Fundamentals
of
chemistry
a
modern
introduction

Fundamentals of chemistry

a modern introduction

FRANK BRESCIA

JOHN ARENTS

HERBERT MEISLICH

AMOS TURK

Department of Chemistry
The City College of the
City University of New York

ACADEMIC PRESS

New York and London

The text of this book was set in Monotype
MODERN 8A *printed and bound by The Maple Press Company.*
The book is printed on Thor Cote Plate by Bergstrom Paper Company.
The design of the text and cover was created by Betty Binns.
The drawings are by F. W. Taylor.

ACADEMIC PRESS INC.
111 Fifth Avenue, New York, New York 10003

United Kingdom Edition published by
ACADEMIC PRESS INC. (LONDON) LTD.
Berkeley Square House, London W.1

Library of Congress catalog card number: 65-26049
First Printing, February 1966
Second Printing, June 1966
Third Printing, August 1966
Fourth Printing, September 1966
Fifth Printing, November 1966

PRINTED IN THE UNITED STATES OF AMERICA

Preface

THE CONTENTS OF A first-year college chemistry course are being pushed forward by advances in the high school course and pulled forward by ever greater demands of the college chemistry curriculum and of the expanding science of chemistry.

Students who have taken improved high school courses are familiar with much of the terminology, descriptive matter, and theoretical background of general chemistry; they are not eager to repeat "that same old stuff." But we do not believe that the fundamental introduction to chemistry should be omitted from the first-year college course. Rather, such background should be presented at a more comprehensive and rigorous level that interests and challenges, but does not dumbfound the student. This text, therefore, does not presume any specific previous chemical training; it can be handled, with some perseverance, even by the student who has not had the high school course.

After general chemistry, the student is confronted by courses in organic, physical, analytical, and inorganic chemistry that are more sophisticated and comprehensive than ever before. Even if he does not elect the advanced chemistry courses, he is better educated if he is introduced to the subject in a way that reflects more closely what chemists are concerned with today. We therefore believe that a modern introduction to general chemistry should not be a condensed physical chemistry, an organic chemistry, or (as it once was) an inorganic chemistry course. It should be a balanced introduction to all of these topics, and to analytical chemistry as well. Important subjects of study or chemical concepts should be broadly presented at the level that is needed to show how they are applied by chemists. For example, this text does not present a course in chemical thermodynamics—that is left for the curriculum in physical chemistry—but the topics of heat, work, enthalpy, entropy, and free energy are introduced. Nor are these topics dropped after they are introduced in the text; they reappear in many contexts, including an explanation of why it is advantageous to roast sulfide ores before reducing them to metal.

The contents of this text are a consequence of our efforts to present a balanced introduction to chemistry that reflects today's realities in education and in science. In accordance with this objective we have offered a fairly sophisticated first presentation of (1) the quantum mechanical concept of electronic structure and chemical bonding; (2) thermodynamics; (3) chemical equilibrium and calculations of ionic equilibria; (4) acid-base theory; (5) relationship of structure and reactivity; (6) stoichiometry; and (7) states of aggregation of matter. Other topics that instructors may consider to be optional additions to an essential core are provided in chapters on (1) structure of complex ions; (2) reactions of the covalent bond; (3) instrumental methods of analysis; (4) metals and metallurgy; (5) nuclear chemistry; and (6) polymer chemistry. The text is arranged, and the sections numbered, so as to give the instructor the greatest individual latitude in his selections and omissions. Many omissions, both in section and chapter, can be made without undue disruption of continuity.

A word should be said concerning the homework problems. We have provided a copious supply that obviates the need to supplement the text with problem books. Answers are given for about half of the problems requiring computation. Each chapter, with a few exceptions, has an initial set of problems which, if assigned *in toto*, will give the student the amount of practice deemed necessary for an understanding of the essential ideas of the chapter. Additional problems are also provided, some of which are suitable as routine drill; some are expected to provide additional challenge to the students; and others serve to extend the content of the chapter.

General chemistry courses include laboratory work, much of which now is analytical chemistry. The chapters in this text covering analytical chemistry will provide background for such laboratory exercises. The laboratory manual that is an optional accompaniment of this text, *Fundamentals of Chemistry: Laboratory Studies*, emphasizes the critical selection of experimental procedures and the use of techniques of quantitative chemistry.

We wish to express our gratitude to our wives for their patience, to our students who used and made helpful comments on the Preliminary Edition, and to our colleagues at City College for their cooperation. In addition we wish to thank Dr. W. L. Rellahan (University of Cincinnati), Dr. Paul Ander (Seton Hall University), Dr. J. M. Alexander (State University of New York at Stony Brook), and Dr. Mary Hillis (Vassar College) for their excellent cooperation in their use of the Preliminary Edition.

New York City

FRANK BRESCIA
JOHN ARENTS
HERBERT MEISLICH
AMOS TURK

Contents

8: Electronic structures of atoms

9: Types of chemical bonds

10: Hydrocarbons and their derivatives

11: The covalent bond

12: Intermolecular forces

13: Solutions

14: Chemical equilibrium

15: Ionic solutions

16: Galvanic cells and the driving force of chemical reactions

17: Acids and bases

18: Hydrides and oxides; structure and basicity

19: Calculations of ionic equilibrium

24: Molecular geometry and bonding; Symmetry

25: Transition metal complexes

26: Reactions of covalent bonds

27: Metals and metallurgy

1

Introduction

1.1 GENERAL AND HISTORICAL REMARKS

The American Chemical Society* has defined chemistry as that science which deals with

(1) the chemical elements alone or in combination;
(2) reactions, transformations, transmutations, and interactions of the chemical elements and their combinations;
(3) determination of, control of, prediction of, interpretation and evaluation of (by direct or indirect methods), application of, preparation of, and mechanisms of processes listed in (2);
(4) basic natural phenomena and forces in their application to reactions, extractions, combinations, processes, additions, syntheses, decompositions, and analyses.

The journal *Chemical Abstracts*, which endeavors to summarize and index all "scientific and technical papers containing new information of chemical interest," refers to sources in about one hundred countries and written in more than fifty languages. The subject matter is divided into about seventy-five separate sections.

This extent and diversity of chemical subjects pose a real problem for one who begins the study of chemistry. Shall he assume that general mastery is impossible and confine himself to a selected group of specialties? Or can he learn a body of "general principles" that makes it unnecessary for him to consider special areas except for vocational training? Are the logical (frequently illogical) and historical antecedents of our current thinking of interest or value to him?

To approach these questions, it will be helpful to trace the time sequence of the early developments which led man toward his present chemical

* Council Committee on Professional Relations and Status.

1

knowledge and industrial capacity. Let us begin, say, in 1620, the year of the Pilgrims' landing. Western technology was then restricted largely to the pursuit of the crafts—the skilled working of materials. Chemical processes, which involve changes in the composition of materials, occurred in metallurgy, leather tanning, fermentation, and manufacture of soap and glass, but there existed no ideas that included these changes in a broad conceptual system. Mechanical ingenuity yielded impressive accomplishments in the construction of large works, as it had since ancient times, but a satisfactory explanation for the fact that a suction pump at sea level could not raise water higher than about 34 feet was not yet at hand.

During the ensuing half century, studies of systems comprising gases and liquids at varying pressures (a discipline then called "pneumatics") by Evangelista Torricelli, Blaise Pascal, Otto von Guericke, and Robert Boyle led to satisfactory concepts of vacuum and of gas compression. Those studies were necessarily accompanied by improvements in methods of handling gases at high and low pressures. As a result of the advances in method and theory, it became possible for a later generation of scientists (notably Karl Wilhelm Scheele, Henry Cavendish, Joseph Priestley, and Antoine Lavoisier), approximately during the period between the American and French Revolutions (1776–1789), to initiate a "chemical revolution." Their efforts served to provide concepts for the understanding of combustion and of calcination (oxidation) of metals, and to establish a quantitative basis for these and other chemical changes.

Thus was the stage set for the most valuable and productive group of ideas about chemical changes—the atomic and molecular hypotheses, and rational systems for atomic and molecular weights and for molecular formulas. These ideas (over the half century 1808–1858) are credited largely to John Dalton, Amadeo Avogadro, and Stanislao Cannizzaro. During the more than a hundred years since Cannizzaro's time, chemical methods and theories have advanced at greatly accelerated rates and in many directions. It is important to remember, however, that the fundamental ideas of chemistry evolved gradually over a period of about two hundred years from concepts concerned largely with the behavior of matter in the gaseous state and in gas-liquid systems.

We have not time, in an introductory study of chemistry, to retrace historical sequences in detail. The retention of some historical perspective in the approach to atomic theory, however, is both intellectually and culturally satisfying; it avoids an impression that atoms were "discovered" during the development of the uranium bomb. We will therefore start by studying the behavior of gases and other states of matter, and thus lay the basis for the study of quantitative chemistry and for the consideration of the structure and behavior of chemical substances and systems.

When the student reaches the point at which he concerns himself with some of the specialized subjects of chemistry, he will learn that there is no sharp demarcation between practice and theory, just as there was none in the days of Boyle, Lavoisier, or Cannizzaro. It is always valuable to study the way in which descriptive information ("the facts") serves as the raw material for the construction of theories, and how, in turn, theoretical concepts guide us in asking meaningful questions, suggesting valuable experiments, and enlarging our store of useful information and techniques.

Refer to Appendix I (page 775) for a review of physical concepts, measurement scales, and significant figures. This material is fundamental to discussions throughout the book. Some of the problems at the end of this chapter are based on material in the Appendix.

1.2 DEFINITIONS OF SOME CHEMICAL TERMS

We will define and discuss briefly some terms which, over a period of many years, have become part of the language of chemists.

A **substance** is any variety of matter of recognizably definite composition and character. The term is used in distinction to **body,** or **object,** which refers to a particular item of matter. Thus, a chair (object) is made of wood (substance). The **composition** of a substance is its makeup of constituent substances, usually expressed in terms of percent or fraction by weight.

Some substances have precisely fixed compositions, which are associated with their properties; they are said to be **pure substances.** For example, red iron rust can be obtained as a pure substance comprising 69.94% iron and 30.06% oxygen. Coal, on the other hand, is not a pure substance; its carbon content ranges from 35% to 84%. Of course, a pure substance may be contaminated by admixture of foreign matter. The important point, however, is that the pure substance, when it is recovered from such a **mixture,** retains its definite composition and character.

It is believed that the constant compositions associated with pure substances are maintained by linkages among elementary units of matter; such linkages are called **chemical bonds.** Any transformation that involves a change of such definite composition is considered to be accompanied by the making or breaking of chemical bonds and is called a **chemical change,** or **chemical reaction.** Examples are combustion, corrosion, photosynthesis, and digestion.

A **physical change** of a substance does not involve change of definite composition or character. Alterations in the dimensions of objects, or in the states of aggregation of their constituents (discussed in the next section), are considered to be physical changes. Examples are fracture, deformation, pulverizing, drawing (as of a metal wire), thermal expansion or contraction, melting, boiling, and freezing.

The types of behavior that a substance exhibits in chemical reactions are called its **chemical properties;** other characteristics that are typical of a substance are called its **physical properties.** Taken together, the chemical and physical properties of a substance are called its **specific properties;** this term is sometimes used in contradistinction to **accidental properties** (for example, length or mass), which describe a given object but are not typical of a substance.

Decomposition is a chemical reaction in which the constituent entities of a substance break down into simpler forms. Most of the many substances known to man can undergo decompositions that involve net energy changes up to about 2×10^3 calories/gram (released) or 3×10^4 calories/gram (absorbed) and which yield two or more decomposition products. A relatively few substances (somewhat over one hundred) do not decompose at all within these ranges of energy change or, if they do, give only one ultimate decomposition product (for example, ozone → oxygen). Such substances are considered to be the stuff of which all other substances are made, and are called **elements.** The fundamental unit of the element is the **atom.**

A nonelemental pure substance is called a **compound substance** or a **compound.**

1.3 THE CLASSIFICATION OF MATTER; STATES OF AGGREGATION

It is often convenient, in determining the properties of a body, to use only a portion, or sample, of it for examination or measurement. If all samples of a body have the same specific properties, the body is said to be **homogeneous;** if not, it is **heterogeneous.** The decision as to the homogeneity or heterogeneity of a body will depend on the size of the sample taken for measurement. The chemist frequently uses the practical criterion that a body is homogeneous if it has no discontinuities larger than about the wavelength of visible light, or 0.4–0.7 micron. By this standard, substances that appear discontinuous on examination with a microscope using visible light are heterogeneous. A worker who uses an instrument that can detect the presence of still smaller particles (for example, an electron microscope) will necessarily establish a finer standard of homogeneity.

In any system, the portion of matter that is homogeneous and uniform in specific properties is called a **phase.** A phase may consist of one or more discrete entities in space, each entity separated from the rest of the system by a definite boundary. Thus, a layer of oil floating on a column of water is a two-phase system (oil and water). If the mixture is shaken until the oil is dispersed as droplets in the water (an **emulsion**), the system still consists of two phases (oil and water). Before taking up the classification of phases of matter, it will be helpful to consider three concepts: molecular structure, cohesiveness, and orderliness.

Molecular Structure. One may be tempted to infer that matter that is microscopically homogeneous would continue to appear uniform no matter how closely it were examined. Evidence against such an idea of the absolute uniformity of matter, however, is overwhelmingly convincing; some of it was recognized even by the ancients: 1.00 liter of ethyl alcohol and 1.00 liter of water, each at 15°C, when mixed and held at the same temperature, produce a new homogeneous liquid which occupies 1.92 liters. Where did the loss of 0.08 liter go? A lump of sugar left at the bottom of an undisturbed glass of water will eventually disappear and sweeten all the water uniformly. By what path does the sugar travel? What happens to the matter in a gas that is compressed? All of these questions are most satisfactorily answered by assuming that matter is discontinuous, consisting of particles, strands, layers, or a network of substance arranged in space. The voids then provide volume which is sacrificed when the substance is compressed, and provide paths for the diffusion of matter. Astronomical evidence that matter can exist in states of extreme density (white dwarf stars, 2×10^5 grams/milliliter) also supports the idea that the matter we know on earth includes a large proportion of empty space.

How are matter and voids disposed within the total volume they occupy? Many patterns, both orderly and random, can be imagined, and the variety known to exist is indeed great. Some matter is arranged as small separate particles in space (gases) or as particles loosely aggregated to each other (for example, iodine crystals). Matter may also be arranged in continuous layers in space (for example, graphite) or in rigid networks (for example, diamond or quartz) that do not separate except under severe stress, such as heating to several thousand degrees.

Electrically neutral individual particles of ordinary matter whose atoms are linked together by chemical bonds are called **molecules.** There is no absolute upper limit of size for molecules. Viruses, for example, which reach dimensions of hundreds of angstrom units, are sometimes called "giant molecules." Strands of tobacco mosaic virus are $(280 \pm 9) \times 10^{-7}$ cm long by 15.2×10^{-7} cm in cross-sectional diameter. Virus particles are illustrated in Fig. 1.1. Molecules of substances that are gaseous in ordinary terrestrial environments are usually less than 10 A; small molecules like those of water and hydrogen chloride are around 2 to 4 A (1 A = 10^{-8} cm, see Appendix I, page 778).

Electrically charged atoms or groups of atoms are called **ions.** Positive ions are **cations,** negative ones **anions.** The smallest ions are individual charged atoms (for example, sodium ion, Na^+, or fluoride ion, F^-). Ions may also be groups of relatively few atoms, such as sulfate ion, SO_4^{2-}, or hexacyanoferrate(III) ion, $[Fe(CN)_6]^{3-}$. Scientists concerned with air use the term "atmospheric ions" to denote charged dust particles; sizes are less than 50 A for "small ions," 50–150 A for "intermediate ions," and up to about 1 micron for "large ions." There is, of course, no upper limit to the size of charged bodies, but the term "ion" does not ordinarily refer to sizes above the micron range. When ions are arranged in some closely packed pattern, it is sometimes conventional to designate as a molecule the smallest group of ions whose charges just neutralize each other, for example, a molecule of calcium chloride consisting of one Ca^{2+}

Fig. 1.1. *Crystalline tobacco necrosis virus, magnification 160,000 times (J. Ultrastructure Research, Vol. 2, page 8, 1958; courtesy of Dr. R. W. G. Wyckoff).*

and two Cl⁻ ions. We will, however, apply the word "molecule" only to individual entities as outlined above.

Cohesiveness. The molecules or ions of which matter is composed may have a greater or lesser tendency to stick together, or cohere. This proclivity is a resultant of two effects: (a) the mutual forces of attraction or repulsion that may exist among all material particles, and (b) the natural tendency for all particles with kinetic energy to separate from one another, because motion away from the center of mass is less likely to be interrupted by collision than is motion toward the center. The tendency to separate increases with rise of temperature.

Generally, the stronger the cohesive forces of a substance, the greater are the density, hardness, strength, and ability to resist the effects of heating. The interplay of cohesive and repulsive forces helps to determine what patterns of molecular arrangement are favored or permitted.

Orderliness. Matter is found to occur in conditions ranging from complete disorder of its particles to patterned arrangements in which only very few particles are out of place. Figure 3.12 (page 45) shows crystalline shapes suggesting orderly arrangements among the particles making up the substances.

The degrees of cohesiveness and of order serve as the bases for classification of matter according to the way it is "put together" or aggregated. These criteria are applicable, of course, only to homogeneous samples, since the properties of nonhomogeneous matter vary from sample to sample.

The States of Matter. For purposes of classification, then, matter may be said (1) to be arranged

(a) randomly, or
(b) in an orderly manner

TABLE 1.1   *States of Aggregation of Matter*

Predominant arrangement of particles	Degree of cohesiveness	Common name of state
Random	Low (no well-defined boundary)	Gas
Random	Intermediate (well-defined boundary, but no rigidity)	Liquid
Random	High (rigid)	Glass (also called noncrystalline solid)
Orderly	Low	Does not ordinarily exist[a]
Orderly	Intermediate	Does not ordinarily exist[b]
Orderly	High	Crystalline solid

[a] Exception: solid helium near 0°K.   [b] Exception: "liquid crystals"—liquids that have some optical properties typical of crystals.

and (2) to cohere

(a) so little that diffusion prevents the maintenance of a well-defined boundary, or
(b) enough to maintain itself as a mass with a well-defined boundary but not to maintain rigidity under the stress of gravity, or
(c) so well that it maintains a rigid shape in spite of the stress imposed by gravity.

This classification yields six combinations, four of which exist in ordinary substances. These are listed and named in Table 1.1.

None of the distinctions given in Table 1.1 is absolute, but some are sharper than others. The distinction between liquid and glass, for example, depends only on assignment of degree of rigidity, and is often quite poorly defined. The randomness of molecular arrangements in liquids is far less than it is in gases.

Some substances, especially those composed of large molecules, such as gels, rubber, and plastics, are not at all well classified by this system. Attempts to apply this classification are made, nonetheless; a textile chemist who examines cellulose fibers by x ray diffraction patterns will say that a well-ordered (repetitive) pattern indicates that the cellulose has a high degree of "crystallinity."

Problems

1. Divisions of chemistry.   Refer to the table of contents of a recent issue of *Chemical Abstracts* in the library and list sections you would expect to scan if you were

(a) an archaeologist concerned with examination of ceramic and metallic artifacts and with radiochemical dating;

(b) an air pollution chemist who must sample and analyze air for gases and dust, and prescribe control remedies;

(c) a research director for a doughnut manufacturer;

(d) a teacher of physical chemistry;

(e) a chemical engineer in a petroleum refinery;

(f) a chemist employed to develop missile fuels.

2. Chemical and physical change. Identify the chemical and the physical changes in each of the following sequences. (a) An egg is hard-boiled, shelled, sliced, eaten, and digested. (b) Gasoline is sprayed into the carburetor, mixed with air, converted to vapor, burned, and the combustion products expand in the cylinder.

3. Definitions of terms. Discuss the inadequacies and limitations of the following definitions. Supply better ones. (a) **Homogeneity** is the property of uniformity of matter. (b) A **molecule** is the smallest particle of matter that retains the specific properties of the matter. (c) A **solid** is matter that retains its shape. (d) A **liquid** is matter that takes the shape of its container. (Is this true of a liquid in a vehicle in interplanetary space?) (e) An **element** is a substance that cannot be decomposed by chemical means.

4. States of matter. Suppose we classified the orderliness of arrangements of molecules in matter as (1) none, (2) intermediate, (3) high, and the degree of cohesiveness as (a) low, unable to maintain a rigid shape under the stress of gravity, (b) high, able to maintain a rigid shape under the stress of gravity. Outline the states of aggregation of matter based on this classification and, where feasible, assign the appropriate common name of a state of matter to each category.

The following problems are related to material in Appendix I (page 775)

5. Matter and energy. Explain the fallacy in each of the following statements:

(a) The energy expended in closing a safety pin is lost when the pin is dissolved in nitric acid.

(b) Smoke pollution from power plants could be profitably controlled by collecting all the stack emissions and chemically reconverting them to fuel.

(c) To cool the kitchen, keep the refrigerator door open.

6. Significant figures. How many significant figures are there in each of the following quantities: (a) 4.81 %; (b) 1.70×10^{-3} torr; (c) 100 dollars; (d) 0.0007 g; (e) 62.61430 g.

7. Units; significant figures. A spherical cloud droplet is 5.0 microns in diameter. What is its equatorial cross-sectional area in square centimeters?

Answer. 2.0×10^{-7} cm².

8. Units; significant figures. It has been said that a number as large as 10^{100} is never needed to express any magnitude that has physical significance. What is the ratio between the distance to the farthest detectable nebulae (1×10^9 light years; velocity of light $= 3.00 \times 10^{10}$ cm/sec) and the radius of the hydrogen atom (0.53 A)?

9. Units; significant figures. An automobile weighing 1.230×10^3 kg is sprayed with 5.02 liters of lacquer that contains 58.2% by weight of volatile thinner. The density of the lacquer is 0.89 g/ml. (a) After the lacquer dries (the thinner evaporates), what weight has been added to the automobile? (b) What weight portion of the coated auto is dried lacquer, in percent, in parts per million, fractionally? (c) What is the weight of the lacquered automobile?

Answer. (a) 1.9×10^3 g; (b) $1.5 \times 10^{-1}\%$; 1.5×10^3 ppm; 1.5×10^{-3} fractional; (c) 1.232×10^3 kg.

10. Density. The label on a bale of peat moss states that the volume is 1.45 cu ft and that the contents will cover a garden area 6 ft by 6 ft to a depth of 1 inch. Account for the discrepancy between the two volumes. Calculate the ratio of packing density of the moss in the bale to that of the moss spread out on the ground.

11. Density. Copper pellets are poured into a measuring cylinder up to the 50-ml mark. The cylinder is then filled with water to the same mark. Data are

Weight of empty cylinder	104 g
Weight of cylinder + copper	371 g
Weight of cylinder + copper + water	391 g
Temperature of system	20°C

Calculate (a) the packing density, and (b) the absolute density, of the copper at 20°C. (c) What is the percent void space?

Answer. (a) 5.3 g/ml; (b) 8.9 g/ml; (c) 40%.

12. Density. A truck of 6.0 m³ capacity delivers 1.10×10^4 kg of crushed limestone. A representative piece of the stone weighs 20.4 g and displaces 7.50 ml of water at 4°C. (a) What is the absolute density of the stone in g/ml? (b) What is the bulk density of the trucked stone in g/ml? (c) What is the percent voids in the trucked stone?

13. Pressure. The density of mercury at 0°C is 13.595 g/cm³. Prove that 1 torr = pressure exerted by a mass of 1.3595 g on an area 1 cm².

14. Specific heat. (a) How many calories are needed to warm 1.0 kg of water from 10°C to 90°C? (Assume that the specific heat of water in this range is 1.0 cal/g deg.) (b) A certain quantity of heat warms 100 g of water in an insulated container at 10.00°C to 12.50°C. An equivalent quantity of heat warms 120 g of alcohol from 60.0° to 63.6°C. What is the specific heat of the alcohol? (c) How many Celsius degrees could 100 g of mercury (specific heat 0.033) be warmed by the same quantity of heat?

Answer. (a) 8.0×10^4 cal; (b) 0.58 cal/g deg; (c) 76 deg.

2
Gases

2.1 INTRODUCTION

From the classification scheme derived in Chapter 1, gases are considered to be composed of molecules whose random motion causes rapid diffusion and prevents the maintenance of a well-defined boundary. As a result, the arrangement of the molecules at any time is random or disorderly. Gaseous materials are well known in our experience, and, under ordinary conditions, we have no trouble in differentiating them from solids, liquids, or glasses. It is possible, however, to describe conditions where such distinction is not so simple or obvious. Consider the detonation of an explosive: TNT is a pale yellow crystalline solid, specific gravity 1.65, which detonates at a velocity of nearly 7000 meters/second to produce carbon monoxide, nitrogen, hydrogen, and other gases, as well as some carbon smoke. During the detonation, the destruction of crystallinity occurs before the energy of the reaction overcomes the cohesive and inertial forces that hold the solid together. There is a short interval during the formation of this "fireball" in which the distinction between solid and gas is not at all clear. Such a state, moreover, can be stabilized at high (stellar) pressures. This example is given to show that classification systems, even when they appear to be entirely obvious and natural, are nonetheless arbitrary, and designed to be useful only within limited ranges of conditions.

A qualitative summary of the characteristic properties of gases under ordinary terrestrial environments is given in Table 2.1.

Quantitative experimental investigations of gases were begun in the 17th century. The first scientist to propose a concept of gas behavior based on molecular motion (kinetic theory) was Daniel Bernoulli in 1738. This idea was not accepted, however, until it was revived about a century later by John Herapath, and eventually assumed ascendancy

TABLE 2.1 *Characteristic Properties of Gases (Qualitative Description)*

Color	All gases are transparent; almost all are colorless; some exceptions: fluorine, chlorine (both green-yellow), bromine (red-brown), iodine (violet), nitrogen dioxide, nitrogen trioxide (both red-brown)
Mobility	Compared with other forms of matter, gases show little resistance to flow; gases diffuse rapidly in space and through porous barriers
Response to changes of pressure, temperature	Compared with other forms of matter, gases expand greatly on heating and/or on reduction of applied pressure

over rival theories. Meanwhile, of course, experimental knowledge of gases continued to grow.

Any account which presents facts and theory in rigid sequence (in either direction) is historically inaccurate. A historically accurate account, however, would be needlessly confusing. For the purposes of study, it will be most satisfactory to describe the kinetic theory in modern terms, and then to interpret experimental findings in the conceptual framework that the theory provides.

2.2 IDEAL GASES

The study of natural phenomena can often be simplified for our limited intellectual capacities by the use of abstract models. A model is a representation of reality, and a good model is a successful compromise between (a) simplicity and (b) faithful representation of the phenomenon to be studied. The model called the "ideal gas" is very successful because it is easy to understand in quantitative terms and conforms quite well to the properties of real gases, especially if high pressures and low temperatures are avoided.

The ideal gas consists of molecules which are points in space, have mass and velocity, exhibit no attractive or repulsive forces among themselves or with other matter, and undergo collisions with no net loss of kinetic energy.*

The ideal gas, when unconfined, will rapidly disperse into space. In a rigid container, however, the molecules will bounce off the inside walls and at all times be distributed in some arrangement within the volume of

* This model has some inconsistency in that it describes collisions between points, which would be events of infinitesimal probability.

confinement. Any one molecule will move at constant speed in a straight line until it suffers a collision; the molecule will then have a new speed and direction until the next collision, etc. Considering all the molecules in the container at any one time, some will therefore have abnormally high speeds, others will be relatively slow, and most will be moving at a rate close to some average value. The distribution of speeds is not symmetrically arranged around the average value, because there is a lower limit (at rest) but no upper one.

Figure 2.1 shows the expected shape of a curve of distribution of molecular speeds in an ideal gas. (See also Fig. 23.3, page 611.) If the container is insulated from the outside, no energy enters or leaves the gas and the average speed of the molecules remains constant.

The **pressure** of the gas is the force that it exerts per unit area of its container (Fig. 2.2). This force is applied by the collisions of the molecules with the walls. Consider a molecule of mass m which approaches the wall at velocity $+u$ and rebounds at equal speed with velocity $-u$. The difference between the velocities before and after collision is $+u - (-u)$, or $2u$. The force exerted by this collision is

$$\text{force} = \text{mass} \times \text{acceleration (see page 776)}$$

$$= \text{mass} \times \frac{\text{change in velocity}}{\text{time}}$$

$$= m \times \frac{2u}{\text{time}} \quad \text{(this is the force per collision)}$$

Let us make the simplifying assumption, which we shall soon discard, that all the molecules collide with the walls at the same velocity u. Now, let Z be the number of collisions per unit time per unit area. We assume that collisions occur so frequently that any variations in pressure from time to time due to variations in collision frequency are entirely indis-

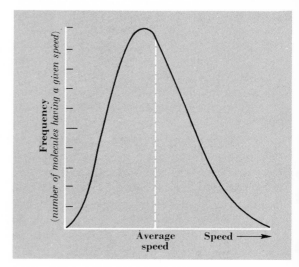

Fig. 2.1. *Distribution of molecular speeds.*

Frequency
(number of molecules having a given speed)

Average speed

Speed ⟶

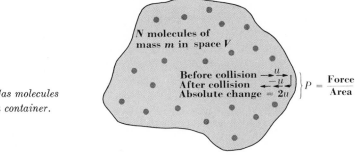

Fig. 2.2. Gas molecules
confined in a container.

tinguishable. Then

$$\text{pressure } (P) = \frac{\text{force}}{\text{collision}} \times \frac{\text{collisions}}{\text{area}}$$

$$= \frac{2mu}{\text{time}} \times \frac{\text{collisions}}{\text{area}}$$

$$= 2mu \times \frac{\text{collisions}}{\text{time} \times \text{area}}$$

Substituting the value

$$Z = \frac{\text{collisions}}{\text{time} \times \text{area}}$$

we have

$$P = 2muZ \tag{1}$$

For a space of volume V, containing N molecules,

Z is	*because*
directly proportional to the number of molecules, N, in the space,....	the more molecules, the more collisions with the walls;
directly proportional to the velocity of the molecules, u,.........	the faster they travel, the more collisions with the walls;
inversely proportional to the volume of the container, V,.......	the larger the container, the greater is the average distance that a molecule must travel to reach the wall, and the greater is the wall area that must be hit; the distance times the area (length³) is directly proportional to the volume.

Thus

$$Z \propto \frac{Nu}{V}$$

and

$$Z = \frac{aNu}{V} \tag{2}$$

where a is the proportionality constant. Substituting this value for Z in Equation (1) we have

$$P = \frac{2aNmu^2}{V} \tag{3}$$

The reader will recognize that the term u^2 in Equation (3) cannot be the square of the velocity of *each* molecule in the gas, because the values are not the same for all the molecules. Instead, u^2 is the average (mean) of the squares of the velocities, sometimes designated $\overline{u^2}$. Then, u, which is the square root of u^2, may be written $\sqrt{\overline{u^2}}$; it is called the **root mean square velocity.**

It will be convenient to write Equation (3) in the form

$$PV = 4aN(\tfrac{1}{2}mu^2) \tag{4}$$

The term $\tfrac{1}{2}mu^2$ gives the kinetic energy of any moving particle; in this case, the particles are molecules. It follows from Equation (4) that an increase in the pressure of a given quantity of an ideal gas in a rigid container (N, V, and a are constant) can occur only when there is a corresponding increase in some property of the gas that depends only on the kinetic energy of its molecules. Both theory and experiment (see ensuing Section 2.3) lead us to believe that this property is the **absolute temperature,*** T. We express the relationship as a proportionality involving the four variables. Thus

$$PV \propto N(\tfrac{1}{2}mu^2)$$

But,

$$(\tfrac{1}{2}mu^2) \propto T \tag{5}$$

Therefore,

$$PV \propto NT \tag{6}$$

This is one form of the **equation of state** of that model of matter called the **ideal gas.** It is also called the **Ideal Gas Law.** As we shall see, it is not a bad equation for real gases, under a fairly broad range of conditions.

Six different equations, each involving only two variables, can be derived from Equation (6) by assuming, in each case, that the other two factors are held constant. Some experimental methods or conditions for holding the various factors constant are

P A constant force (weight) on a frictionless piston maintains a constant pressure.

V A rigid container is a constant volume.

---

* The relationship between the kinetic energy of the molecules and T is $(\tfrac{1}{2}mu^2) = \tfrac{3}{2}kT$, where k is a fundamental constant (Boltzmann's constant) whose value is 1.38×10^{-16} erg/deg molecule.

N A constant weight of gas represents a constant number of molecules; therefore N is constant if the container is sealed. It is assumed that no chemical reactions occur.

T An uninsulated container in a thermostatted (isothermal) environment will reach the constant temperature of the environment.

The six deductions are summarized in Table 2.2.

A valuable deduction may be made from Equation (5): at constant temperature, $\frac{1}{2}mu^2$ is constant. Rearranging, and expressing the relationship as a proportionality,

$$u \propto \frac{1}{\sqrt{m}} \tag{7}$$

The statement is: the average velocity of a molecule in a gas at constant temperature is inversely proportional to the square root of its mass. This expression is related to **Graham's Law,** to be elaborated upon later.

As another consequence of $PV \propto NT$, it is meaningless to specify the volume of a gas unless 2 of the 3 variables, P, N, and T, are also specified. For example, if a rigid container of an ideal gas is held at a definite temperature and a definite pressure, the number of molecules is automatically fixed.

Having made these various deductions from $PV \propto NT$, let us now examine some of them in more detail.

2.3   THE LAW OF CHARLES AND GAY-LUSSAC; ABSOLUTE TEMPERATURE; $V \propto T$, OR $V = constant \times T$

Jacques Charles, a French physicist, measured the relationship between temperature* and volume of gases around 1787, but his data are not available. His work was confirmed in 1802 by his countryman, Joseph Gay-Lussac.

The results of such a study give a straight-line plot of gas volume vs. temperature, such as appears in Fig. 2.3.

   * Thermometers had been developed in Europe starting around 1600. Earliest Western concepts of gas expansion by heating probably originated in the mechanical toys of the Hellenic period, such as Hero's engine.

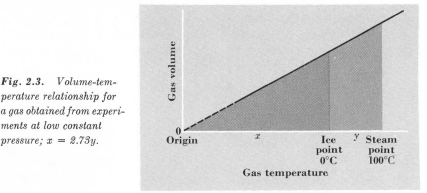

Fig. 2.3. Volume-temperature relationship for a gas obtained from experiments at low constant pressure; $x = 2.73y$.

TABLE 2.2 *Deductions from* $PV \propto NT$

Factors held constant	Descriptions	Deductions
V,N	**A fixed quantity of gas is confined in a rigid, insulated container** 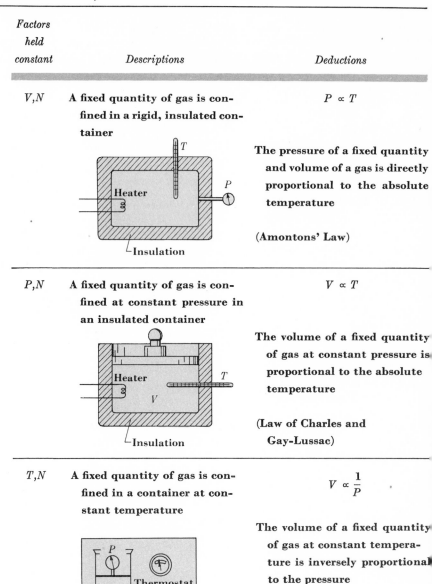	$P \propto T$ The pressure of a fixed quantity and volume of a gas is directly proportional to the absolute temperature (Amontons' Law)
P,N	**A fixed quantity of gas is confined at constant pressure in an insulated container**	$V \propto T$ The volume of a fixed quantity of gas at constant pressure is proportional to the absolute temperature (Law of Charles and Gay-Lussac)
T,N	**A fixed quantity of gas is confined in a container at constant temperature**	$V \propto \dfrac{1}{P}$ The volume of a fixed quantity of gas at constant temperature is inversely proportional to the pressure (Boyle's Law)

TABLE **2.2** (*Continued*)

Factors held constant	Descriptions	Deductions
P,T	**A gas is confined in a container at constant temperature and pressure**	$V \propto N$
		The volume of a gas at fixed temperature and pressure depends directly on the number of its molecules, or, equal volumes of all gases (*P,T* constant) have the same number of molecules (Avogadro's Law)
V,T	**A gas is confined in a rigid container at constant temperature**	$P \propto N$
		The pressure of a fixed volume of gas at constant temperature depends directly on the number of its molecules (Dalton's Law of Partial Pressures)
P,V	**A gas is confined in a rigid, insulated container at constant pressure**	$N \propto \dfrac{1}{T}$
		The number of molecules of gas in a fixed volume at constant pressure is inversely proportional to the absolute temperature

The temperature scale designates three points: (1) the steam point, 100°C; (2) the ice point, 0°C; and (3) the temperature at the origin, where the extension of the straight line would reach the point of zero gas volume. It is found experimentally that the distance x (between the origin and the ice point) is close to 2.73 times as great as the distance y (between the ice point and the steam point), or

$$x = 2.73y \tag{8}$$

But $y = 100°C$ minus $0°C$, and $x = 0°C$ minus temperature at origin. Substituting these values for x and y in Equation (8), and solving for the temperature at the origin, we get

$$0°C - \text{temperature at origin} = 2.73(100°C - 0°C)$$
$$\text{temperature at origin} = -273°C$$

For an ideal gas, whose molecules are points (occupying no volume), the lowest possible temperature corresponds to total loss of volume. This temperature is called "absolute zero" because it is irrational to assume that the ideal gas molecules might possess a negative volume. The best current value for absolute zero, obtained from volume-temperature studies at low pressures, is $-273.15°C$. This temperature is taken as the zero point of the absolute or **Kelvin* scale,** and

$$°K = °C + 273.15 \tag{9}$$

Real gases do not in fact approach zero volume near $0°K$. Even though the free space between molecules decreases as the temperature decreases, the molecules themselves occupy volume that is relatively independent of the temperature.

Some residual energy would be retained by molecules even at $0°K$; this quantity is called the **zero-point energy.**

Charles' Law can be used in a simple way to solve problems concerning V-T relationships of gases at constant pressure. If V_1, T_1 refer to one set of conditions and V_2, T_2 refer to another set of conditions of the same quantity of gas, then $V_1 = constant \times T_1$, and $V_2 = constant \times T_2$.

Dividing one equation by the other,

$$\frac{V_2}{V_1} = \frac{T_2}{T_1} \tag{10}$$

The "common sense" application of correction factors can also be used (see below).

The term "**standard temperature,**" as used in calculations involving gases, means $0°C$.

EXAMPLE 1   **10.0 ml of gas at 20.0°C is cooled at constant pressure to the ice point. What will the new volume be?**

---

* Named after Lord Kelvin (1824–1907), who suggested the scale.

ANSWER $V_1 = 10.0$ ml, $T_1 = (20 + 273)°K$, $T_2 = (0 + 273)°K$.

From Equation (10)	*"Common sense" method*
Solving for V_2,	**New volume = original volume × temperature correction**
$$V_2 = V_1 \times \frac{T_2}{T_1}$$	**(because cooling reduces gas volume, correction factor must be less than unity)**
$$= 10.0 \text{ ml} \times \frac{273°K}{293°K}$$	$$= 10.0 \text{ ml} \times \frac{273°K}{293°K}$$

Therefore $V_2 = 9.32$ ml.

2.4   BOYLE'S LAW; $V \propto 1/P$, OR $PV = constant$

Robert Boyle (1627–1691) investigated *P-V* relationships in air by pouring successive quantities of mercury into the open arm of a ∪-shaped tube as shown in Fig. 2.4. After each addition, he measured (a) the volume of air in the lower section of the tube, and (b) the difference between the heights of the mercury columns in the two arms. The pressure on the trapped air is the difference between the mercury levels plus the atmospheric pressure (the height of mercury in a barometer).* Boyle's *PV* values were constant to within about 1% relative error.

* Addition of barometer reading takes into account the atmospheric pressure on the right arm of the tube.

Fig. 2.4.   *Boyle's apparatus.* P_{atm} *refers to barometric pressure*

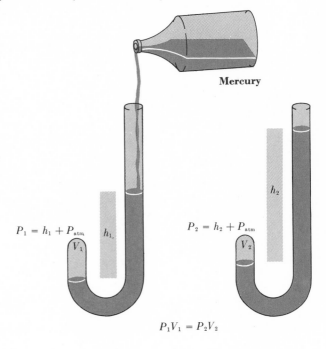

$$P_1 V_1 = P_2 V_2$$

Problems dealing with V-P relationships among gases can be solved by using the relationship derived from $PV = constant$ at constant temperature for a given quantity of gas,

$$P_2V_2 = P_1V_1 \tag{11}$$

or by the "common sense" use of ratios.

The term "**standard pressure**," as used in calculations involving gases, means standard atmospheric pressure, or 760 torr.*

EXAMPLE 2   **The pressure on 10.0 liters of gas at 760 torr is reduced to 700 torr at constant temperature. What will the new volume be?**

ANSWER $V_1 = 10.0$ liters, $P_1 = 760$ torr, $P_2 = 700$ torr.

From Equation (11)	"Common sense" method
$$V_2 = V_1 \times \frac{P_1}{P_2}$$	**New volume = original volume × pressure correction** (the gas will expand because of pressure reduction, so correction is greater than unity)
$$= 10.0 \text{ liters} \times \frac{760 \text{ torr}}{700 \text{ torr}}$$	$$= 10.0 \text{ liters} \times \frac{760 \text{ torr}}{700 \text{ torr}}$$

Therefore $V_2 = 10.9$ liters.

2.5   DALTON'S LAW OF PARTIAL PRESSURES; $P \propto N$; $P = constant \times N$; $P_T = p_1 + p_2 + \cdots$

The $P = constant \times N$ equation states that the pressure of a given volume of gas at constant temperature depends directly on the number of molecules. This relationship, like all the others that derive from $PV \propto NT$, applies to mixtures of ideal gases containing more than one kind of molecule, as well as to pure gases. Now, consider a mixture of N_1 molecules of gas₁, plus N_2 molecules of gas₂, etc., which exerts a total pressure P_T. Then

$$P_T = constant \times (N_1 + N_2 + \cdots) \tag{12}$$

Let us now separate the gases into individual containers,† each of which has the original volume. The pressure exerted in each of the new containers is called the **partial pressure** p, which is defined simply as the pressure that one component of a gas mixture would exert if it occupied the same volume alone. Then, $p_1 = constant \times N_1$, $p_2 = constant \times N_2$, etc., and, by addition,

$$p_1 + p_2 + \cdots = constant \times (N_1 + N_2 + \cdots) \tag{13}$$

---

* See Appendix I (page 780) for definitions of units.

† This experiment need not be performed. It is sufficient just to think of it. Heisenberg called such efforts "*gedanken*" (imaginary) experiments.

By combining Equations (12) and (13) we have

$$P_T = p_1 + p_2 + \cdots \tag{14}$$

Equation (14) is Dalton's Law of Partial Pressures (1801), which states that, in a mixture of gases, the total pressure equals the sum of the partial pressures.

This relationship is important in measurements of gases confined by volatile liquids. The evaporation of the liquid contributes a new component to the gas and makes up a part of its total pressure in accordance with Dalton's Law. Fortunately for measurement purposes, the pressure contribution from such evaporation at constant temperature reaches a constant value called the **vapor pressure of the liquid.**[*] In laboratory practice, the confining liquid is often water, for which vapor pressures are found in Appendix V (page 800).

EXAMPLE 3   **The composition of dry air by volume is 78.1% nitrogen, 20.9% oxygen, and 1.0% of other gases. Calculate the partial pressures, in atmospheres, in a tank of dry air compressed to 10.0 atmospheres.**

ANSWER   **According to the data, if the nitrogen were removed to a separate container and compressed to 10.0 atm it would occupy 78.1% of the original volume. If the volume were then expanded to 100% of the original volume, the pressure would drop to 78.1% of the original pressure, or (78.1/100) × 10.0 atm, or 7.81 atm. This is the partial pressure of nitrogen in the original container. By Dalton's Law, the sum of the partial pressures is the total pressure. In short,**

$$\text{partial pressure} = \text{proportion by volume} \times \text{total pressure}$$

$$p_{\text{nitrogen}} = \frac{78.1}{100} \times 10.0 \text{ atm} = 7.81 \text{ atm}$$

$$p_{\text{oxygen}} = \frac{20.9}{100} \times 10.0 \text{ atm} = 2.09 \text{ atm}$$

$$p_{\text{other gases}} = \frac{1.00}{100} \times 10.0 \text{ atm} = 0.10 \text{ atm}$$

2.6   THE PRESSURE OF A GAS CONFINED BY A LIQUID

A quantity of gas confined by a liquid will undergo a change of pressure simply by raising or lowering the liquid level. Such changes commonly occur in laboratory manipulations of gases in **eudiometers** (inverted graduated gas-collecting tubes, such as are pictured in Fig. 2.5).

To find the total pressure of a confined gas, note the level of the liquid with which it is in contact. If this level is lower than that of the unconfined liquid, the pressure of the confined gas (P_2 in Fig. 2.5) must be

[*] The vapor pressures of solids are usually too small to influence gas pressures significantly. The subject is treated in more detail in the next chapter.

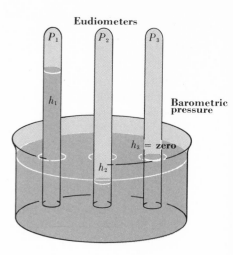

Eudiometers

P_1 P_2 P_3

Barometric pressure

h_1

$h_3 = $ **zero**

h_2

Fig. 2.5. *Gas confined by a liquid.*

greater than barometric pressure,

P_2 = barometric pressure + pressure exerted by confined liquid of
    height h_2

This difference can be thought of as an excess gas pressure that depresses
the liquid level in the tube. If the confined liquid level is elevated, then
the pressure (P_1 in Fig. 2.5) of the gas must be less than barometric
pressure,

P_1 = barometric pressure − pressure exerted by confined liquid of
    height h_1

This condition can be thought of as a rarefied gas that sucks the liquid
up in the tube. The general relationship is

$$\begin{matrix}\text{pressure of} \\ \text{confined gas } (P)\end{matrix} = \begin{matrix}\text{barometric} \\ \text{pressure}\end{matrix} \begin{matrix}+\text{ pressure exerted by} \\ \text{depressed liquid} \\ or \\ -\text{ pressure needed to support} \\ \text{elevated liquid}\end{matrix} \qquad (15)$$

The pressure exerted by a column of any liquid is the product of its
height (h) and density (d),

$$\text{height (cm)} \times \text{density}\left(\frac{\text{g}}{\text{cm}^3}\right) = \text{pressure}\left(\frac{\text{g}}{\text{cm}^2}\right)$$

Therefore, for a given height of liquid, the greater the density, the greater
the pressure it exerts. If we compare any liquid at $t°C$ with mercury at
$0°C$, we have

$$\begin{matrix}\text{height of mercury} \\ \text{column (mm, } 0°C)\end{matrix} = \begin{matrix}\text{height of liquid} \\ \text{column (mm, } t°C)\end{matrix} \times \frac{\begin{matrix}\text{density of liquid} \\ \text{(at } t°C)\end{matrix}}{\begin{matrix}\text{density of mercury} \\ \text{(at } 0°C)\end{matrix}}$$

But the height of a mercury column in mm at 0°C is numerically the same as the pressure in torr units, and the density of mercury at 0°C is 13.5951 g/ml. Substituting these values in the previous equation, and solving for the pressure, we have

$$\begin{array}{c}\text{pressure of} \\ \text{liquid column} = \\ \text{(torr)}\end{array} \begin{array}{c}\text{height of} \\ \text{liquid column} \\ \text{(mm)}\end{array} \times \frac{\text{density of liquid (g/ml)}}{13.5951 \text{ g/ml}}$$

Substituting the above expression for pressure of a liquid column in Equation (15),

$$\begin{array}{c}\text{pressure of} \\ \text{confined} \\ \text{gas } (P) \\ \text{(torr)}\end{array} = \begin{array}{c}\text{barometric} \\ \text{pressure} \pm \\ \text{(torr)}\end{array} \begin{array}{c}\text{depth or height} \\ \text{of confining} \\ \text{liquid} \\ \text{(mm)}\end{array} \times \frac{\begin{array}{c}\text{density of confining} \\ \text{liquid (g/ml)}\end{array}}{13.5951 \text{ g/ml}}$$

(16)

EXAMPLE 4   **Referring to Fig. 2.5, the confining liquid is water at 20°C, h_1 is 15.00 cm above the liquid level in the vessel, and h_2 is 6.31 cm below the liquid level. The barometer reading is 767.5 torr. Density of water at 20°C is 0.9982 g/ml. What are the values of P_1, P_2, and P_3?**

ANSWER   **From Equation (16),**

$$P_1 = 767.5 \text{ torr} - \left(150.0 \text{ torr} \times \frac{0.9982 \text{ g/ml}}{13.60 \text{ g/ml}} \right)$$

$$= 756.5 \text{ torr}$$

$$P_2 = 767.5 \text{ torr} + \left(63.1 \text{ torr} \times \frac{0.9982}{13.60} \right)$$

$$= 772.1 \text{ torr}$$

$$P_3 = 767.5 \text{ torr}$$

EXAMPLE 5   **Referring to Fig. 2.5, if oxygen is collected over water at 20°C in the three tubes, what is the partial pressure of the oxygen in each tube?**

ANSWER   **From Dalton's Law,**

$$P = p_{\text{oxygen}} + p_{\text{water vapor}}$$

and, from Appendix V (page 800), the vapor pressure of water at 20°C is 17.5 torr. Therefore

$$p_{\text{oxygen}} = P - 17.5 \text{ torr}$$

$$= 756.5 \text{ torr} - 17.5 \text{ torr} = 739.0 \text{ torr (first tube)}$$

$$= 772.1 \text{ torr} - 17.5 \text{ torr} = 754.6 \text{ torr (second tube)}$$

$$= 767.5 \text{ torr} - 17.5 \text{ torr} = 750.0 \text{ torr (third tube)}$$

2.7   AVOGADRO'S LAW; $V \propto N$; $V = constant \times N$

The hypothesis "equal volumes of all gases at the same temperature and pressure contain the same number of molecules" was vaguely conceived by scientists as early as about 1760; it was first clearly delineated by Amadeo Avogadro in 1811, and is therefore named in his honor. The concept is highly useful, since it teaches us that we may select equal numbers of molecules simply by selecting equal gas volumes at constant temperature and pressure.

EXAMPLE 6   One gram of radium emits alpha particles at the rate of 11.6×10^{17} per year. Each alpha particle becomes a molecule of helium. The total volume of the 11.6×10^{17} molecules is 0.0430 ml at standard conditions. How many molecules are there in one liter of helium under standard conditions? In one liter of oxygen? In one liter of any gas?

ANSWER

$$\frac{N}{V} = \frac{11.6 \times 10^{17} \text{ molecules}}{0.043 \text{ ml}} \times 1000 \frac{\text{ml}}{\text{liter}}$$

$$= 2.70 \times 10^{22} \frac{\text{molecules}}{\text{liter}}$$

Since N/V is a constant regardless of the nature of the gas, the ratio applies to helium, oxygen, or any other gas.

2.8   GRAHAM'S LAW; $u \propto \dfrac{1}{\sqrt{m}}$; $u = \dfrac{constant}{\sqrt{m}}$

This relationship states that the average velocity of a molecule at a given temperature is inversely proportional to the square root of its mass. The velocity of a molecule directly controls two closely related phenomena: **diffusion** and **effusion** (Fig. 2.6). Diffusion refers to the translational kinetic movement (see Appendix I, page 776) of one set of molecules within another set. Effusion refers to the escape of molecules

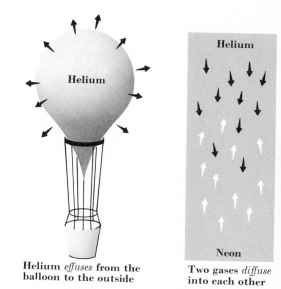

Fig. 2.6. Diffusion and effusion.

Helium *effuses* from the balloon to the outside

Two gases *diffuse* into each other

through orifices or porous barriers. Faster molecules diffuse more rapidly because they get past obstacles (other molecules) in less time; they effuse more rapidly because they have a better chance of hitting a hole in a given time.

The density of a gas, as measured at a given temperature and pressure, is its mass divided by its volume, or $d = mN/V$, where m is the mass per molecule of the gas. But, by Avogadro's Law, N/V is a constant at a given temperature and pressure. Therefore, the density is proportional to m. It follows from

$$u \propto \frac{1}{\sqrt{m}}$$

that

$$u \propto \frac{1}{\sqrt{d}}$$

or the rate of diffusion or effusion of a gas is inversely proportional to the square root of its density. This statement is the usual expression of Graham's Law.

EXAMPLE 7 **Two balloons at the same temperature, of equal volume and porosity, are each filled to a pressure of 4 atmospheres, one with 16 kg of oxygen, the other with 1 kg of hydrogen. The oxygen balloon leaks to a pressure of $\frac{1}{2}$ atmosphere in one hour. How long will it take for the hydrogen balloon to reach a pressure of $\frac{1}{2}$ atmosphere?**

ANSWER **From Graham's Law,**

$$\frac{rate_{hydrogen}}{rate_{oxygen}} = \frac{\sqrt{16 \text{ kg per unit volume}}}{\sqrt{1 \text{ kg per unit volume}}} = 4$$

The hydrogen effuses 4 times as rapidly; it will reach $\frac{1}{2}$ atmosphere in $\frac{1}{4}$ hour.

2.9 THE IDEAL GAS LAW; THE MOLE; GAS DENSITIES; $PV = nRT$

The relationship $PV \propto NT$ may be expressed as $PV = constant \times NT$. To evaluate the constant, we must adopt standard values for any three of the variables; the value of the fourth variable will be fixed by this selection. The standard values are

P = one standard atmosphere.
T = 273.15°K (the ice point).
V = the volume occupied by 31.9988 grams of oxygen at the standard temperature and pressure = 22.4136 liters. (The rationale for the selection of this particular volume will be elaborated in the discussion of molecular weights in Chapter 4.)

N = the number of molecules fixed by the selection of the above values for P, T, and V. Since the quantity is fixed it need not be measured, only named. It is called the **Avogadro number** of molecules, designated $\mathfrak{N}$, and the quantity of substance that contains this number of molecules is called **one mole.** The designation for number of moles is n. The relationship between moles and molecules is

$$n(\text{moles}) \times \mathfrak{N}(\text{Avogadro number, molecules/mole}) = N(\text{molecules})$$

The ideal gas equation may now be expressed in terms of moles (n) and a constant, usually designated R:

$$PV = nRT \tag{17}$$

To evaluate R,

$$
\begin{aligned}
R &= PV/nT \\
&= \frac{1.0000 \text{ atm} \times 22.4136 \text{ liters}}{1.0000 \text{ mole} \times 273.15° \text{ K}} \\
&= 0.082056 \text{ liter atm/mole deg}
\end{aligned}
$$

It will now be possible to execute calculations on a broader basis than is permitted by the two-variable laws described in the preceding sections. There are three approaches:

(a) **Use** $PV = nRT$. Conditions *must* be expressed in the units consistent with those used for R.

(b) **Refer to two sets of conditions,**

$$P_2V_2 = n_2RT_2$$
$$P_1V_1 = n_1RT_1$$

Therefore

$$\frac{P_2V_2}{P_1V_1} = \frac{n_2T_2}{n_1T_1} \tag{18}$$

Solve Equation (18) for the desired term.

(c) **Use the "common sense" method.**

Methods (b) and (c) make it unnecessary to memorize the value of R. The total mass of a gas, w, is the mass of its moles; n and w are therefore in direct proportion to each other,

$$w(\text{grams}) = n(\overline{\text{moles}}) \times \mathfrak{N} \left(\frac{\text{molecules}}{\overline{\text{mole}}} \right) m \left(\frac{\text{grams}}{\overline{\text{molecule}}} \right)$$

Since $\mathfrak{N}$ and, for a given gas, m are constant,

$$w \propto n$$

Then

$$PV = constant \times wT$$

or

$$P = constant \times \frac{w}{V} T$$

But w/V is the density d of the gas. Therefore

$$P = constant \times dT$$

Referring to two sets of conditions for the same gas and dropping the constant, we have

$$\frac{P_2}{P_1} = \frac{d_2}{d_1} \frac{T_2}{T_1} \qquad (19)$$

EXAMPLE 8   (**Compare with Examples 1 and 2.**) **A gas occupies 10.0 liters at standard conditions. What volume will it occupy at 20.0°C and 700 torr?**

ANSWER $V_1 = 10.0$ **liters,** $P_1 = 760$ **torr,** $T_1 = 273°K, P_2 = 700$ **torr,** $T_2 = 293°K.$

From Equation (17)	*"Common sense" method*
$V_2 = V_1 \times \dfrac{\cancel{n}}{\cancel{n}} \times \dfrac{T_2}{T_1} \times \dfrac{P_1}{P_2}$	**New volume = original volume × temperature correction × pressure correction**
	(temperature correction > 1, pressure correction > 1)
$= 10.0 \text{ liters} \dfrac{293°K}{273°K} \times \dfrac{760 \cancel{\text{torr}}}{700 \cancel{\text{torr}}}$	$= 10.0 \text{ liters} \times \dfrac{293°K}{273°K} \times \dfrac{760 \cancel{\text{torr}}}{700 \cancel{\text{torr}}}$

Therefore $V_2 = 11.7$ **liters.**

EXAMPLE 9   **10.0 ml of oxygen is collected over water at 20°C and 770 torr. What is the volume of the dry gas at standard conditions? The vapor pressure of water at 20°C is 17.5 torr.**

ANSWER $V_1 = 10.0$ **ml,** $T_1 = 293°K.$ **To find** P_1 **use the partial pressure law,** $P_T = p_{oxygen} + p_{water}.$ **Therefore**

$$p_{oxygen} = P_T - p_{water} = 770 \text{ torr} - 17.5 \text{ torr} = 753 \text{ torr}$$

P_2 and T_2 are the standard conditions (abbreviation sc), 760 torr and 273°K. Then ("common sense")

$$V_2 = 10.0 \text{ ml} \times \frac{273°\text{K}}{293°\text{K}} \times \frac{753 \text{ torr}}{760 \text{ torr}}$$

$$= 9.23 \text{ ml.}$$

EXAMPLE 10 To what temperature must 1.00×10^{-4} mole of a gas be heated in a 25.0-liter container to maintain a pressure 1.00×10^{-1} torr?

ANSWER This problem is concerned with a single set of conditions, not with ratios between different sets. It will therefore be best to use Equation (17) directly. Solving for T,

$$T = \frac{PV}{nR}$$

$$= \frac{1.00 \times 10^{-1} \text{ torr} \times 25.0 \text{ liters}}{760 \frac{\text{torr}}{\text{atm}} \times 1.00 \times 10^{-4} \text{ mole} \times 0.0821 \frac{\text{liter atm}}{\text{mole deg}}}$$

$$= 401°\text{K, or } 128°\text{C.}$$

EXAMPLE 11 Using the data of Example 6 (page 24), calculate the Avogadro number.

ANSWER The Avogadro number is the number of molecules in 22.414 liters, or one mole, of a gas. From Example 6, this is

$$2.70 \times 10^{22} \frac{\text{molecules}}{\text{liter}} \times 22.4 \frac{\text{liters}}{\text{mole}} = 6.05 \times 10^{23} \text{ molecules/mole}$$

The significance and utility of the Avogadro number will be developed in subsequent chapters. Its value has been determined by a number of methods in addition to the one described by Example 6, and the best currently accepted value is $(6.0225 \pm 0.0003) \times 10^{23}$ molecules/mole.

EXAMPLE 12 10.0 grams of a gas occupy 50.0 liters at 25.0°C and 600 torr. What is the density of the gas at standard conditions?

ANSWER $P_1 = 600$ torr, $P_2 = 760$ torr, $T_1 = 298°$K, $T_2 = 273°$K, $d_1 = \dfrac{10.0 \text{ g}}{50.0 \text{ liters}}$.

From Equation (19)

$$d_2 = d_1 \times \frac{P_2}{P_1} \times \frac{T_1}{T_2}$$

$$= \frac{10.0 \text{ g}}{50.0 \text{ liters}} \times \frac{760}{600} \times \frac{298}{273}$$

$$= 0.277 \text{ g/liter}$$

"Common sense" method

Solving for new volume at sc,

$$\text{volume}_{sc} = 50.0 \text{ liters} \times \frac{273°\text{K}}{298°\text{K}} \times \frac{600 \text{ torr}}{760 \text{ torr}}$$

$$= 36.1 \text{ liters}$$

$$\text{density}_{sc} = \frac{\text{wt}}{\text{vol}_{sc}} = \frac{10.0 \text{ g}}{36.1 \text{ liters}}$$

$$= 0.277 \text{ g/liter}$$

Real gases do not behave in an ideal way. The important differences between ideal and real gases, and the consequences of these differences, are given in the following tabulation.

Ideal gases	Real gases	Difference
Molecules have no interacting forces	Molecules of gases do exert forces of attraction among themselves and to other matter. A result of such mutual attractions is the formation, at any time, of loosely bonded aggregates of two or more gas molecules. The total number of molecules, and hence of moles, is, in effect, reduced by such aggregation. The pressure exerted by the gas is therefore reduced ($P \propto N$, see discussion of Dalton's Law).	The pressure exerted by a given quantity of a real gas in a rigid container at a definite temperature is less than that predicted by the ideal gas law. Therefore, since $(PV)_{ideal} = nRT$, or $$\frac{(PV)_{ideal}}{nRT} = 1$$ and P_{real} is less than P_{ideal}, $$\frac{(PV)_{real}}{nRT} < 1$$
Molecules are points that have no volume	Molecules occupy volume that is relatively independent of P and T	The volume occupied by a given quantity of a real gas at a definite T and P is greater than that predicted by the ideal gas law. Therefore, since $V_{real} > V_{ideal}$, $$\frac{(PV)_{real}}{nRT} > 1$$

Deviations from ideal behavior are shown in Fig. 2.7. For hydrogen, the molecular attractive forces are low and do not produce a predominant PV effect; instead, the volume added by the molecules yields PV values exceeding the ideal values at all pressures shown on the graph. For nitrogen, the interattractive forces are great enough to yield negative PV deviations up to about 150 atmospheres. Intermolecular attractions in carbon dioxide, even at 40°C, are obviously much more important than those in nitrogen at 0°C. For both nitrogen and carbon dioxide a pressure exists (150 atmospheres and 600 atmospheres, respectively) at which the two effects cancel each other and the PV product is ideal.

At low pressures, the volume of a given quantity of gas becomes large,

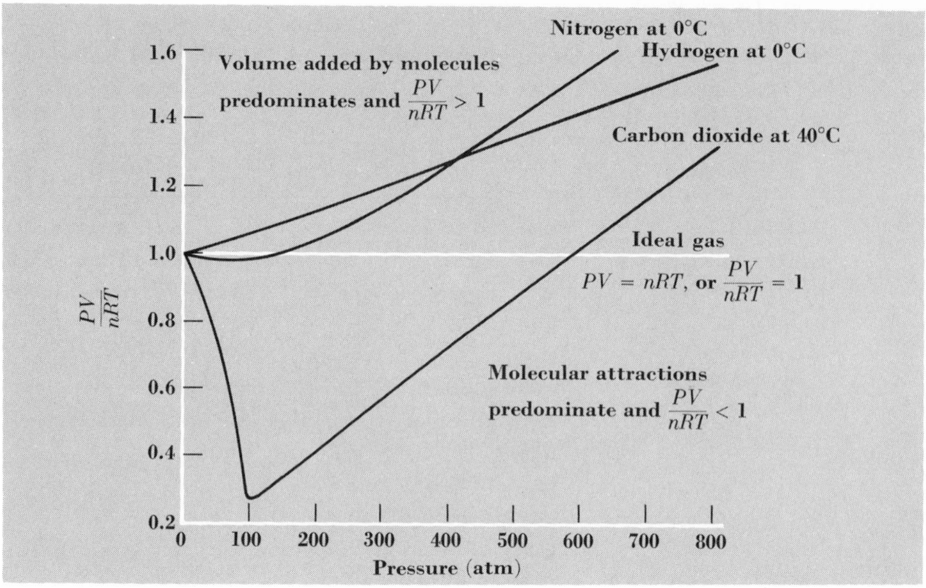
Nitrogen at 0°C
Hydrogen at 0°C
Volume added by molecules
predominates and $\frac{PV}{nRT} > 1$
Carbon dioxide at 40°C
Ideal gas
$PV = nRT$, or $\frac{PV}{nRT} = 1$
Molecular attractions
predominate and $\frac{PV}{nRT} < 1$
$\frac{PV}{nRT}$
1.6
1.4
1.2
1.0
0.8
0.6
0.4
0.2
0
100
200
300
400
500
600
700
800
Pressure (atm)

Fig. 2.7. *Deviations from ideal gas behavior.*

and the volume occupied by the molecules becomes relatively small. Since the molecules become more widely separated at low pressures, their mutual attractions and tendencies to aggregate lessen. At high temperatures, the molecules have greater kinetic energy and their tendencies to aggregate lessen. Thus, high temperatures and low pressures both favor ideal gas behavior.

At one atmosphere, deviations from ideality are of the order of 1% for most gases.

Problems

1. Properties of gases. Offer an explanation for the fact that all gases are transparent.

2. Kelvin scale. Make the following conversions to the Kelvin scale: $-79°C$, $-272.1°C$, $0.000°C$, $5 \times 10^3 °C$. Convert to the Celsius scale: $373.150°K$, $5 \times 10^3 °K$, $0.1°K$.

3. Charles' and Gay-Lussac's Law. A near-frictionless piston of the type schematically shown in the second sketch in Table 2.2 can actually be constructed from a ground-glass syringe whose plunger is spinning at high speed. If such a syringe holds 5.31 ml of air at 20.0°C, what volume will it hold if the air cools to 10.0°C?

4. Boyle's Law. A sample of helium occupies 100.0 ml at 1.00 standard atmosphere. Assuming that the temperature remains constant, what volume will the helium occupy (a) at 2.0 atm, (b) at 100 torr, (c) at 1.00×10^{-2} torr?

Answer. (a) 50 ml; (b) 760 ml; (c) 7.60×10^6 ml.

5. Dalton's Law. A mixture of nitrogen and oxygen at 1.00 atmosphere pressure is stored in a 2.0-ft^3 iron container at constant temperature. The iron eventually reacts with all the oxygen, converting it to a solid oxide of negligible volume. The final pressure is 600 torr. (a) What is the final volume of the nitrogen? (b) What are the initial and final partial pressures?

6. Avogadro's Law. A 10-ml container holds 1.8×10^{19} molecules of nitrogen at a certain temperature and pressure. (a) How many molecules would remain if the container volume were compressed to 5.0 ml? (b) What volume in liters is needed to hold 6.0×10^{23} molecules at the same temperature and pressure? (c) What volume in ml would be occupied by 1.8×10^{10} molecules at the same temperature and pressure?

      Answer. (a) 1.8×10^{19} molecules; (b) 3.3×10^2 liters; (c) 1.0×10^{-8} ml.

7. Graham's Law. Argon gas is 10 times as dense as helium gas at the same temperature and pressure. Which gas diffuses faster? How much faster?

      Answer. Helium, 3.2 times as fast.

8. Ideal gas law. A sample of gas occupies 12.2 liters at 15°C and 800 torr. What will its volume be at 20°C and 400 torr?

      Answer. 24.8 liters.

9. Ideal gas law. 50.0 ml of oxygen is collected over water at 25.0°C and 760 torr. Calculate the volume of the dry gas at standard conditions.

Additional problems*

10. Properties of gases. Suppose you were asked to supply a stated mass of gas in a given rigid container at a specified pressure and temperature. Would it be likely that you could fulfill the request? Explain.

11. Charles' and Gay-Lussac's Law. The device shown in Fig. 2.8 is a gas thermometer. (a) At the ice point, the gas volume is 1.00 liter. What is the temperature in °C when the volume is 1.01 liters? (b) What volume in liters would the gas occupy at the steam point? (c) What modifications may be made to increase the sensitivity of the thermometer?

      Answer. (a) 3°C; (b) 1.37 liters.

12. Absolute zero. The densities of dry air at 0°C and 100°C are 12.9×10^{-4} and 9.46×10^{-4} g/ml, respectively. Calculate the value of absolute zero in

    * Problems 1–9 are a minimal assignment for covering the chapter. The following problems are additional drill and include some more difficult calculations.

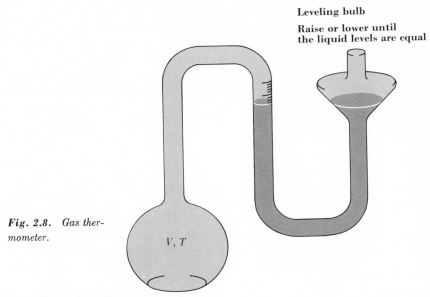

Leveling bulb

Raise or lower until the liquid levels are equal

Fig. 2.8. Gas thermometer.

V, T

degrees C. *Hint:* extrapolate the specific volumes (reciprocals of densities) to zero volume.

13. Pressure. (a) A diver descends to a depth of 15.0 m in pure water (density 1.00 g/cm³). The barometric pressure is 1.02 standard atmospheres. What is the total pressure on the diver, expressed in atmospheres? (b) If, at the same barometric pressure, the water were the Dead Sea (1.20 g/cm³), what would the total pressure be?

Answer. (a) 2.48 atm; (b) 2.97 atm.

14. Gas pressure. A glass vessel is strong enough to resist implosion when it is evacuated to 1×10^{-2} torr and when the outside pressure is as high as one standard atmosphere. By what factor must the vessel be strengthened if it is to resist evacuation to 1×10^{-9} torr at the same outside pressure?

15. Boyle's Law. Assume that the value of k in $PV = k$ is 12. Plot the graph of P (abscissa) vs. V (ordinate) for the values $V = 1, 2, 3, 4, 6,$ and 12. What is the shape of the curve? Plot the graph of $1/P$ (abscissa) vs. V (ordinate) for the same values of V. What plot is obtained?

16. Eudiometer. Referring to the first eudiometer, Fig. 2.5 (page 22), assume that the confining liquid is mercury at 0°C, the barometric pressure is 755.0 torr, h_1 is 15.0 cm, and the eudiometer contains 21.3 ml of hydrogen. The eudiometer is now lifted up at constant temperature until h_1 is 17.0 cm. (a) What was the initial pressure of the hydrogen? (b) What is the pressure after the tube is lifted? (c) What is the new gas volume in the tube?

Answer. (a) 605 torr; (b) 585 torr; (c) 22.0 ml.

17. Boyle's Law. An experiment is conducted at 50°C and 750 torr in a 2.00-liter flask which contains an evacuated bulb of 100-ml capacity. The bulb breaks (implodes). What is the new pressure in the flask, assuming negligible change in temperature?

18. Boyle's Law. A balloon is filled with air to a gage pressure of 5.0 lb/in². Barometric pressure is 15 lb/in². It is then squeezed to half its volume. What is the new gage pressure? See discussion of gage pressure in Appendix I (page 780).

Answer. 25 lb/in².

19. Dalton's Law. 100 ml of hydrogen gas is collected over water at 283°K and 800 torr. The vapor pressure of water at this temperature is 9.2 torr. The hydrogen is separated from the water and dried at constant temperature. (a) What is the new volume of the dry hydrogen at standard conditions? (b) If the water vapor that was removed from the hydrogen were stored at 100°C and 12.1 torr, what volume would it occupy?

20. Dalton's Law. The irradiation of oxygen gas with ultraviolet light changes some oxygen to ozone (page 712). Two molecules of ozone are produced from three molecules of oxygen. If oxygen at 760 torr is irradiated at constant volume and temperature until 5.00% of it is converted to ozone, what will the final pressure be?

Answer. 747 torr.

21. Graham's Law. The average velocity of hydrogen molecules at 25°C is 0.32 mile/sec. Pentane vapor is about 36 times as dense as hydrogen under the same conditions of temperature and pressure. What is the average velocity of the pentane molecules at 25°C?

Answer. 0.053 mile/sec.

22. Ideal gas law. Evaluate and assign units to the constant R for the ideal gas law expressed in the form $PV = \mathfrak{N}RT$, where $\mathfrak{N} = 6.02 \times 10^{23}$ molecules and the other factors have the same standard values as given in Section 2.9.

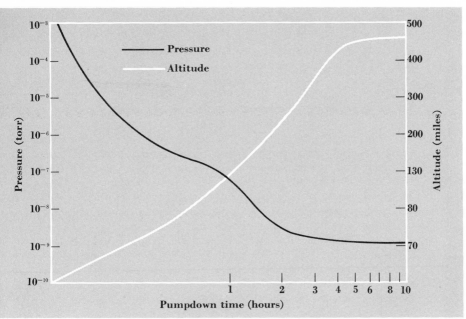

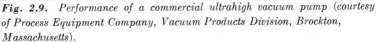

Fig. 2.9. *Performance of a commercial ultrahigh vacuum pump (courtesy of Process Equipment Company, Vacuum Products Division, Brockton, Massachusetts).*

23. Ideal gas law. A sample of gas occupies 0.022 ml at standard conditions. What will its volume be at 300°K and 770 torr?

24. Ideal gas law. 22.4 liters of oxygen at standard conditions weigh 32.0 grams. What is the density of oxygen in g/liter at 100°C and 1.20 atmospheres?

Answer. 1.25 g/liter.

25. Ideal gas law. An automobile tire of 50.0-liter capacity is filled with air to a gage pressure of 30.0 lb/in², at 25.0°C. The barometric pressure is 14.7 lb/in². After being driven at high speed for some distance, the tire warms to 40.0°C and its volume expands to 50.5 liters. What is the new gage pressure?

26. Ideal gas law. Modern vacuum techniques make it possible to reach 10^{-10} torr in laboratory systems. What volume (ml) would 1.00×10^6 molecules of gas occupy at this pressure and 0°C?

Answer. 0.3 ml.

27. Ideal gas law. An article on ultrahigh vacuum which appeared in *Scientific American* states, "In interplanetary space the pressure is estimated to be of the order of 10^{-16} torr. This corresponds to a density of about four molecules per cubic centimeter." What temperature must be assigned to the molecules in interplanetary space for this statement to be true? How do you think a mercury-in-glass thermometer would behave in interplanetary space? Reconcile your answers.

28. Ideal gas law. Figure 2.9 illustrates the performance of a commercial ultrahigh vacuum pumping system in a test space of 2 cubic feet.

(a) What pumpdown time is needed to prepare the test space at 200-mile simulated altitude?

(b) What pressure does the system reach at this condition?

(c) To what expansion of the test space (in cubic miles) is this evacuation equivalent, assuming that original pressure is 1 atmosphere and the temperature is constant at 0°C?

(d) What is the concentration of gas in molecules/cm³ after evacuation?

(e) The pumping system consists of a mechanical pump for initial evacuation and a molecular diffusion pump for attaining the higher vacuum. Judging from the shape of the pumpdown curve, at about what pressure do you think the diffusion pump begins to operate?

Answer. (a) 1.7 hours; (b) 8×10^{-9} torr;
(c) 1.3 miles³; (d) 3×10^8 molecules/cm³.

29. Ideal gas law. The lowest pressures are obtainable by cooling matter to temperatures close to absolute zero. At 0.1°K, it is estimated that the vapor pressure of helium (the only pressure that need be considered) is so low that it contributes 3×10^{-11} atom per ml of space. Each molecule of helium consists of one atom. (a) Since the molecules of helium do not divide, what is the meaning of "3×10^{-11} atom per ml"? (b) Calculate the pressure under the conditions stated.

30. Ideal gas law. A monkey rides in a rocket capsule filled with oxygen at 1 atm pressure. He breathes 20 times per minute and consumes 0.05 liter of oxygen per breath; the carbon dioxide that he exhales is removed by a chemical absorbent. This oxygen supply is replenished from a 1-liter tank, initially at 100 atm pressure, which releases oxygen at a rate just sufficient to maintain constant pressure in the capsule. How long will it take before the tank can no longer deliver oxygen to the capsule (assume constant temperature)? (*Hint:* at what tank pressure will gas delivery stop?)

31. Deviations from ideal behavior. (a) Referring to Fig. 2.7 (page 30), compare, qualitatively, the intermolecular attractive forces among nitrogen, hydrogen, and carbon dioxide at 100 atm pressure. (b) At 600 atm and 0°C, the PV product for nitrogen exceeds that for hydrogen. Does this mean that the intermolecular forces in hydrogen are the greater at this pressure? Why or why not?

32. Molecular motion. Use a blank sheet of paper, a rule, and a protractor to plot a model of molecular motion as follows. Place a point anywhere on the paper. Starting from this point, draw a straight line according to the following instructions:

(a) Angle of the line from the horizontal: draw a card at random from a poker deck from which the Kings have been removed. Count the value of your card on a scale of 1–12 (Ace = 1, . . . Jack = 11, Queen = 12). Let the angle = value of your card × 30 degrees.

(b) Length of the line: return the Kings and add 3 Jokers to your deck and draw another card at random. Toss a coin. Now refer to Fig. 2.1 (page 12) which plots frequency number vs. molecular speed. Select from the tabulation below a frequency number that corresponds to your card.

Card			Frequency number	Card			Frequency number
♠ A			1	♡ 3–8			6
♠ 2, 3			2	♡ 9–K	♣ A, 2		7
♠ 4–6			3	♣ 3–10			8
♠ 7–10			4	♣ J–K	◇ A–6		9
♠ J–K	♡ A, 2		5	◇ 7–K, Jokers			10

Let the length of your line be the horizontal distance from your frequency number (ordinate scale of Fig. 2.1) to the first intersection with the curve (if the coin was heads) or to the second intersection (if the coin was tails).

Repeat the procedure at least 10 times, the end of each line being the point at which the next line starts.

Discuss the aptness and limitations of this model of molecular motion.

3

Aggregated
states
of
matter

3.1 INTRODUCTION

Solids, liquids, and glasses were characterized in Chapter 1 as coherent states of matter, distinguished from the noncoherent gaseous state. Solids were further characterized as being orderly in the arrangement of their atomic and molecular particles, distinguished from the disordered liquid and glassy states. Finally, liquids and glasses were distinguished from each other according to their degree of rigidity.

3.2 SOLIDS; METHODS OF INVESTIGATION

The geometrical patterns of crystals have been of interest to man since earliest civilization, and more especially since the invention of the microscope. The study of such patterns is the science of **crystallography.** Crystal structures have been classified by systems that depend on the shape of the crystals—the number and relative size of the faces, and the angles between them. The reflection or scattering of electromagnetic radiation by crystals can be related to their internal structure. Since the distances between atoms in matter are of the same order of magnitude as x ray wavelengths, x ray patterns may be expected to give useful information about the arrangement of atoms in crystals. This idea was experimentally verified by Max von Laue in 1912. The diffraction of x rays through crystals, the array of atoms being a diffraction grating, was found to produce patterns of reinforcement and attenuation of the

Fig. 3.1. X ray diffraction pattern of quartz powder (courtesy of Dr. R. H. Bell, Lucius Pitkin, Inc., New York).

radiation. X ray diffraction patterns, as illustrated in Fig. 3.1, give a good picture of the symmetry of a crystal and of the relative intensities of different crystal planes, but provide no information on the spacing between the planes. In 1913, William Henry Bragg and William Lawrence Bragg (father and son) devised a satisfactory method for measuring the spacing of crystal planes by measuring reflectance angles (Fig. 3.2). Developments and refinements by many other investigators have made x ray analysis a very powerful, if complicated, method of examining orderly arrangements in crystals, crystalline powders, and large molecules like those of proteins, rubber, and textiles.

3.3 THE SPACE LATTICE; THE UNIT CELL

A complete elucidation of the internal structure of a crystal gives all the information about the spatial arrangement of the constituent particles (atoms, ions, or molecules). To describe such an arrangement, we may represent the particles by points or other designations and illustrate

Fig. 3.2. Examination of crystals by x ray reflectance.

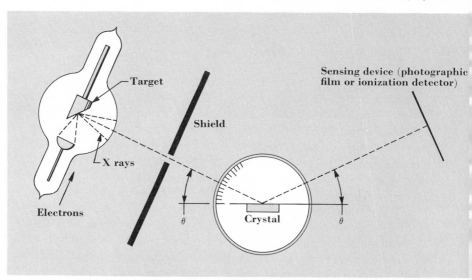

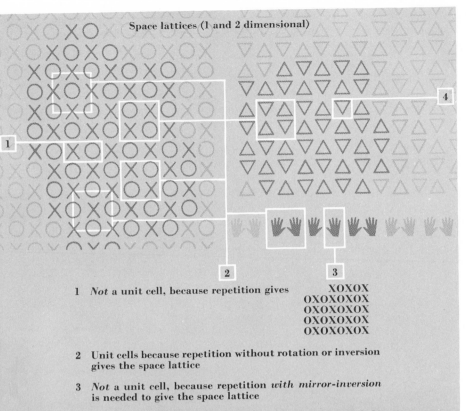

Space lattices (1 and 2 dimensional)

1 *Not* a unit cell, because repetition gives

XOXOX
OXOXOXOX
OXOXOXOX
OXOXOXOX
OXOXOXOX

2 Unit cells because repetition without rotation or inversion gives the space lattice

3 *Not* a unit cell, because repetition *with mirror-inversion* is needed to give the space lattice

4 Not a unit cell, because repetition with rotation is needed to give the space lattice

Fig. 3.3. *The space lattice and the unit cell.*

them in their relative positions in space. Since the atoms vibrate in the crystal because of their thermal energy, each designated position is actually a "center of vibration." Such a representation is called a **space lattice.**

The smallest sample that represents the entire crystal is called the **unit cell** (Fig. 3.3). The crystal may be considered to consist of an indefinite number of unit cells, each one in direct contact with its nearest neighbors, and all similarly oriented in space (not rotated or reflected). If a crystal consists of more than one kind of lattice particle (for example, sodium chloride crystals consist of lattices of sodium ions and chloride ions), we must describe either a separate space lattice for each kind of particle, or else a space lattice for the compound substance in which each point is identified according to the kind of particle that it represents.

What varieties of space lattice can exist in crystalline forms? The number of classifications is surprisingly limited. To understand the nature of the limitation, consider first what types of *regular* polygon can completely fill a 2-dimensional space. Answer: only triangles, squares, and hexagons, all of which have internal angles that are integral fractions of

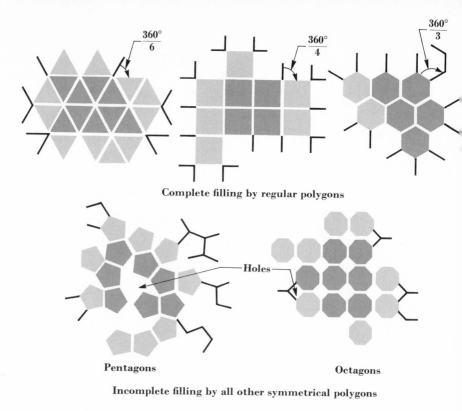

Complete filling by regular polygons

Holes

Pentagons   Octagons

Incomplete filling by all other symmetrical polygons

Fig. 3.4. *Filling two-dimensional space (or "how to tile a bathroom floor").*

360° (see Fig. 3.4). Filling can also be accomplished with *irregular* symmetrical polygons (for example, rectangles or parallelograms), but again we are restricted to 3-, 4-, and 6-sided figures. Extending this to 3-dimensional space leads to the following important conclusion: *symmetrical polyhedra used to fill 3-dimensional space must have faces that are all triangles, quadrilaterals, or hexagons.* One may ask—are there not, for example, pentagonal arrangements of particles in nature? There are—but such shapes do not constitute the lattice pattern in crystalline forms.

In the space lattice, the points (centers of particles) may be assigned to the corners, face-centers, or body-centers of the polyhedra. Crystallographers have classified known lattices into 7 different polyhedral types with one or more assignments of atomic centers to each. These types are illustrated in Fig. 3.5. The cubic type occurs in three different varieties of distribution of atomic centers: simple, body-centered, and face-centered. These appear in Fig. 3.6.

Figure 3.7 illustrates, by means of unit cells, the type of packing that would fill the three different types of cubic space lattice. Note that the **center** of each particle corresponds to a lattice point. Two questions may be asked: (a) how many particles exist within the space defined by the cubic unit cell, and (b) how many particles touch a given particle?

Assignment of Spherical Particles to the Unit Cell. Assignment of particles to the cubic unit cell is made on the following basis (see Fig. 3.7).

A **corner particle** is shared equally by all the unit cells that touch the same point. In two dimensions, four squares can touch a given point. In

Fig. 3.5.   *Types of crystal system.*

Nomenclature	Relation of sides	Relation of angles	Examples
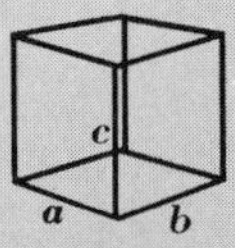 Cubic	$a = b = c$	$\alpha = \beta = \gamma = 90°$	NaCl
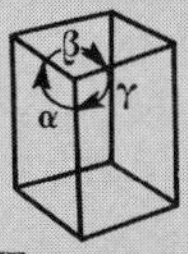 Tetragonal	$a = b \neq c$	$\alpha = \beta = \gamma = 90°$	SnO_2, TiO_2
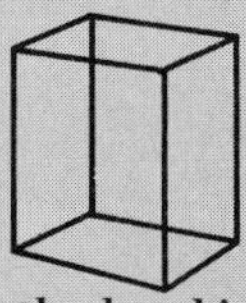 Orthorhombic, or rhombic	$a \neq b \neq c$	$\alpha = \beta = \gamma = 90°$	$BaSO_4$, KNO_3, α-S
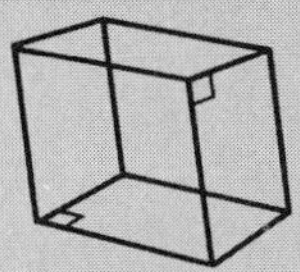 Monoclinic	$a \neq b \neq c$	$\beta = \gamma = 90° \neq \alpha$	$CaSO_4(H_2O)_2$, β-S
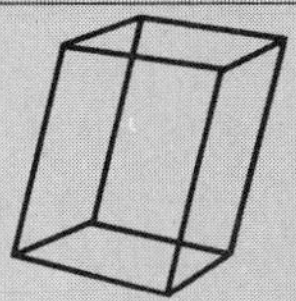 Triclinic	$a \neq b \neq c$	$\alpha \neq \beta \neq \gamma \neq 90°$	$CuSO_4(H_2O)_5$
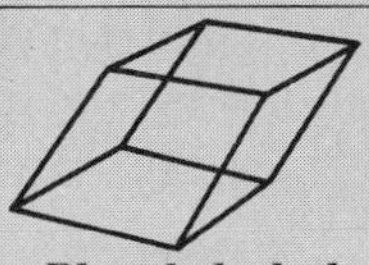 Rhombohedral	$a = b = c$	$\alpha = \beta = \gamma \neq 90°$	Graphite, ice, Cd
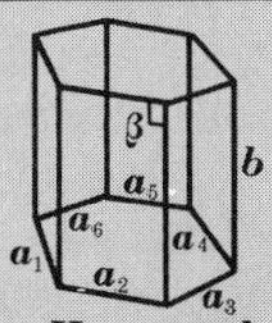 Hexagonal	$a_1 = a_2 = \ldots a_6 =$ or $\neq b$	$\alpha = 120°$, $\beta = 90°$	Quartz, Bi

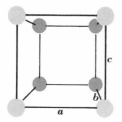
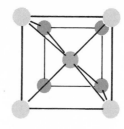
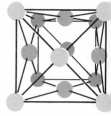

Simple cubic

Body-centered cubic
(CsCl)

Face-centered cubic
(NaCl)

Fig. 3.6. *Cubic crystal systems.*

three dimensions, eight cubes can touch a given point. Therefore only $\frac{1}{8}$ of a corner particle is assigned to one unit cell.

A **face particle** is shared equally between the two cells that face each other. Therefore $\frac{1}{2}$ of a face particle is assigned to one unit cell.

An **edge particle** (not shown in Fig. 3.6 or 3.7) is shared equally among the 4 unit cells that have a common edge. Therefore $\frac{1}{4}$ of an edge particle is assigned to one unit cell.

A **body-centered particle** belongs entirely to its unit cell.

In summary:

Particle	Portion in cubic unit cell
Corner	$\frac{1}{8}$
Edge	$\frac{1}{4}$
Face	$\frac{1}{2}$
Center	1

EXAMPLE 1   **How many atoms are assigned to the unit cell of the body-centered cube?**

ANSWER   **8 corners = 1; 1 center = 1; total = 2.**

Coordination Number or Ligancy.   The number of particles touching* a given particle is an important value called the **coordination number** or **ligancy**. The ligancy for a given space lattice may be determined by inspection of the real or projected model (Fig. 3.7).

In the **simple cube,** each particle touches six adjacent particles (Fig. 3.7).

In the **body-centered cube,** each particle may be considered to be in the center of a cube and touching the eight corner particles (Fig. 3.7).

In the **face-centered cube** the ligancy cannot readily be visualized

---

* "Touching" is a macroscopic concept that is less meaningful on an atomic scale. The ligancy of a particle may therefore be defined simply as its number of nearest neighboring particles.

from the model of Fig. 3.7. An extended face-centered cubic packing is shown in Fig. 3.8, with some spheres removed from the corners. Note that sphere X touches 6 other spheres (numbered 1 through 6) in a single plane that is diagonal to the side of the cube. Above this plane there is room for 3 more spheres to touch X. One would fit in the depressions bounded by 1, 2, X, another by 3, 4, X, and a third by 5, 6, X. Below this plane there are 3 additional spheres (not visible) touching X. The total number of X's nearest neighbors is therefore 12. This ligancy

Fig. 3.7. *Cubic packings.*

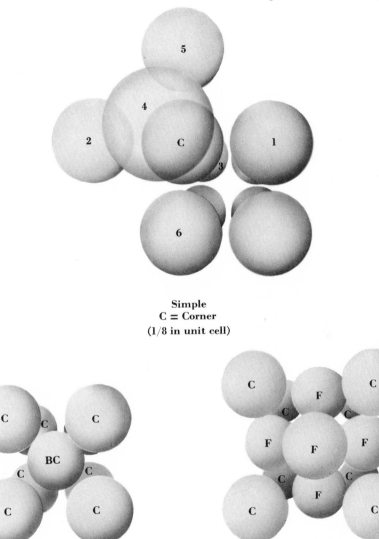

Simple
C = Corner
(1/8 in unit cell)

Body-centered
BC = Body center
(all in unit cell)

Face-centered
F = Face
(1/2 in unit cell)

of 12 is called *cubic closest packing;* it is impossible to pack more uniform spheres into a given space by any other arrangement.*

In summary:

Lattice of uniform spheres	Ligancy
Simple cubic	6
Body-centered cubic	8
Face-centered cubic	12
Hexagonal	12

EXAMPLE 2 **The element chromium exists as a body-centered cubic lattice whose unit cell edge is 2.88 A. The density of chromium is 7.20 g/cm³. How many atoms does 52.0 g of chromium contain?**

ANSWER

$$\text{volume of unit cell} = (2.88 \text{ A})^3 = 23.9 \text{ A}^3$$

$$\text{volume of 52.0 g of chromium} = \frac{52.0 \text{ g}}{7.20 \text{ g/cm}^3}$$

$$= 7.22 \text{ cm}^3$$

$$\text{number of unit cells in this volume} = \frac{7.22 \text{ cm}^3}{23.9 \text{ A}^3/\text{unit cell}} \times (10^8 \text{ A/cm})^3$$

$$= 3.02 \times 10^{23} \text{ unit cells}$$

Since each body-centered cube contains 2 atoms, the total number is

2 atoms/unit cell $\times$ 3.02 $\times$ 10²³ unit cells = 6.04 $\times$ 10²³ atoms

Compound Lattices. Compound lattices, as previously mentioned, are more complicated than the elemental ones just described; the different kinds of atom may differ both in number and in size. The relative number and size of the different kinds of atom will, in turn, determine which types of crystal packing may be favored. Figure 3.9 illustrates the lattices and the packing models of sodium chloride and of cesium chloride. Note that the ligancies in compound lattices do not necessarily correspond to those of elemental lattices. In sodium chloride, for example, the ligancy

* There is another equally closely packed arrangement based on the hexagonal crystal type (Fig. 3.5), called *hexagonal closest packing.*

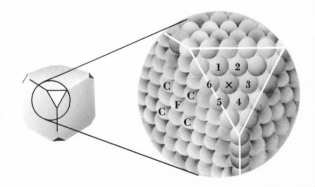

Fig. 3.8. *Cubic closest packing.*

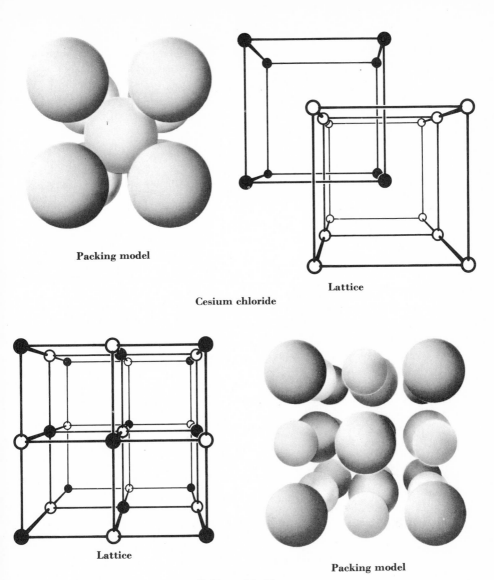

Fig. 3.9. *Compound lattices and packing models. Lighter spheres: sodium or cesium ions. Darker spheres: chloride ions.*

of each ion, taken to be the number of its nearest neighbors *of opposite charge*, is 6.

3.4 THE TETRAHEDRON; THE OCTAHEDRON

White phosphorus is a simple cubic crystal lattice in which only alternate corners of the cube are occupied by phosphorus atoms. The shape defined by four such points is a regular **tetrahedron** (Fig. 3.10b and c). This is a body whose four faces are equilateral triangles. The body-centered

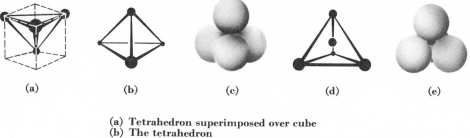

(a) Tetrahedron superimposed over cube
(b) The tetrahedron
(c) Tetrahedral packing
(d) The body-centered tetrahedron (Ligancy = 4)
(e) Body-centered tetrahedral packing

Fig. 3.10.   The tetrahedron.

tetrahedron (Fig. 3.11d and e), with a ligancy of 4, is the geometric basis of a very great number of compounds, notably those of the element carbon.

In the simple cube of uniform spheres (Fig. 3.7), the ligancy is 6. The 6 spheres that touch any given sphere define a regular **octahedron** (Fig. 3.11), a bipyramidal body with eight triangular faces. This shape is the geometric basis of many inorganic compounds.

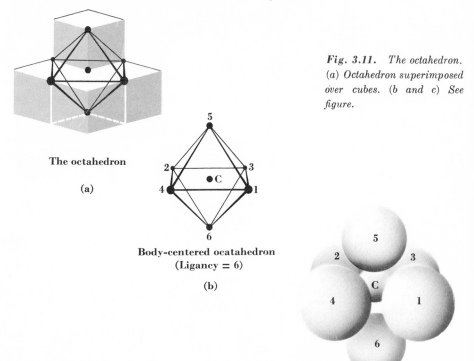

Fig. 3.11.   The octahedron.
(a) Octahedron superimposed over cubes. (b and c) See figure.

The octahedron

(a)

Body-centered ocatahedron
(Ligancy = 6)

(b)

Body-centered octahedral packing

(c)

Real crystals do not necessarily look like the space lattices or unit cells of which they are composed. The shape of real crystals is determined in large part by their relative rates of growth in different directions. For example, an end-face centered monoclinic structure that grows relatively faster at its end-faces than at other planes will develop a long or needle-like crystal shape. A face-centered cubic structure may grow so as to enlarge only its cubic faces (to form a cube) or only its octahedral faces (to form an octahedron) or both (to form a cube with octahedral faces). These forms are shown in Fig. 3.12.

The perfect order depicted in the foregoing sections, like the complete randomness discussed for gases, is an ideal picture. Real crystals are very likely to be imperfect. The importance of lattice imperfections was highlighted by an experience noted by scientists at the Bell Telephone Laboratories. Unexplained short circuits in telephone filter networks were traced to the growth of whisker-like metallic particles on some of the filter-mounting brackets. These "whiskers" were found to be substantially perfect crystals of unusually high strength relative to their cross-sectional areas (Fig. 3.13). Synthesis of the first "perfect" crystals of iron was reported in 1954. Representative data appear in Table 3.1.

This means that the imperfections in ordinary crystals, although only relatively few atoms may be involved, exert marked weakening effects. It seems unlikely that an occasional misplaced or empty lattice point could weaken the crystal so greatly. More plausible is the hypothesis that, in imperfect crystals, entire lines of lattice points are slightly shifted, distorted, or otherwise dislocated. Such defects arise during the growth of the crystal. The crystal then preferentially yields to stress along the defect lines or planes.

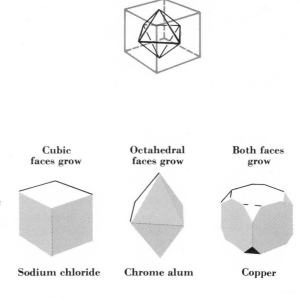

Cubic faces grow	Octahedral faces grow	Both faces grow

Fig. 3.12. *Crystal habits from a face-centered cubic lattice.*

Sodium chloride	Chrome alum	Copper

TABLE 3.1 *Strength of Crystals*

| Substance | Strength (lb/in² of stress needed to break crystal) | |
	Ordinary crystal	Whiskers
Iron	4,000	1,900,000
Gold	200	230,000
Graphite	40,000	3,000,000
Copper	5,000	600,000

Fig. 3.13. *Crystal whiskers. (Courtesy of S. M. Arnold, Bell Telephone Laboratories, Murray Hill, New Jersey.)*

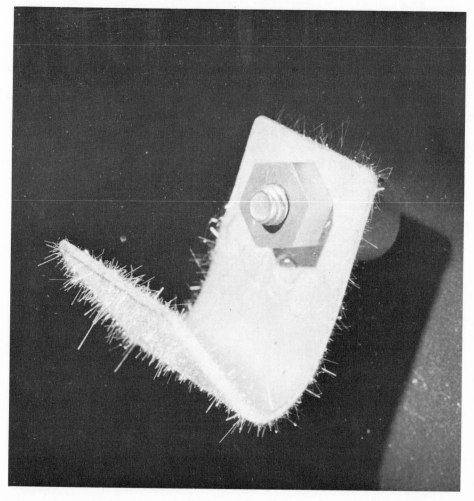

Another effect of lattice imperfection is solid-state diffusion. It is found, for example, that a disk of gold that is sealed (or even tightly pressed) onto the end of a cylinder of lead will gradually diffuse into it, forming a lead-gold alloy. At 200°C, substantial diffusion occurs within a matter of days. It is postulated that lattice vacancies in the lead allow the almost equal-sized gold atoms to occupy the empty sites. The random shifting of atoms into these holes promotes diffusion. Unequally sized atoms may exhibit solid-state diffusion if the smaller atoms can slip among the larger ones (for example, carbon in iron), like a cyclist in stalled truck traffic.

3.6 LIQUIDS; GLASSES

The liquid state cannot yet be described by any concept that has the intellectual elegance of the theories of the gaseous or crystalline states. Nonetheless, important advances have been made by Henry Eyring, J. D. Bernal, and others.

Is there any order at all in liquid structure? X ray examination shows diffuse diffraction patterns indicating some limited regularity—but greatly contrasting with the sharp patterns obtained from crystalline solids. There are, of course, conditions (at or somewhat below the freezing point) under which a given substance may exist as either a liquid or a solid, with not much difference in density between the two states. Under such conditions the coordination number, or ligancy, in the liquid state cannot differ greatly from that of the solid. Thus, in a liquid, each individual atom or molecule may be thought of as occupying a lattice point and having an immediate environment that is crystalline-like. The lattice itself, however, is so defective that no long-range order exists. A highly defective lattice of this type offers little resistance to stress—hence a liquid has fluidity. Another way of looking at this is to consider that there are many alternative types of disordered structure differing little in energy among themselves; hence movement of the liquid, which involves a series of shifts from one structure to another, can be accomplished with little work. Still another way to regard the liquid state is as a crystalline-like mass interspersed with molecular-sized spaces whose arrangements are entirely random, or gas-like. Molecules may enter or leave these "holes"; this interchange produces over-all randomizing and fluidity. As may be visualized from Fig. 3.4, a favored geometrical arrangement in the liquid state is pentagonal—producing local regularities but precluding over-all order.

If a liquid is cooled until the decrease in molecular energy and the increase in density rob it of its fluidity, and if crystallization does not occur, then the substance becomes a **glass**. A glass thus has the over-all randomness of a liquid. When a glass is heated, fluid properties appear gradually, since no sudden breakup of an orderly structure is required.

Examples of liquids which, on cooling, are likely to produce glasses rather than crystalline solids include the following:

(a) A molten mixture of metal silicates cools to give the material whose common name is "glass."

(b) Molten tar, on cooling, forms a glassy product. If a piece of cold "solid" tar is cracked, the vitreous (glassy) appearance of the fresh surface is apparent.

(c) Melted sugar compositions frequently fail to crystallize on cooling. Ordinary "hard candy" is a glassy solid obtained from such melts. "Rock candy," by contrast, is crystalline sugar.

3.7 VISCOSITY; FLUIDITY; SURFACE TENSION; WETTING; CAPILLARITY

The **viscosity** of a liquid is its resistance to flow; one may think of it as a kind of internal friction. A liquid of high viscosity is said to be **viscous** or, simply, "thick." When viscosity is so high that flow becomes negligible, the matter is said to be **glassy** or **vitreous.** As elaborated above, there is no sharp demarcation between being viscous and being glassy. The reciprocal of viscosity is **fluidity;** a highly fluid liquid is said to be **free-flowing, mobile,** or "thin."

A molecule can be moved from one point in the body of a liquid to another (point A to point B, Fig. 3.14) with an expenditure of work depending on the viscosity of the liquid and the speed of the displacement. If the displacement is infinitesimally slow, no work at all is needed. But consider the requirements for moving a molecule from the body of a liquid to the surface (point C). As it approaches the surface, it is subjected to a greatly unbalanced force toward the body of the liquid, where there are more molecules to exert attraction. Thus, extra work must be done to move a molecule to the surface, and the surface molecules are therefore a higher-energy group than the nonsurface molecules. The surface molecules, being constrained to two dimensions, are also more highly ordered than the nonsurface molecules. It is "natural" (see discussion of entropy in Section 3.9, page 51) for matter to tend to avoid such highly energized, orderly situations; the liquid accomplishes this by minimizing its ratio of surface to volume—it therefore assumes a spherical or drop-like shape. The surface behaves as if it is being pulled by a force along its length—the measure of this effect is called **surface tension,** expressed as force per unit length along the surface, dynes/cm. A dimensionally equivalent expression is **surface energy,** work required to increase the surface by unit area, ergs/cm². When a liquid surface is in

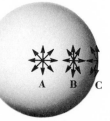

Fig. 3.14. *Surface tension of a liquid.*

A and B show balanced forces; C shows unbalanced forces at the surface

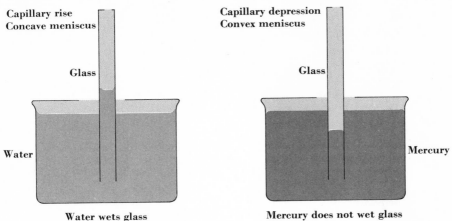

Fig. 3.15. *Capillarity.*

contact with a solid, the molecules at the surface may be more attracted to the solid than to the bulk liquid. If so, they tend to spread out over the solid; the surface area of the liquid is thereby increased. This phenomenon is called **wetting.** If the liquid surface is less attracted by the solid than by the bulk liquid, the spreading phenomenon does not occur and the liquid is said to be **nonwetting.** (These phenomena are also observed between liquids.) Thus, water wets glass; it does not wet candle wax.

If a solid is set perpendicular to the surface of a liquid, then the liquid will be pulled up along the solid (if wetting occurs) or will pull away from it (if it is nonwetting). If the wetted solid is a tube or a set of parallel walls sufficiently close together, then the wetting force can actually pull the liquid up into the tube or between the walls. This phenomenon is called **capillarity,** or **capillary rise.** Under nonwetting conditions, the liquid falls (**capillary depression**). The convex or concave upper surface of the column is called the **meniscus** (Fig. 3.15).

3.8 CHANGES OF STATE

The various states of matter are frequently interconvertible. As the internal energy of matter is increased, the arrangement of its constituent particles becomes more disordered; as the energy is decreased, the opportunities for orderly arrangements increase. There are limitations, however, in both directions. Increase of energy tends to destroy particles as well as to disorder them; sometimes the destruction occurs first. For example, crystalline insulin (a protein) cannot be liquefied; less energy is required to destroy the molecules than to make them exhibit mobile flow. Therefore, for insulin, decomposition precedes melting. In the reverse direction, loss of energy may afford a better chance for an orderly pattern, but it does not assure it. Instead (as discussed earlier), a glass may form.

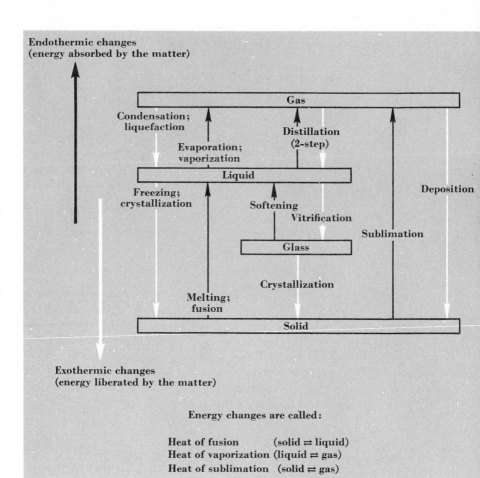

Endothermic changes
(energy absorbed by the matter)

Gas

Condensation;
liquefaction

Distillation
(2-step)

Evaporation;
vaporization

Liquid

Deposition

Freezing;
crystallization

Softening

Vitrification

Sublimation

Glass

Crystallization

Melting;
fusion

Solid

Exothermic changes
(energy liberated by the matter)

Energy changes are called:

Heat of fusion   (solid ⇌ liquid)
Heat of vaporization (liquid ⇌ gas)
Heat of sublimation (solid ⇌ gas)

Fig. 3.16.   Vocabulary of changes of state.

It will be helpful to learn the vocabulary of changes of state, as illustrated in Fig. 3.16. A change of state involves gain or loss of heat that is not related to warming or cooling. Thus the **heat of fusion** of a substance is the amount of heat necessary to melt 1 gram of the solid to a liquid *at the same temperature*. The energy of fusion, as illustrated in Fig. 3.16, is absorbed by the substance from the environment (**endothermic**); the opposite process (freezing) involves the same quantity of heat per gram of substance, but the heat is released by the substance to the environment (**exothermic**). Analogous expressions are used for the other changes of state. The heats are often referred to 1 mole, rather than 1 gram, of a substance.

Any of the endothermic processes in Fig. 3.16 that proceed in the direction solid → liquid → gas, produce a twofold change in the affected matter:

(1) The internal energy of the matter is increased because work is being done to overcome attractive forces.

(2) The orderliness of the molecular arrangement is decreased.

Substance	Melting point (°C)	Boiling point (°C)	Heat (cal/g) of	
			Fusion	Vaporization
Aluminum	658	2057	94	2.5×10^3
Mercury	−39	357	2.8	70.6
Water	0	100	79.7	539.6
Beeswax	62	—	42.3	—
TNT	79	—	22.3	—
Carbon tetrachloride	−24	76.8	4.2	46.4
Ethyl alcohol	−114	78.3	24.9	204

Conversely, in any of the exothermic processes that proceed in the direction gas → liquid → solid, the internal energy is decreased and the order is increased.

Table 3.2 presents data on heats of fusion and vaporization.

3.9 SPONTANEOUS CHANGE; ENTROPY

Which set of processes shown in Fig. 3.16, the exo- or the endothermic ones, would be expected to be "natural" or "spontaneous"? The direction of energy flow will be influenced by the relative temperatures of the system and the environment; if the environment is cold, then heat will tend to flow out of the matter, and the gas → solid processes will be favored. The reverse will be true in a hot environment.

There is also, however, *a natural tendency for disorder.* This deceptively simple idea has consequences of the most far-reaching nature. For changes of state, it means there is *always* a drive that favors the solid → gas processes, regardless of the outside temperature. Thus, it is not necessary to place solids or liquids in a warm environment for them to evaporate; evaporation will occur even when they are cooling. Examples: snow sublimes even on a cold winter day; moth-repellent crystals sublime in a closet, even though the temperature may be falling. In fact, practically all the matter in the universe is in the gaseous state; aggregated states of matter may be regarded as freakish exceptions of very rare occurrence.

The attribute expressing the disorder or randomness of a system is called the **entropy.** The relationship between the entropy and the properties of a system can be arrived at either from statistical or from thermodynamic (heat-work) considerations.

Statistically, we may argue that disordered conditions are more probable than ordered ones because there are many more of the former. We may visualize this with the simple model of a tic-tac-toe field used by a

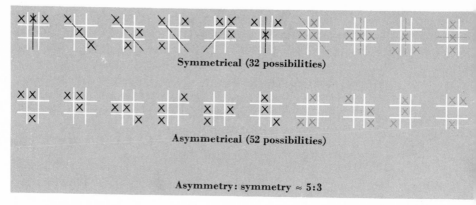

Symmetrical (32 possibilities)

Asymmetrical (52 possibilities)

Asymmetry: symmetry ≈ 5:3

Fig. 3.17. *Entropy on a tic-tac-toe field*

single player (Fig. 3.17). If he makes his three marks without plan, what are his chances of obtaining an orderly arrangement? Order is characterized by symmetry, or repetition of unit parts. Let us therefore say that an orderly arrangement is one which can be folded so that the facing sides superimpose exactly on each other. The "fold line" is then called a line of symmetry. The total possible number of plays is 84. Of these, 32 have a line of symmetry; the chances for disorder are thus 52 to 32, or about 5 to 3. With matter in the quantities usually handled in the laboratory ($\sim 10^{-3}$ to 10^{+3} grams), we deal not with 3 units but with the order of 10^{23} units. Based on chance alone, the preponderances of disorder over order are overwhelming, and are expressed by the largest numbers of any physical significance to man (far larger than the numbers used, say, by astronomers). Statistically, then, there is a natural tendency to disorder. Because chance favors disorder, it follows that there is a *tendency for the entropy of a system to increase.* For change-of-state processes, then, the likely entropy change favors the solid → gas conversions.

Thermodynamically, we may argue that ordered states such as solids are usually lower in energy than disordered states such as gases. (Exception: surface energy—see preceding section.) This preference for low energy decreases, however, as the temperature increases, because at higher temperatures the tendency to disorder becomes more predominant. A mechanical illustration is afforded by a vertically vibrating tray with a shallow depression in the middle (Fig. 3.18). If some balls are placed in

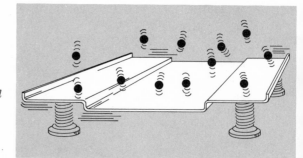

Fig. 3.18. *Energy and disorder in a vibrating tray.*

the tray, and the vibration is gentle, the balls will tend to accumulate in the depression. This accumulation is an ordered arrangement. As the vibration of the tray becomes more vigorous (analogous to a rise of temperature), the balls show less and less preference for the depression. Such a dispersed arrangement is disordered.

3.10 LIQUID-GAS INTERCONVERSION; VAPOR PRESSURE

Molecules of a liquid, like those of a gas (See Fig. 2.1 page 12), exhibit a distribution of energies. The molecules that are energetic, close to the surface, and directed toward the surface, have the best chance to escape (vaporize). The vaporized molecules may be condensed if, in their kinetic path, they reach and are held by the attractive forces of the liquid. Any condensable gas is, in fact, called a **vapor.**

A high *net* rate of vaporization (evaporation) is therefore favored by (1) high temperature of the liquid, (2) small attractive forces in the liquid, (3) a large surface area, (4) low atmospheric pressure above the liquid—to decrease the number of collisions and thereby minimize return of molecules to the liquid, and (5) a mass motion of the atmosphere (breeze) above the liquid to carry away vaporized molecules and minimize re-entry. The housewife takes advantage of these factors when she spreads out her wash on a clothesline on a warm, dry, windy day.

If the enclosed space above a liquid is small enough, and if environmental factors are held constant, a condition will be reached in which the rates of vaporization and of condensation will be equal. This occurs because the rate of vaporization depends on factors that are constant,* while the rate of condensation increases directly with increase in the concentration of vaporized molecules. The increasing rate of condensation will therefore approach the constant rate of vaporization until the two rates are equal. This condition of equal rates is a stable one that tends to perpetuate itself; the system is now said to be in **dynamic equilibrium,** or simply in **equilibrium.**

A system at equilibrium is defined as one in which two opposing processes are going on simultaneously at the same rate. The effect is one of no net change.

The **vapor pressure** of a liquid is the pressure exerted by the vapor that is in equilibrium with the liquid at a definite temperature. The vapor pressure depends on the temperature and on the nature of the liquid; it is, within the limits of the ideal gas law, independent of the presence of other gases.

Vapor pressure may be measured in a number of ways. A direct method makes use of the mercury barometer, illustrated in Fig. 3.19. If a small quantity of liquid is allowed to float up to the top of the mercury column and evaporate into the Torricellian vacuum there, then the vapor establishes equilibrium with the remaining liquid and the vapor pressure in torr

---

* The surface area may change, but in a closed space this provides as much opportunity for condensation as for vaporization, and any effect is therefore compensated.

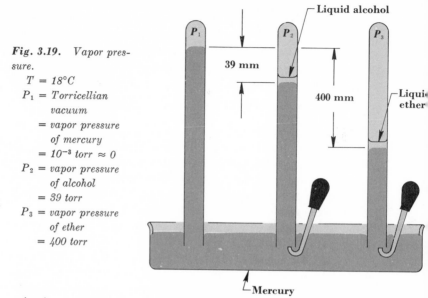

Fig. 3.19. *Vapor pressure.*
$T = 18°C$
P_1 = *Torricellian vacuum*
= *vapor pressure of mercury*
= 10^{-3} *torr* ≈ 0
P_2 = *vapor pressure of alcohol*
= *39 torr*
P_3 = *vapor pressure of ether*
= *400 torr*

39 mm

400 mm

Liquid alcohol

Liquid ether

Mercury

units is numerically equal to the depression of the mercury column in mm. Figure 3.20 illustrates vapor pressure-temperature relationships for several substances.

3.11 THE VAPOR PRESSURE OF WATER; HUMIDITY

The vapor pressure of water at different temperatures is tabulated in Appendix V (page 800) and illustrated in Fig. 3.20 (below). These

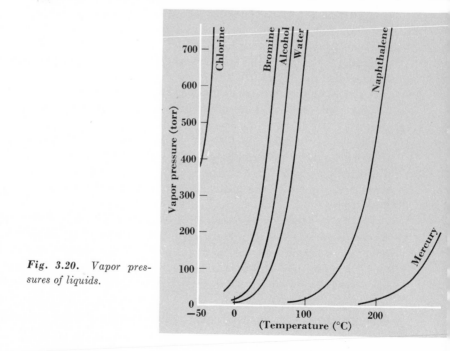

Fig. 3.20. *Vapor pressures of liquids.*

data are *equilibrium values.* The ordinary environments of our daily experience—living and working spaces, indoors and outdoors—all contain water vapor, but equilibrium between the evaporating source and the atmospheric water vapor is seldom reached. The *actual* concentration of water vapor in any space may conveniently be expressed as the partial pressure of water vapor, in torr units. This value is called the **absolute humidity,** or sometimes simply the **humidity.** Then,

$$\text{absolute humidity at temperature } T = \text{partial pressure (torr) of } H_2O \text{ at temperature } T$$

$$\text{equilibrium humidity at temperature } T = \text{vapor pressure (torr) of } H_2O \text{ at temperature } T$$

The ratio of the two values is the **relative humidity** (R.H.),

$$\substack{\text{relative humidity} \\ \text{at temperature } T \\ \text{(percent)}} = \frac{\text{absolute humidity at } T}{\text{equilibrium humidity at } T} \times 100$$

$$= \frac{\text{partial pressure of } H_2O \text{ at } T}{\text{vapor pressure of } H_2O \text{ at } T} \times 100 \qquad (1)$$

Relative humidity of an atmosphere is cited in meteorological reports because it has an important bearing on our physical comfort, on the corrosion and deterioration of materials, and on the growth of molds and bacteria.

The Measurement of Relative Humidity. If air at a given pressure and absolute humidity is warmed or cooled, the partial pressure of water in the air remains unchanged. The vapor pressure of water, however, which depends on the temperature, changes, and therefore so does the relative humidity (Equation 1). Air is said to become "drier" when it is heated, because of the decrease in relative humidity. On cooling, the vapor pressure of water decreases, while the partial pressure remains constant; hence the relative humidity increases. When the vapor pressure equals the partial pressure, the relative humidity reaches 100%, equilibrium is established, and atmospheric moisture condenses onto surfaces. This deposition is **dew,** and the temperature at which it occurs is the **dew point.** The vapor pressure at the dew point therefore equals the partial pressure, and, if the temperature is measured, the vapor pressure value can be found in a table. Now, the vapor pressure at the dew point equals the partial pressure at the original temperature T, because cooling did not produce an actual change of composition. Then we may write

$$\text{partial pressure of } H_2O \text{ at } T = \text{vapor pressure of } H_2O \text{ at dew point}$$

and, substituting the value in Equation (1),

$$\substack{\text{relative humidity} \\ \text{at } T \text{ (percent)}} = \frac{\text{vapor pressure of } H_2O \text{ at dew point}}{\text{vapor pressure of } H_2O \text{ at } T} \times 100 \qquad (2)$$

Equation (2) is convenient because it asks us only to measure two temperatures (T and the dew point) and then to look up appropriate values in a table to obtain the data needed to calculate relative humidity. The dew point can be determined by cooling an object (**dew point cup**) that has a smooth lustrous surface, and measuring the temperature at which dew forms on it. Another method of measuring the dew point makes use of the fact that evaporation, which produces cooling, occurs at any relative humidity less than 100%; when the temperature of a wet body from which water is evaporating has been cooled to the dew point, evaporation stops and so does cooling. Therefore the lowest temperature that can be produced by evaporative cooling is the dew point. For ordinary laboratory thermometers, kept moist around the bulb by a wet fabric sleeve, an air velocity of about 1000 ft/min is needed to reach dew point equilibrium. These principles are embodied in the **sling psychrometer,** a two-thermometer device—one dry (**dry-bulb thermometer**), the other whose bulb is covered with wet wicking (**wet-bulb thermometer**). The thermometers are whirled around manually until constant temperatures are read. The dry bulb gives the room temperature, the wet bulb the dew point.

EXAMPLE 3   **The dry and wet bulbs of a psychrometer read, respectively, 25°C and 15°C. What is the relative humidity (R.H.)?**

ANSWER   **The temperature of the room is 25°C. From Equation (2),**

$$\textbf{R.H. at 25°C} = \frac{\textbf{vapor pressure of } H_2O \textbf{ at 15°C}}{\textbf{vapor pressure of } H_2O \textbf{ at 25°C}} \times 100$$

$$\textbf{(from Appendix V, page 800)} = \frac{\textbf{12.8 torr}}{\textbf{23.8 torr}} \times 100$$

$$= 54\%$$

3.12   CRITICAL CONSTANTS

For any volatile liquid, there is a vapor pressure at which any distinction between vapor and liquid ceases to exist. This pressure is called the **critical pressure,** and the temperature at which it is exerted is the **critical temperature.** The critical phenomena may be observed in either of the following ways:

(a) If a strong, sealed glass vessel contains a sufficient amount of liquid, and is gradually heated, the boundary between liquid and vapor is observed to disappear at a definite temperature and to reappear on cooling back to the same temperature. The temperature and pressure at which these phenomena occur are the critical constants. *THE STUDENT IS WARNED AGAINST ATTEMPTING SUCH AN EXPERIMENT UNDER ANY CONDITIONS*, because critical pressures (see Table 3.3) are usually high enough to cause even strong vessels to explode.

(b) If a vapor is compressed at constant temperature, its volume will shrink in approximately inverse proportion (Boyle's law). When the conditions for vapor-liquid equilibrium are reached, liquefaction occurs, and

TABLE 3.3 *Critical Constants*

Substance	Temperature (°C)	Pressure (atm)
Air	−140.7	37.2
Carbon dioxide	31.1	73.0
Ethyl alcohol	243.1	63.1
Helium	−267.9	2.26
Hydrogen	−239.2	12.8
Mercury	>1550	>200
Oxygen	−118.8	49.7
Water	374.0	217.72

further squeezing converts vapor to liquid while the equilibrium vapor pressure is maintained. After all the vapor has been liquefied, additional reduction of volume is accomplished only by greatly increased pressurization, because of the relative incompressibility of the liquid. The higher the temperature, the smaller is the range in which liquid and vapor can coexist. At a sufficiently high temperature (the critical temperature), no distinction between liquid and vapor can be observed.

These sequences are illustrated by the pressure-volume isotherms (curves at constant temperature) for carbon dioxide, the gas for which these phenomena were first studied (Fig. 3.21). Referring to the 13° isotherm, point A represents a pressure at which carbon dioxide exists in the gaseous (vapor) state. If the vapor is isothermally compressed, its volume shrinks along the line AB until liquefaction starts at point B. Further compression along the line BC rapidly converts the remainder of the vapor to liquid. Any reduction of volume beyond point C occurs by the increase in the density of the pure liquid, and is therefore accomplished only by great pressurization (line CD). A similar sequence may be followed along the 21° isotherm, but the range of liquid-vapor coexistence (B′C′) is less than it is at 13° (BC). A temperature is finally reached (31°) at which the vapor-liquid coexistence just disappears. The pressure-volume curve, instead of having a horizontal section, becomes only momentarily horizontal. This occurs at a pressure of 73 atm (the critical pressure). These conditions fulfill the requirements of criticality (equivalence of liquid and vapor), and are therefore the critical constants. Above 31°, carbon dioxide is a noncondensable gas, and its *P-V* plot follows Boyle's law (hyperbola) with increasing faithfulness at increasingly high temperatures. The *P-V* curve never becomes horizontal, even momentarily, at these temperatures. It is found that, above 31°C, pressures of even hundreds of atmospheres do not liquefy carbon dioxide gas.

At the critical state, the condition of molecular aggregation can be described either (a) as a gas whose molecular motion is so curtailed by

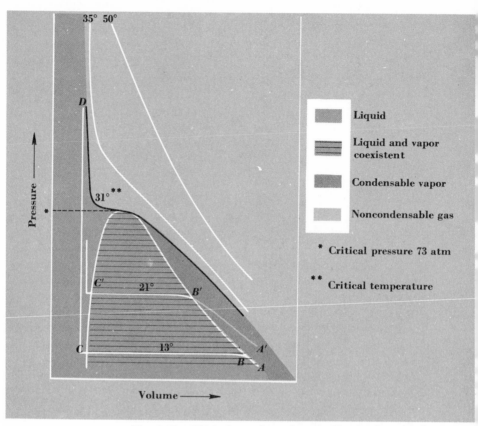

Fig. 3.21. *PV isotherms for carbon dioxide, showing critical constants.*

high pressure that it is like a liquid, or (b) as a liquid whose molecular motion is so disordered by high temperature that it is like a gas. Under the circumstances, the distinction between gas and liquid is arbitrary.

The critical temperature of a substance is related to the magnitude of the attractive forces among its molecules. If the attractive forces are great, liquefaction can be achieved in spite of kinetic opposition at elevated temperatures. The critical temperature is, therefore, high. If attractive forces are small, liquefaction is easily opposed by kinetic motion, and the critical temperature is low. Refer to Table 3.3 for data.

3.13 BOILING

Boiling is a phenomenon so common to our experience that we overlook its complexity. We observe that, as we heat a quantity of liquid in a container, the vapor pressure (Fig. 3.20) and the rate of evaporation increase until, at a more or less definite temperature, bubbles of vapor begin to form below the liquid surface. We note that this phenomenon usually (but not always) occurs close to the temperature at which the vapor pressure of the liquid equals the total (atmospheric) pressure above the liquid. We call this action **boiling, or ebullition.**

Why do liquids boil? A moment's reflection will convince one that nothing in the previous discussion of liquid-vapor interconversions leads to the prediction of ebullition. One would simply guess that evaporation of a liquid would proceed more and more rapidly as the temperature is raised. Let us explore the problem by means of an imaginary experiment.

The vapor pressure of water is 1 atmosphere at 100°C. Let us gradually warm an open pot of water at 1 atmosphere outside pressure, starting, say, at 20°C. At the same time, we inject a steady stream of steam bubbles at 100°C and 1 atmosphere into the liquid. At 20°C, each steam bubble will quickly cool, its pressure will drop, and it will collapse and disappear by condensation. As the water temperature rises, the steam bubbles will cool more slowly. At a water temperature of 100°C no cooling will occur and the bubbles will therefore be stable. The liquid will be agitated as they rise to the surface, and the entire action can be described as ebullition. Injected bubbles of any other gas would serve the same function as the steam bubbles. A bubble of air, for example, injected into water at 20°C (assume it is near the surface and neglect the hydrostatic pressure of the water) will accommodate the vapor pressure of water at this temperature, 17.5 torr. To maintain its total pressure of 760 torr, the bubble will expand until the partial pressure of the air drops to 742.5 torr ($760 - 17.5 = 742.5$ torr, partial pressure law). At higher temperatures, the air bubble will expand correspondingly more to accommodate the higher vapor pressure of the water. But at 100°C, the water contributes *all* the pressure needed to maintain the atmospheric pressure of the bubble; stabilization does not occur; the bubble continues to expand by evaporation of steam into it, and again we have ebullition. On the other hand, if we introduce no bubbles at all, ebullition does not occur even if the water temperature exceeds 100°C.

What conclusion or insight may we gain from this imaginary experiment? It would seem that the ebullition of a liquid must be initiated around small pockets of vapor or air; in the absence of such nuclei, evaporation may proceed rapidly at high temperatures, but the bubbles characteristic of ordinary boiling could not form. This picture helps us understand a number of real phenomena: when filtered deaerated water is heated carefully at standard atmospheric pressure in a smooth vessel, temperatures over 120°C may be reached without ebullition. This phenomenon is called **superheating,** and is considered to be caused by a scarcity of nucleating bubbles. If a piece of pumice stone, which releases air bubbles readily, is dropped into such superheated water, boiling occurs explosively for a while until the system settles down to ordinary ebullition, or **nuclear boiling** as it is sometimes called. Some organic liquids, when heated, tend to oscillate between superheating and nuclear boiling, a disconcerting action that the chemist calls **bumping.** Smooth ebullition can, in fact, be nucleated by introducing a fine stream of gas bubbles into the liquid. The inner surfaces of ordinary containers are known to be uneven on a microscopic scale and to hold quantities of gas that are released on heating. That such gas may nucleate boiling is consistent with the observation that bubbles usually originate from locations on the inside wall of the container. Since liquid structure may be considered to be arranged around molecular "holes" (Section 3.6, page 47), it is also possible that the source of some bubbles may be in the random structure of the liquid itself.

When nuclear boiling does not occur, a hot liquid may evaporate rapidly from its outer surface only; this phenomenon is called **film boiling.** An example is a drop of water dancing around on a hot iron.

The **boiling point** of a liquid is best defined as the temperature at which the liquid is in equilibrium with its vapor at the pressure of the atmosphere in contact with the liquid. The boiling point of a liquid may therefore be varied by changing the pressure to which it is subjected. When the pressure is one standard atmosphere, the equilibrium temperature is called the **normal boiling point.**

For precise measurement, elaborate precautions must be taken to minimize any departure from equilibrium conditions.

3.14   MELTING POINT; FREEZING POINT; WARMING AND COOLING CURVES

Ideally, the melting point and freezing point of a substance are equivalent; they are the temperatures at which liquid and solid are in equilibrium at atmospheric pressure. The effect of change of atmospheric pressure is usually relatively small; this will be illustrated in the next section.

At the melting point, the tendencies for increase of entropy (→liquid) and for decrease of energy (→solid) just balance and equilibrium is established. If the substance is pure, continued heat input at a very slow rate causes liquefaction without rise in temperature. After melting is completed, continued heat input warms the liquid. An idealized warming curve of a pure solid is pictured in Fig. 3.22. A curve such as this would be very difficult to obtain in practice, however, because heating would have to be extremely slow to keep the mixture uniform in temperature. The alternative, stirring the solid, is not experimentally feasible because of the lack of mobility of the solid.

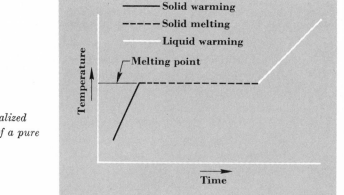

Fig. 3.22. Idealized warming curve of a pure solid.

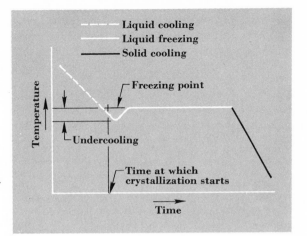

Fig. 3.23. *Idealized cooling curve of a pure liquid, with undercooling.*

Theoretically, the cooling curve should be the backward trace of the warming curve; in practice there are significant differences. A liquid usually cools *below* its freezing point before crystallization occurs; this phenomenon is called **supercooling** or, more aptly, **undercooling.** At temperatures somewhat below the equilibrium freezing point, the pseudo or short-range crystal structure of liquids competes favorably in stability with the crystal structure of the solid, and the liquid state may therefore survive. Once a crystal of the solid is produced (by chance, or from mechanical effects such as vibration, or by outside injection or "seeding"), the residual orienting forces at its surface quickly facilitate the crystallizing process. The heat liberated by this crystallization warms the mixture back to the equilibrium temperature, equilibrium is re-established, and the cooling curve "behaves." If crystallization is not initiated, the liquid may cool down to a glass. Figure 3.23 shows an idealized cooling curve of a pure liquid.

3.15 THE PHASE DIAGRAM

The temperature-pressure relationships among the solid, liquid, and gaseous states of a substance may be illustrated in a single diagram, called the **phase diagram.** The phase diagram is unique for each substance, and is determined experimentally. Figure 3.24 illustrates the phase diagram for water. In a two-dimensional diagram, an area represents one phase, a line two phases, and a point three phases. If we specify a combination of temperature and pressure, the location of these coordinates on the diagram will indicate what the *most stable condition* for water will be. Thus it is seen, for example, that the melting point of ice (water-ice equilibrium line) decreases as the pressure increases.

The reader should verify that there are 7 possibilities: three single phases (ice,* water, and steam), three 2-phase equilibria (water-ice, water-steam, and steam-ice), and one 3-phase equilibrium (steam-water-ice at point *f*). The diagram will be further illustrated by describing 5

* At high pressures, several different ice phases are known to exist.

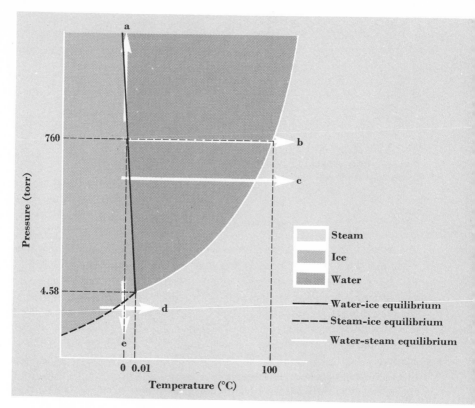

Fig. 3.24. *Phase diagram for water (not to scale)*.

transformations and one equilibrium (refer to the corresponding arrows and letters):

(a) *Ice skating.* Ice at a temperature below 0°C is subjected to supra-atmospheric pressure. It melts.

(b) *Heating ice at sea level.* Ice is heated at standard atmospheric pressure. It melts at 0°C. The liquid, on continued heating, reaches equilibrium with the atmosphere at 100°C, its normal boiling point. Eventually all becomes steam.

(c) *Himalayan cookout.* Ice, heated at less than standard atmospheric pressure, melts a little above 0°C. The water boils below 100°C.

(d) *Space kitchen.* Ice, heated below 4.58 torr, does not melt; it vaporizes.

(e) *Ice in a flask that is being evacuated at constant temperature.* As the pressure is lowered, the ice vaporizes.

(f) *The triple point.* Ice, water, and water vapor coexist at equilibrium at 0.01°C. The vapor pressure of the system is 4.58 torr.

The small effect of pressure variation on the freezing point is illustrated by the steepness of the solid-liquid equilibrium line. Its negative slope is not typical of most substances.

Figure 3.25 illustrates the phase diagram for carbon dioxide. Note that sublimation, which is exhibited by ice only at pressures below 4.58 torr, occurs for carbon dioxide at pressures up to 5.2 atmospheres.

3.16 COLLOIDS; ADSORBENTS

It was pointed out in the discussion of surface tension (Section 3.7, page 48) that molecules at the surface of a liquid differ in energy from molecules inside. Molecules at the surface of a solid, too, have fewer opportunities to interact with other parts of the body than do the inside molecules, and therefore constitute an atypical group. When the surface area of any body is very large compared with its bulk volume, the special properties of the surface molecules influence the over-all properties of the body to a significant degree. Large surface-to-volume ratios exist when either

(a) the particles of the substance are very small, or
(b) the body is interlaced with small pores throughout its bulk volume.

Particles so small that surface effects assume great relative importance in determining their properties or behavior are called **colloids.** Colloidal particles dispersed in air are called **aerosols,** or **atmospheric dispersoids,** or **aerocolloids.** It will be helpful to refer to Fig. 3.26 to note the particle sizes of some common aerocolloids in comparison with coarse matter (such as beach sand) and with gas molecules. Particles smaller than the wavelength range of visible light cannot be seen with the ordi-

Fig. 3.25. *Phase diagram for carbon dioxide (not to scale).*

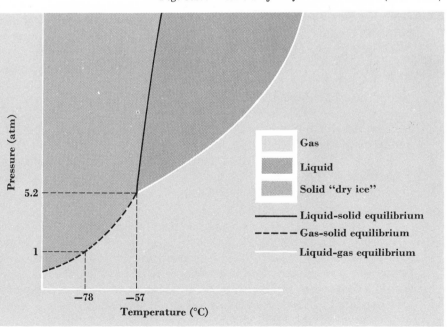

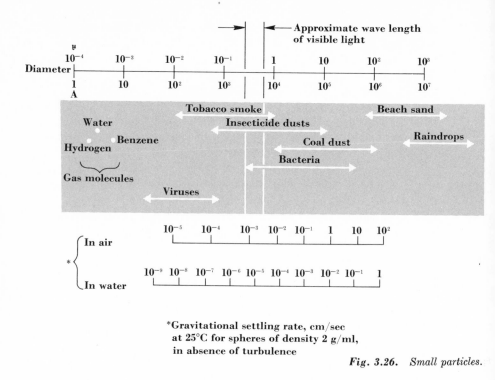

Fig. 3.26.   Small particles.

nary microscope. The lower limit of microscopic visibility, about 0.2 micron, is frequently taken to be the upper limit of colloidal particle sizes. The lower size limit of the colloid range is taken to be the size of such known particles as protein or starch molecules and some small viruses, roughly 50 A. The particle-size interval between ordinary gas molecules (up to about 8 A) and the smallest colloids (about 50 A) is a sort of "no man's land" about which our knowledge is relatively meager.

Colloidal particles have the ability to scatter visible light. A thin beam of light passing through a colloid in a gas or a liquid can be seen at right angles because of the scattering. This phenomenon, called the **Tyndall effect,** was discovered in 1857, and constituted a simple (and still reliable) criterion of the colloidal state of matter. Colloids are characterized by very slow settling rates. Note (Fig. 3.26) that at 0.2μ, settling in air is about 5×10^{-4} cm/sec and in water is several hundredfold slower. Some special properties of colloids in liquid media will be mentioned in Chapter 29 on polymers.

The high energy characteristic of surface molecules may be lessened if foreign molecules move to the surface under the influence of the residual attractive forces available there. Any gas, vapor, or liquid will, therefore, adhere to some degree to any surface of a body. This phenomenon is called **adsorption,** or **sorption.** Solid bodies having large surface areas compared to their bulk volumes are therefore called **adsorbents.** Colloids, as described above, fulfill this requirement because of their small size.

All colloidal matter is therefore highly adsorbent. Even large bodies, however, may have large surface-to-volume ratios if a network of pores within them provides extensive surface area. Matter of this type can be produced from coconut shells, for example, by charring and then heating them in a steam atmosphere to about 1500°C to drive out all material which can be gasified at that temperature. This process is called **activation.** The matter left behind, consisting mainly of carbon and retaining the many pores created by the activation process, is called **activated carbon.** Its surface area may be as much as about 1000 m² per gram. The adsorbing capacity of such material is startlingly high. For example, activated carbon at 20°C can adsorb up to $\frac{3}{4}$ its own weight of carbon tetrachloride (dry cleaning solvent) vapor from air that is saturated with the vapor at 0°C (vapor pressure = 30 torr). Other effective adsorbents may be made from metallic oxides, silicates, and metals.

Problems

1. Crystal structure. Outline the kinds of information about crystalline substances that may be obtained by (1) visual observation; (2) microscopy using visible light; (3) x ray examination by the von Laue method; (4) x ray examination by the Bragg method.

2. Unit cell. What portion of a circle in each of the following locations is assigned to the two-dimensional square unit cell: (a) corner; (b) side; (c) face?

3. Space lattice. The metal lead exists as a face-centered cubic lattice whose unit cell edge is 4.94 A. (a) How many atoms are there in the unit cell? (b) There are 6.02×10^{23} atoms of lead in 207 g (the atomic weight). Predict the density of lead. Compare your answer with the value 11.34 g/cm³ at 16°C (from the *Handbook of Chemistry and Physics*).

Answer. (a) 4 atoms.

4. Liquid and glassy states. A zinc metal rod and a glass rod are each heated in the absence of air to a temperature somewhat above 419°C. The zinc rod remains rigid, but liquid zinc begins to drip from it. The glass rod sags, but dripping does not occur. Account for these phenomena.

5. Wetting. It is observed that rain droplets accumulate on a windowpane, and run down its surface in irregular paths from time to time. The pane is washed with strong, hot detergent solution. It is now observed that drops do not gather on the glass. Instead, rain that strikes it falls off in a clear, continuous film. Account for these phenomena.

6. Heats of fusion and vaporization. (a) How many calories of heat are needed to melt 10.0 g of ice at 0°C, warm it to 100°C, and boil the water at 100°C. [See Table 3.2 (page 51) for data.] (b) Do you think the answer would be the same if the operations were carried out at different temperatures but ended at the same conditions specified in (a)?

Answer. 7.19×10^3 cal.

7. Entropy. (a) An atmosphere contains soot from chimneys and pollen from vegetation. Discuss the chances that, if two equivalent air samplers are placed side by side, one collects only soot, the other only pollen. Explain in terms of the entropy concept. (b) Assume that your room has a specific arrangement of clothing, books, papers, and other personal effects. For one month, whenever you have finished using any item, you replace it without plan in any location in the room. Does the room become more orderly or more disorderly? Explain in terms of the entropy concept.

8. Vapor pressure. Refer to Fig. 3.20. (a) What are the approximate normal boiling points of chlorine, bromine, alcohol, water, and naphthalene? (b) At what pressure is it possible to boil bromine at 41.6°C, alcohol at 63.5°C, and water at 83°C?

9. Relative humidity. Air at 20°C must be cooled to 0°C to deposit dew. What is the relative humidity of the air (a) at 20°C, (b) at 0°C?

Answer. (a) 26%; (b) 100%.

10. Critical temperature. The intermolecular attractive forces in liquid A are greater than those in liquid B. Predict which liquid will have the higher critical temperature. Explain.

11. Cooling curve. Draw a complete time (x axis)–temperature (y axis) cooling curve for water at an outside pressure of 1 atmosphere, showing the cooling of steam, its condensation at 100°C, the cooling, undercooling, and freezing of water, and the cooling of ice. The specific heat of steam and of ice are both about 0.5 cal/g°C. Label all parts.

12. Phase diagram. Do you think that it would be possible to ice-skate on solid carbon dioxide? Explain.

Additional problems

13. Unit cell. Designate the unit cell in (a) a sheet of postage stamps; (b) black and white squares arranged in a striped pattern; (c) black and white squares arranged in a checkerboard pattern.

14. Unit cell. Draw a diagram showing how the diameter of a sphere may be part of the edge of a cube. If each edge contains one such sphere, what is the total number of spheres assigned to the space within the cube?

15. Space lattice. Refer to the diagram of the sodium chloride lattice (Fig. 3.9). What is the coordination number (a) of the sodium; (b) of the chlorine? (c) What are the individual lattice structures of sodium and chlorine in sodium chloride? (d) Tabulate the number of corner, edge, face, or center particles of sodium atoms (smaller spheres) and of chlorine atoms (larger spheres) in the unit cell of sodium chloride. How many atoms of each are assigned to the unit cell?

Answer. (a) 6; (b) 6; (c) face-centered cubes; (d) 4 of sodium and 4 of chlorine.

16. Space lattice. Refer to the diagram of the cesium chloride lattice (Fig. 3.9). What is the coordination number (a) of the cesium; (b) of the chlorine? (c) What are the lattice structures of the individual elements? (d) How many atoms of each are assigned to the packing model illustrated?

17. Space lattice. You are given your choice of pea-sized or baseball-sized spheres of the same material. You are to pack the spheres as closely as possible. Which choice will yield the greater packing density?

Answer. The densities are the same.

18. Crystal habits. Draw a picture of the crystal habit likely to be formed if (a) a face-centered cubic lattice grew at equal rates from its octahedral and its cubic faces, or (b) more rapidly from its octahedral faces; (c) a simple cubic lattice grew at equal rates from two sets of cubic faces but very slowly from the third set of faces.

19. Space lattice. The unit cell of potassium chloride (KCl) is a face-centered cube that contains four K^+ ions and four Cl^- ions. The edge of the unit cell is 6.29 A, and the density of KCl is 1.99 g/cm³. (a) How many K^+ ions are there in 1 g of KCl? (b) How many Cl^- ions?

Answer. (a) 8.07×10^{21} ions; (b) 8.07×10^{21} ions.

20. The liquid state. A traveler in a space vehicle (zero gravity) must have a usable supply of drinking fluid. What would be the result of attempting to use earth-bound kitchen methods of storage, handling, and drinking? Suggest methods appropriate for space travel.

21. Liquid and glassy states. A man wearing spiked shoes finds that he sinks slowly when he stands on a tar road or on an ice rink. Ice is crystalline; tar is not. Account for both phenomena.

22. The mesomorphic state. Some soapy solids (for example, potassium oleate), on heating, melt sharply to form homogeneous, turbid liquids that have some of the optical properties of crystalline solids, and that give much sharper x ray diffraction patterns than ordinary liquids do. On further heating, an abrupt change to a clear liquid occurs. Such turbid liquids are sometimes called "liquid crystals" and their state of aggregation is called the "mesomorphic state." Suggest a theory of molecular arrangement to account for the mesomorphic state.

23. Viscosity. A granular solid resting on an inclined plane can be made to flow down the slope by vibrating the plane. Is this phenomenon more closely analogous to the melting of a crystal or to the softening of a glass? Explain.

24. Entropy. The Haber process for fixing nitrogen from the air and the Dow process for extracting magnesium from the sea are said to be anti-entropic processes. These are in contrast to procedures of the type that involve the mining of a concentrated ore and the wide distribution of the final product; such procedures are said to be entropic. An example is the mining of mercury and its widespread use in industrial and commercial products. Explain how the concept of entropy is related to these considerations.

25. Relative humidity. Air at 24°C has a relative humidity of 47%. (a) To what relative humidity is the air reduced by warming it to 30°C? (b) To what temperature must it be cooled to deposit dew?

Answer. (a) 33%; (b) 12°C.

26. Critical constants. Large quantities of liquid oxygen are transferred to and kept at missile sites in containers that are vented to the atmosphere. Liquid carbon dioxide, on the other hand, is handled and shipped in closed steel cylinders. Explain.

27. Film boiling. The following phenomena have been reported:

(a) If a man's hand is somewhat damp, he can pass it quickly through a stream of molten iron (melting point 1535°C) without injury (steel mills, United States).

(b) Men can walk barefoot over glowing charcoal beds, $> 1400°C$, without injury (Argentina; India).

(c) A man can hold liquid nitrogen (boiling point $= -196°C$) in his mouth briefly without freezing his tongue (liquid air plants, United States).

Account for these reported phenomena.

28. Warming curve. Figure 3.22 shows that, for the same rate of heat gain, the slope of the solid warming line is different from that of the liquid warming line. Explain why such a difference may exist.

29. Colloids. Consider a 1-cm cube whose weight is 1 g. (a) What is its surface area? (b) If the cube is cut in half by a slice that is parallel to one set of sides, how much surface area is added? (c) How many such slicings would be needed to produce a total surface area of 10^3 m²? (d) How much volume would each piece occupy? (e) If each sliced particle were a cube, how long would its edge be, in microns? **Answer.** (a) 6 cm²; (b) 2 cm²; (c) 5×10^6 slices (d) 2×10^{-7} cm³; (e) 6×10 μ.

30. Adsorption. It is observed that when air containing gasoline vapor passes through a bed of activated carbon, the gasoline vapor is removed from the air and the temperature of the carbon bed rises. Account for these phenomena.

31. Phase diagram. Sulfur hexafluoride resembles carbon dioxide in that the solid, when heated at standard atmospheric pressure, vaporizes completely without melting. What is characteristic of the phase diagrams of substances that behave in this way?

4

Atoms
and
molecules

TODAY ALMOST EVERYONE knows something about atoms and believes that atoms exist. Most likely atoms do exist; nevertheless, their existence is an assumption of a theory of the structure of matter. Although Leucippus and Democritus (about the 5th century B.C.) assumed matter to be composed of indivisible particles that they called atoms,* the atomic theory was not reaffirmed until chemical changes were studied quantitatively. These studies, made during the 18th and 19th centuries, are summarized in the laws describing chemical changes: the law of conservation of matter, the law of definite proportions, the law of multiple proportions, and the law of combining volumes.

4.1 THE LAW OF CONSERVATION OF MATTER

Measurements show that, within the experimental error, the weight (mass)† of substances in a sealed container does not change during a chemical change. Thus, air containing oxygen, O_2, and hydrogen, H_2, is enclosed in a tube; no matter can now enter or escape from the tube. The tube and contents are weighed. Passage of an electric spark across the tube causes hydrogen and oxygen gases to disappear, but liquid water, H_2O, and heat are produced. After restoring the original temperature, the tube and contents are reweighed. The observed weights, before and after the chemical change, are identical within the precision of the balance. Such observations are summarized in the *law of conservation of*

* *A-tomos* means without cutting.
† "Weight" and "mass" will be used synonymously (considered in Section 4.13, page 88).

matter: the mass of a chemically reacting system remains constant. This law is consistent with the data obtained with the most precise balances available. If matter is created or destroyed, the quantity is less than can be detected with the best available balance.

4.2 THE LAW OF DEFINITE PROPORTIONS

Analyses of compounds show that when elements form a given compound, they always combine in the same ratio by weight. For example, independently of the source or method of formation, silicon dioxide, SiO_2, contains 46.7% by weight of silicon and 53.3% of oxygen. This knowledge is summarized in the *law of definite proportions: the weight composition of a given compound is constant.*

EXAMPLE 1   **10.0 g of silicon dust, Si, is exploded with 100.0 g of oxygen, O_2, forming silicon dioxide, SiO_2. How many grams of SiO_2 are formed and how many grams of O_2 remain uncombined?**

ANSWER   **Since 46.7 g of Si combines with 53.3 g of O_2, the quantity of O_2 required per gram of Si is**

$$\frac{53.3 \text{ g } O_2}{46.7 \text{ g Si}}$$

and, therefore, for 10.0 g of Si, the quantity of O_2 required is

$$10.0 \text{ g Si} \frac{53.3 \text{ g } O_2}{46.7 \text{ g Si}} = 11.4 \text{ g } O_2$$

Hence, the weight of SiO_2 formed is 10.0 g + 11.4 g = 21.4 g and the weight of uncombined O_2 is 100.0 g − 11.4 g = 88.6 g.

4.3 THE ATOMIC THEORY

The weight relationships of substances participating in chemical reactions are clearly explained in terms of the atomic theory. Although John Dalton (1803) is generally recognized as the inventor of the theory, he was anticipated by other scientists, particularly William Higgins (1789). Thus, it appears that the law of multiple proportions (Section 4.4) was foreshadowed by Higgins and Dalton from their respective atomic theories. A verified prediction made by a theory constitutes the strongest argument in its favor. However, the novel and central point of Dalton's activities was the attempt to determine the relative weights of atoms. This goal focused attention upon the theory, and revealed a new field of human endeavor that ultimately made chemistry a systematized body of knowledge.

The assumptions of the atomic theory were

(*i*) *The elements are composed of indivisible particles called atoms.*
(*ii*) *All the atoms of a given element possess identical properties, for example, mass.*

(iii) *The atoms of different elements differ in properties.*

(iv) *These atoms are the units of chemical changes; chemical changes merely involve the combination or the rearrangement of atoms; atoms are not destroyed, created, or changed.*

(v) *When atoms combine, they combine in fixed ratios of whole numbers forming particles known as molecules.**

This theory differs fundamentally from previous theories of matter in that it endows atoms with definite properties, particularly with definite masses, and limits the number of different kinds of atoms to the number of elements known.†

The theory offers an acceptable explanation of the laws of chemical change. First, the conservation of matter: since atoms merely combine or rearrange during a chemical change, the number of atoms of each element in the **products** of the reaction is the same as the original number in the **reactants** or starting materials. Since it is further assumed that the mass of an atom does not change, the mass of a chemically reacting system remains constant. Thus, treat 100×10^{10} sulfur atoms, S, and 65×10^{10} oxygen atoms, O, in a tube at $1000°C$ so that 20×10^{10} S atoms combine with 20×10^{10} atoms of O, forming sulfur monoxide, SO. The tube now contains 20×10^{10} S atoms combined in the oxide, 80×10^{10} S atoms uncombined, 20×10^{10} O atoms combined, and 45×10^{10} O atoms uncombined.‡ These add up to the original number of atoms and, since the mass of an atom is assumed to remain constant, the weight remains constant during the chemical change.

Second, the law of definite proportions: since the mass of the atoms of any given element is constant and since the atoms, by assumption, combine in fixed whole number ratios for a given combination, the weight ratio of the elements in a given compound must be constant. For example, 20×10^{10} S atoms combine with 20×10^{10} O atoms forming 20×10^{10} SO molecules. Each SO molecule contains 1 S atom and 1 O atom. Since each molecule contains the same number of S and O atoms and since the masses of these atoms are also constant, the mass ratio of sulfur to oxygen must be constant in any given quantity of sulfur monoxide.

EXAMPLE 2 **As most people know, although few understand how the chemist arrived at the conclusion (page 81), water vapor consists of molecules com-**

---

* The term **molecule,** meaning a particle composed of similar or dissimilar atoms, was introduced by Avogadro in 1811.

† Present knowledge recognizes that the atoms of a given element do not possess uniform masses. Silver, for example, occurs as two isotopes (page 87), atoms of different masses, but, as found in nature, these silver atoms are always mixed in the same number ratio so that the average mass of the silver atoms is always the same. Thus, the two atoms have relative masses of 107 and 109, and relative abundances of 51 atoms to 49 atoms. The average relative mass of the atoms is then given by $107 \times 0.51 + 109 \times 0.49 = 108$. And the atoms of *any natural source* of silver will have a constant relative mass of 108.

‡ Very frequently, the conversion of reactants to products is incomplete (Chapter 14).

posed of 1 oxygen atom to 2 hydrogen atoms, H_2O. Assume the weight of a hydrogen atom is 2.0×10^{-24} g and that of oxygen is 3.2×10^{-23} g. (a) Calculate the weight of one molecule.

ANSWER

$$2 \text{ atoms } (2.0 \times 10^{-24}) \frac{g}{\text{atom}} + 1 \text{ atom } (3.2 \times 10^{-23}) \frac{g}{\text{atom}} = 3.6 \times 10^{-23} \text{ g}$$

(b) Calculate the weight percent of hydrogen in one molecule.

ANSWER

$$\frac{2(2.0 \times 10^{-24})g}{2(2.0 \times 10^{-24})g + 3.2 \times 10^{-23}g} (100) = 11.1\%$$

(c) Calculate the weight of 10^3 water molecules.

ANSWER   Since 10^3 molecules contain 2×10^3 hydrogen atoms and 10^3 oxygen atoms,

$$2 \times 10^3 \text{ atoms } (2.0 \times 10^{-24}) \frac{g}{\text{atom}}$$
$$+ 10^3 \text{ atoms } (3.2 \times 10^{-23}) \frac{g}{\text{atom}} = 10^3 (3.6 \times 10^{-23})g$$
$$= 3.6 \times 10^{-20} \text{ g}$$

(d) Calculate the weight percent of hydrogen in 10^3 molecules or in 3.6×10^{-20} g of water.

ANSWER

$$\frac{2 \times 10^3 (2.0 \times 10^{-24})g}{2 \times 10^3 (2.0 \times 10^{-24})g + 10^3 (3.2 \times 10^{-23})g} (100) = 11.1\%$$

4.4   THE LAW OF MULTIPLE PROPORTIONS

The atomic theory restricts combinations to whole numbers of atoms; fractional numbers are excluded. Further, the number ratio is fixed for any given combination. The theory, however, does not restrict the number of possible combinations between atoms. Thus, using Dalton's symbols, hydrogen atoms ⊙ and oxygen atoms ○ may, for example, combine

(a) in a 1:1 ratio, ⊙○, to form one compound;
(b) in a 2:1 ratio, ⊙○⊙, to form a second compound;
(c) in a 1:2 ratio, ○⊙○, to form a third compound.

Now, the theory *does not predict* that these combinations must occur; in fact, the theory is *not even capable* of predicting whether or not hydrogen and oxygen will combine. But it does predict that, if hydrogen and oxygen do form more than one compound, a relationship must exist among the weights of hydrogen and oxygen in these compounds. Thus, let us arbi-

trarily make the weight of one element, hydrogen, identical in the three
postulated combinations by using the same number of hydrogen atoms,

Compound (a)	*Compound* (b)	*Compound* (c)
two molecules contain	one molecule contains	two molecules contain
two hydrogen atoms	*two hydrogen atoms*	*two hydrogen atoms*
and two oxygen atoms	and one oxygen atom	and four oxygen atoms

It is evident now that the oxygen atoms in each case are related as whole
numbers, $2:1:4$; since each oxygen atom has the same weight, the weights
of the oxygen atoms in each case are also related as whole numbers,
$2:1:4$. Stated otherwise, when *two elements form more than one compound,
the weights of one element, combined with an arbitrarily fixed weight of the
other element*, are *in ratios of whole numbers*. This statement, *the law of
multiple proportions*, is illustrated in Example 3.

EXAMPLE 3   **When an electric discharge is passed through hydrogen and oxygen gases at ordinary temperatures, water is formed; but at about 90°K,
more than 50% of the product is hydrogen peroxide. It appears that a hydrogen superoxide may exist below about 160°K. Water contains 11.2% hydrogen
and 88.8% oxygen by weight; hydrogen peroxide, 5.93% hydrogen and 94.1%
oxygen; hydrogen superoxide, 3.05% hydrogen and 97.0% oxygen. Show that
the given experimental data confirm the law of multiple proportions.**

ANSWER   **First, calculate the weight of one element, let us say the hydrogen,
that combines with a fixed weight of the other element, let us say 1.00 g of
oxygen. Then, in water,**

$$\frac{11.2 \text{ g H}_2}{88.8 \text{ g O}_2} = 0.126 \text{ g of hydrogen per g of oxygen}$$

in hydrogen peroxide,

$$\frac{5.93 \text{ g H}_2}{94.1 \text{ g O}_2} = 0.0630 \text{ g of hydrogen per g of oxygen}$$

in hydrogen superoxide,

$$\frac{3.05 \text{ g H}_2}{97.0 \text{ g O}_2} = 0.0314 \text{ g of hydrogen per g of oxygen}$$

Second, show that these weights of hydrogen are in ratios of whole numbers,

   $0.126:0.0630:0.0314$ are in the same ratios as $4:2:1$

4.5   THE LAW OF COMBINING VOLUMES; THE AVOGADRO HYPOTHESIS

As a result of his experimental studies of the volumes of gases involved in
chemical changes, Joseph Louis Gay-Lussac concluded (1808) that *when
gases react, the volumes consumed and produced, measured at the same tem-*

perature and pressure, are in ratios of small whole numbers. For example, at the same temperature and pressure,

> 10.6 ml hydrogen gas combines with 10.6 ml chlorine gas
> > to produce 21.2 ml hydrogen chloride gas
> 20.4 ml hydrogen gas combines with 10.2 ml oxygen gas
> > to produce 20.4 ml water vapor
> 12 ml hydrogen gas combines with 4.0 ml nitrogen gas
> > to produce 8.0 ml ammonia gas
> 6.3 ml water vapor combines with solid carbon
> > to produce 6.3 ml hydrogen and 6.3 ml carbon monoxide gas

In 1811 Amadeo Avogadro, whose theoretical work was ignored for half a century, showed that these results may be explained by the assumption that molecules of elements are composed of similar atoms, molecules of compounds are composed of dissimilar atoms, and, further, that *equal volumes of all gases under the same conditions of temperature and pressure contain the same number of molecules* (pages 17; 26). Thus, let N be the number of molecules in a given volume of gas; then, according to the Avogadro hypothesis, the experimental observation

$$\text{1 volume of hydrogen} + \text{1 volume of chlorine} \rightarrow \text{2 volumes of hydrogen chloride}$$

means that

$$\text{N molecules of hydrogen} + \text{N molecules of chlorine} \rightarrow \text{$2N$ molecules of hydrogen chloride}$$

and dividing by N yields

$$\text{1 molecule of hydrogen} + \text{1 molecule of chlorine} \rightarrow \text{2 molecules of hydrogen chloride}$$

Since a molecule of hydrogen chloride must contain at least one atom of hydrogen and one atom of chlorine, the symbol HCl may be used to represent a hydrogen chloride molecule. But there are 2 hydrogen chloride molecules for every 1 hydrogen molecule and 1 chlorine molecule. Whence, to satisfy the law of conservation of matter, 1 hydrogen molecule must contain at least 2 hydrogen atoms and 1 chlorine molecule must contain at least 2 chlorine atoms, or

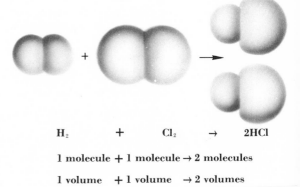

$$H_2 \quad + \quad Cl_2 \quad \rightarrow \quad 2HCl$$

1 molecule + 1 molecule → 2 molecules

1 volume + 1 volume → 2 volumes

This explanation, however, does not prove that hydrogen and chlorine molecules in the gaseous state are composed of 2 atoms (**diatomic**). Nor does it prove that hydrogen chloride molecules are composed of 1 atom of each constituent element. Thus, if we assume H_4, Cl_4, and H_2Cl_2 to be the molecular species, we can write

$$H_4 \quad + \quad Cl_4 \quad \rightarrow \quad 2H_2Cl_2$$
1 molecule + 1 molecule → 2 molecules
1 volume + 1 volume   → 2 volumes

which also explains the volume relations experimentally observed, $1:1:2$. We have, however, proved that the gaseous molecules of hydrogen and chlorine contain an even number of atoms, e.g., H_2 or H_4, Cl_2 or Cl_4, and not an odd number, e.g., H or H_3, Cl or Cl_3.

4.6 MOLECULAR WEIGHTS OF GASES

We cannot weigh a single molecule by any method. However, if molecules really exist, it should be possible to determine their relative weights by weighing *large* but *identical* numbers of molecules. Illustrating with the fictitious molecules AB and CD,

Number weighed	Total weight
2.00×10^{22} molecules of AB	33.4 grams
2.00×10^{22} molecules of CD	6.2 grams
4.00×10^{22} molecules of AB	66.8 grams
4.00×10^{22} molecules of CD	12.4 grams

The relative weights of the molecules of AB and CD are then 33.4 to 6.2, the same as 66.8 to 12.4. Observe that identical relative weights are obtained when an *equal number* of molecules is weighed, irrespective of the value of that number. Further observe that relative weights of the molecules are obtainable without knowing the number being weighed, provided the number weighed is identical.

Thus when a chemist says, "The molecular weight of water is 18, the molecular weight of carbon dioxide is 44, and the molecular weight of sulfur dioxide is 64," he means there are as many molecules in 18 grams of water as in 44 grams of carbon dioxide, or in 64 grams of sulfur dioxide. Also, since these weights contain the same number of molecules, 18, 44, and 64 may be used to represent the relative weights of one molecule of each of these substances.

The question now is, "How do we know when we are weighing equal numbers of molecules?" Stanislao Cannizzaro showed in 1858 that the Avogadro hypothesis may be used to determine molecular weights of gases: by common consent,* we take 31.9988 grams of oxygen, using air as the source of oxygen. This quantity contains a definite number of

---

* By a majority vote of chemists taken in 1905 through the International Union of Pure and Applied Chemistry, 32.0000 grams of oxygen was chosen to avoid a number smaller than one for the atomic weight of hydrogen. In 1961, this was changed to 31.9988 grams with the adoption of the atomic weight scale based on the isotope of carbon, C^{12} = exactly 12 (further treated on page 88).

molecules; we call this number the **Avogadro number** $\mathfrak{N}$. Next, we determine the volume occupied by this quantity of oxygen at standard conditions (sc), 0°C and 760 torr.

EXAMPLE 4 **The density of oxygen, determined by Gregory Baxter and Howard Starkweather in 1926, is 1.42765 g per liter at sc. Calculate the volume occupied by 31.9988 g of oxygen at sc.**

ANSWER

$$\frac{31.9988 \text{ g}}{1.42765 \dfrac{\text{g}}{\text{liter (sc)}}} = 22.4136 \text{ liters (sc)}$$

It follows, then, from the Avogadro hypothesis that 22.4 liters, sc, of any other gas also contains $\mathfrak{N}$ molecules. Hence, the weight in grams of 22.4 liters at sc of any gas will be its gram molecular weight because it contains $\mathfrak{N}$ molecules. The quantity containing $\mathfrak{N}$ molecules, or in general $\mathfrak{N}$ particles regardless of their nature, is known as a **mole.** Thus a mole of atoms contains $\mathfrak{N}$ atoms, a mole of molecules contains $\mathfrak{N}$ molecules, and a mole of protons contains $\mathfrak{N}$ protons. The value of $\mathfrak{N}$, experimentally determined (page 28), is $6.0225 \pm 0.0003 \times 10^{23}$ particles. Then, the quantity of matter in a mole may be expressed as 6.02×10^{23} particles per mole, 22.4 liters (sc) per mole of gas, and 22.4×10^3 ml (sc) per mole of gas. The dimensional units of a gram molecular weight are grams per mole. The volume (sc) occupied by one mole of a gas is known as the molar volume or the gram molecular volume.

EXAMPLE 5 **Hydrocarbons are compounds composed of hydrogen and carbon. 0.482 g of the hydrocarbon pentane occupies 204 ml as a vapor at 100°C and 765 torr. Calculate the molecular weight of pentane.**

ANSWER **Since the molecular weight is the weight of 22.4 liters (sc) of the vapor, first convert the given volume to its corresponding volume at sc using the gas laws and then, since the volume is given in ml, calculate the weight of 22.4×10^3 ml,**

$$V(\text{sc}) = 204 \text{ ml} \frac{273°\text{K} \, 765 \text{ torr}}{373°\text{K} \, 760 \text{ torr}} = 150 \text{ ml (sc)}$$

Since 150 ml weighs 0.482 g, the weight of 1.00 ml, the density of the vapor, is given by

$$\frac{0.482 \text{ g}}{150 \text{ ml (sc)}}$$

and therefore the weight of 22.4×10^3 ml is

$$\frac{0.482 \text{ g}}{150 \text{ ml (sc)}} \, 22.4 \times 10^3 \frac{\text{ml (sc)}}{\text{mole}} = 72.0 \frac{\text{g}}{\text{mole}} \quad *$$

* The use of dimensional units is strongly urged to verify your calculations. Thus, multiplying incorrectly by

$$\frac{150 \text{ ml (sc)}}{0.482 \text{ g}}$$

ALTERNATE SOLUTION Since the numerical value of R in the equation for an ideal gas (page 26) is calculated from the experimental values for one mole of oxygen gas, namely, $n = 1$ exactly, $T = 273.15°K$, $P = 1.0000$ atm, and $V = 22.4136$ liters, the equation can be used to calculate the number of moles in a given volume of gas. From the equation $PV = nRT$,

$$n = \frac{PV}{RT}$$

But n, the number of moles, is given by

$$n = \frac{w}{M}$$

in which w is the weight of the gas, and M is its molecular weight. Hence

$$PV = \frac{w}{M} RT$$

$$M = \frac{wRT}{PV}$$

$$w = 0.482 \text{ g}$$

and

$$M = \frac{0.482 \text{ g } 0.0821 \dfrac{\text{liter atm}}{\text{mole deg}} 373 \text{ deg}}{1.006 \text{ atm } 0.204 \text{ liter}}$$

$$= 72.0 \frac{\text{g}}{\text{mole}}$$

EXAMPLE 6 The molecular weight of the hydrocarbon butane is 58.1. Calculate the number of moles, the number of molecules, and the volume in liters (sc) corresponding to 12.0 g of butane.

ANSWER One mole weighs 58.1 g; hence, the number of moles is given by

$$\frac{12.0 \text{ g}}{58.1 \dfrac{\text{g}}{\text{mole}}} = 0.207 \text{ mole}$$

and since there are 6.02×10^{23} molecules in one mole,

$$0.207 \text{ mole } 6.02 \times 10^{23} \frac{\text{molecules}}{\text{mole}} = 1.25 \times 10^{23} \text{ molecules}$$

and since one mole occupies 22.4 liters (sc),

$$0.207 \text{ mole } 22.4 \frac{\text{liters (sc)}}{\text{mole}} = 4.64 \text{ liters (sc)}$$

---

would yield

$$\frac{150 \text{ ml (sc)}}{0.482 \text{ g}} 22.4 \times 10^3 \frac{\text{ml (sc)}}{\text{mole}} = 6.96 \times 10^6 \frac{\text{ml}^2 \text{ (sc)}}{\text{g mole}}$$

and the error would be obvious, since $\dfrac{\text{ml}^2 \text{ (sc)}}{\text{g mole}}$ does not correspond to the desired

answer, $\dfrac{\text{g}}{\text{mole}}$.

4.7 ATOMIC WEIGHTS FROM MOLECULAR WEIGHTS; THE CANNIZZARO METHOD

The first set of atomic weights which had the confidence of a large number of scientists was deduced from the molecular weights of substances by Cannizzaro. Analogous to the term molecular weight, the atomic weight of an element is not the weight of one atom; it is the weight of $\mathfrak{N}$ or 6.0225×10^{23} atoms of the element. The weight in grams of one Avogadro number (one mole) of atoms of an element is called a **gram-atom.** Thus when a chemist says, "The atomic weight of mercury, Hg, is 200.6, the atomic weight of oxygen, O, is 16.00, and the atomic weight of lead Pb, is 207.2," he means that 6.02×10^{23} mercury atoms weigh 200.6 g, the same number of oxygen atoms weigh 16.00 g, and the same number of lead atoms weigh 207.2 g. The problem, then, is, "How do we know when we are weighing $\mathfrak{N}$ atoms?"

Molecules are composed of *whole numbers of atoms;* the molecular weight then must be the sum of the atomic weights of all the atoms in the molecule. Also, it is reasonable to suppose that at least one compound of each element contains only one atom of the element per molecule. Thus, if hydrogen chloride molecules are composed of 1 hydrogen atom and 1 chlorine atom, then the molecular weight of hydrogen chloride is the sum of the atomic weight of hydrogen and the atomic weight of chlorine. If the molecules of pentane are composed of 5 atoms of carbon and 12 atoms of hydrogen, then its measured molecular weight (above) is the sum of 5 × atomic weight of carbon and 12 × atomic weight of hydrogen. If carbon monoxide molecules are composed of 1 carbon atom and 1 oxygen atom, then its measured molecular weight is the sum of the atomic weight of carbon and the atomic weight of oxygen. We can therefore conclude that *the weight of an element found in one mole of any of its compounds is the atomic weight or a whole number multiple of the atomic weight of the element.*

EXAMPLE 7 **Find the weight in grams of hydrogen and chlorine in one mole of hydrogen chloride. The experimentally determined molecular weight is 36.5 g per mole and weight composition is 2.74% hydrogen and, therefore, 97.26% chlorine.**

ANSWER **The weight percent means that in 100 g of the compound there are 2.74 g of hydrogen and 97.26 g of chlorine. Therefore in 36.5 g of the compound**

$$36.5 \frac{\text{g compd}}{\text{mole}} \frac{2.74 \text{ g hydrogen}}{100 \text{ g compd}} = 1.00 \frac{\text{g hydrogen}}{\text{mole}}$$

$$36.5 \frac{\text{g compd}}{\text{mole}} \frac{97.26 \text{ g chlorine}}{100 \text{ g compd}} = 35.5 \frac{\text{g chlorine}}{\text{mole}}$$

there are 1.00 g hydrogen and 35.5 g chlorine.

We can conclude that 1.00 is either the atomic weight or a whole number multiple of the atomic weight of hydrogen. Similarly, 35.5 is either the atomic weight or an integral multiple of the atomic weight of chlorine.

EXAMPLE 8 **The molecular weight of pentane is 72.0 g per mole and weight composition is 16.7% hydrogen and 83.3% carbon. What statement can you make regarding the atomic weights of hydrogen and carbon?**

ANSWER **First, calculate the weight of each element in one mole of the compound,**

$$72.0\, \frac{\text{g compd}}{\text{mole}} \times \frac{16.7 \text{ g hydrogen}}{100 \text{ g compd}} = 12.0\, \frac{\text{g hydrogen}}{\text{mole}}$$

$$72.0\, \frac{\text{g compd}}{\text{mole}} \times \frac{83.3 \text{ g carbon}}{100 \text{ g compd}} = 60.0\, \frac{\text{g carbon}}{\text{mole}}$$

We can therefore state that 12.0 is either the atomic weight or an integral multiple of the atomic weight of hydrogen; similarly, 60.0 is either the atomic weight or an integral multiple of the atomic weight of carbon.

We are now at an important junction. The calculations with hydrogen chloride lead us to the conclusion that 1.0 may be the atomic weight or a multiple of the atomic weight of hydrogen, whereas our calculations with pentane lead us to the value of 12.0 as the atomic weight or a multiple of the atomic weight of hydrogen. Since 12.0 is larger than 1.0, 12.0 cannot be the atomic weight of hydrogen. But 1.0 is a multiple of $\frac{1}{4}$, $\frac{1}{2}$, or some such other fraction; how can we decide whether the atomic weight of hydrogen is $\frac{1}{4}$, $\frac{1}{3}$, $\frac{1}{2}$, or 1.0? Let us continue our investigation, as in Examples 7 and 8, determining the weight of hydrogen in 1 mole of many more compounds of hydrogen. If $\frac{1}{4}$, $\frac{1}{3}$, or $\frac{1}{2}$ is the atomic weight of hydrogen, then we should discover $\frac{1}{4}$ g, $\frac{1}{3}$ g, or $\frac{1}{2}$ g in 1 mole of at least one hydrogen compound. But, although hundreds of thousands of hydrogen compounds have been studied, the smallest weight ever found is 1.0 g of hydrogen per mole of compound and the weight of hydrogen in a mole of every compound is a multiple of 1.0 g. Hence, 1.0 is almost certainly the atomic weight of hydrogen. Generalizing, *the atomic weight of an element is the smallest weight of the element found in one mole of its compounds.**

EXAMPLE 9 **Determine the probable atomic weight of carbon from the following data:**

Compound	Molecular weight (g per mole)	Weight % of carbon	Grams of carbon (per mole of compound)
Pentane	72.0	83.3	60.0
Carbon monoxide	28.0	42.9	12.0
Benzene	78.0	92.3	72.0
Chloroform	119.5	10.0	12.0

* More generally, the atomic weight is the greatest common divisor of the weights of the element found in one mole of its compounds.

ANSWER   12.0 g is the smallest weight of carbon found in the gram molecular weight of its compounds and all the weights of carbon per mole are divisible by 12.0; therefore, 12.0 is probably the atomic weight of carbon.

The dimensional units of an atomic weight are g per mole or g per gram-atom (g per g-atom).

The precision of atomic weights so obtained may be very high. Nevertheless, we can still ask, "How certain can we be that 1.0 is the atomic weight of hydrogen, and 12.0 the atomic weight of carbon?" What, for example, is the probability of discovering a compound that contains 6.0 grams of carbon per mole? Because the number of compounds studied is very large, the probability of such an event is vanishingly small. Furthermore, these atomic weights have been verified by an independent method (page 86). And, again, this success, the verification of deductions based on the atomic theory of matter, serves to increase our confidence in the existence of atoms and molecules.

4.8   ATOMIC WEIGHTS FROM SPECIFIC HEATS; THE METHOD OF PETIT AND DULONG

Alexis Petit and Pierre Dulong in 1819 reasoned that, although the atoms of different elements differ in such properties as mass, *the ability of atoms to absorb heat is independent of the specific nature of the atom.* This means that *equal numbers of atoms* of different elements should require the *same number of calories** for an *identical rise* in temperature. The determination of atomic weights by the Cannizzaro method makes it possible to test this idea.

Since a gram-atom of any element contains the same number of atoms, the same quantity of heat should be required to raise one gram-atom of an element one degree Celsius. Thus, if we multiply a gram-atom of an element by the specific heat of the element, the product should be a constant. Some typical data (Table 4.1) show that the principle of Petit and Dulong is only approximately correct. If we eliminate the liquids, and the solids boron and carbon, then the *product of the atomic weight of a solid element and its specific heat,* measured at room temperature, *is approximately* 6.2 calories per gram-atom per degree. The relationship may be used to *estimate* the atomic weight of solid elements, particularly those that form few or no volatile compounds. Also, this principle is the basis for theoretical studies of the specific heats of solids; there is actually greater validity to the idea of Petit and Dulong than appears from the data in Table 4.1.

EXAMPLE 10   **Estimate the atomic weight of platinum from its specific heat, 0.0314 cal per g per deg.**

* See Appendix I (page 782).

Element	Atomic weight $\dfrac{g}{g\text{-}atom}$	Specific heat $\dfrac{cal}{g,\ deg}$	At. wt. $\times$ sp. heat $\dfrac{cal}{g\text{-}atom,\ deg}$
Sulfur (solid)	32.0	0.18	5.8
Antimony (solid)	122	0.050	6.1
Arsenic (solid)	74.9	0.082	6.1
Phosphorus (solid)	31.0	0.19	5.9
Mercury (liquid)	201	0.033	6.7
Tin (solid)	119	0.054	6.4
Iodine (solid)	127	0.052	6.6
Carbon (solid)	12.0	0.17	2.4
Boron (solid)	10.8	0.31	3.4
Uranium (solid)	238	0.028	6.7
Lithium (solid)	6.94	0.94	6.5
Bromine (liquid)	79.9	0.11	8.8
Gallium (liquid)	69.7	0.080	5.6

ANSWER **From the Petit and Dulong principle,**

$$\text{atomic weight} \times \text{specific heat} \approx^* 6.2 \ \frac{cal}{g\text{-atom, deg}}$$

hence

$$\frac{6.2 \ \dfrac{\cancel{cal}}{g\text{-atom, }\cancel{deg}}}{0.0314 \ \dfrac{\cancel{cal}}{g,\ \cancel{deg}}} \approx 198 \ \frac{g}{g\text{-atom}}$$

The approximate atomic weight of platinum is therefore 198.

4.9 MOLECULAR FORMULAS

A chemical symbol such as C represents not only the element C but also a definite quantity of carbon, one g-atom or 12.0 g. A molecular formula such as C_8H_8, cyclo-octatetraene, gives the actual composition in number of atoms per molecule or in number of gram-atoms per mole of compound; it also represents a definite quantity of the substance, 1 mole or 104 g $(8 \times 12.0 + 8 \times 1.0)$. A molecular formula summarizes the weight composition as the number of gram-atoms per mole of compound. Hence, to calculate such a formula, the molecular weight, the weight composition of the substance, and the atomic weights of the constituent elements must be known. For example, in Example 8 (page 79) from the molecular

* The symbol $\approx$ means "equals approximately."

weight and weight composition, we calculated that pentane contains 12.0 g hydrogen per mole and 60.0 g carbon per mole. Since the atomic weight of hydrogen is 1.0 g/g-atom and that of carbon is 12.0 g/g-atom, the number of gram-atoms per mole is given by

$$\frac{12.0 \ \frac{\text{g hydrogen}}{\text{mole}}}{1.0 \ \frac{\text{g hydrogen}}{\text{g-atom}}} = 12.0 \ \frac{\text{g-atoms}}{\text{mole}} = 12.0 \ \frac{\text{atoms}}{\text{molecule}}$$

$$\frac{60.0 \ \frac{\text{g carbon}}{\text{mole}}}{12.0 \ \frac{\text{g carbon}}{\text{g-atom}}} = 5.00 \ \frac{\text{g-atoms}}{\text{mole}} = 5.00 \ \frac{\text{atoms}}{\text{molecule}}$$

The molecular formula of pentane is therefore C_5H_{12}.

EXAMPLE 11 **Hexachlorocyclohexane, synthesized from benzene and chlorine and used as an insecticide, has a molecular weight of 291. Analysis shows 24.7% carbon, 2.06% hydrogen, and 73.2% chlorine. Using 12.0, 1.0, and 35.5 as the atomic weights, respectively, of these elements, calculate the molecular formula of the hexachlorocyclohexane.**

ANSWER **Since a molecular formula represents the number of gram-atoms of the elements per mole of compound, first calculate the weight of each element in one mole:**

$$291 \ \frac{\text{g compd}}{\text{mole}} \frac{24.7 \ \text{g carbon}}{100 \ \text{g compd}} = 71.9 \ \frac{\text{g carbon}}{\text{mole}}$$

$$291 \ \frac{\text{g compd}}{\text{mole}} \frac{2.06 \ \text{g hydrogen}}{100 \ \text{g compd}} = 6.00 \ \frac{\text{g hydrogen}}{\text{mole}}$$

$$291 \ \frac{\text{g compd}}{\text{mole}} \frac{73.2 \ \text{g chlorine}}{100 \ \text{g compd}} = 213 \ \frac{\text{g chlorine}}{\text{mole}}$$

Then convert these weights to the corresponding number of gram-atoms:

$$\frac{71.9 \ \frac{\text{g carbon}}{\text{mole}}}{12.0 \ \frac{\text{g carbon}}{\text{g-atom}}} = 5.99 \ \frac{\text{g-atoms}}{\text{mole}} = 6.00^* \ \frac{\text{g-atoms}}{\text{mole}} = 6.00 \ \frac{\text{atoms}}{\text{molecule}}$$

$$\frac{6.00 \ \frac{\text{g hydrogen}}{\text{mole}}}{1.0 \ \frac{\text{g hydrogen}}{\text{g-atom}}} = 6.00 \ \frac{\text{g-atoms}}{\text{mole}} = 6.00 \ \frac{\text{atoms}}{\text{molecule}}$$

$$\frac{213 \ \frac{\text{g chlorine}}{\text{mole}}}{35.5 \ \frac{\text{g chlorine}}{\text{g-atom}}} = 6.00 \ \frac{\text{g-atoms}}{\text{mole}} = 6.00 \ \frac{\text{atoms}}{\text{molecule}}$$

The molecular formula is, therefore, $C_6H_6Cl_6$.

  * The difference between 5.99 and 6.00 is within the experimental error.

4.10 EMPIRICAL FORMULAS; IONIC SOLIDS

It is evident that if the molecular weight of a substance is unknown, then its molecular formula cannot be calculated. For such substances, it is, however, possible to calculate the empirical formula—*the simplest integral ratio in which the atoms combine*. The weight composition expresses the relative weights of the constituent elements in a particular compound. If we divide each relative weight by the atomic weight of the corresponding element, the relative number of gram-atoms of each constituent element is obtained.

EXAMPLE 12 **Potassium osmate, a pink solid synthesized in 1960, contains 21.3% potassium, 51.6% osmium, 26.1% oxygen, and 1.10% hydrogen by weight. What is its simplest formula?**

ANSWER **Dividing the relative weight of each element by its atomic weight gives the relative number of gram-atoms of the elements,**

$$\text{for potassium:} \quad \frac{21.3 \text{ g}}{39.1 \dfrac{\text{g}}{\text{g-atom}}} = 0.545 \text{ g-atom K}$$

$$\text{for osmium:} \quad \frac{51.6 \text{ g}}{190 \dfrac{\text{g}}{\text{g-atom}}} = 0.272 \text{ g-atom Os}$$

$$\text{for oxygen:} \quad \frac{26.1 \text{ g}}{16.0 \dfrac{\text{g}}{\text{g-atom}}} = 1.63 \text{ g-atoms O}$$

$$\text{for hydrogen:} \quad \frac{1.10 \text{ g}}{1.01 \dfrac{\text{g}}{\text{g-atom}}} = 1.09 \text{ g-atoms H}$$

The ratios of the numbers of gram-atoms of the elements are thus

$$0.545 \text{ K} : 0.272 \text{ Os} : 1.63 \text{ O} : 1.09 \text{ H}$$

To find the relative whole number ratios, divide by the smallest number, 0.272; thus

$$\frac{0.545}{0.272} \text{ K}: \frac{0.272}{0.272} \text{ Os}: \frac{1.63}{0.272} \text{ O}: \frac{1.09}{0.272} \text{ H}$$

yielding

$$2 \text{ K} : 1 \text{ Os} : 6 \text{ O} : 4 \text{ H}$$

For each Os atom, there are 2 K atoms, 6 O atoms, and 4 H atoms; the simplest formula is therefore $K_2OsO_6H_4$.

The sum of the atomic weights of all the atoms indicated by an empirical formula is called the formula weight; the molecular weight is, of course, related to the formula weight by a whole number. By general usage, one mole of a substance means one gram molecular weight or one formula weight expressed in grams; the dimensional units of a gram formula weight are then g per mole.

EXAMPLE 13   **What is the formula weight of potassium osmate, $K_2OsO_6H_4$?**

ANSWER   **The formula weight = 2(atomic weight of potassium) + 1(atomic weight of osmium) + 6(atomic weight of oxygen) + 4(atomic weight of hydrogen) = 368. The formula weight is 368 or 368 g per mole.**

Formulas derived from molecular weights of substances in the gaseous state are valid only for the gaseous state. We are not justified in assuming that the ultimate particles of liquids and solids must be identical with the molecules of the corresponding gaseous state. For example, the molecular weight of sodium chloride vapor is about 59, determined at 1970°C and atmospheric pressure by Walther Nernst in 1904. This indicates that the vapor consists essentially of NaCl molecules; NaCl is thus the molecular formula for sodium chloride in the vapor state at about 2000°C. But *solid sodium chloride* is a typical ionic compound. The solid is not composed of NaCl or $(NaCl)_2$ or $(NaCl)_x$ molecules; nor is it composed of sodium atoms and chlorine atoms. Rather, it is composed of positively charged sodium ions (Na^+) and negatively charged chloride ions (Cl^-). It is therefore manifestly impossible to write a molecular formula for an ionic solid; an empirical formula* is, however, acceptable. Nevertheless, we do refer to the gram formula weight of an ionic substance as one mole, so that the dimensional units of a gram formula weight of an ionic substance are g per mole.

4.11   MORE ACCURATE ATOMIC WEIGHTS

The accuracy of atomic weights determined by the Cannizzaro method is limited by the accuracy of the gas laws—Boyle's, Charles', Avogadro's— at the conditions under which the molecular weights are determined. The usual accuracy is within about 1%, although at very low pressures the accuracy may be within 0.01% or better. The accuracy of the Petit-Dulong rule is within about 5%. These approximate atomic weight values may be converted to accurate values by utilizing highly accurate weight composition data. For example, from data accurate to about 1%, it is established that the atomic weight of hydrogen is 1.0 and that the formula for water is H_2O; this formula means that *exactly* two gram-atoms of hydrogen combine with *exactly* one gram-atom of oxygen. Since the molecular weight of oxygen is 31.9988, by definition, and oxygen is diatomic (Problem 10, page 90), the atomic weight of oxygen is 15.9994. Hence, the weight in grams of hydrogen that combines with 15.9994 grams of oxygen will be *exactly twice* the atomic weight of hydrogen. The

* Ionic solids such as sodium chloride and aluminum fluoride might be more clearly represented by ionic formulas, Na^+Cl^-, $Al^{3+}3F^-$, but common practice dictates the use of empirical formulas, NaCl and AlF_3.

results of over 200 experiments made by several scientists over the years 1887–1917 show that 2.01547 ± 0.00004 g of hydrogen combines with 15.9994 g of oxygen. The more precise atomic weight of hydrogen is therefore 2.01547 ± 0.00004 divided by exactly 2, or 1.00774 ± 0.00002.*

EXAMPLE 14   The formula for silver oxide is established as Ag_2O. Exhaustive measurements by Theodore Richards established that 215.74 g of silver combines with 15.9994 g of oxygen. Calculate a highly precise value for the atomic weight of silver.

ANSWER   The formula Ag_2O means that *exactly* 2 gram-atoms of silver combine with 15.9994 g of oxygen. Hence, 215.74 g represents *exactly* 2 gram-atoms of silver; its atomic weight is therefore exactly one-half of 215.74, or 107.87.

EXAMPLE 15   From data precise to 1%, it is established that the formula of carbon dioxide is CO_2; 6.00500 g of carbon combines with 15.9994 g of oxygen in carbon dioxide. Calculate a precise value for the atomic weight of carbon.

ANSWER   The formula CO_2 means that *exactly* one-half gram-atom of carbon combines with 15.9994 g of oxygen. Hence, the 6.00500 g of carbon represents exactly one-half its atomic weight and therefore the more precise atomic weight of carbon is 6.00500 multiplied by exactly 2, or 12.010.†

Generalizing, we can state that *the weight of an element that combines with exactly one gram-atom of another element*—15.9994 g of oxygen or 107.870 g of silver—*is either the atomic weight of the element or the atomic weight multiplied by a small integer or a ratio of small integers.* Because of the relative ease with which pure silver can be prepared and the ease with which it forms insoluble solids, silver is an important secondary standard for determining atomic weights.

EXAMPLE 16   From the Cannizzaro method, the atomic weight of sulfur is 32.0. O. Hönigschmid determined that 53.935 g of silver combines with 8.016 g of sulfur. Calculate a highly precise value for the atomic weight of sulfur.

ANSWER   From the given data, 16.032 g of sulfur combines with one *gram-atom of silver*, 107.870 g. Hence, 16.032 g is either the atomic weight of sulfur or is related to it by a simple whole number or fraction. By comparison with the known value of 32.0, it is evident that 16.032 must be one-half the atomic weight. Therefore, the more precise value is given by 16.032 multiplied by 2, or 32.064.

* The accepted atomic weight, 1.00797 ± 0.00001, is based upon mass spectroscopy (page 86).
† The accepted atomic weight, 12.01115 ± 0.00005, is based upon mass spectroscopy.

EXAMPLE 17 **The specific heat of the metallic element calcium at ordinary temperatures is 0.16 cal per g per deg. It is determined that 10.02 g of calcium combines with 3.999 g of oxygen. Calculate a precise value for the atomic weight of calcium.**

ANSWER **From the Petit and Dulong rule,**

$$\frac{6.2 \frac{\text{cal}}{\text{g-atom, deg}}}{0.16 \frac{\text{cal}}{\text{g, deg}}} \approx 39 \frac{\text{g}}{\text{g-atom}}$$

The atomic weight of calcium is therefore about 39. From the data, 40.08 g of calcium combines with one gram-atom of oxygen, 15.9994 g. Hence, 40.08 is either the atomic weight of calcium or is related to it by a simple whole number or fraction. By comparison with the known value of 39, 40.08 must be the more precise value.

4.12 MASS SPECTROSCOPY

The methods we have considered are known as the "chemical methods" of determining atomic weights.

Very precise atomic weights have also been obtained by the method of **mass spectroscopy;** among the early pioneers, Sir J. J. Thomson (about 1910), Francis Aston, Arthur Dempster, Kenneth Bainbridge, and Alfred Nier may be mentioned. The principle of mass spectroscopy is based on the fact that when a charged particle enters a magnetic field perpendicularly, the particle *moves in a circular path*. The radius r of the path is given by

$$r = \frac{mv}{Hq}$$

from which

$$m = \frac{Hqr}{v} \tag{1}$$

For a given magnetic field strength H, and identical velocity v, the *radius is proportional to the mass* of the particle, m, but *inversely proportional to the charge*, q, on the particle.

Although it appears possible to measure the mass of a single charged atom from its motion in a magnetic field, this has not proved practical. In practice, an apparatus is set up so that H, q, and v remain identical during the operation of the apparatus; Equation (1) then becomes

$$m = Cr$$

in which C is a constant, or

$$\frac{m_1}{m_2} = \frac{Cr_1}{Cr_2} = \frac{r_1}{r_2} \tag{2}$$

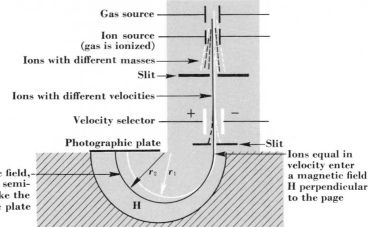

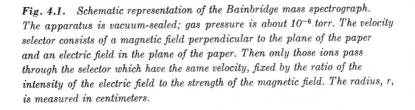

Gas source

Ion source
(gas is ionized)

Ions with different masses

Slit

Ions with different velocities

Velocity selector

Photographic plate

In the magnetic field,
ions travel in a semi-
circle and strike the
photographic plate

Slit

Ions equal in
velocity enter
a magnetic field
H perpendicular
to the page

Fig. 4.1. *Schematic representation of the Bainbridge mass spectrograph. The apparatus is vacuum-sealed; gas pressure is about 10^{-6} torr. The velocity selector consists of a magnetic field perpendicular to the plane of the paper and an electric field in the plane of the paper. Then only those ions pass through the selector which have the same velocity, fixed by the ratio of the intensity of the electric field to the strength of the magnetic field. The radius, r, is measured in centimeters.*

Hence, the *relative masses* of identically charged particles may be determined directly from the radii described by the particles in a magnetic field.

To utilize Equation (2) the apparatus (Fig. 4.1) should consist of

(1) A source of gaseous ions; this is generally accomplished by passing an electrical discharge through a gas.

(2) A velocity selector to ensure that the ions entering the magnetic field have the same velocity.

(3) A magnetic field to impart a circular path to the ions.

(4) An ion detector; this may be a photographic plate or a metal plate connected to a galvanometer.

EXAMPLE 18 **Atoms of the element nitrogen, with identical positive charges and velocities, produce two circular paths in a magnetic field; the radius ratio is 1.0712. What are the relative weights of the atoms of the element nitrogen?**

ANSWER **Since the masses of the ions are directly proportional to the radii of the circular paths, the relative masses (weights) of the ions are in the ratio of 1.0712, or one atom of nitrogen is 1.0712 times heavier than the other atom.**

The atoms of the same element having different weights are called **isotopes;** nitrogen thus consists of two isotopes. Oxygen possesses three isotopes with relative weights of 1.0000:1.06277:1.12531. To compare the weights of the atoms of the elements, a standard must be established; the presently accepted standard is the isotope of carbon C^{12} = exactly 12. 12.0000 grams of C^{12} contains as many atoms as there are atoms of oxygen in 15.9994 grams of oxygen obtained from air.

From the radii described by C^{12} and O^{16}, the atomic weight of the isotope O^{16} is 15.9949. The atomic weights of the other isotopes of oxygen are thus 15.9949×1.06277 and 15.9949×1.12531, or 16.9991 and 17.9992, abbreviated as O^{17} and O^{18}. The atomic weights of the isotopes of nitrogen are 14.003 and 14.003×1.0712, or 14.003 and 15.000, abbreviated as N^{14} and N^{15}. In these symbols, the superscript, the nearest whole number to the atomic weight of an isotope, is called the **mass number.**

The chemical methods yield an average value of the atomic weights of the isotopes of a particular element. But to convert the atomic weights of the isotopes of an element to an atomic weight of the element, the relative number of atoms of each isotope present must also be known. In mass spectroscopy, the relative abundance of isotopes is obtained from the relative darkness of the lines developed on the photographic plate or from the relative currents produced by the ions of the isotopes.

EXAMPLE 19   **Calculate the atomic weight of oxygen found in air and of naturally occurring nitrogen from the previous and the following data. Atmospheric oxygen contains 99.7587% O^{16}, 0.0374% O^{17}, and 0.2039% O^{18}. Natural nitrogen contains 99.625% N^{14} and 0.375% N^{15}.**

ANSWER   **To obtain the atomic weight of an element from mass spectroscopic data, calculate the average relative weight from the relative weight and the relative abundance of each isotope. Thus, the atomic weight of atmospheric oxygen is**

$$15.9949 \times 0.997587 + 16.9991 \times 0.000374 + 17.9992 \times 0.002039 = 15.9994$$

and the atomic weight of nitrogen is

$$14.003 \times 0.99625 + 15.000 \times 0.00375 = 14.007$$

The International Commission on Atomic Weights was established in 1900 by the International Union of Pure and Applied Chemistry and given the duty of issuing periodically a table of atomic weights after the consideration of all papers dealing with the subject. The values chosen by the Commission (see back cover) become the **accepted atomic weights.**

4.13   INERTIAL AND GRAVITATIONAL MASS

An automobile or a golf ball at rest is inert; they will stay at rest unless an unbalanced force acts upon them. It is the mass of these bodies that necessitates the use of an unbalanced force to set them in motion. But an equal force applied for the same duration to the golf ball and the automobile produces a larger change in the velocity of the golf ball. This difference results from the difference in the masses of the two bodies. The greater the force, f, required to produce a given acceleration, a, the greater is the mass of the body, m. Namely,

$$f \propto a$$

and for a body of constant mass,

$$f = ma$$

This mass, m, is called the **inertial mass.**

The **weights,** w, of these bodies at the same spot on the earth are proportional to their **gravitational mass,** m,

$$w \propto m$$
$$w = mg$$

where g is the acceleration due to gravity. Experimentally, the inertial mass and gravitational mass of a given body are exactly identical.

Problems

1. **Conservation.** J. J. Manley performed the following experiment in 1913: a small flask containing sodium sulfate, Na_2SO_4, solution was placed in a large jar containing barium chloride, $BaCl_2$, solution; the jar was then shaped into a flask and sealed, thereby producing a closed system containing two unmixed solutions. The system was then weighed; upon tilting the system, the two solutions mixed and a chemical change occurred, producing insoluble barium sulfate, $BaSO_4$, and sodium chloride, $NaCl$. After restoring the original temperature, the system was reweighed. The data obtained may be reproduced as

> weight of system before reaction = 109.000000 g
> weight of system after reaction = 109.000001 g

The precision of the balance is 6 parts in 100,000,000. What conclusion can you draw regarding the creation of matter in this experiment? Justify your answer.

2. **Weight composition.** The combustion of a hydrocarbon, a compound composed of carbon and hydrogen, produces water and carbon dioxide. A weighed quantity of a hydrocarbon, 2.246 g, on complete combustion, yields 4.532 g carbon dioxide and a quantity of water containing 1.010 g hydrogen. Calculate (a) the weight of carbon in the hydrocarbon; (b) the weight of carbon in the carbon dioxide; (c) the weight of oxygen in the carbon dioxide; (d) the weight of carbon that combines with 16.0 g of oxygen.
    Answer. (a) 1.236 g; (b) 1.236 g; (c) 3.296 g; (d) 6.01 g.

3. **Definite proportions.** Are the following data on silver bromide, taken from Baxter (1906), in accord with the law of definite proportions?

Initial weight of silver	Weight of silver bromide formed (from weight of silver given in column 1)
4.80711 g	8.36827 g
6.23696 g	10.85722 g
8.13612 g	14.16334 g

4. Atomic theory. (a) Assume a mass for atoms of element A and element B. Show how these atoms must combine to satisfy the law of definite proportions. Justify your assumptions. (b) 10.0 g of element X combines with 20.0 g of element Y, forming a compound X_2Y. What are the relative weights of the atoms of X and Y?

5. Multiple proportions. Show whether or not the following data are in accord with the law of multiple proportions:

	Methane	Ethylene	Benzene
Wt % carbon...........	75.0	85.7	92.3
Wt % hydrogen........	25.0	14.3	7.7

6. Avogadro hypothesis. (a) Try to explain the following observation, volumes being measured at the same temperature and pressure,

5 ml hydrogen gas + 5 ml chlorine gas → 10 ml hydrogen chlorlde gas

by assuming a hydrogen molecule consists of 1 atom of hydrogen, H, and a chlorine molecule consists of 1 atom of chlorine, Cl. (b) Check the correct word in parentheses: the Avogadro hypothesis is a more nearly exact expression of the behavior of gases at (high, low) pressures.

7. Avogadro hypothesis. Assuming that hydrogen molecules are diatomic, H_2, use the measured volume relationships in the formation of water vapor from hydrogen and oxygen gases to show that an oxygen molecule more likely consists of 2 oxygen atoms rather than 1.

8. Mole. (a) One gross of $\frac{1}{4}$-inch ball bearings weighs 7.20 lb. Calculate the weight of 0.50 gross and the number of ball bearings in 3.60 lb of these bearings. (b) One mole of bismuth pentafluoride weighs 304 g. Calculate the weight of 0.50 mole and the number of molecules in 152 g of bismuth pentafluoride. (c) Calculate the number of moles and number of molecules in 32.0 lb of oxygen.
Answer. (a) 3.60 lb, 72; (b) 152 g, 3.01×10^{23} molecules; (c) 454 moles, 2.73×10^{26} molecules.

9. Molecular weight. The weight of formaldehyde vapor in a 1.20-liter globe sealed at 30.0°C and 1.10 atm is 1.61 g. (a) Calculate the molecular weight of the formaldehyde. (b) Calculate the weight, the number of molecules, and volume (sc) of the vapor corresponding to 1.35 moles. (c) Calculate the number of moles corresponding to 75.6 g and to 75.6 liters (sc) of vapor.

10. Cannizzaro method. Given the experimental data:

Substance	Molecular weight (g per mole)	Weight % composition Sulfur	Oxygen	Fluorine
Oxygen	32.0	—	100.0	—
Fluorine fluorosulfonate	118.1	27.2	40.6	32.2
Thionyl tetrafluoride	124.1	25.9	12.9	61.2
Pentafluorosulfur hypofluorite	162.1	19.8	9.88	70.4
Sulfur monofluoride	102.2	62.9	—	37.2
Hydrogen fluoride	20.1	—	—	94.5

Calculate the atomic weight of sulfur, oxygen, and fluorine and the molecular formulas of each of the substances. What data would you have to discover to compel a change in the atomic weight of sulfur or oxygen? Would you undertake such a research project?

11. Petit and Dulong rule. A 45-gram sample of a solid metallic element raised the temperature of 50 grams of water 4.2°C when the metal cooled from 100°C to 25°C. Estimate the atomic weight of the metal. The specific heat of water may be taken as 1.0 cal per g per deg. From an inspection of the table of International Atomic Weights (back cover), name two elements that might be the metal involved in this problem.

$$\text{Answer. } 100 \frac{g}{\text{g-atom}}.$$

12. Molecular formula. (a) The molecular weight of nicotine, a colorless oil, is 162.1 and it contains 74.0% carbon, 8.7% hydrogen, and nitrogen. Using three significant figures for the atomic weights, calculate the molecular formula of nicotine. (b) If a scientist synthesized a nitrogen compound containing 7.0 g of nitrogen per mole, would this affect the formula for nicotine? If your answer is yes, explain your answer and give the "new" formula for nicotine.

13. Empirical formula. Several alkylthiopurines were synthesized in 1960 in the search for substances with antitumor activity. One reported compound contains by weight 35.9% carbon, 3.0% hydrogen, 41.8% nitrogen, and sulfur. What is its simplest formula and formula weight? Give at least two possible values for the molecular weight of this compound.

$$\text{Answer. } C_5H_5N_5S, 167 \frac{g}{\text{mole}}.$$

14. Atomic weights. (a) The specific heat of copper at room temperature is 0.093 cal per g per deg. Hönigschmid (1944) determined that 7.9420 g of copper combines with exactly $\frac{1}{8}$ of a gram-atom of chlorine. Calculate a highly precise value for the atomic weight of copper. (b) How many gram-atoms and atoms are there in 83 g of copper?

15. Mass spectroscopy. (a) The isotope C^{12}, singly charged, describes a radius of 2.754 inches; calculate the radius in centimeters described by C^{13}, 13.003, singly charged, and by C^{12}, doubly charged. (See page 778 for necessary unit conversion.) (b) Mass spectroscopic analysis of naturally occurring carbon reveals a mixture of 98.89% C^{12}, 1.11% C^{13}, 13.003, and about $10^{-10}\%$ C^{14}, 14.008. Calculate the atomic weight of natural carbon.

$$\text{Answer. (a) } 7.580 \text{ cm}, 3.498 \text{ cm};$$
$$\text{(b) } 12.01.$$

Additional problems

16. Quantitative studies. While seeking evidence relevant to the phlogiston theory, Lavoisier in the 18th century made measurements illustrated by the following data:

- (*i*) Volume of air (room temperature, 1 atm pressure).......... 100 ml; excess mercury is heated in this volume of air forming mercuric oxide;
- (*ii*) volume of residue (room temperature, 0.5 atm pressure) after reaction with mercury.................................. 160 ml;
- (*iii*) this residue does not support combustion;
- (*iv*) volume of gas obtained from decomposition of mercuric oxide (room temperature, 2 atm pressure)...................... 10 ml;
- (*v*) this gas supports combustion;

(*vi*) volume of residue (*ii*) + volume of gas (*iv*) (room temperature, 2 atm)... 50 ml;

(*vii*) this mixture (*vi*) has all the properties of the original air.

What conclusions may you draw regarding (a) the nature of combustion; (b) the conservation of matter?

17. Conservation. Would you accept or reject as incomplete the following statements?

(a) The total quantity of matter within a chemically reacting system remains constant.

(b) In a chemical change, mass is neither created nor destroyed.

(c) In a chemical change, mass is neither created nor destroyed to any detectable extent.

(d) Mass is neither created nor destroyed.

(e) The weights of bodies at the same place are in the same ratio as their masses. Hence, the validity of the law of conservation of matter is independent of the laboratory location, making it unnecessary to study the effect of such variables as latitude, longitude, and altitude.

18. Conservation. A photographic flash bulb, containing a metal and oxygen, is weighed and fired, producing a metal oxide, and immediately reweighed without restoring the original temperature. Under the conditions of the experiment, will the sum of the weights (masses) required to balance the bulb be different after the firing than before? If not, why not? If different, does the difference prove that a change in the mass of the bulb has occurred? Explain your answer.

19. Conservation. An enclosed tube containing 21.427 g of silver oxide, Ag_2O, and 3.000 g of iron, Fe, is heated, converting some Ag_2O to silver, Ag, and some Fe to iron oxide. After the experiment, the Ag_2O weighs 20.512 g and the iron oxide weighs 3.504 g. What is the weight of Ag and Fe in the tube? What major assumption is made in arriving at your answer?

20. Definite proportions. When 0.954 g of iron, Fe, and 0.211 g of sulfur, S, are heated, 0.186 g of iron combines with 0.107 g of sulfur to form solid iron(II) sulfide. Calculate the percent composition of a piece of iron(II) sulfide located in Tibet. If all the S combined with iron, how many grams of iron(II) sulfide would form?

Answer. 63.5% Fe, 36.5% S, 0.578 g.

21. Definite proportions. Calculate the weight of arsenic in 20.0 g of calcium orthoarsenate, $Ca_3(AsO_4)_2$.

22. Weight composition. Jean Dumas in 1843 used the reaction

$$H_2 + CuO \rightarrow H_2O + Cu$$

to determine the weight composition of water. Hydrogen gas is passed through a heated tube containing solid cupric oxide, CuO. The tube and its contents are weighed before and after the experiment. The water vapor formed is condensed, collected, and weighed. The copper, Cu, formed remains in the tube. The data may be summarized as follows:

Weight of tube + cupric oxide (before experiment)	54.33 g
Weight of tube + cupric oxide + Cu (after experiment)	10.11 g
Weight of water produced	49.76 g

Calculate (a) the weight of oxygen used to produce the water; (b) the weight of hydrogen used to produce the water; (c) the weight of hydrogen that combines with 16.0 g of oxygen; (d) the weight percent of oxygen in water.

Answer. (a) 44.22 g; (b) 5.54 g; (c) 2.01 g; (d) 88.9%.

23. Atomic theory. Would you accept as correct the statement, "The existence of atoms is now accepted as a fact"?

24. Multiple proportions. (a) Use the Dalton symbols, ⊕ for sulfur and ○ for oxygen, to illustrate and explain the law of multiple proportions. (b) William Higgins in discussing the forces between atoms used the following diagram to illustrate the combination of particles:

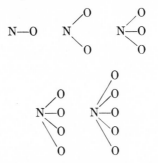

Show how this foreshadows the law of multiple proportions.

25. Combining volumes. Are the following data in accord with the law of combining volumes?

(a) A tube is loaded with 25.0 ml of hydrogen, 27°C and 1.2 atm, and 25.0 ml of oxygen, 27°C and 1.2 atm. The temperature of the mixture is raised to 227°C, and the pressure decreased to 0.1 atm; during this operation, water vapor forms. Upon restoring the tube to 27°C, the gaseous phase is found to contain oxygen and water vapor, the volume being 12.5 ml when the total pressure is 938.7 torr.

(b) 40 ml of hydrogen gas, 40 ml of nitrogen gas, and 2 ml of ammonia gas are heated under conditions such that 75% of the hydrogen and 25% of the nitrogen react to produce an additional 20 ml of ammonia. All volume measurements are made at the same temperature and pressure.

26. Avogadro hypothesis. Q and R are gaseous elements. They combine to form two different compounds, X and Y (Q + R → X; Q + R → Y), which are also gases. When the volumes of the gases are measured at the same temperature and pressure, it is found that 2 volumes of Q and 1 volume of R react to give 2 volumes of X; 2 volumes of Q and 3 volumes of R react to give 6 volumes of Y. (a) How many atoms are there in a molecule of Q and in a molecule of R? How many Q atoms and how many R atoms are there in a molecule of X? In a molecule of Y? (In short, what are the molecular formulas of Q, R, X, and Y?) (b) Are your answers to (a) the only possible answers? If they are not, give another set of molecular formulas consistent with the experimental facts.

27. Molecular weight. The molecular weight of bismuth pentafluoride is 304.0, and that of sulfur pentafluoride monochloride is 162.6. If there are X molecules in 304 grams of bismuth pentafluoride, (a) how many grams in 0.100 X molecules of the sulfur compound, and (b) how many molecules in 12 grams of the sulfur compound? (c) If 0.200 X molecules of disulfur decafluoride weigh 50.8 grams, what is its molecular weight?

Answer. (a) 16.3 g; (b) 0.074 X; (c) 254.

28. Mole. The molecules of a crystal are arranged in a simple cubic lattice, separated by 3.0×10^{-8} cm. How many molecules correspond to one unit cell? What is the volume occupied by 0.50 mole of these molecules?

29. Mole. Express in your own words and illustrate the meaning of the following definition adopted by the International Union of Pure and Applied Chemistry:

"The mole is defined as the amount of substance which contains the same number of molecules (or ions, or atoms, or electrons, as the case may be) as there are atoms in exactly 12 grammes of the pure carbon nuclide ^{12}C."

30. Mole. How many

(*i*) molecules in 2.0 moles of hydrogen,
(*ii*) ions in 2.0 moles of sodium ions,
(*iii*) particles in 2.0 moles of platinum oxide sol,
(*iv*) electrons in 2.0 moles of electrons,
(*v*) nuclei in 2.0 moles of nuclides,
(*vi*) atoms in 2.0 moles of helium,
(*vii*) radicals in 2.0 moles of sulfate radicals?

31. Molecular weight. The **Dumas method** for determining molecular weights involves the measurement of the weight of a gas or vapor enclosed in a globe of known capacity under known temperature and pressure. The data obtained by E. Moles and T. Batuecas in 1919 with methyl fluoride, a gas composed of carbon, hydrogen, and fluorine, may be presented as follows:

Weight of globe + gas	56.7642 g
Weight of globe, empty	55.2463 g
Volume of globe	2.7000 liters
Ratio of measured temperature to standard temperature (in degrees Kelvin)	1.3500
Ratio of measured pressure to standard pressure	0.50000

Calculate the molecular weight of methyl fluoride.

Answer. 34.022 $\dfrac{\text{g}}{\text{mole}}$.

32. Molecular weight. At 1000°K and 1.0 torr sodium chloride exists as **monomer** molecules, NaCl, and **dimer** molecules, (NaCl)$_2$, in the ratio of about 1:1. Estimate the apparent average molecular weight of sodium chloride under these conditions.

33. Atomic weight. The compound tetrallyldiborane, (C$_3$H$_5$)$_4$B$_2$, was first synthesized in 1960; its molecular weight, experimentally determined, is 186 and weight composition is 11.6% boron. (a) What atomic weight for boron is calculated from these data? (b) How many atoms of hydrogen are there in 1.86 grams of the compound?

Answer. (a) 10.8; (b) 1.20×10^{21} atoms.

34. Atomic weights. In his 1818 table of atomic weights, Jöns Jakob Berzelius listed aluminum with an atomic weight of 54.77 (on the scale O = 16.00). What experiments would you pursue to test this value?

35. Petit and Dulong rule. (a) The ideas of Petit and Dulong, based on the assumption of the existence of atoms, do not agree completely with experimental results; does this fact tend to invalidate the atomic theory of matter? (b) x atoms of the solid element X with a particular atomic weight require 2.6 cal for a rise of one deg C. How many calories would be required to raise the temperature of 1.1x atoms of the solid element Y one deg C? (c) 2.01 calories are required to raise 1.90×10^{23} atoms of a solid one deg C. How many calories would be required to raise the temperature of one gram-atom one deg C?

36. Petit and Dulong rule. Helium and mercury form monatomic gases; this means there is only one atom in the molecule. It requires 5.00 cal to raise

4.00 g helium one degree Centigrade (pressure constant), and 4.97 cal to raise 200.6 g gaseous mercury one degree Centigrade (pressure constant). Is the ability of an atom of helium or mercury to absorb heat dependent on the weight of the atom? Would it be fruitful to search for some general relationship between number of calories and number of moles of gases? Justify your answer.

37. Molecular formula. (a) Millions of pounds of tetrachloroethylene (b.p. 121°C) are synthesized annually for the "dry cleaning" and "vapor degreasing" industries; 310 ml of the vapor at 177°C and 765 torr weighs 1.40 g. The weight composition of the compound is 14.5% carbon and 85.5% chlorine. Calculate the molecular formula of the compound. (b) How many moles, molecules, and grams of the tetrachloroethylene would have to be vaporized to operate a vapor degreasing chamber, capacity 2.26×10^4 liters, at 127°C and 759 torr?

Answer. (a) C_2Cl_4; (b) 688 moles, 4.14×10^{26} molecules, 1.14×10^5 g.

38. Molecular formula. (a) The molecular weight of gaseous tin was recently determined with an experimental error of 30%; 0.090 g of tin at 1800°K and 1 atm occupied 147 ml. Is tin essentially a monatomic, diatomic, triatomic, or tetratomic gas? (b) Under a pressure of 10 atm, room temperature, carbon dioxide consists of 1.0% $(CO_2)_2$, 0.60% $(CO_2)_6$, 0.40% $(CO_2)_{10}$, and 98.0% CO_2; what would be the effective average molecular weight of carbon dioxide under these conditions?

Answer. (b) 47.3.

39. Empirical formula. The weight composition of a compound is 88.9% carbon and 11.1% hydrogen; 4.0 moles of fluorine reacts with 54.0 g of the compound. Without additional knowledge, what can you say about the relationship between the empirical and molecular formulas of the compound?

40. Empirical formula. 1.69 g of a solid barium-oxygen compound, treated with aqueous sulfuric acid, evolves oxygen gas and produces 2.33 g solid barium sulfate, $BaSO_4$. Calculate the empirical formula of the barium-oxygen compound.

41. Empirical formula. When a mixture of fluorine and xenon in a nickel container is heated to 400°C and then cooled rapidly to room temperature, a number of compounds is obtained. The composition of one of these compounds expressed in ml at standard conditions is

Experiment number	Xe(ml)	F₂(ml)
(1)	2.248	4.558
(2)	2.745	5.453

Calculate the empirical formula of the compound.

42. Atomic weights. Use these data to calculate a highly precise value for the atomic weight of chlorine:

Substance	Molecular weight (g per mole)	Weight % chlorine
Chlorine	71.0	100
Chloroform	119.5	89.2
Dichloromethane	85.0	83.5
Ethyl chloride	64.5	55.0

Silver chloride composition (Richards, 1907): 0.32866 g chlorine per gram of silver.

Answer. 35.453.

43. Atomic weight standard. (a) See page 88 and table of atomic weights, back cover. Choose the weights that contain the same number of atoms: 16.0000

grams of oxygen from the air, 15.9994 grams of oxygen from the air, 15.9949 grams of pure O^{16}, 16.9991 grams of pure O^{17}, 14.003 grams of natural nitrogen, 14.0067 grams of natural nitrogen, 12.0000 grams of pure C^{12}, 12.0000 grams of natural carbon. (b) Is the Avogadro number for 12.0000 grams of pure C^{12} smaller than, larger than, or the same as the number for 16.0000 grams of oxygen from air? Explain your answer.

44. Mass spectroscopy. An element A is composed of two isotopes of masses 4.20×10^{-23} g per atom and 4.27×10^{-23} g per atom. The isotopic abundance is, respectively, 3.00 atoms to 4.00 atoms. Calculate the atomic weight of this element.

Answer. 25.8.

45. Mass spectroscopy. The isotopic abundance ratio of natural chlorine, redetermined recently at the U.S. National Bureau of Standards, is

$$Cl^{35}/Cl^{37} = 3.1272 \pm 0.0080.$$

On the scale, $C^{12} = 12$, the isotopic weights are $Cl^{35} = 34.9689$ and $Cl^{37} = 36.9659$. Calculate the atomic weight of natural chlorine.

46. Definite proportions. The weight composition of lead chloride generally found throughout the world is 207.19 g Pb : 35.453 g Cl. However, the composition of lead chloride found in various uranium minerals from different parts of the world is 206.03 : 35.453. Are these accepted measurements in disagreement with the law of definite proportions?

47. Isotopes. Deuterated solvents are now available in high isotopic purity for general spectroscopic research. How many deuterium atoms are there in 1.00 mg of acetone-d_6, D_3CCOCD_3, isotopic purity 99.500 %? The atomic weight of D is 2.01410 on the scale $C^{12} = 12$.

Answer. 5.60×10^{19} atoms.

48. Time-of-flight spectrograph. This is another type of mass spectrograph. In this model, the positive ions are accelerated by a potential difference to the *same kinetic energy* into a long straight tube in a field-free region. The lighter the ion, the shorter is the time required to reach a collector at the end of the tube. The collector current measured as a function of time yields a mass spectrum. A chemist is seeking evidence for the presence of CH_2^+ and CH_3^+ as opposed to the presence of $C_2H_4^+$ and $C_2H_6^+$ as products of molecules cleaved during the ionization process in the mass spectrograph. The free flight time corresponds to 2.500×10^{-3} sec for $C_2H_5^+$; if the instrument yields readings corresponding to 2.457×10^{-3} sec and 1.737×10^{-3} sec, what species are present? (Chemical formulas refer to the most naturally abundant isotopes.)

49. History. Comment on Galen's account of the Democritean explanation of our sense perceptions. " 'For by convention color exists, by convention bitter, by convention sweet, but in reality all are atoms and void,' says Democritus, believing that from the conjunction of atoms all sensible qualities come into being for us who perceive them, but by nature nothing is white, black, yellow, red, bitter, or sweet."

5

Chemical
equations
and
chemical
arithmetic

5.1 FORMULAS AND VALENCE

The calculation of the formulas of such compounds as HCl, H_2O, NH_3, NaCl, $CaCl_2$, H_2SO_4, and H_3PO_4 immediately reveals that the **combining capacity** of atoms is not uniform. The combining capacity of an atom is commonly referred to as its **valence.** The formula HCl shows that the atoms of hydrogen and chlorine have the same combining capacity and therefore the same valence. The formula H_2O, however, shows that the combining capacity of an oxygen atom is twice that of the hydrogen atom and therefore the valence of oxygen is twice that of hydrogen. If we assign a valence of 1 to the hydrogen atom, then the valence of the chlorine atom becomes 1 and that of the oxygen atom 2. It also follows from the formula $CaCl_2$ that the combining capacity of the calcium atom is twice that of the chlorine atom; the valence of calcium is therefore 2.

Certain combinations of elements, known as **groups** or **polyatomic ions,** remain combined and behave as characteristic units during many chemical reactions. Such a combination is the sulfate group. Thus from the formula for sulfuric acid, H_2SO_4, a valence of 2 may be assigned to the sulfate, (SO_4), group.

In ionic compounds, the valence corresponds to the charge on the ion. Thus, the valence of aluminum is 3 in aluminum fluoride, $Al^{3+}(F^-)_3$, more commonly written as AlF_3, as well as in aluminum iodide, AlI_3, a nonionic compound.

Reversing the process, the knowledge of the valences of the atoms and groups furnishes adequate information for writing the empirical formulas of many compounds. The valence (see Table 5.1) of sodium is 1 and the valence of the phosphate group is 3. This means the combining capacity of the phosphate group is 3 times greater than that of the sodium atom; thus, if we take 3 sodium atoms to one phosphate group, the total combining capacity of the sodium atoms and of the phosphate group becomes

TABLE 5.1 *Common Valences of Some Elements and Groups*

| | | Illustrative compound | |
Name	Valence	Ionic	Nonionic
Ammonium	1	$NH_4^+Cl^-$	—
Copper			
Cuprous	1	—	Cu_2O
Cupric	2	$Cu^{2+}(Cl^-)_2$	—
Hydrogen	1	—	H_2O
Mercury			
Mercurous	1	—	Hg_2S
Mercuric	2	$Hg^{2+}(F^-)_2$	$HgICl$
Potassium	1	$(K^+)_2SO_4^{2-}$	—
Silver	1	$Ag^+NO_3^-$	AgI
Sodium	1	Na^+Cl^-	—
Barium	2	$Ba^{2+}CO_3^{2-}$	—
Cadmium	2	$Cd^{2+}(F^-)_2$	—
Calcium	2	$Ca^{2+}O^{2-}$	—
Cobalt	2	$Co^{2+}(NO_3^-)_2$	$CoCl_2$
Iron			
Ferrous	2	$Fe^{2+}SO_4^{2-}$	$FeBr_2$
Ferric	3	$(Fe^{3+})_2(SO_4^{2-})_3$	$FeCl_3$
Lead	2	$Pb^{2+}(F^-)_2$	$Pb(CH_3COO)_2$
Magnesium	2	$Mg^{2+}SO_4^{2-}$	—
Nickel	2	$Ni^{2+}O^{2-}$	$NiCl_2$
Strontium	2	$Sr^{2+}(Cl^-)_2$	—
Tin			
Stannous	2	$Sn^{2+}SO_4^{2-}$	$SnCl_2$
Stannic	4	$Sn^{4+}(O^{2-})_2$	$SnCl_4$
Zinc	2	$Zn^{2+}(F^-)_2$	$ZnBr_2$
Aluminum	3	$(Al^{3+})_2(O^{2-})_3$	AlI_3
Antimony	3	—	SbI_3
Bismuth	3	—	$BiCl_3$
Chromium	3	$(Cr^{3+})_2(SO_4^{2-})_3$	$CrCl_3$

TABLE **5.1** (*Continued*)

		Illustrative compound	
Name	*Valence*	*Ionic*	*Nonionic*
Acetate	1	$Na^+CH_3COO^-$	CH_3COOH
Arsenite	1	$K^+AsO_2^-$	—
Bicarbonate	1	$Na^+HCO_3^-$	—
Bromide	1	Na^+Br^-	HBr
Bromate	1	$Na^+BrO_3^-$	$HBrO_3$
Chloride	1	Na^+Cl^-	HCl
Chlorate	1	$K^+ClO_3^-$	$HClO_3$
Cyanide	1	K^+CN^-	HCN
Dihydrogen phosphate	1	$Na^+H_2PO_4^-$	—
Fluoride	1	K^+F^-	HF
Hydride	1	Li^+H^-	B_2H_6
Hydroxide	1	Na^+OH^-	HOH
Iodide	1	K^+I^-	HI
Nitrate	1	$Na^+NO_3^-$	HNO_3
Nitrite	1	$Na^+NO_2^-$	HNO_2
Permanganate	1	$K^+MnO_4^-$	$HMnO_4$
Carbonate	2	$Ca^{2+}CO_3^{2-}$	—
Chromate	2	$(K^+)_2CrO_4^{2-}$	—
Dichromate	2	$(K^+)_2Cr_2O_7^{2-}$	—
Hydrogen phosphate	2	$(Na^+)_2HPO_4^{2-}$	—
Oxygen			
Oxide	2	$(Na^+)_2O^{2-}$	HgO
Peroxide	2	$(Na^+)_2O_2^{2-}$	H_2O_2
Sulfate	2	$(Na^+)_2SO_4^{2-}$	H_2SO_4
Sulfide	2	$(K^+)_2S^{2-}$	CdS
Sulfite	2	$(Na^+)_2SO_3^{2-}$	—
Arsenate	3	$(K^+)_3AsO_4^{3-}$	H_3AsO_4
Phosphate	3	$(Na^+)_3PO_4^{3-}$	H_3PO_4

identical. The empirical formula for sodium phosphate may then be written as Na_3PO_4; since it is an ionic compound, it may also be written as $(Na^+)_3PO_4^{3-}$. Similarly, to make the total combining capacity of aluminum atoms and of sulfate groups identical, we take these in the ratio of 2:3; the simplest formula for aluminum sulfate is then $Al_2(SO_4)_3$ or, more correctly, $(Al^{3+})_2(SO_4^{2-})_3$, in which the subscript outside refers to all atoms within the parenthesis.

The fact that we can write a formula for a compound from the valences of the constituent atoms does not mean the compound must exist. We can write AgOH for the compound "silver hydroxide" but no compound

of this definite composition has yet been isolated. Conversely, man
compounds do exist, for example benzene, C_6H_6, and carbon suboxide
C_3O_2, whose formulas cannot be deduced by this scheme.

It is not fruitful to speak of a valence of the individual atoms combine
in a group. It is nevertheless useful to assign a number to an individua
atom or ion in any combination. The number is known as the **oxidatio
number** or **oxidation state** of the atom or the ion (treated further o
page 222).

5.2 NOMENCLATURE

Inspection of Table 5.1 reveals:

(a) The name of a **binary compound,** a compound composed of
elements, is usually derived from the names of the elements (see bac
cover); most commonly the metallic or electropositive element is writte
first and the second element is given the suffix **-ide.** Although frequentl,
omitted, a Greek prefix should be used to indicate the number of atom
when more than one atom is involved.

(b) When an element exhibits more than one valence, the higher stat
is denoted by the suffix **-ic** and the lower by **-ous;** however, the use o
Roman numbers placed after the name of the element to denote it
valence state is preferable. Examples:

BN	Li_3N	$SnCl_2$	$SnCl_4$	HCl
boron	*trilithium nitride*	*tin(II) chloride*	*tin(IV) chloride*	*hydrogea*
nitride	lithium nitride	*tin dichloride*	*tin tetrachloride*	*chlorid*
borazon		stannous chloride	stannic chloride	

Preferred names are in italics. Traditional names are used for very com
mon compounds such as water (dihydrogen oxide) and ammonia (tri
hydrogen nitride).

Binary acids are compounds in which a hydrogen atom combines wit
one other atom, HX or H_2X. They are named by bracketing the root
derived from the name of the element X, by the prefix **hydro-** an
suffix **-ic** followed by the word **acid.** The common binary acids ar
restricted mainly to the elements of the halogen and oxygen familie
(page 134), since the water solutions of the hydrogen compounds of othe
elements are not sufficiently acidic to warrant the use of the name acid
The corresponding negative ion is named by adding the suffix **-ide** to th
root as shown in the tabulation:

HF	*Hydrofluoric acid*	F^-	Fluoride ion
HCl	*Hydrochloric acid*	Cl^-	Chloride ion
HBr	*Hydrobromic acid*	Br^-	Bromide ion
HI	*Hydroiodic acid*	I^-	Iodide ion
H_2S	*Hydrosulfuric acid*	S^{2-}	Sulfide ion
H_2Se	*Hydroselenic acid*	Se^{2-}	Selenide ion
H_2Te	*Hydrotelluric acid*	Te^{2-}	Telluride ion
HCN	*Hydrocyanic acid*	CN^-	Cyanide ion

Included in the list is hydrocyanic acid, HCN, which is named as if it were a binary acid.

(c) **Ternary compounds,** composed of three elements, are most frequently characterized by the presence of a group; the name is therefore usually derived from the name of the element and the group. Groups containing oxygen are named relative to the number of oxygen atoms, as shown in the accompanying tabulation.

Prefix	Suffix	Refers to	Examples	
	-ate	group containing as many O atoms as the oxyacid whose suffix is -ic	H_2SO_4, sulfuric acid; $\overset{\displaystyle O}{\underset{\displaystyle O}{-OSO-}}$	sulfate
			H_3PO_4, phosphoric acid; $\overset{\displaystyle O}{\underset{\displaystyle O}{\underset{\displaystyle \mid}{-OPO-}}}$	phosphate
			HNO_3, nitric acid; $\overset{\displaystyle O}{ONO-}$	nitrate
			$HClO_3$, chloric acid; $\overset{\displaystyle O}{OClO-}$	chlorate
	-ite	one less O atom than -ate	H_2SO_3, sulfurous acid; $\overset{\displaystyle O}{-OSO-}$	sulfite
			$HClO_2$, chlorous acid; $OClO-$	chlorite
hypo-	-ite	one less O atom than -ite	$HClO$, hypochlorous acid; $ClO-$	hypochlorite
per-	-ate	one more O atom than -ate	$HClO_4$, perchloric acid; $\overset{\displaystyle O}{\underset{\displaystyle O}{OClO-}}$	perchlorate

Thus, Na_2SO_3, $FeSO_4$, $Fe_2(SO_4)_3$, $Ba(ClO_4)_2$, $Ca(ClO_3)_2$, $KClO_2$, $NaClO$ are named, respectively, **disodium sulfite** (sodium sulfite), **iron(II) sulfate** (ferrous sulfate), **iron(III) sulfate** (ferric sulfate), barium perchlorate, calcium chlorate, potassium chlorite, and sodium hypochlorite.

The nomenclature of oxyacids and related ions is further treated on page 437; complex ions are treated on page 672.

5.3 CHEMICAL EQUATIONS

Chemical equations tell us what substances react and what substances are produced. The products of a reaction are determined by experimentation. Thus propane, a typical hydrocarbon, burns in the presence of oxygen to form carbon dioxide and water. First, since the formulas for these substances are known, we may write*

$$C_3H_8(g) + O_2(g) \rightarrow CO_2(g) + H_2O(g)$$

Second, since atoms are not created or destroyed but merely rearranged in chemical changes, we **balance the equation** by making the number of atoms of each element participating in the reaction the same as that appearing in the products. This is accomplished by placing the required number before each formula.† Thus, the 8 atoms of hydrogen in the C_3H_8 must form 4 molecules of H_2O, while the 3 atoms of carbon must form 3 molecules of CO_2; but the 3 molecules of CO_2 and the 4 molecules of H_2O require 10 atoms or 5 molecules of oxygen, hence

$$C_3H_8(g) + 5O_2(g) \rightarrow 3CO_2(g) + 4H_2O(g)$$

The number before each formula is known as its **coefficient.** The coefficient is a multiplier for the entire formula, never for only a part of it. Thus, $3CaCl_2(H_2O)_6$ includes $3Ca$ atoms, $36H$ atoms, and $18O$ atoms. It should be stressed that the *subscripts in the formulas must not be altered.* This would alter the nature of the substances involved, thereby violating the experimental observation. Also, the balanced equation is a statement of the stoichiometric relations between the reactants and products involved in a chemical change; it does not, however, show the actual processes (Chapter 23) by which reactants are converted to products.

5.4 QUANTITATIVE INFORMATION FROM CHEMICAL EQUATIONS

The subject referred to as stoichiometry, in a generalized sense, deals with the weight and volume relationships determined by formulas and chemical equations. The balanced equation, for example

$$C_3H_8(g) + 5O_2(g) \rightarrow 3CO_2(g) + 4H_2O(g)$$

summarizes the chemical reaction and also gives the relative amounts of reactants and products involved in the chemical change. Thus, for every 1 molecule of propane, 5 oxygen molecules react, producing 3 carbon dioxide molecules and 4 water molecules; or, in more practical terms, for every 6.02×10^{23} molecules of propane consumed, $5(6.02 \times 10^{23})$ molecules of oxygen react, producing $3(6.02 \times 10^{23})$ molecules of carbon dioxide and $4(6.02 \times 10^{23})$ molecules of water, abbreviated as

1 molecule C_3H_8 + 5 molecules O_2
$$\rightarrow 3 \text{ molecules } CO_2 + 4 \text{ molecules } H_2O$$
or
6.02×10^{23} molecules C_3H_8 + $5(6.02 \times 10^{23})$ molecules O_2
$$\rightarrow 3(6.02 \times 10^{23}) \text{ molecules } CO_2 + 4(6.02 \times 10^{23}) \text{ molecules } H_2O$$
or
1 mole C_3H_8 + 5 moles $O_2 \rightarrow$ 3 moles CO_2 + 4 moles H_2O

* The symbol (l) denotes a liquid, (c) crystalline solid, $(amorph)$ amorphous solid, (g) gas, (sol) solution, and (aq) aqueous solution.
† A systematic method is considered later (page 367) for more complicated reactions.

or

$\qquad$ 22.4 liters(sc) C_3H_8 + 5(22.4) liters(sc) O_2
$\qquad\qquad \rightarrow$ 3(22.4) liters(sc) CO_2 + 4(22.4) liters(sc) H_2O

or

$\qquad$ 1 molecular wt C_3H_8 + 5 molecular wt O_2
$\qquad\qquad \rightarrow$ 3 molecular wt CO_2 + 4 molecular wt H_2O

or

$\qquad$ 44.1 g C_3H_8 + 5(32.0)g $O_2 \rightarrow$ 3(44.0)g CO_2 + 4(18.0)g H_2O

or

$\qquad$ 1 mole C_3H_8 + 5(6.02 × 10^{23}) molecules O_2
$\qquad\qquad \rightarrow$ 3(22.4) liters(sc) CO_2 + 4(18.0)g H_2O

Similarly, from the coefficients in the balanced equation,

$\qquad$ $3H_2(g)$ + $Fe_2O_3(c) \rightarrow 2Fe(c)$ + $3H_2O(g)$

$\qquad$ 3 moles H_2 + 1 mole $Fe_2O_3 \rightarrow$ 2 moles Fe + 3 moles H_2O

or

$\qquad$ 3(22.4) liters(sc) H_2 + 160 g Fe_2O_3
$\qquad\qquad \rightarrow$ 2(55.9)g Fe + 3(22.4) liters(sc) H_2O

or

$\qquad$ 3(2.02)g H_2 + 160 g $Fe_2O_3 \rightarrow$ 2(55.9)g Fe + 3(18.0)g H_2O

Note that each *quantity includes a unit;* refer to page 787 for a review of dimensional numbers. The rigorous use of dimensional units is particularly important in chemical stoichiometry.

$\qquad$ Chemical equations thus make it possible to calculate quantities of materials required to produce a definite quantity of a desired product.

EXAMPLE 1 **A process for manufacturing the dry cleaning fluid, tetrachloro-ethylene, C_2Cl_4, from acetylene, C_2H_2, may be summarized as**

$\qquad$ $C_2H_2(g)$ + $3Cl_2(g)$ + $Ca(OH)_2(c) \rightarrow C_2Cl_4(l)$ + $CaCl_2(c)$ + $2H_2O(l)$

$\qquad$ **(a) What weight in grams of C_2Cl_4 is produced from 50.0 g of Cl_2?**

ANSWER **From the balanced equation**

$\qquad$ **3 moles Cl_2 yields 1 mole C_2Cl_4**

or, since the molecular weight of Cl_2 is 71.0 and that of C_2Cl_4 is 166 (2 × 12.0 + 4 × 35.5 = 166),

$\qquad$ **3(71.0)g Cl_2 yields 166 g C_2Cl_4**

Hence, the number of grams of C_2Cl_4 obtained from 1 gram of chlorine is

$$\frac{166 \text{ g } C_2Cl_4}{3(71.0)\text{g } Cl_2}$$

Then the number of grams of C_2Cl_4 obtained from 50.0 g of Cl_2 is

$$50.0 \text{ g } Cl_2 \frac{166 \text{ g } C_2Cl_4}{3(71.0)\text{g } Cl_2} = 39.0 \text{ g } C_2Cl_4$$

(b) What volume of Cl_2 in liters at 27°C and 810 torr is required to produce 100 g of C_2Cl_4?

ANSWER   From the balanced equation

1 mole of C_2Cl_4 requires 3 moles Cl_2

or

166 g of C_2Cl_4 requires 3(22.4) liters(sc) Cl_2

Hence, the number of liters (sc) of Cl_2 required for 1 gram of C_2Cl_4 is

$$\frac{3(22.4) \text{ liters(sc) } Cl_2}{166 \text{ g } C_2Cl_4}$$

Then the number of liters of Cl_2 (sc) required for 100 g of C_2Cl_4 is

$$100 \text{ g } C_2Cl_4 \frac{3(22.4) \text{ liters(sc) } Cl_2}{166 \text{ g } C_2Cl_4} = 40.5 \text{ liters(sc) } Cl_2$$

The gas laws are used to calculate the volume corresponding to the conditions of the problem (cp),

$$V(\text{cp}) = 40.5 \text{ liters(sc) } Cl_2 \frac{300°K}{273°K} \frac{760 \text{ torr}}{810 \text{ torr}} = 41.8 \text{ liters(cp) } Cl_2$$

(c) What weight in grams of chlorine will react with 75.0 liters of C_2H_2 measured at 24.0°C and 790 torr?

ANSWER   From the balanced equation

3 moles Cl_2 reacts with 1 mole C_2H_2

or

3(71.0)g Cl_2 reacts with 22.4 liters(sc) C_2H_2

Hence, the number of grams of Cl_2 that reacts with 1 liter (sc) of C_2H_2 is

$$\frac{3(71.0) \text{g } Cl_2}{22.4 \text{ liters(sc) } C_2H_2}$$

Then the number of grams of Cl_2 that reacts with 75.0 liters(cp) of C_2H_2 is

$$75.0 \text{ liters(cp) } C_2H_2 \frac{3(71.0) \text{g } Cl_2}{22.4 \text{ liters(sc) } C_2H_2}$$

But this is incorrect because we cannot cancel liters(cp) and liters(sc); consequently, the 75 liters(cp) must be converted to the corresponding volume at sc,

$$V(\text{sc}) = 75.0 \text{ liters(cp) } C_2H_2 \frac{273°K}{297°K} \frac{790 \text{ torr}}{760 \text{ torr}} = 71.7 \text{ liters(sc) } C_2H_2$$

Then the number of grams of Cl_2 that reacts with 75.0 liters(cp) or 71.7 liters(sc) of C_2H_2 is

$$71.7 \text{ liters(sc) } C_2H_2 \frac{3(71.0) \text{g } Cl_2}{22.4 \text{ liters(sc) } C_2H_2} = 682 \text{ g } Cl_2$$

Notice that the *choice of units* is determined by the statement of the problem; also notice that the use of units verifies the method used for the solution of these problems, because the correct unit is obtained for the answer. If we inadvertently had inverted the ratio in the last step of the previous problem

$$71.7 \text{ liters(sc) } C_2H_2 \frac{22.4 \text{ liters(sc) } C_2H_2}{3(71.0)\text{g } Cl_2} = 7.54 \frac{[\text{liters(sc)}]^2 C_2H_2}{\text{g } Cl_2}$$

the error would be obvious since

$$\frac{[\text{liters(sc)}]^2 C_2H_2}{\text{g } Cl_2}$$

is meaningless in terms of the desired answer, g Cl_2. Note finally that the arithmetical procedure is similar to that used in everyday life; a typical problem is, "What is the cost in dollars of 12.2 gross of nails selling at 11.2 cents per hundred?" From the price, the number of cents for one nail is

$$\frac{11.2 \text{ cents}}{100 \text{ nails}}$$

Then the number of cents required for 12.2 gross of nails is

$$12.2 \text{ gross} \frac{144 \text{ nails}}{\text{gross}} \frac{11.2 \text{ cents}}{100 \text{ nails}}$$

and, converting to dollars,

$$12.2 \text{ gross} \frac{144 \text{ nails}}{\text{gross}} \frac{11.2 \text{ cents}}{100 \text{ nails}} \frac{1 \text{ dollar}}{100 \text{ cents}} = 1.97 \text{ dollars}$$

Terms such as

$$\frac{100 \text{ cents}}{1 \text{ dollar}} \quad \text{or} \quad \frac{12 \text{ inches}}{1 \text{ foot}} \quad \text{or} \quad \frac{91.4 \text{ centimeters}}{1 \text{ yard}}$$

are known as conversion factors because they are used to convert a given unit to another. But the terms used in Example 1,

$$\frac{166 \text{ g } C_2Cl_4}{3(71)\text{g } Cl_2}, \quad \frac{3(22.4) \text{ liters(sc) } Cl_2}{166 \text{ g } C_2Cl_4}, \quad \frac{3(71.0)\text{g } Cl_2}{22.4 \text{ liters(sc) } C_2H_2}$$

are also "conversion factors." The first term, for example, "converted" the given quantity of Cl_2 to the quantity of C_2Cl_4 that it produces in this particular reaction. This offers an alternate method for solving problems involving quantity relations in chemical equations.

In analytical chemistry, "conversion factors" involving gram per gram relations are called **"gravimetric factors."**

EXAMPLE 2   **When an iodate is mixed with an excess of iodine in sulfuric acid, a solution is formed having the brown-red color of the ion I_3^+ formed by the reaction**

$$HIO_3 + 7I_2 + 8H_2SO_4 \rightarrow 5I_3^+ + 3H_3O^+ + 8HSO_4^-$$

How many I_3^+ ions are produced when 1.5 grams of HIO_3 so reacts?

ANSWER Essentially, we wish to "convert" 1.5 grams of HIO_3 to a number of ions of I_3^+. From the given chemical equation, the relation between these two quantities is

$$\frac{5 \text{ moles } I_3^+}{1 \text{ mole } HIO_3} \quad \text{or} \quad \frac{5(6.0 \times 10^{23}) \text{ ions } I_3^+}{176 \text{ g } HIO_3}$$

Then, following the same arithmetical procedure by which feet are converted to inches,

$$1.5 \text{ g } HIO_3 \frac{5(6.0 \times 10^{23}) \text{ ions } I_3^+}{176 \text{ g } HIO_3} = 2.6 \times 10^{22} \text{ ions } I_3^+$$

EXAMPLE 3 2.00 g of lead nitrate, $Pb(NO_3)_2$, is added to a solution containing 1.00 g of potassium iodide, KI; insoluble lead iodide forms,

$$Pb(NO_3)_2(aq) + 2KI(aq) \rightarrow PbI_2(c) + 2KNO_3(aq)$$

How many grams of PbI_2 are formed? Which reactant is present in excess and by how many grams?

ANSWER Let us first determine which reactant is present in excess by calculating the amount of one reactant required to react with the given amount of the second reactant. This calculation, *regardless of the choice* we make for the first reactant, decides which reactant is in excess. Thus, suppose we decide to calculate how many grams of $Pb(NO_3)_2$, molecular weight 331, are needed for the 1.00 g of KI, molecular weight 166,

$$1.00 \text{ g } KI \frac{331 \text{ g } Pb(NO_3)_2}{2 \times 166 \text{ g } KI} = 0.997 \text{ } Pb(NO_3)_2 \tag{1}$$

However, 2.00 g of $Pb(NO_3)_2$ is given; therefore, $Pb(NO_3)_2$ is in excess by 1.00 g.

If we had decided to calculate how many grams of KI are needed for the 2.00 g of $Pb(NO_3)_2$,

$$2.00 \text{ g } Pb(NO_3)_2 \frac{2 \times 166 \text{ g } KI}{331 \text{ g } Pb(NO_3)_2} = 2.01 \text{ g } KI$$

we would have concluded that 1.00 g of KI is insufficient to react with 2.00 g of $Pb(NO_3)_2$. Then, to determine the quantity of $Pb(NO_3)_2$ in excess, we would have to proceed as above (Equation 1).

These calculations also show that the quantity of PbI_2, molecular weight 461, formed is determined by the 1.00 g of KI [or 0.997 g of $Pb(NO_3)_2$] consumed. Hence

$$1.00 \text{ g } KI \frac{461 \text{ g } PbI_2}{2 \times 166 \text{ g } KI} = 1.39 \text{ g } PbI_2$$

or

$$0.997 \text{ g } Pb(NO_3)_2 \frac{461 \text{ g } PbI_2}{331 \text{ g } Pb(NO_3)_2} = 1.39 \text{ g } PbI_2$$

Equations such as

$$H_2(g) + \tfrac{1}{2}O_2(g) \rightarrow H_2O(l)$$

are frequently used; this balanced equation is read as: 1 mole of H_2 combines with $\frac{1}{2}$ mole of O_2 to form 1 mole of H_2O (not as 1 molecule of H_2 combining with $\frac{1}{2}$ molecule of O_2).

5.5 PERCENT YIELD

Reactants often yield quantities of products that are **less** than those calculated on the basis of the formulated chemical reaction. Reasons for such material deficiencies may be (a) some of the reactants fail to undergo reaction; (b) some of the reactants react in a way different from that expected or desired ("side reactions" occur); (c) some of the expected products react to form other products or revert to the original reactants.

The calculated quantity is referred to as the "theoretical yield" and the percent yield is given by

$$\% \text{ yield} = \frac{\text{actual yield}}{\text{theoretical yield}} (100)$$

EXAMPLE 4 **Ethylene oxide, C_2H_4O, is manufactured by the oxidation of ethylene in air,**

$$C_2H_4 + \tfrac{1}{2}O_2 \rightarrow C_2H_4O$$

Undesirable events are (a) the escape of some ethylene to the atmosphere; (b) the more complete oxidation of some ethylene to formaldehyde (H_2CO), CO, and CO_2; (c) the decomposition of some ethylene to carbon (smoke) and other products. If 60 g of C_2H_4O is obtained from 42 g of C_2H_4, what is the percent yield?

ANSWER **The theoretical yield, the quantity of C_2H_4O that should be obtained from 42 g of C_2H_4, is 66 g C_2H_4O,**

$$42 \text{ g } C_2H_4 \frac{44 \text{ g } C_2H_4O}{28 \text{ g } C_2H_4} = 66 \text{ g } C_2H_4O$$

The actual yield, however, is 60 g C_2H_4O. The percent yield is therefore

$$\frac{60 \text{ g } C_2H_4O}{66 \text{ g } C_2H_4O}(100) = 91\%$$

Problems

1. Valence and formula. (a) What is the valence of the element combined with oxygen in each of the following oxides: OsO, WO_3, Tl_2O, and Tl_2O_3? (b) Write the simplest formula for each of the following compounds: zinc chlorate, sodium peroxide, magnesium phosphate, and lead nitrate. (c) The formula for radium chloride is $RaCl_2$. Write the formula for each of the following compounds of radium: the sulfate, the carbonate, the sulfide.

2. Nomenclature. (a) HNO_3 is the formula for nitric acid; write the formula for nitrous acid and calcium nitrite. (b) H_3PO_4 is the formula for phosphoric acid; name the acids H_3PO_3 and H_3PO_2. (c) Name $Mg(ClO_4)_2$. (d) HIO_3 is the formula for iodic acid; write the formula for periodic acid and hypoiodous acid.

3. Chemical equations. Each of the following reactions is the basis of an industrial process. Write a balanced equation for each reaction:

(a) $NH_3(g) + O_2(g) \rightarrow NO(g) + H_2O(g)$
(b) $C_6H_{12}O_6(c) \rightarrow C_2H_5OH(l) + CO_2(g)$
(c) $C_2H_5Cl(g) + Pb(c) + Na(c) \rightarrow Pb(C_2H_5)_4(l) + NaCl(c)$
(d) $Fe_3O_4(c) + CO(g) \rightarrow Fe(l) + CO_2(g)$
(e) $Fe_2O_3(c) + CH_4(g) \rightarrow Fe(c) + CO_2(g) + H_2O(g)$
(f) $C_2H_2 + O_2 \rightarrow$ ——— $+$ ———

4. Chemical equations. Would you accept

$$\tfrac{3}{2}H_2(g) + \tfrac{1}{2}N_2(g) \rightarrow NH_3(g)$$

as a balanced chemical equation? Justify your answer.

5. Conversion factors. Write the conversion factor you would use for each of the following problems:

(a) How many square inches in 10.1 square feet?
(b) How many grams of iodine triperchlorate may be prepared by the reaction

$$3AgClO_4 + 2I_2 \rightarrow 3AgI + I(ClO_4)_3$$

(*i*) if 2.0 moles of silver perchlorate reacts?
(*ii*) if 32 ml, as a gas at sc, of iodine reacts?
(*iii*) if 1.1 grams of silver iodide is produced?
(c) How many liters in 10.0 ml?
(d) How many molecules of hydrogen fluoride are obtained when 10^{-2} mole of XeF_4 reacts as follows?

$$XeF_4 + 2H_2 \rightarrow Xe + 4HF$$

(e) How many grams of Cl^- are present in a sample that yields 0.5679 gram of silver chloride when all the Cl^- in the sample reacts as follows?

$$Ag^+ + Cl^- \rightarrow AgCl$$

Answer. (a) $\dfrac{144 \text{ in}^2}{\text{ft}^2}$; (b) (*i*) $\dfrac{426 \text{ g } I(ClO_4)_3}{3 \text{ moles } AgClO_4}$; (*ii*) $\dfrac{426 \text{ g } I(ClO_4)_3}{2(22.4 \times 10^3) \text{ ml(sc) } I_2}$;

(*iii*) $\dfrac{426 \text{ g } I(ClO_4)_3}{3(235) \text{ g } AgI}$; (c) $\dfrac{\text{liter}}{10^3 \text{ ml}}$; (d) $\dfrac{4(6 \times 10^{23}) \text{ molecules HF}}{1 \text{ mole } XeF_4}$;

(e) $\dfrac{35.453 \text{ g } Cl^-}{143.32 \text{ g } AgCl}$.

6. Chemical arithmetic. How many grams of oxygen may be obtained by decomposing completely, as shown, 17 g of barium peroxide?

$$2BaO_2(c) \rightarrow 2BaO(c) + O_2$$

7. Chemical arithmetic. How many liters of nitrogen, (*i*) at standard conditions, (*ii*) at 27.0°C and 2.00 atm, may be obtained by the complete decomposition of 4.60 g NO_2?

$$2NO_2(g) \rightarrow N_2(g) + 2O_2(g)$$

Answer. (*i*) 1.12 liters; (*ii*) 0.618 liter.

8. Chemical arithmetic. When diborane, B_2H_6, is passed at low pressure through a tube at 400°C, the high energy fuel pentaborane, B_5H_9, is largely obtained,

$$5B_2H_6(g) \rightarrow 2B_5H_9(g) + 6H_2(g)$$

(a) What weight in grams of B_5H_9 is produced from 45.0 g of B_2H_6? (b) What volume of B_5H_9 in liters at 400°C and 120 torr is produced from 100 g of B_2H_6? (c) What is the weight in grams of hydrogen, H_2, obtained for the production of 20.0 liters of B_5H_9 measured at 27°C and 780 torr?

Answer. (a) 39.7 g; (b) 506 liters; (c) 5.05 g.

9. Chemical arithmetic. The production of **sponge iron** from iron oxides and natural gas, which requires no blast furnace, may be represented as

$$4Fe_2O_3(c) + 3CH_4(g) \rightarrow 8Fe(c) + 3CO_2(g) + 6H_2O(g)$$

How many liters of gas (CO_2 and H_2O) would be produced at 300°C and 775 torr for every kilogram of Fe_2O_3 converted to iron?

10. Yield. In the laboratory, oxygen may be prepared by the thermal decomposition of solid potassium chlorate. During the decomposition of potassium chlorate, $2KClO_3(c) \rightarrow 2KCl(c) + 3O_2$, a number of side reactions occur; for example, oxides of chlorine are also produced. If 10 g of $KClO_3$ yields 3.8 g of oxygen, calculate the theoretical yield, the percent yield.

11. Chemical arithmetic. 4.0 g of magnesium is ignited in 4.0 g of oxygen, producing magnesium oxide,

$$2Mg(c) + O_2(g) \rightarrow 2MgO(c)$$

(i) Which reactant is present in excess, and (ii) by how many grams? (iii) How many grams of MgO are formed?

Answer. (ii) 1.3 g; (iii) 6.7 g.

Additional problems

12. Nomenclature. Write the formula for (a) cerium(III) sulfate and cerium(IV) sulfate; (b) diarsenic pentoxide; (c) sulfur hexafluoride. (d) Give another name for each of the compounds given in part (a). (e) Of what elements is the compound trichromium dicarbide composed?

13. Chemical arithmetic. At 77°K atomic hydrogen reacts with dioxygen difluoride (m.p. $\sim$ 110°K),

$$O_2F_2 + 5H \rightarrow 2HF + 0.5\ H_2O_2 + H_2O$$

(a) What weight of hydrogen peroxide H_2O_2 in mg is produced for every 10×10^2 ml of atomic hydrogen consumed at 77°K and 1.5 atm? The formation of H_2O_4 in trace amounts may be neglected.

(b) Calculate the weight of water in grams formed from 2.5 moles of atomic hydrogen and the corresponding volume of steam at 300°C and 790 torr in liters.

Answer. (a) 8.1×10^2 mg; (b) 9.0 g, 23 liters.

14. Chemical arithmetic. The solution of 5.1 g of iodine in 200 g of iodine pentafluoride yields the positive iodine ion and the IF_6^- complex negative ion,

$$2I_2 + 6IF_5 \rightarrow 5I^+ + 5IF_6^-$$

Calculate the number of grams of (i) the reactant present in excess, and (ii) IF_6^- produced.

Answer. (i) 187 g; (ii) 12 g.

15. Chemical arithmetic. Carbon monoxide, CO, is used as an ashless fuel, the reaction being

$$2CO(g) + O_2(g) \rightarrow 2CO_2(g)$$

Calculate the approximate volume of air (20% oxygen by volume) in liters at 25°C and 763 torr required per hour to burn 6.0 liters of CO per hour at the same temperature under a pressure of 20 atm.

16. Chemical arithmetic. Nitrogen atoms react with solid acetylene at 80°K to produce a polymer, $(CN)C_4H_4(CN)$,

$$2N + 3C_2H_2(c) \rightarrow (CN)C_4H_4(CN)(amorph) + 2H$$

If 2.80 g of atomic nitrogen yields 1.09 g of polymer, have all of the nitrogen atoms reacted as shown in the above equation?

17. Chemical arithmetic. Assuming complete reaction between lithium and the isotope of astatine, At^{211}, producing lithium astatide, $LiAt^{211}$, what is the composition of the mixture formed from 7.4 pg lithium and 216 pg astatine-211? (If required, see page 778 for definition of pg.)

18. Chemical arithmetic. Difluoramine reacts with anhydrous HCl in the gas phase in accord with the reaction

$$3HCl + 3HNF_2 \rightarrow 2ClNF_2 + NH_4Cl + 2HF$$

In this reaction, only 78% of the HCl reacts. A mixture is prepared with 4.00 g HCl and 6.00 g HNF_2. After reaction has occurred, what is the composition of the mixture, in grams, in the reaction vessel with respect to HCl, HNF_2, and $ClNF_2$?

Answer. 1.5 g HNF_2, 0.88 g HCl, 5.1 g $ClNF_2$.

6

Thermochemistry;
The
first
law of
thermodynamics

6.1 THERMOCHEMISTRY

Chemical changes are nearly always accompanied by energy changes. These energy changes are of theoretical and practical importance. The results of quantitative measurements of these energy changes support the law of conservation of energy and show that the energy change is a most important factor in determining the extent to which a chemical reaction will occur (pages 403). The combustion of fossil fuels, such as coal, petroleum products, and natural gas, now constitutes man's major energy source. Chemical reactions evolving heat to the surroundings are known as **exothermic;** if heat is absorbed from the surroundings, the reaction is called **endothermic.** The amount of heat removed in an exothermic reaction or added in an endothermic reaction is *that neces-sary to restore the reaction mixture to its original temperature.* Heat measurements are made by mixing known amounts of reactants in a calorimeter (Fig. 6.1). The heat evolved by the reaction is equal to the heat absorbed by a known quantity of water, the metal bucket, the metal reaction chamber containing known quantities of reactants, the stirrer, and the thermometer. The water equivalent of a calorimeter is the quantity of water required to absorb the same quantity of heat absorbed by the calorimeter and its component parts.

EXAMPLE 1   The combustion of 0.100 g of liquid benzene, C_6H_6, in a calorimeter, whose water equivalent is 383.6 g of water, produced a temperature rise of

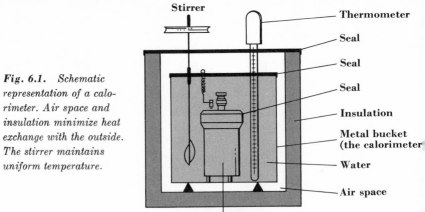

Fig. 6.1. Schematic
representation of a calo-
rimeter. Air space and
insulation minimize heat
exchange with the outside.
The stirrer maintains
uniform temperature.

Stirrer

Thermometer

Seal

Seal

Seal

Insulation

Metal bucket
(the calorimeter)

Water

Air space

Reaction Chamber

2.609°C. Calculate the molar heat of combustion of C_6H_6, the heat change accompanying the combustion of one mole of a substance. The molecular weight of C_6H_6 is 78.1. There are 10^3 cal in a kilocalorie (kcal).

ANSWER The specific heat of water is 0.9983 cal per g per deg; hence, the quantity of heat emitted is

$$0.9983 \; \frac{\text{cal}}{\text{g, deg}} \; 383.6 \; \text{g} \; 2.609 \; \text{deg} = 999 \text{ cal}$$

Since 999 cal are emitted during the combustion of 0.100 g of C_6H_6, the heat emitted by 1 gram of C_6H_6 is

$$\frac{999 \text{ cal}}{0.100 \text{ g}}$$

Then the heat emitted by 1 mole of C_6H_6 is

$$\frac{999 \text{ cal}}{0.100 \text{ g}} \; 78.1 \; \frac{\text{g}}{\text{mole}} \; \frac{1}{10^3 \; \dfrac{\text{cal}}{\text{kcal}}} = 780 \; \frac{\text{kcal}}{\text{mole}}$$

Since calorimetric measurements are generally made in a container of fixed volume, *the chemical reaction occurs at constant volume.* Since work (Appendix I, page 776) is done only when the force acting on a body moves the body through a distance, no work is done by the chemically reacting system against the surrounding atmosphere and no work is done by the surrounding atmosphere on the chemically reacting system. The heat liberated or absorbed under conditions of *constant volume and constant temperature* is given the symbol ΔE. ΔE, the change in the "energy" of a chemical system, is equal to the energy of products, E_2, less the energy of the reactants, E_1,

$$\Delta E = \text{energy of products} - \text{energy of reactants}$$
$$= E_2 - E_1$$

Thus the **thermochemical** equation for the combustion of liquid C_6H_6,

$$C_6H_6(l) + 7\tfrac{1}{2}O_2(g) \rightarrow 3H_2O(l) + 6CO_2(g) \qquad \Delta E = -780 \text{ kcal}$$
$$(\textit{exothermic reaction})$$

means that when 1 mole of liquid benzene reacts with $7\tfrac{1}{2}$ moles of oxygen, forming 3 moles of liquid water and 6 moles of carbon dioxide at *constant volume*, and the *temperature* of the products *is restored* to the original temperature of the reactants, 780 kilocalories are evolved. The energy of the 3 moles of $H_2O(l)$ and 6 moles of $CO_2(g)$ is therefore 780 kcal less than the energy of 1 mole of $C_6H_6(l)$ and $7\tfrac{1}{2}$ moles of $O_2(g)$.

The thermochemical equation for the decomposition of nickel oxide is

$$NiO(c) \rightarrow Ni(c) + \tfrac{1}{2}O_2(g) \qquad \Delta E = +57.0 \text{ kcal}$$
$$(\textit{endothermic reaction})$$

This means that when 1 mole of solid NiO is decomposed to 1 mole of solid Ni and $\tfrac{1}{2}$ mole of $O_2(g)$ at *constant volume* and *constant temperature*, 57.0 kcal is absorbed from the surroundings so that the energy of the 1 mole of Ni and $\tfrac{1}{2}$ mole of O_2 is 57.0 kcal larger than the energy of 1 mole of NiO.

Since the energy of a substance is a function of its physical state and temperature, the ΔE of a reaction is also a function of these variables. Thus the state of each reactant and product must be clearly indicated. The data given in this text are for substances in their stable states at 25.0°C and 1 atm pressure; graphite is the stable state for carbon.

However, reactions most frequently occur in open vessels at constant barometric pressure. But when one mole of liquid C_6H_6 is burned at constant pressure, the heat evolved is 781 kcal, not 780 kcal. This difference results from the fact that when gases are involved in chemical reactions at **constant pressure,** *appreciable volume changes may occur.* Consequently, work may be done. If the volume of the products is larger than the volume of the reactants, then the chemically reacting system **does work against** the surrounding atmosphere. Conversely, if a decrease in volume accompanies a chemical reaction, then the surrounding atmosphere **does work** on the chemical system. Thus, the combustion of benzene

$$C_6H_6(l) + 7\tfrac{1}{2}O_2(g) \rightarrow 3H_2O(l) + 6CO_2(g)$$

in air is accompanied by a decrease in volume, $7\tfrac{1}{2}$ moles of gaseous oxygen to 6 moles of gaseous carbon dioxide. Hence, the *surrounding air does work on the chemical system* and the heat evolved at constant temperature and constant pressure is therefore greater than the heat evolved in a calorimeter at *constant temperature* and constant volume. The data for heats of reaction are commonly given for the quantity of heat emitted or absorbed at constant temperature and *constant pressure;* this quantity is given the symbol ΔH. ΔH, called the change in the **enthalpy*** of a

---

* The term "enthalpy" is derived from the Greek word *enthalpo*, meaning "warming up." The more descriptive but misleading term, "heat content," is sometimes used synonymously with enthalpy. The relation between ΔE and ΔH is treated more fully in Section 6.5 (page 119).

chemical system, is equal to the enthalpy of the products, H_2, less the enthalpy of the reactants, H_1,

$$\Delta H = H_2 - H_1$$

Thus the thermochemical equation for the combustion of C_6H_6 is

$$C_6H_6(l) + 7\tfrac{1}{2}O_2(g) \rightarrow 3H_2O(l) + 6CO_2(g) \qquad \Delta H = -781 \text{ kcal}$$

This means that when 1 mole of liquid benzene reacts with $7\tfrac{1}{2}$ moles of oxygen forming 3 moles of liquid water and 6 moles of carbon dioxide at *constant pressure*, and the temperature of the products is restored to the original temperature of the reactants, 781 kilocalories are evolved; therefore, the enthalpy of the 3 moles of $H_2O(l)$ and 6 moles of $CO_2(g)$ 781 kcal less than the enthalpy of 1 mole of $C_6H_6(l)$ and $7\tfrac{1}{2}$ moles of $O_2(g)$. When ΔH is $+$, heat is absorbed during the reaction. For example the thermochemical equation for the formation of hydrogen iodide is

$$\tfrac{1}{2}H_2(g) + \tfrac{1}{2}I_2(c) \rightarrow HI(g) \qquad \Delta H = +6.20 \text{ kcal}$$

This means that when $\tfrac{1}{2}$ mole of hydrogen reacts with $\tfrac{1}{2}$ mole of solid iodine forming 1 mole of gaseous hydrogen iodide at *constant temperature* and *constant pressure*, 6.20 kcal is absorbed from the surroundings; the enthalpy of the products is therefore larger than the enthalpy of reactants.

6.2 HESS'S LAW

In accord with the law of conservation of energy, thermochemical equations possess two important properties:

(a) They may be reversed, in which case the sign of ΔE or ΔH is changed. For example,

$$H_2(g) + \tfrac{1}{2}O_2(g) \rightarrow H_2O(l) \qquad \Delta H = -68.3 \text{ kcal}$$
$$H_2O(l) \rightarrow H_2(g) + \tfrac{1}{2}O_2(g) \qquad \Delta H = +68.3 \text{ kcal}$$

means the heat evolved in the formation of 1 mole of liquid water is equal to the heat required to decompose 1 mole of liquid water.

(b) They may be added and subtracted as ordinary algebraic equations. This generalization is known as **Hess's law.** For example, the addition of the two thermochemical equations

$$C_2H_4(g) + H_2(g) + \tfrac{3}{2}O_2(g) \rightarrow 2CO_2(g) + 3H_2O(l)$$
$$\Delta H = -405.5 \text{ kcal}$$
$$2CO_2(g) + 3H_2O(l) \rightarrow C_2H_6(g) + \tfrac{3}{2}O_2(g)$$
$$\Delta H = +372.8 \text{ kcal}$$

predicts that the heat of hydrogenation of ethylene, C_2H_4, to ethane C_2H_6, is

$$C_2H_4(g) + H_2(g) \rightarrow C_2H_6(g) \quad \Delta H = -405.5 + 372.8 = -32.7 \text{ kcal}$$

When a formula appears on the right of one equation and on the left of another, the substance will not appear in the final equation if it is produced and consumed in equal quantities.

The experimentally determined heat of reaction is

$$C_2H_4(g) + H_2(g) \rightarrow C_2H_6(g) \qquad \Delta H = -32.6 \pm 0.1 \text{ kcal}$$

Hess's law shows that the heat of a reaction, ΔE or ΔH, depends only on the nature of the final products and initial reactants, and is independent of the path (how the chemical change is carried out, in one or several steps).

Since the enthalpy of a substance is a function of its physical state and temperature, the ΔH of a reaction is also a function of these variables. For example, the enthalpy of $H_2O(g)$ is greater than that of $H_2O(l)$ by 10.5 kcal per mole,

$$H_2O(l) \rightarrow H_2O(g) \qquad \Delta H = +10.5 \text{ kcal}$$

EXAMPLE 2   **Use the thermochemical equations**

$\frac{1}{2}H_2(g) + \frac{1}{2}I_2(c) \rightarrow HI(g)$	$\Delta H = +6.20$ kcal	(1)
$\frac{1}{2}H_2(g) \rightarrow H(g)$	$\Delta H = +52.1$ kcal	(2)
$\frac{1}{2}I_2(g) \rightarrow I(g)$	$\Delta H = +18.1$ kcal	(3)
$I_2(c) \rightarrow I_2(g)$	$\Delta H = +14.9$ kcal	(4)

to calculate the ΔH for the formation of gaseous hydrogen iodide, HI, from gaseous atomic hydrogen and gaseous atomic iodine,

$$H(g) + I(g) \rightarrow HI(g)$$

ANSWER   **Basically, the problem is to manipulate the given chemical equations as we would algebraic equations so as to eliminate those substances not appearing in the final desired equation. Thus, transpose Equations (2), (3), and (4) and also multiply Equation (4) by $\frac{1}{2}$, yielding**

$\frac{1}{2}H_2(g) + \frac{1}{2}I_2(c) \rightarrow HI(g)$	$\Delta H = +6.20$ kcal	(1)
$H(g) \rightarrow \frac{1}{2}H_2(g)$	$\Delta H = -52.1$ kcal	(5)
$I(g) \rightarrow \frac{1}{2}I_2(g)$	$\Delta H = -18.1$ kcal	(6)
$\frac{1}{2}I_2(g) \rightarrow \frac{1}{2}I_2(c)$	$\Delta H = -7.5$ kcal	(7)

which on addition yield

$$H(g) + I(g) \rightarrow HI(g) \qquad \Delta H = +6.20 - 52.1 - 18.1 - 7.5 = -71.5 \text{ kcal}$$

6.3   BOND DISSOCIATION ENERGY

The formation of 1 mole of $HI(g)$ from gaseous atoms evolves 71.5 kcal while the dissociation of 1 mole of $HI(g)$ into gaseous atoms requires 71.5 kcal. The quantity of energy required to decompose a gaseous molecule into two individual fragments or to break one bond in a molecule is called the **bond dissociation energy,** commonly expressed in kcal per mole. Bond dissociation energies for a number of bonds are given in Table 6.1.

HF	136	**H₂**	104.2	**N₂**	225.9
HCl	103	**F₂**	38	$NF_3 \rightarrow NF_2 + F$	74.0
HBr	87.4	**Cl₂**	57.9	$NF_2 \rightarrow NF + F$	62.6
HI	71.5	**Br₂**	46.1	$NF \rightarrow N + F$	62.6

^{a} ΔH **in kcal per mole.**

The heats of dissociation illustrated in Table 6.1 are obtained without assumptions regarding the nature of the forces holding atoms together in molecules.

From the data in Table 6.1, Hess's law predicts that the decomposition of nitrogen trifluoride, NF_3, into its constituent atoms, $N + 3F$, will require 199.2 kcal per mole:

$$NF_3(g) \rightarrow NF_2(g) + F(g) \qquad \Delta H = +74.0$$
$$NF_2(g) \rightarrow NF(g) + F(g) \qquad \Delta H = +62.6$$
$$NF(g) \rightarrow N(g) + F(g) \qquad \Delta H = +62.6$$
$$\overline{NF_3(g) \rightarrow N(g) + 3F(g) \qquad \Delta H = +199.2}$$

But the same prediction may be made by another means. Assume that the energy required to remove the fluorine atoms successively from the nitrogen atom is equal; then we may *assign* to each N—F bond an **average energy** of $(199.2)/3$ or 66.4 kcal per mole, called the **average bond energy** of the N—F bond. The decomposition of NF_3 into its constituent atoms will then require 3×66.4 or 199.2 kcal per mole.

Since no experimental data for the stepwise dissociation of most polyatomic molecules exist, the assignment of average bond energies to chemical bonds is common practice.

EXAMPLE 3 **Calculate the average bond energy for the C—H bond from the following experimental data:**

$$C(graphite) + 2H_2(g) \rightarrow H-\overset{\displaystyle H}{\underset{\displaystyle H}{\overset{|}{\underset{|}{C}}}}-H(g) \qquad \Delta H = -17.9 \text{ kcal}$$
$$\text{methane}$$

$$C(g) \rightarrow C(graphite) \qquad \Delta H = -170.9 \text{ kcal}$$
$$2H(g) \rightarrow H_2(g) \qquad \Delta H = -104.2 \text{ kcal}$$

ANSWER **First, multiplying the third equation by 2 and adding the three equations yields**

$$C(g) + 4H(g) \rightarrow CH_4(g) \qquad \Delta H = -397.2 \text{ kcal}$$

Notice that the only reaction now occurring is the formation of four C—H bonds; *assuming* they are identical, it follows that in forming one bond

$$C(g) + H(g) \rightarrow C\text{—}H(g) \qquad \Delta H = \frac{-397.2}{4} = -99.3 \frac{kcal}{mole}$$

or breaking one bond

$$C\text{—}H(g) \rightarrow C(g) + H(g) \qquad \Delta H = +99.3 \frac{kcal}{mole}$$

The average bond energy for the C—H bond is therefore 99.3 kcal per mole.

Average bond energies are usually called simply **"bond energies"**; Table 6.2 lists a number of bond energy values. Since the bond dissociation energy and the bond energy are necessarily the same for **diatomic molecules,** they may also be included in Table 6.2.

The energy required to decompose a gaseous molecule completely into isolated atoms must equal the sum of the bond energies for all the bonds within the molecule. Precise values may of course be calculated, as in Example 2 or 3, if thermochemical data are available. But suppose, as frequently is the situation, that experimental data are not available. If we *assume that the bond between a given pair of atoms is independent of the molecule in which it resides,* then the type of data given in Table 6.2 can be used to predict the energy required to dissociate any molecule into its constituent atoms.

EXAMPLE 4   **Calculate the heat of the reaction**

$$\begin{array}{c} H \\ | \\ H\text{—}C\text{—}H(g) \rightarrow C(g) + 3H(g) + Cl(g) \qquad \Delta H = ? \\ | \\ Cl \end{array}$$

ANSWER   **This reaction involves**

(a) breaking three C—H bonds:

$$3C\text{—}H \rightarrow 3C + 3H \qquad \Delta H = +3(99.3) = +298 \text{ kcal}$$

(b) breaking one C—Cl bond:

$$C\text{—}Cl \rightarrow C + Cl \qquad \Delta H = +78 \text{ kcal}$$

TABLE 6.2   *Average Bond Energy Values*[a] *for the Process: Bond AB in a Gaseous Molecule* $\rightarrow A(g) + B(g)$

C—H	99.3	C—F	116	H—F	136
C—C (ethane)	83	C—Cl	78	H—Cl	103
C=C (ethylenic bond)	143	C—Br	68	H—Br	87.4
C≡C (acetylenic bond)	194	O—H	111	H—I	71.5

[a] ΔH in kcal per mole.

The ΔH for the reaction is therefore $298 + 78$ or $+376$ kcal per mole of CH_3Cl. The experimental value is 375.8 kcal per mole.

EXAMPLE 5   Calculate the heat of the reaction

$$CH_4(g) + 4F_2(g) \rightarrow CF_4(g) + 4HF(g)$$

ANSWER   This reaction involves

(a) breaking four C—H bonds:

$$4C—H \rightarrow 4C + 4H \qquad \Delta H = +4(99.3) \text{ kcal}$$

(b) breaking four F—F bonds:

$$4F—F \rightarrow 8F \qquad \Delta H = +4(38) \text{ kcal}$$

(c) forming four C—F bonds:

$$4C + 4F \rightarrow 4C—F \qquad \Delta H = -4(116) \text{ kcal}$$

(d) forming four H—F bonds:

$$4H + 4F \rightarrow 4H—F \qquad \Delta H = -4(136) \text{ kcal}$$

The calculated ΔH for the reaction is therefore $+4(99.3) + 4(38) - 4(116) - 4(136) = -459$ kcal per mole of CH_4. The measured value is -457 kcal per mole.

Although the agreement is usually gratifying, for many reactions a significant difference occurs between the heat of the reaction as calculated in Examples 4 and 5 and the experimental heat of reaction. These discrepancies, annoying to the uninitiated, compel the re-examination of our assumption that the property of a bond is independent of its molecular environment. This re-examination will, in fact, lead us (page 286) to a better understanding of the nature of the bonds holding atoms together in molecules.

6.4   THE INTERCONVERTIBILITY OF MATTER AND ENERGY

Regardless of the name given to reactions—"chemical change," "ordinary chemical change," "nuclear reaction," "nuclear chemical reaction," or "nuclear formation"—the conversion of one form of matter to another involves the conversion of matter to energy if the reaction is exothermic; conversely, in an endothermic reaction, the heat energy absorbed is converted into matter. This means matter and heat energy are not conserved separately; rather, the principle of conservation of energy is broadened to include matter as another form of energy. Thus, the quantity of energy, expressed in grams, liberated or absorbed is *exactly equal* to the quantity of matter, expressed in grams, destroyed or created.

The interconvertibility of matter and energy is described by the equation $E = mc^2$, predicted by Albert Einstein in 1905: E is the energy in ergs when m, the quantity of matter converted, is in grams; the constant

c, the speed of light, is 3.00×10^{10} cm per sec. An erg has the dimensions of g cm^2/sec^2, and there are 4.18×10^7 ergs in one calorie.

EXAMPLE 6   **In an explosion of a gasoline-air mixture 4.9×10^6 cal are evolved,**

$$\text{reactants} \rightarrow \text{products} \qquad \Delta E = -4.9 \times 10^6 \text{ cal}$$

Calculate the decrease in mass (weight) in grams accompanying this reaction.

ANSWER   **The mass (weight) of the products will be less by an amount calculated from the Einstein equation ($E = mc^2$),**

$$4.9 \times 10^6 \, \cancel{\text{cal}} \; 4.2 \times 10^7 \frac{\text{ergs}}{\cancel{\text{cal}}} = m(3.0 \times 10^{10})^2 \frac{\text{cm}^2}{\text{sec}^2}$$

from which

$$m = 2.3 \times 10^{-7} \text{ ergs} \, \frac{\text{sec}^2}{\text{cm}^2}$$

and since an erg has the dimensions of g $\dfrac{\text{cm}^2}{\text{sec}^2}$

$$m = 2.3 \times 10^{-7} \frac{\text{g} \, \cancel{\text{cm}^2} \, \cancel{\text{sec}^2}}{\cancel{\text{sec}^2} \, \cancel{\text{cm}^2}} = 2.3 \times 10^{-7} \text{ g}$$

Thus 2.3×10^{-7} g is the quantity of matter liberated as heat to the surroundings.

This quantity is so small that unless nuclear reactions (Chapter 28) are involved, we can say that the total mass of matter of a chemically reacting system is *practically* constant.

6.5   THE FIRST LAW OF THERMODYNAMICS

The interconvertibility of matter and energy, Hess's law, the failure to produce a practical perpetual motion machine, and the experiments on the mechanical equivalent of heat* are among the facts summarized in the first law of thermodynamics: *the energy of a system in a definite state is fixed and independent of the method of preparation.* For example, the energy of, say, 1.72643 grams of natural nitrogen gas at 425.270°K and 2.54361 atm is a fixed value, E_1. When a system undergoes a change in state, its energy also changes; for example, E_1 changes if the temperature of the nitrogen is raised to 526.371°K and the pressure is increased to 4.53205 atm. But, since the energy of the system in the second state is also a fixed value, E_2, independent of the method of preparation, it follows that the difference in the energies of these two states, $E_2 - E_1$, must have a definite value regardless of the method of arriving at these

* This refers to the experiments, performed in 1845–1878 by James P. Joule, showing that the same amount of work, 4.18×10^7 ergs, always produces the same change in temperature as one calorie of heat. His experiments proved that heat is another form of energy.

two states: $E_2 - E_1 = \Delta E$, regardless of how state 1 is changed to state 2 If we restrict the technique of changing the state of a system to the utilization of heat (**"thermo"**) and work (**"dynamics"**), then the change in the energy of a system is independent of how the heat is added or removed or how work is done on the system or how the system is permitted to perform work. This relation may be written as

$$E_2 - E_1 = \Delta E = q \ (heat \ absorbed) - w \ (work \ done \ by \ system)$$

where q is the heat absorbed from the surroundings, and w is the work done by the system upon the surroundings. The energy of the system increases by the amount of heat added, and decreases by the amount of work done by the system. If the system releases heat to the surroundings then the sign of q is *minus*. If work is done *on* the system by the surroundings, then the minus sign in Equation (1) becomes *plus*.

When the final and initial states of the system are fixed, ΔE is fixed, but the heat gained or lost by the system and the work done on or by the system are not fixed. For example, let us assign arbitrarily an energy value of 90 cal to a particular quantity of a gas in an initial state, and a value of 100 cal in a final state; then

$$\Delta E = E_2 - E_1 = 100 \ \text{cal} - 90 \ \text{cal} = 10 \ \text{cal}$$

This change may be effected by any of an infinite number of methods (paths). For example,

Path I.   Add 10 cal of heat to the gas, keeping the volume constant so that no work is done by or on the gas; then

$$\Delta E = q - w$$
$$= 10 \ \text{cal} - 0 = 10 \ \text{cal}$$

Path II.   Add 25 cal of heat to the gas and remove 15 cal, keeping the volume constant; then

$$\Delta E = 25 \ \text{cal} - 15 \ \text{cal} - 0 = 10 \ \text{cal}$$

Path III.   Do 10 cal of work on the gas without permitting the evolution or absorption of heat; then

$$\Delta E = 0 \ \text{cal} + 10 \ \text{cal} = 10 \ \text{cal}$$

Path IV.   Add 35 cal of heat and let the system perform 25 cal of work; then

$$\Delta E = 35 \ \text{cal} - 25 \ \text{cal} = 10 \ \text{cal}$$

Path V.   Do 40 cal of work on the gas and let the gas evolve 30 cal of heat; then

$$\Delta E = -30 \ \text{cal} + 40 \ \text{cal} = 10 \ \text{cal}$$

The student can imagine many other schemes by which this gas may pass from the initial to the final state. In words, we say ΔE *is independent of the path between the initial and the final state but q and w are path-dependent.*

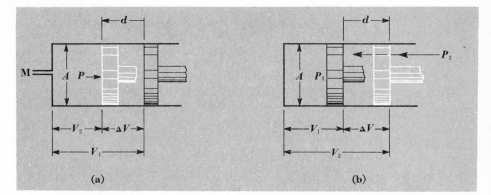

Fig. 6.2. (a) *Illustrating the work done by a piston of cross-sectional area A on a gas by moving through the distance d against the gas at constant pressure P; V_1 is the initial volume of the gas, V_2 the final volume, and ΔV the decrease in the volume. **M** is a mechanism to maintain constant pressure. (b) Illustrating the work done by a gas expanding against a piston with a resistance equal to a constant pressure P_2. The pressure of the gas P_3 is, of course greater than P_2. The piston is assumed to be frictionless.*

The work done by a gas in expanding from V_1 to V_2 against a constant pressure P is

$$w = P(V_2 - V_1) = P\Delta V$$

When P is expressed in atm and V in liters, the units of w are atm-liter and may be converted to cal:

$$\require{cancel}\cancel{\text{atm-liter}}\,10^3\,\frac{\cancel{\text{cm}^3}}{\cancel{\text{liter}}}\,76\,\frac{\cancel{\text{cm}}}{\cancel{\text{atm}}}\,13.6\,\frac{\cancel{\text{g}}}{\cancel{\text{cm}^3}}\,981\,\frac{\cancel{\text{cm}}}{\sec^2}\,\frac{\cancel{\text{erg}}}{\cancel{\text{g}\,\frac{\cancel{\text{cm}^2}}{\cancel{\sec^2}}}}\,\frac{\text{cal}}{4.18 \times 10^7\,\cancel{\text{ergs}}}$$

$$= 24.2\ \text{cal}$$

Proof that work $w = P\Delta V$. Work can be done only against a force. A (frictionless) piston moving against a vacuum does no work. The **work** done by a body (solid, liquid, or gas) is the *product of the force, F,* and *the distance, d,* through which the body *moves* **against** *the force,*

$$w = Fd$$

A gas is confined in a cylinder fitted with a movable (frictionless) piston and attached to a mechanism which will maintain a constant pressure, P, in the cylinder (Fig. 6.2a). The cross-sectional area of the cylinder, A, is also the cross-sectional area of the piston. Suppose the piston moves through a distance d without changing the pressure P. The force exerted by the gas *against* the piston is

$$F = PA$$

Then

$$w = PAd$$

But the cross-sectional area of the piston multiplied by the distance through which it moves equals the change of volume, ΔV. Hence

$$w = P\Delta V$$

For the illustration (a) in Fig. 6.2, $w = P(V_2 - V_1)$ and w is a minus quantity, informing us that work is done *on* the gas.

If, as in illustration (b), a gas pushes (expands) against a piston whose resistance is constant and equal to P_2 through a volume change, ΔV, then $w = P_2\Delta V$. However, V_2 is larger than V_1 and w is now a positive quantity, informing us that work is done *by* the gas.

The first law, in the case that the *only* work is $P\Delta V$, may then be written

$$\Delta E = q - P\Delta V$$

For calorimetric measurements made in a container of fixed volume $P\Delta V = 0$ and

$$\Delta E = q_v \tag{1}$$

In words, the change in energy is equal to the heat absorbed by the system when the process occurs at constant volume, q_v.

However, chemical reactions occur more frequently in open vessels at constant barometric pressure; then

$$\Delta E = q_p - P\Delta V$$

In words, the change in energy is equal to the heat absorbed by the system at constant pressure, q_p, less the work done by the system at constant pressure. Or,

$$q_p = \Delta E + P\Delta V \tag{2}$$

Since it is common practice to conduct reactions at constant pressure, we define a new quantity, called the **enthalpy H,** by the equation

$$H = E + PV$$

As with E, no attempt is made to define absolute values of H for a system. Rather, of interest is the change in H that occurs when the state of a system is changed at constant pressure. Then

$$\Delta H = H_2 - H_1 = \Delta E + P\Delta V$$

But from Equation (2),

$$\Delta E + P\Delta V = q_p$$

and therefore

$$\Delta H = q_p \tag{3}$$

In words, the change in enthalpy is equal to the heat absorbed when the process occurs at constant pressure and the only work is $P\Delta V$ (no electrical work).

Equations (1) and (2) yield the relationship between q_v and q_p,

$$q_p = q_v + P\Delta V$$
$$= q_v + P(V_2 - V_1)$$
$$= q_v + PV_2 - PV_1$$

Thus, for chemical reactions *involving only solids and liquids*, V_2 practically equals V_1, and q_v is practically equal to q_p. However, if *gases are involved* in the chemical reaction, appreciable volume changes may occur and the heat absorbed or evolved at constant pressure may differ appreciably from the heat absorbed or evolved at constant volume. Assuming ideal behavior and constant temperature,

$$PV_2 = n_2RT$$

and

$$PV_1 = n_1RT$$

Then

$$q_p = q_v + n_2RT - n_1RT$$
$$= q_v + (n_2 - n_1)RT$$
$$= q_v + \Delta nRT$$

or

$$\Delta H = \Delta E + \Delta nRT$$

where Δn is the total number of moles of gaseous products minus the total number of moles of gaseous reactants. The value of R is 1.99 cal per mole-deg.

EXAMPLE 7 **For the combustion of liquid benzene (page 113) at 25.0°C,**

$$C_6H_6(l) + 7\tfrac{1}{2}O_2(g) \rightarrow 3H_2O(l) + 6CO_2(g) \qquad \Delta E = -780 \text{ kcal}$$

Calculate ΔH.

ANSWER **Since 6 moles of gas are produced for 7.5 moles of gas consumed,**

$$\Delta n = 6.00 \text{ moles} - 7.50 \text{ moles} = -1.50 \text{ moles}$$

and

$$\Delta H = \Delta E + \Delta nRT$$
$$= -780 \text{ kcal} + [-1.50 \text{ moles}]\,1.99\,\frac{\cancel{\text{cal}}}{\text{mole deg}\,10^3\,\cancel{\text{cal}}}\,\frac{\text{kcal}}{}\,298\,\cancel{\text{deg}}$$
$$= -781 \text{ kcal}$$

Compare this result with the thermochemical equation on page 114.

EXAMPLE 8 **For the decomposition of nickel oxide (page 113) at 25.0°C,**

$$NiO(c) \rightarrow Ni(c) + \tfrac{1}{2}O_2(g) \qquad \Delta E = +57.0 \text{ kcal}$$

Calculate ΔH.

ANSWER **From the equation,**

$$\Delta n = 0.500 \text{ mole} - 0.000 = 0.500 \text{ mole}$$

Hence

$$\Delta H = 57.0 \text{ kcal} + [0.500 \text{ mole}] \ 1.99 \ \frac{\cancel{\text{cal}}}{\text{mole deg} \cdot 10^3 \cancel{\text{cal}}} \ \frac{\text{kcal}}{} \ 298 \cancel{\text{deg}}$$

$$= 57.3 \text{ kcal}$$

The energy, E, of a system depends only on its state, and is inde-pendent of the path taken to reach that state. But the same is true of the product, PV. Therefore, H, the sum of $E + PV$, like E, depends only on the state of a system. Consequently, ΔH, like ΔE, depends only on the final and initial states, in agreement with Hess's law.

Although the First Law summarizes important experimental observa-tions, it cannot tell us whether a given process will occur. It tells us that if carbon and hydrogen, state 1, change to methane gas, state 2, energy is conserved. However, it cannot tell us whether the change can occur. This subject is pursued further in Chapter 16.

Problems

1. Thermochemistry. (a) The thermochemical equation for the heat of combustion of acetylene, C_2H_2, is

$$C_2H_2(g) + 2\tfrac{1}{2}O_2(g) \rightarrow 2CO_2(g) + H_2O(l) \qquad \Delta H = -311 \text{ kcal}$$

Calculate the heat evolved when 3.00 g of C_2H_2 is burned at constant pressure
(b) Predict the ΔH for the molar heat of formation of carbon disulfide, CS_2

$$C(graphite) + 2S(c) \rightarrow CS_2(l)$$

from the following thermochemical equations:

$$
\begin{array}{ll}
C(graphite) + O_2(g) \rightarrow CO_2(g) & \Delta H = -94.1 \text{ kcal} \\
S(c) + O_2(g) \rightarrow SO_2(g) & \Delta H = -70.9 \text{ kcal} \\
CS_2(l) + 3O_2(g) \rightarrow 2SO_2(g) + CO_2(g) & \Delta H = -256.9 \text{ kcal}
\end{array}
$$

Answer. (a) 35.9 kcal; (b) $\Delta H = +21.0$ kcal

2. Thermochemistry. Calculate the ΔH for the reaction

$$H(g) + Cl(g) \rightarrow HCl(g)$$

from the following thermochemical equations:

$$
\begin{array}{ll}
H_2(g) + Cl_2(g) \rightarrow 2HCl(g) & \Delta H = -44.2 \text{ kcal} \\
H_2(g) \rightarrow 2H(g) & \Delta H = +104.2 \text{ kcal} \\
\tfrac{1}{2}Cl_2(g) \rightarrow Cl(g) & \Delta H = +29.0 \text{ kcal}
\end{array}
$$

Explain the difference in the heat of formation of the gaseous hydrogen chloride from the elements in the molecular and the atomic states.

3. Bond energies. Use data in Tables 6.1 and 6.2 (pages 116; 117) to predict ΔH, the heat of hydrogenation of ethylene to ethane,

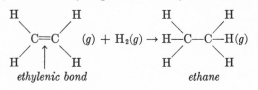

and compare with data on page 115. Note: use C=C (ethylenic bond) value for ethylene and C—C (ethane) value for ethane.

4. Thermochemistry. (a) Do the products of an exothermic reaction contain more or less energy than the reactants at the same temperature? Explain your answer. (b) For each of the following reactions, explain whether the heat evolved at constant pressure is smaller than, larger than, or the same as the heat evolved at constant volume:

$$CO(g) + \tfrac{1}{2}O_2(g) \rightarrow CO_2(g)$$
$$\tfrac{1}{2}H_2(g) + \tfrac{1}{2}Cl_2(g) \rightarrow HCl(g)$$
$$\tfrac{1}{2}N_2(g) + \tfrac{3}{2}H_2(g) \rightarrow NH_3(g)$$

5. $E = mc^2$. (a) Explain the statement, "If the heat of a reaction is considered as one of the products of the reaction and the heat is not removed, then the mass (weight) of the products *exactly* equals the mass (weight) of the reactants." (b) In an explosion 0.84 g of matter is converted into some other form of energy. Calculate the energy obtained in kcal. *If it were possible to weigh* this number of kcal, what would be its mass (weight) in grams?

Answer. (b) 1.8×10^{10} kcal, 0.84 g.

6. First law. To convert one gram of water at 100°C, volume 1.00 ml, at 1.00 atm to water vapor at 100°C at *constant volume* requires 499 calories. Predict the number of calories required to convert one gram of water at 100°C, volume 1.00 ml, at 1.00 atm, to steam at 100°C at 1.00 atm. The volume of the steam is 1.67 liters. The measured value is 539.4 cal. (Units: one liter-atm = 24.2 cal.)

7. First law. The combustion of 0.500 mole of methane gas, CH_4, in a bomb calorimeter (a vessel of fixed volume) evolves 105.8 kcal at 25.00°C. For the reaction

$$CH_4(g) + 2O_2(g) \rightarrow CO_2(g) + 2H_2O(l)$$

calculate (a) q_v, (b) q_p, (c) ΔE, and (d) ΔH. During the course of the reaction, is work done on or by the system?

Answer. (a) -211.6 kcal; (b) -212.8; (c) -211.6; (d) -212.8.

Additional problems

8. Bond energy. Use the thermochemical equation

$$XeF_4 \rightarrow Xe^+ + F^- + F + F_2 \qquad \Delta H = +286 \text{ kcal/mole}$$

obtained (150°C) from a study in a time-of-flight mass spectrograph (Problem 48, page 96) and the following data

$$
\begin{array}{ll}
Xe - e^- \rightarrow Xe^+ & \Delta H = +280 \\
F + e^- \rightarrow F^- & \Delta H = -83.5 \\
F_2 \rightarrow 2F & \Delta H = +38
\end{array}
$$

to calculate the Xe—F bond energy. The value from heats of reaction data (125°C) is 131 kcal/mole. All species are in the gaseous state. (For this problem, the temperature difference may be ignored.)

9. Bond energy. The Mn—F bond energy is 101 kcal. Calculate the heat of atomization of solid MnF_2,

$$MnF_2(c) \rightarrow Mn(g) + 2F(g)$$

Additional data:

$$MnF_2(g) + Mn(g) \rightarrow 2MnF(g) \qquad \Delta H = +18 \text{ kcal}$$
$$MnF_2(g) \rightarrow MnF_2(c) \qquad \Delta H = -76 \text{ kcal}$$

Answer. $\Delta H = +296$ kcal

10. Hess's law. Given:

$$H_2(g) + \tfrac{1}{2}O_2(g) \rightarrow H_2O(l) \qquad\qquad \Delta H = -68.3 \text{ kcal}$$
$$C(graphite) + O_2(g) \rightarrow CO_2(g) \qquad\qquad \Delta H = -94.1 \text{ kcal}$$
$$C_6H_{12}O_6(c) + 6O_2(g) \rightarrow 6CO_2(g) + 6H_2O(l) \qquad \Delta H = -673 \text{ kcal}$$

Find ΔH for

(*i*) the formation of glucose, $C_6H_{12}O_6(c)$, from carbon, hydrogen, and oxygen

$$6C(graphite) + 6H_2(g) + 3O_2(g) \rightarrow C_6H_{12}O_6(c)$$

(*ii*) the decomposition of glucose into carbon and water,

$$C_6H_{12}O_6(c) \rightarrow 6C(graphite) + 6H_2O(l)$$

11. Thermochemistry. (a) An exothermic reaction is allowed to occur very rapidly in the air. Will the temperature of the surrounding air increase or decrease? (b) An endothermic reaction is allowed to occur very rapidly in the air. Will the temperature of the surrounding air increase or decrease? (c) A person pours a liquid into the palm of his hand. As the liquid evaporates, his hand "feel cold." Is the evaporation of this liquid an exothermic or endothermic reaction

12. Thermochemistry. Explain how these incorrect thermochemical equations violate the law of conservation of energy:

$$C(graphite) + O_2(g) \rightarrow CO_2(g) \qquad \Delta H = -94.1 \text{ kcal}$$
$$CO_2(g) \rightarrow C(graphite) + O_2(g) \qquad \Delta H = +84.1 \text{ kcal}$$

13. Thermochemistry. When 2.00 g of iron is burned to ferric oxide at constant pressure, 3.50×10^3 cal are evolved. Calculate the ΔH in kcal for the molar heat of formation of Fe_2O_3, the heat evolved or absorbed in the preparation of one mole of a substance from its elements,

$$2Fe(c) + \tfrac{3}{2}O_2(g) \rightarrow Fe_2O_3(c) \qquad\qquad \textbf{Answer.} \ \Delta H = -195 \text{ kcal}$$

14. Bond energies. (a) How much energy (ΔH) in kcal per mole and in cal per molecule is necessary to split the gaseous H—F molecule into its constituent gaseous atoms? (b) Calculate the energy (ΔH) in kcal per mole required to decompose gaseous ethane

into isolated atoms.

Answer. (a) $\Delta H = +136$ kcal per mole, $+2.26 \times 10^{-19}$ cal per molecule
(b) $\Delta H = +679$ kcal per mole.

15. Bond energies. From the measured heat of reaction

$$C(graphite) + \tfrac{1}{2}Cl_2(g) + \tfrac{3}{2}H_2(g) \rightarrow CH_3Cl(g) \qquad \Delta H = -19.6 \text{ kcal}$$

and data in the text, calculate ΔH for the reaction

$$C(g) + Cl(g) + 3H(g) \rightarrow CH_3Cl(g)$$

and check your answer with Example 4 (page 117).

16. Thermochemistry. (a) Given the following data:

$$H_2(g) + \tfrac{1}{2}O_2(g) \rightarrow H_2O(l) \qquad\qquad \Delta H = -68.3 \text{ kcal}$$
$$B_5H_9(g) + 6O_2(g) \rightarrow \tfrac{5}{2}B_2O_3(c) + \tfrac{9}{2}H_2O(l) \qquad \Delta H = -1047 \text{ kcal}$$

Pound for pound, which is theoretically the better rocket fuel, hydrogen or penta-borane? (b) Energy is emitted by the sun at the rate of 2 ergs per gram of sun per sec (for comparison, the rate of heat energy generated during animal metabolism is about 250 ergs per gram per sec). The estimated mass of the sun is 2×10^{33} tons. Estimate the decrease in tons and percent decrease in the mass of the sun per day.

17. First law. Calculate the number of kilocalories required to convert 10.0 g of ice at 0.00°C and 1.00 atm to water vapor at 110°C and 1.00 atm by the following two methods: (a) The ice is melted at 0.00°C and the liquid temperature is raised to 100°C under 1.00 atm pressure; the liquid is then vaporized and the vapor is heated to 110°C under a constant pressure of 1 atm. (b) The ice is vaporized at 0.00°C and 1.00 atm and the resulting vapor is heated to 110°C at constant pressure. Required data:

Heat of fusion (0°C and 1 atm)	79.7 cal per g
Heat of sublimation (0°C and 1 atm)	675.6 cal per g
Heat of vaporization (100°C and 1 atm)	539.4 cal per g
Specific heat of water	1.00 cal per g per deg
Average specific heat of water vapor between 0°C and 110°C at 1 atm	0.44 cal per g per deg

Answer. (a) 7.24 kcal; (b) 7.24 kcal.

18. First law. A gas, initial pressure 6.00 atm, expands from 10.0 liters to 12.0 liters against a constant pressure of 3.00 atm. Calculate the work done by the gas in liter-atm. If the gas absorbs 30 cal during this change, find ΔE and ΔH in cal.

Answer. 6.00 liter-atm, -115 cal, -696 cal.

19. Noble gases. By experiment, the heat evolved at constant pressure in forming the compound $Xe_8(H_2O)_{46}$ is 22.5 cal per g of ice at 0°C. Calculate the enthalpy (heat) of formation at 0°C for the reaction

$$8Xe(g) + 46H_2O(c) \rightarrow Xe_8(H_2O)_{46}(c)$$

7

Chemical periodicity

████████████

7.1 BEFORE MENDELEEV

According to the Daltonian concept, elements are substances that ar
aggregates of identical fundamental units—atoms—ultimate and im
mutable particles whose intimate structures defy examination. Element
can, however, be grouped by properties into various classes or families
somewhat as living things are classified by biologists. For example, th
metals iron, copper, and lead differ as a class from the nonmetals sulfu
phosphorus, and carbon. Within the metallic class, copper, silver, an
gold (coinage metals) differ as a group from calcium, strontium, an
barium (alkaline earth metals). These facts suggest that atoms are no
ultimate particles at all, but are themselves aggregates of other funda
mental entities, and that some of the similarity in properties of differen
elements are manifestations of a common pool of subatomic units.

Hence, the effort of chemists to set up rational systems for classifyin
the elements was one of the necessary first steps leading to our curren
progress in understanding the complexities of atomic structure. Lik
other fundamental scientific concepts, the idea of chemical periodicit
developed at an accelerating rate from quite unsophisticated beginning
to its current status as a very broad conceptual system. The first moder
classification systems were based on relating chemical properties (espe
cially valence) to the atomic weights of the elements; such systems there
fore could not be formulated until methods for determining valences an
atomic weights began to become available in the early part of the nine
teenth century. In 1829, Johann Wolfgang Döbereiner reported severa
instances in which elements with closely related chemical properties
when arranged in order of atomic weight, showed approximately constan
increments of atomic weight. These groups consisted of three elements each
and he therefore called them **triads.** Examples are given in Table 7.1.

TABLE 7.1 *Döbereiner's Triads*

Triad	Properties	Atomic weight (approximate)	Atomic weight increment
Chlorine		35	
	Corrosive colored vapors		→ 45
Bromine		80	
			→ 47
Iodine		127	
Sulfur		32	
	Solids whose hydrides		→ 47
Selenium	(H_2S, H_2Se, H_2Te)	79	
	are stenches		→ 49
Tellurium		128	
Lithium		7	
			→ 16
Sodium	Very reactive metals	23	
			→ 16
Potassium		39	

In 1864, John Newlands made a great step forward by relating the properties of elements, not to a plot or scale of atomic weights, but simply to the **ordinal numbers*** *of the elements when they are arranged in an increasing series of atomic weights.* Newlands found that, in such a list, elements with similar properties recur at intervals of seven. He called this relationship, by a rather inept analogy to the musical scale, the **law of octaves.** Thus, lithium (thought then to be the second lightest element) and sodium (thought to be the ninth) are an "octave" apart.†
This serialization was the beginning of our idea of "atomic number"—a concept vital to our present expressions of chemical periodicity and the electronic structures of atoms. Newlands' contribution, ridiculed at first, was later given recognition (Davy Medal, 1887).

7.2 MENDELEEV; MEYER

In 1869 Dmitrii Ivanovich Mendeleev and several months later Julius Lothar Meyer published independent versions of a periodic system of the

* "Ordinal numbers" express order or succession in a series: first, second, third, etc., or 1st, 2nd, 3rd · · · · . They are distinguished from **cardinal numbers,** the numbers used in counting: one, two, three · · · · .
† Helium and neon had not yet been discovered.

elements. Credit for the "Periodic Law" is given to these two scientists (especially to Mendeleev) not because they were the first to describe periodic classifications of the elements, but more particularly for the following reasons:

(a) The significance of periodicity was more fully appreciated, the system of classification was more elaborate, and attention was given to a broader range of physical and chemical properties than was examined by earlier investigators. Table 7.2 is an adaptation of Mendeleev's Periodic Table of 1871.

(b) Mendeleev recognized that, when the atomic weight order demanded a chemically incongruous location of elements in the periodic system, adherence to atomic weight order must be sacrificed. For example, if iodine (atomic weight in 1869: 127) is placed before tellurium

TABLE 7.2 *Periodic Table of the Elements (Adapted from Mendeleev, 1871)*

Groups:	I	II	III	IV	V	VI	VII	VIII
Type	R_2O	RO	R_2O_3	RH_4	RH_3	RH_2	RH	RO_4
formulas:	RCl	RCl_2	RCl_3	RO_2	R_2O_5	RO_3	R_2O_7	
Subgroup or family:	A B	A B	A B	A B	A B	A B	A B	A B
1	H							
2	Li	Be	B	C	N	O	F	
3	Na	Mg	Al	Si	P	S	Cl	
4	K	Ca	—	Ti	V	Cr	Mn	Fe, Co, Ni, (Cu)
5	(Cu)	Zn	—	—	As	Se	Br	
6	Rb	Sr	Yt?	Zr	Nb	Mo	—	Ru, Rh, Pd, (Ag)
7	(Ag)	Cd	In	Sn	Sb	Te	I	
8	Cs	Ba	Di?	Ce?	—	—	—	— — — —
9	—	—	—	—	—	—	—	
10	—	—	Er?	La?	Ta	W	—	Os, Ir, Pt, (Au)
11	(Au)	Hg	Tl	Pb	Bi			
12	—	—	—	Th	—	U	—	— — — —

Series

TABLE **7.3** *Prediction of the Properties of Germanium*

Property	"Eka-silicon" (Es) Predicted in 1871 by Mendeleev	Germanium (Ge) Reported in 1886 by Clemens Alexander Winkler	Currently accepted
Atomic weight	72	72.32	72.59
Specific gravity	5.5	5.47	5.35
Melting point	High	—	947°C
Specific heat (cal/g°)	0.073	0.076	0.074
Gram-atomic volume (cm³)	13	13.22	13.5
Color	Dark gray	Grayish white	Grayish white
Valence	4	4	4
Reaction with acids and alkalies	Es will be slightly attacked by such acids as HCl, but will resist attack by such alkalies as NaOH	Ge is dissolved by neither HCl nor NaOH, but is dissolved by concentrated NaOH	Ge is dissolved by neither HCl nor NaOH, but is dissolved by concentrated NaOH
Boiling point of the tetraethyl derivative	160°C	160°C	185–187°C
Specific gravity of the dioxide	4.7	4.703	4.228
Specific gravity of the tetrachloride	1.9	1.887	1.8443
Boiling point of the tetrachloride	100°C	86°C	84°C

(atomic weight in 1869: 128), iodine appears in a group with sulfur and selenium, and tellurium finds itself in the company of chlorine and bromine. This is obvious chemical mismatching and must mean that the atomic weights either are wrong or are not the fundamental basis of chemical periodicity. Mendeleev imagined that the weights were in error; actually they were not far from today's accepted values.

(c) Mendeleev avoided what would otherwise be additional chemical inconsistencies by boldly leaving gaps in his table, predicting that elements would be discovered to fill the gaps, and describing the properties that the to-be-discovered elements would have. For example, the element

TABLE 7.4   *Prediction of the Properties of Gallium*

Property	"Eka-aluminum" (Ea) Predicted in 1871 by Mendeleev	Gallium (Ga) Reported in 1875 by Lecoq de Boisbaudran	Currently accepted
Atomic weight	68	69.9	69.72
Specific gravity	5.9	5.94	5.904
Melting point	Low	30.15°C	29.78°C
Solubility in acid and alkali	Ea will dissolve slowly in both acid and alkali	Ga dissolves slowly in both acid and alkali	Ga dissolves slowly in both acid and alkali
Formula of oxide	Ea_2O_3	Ga_2O_3	Ga_2O_3 (α and β forms)
Specific gravity of oxide	5.5	—	6.44 α form 5.88 β form
Reactions of sulfates	$Ea_2(SO_4)_3$ will form alums[a]	Gallium alums are known	Gallium alums are known, e.g. $NH_4Ga(SO_4)_2 \cdot (H_2O)_{12}$
Preparation of sulfides	Ea_2S_3 will be precipitated by H_2S or $(NH_4)_2S$	Ga_2S_3 can be precipitated by H_2S or $(NH_4)_2S$	Ga_2S_3 can be precipitated by H_2S or $(NH_4)_2S$
Properties of chloride	$EaCl_3$ will be more volatile than $ZnCl_2$	$GaCl_3$ is more volatile than $ZnCl_2$	$GaCl_3$ is more volatile than $ZnCl_2$

[a] Alums are complex sulfates containing one cation of $+1$ charge and one of $+3$ charge, for example, $NaAl(SO_4)_2(H_2O)_{12}$.

after zinc was, in 1871, arsenic. But arsenic does not belong in the same chemical group with aluminum or with silicon (see Table 7.2, Groups III and IV). Arsenic is chemically like phosphorus, and therefore belongs in Group V. Succeeding elements (selenium, bromine, etc.) also fall into reasonable locations if they follow arsenic located in Group V. This means that two elements, one like aluminum and one like silicon, are missing.

For testing a theory, there is nothing like a prediction. The more spectacular the confrontation between predicted and observed data, the better the test. Tables 7.3, 7.4, and 7.5 show the degree to which such predictions were successful for eka-silicon (germanium), eka-aluminum (gallium), and eka-boron (scandium).*

* *Eka* (Greek) means "first after" or "first beyond."

TABLE 7.5   *Prediction of the Properties of Scandium*

Property	"Eka-boron" (Eb) Predicted in 1871 by Mendeleev	Scandium (Sc) Reported in 1879 by Lars Frederick Nilson	Currently accepted
Atomic weight	44	—	44.956
Formula of the oxide	Eb_2O_3	Sc_2O_3	Sc_2O_3
Specific gravity of the oxide	3.5	3.86	3.86
Basicity of the oxide	Eb_2O_3 will be more basic than Al_2O_3, but less basic than Y_2O_3 or MgO	Sc_2O_3 is more basic than Al_2O_3, but less than Y_2O_3 or MgO	Sc_2O_3 is more basic than Al_2O_3, but less basic than Y_2O_3 or MgO
Salts	The salts of Eb will be colorless; they will give gelatinous precipitates with KOH and Na_2CO_3	Sc salts are colorless, and give gelatinous precipitates with KOH and Na_2CO_3	Sc salts are colorless, and give gelatinous precipitates with KOH and Na_2CO_3
Chloride	$EbCl_3$ will be less volatile than $AlCl_3$	$ScCl_3$ sublimes at 850°C $AlCl_3$ sublimes at 100°C	$ScCl_3$ sublimes above 1000°C $AlCl_3$ sublimes at 178°C

7.3   THE PERIODIC LAW AND THE PERIODIC TABLE

The properties of the elements are periodic functions of their atomic numbers.
This oft-cited statement does not sound like a "law" at all, in the sense
that it is not a quantitative expression. One must not, however, confuse
precision with reliability. The Periodic Law is a broad, imprecise statement that grew out of early efforts, such as those described in the preceding section, and that still functions as a much-used framework on which
comparisons and generalizations of chemical behavior are based. Chemists
everywhere agree that the Periodic Law expresses deep-seated relationships in chemical properties and in the structures of atoms, but no two
chemists are likely to offer the same detailed interpretation of the Law.

Starting with Mendeleev and Meyer, and continuing to the present,
enough periodic tables have been published to fill a book.* We will

* Literally. See Edward Mazurs, "Types of Graphic Representations of the Periodic
System of Chemical Elements," La Grange, Illinois, 1957.

examine the Mendeleev Table of 1871 (Table 7.2), because some of its usages and conventions still persist. We will then exploit modern classifications in subsequent discussions for a more detailed consideration of chemical periodicity.

Mendeleev's Table. After earlier efforts with other arrangements, Mendeleev in 1871 divided the elements into eight vertical columns, called **groups.** The most important characteristic common to elements in the same group is **valence**—the numerical capacity of atoms of the element to combine with other atoms. If the other atoms are taken to be H, Cl, or O, it is possible to write "type formulas" that characterize the valence of elements within a group. Such formulas appear in Table 7.2, R denoting any element in the group. It was apparent to Mendeleev, however, that the elements within a given valence group exhibited not one, but two, more or less distinct sets of properties. Accordingly, he divided each group into two **subgroups** or **families,** to correspond to this chemical duality. In Group I, for example, all the metals form univalent oxides. Of these, Cu_2O, Ag_2O, and Au_2O lose oxygen on relatively mild heating, while Li_2O, K_2O, Rb_2O, and Cs_2O retain oxygen even under much more stringent conditions. Similar subgrouping continues through Group VII. The make-up of Group VIII is atypical—it consists of sets of chemically similar metals, only some of which exhibit octavalence (RuO_4, OsO_4).

Mendeleev noted that the assignments of elements to families alternated with increasing atomic number within each group, with confusing exceptions in Series 2 and 3. The uncertain assignments of Cu, Ag, and Au, and the misplacements of Na, O, and F are some consequences of this confusion. We are now aware that the subgroup classifications foreshadowed our modern understanding of the differences among elements based on electronic structure. Mendeleev's subgroup designations were based on metallic character, A being the more and B the less metallic family of any given Group. Thus, in Group II, for example, Ca, Sr, and Ba are more metallic than Mg, Zn, and Cd, respectively. The A and B subgroup designations are now made on a different basis, as elaborated later.

Mendeleev's horizontal rows were called **series.** The important characteristic of such a series of elements is its *regular progression of valence*. In Series 2, 3, 5, and 7 this progression is accompanied by a marked shift from metallic to nonmetallic character with increasing Group number.

A Modern Periodic Table: the Long-Period Form. Modern periodic tables attempt to depict both chemical and electronic relationships. In all modern tables, the horizontal rows are called **"periods."** The so-called "short-period form," most popular up to about 1950, is a direct adaptation of Mendeleev's table, with inclusion of "Group 0" to accommodate the noble gases, once thought to have "zero valence." The "long-period form" (Table 7.6), now widely used, has 18 vertical columns instead of eight, and uses this expansion to separate the A subgroups

TABLE 7.6[a] *Periodic Table, Long-Form*

Periods	I A	II A	III B	IV B	V B	VI B	VII B	VIII			I B	II B	III A	IV A	V A	VI A	VII A	0
1	H 1																H 1	He 2
2	Li 3	Be 4											B 5	C 6	N 7	O 8	F 9	Ne 10
3	Na 11	Mg 12											Al 13	Si 14	P 15	S 16	Cl 17	Ar 18
4	K 19	Ca 20	Sc 21	Ti 22	V 23	Cr 24	Mn 25	Fe 26	Co 27	Ni 28	Cu 29	Zn 30	Ga 31	Ge 32	As 33	Se 34	Br 35	Kr 36
5	Rb 37	Sr 38	Y 39	Zr 40	Nb 41	Mo 42	Tc 43	Ru 44	Rh 45	Pd 46	Ag 47	Cd 48	In 49	Sn 50	Sb 51	Te 52	I 53	Xe 54
6	Cs 55	Ba 56	La 57	Hf 72	Ta 73	W 74	Re 75	Os 76	Ir 77	Pt 78	Au 79	Hg 80	Tl 81	Pb 82	Bi 83	Po 84	At 85	Rn 86
7	Fr 87	Ra 88	Ac 89															

Transition Elements

Lanthanide Series

Ce 58	Pr 59	Nd 60	Pm 61	Sm 62	Eu 63	Gd 64	Tb 65	Dy 66	Ho 67	Er 68	Tm 69	Yb 70	Lu 71

Actinide Series

Th 90	Pa 91	U 92	Np 93	Pu 94	Am 95	Cm 96	Bk 97	Cf 98	Es 99	Fm 100	Md 101	No 102	Lw 103

[a] The heavy black line separates the metallic from the nonmetallic elements; the distinction, however, is not so sharp as shown.

from the B subgroups. In the second and third periods, where no subgroup distinction exists, this wide separation, occurring between Groups II and III, has no meaning at all. More serious, and common to both long and short forms, is the obscuration of sequences of properties (including valence) that are exhibited by certain elements in a given period (for example, K, Ca, Ga, Ge, As, Se, Br, Kr).

The interposition of lanthanide (rare earth) and actinide (heavy rare earth) elements into the body of the table would impose strains on the dimensions of charts and books, and is therefore not usually attempted.

Another Modern Table: the Separated Form; Types of Elements. Another modern form of the Periodic Table is shown in Table 7.7. This arrangement has the advantages of preserving traditional group, subgroup, and period designations, of presenting meaningful separations based on electronic structures, and of facilitating the examination of many physical and chemical relationships that are the basis of the Periodic Law.

Note, particularly, the following characteristics of Table 7.7:

(a) The upper section of Table 7.7 comprises the elements that represent the regular progression of valence on which all original periodic systems were based. They are therefore called **representative elements,** and the section in which they appear is a sort of "ideal" periodic table. As we shall see in the next chapter, the concept of "representative elements" is related to the progressive accretion of electrons in the highest principal energy levels of the atoms. The subgroup designation A is here reserved for representative elements.

(b) The middle section of Table 7.7 comprises the elements that interrupt the representative series. Interruption by ten elements first occurs in the 4th Period between Groups II and III, or between calcium and gallium. Ten elements also constitute the transition between Groups II and III in the 5th and in the 6th Periods. These groups of elements are called **transition elements.**[*] In comparison with the representative elements, the progression of valence and of chemical properties among the transition elements is not so marked. The transition elements thus constitute, chemically, a much more homogeneous group than the representative ones. As we shall see in the next chapter, the concept of "transition elements" is related to the progressive accretion of electrons in the next-to-highest principal energy levels of the atoms. The subgroup designation B is here reserved for transition elements.

(c) The lower section of Table 7.7 comprises the elements that interrupt the transition elements. This section originated as a reluctant footnote to accommodate a frustrating group of fourteen elements that all seemed to want to crowd into the one space in the 6th Period of Group III occupied by lanthanum. The elements were frustrating because they all seemed to be alike; it was difficult to characterize them, to separate them,

---

[*] The zinc subgroup elements (Zn, Cd, and Hg) have many properties of representative elements and therefore could be so classified. This point is elaborated in Chapters 8 and 9.

TABLE 7.7 *Periodic Table, Separated Form*

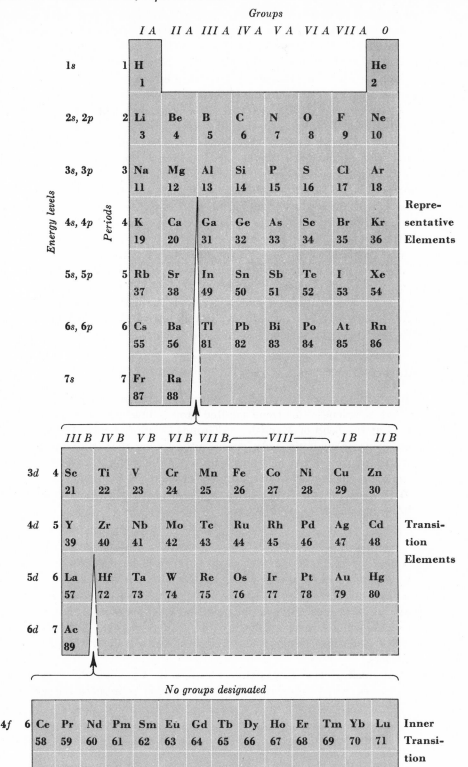

to find out how many there were, to be sure indeed that some of the "elements" would not prove to be mixtures after further attempts at purification. This series came to be called the **"rare earth elements,"** or the **"lanthanides"*** (the word "earth" was used in the sense of "oxide"). That the fourteen elements following actinium in the 7th Period constitute an analogous series was learned much later; accordingly its members are called the **"heavy rare earth elements,"** or the **"actinides."*** Taken together, the two series are called the **"inner transition elements."** The actinides are *presumed* to be an interruption in the 7th Period transition elements, although the elements that would continue after this interruption (starting with atomic number 104) have not yet been prepared (1965). As we shall see in the next chapter, the concept of "inner transition elements" is related to the progressive accretion of electrons in the second-from-highest principal energy levels of the atoms.

(d) The slashes in the upper and middle sections show the interruptions in atomic number sequences that are filled by the transition and inner transition elements.

(e) The designations of energy levels in the listing to the left of the table affords, except for certain irregularities, a quick count of the number of electrons in the various sublevels (as elaborated in Chapter 8).

7.4 **THE PERIODICITY OF VALENCE**

The most striking and significant periodic variation among the elements is that of valence; this trend merited "top billing" in the type formulas listed at the head of Mendeleev's Groups (Table 7.2, page 130). Valence periodicity is exhibited most consistently among the representative elements; it is somewhat of a strain to apply the system to the transition elements, and hopeless for the inner transition elements.

Valences of the Representative Elements. If we designate the Group number as G, we may write

$$\text{valence of representative elements} = G \text{ and/or } 8 - G \tag{1}$$

Table 7.8 presents a sampling of compounds of representative elements and separates them into two groups, depending on whether the valences do or do not correspond to Equation (1). On the basis of these and other data, it is reasonable to designate those valences of the representative elements which correspond to Equation (1) as "typical." The interpretation of Equation (1) and its many exceptions will evolve in subsequent chapters.

Valences of the Transition Elements. Consider the first transition series, which interrupts the progression of representative elements

---

* Lanthanum and actinium, by virtue of their properties, are included in the classification of "lanthanide" and "actinide," respectively. Thus, the space corresponding to Group IIIB, Period 6, may be assigned to *all* the elements $La_{57} \rightarrow Lu_{71}$, and the corresponding space in Period 7 to $Ac_{89} \rightarrow Lw_{103}$.

TABLE 7.8   *Some Compounds of the Representative Elements*

			Group				
	I	*II*	*III*	*IV*	*V*	*VI*	*VII*
Some compounds whose formulas correspond to Equation (1) (page 138)	H_2O	$BeCl_2$	BF_3	CH_4	NH_3	H_2O	HF
	Li_2O	Be_2C	Al_2O_3	CO_2	N_2O_5	H_2S	HCl
	NaH	CaH_2	$InCl_3$	$SiHF_3$	PCl_3	SO_3	Cl_2O_7
	KCl	SrO	TlF_3	$GeBr_4$	PCl_5	SF_6	$BrCl$
	$RbNO_3$	BaO		SnS_2	AsI_3	SeO_3	Br_2O
	CsF	$Ra(NO_3)_2$		PbO_2	AsI_5	TeO_3	KI
					AsP		BaI_2
					Sb_2O_3		
					$BiOCl$		
Some compounds whose formulas do not correspond to Equation (1) (page 138)	H_2O_2 [a]	BaO_2 [a]	$B_{10}H_{14}$	CO	N_2O	SO_2	ClO_2
	Na_2O_2 [a]		InO	$C_{10}H_{22}$	AsI_2	SeO_2	BrF_5
			TlF	PbO	$BiCl_4$	TeF_4	ICl_3

[a] These substances are peroxides, in which oxygen atoms are bonded to each other. Although the formulas do not correspond to Equation (1) if the valence of oxygen is assumed to be 2, they correspond properly on the basis that the average valence of each oxygen in a peroxide is 1; thus, $(Na^+)_2(O_2)^{2-}$ and $Ba^{2+}(O_2)^{2-}$.

between calcium (No. 20) and gallium (No. 31). This transition series starts with scandium (No. 21) and ends with zinc (No. 30). We can attempt to rationalize the valences of these elements on the basis of either of two different ideas:

(a) These transition elements fall into Periodic Groups that follow the same sequence as those of the representative elements. The transition groups are designated B to distinguish them from the designation A reserved for the representative elements. Therefore, after calcium (Group IIA) the transition Group designations following numerically are scandium (IIIB), titanium (IVB), etc. But the sequence is bound to become embarrassing because there are ten transition elements whose classifications are to correspond to seven representative groups. (We do not consider the noble gases, Group 0, for which there are no conceivable counterparts among the transition elements.) Copper and zinc exhibit valences of 1 and 2, respectively, and so can be classified into Groups IB and IIB, respectively. The unmatched three then are iron, cobalt, and nickel. The facts that these elements cannot be matched with any representative counterparts, and that they are quite similar in properties to each other, have led to their somewhat awkward assignment to a common Group

TABLE 7.9 *The Oxides of the Transition Elements (peroxides are not included)*

Group

	IIIB	IVB	VB	VIB	VIIB	VIII			IB	IIB
4	Sc_2O_3	TiO Ti_2O_3 TiO_2	VO V_2O_3 VO_2 V_2O_5	CrO Cr_2O_3 CrO_2 CrO_3	MnO Mn_3O_4 MnO_2 MnO_3 Mn_2O_7	FeO Fe_3O_4 Fe_2O_3	CoO Co_3O_4 Co_2O_3	NiO	Cu_4O Cu_2O CuO	ZnO
5	Y_2O_3	ZrO_2	NbO Nb_2O_3 NbO_2 Nb_2O_5	Mo_2O_3 MoO_2 Mo_2O_5 MoO_3		RuO_2 RuO_4	Rh_2O_3 RhO_2	PdO PdO_2	Ag_2O	CdO
6	La_2O_3	HfO_2	Ta_2O_4 Ta_2O_5	WO_2 W_2O_5 WO_3	ReO_2 ReO_3 Re_2O_7	OsO Os_2O_3 OsO_2 OsO_4	IrO_3 IrO_2	PtO Pt_2O_3 Pt_3O_4 PtO_2 PtO_3	Au_2O_3	Hg_2O HgO
7	Ac_2O_3									

VIII. It is unnecessary to specify "VIIIB" because there is no "VIIIA" from which it need be distinguished. Now, if these transition element sub-groupings are to have any justification at all, Equation (1) should be of some value in predicting valences.

(b) A second idea is that these transition elements really all belong in the space in Group II occupied by calcium; they should all have a valence of 2 and we could even think of calling them "calcides." The succeeding transition series could be similarly classified and we could call them, respectively, "strontides" and "barides."

Now, what are the facts? Let us list the known oxides of the transition elements (see Table 7.9). We see, first, that these elements typically exhibit multiple valence. In almost all cases, one of these valences is 2, a fact consistent with the idea that all of the transition elements should really be squeezed into Group II. In almost all cases, another one of these valences is G, the Group number, a fact consistent with the B subgrouping classification. Even the awkward Group VIII finds some valence justification in the octavalent oxides RuO_4 and OsO_4. Thus, both sets of ideas mentioned above can be supported, to some degree, by the data. These various facts and concepts, confusing and limited as they are, nevertheless

TABLE 7.10 The Oxides of the Inner Transition Elements

Period														
6	Ce_2O_3 CeO_2	Pr_2O_3 PrO_2	Nd_2O_3		Sm_2O_3	Eu_2O_3	Gd_2O_3	Tb_2O_3	Dy_2O_3	Ho_2O_3	Er_2O_3	Tm_2O_3	Yb_2O_3	Lu_2O_3
7	ThO_2	PaO_2 Pa_2O_5	UO_2 U_3O_8 UO_3 UO_4	NpO_2 Np_3O_8	PuO_2	Am_2O_3 AmO_2								

constitute a very important part of the basis on which our modern ideas of electronic structure are supported.

Valences of the Inner Transition Elements. To extend a sub-grouping classification to these elements hardly seems worth the effort. The best we can say is that, if they can all be considered to belong in the spaces in Group III occupied by lanthanum or by actinium, one of the valences they should all exhibit is 3. Table 7.10, listing the oxides of the inner transition elements, to some extent justifies this idea.

7.5 THE PERIODICITY OF CHEMICAL PROPERTIES

Table 7.11 gives some of the common names, reflecting common chemical characteristics, of groups of elements from the Periodic Table. It will be helpful to survey briefly some of these group chemical properties.

The Alkali Metals. These elements are soft, lustrous, highly reactive metals. They react vigorously with water, even in the cold, forming a solution of the hydroxide and liberating hydrogen gas and heat,

$$Li(c) + H_2O(l) \rightarrow Li^+(aq) + OH^-(aq) + \tfrac{1}{2}H_2(g)$$

The alkali metals also react very vigorously with nonmetallic elements like oxygen and the halogens; in such reactions the alkali metals are converted to their 1+ ions.

The Alkaline Earth Metals. These elements resemble the alkali metals but are not quite so soft, lustrous, or reactive as the corresponding alkali metals. The alkaline earth metals, when they combine with non-metals, are converted to their 2+ ions,

$$Ba(c) + Cl_2(g) \rightarrow BaCl_2(c),\ or\ Ba^{2+} + 2Cl^-$$

They react with water, but more slowly than the alkali metals,

$$Ca(c) + 2H_2O(l) \rightarrow Ca^{2+}(aq) + 2OH^-(aq) + H_2(g)$$

The Group III Elements. Boron is not classified as a metal; the other Group III elements are. Boron is a hard, brittle, dull, rather inert element. It forms a series of hydrides and a series of complex borates (borate ion is BO_3^{3-}). Aluminum is a light, soft, abundant metal that protects itself from oxidation in air by forming a film of the oxide, Al_2O_3. Gallium, indium, and thallium are lustrous, moderately reactive metals.

The Group IV Elements. These elements show a progression of metallic character from carbon (nonmetallic) to silicon and germanium (some metallic properties) to tin and lead (metals). Elemental carbon occurs in the forms graphite and diamond. Such different forms of the same element are called **allotropic forms.** Carbon occurs in chemical combination in all living matter and in its derivatives such as coal and petroleum, in the atmosphere as CO_2, in the toxic oxide CO, and in carbonate (CO_3^{2-}) minerals such as limestone, $CaCO_3$. Silicon is a dull solid somewhat metallic in appearance. It forms hydrides which burn in oxygen to yield SiO_2 and water. A typical reaction is

$$SiH_4(g) + 2O_2(g) \rightarrow SiO_2(c) + 2H_2O(g)$$

TABLE 7.11 *Nomenclature of the Periodic Table of the Elements*

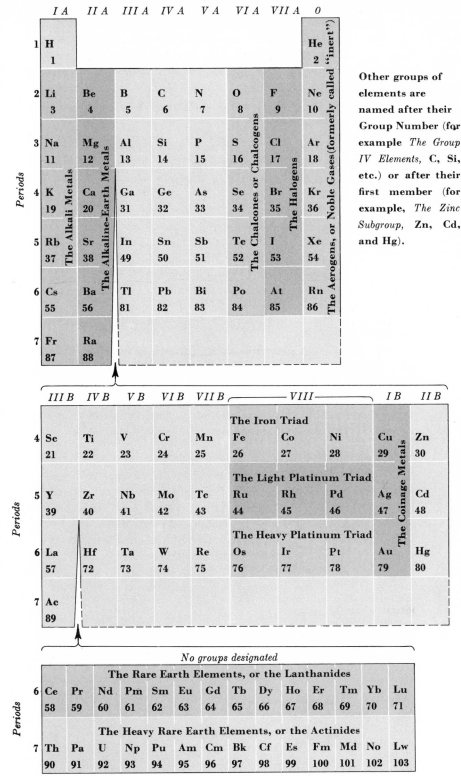

Groups

	I A	II A	III A	IV A	V A	VI A	VII A	0
1	H 1							He 2
2	Li 3	Be 4	B 5	C 6	N 7	O 8	F 9	Ne 10
3	Na 11	Mg 12	Al 13	Si 14	P 15	S 16	Cl 17	Ar 18
4	K 19	Ca 20	Ga 31	Ge 32	As 33	Se 34	Br 35	Kr 36
5	Rb 37	Sr 38	In 49	Sn 50	Sb 51	Te 52	I 53	Xe 54
6	Cs 55	Ba 56	Tl 81	Pb 82	Bi 83	Po 84	At 85	Rn 86
7	Fr 87	Ra 88						

Periods (vertical label on left)

The Alkali Metals · The Alkaline-Earth Metals · The Chalcones or Chalcogens · The Halogens · The Aerogens, or Noble Gases (formerly called "inert")

Other groups of elements are named after their Group Number (for example *The Group IV Elements*, **C, Si,** etc.) or after their first member (for example, *The Zinc Subgroup*, **Zn, Cd,** and **Hg**).

	III B	IV B	V B	VI B	VII B		VIII		I B	II B
						The Iron Triad				
4	Sc 21	Ti 22	V 23	Cr 24	Mn 25	Fe 26	Co 27	Ni 28	Cu 29	Zn 30
						The Light Platinum Triad				
5	Y 39	Zr 40	Nb 41	Mo 42	Tc 43	Ru 44	Rh 45	Pd 46	Ag 47	Cd 48
						The Heavy Platinum Triad				
6	La 57	Hf 72	Ta 73	W 74	Re 75	Os 76	Ir 77	Pt 78	Au 79	Hg 80
7	Ac 89									

Periods (vertical label on left)

The Coinage Metals

No groups designated

				The Rare Earth Elements, or the Lanthanides									
6	Ce 58	Pr 59	Nd 60	Pm 61	Sm 62	Eu 63	Gd 64	Tb 65	Dy 66	Ho 67	Er 68	Tm 69	Yb 70	Lu 71
				The Heavy Rare Earth Elements, or the Actinides									
7	Th 90	Pa 91	U 92	Np 93	Pu 94	Am 95	Cm 96	Bk 97	Cf 98	Es 99	Fm 100	Md 101	No 102	Lw 103

Periods (vertical label on left)

Silicon is widely distributed in the earth's crust as silicate rocks. Germanium is an element roughly midway between metallic and nonmetallic in character; the subject of semimetals in general will be discussed in Chapter 27. Tin and lead are relatively inert metals, widely used in the home and in industry. Tin dissolves in acid solutions to form stannous (2+) salts,

$$Sn(c) + 2H^+(aq) + 2Cl^-(aq) \rightarrow Sn^{2+}(aq) + 2Cl^-(aq) + H_2(g)$$
hydrochloric acid

Most of the salts of lead are insoluble in water; as a result, the action of acids on lead deposits an impervious layer, enabling the lead to resist further attack. Lead is therefore used widely as an "acid-proof" material of construction.

The Group V Elements. These elements, like those of Group IV, also show a marked progression from nonmetallic (nitrogen, phosphorus, and arsenic) to metallic character (antimony and bismuth). Nitrogen is an odorless, colorless, relatively inert gas that constitutes about 80% of the earth's atmosphere. In combustion reactions in air, atmospheric nitrogen combines with oxygen to form nitric oxide and nitrogen dioxide,

$$N_2(g) + O_2(g) \rightarrow 2NO(g)$$
$$2NO(g) + O_2(g) \rightarrow 2NO_2(g)$$

Nitrogen also combines with metals to form **nitrides,** such as Mg_3N_2. The hydrides of nitrogen include ammonia (NH_3), and hydrazine (N_2H_4). Phosphorus is a soft solid that occurs in white and red allotropic forms. The white form, dangerous to handle, corresponds to a vapor whose formula is P_4. This vapor ignites spontaneously in air or oxygen to form an oxide in which phosphorus is pentavalent,

$$P_4(g) + 5O_2(g) \rightarrow P_4O_{10}(c)$$

The hydride of phosphorus is phosphine, PH_3, a very toxic gas. Arsenic exists in nonmetallic (yellow) and metallic (gray) modifications. It forms a hydride (arsine, AsH_3) and both trivalent and pentavalent oxides, As_2O_3 and As_2O_5, all very toxic compounds. Antimony and bismuth are both metals not useful in applications requiring great structural strength. Antimony forms the unstable hydride **stibine,** SbH_3. Both metals form the trivalent oxide (Sb_2O_3 and Bi_2O_3) and the pentavalent oxide (Sb_2O_5 and Bi_2O_5). All the Group V elements form the trifluoride and the trichloride.

The Group VI Elements. These elements are nonmetals except for the highest member, polonium. Gaseous oxygen is colorless and odorless; liquid oxygen is blue. Oxygen is a reactive element that combines with all the elements except some noble gases. In a number of combinations, oxygen atoms are bonded to each other; such compounds are called **peroxides.** Oxygen, when energized by ultraviolet irradiation or other means, produces ozone, an irritating, chemically reactive gas,

$$3O_2(g) \xrightarrow{\text{energy}} 2O_3(g)$$

Sulfur is a pale yellow solid obtained from underground beds of the element by melting and forcing it up with a mixture of steam, superheated water (about 175°C), and compressed air (**Frasch process**). The dioxide and trioxide, SO_2 and SO_3, are both well known. Sulfur combines with practically all metals to form sulfides. Its hydride is the foul-smelling gas H_2S. Selenium and tellurium are both semimetallic. Their hydrides, H_2Se and H_2Te, have an even more evil odor than H_2S, and the stench, toxicity, and absorption and retention by the human body of these compounds and their derivatives have discouraged the investigation of their properties. Polonium is highly radioactive and the investigation of its chemistry limited.

The Group VII Elements, the Halogens. These elements are nonmetallic, toxic, reactive, and gaseous or volatile at ordinary temperatures. Fluorine is a pale yellow gas of very high reactivity. It reacts violently with hydrogen,

$$H_2(g) + F_2(g) \rightarrow H_2F_2(g)$$

Chlorine, a greenish-yellow gas, is also very reactive. It will actively support the combustion of hydrocarbons,

$$CH_4(g) + 4Cl_2(g) \xrightarrow{\text{energy}} CCl_4(g) + 4HCl(g)$$

Its hydride is HCl. Bromine at room temperature is a dense, dark red, volatile liquid. It is sufficiently reactive to combine rapidly with most metals,

$$Zn(c) + Br_2(l) \rightarrow ZnBr_2(c), \; or \; Zn^{2+} + 2Br^-$$

Its hydride is HBr. Iodine is a black solid that evaporates to yield a violet vapor. Its hydride is HI. The chemistry of astatine has not been extensively investigated, but it forms compounds in which it exists as astatide ion, At^-. Halogens form compounds with each other called **interhalogen compounds.** Examples are $BrCl$, ClF_3, IF_5, IF_7, and ICl.

The Noble Gases or Aerogens, Group 0. These gaseous elements were once thought to participate in no chemical reactions; they were therefore called "inert." In recent years "inert" gas chemistry (especially that of xenon) has been studied. (This subject is treated on page 219.)

The Transition and Inner Transition Elements. These are all metals, ranging widely in physical properties. The highest melting, most brittle, hardest, and densest metals are found among these elements. (The general subject of metallic character will be treated in Chapter 27.)

Problems

1. Mendeleev Table. Designating the Group number as G, write the type formulas for the oxide, hydride, and chloride of any element, R, expressing the subscripts in terms of G. Criticize the use of such type formulas in predicting the compositions of real compounds.

Answer. R_2O_G, RH_{8-G}, RCl_G.

2. Mendeleev Table. Advance arguments that might have been appropriat in 1871 for the inclusion of Cu, Ag, and Au in Group I; do the same for inclusio of these metals in Group VIII. Which set of arguments do you favor?

3. Mendeleev Table. Suggest a modern explanation for the fact that there ar many uncertainties in Series 8, 9, and 10 of the Mendeleev Table.

4. Modern Periodic Table. If the atomic numbers in yet undiscovered ele ments were to follow a sequence analogous to the structure of the existing Table what atomic numbers would appear in (a) Group VIB, Period 7; (b) Group VA Period 7?

Answer. (a) 106; (b) 11

5. Periodicity. Referring to a Periodic Table and using the data given below predict the values omitted from the following tables. Compare your prediction with data from a chemical handbook. What conclusions do you draw regardin

Group VIIA Halogen family	Period number	Melting point (°C)	Boiling point (°C)	Critical temperature (°C
F_2	2	−223	−188	—
Cl_2	3	−102	−34.1	144
Br_2	4	−7.2	58.2	302
I_2	5	114	185	553
At_2	6	—	—	—

Substance	Period number of elements of Group IVA	Heat of vaporizatio (kcal/mole)
CH_4	2	2.12
SiH_4	3	2.98
GeH_4	4	—
SnH_4	5	4.5

Substance	Period number of elements of Group VIA	Boiling point (°C
H_2O	2	—
H_2S	3	−60.8
H_2Se	4	−41.5
H_2Te	5	− 1.8

	He	Ne	Ar	Kr	Xe	Rn
M.P.	1.0°K	24.6	83.8	—	161.7	202
B.P.	4.23°K	27.13	87.29	—	166.1	208

the value of the concept of periodicity in predicting physical properties of substances? How do your conclusions apply to predicting the properties of water?

6. Periodicity. Plot the following melting points (°C) vs. the atomic number for the following elements. Is the plot periodic?

Li	186	Mg	6.5×10^2	Sc	12×10^2
Be	12.8×10^2	Al	6.6×10^2	Ti	17.3×10^2
B	23×10^2	Si	14.2×10^2	V	17.1×10^2
C	36×10^2	P	44	Cr	16×10^2
N	-210	S	119	Mn	12.6×10^2
O	-218	Cl	-102		
F	-223	Ar	-189		
Ne	-249	K	62		
Na	98	Ca	810		

7. Periodicity. Osmium forms the following compounds: OsO_4, $OsCl_3$, $OsCl_6$, and K_2OsO_4. (a) Write the formulas of the corresponding ruthenium compounds. Can you definitely conclude that these ruthenium compounds must exist? (b) Look up in the *Handbook of Chemistry and Physics* or the *International Critical Tables* the heats of combustion (per mole of oxide) for the first thirty elements and plot against the atomic number (x axis). Is the principle of periodicity applicable? Is this information of value to a missile fuel chemist? Justify your answer.

8. Periodicity. The measured heats of solution of the noble gases in water at 25°C, ΔH in kcal per mole, are Ne -1.4, Ar -2.88, and Kr -3.69. Plot the period number (x axis) vs. the heat of solution for these three gases and predict the heat of solution of Xe; the measured value is -4.29.

9. Periodicity of valence. For each of the following compounds, state whether the valence of the italicized representative element corresponds to G, to $8 - G$, or to neither one. G is the Periodic Group number. Assume for valences of elements not italicized that H, F, Cl, Br, I, $(NO_3) = 1$; O, S, Se, Te, $(SO_4) = 2$; N, P, $(PO_4) = 3$. (a) $Al_2(SO_4)_3$; (b) AlN; (c) Sb_2Te_3; (d) $BaSO_4$; (e) $Be_3(PO_4)_2$; (f) $BiOI$; (g) B_2H_6; (h) B_4H_{10}; (i) BP; (j) $CSTe$; (k) Ga_2O_3; (l) $GeOCl_2$; (m) Ge_3N_2; (n) IF_7; (o) I_2O_5; (p) $LiNO_3$; (q) MgS; (r) NO_2F; (s) OF_2; (t) PBr_2F_3; (u) P_2I_4; (v) $FrNO_3$; (w) NaHS; (x) $TlNO_3$; (y) $In_2(SO_4)_3$; (z) Pb_3O_4; (aa) AsF_5.

10. Periodicity of valence. (a) For each of the compounds in the upper section of Table 7.8, state whether the valence of the element that corresponds to the listed Group number is G or $8 - G$. (b) For each of the compounds in the lower section of Table 7.8, assign a valence to the first element in each formula.

8

Electronic
structures
of
atoms

━━━━━━

IN THIS CHAPTER we consider several of the experiments involving the
use of electricity that ultimately led to the conclusion that the atom is
electrical in nature. The concept of the Daltonian atom provides no
mechanism to explain these observations. These experiments, started
over 125 years ago, also culminated in the discovery of x rays and radioactivity (Section 28.1). The spontaneous disintegration of naturally
radioactive atoms into smaller particles contradicts the Daltonian
hypothesis that atoms are unalterable. In turn, these discoveries inaugu-
rated a more complete theory of the structure of atoms, the nuclear theory
of the atom, and reaffirmed the atom as the unit of chemical changes.

8.1 QUANTIZATION OF ELECTRICITY

When a property of matter exists in discrete amounts, we say the property
is "quantized." For example, in accord with the atomic theory of matter,
mass is quantized. Solid iron, liquid water, gaseous hydrogen are not continuous; they are composed of atoms or molecules and therefore are quantized. Electricity in Dalton's time, however, was regarded as a continuous
fluid.

Electrolysis. The passage of electricity through a metallic conductor
in the solid or liquid state produces no chemical change in the conductor.
However, when a direct current is passed through an electrolytic conductor, such as molten sodium chloride or copper(II) sulfate dissolved in
water, chemical changes occur at the surface of the electrodes. The elec-

trodes are the solid metallic surfaces through which the current enters and leaves the liquid phase. The practical unit of charge or quantity of electricity is the coulomb (coul); one coulomb is the amount of charge obtained from a steady current of one ampere (amp) in one second (sec). Michael Faraday studied the relation between the quantity of electricity and the quantities of the products obtained at the electrodes, and announced in 1833 that the mass of a substance produced at an electrode is proportional to the charge passed through the liquid. Also, he discovered · that the same quantity of charge electroplates one atomic weight of any univalent element (hydrogen, for example, in solution as hydrochloric acid, or silver in solution as silver nitrate). But to discharge one atomic weight of a divalent element, copper in solution as copper(II) sulfate, exactly twice this quantity is required, and for a trivalent element, exactly three times this quantity is required.*

From these results, George Johnstone Stoney in 1874 concluded that electricity, like matter, is atomic in nature and consists of particles. He called the charge of a single particle of electricity the **electron.** Various experiments, based on the work of Faraday, yield 1.60×10^{-19} coul or 4.80×10^{-10} electrostatic unit (esu) for the electronic charge.

Discharge Tubes.   The passage of the electric current through air (gases), the so-called electric discharge, was concurrently studied by Faraday, Johann W. Hittorf, Sir William Crookes, and many other investigators. The results of these studies are best explained in terms of the electron particle suggested by Stoney.

A sealed glass tube with two electrodes attached to a high voltage source constitutes a discharge tube (see Fig. 8.1). When the gas pressure in the tube is reduced to about 10 torr, the gas becomes a conductor, current flows, and the gas fluoresces (emits light); when the pressure is reduced below about 10^{-3} torr, emission of light by the gas ceases. The current, however, still flows between the electrodes and the glass at the anode end of the tube fluoresces. If this end of the tube is coated with a luminescent material, such as impure zinc sulfide, it glows brilliantly. It thus appears that a radiation capable of inducing luminescence is emitted from the cathode; this radiation, because of its origin, is named the **"cathode ray."**

These rays possess momentum, a characteristic property of matter in motion, and they appear also to possess mass. Also, they are deflected in magnetic and electric fields in a manner predicted for negatively charged particles (see Fig. 8.1). These rays leave the cathode at a right angle to its surface, move in practically straight lines, and are capable of penetrating very thin metallic or mica plates. They also affect a photographic plate. These experiments demonstrated the particle character of the cathode rays. Moreover, Sir J. J. Thomson in 1897 showed the particles to be **electrons** by measuring the ratio of the charge of the particle to its mass, symbolized by e/m. From independent measurements, the accepted (rest)

* The subject of electrical conductance and electrolysis is more extensively covered in Chapter 15.

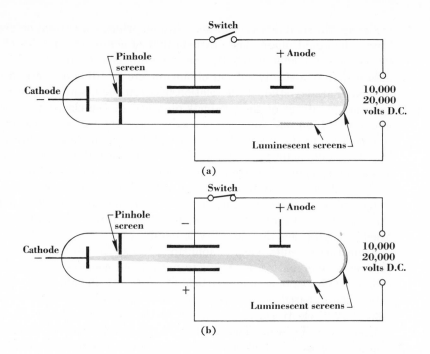

Fig. 8.1. *A discharge tube. Experiment showing that the cathode rays possess a negative charge: (a) position of ray in the absence of electric field, (b) position of ray in an electric field. The pressure in the tube is about 10⁻ torr.*

mass of the particle is 9.11×10^{-28} g. From the accepted value of e/m,[*] 1.76×10^8 coul/g, the charge of the particle is calculated to be 1.60×10^{-19} coul,

$$\frac{e}{m} \times m = e$$

$$1.76 \times 10^8 \, \frac{\text{coul}}{g} \times 9.11 \times 10^{-28} \, \frac{g}{\text{particle}} = 1.60 \times 10^{-19} \, \frac{\text{coul}}{\text{particle}}$$

in perfect agreement with the previously determined electronic charge based on Faraday's discoveries.

The ratio e/m is independent of the nature of the gas in the discharge tube and of the materials of which the tube is composed. Also, electrons from other sources, such as a hot cathode filament or photoelectrons, yield the same ratio. This, with the observation that the mass of the electron is about 2×10^3 times smaller than the lightest atom known, implies that the electron is a universal constituent of matter.

Originally referred to as "rays" because they were believed to be light waves, the more accurate name for cathode rays would be "electron beams." Electromagnetic radiations (light), in contrast, are not deflected in electric or magnetic fields.

* See Problem 21 (page 198).

Wilhelm Röntgen, while performing experiments on the fluorescence produced by cathode rays, discovered in 1895 a radiation that penetrates glass and metal plates opaque to light and cathode rays. This radiation, named the **x ray,** is produced when high speed electrons strike an object. X rays affect a photographic plate, exhibit the phenomena of diffraction, refraction, and reflection, but are not deflected in electric or magnetic fields. They are therefore electromagnetic waves of the same nature as light, radio waves, and ultraviolet radiation. Their wavelengths are of the order of 1 A, compared to $4\text{--}7 \times 10^3$ A for visible light. In addition, they cause luminescence and ionize gases. The conversion of neutral particles into ions is called **ionization.**

8.2 THE POSITIVE IONS (POSITIVE RAYS)

In the discharge tube, neutral particles—atoms or molecules—are ionized into electrons and positive ions. These charged particles acquire kinetic energy under the influence of the electric field and may, by collision, transfer energy to neutral particles. This energy appears as light, characteristic of the gas in the tube. At pressures below 10^{-3} torr, the number of collisions among the charged particles is comparatively low; therefore, a comparatively large number of highly energetic positive ions hits the cathode. Cathode rays are emitted by the cathode when it is bombarded. Evidently, if a perforated cathode is used, positive ions will emerge behind the cathode. Eugen Goldstein performed such an experiment in 1886 and detected the positive "rays." Their behavior in electric and magnetic fields conforms to that predicted for positively charged particles but, unlike the cathode ray, the nature of the positive ion is *characteristic* of the gas in the tube. As previously discussed (page 86), the masses of the positive ions are determined by mass spectroscopy. The mass of the positive ion depends on the atomic or molecular weight of the gas in the tube; since positive ions are produced by the removal of one or more electrons from neutral particles, the mass of the ion is almost equal to that of the neutral particle.

Natural hydrogen consists of three isotopes. Of all the positive ions whose masses have been determined, the **lightest ion found,** mass number 1, atomic weight 1.00728, is obtained from protium, the lightest isotope of hydrogen, atomic weight 1.007825. This ion, named the **proton,** H^+, bears a charge equal to that of an electron but opposite in sign. The ion obtained from deuterium, an isotope of hydrogen of mass number 2, is known as the **deuteron,** D^+. The removal of two electrons from a neutral helium atom produces an **alpha particle,** He^{2+}.

8.3 THE RUTHERFORD-BOHR NUCLEAR THEORY OF THE ATOM

The existence of nuclei within atoms was suggested by Lord Rutherford in 1911 to explain his experimental results on the scattering of alpha particles (see below), and confirmed by Niels Bohr in 1913 in his attempt

Fig. 8.2. *The Thomson atom; a sphere of positive electricity, distributed more or less uniformly over the volume of the known size of the atom, in which are imbedded a number of electrons so that the atom is electrically neutral. Stability, according to Thomson, results from a balance between the repulsive forces between the electrons and their attraction toward the center of the positive sphere.*

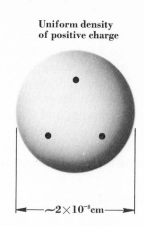

Uniform density
of positive charge

$\sim 2 \times 10^{-8}$ cm

to explain the origin of spectral lines (page 162). These ideas, however, evolved over a period of years in which other scientists contributed significantly.

The first recognized attempt to account for the conclusion that electrons are constituent parts of atoms was made by J. J. Thomson in 1904. He postulated that an atom is composed of a sphere of positive electricity in which are imbedded a number of electrons sufficient to neutralize the positive charge. Since the mass of an electron is exceedingly small compared to the mass of an atom, nearly all the mass of an atom is associated with the positive charge. The model of a **Thomson atom** containing three electrons in a uniform sphere of positive electricity equal to three electrons is illustrated in Fig. 8.2. Let us now make a prediction: if a high velocity alpha particle, possessing great kinetic energy, is impinged upon a "Thomson atom," it should not be deflected from its original path ("scattered"). Recall that to alter the path of a body in motion an *unbalanced force* must act on it. Deflection in this case will result from the mutual repulsion of the positive charges on the alpha particle and the sphere of positive electricity. But the positive electricity would *uniformly* occupy the volume of the atom and, therefore, is not concentrated in any region. An alpha particle entering such an atom, Thomson reasoned, will then be encircled by positive electricity. The alpha particle thus subjected to a balanced force is repelled almost equally on all sides (see Fig. 8.3a). An atom, Thomson concluded, will produce no appreciable deflection of an alpha particle and if, therefore, a beam of alpha particles is impinged upon a metal film, practically all the particles should pass through the film; a few may be deflected through small angles, a degree or two.

Such an experiment (Fig. 8.4) was performed by Lord Rutherford with Hans Geiger and Ernest Marsden in 1909. As predicted, practically all the particles passed through the film without deviation from the original path but, much to their amazement, a small fraction of the particles was

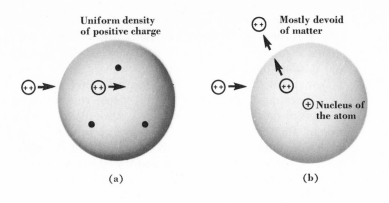

**Uniform density
of positive charge**

**Mostly devoid
of matter**

$\oplus$ **Nucleus of
the atom**

(a)

(b)

Fig. 8.3. *In the postulated Thomson atom (a) the alpha particle, subjected
to a balanced force, suffers little deflection. On approaching the nucleus of a
Rutherford atom (b), the alpha particle, subjected to a strong unbalanced force, is
deflected through large angles. If the nucleus were represented with a diameter
of one foot, the atom would then occupy a sphere of diameter roughly 19 miles.*

Fig. 8.4. *Illustrating the principle of the alpha particle deflection (scattering)
experiments. Positively charged helium atoms are directed at a metal film, and
its effect on the particles observed with detecting devices placed at various angles
relative to the original path. The angle is a measure of the deflection. A Geiger
counter may be used to detect alpha particles. The detector tube consists of a
wire inserted through the center of one end of a cylinder. The other end of the
cylinder is closed by a mica window sufficiently thin to permit passage of the
particles to be counted. A potential difference, insufficient to cause a discharge
through the gas, is maintained between the wire and the side of the cylinder.
However, when a particle enters the cylinder, the gas is ionized, discharge
occurs, and the current flows momentarily. This current is amplified and used
to operate a mechanical counter. Geiger originally employed a zinc sulfide
screen to count alpha particles; each alpha particle that hits the screen produces
a flash (a scintillation).*

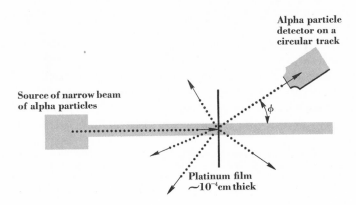

**Alpha particle
detector on a
circular track**

**Source of narrow beam
of alpha particles**

ϕ

**Platinum film
$\sim 10^{-4}$ cm thick**

deflected through large angles; a minute fraction, in fact, was almost completely reversed in direction. In Lord Rutherford's own words, "It was almost as incredible as if you fired a 15-inch shell at a piece of tissue paper and it came back and hit you."

To explain these results, Rutherford in 1911 assumed that the atom must be almost completely empty space; this would account for the passage of most of the particles in a straight line through the film. To account for the repulsive force required to produce large deflections, he further assumed that the positive electricity of the atom, and therefore the mass of the atom, must be concentrated in a very small volume, called the **nucleus of the atom.** When an alpha particle approaches a nucleus, it will be repelled, the angle of deflection being dependent upon the closeness of approach to the nucleus (see Fig. 8.3b). Since the atom is electrically neutral, electrons, sufficient in number to equal the positive charge of the nucleus, reside around the nucleus and determine the effective volume of the atom.

Assuming a nuclear type of atom and the applicability of Coulomb's law, Rutherford calculated a maximum value for the diameter of the nucleus, $\approx 10^{-13}$ cm, and predicted that the *number of unit positive charges on a nucleus* is numerically equal to the **atomic number,** the *ordinal number of the atom in the periodic classification.* Measurements of the nuclear charge from alpha particle deflection experiments by Geiger and Marsden, and later by Sir James Chadwick, verified this prediction.

Composition of the Nucleus.   A hydrogen atom, atomic number 1, consists of a proton, charge $+1$, as its nucleus, surrounded by one electron, charge -1. It is therefore inferred that the proton is a common constituent of atomic nuclei, sufficient in number to give a nucleus its characteristic positive charge. For example, the nucleus of any atom of neon, atomic number 10, contains 10 protons regardless of its mass.

These protons account for only about one half the mass of a neon atom. The currently accepted view attributes the remainder of the mass to the presence of neutrons in the nucleus.* The neutron, an electrically neutral particle with a mass number 1, atomic weight 1.00867, was discovered in 1932 by Chadwick.† The number of neutrons in a nucleus, N, is the difference between the mass number of the atom, A, and the number of protons in the nucleus, Z; symbolically,

$$N \ (number \ of \ neutrons) = A \ (mass \ number) - Z \ (atomic \ number)$$

Thus, the three isotopes of neon, atomic weights 19.99, 20.99, and 21.99, have the same atomic number but different mass numbers. All the nuclei of neon have 10 protons, but the nuclei of the isotope of mass number 20 have 10 neutrons, the isotope of mass number 21 has 11 neutrons, and the

* There is, however, a slight, but significant, difference between the mass of an atom and the sum of the masses of its constituent particles (Section 28.2).

† Rutherford had proposed that protons and neutrons are the fundamental building blocks of nuclei before the discovery of the neutron by Chadwick.

isotope of mass number 22 has 12 neutrons. Symbolically, these nuclei are represented as $_{10}Ne^{20}$, $_{10}Ne^{21}$, $_{10}Ne^{22}$.

When it is unnecessary to distinguish between protons and neutrons, they are referred to as **nucleons.** The mass number thus represents the total number of nucleons in the nucleus.

8.4 THE NATURE OF LIGHT

The discussion of the electronic structure of an atom is so closely interwoven with an understanding of the nature of light that we will pause here for a brief review on the nature and propagation of light.

James Clerk Maxwell in 1864 predicted that an alternating current of high frequency in a circuit would radiate energy in the form of waves— "electromagnetic waves"—traveling into space with the speed of light. A *wave*, by definition, *transmits energy without the transmission of matter.** This prediction led to the development of wireless telegraphy and the radio. The number of waves passing a given point in unit time is known as the **frequency** of the wave, ν; the unit of frequency is sec^{-1}. The distance between two crests of consecutive waves is called the **wavelength,** λ, illustrated in Fig. 8.5; the unit of wavelength is cm. The speed of the wave, given by

$$c = \lambda \nu$$

is the distance traveled by a given point in the wave in one second; the units of c are cm/sec. The quantity, $+a$ or $-a$, is called the amplitude of the wave. The *intensity* of a wave is the quantity of energy crossing a unit area in space in unit time. It may be expressed as ergs per cm^2 per second, or watts† per cm^2, and is related to the amplitude; for a given frequency, the larger the amplitude, the greater the intensity.

Light is radiant energy that produces a visual effect. Light waves are regarded as electromagnetic waves. The only difference between the elec-

* Although the word "wave" connotes a visible shape like that of a water wave or a vibrating wire (Fig. 8.5), the generalized concept of wave motion is simply that of energy in pulsating or periodically varying form. No material form or shape or sequence of waves need be imagined.

† 10^7 ergs $= 1$ joule; 1 watt $= 1$ joule/sec.

Fig. 8.5. *Illustrating the wavelength and the amplitude, $+a$ or $-a$, of the wave set up in a vibrating wire. The distance between two consecutive troughs, AB, is the same as the distance between two consecutive crests, CD.*

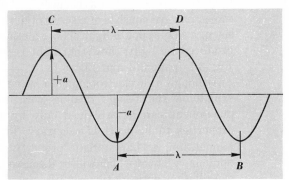

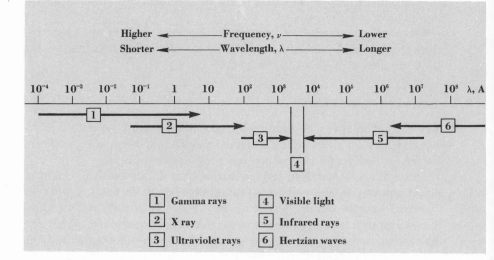

Fig. 8.6.   Electromagnetic spectrum:

Gamma rays	(radiation from atomic nuclei)
X rays	(radiation from electrons striking a target)
Ultraviolet rays	(radiation from arcs and gas discharges)
Visible light	(radiation from stars, hot objects, or gases)
Infrared rays	(radiation from warm objects)
Hertzian waves	(radiation from electric currents:
	radio waves, television, microwaves, radar)

tromagnetic waves emitted by a radio transmitter and the electromagnetic waves emitted by a hot tungsten wire (electric light bulb) or a fluorescent lamp is a difference in frequency; the light waves possess the higher frequencies. The electromagnetic spectrum is given in Fig. 8.6. There are no upper or lower limits to the wavelength.

Sound waves are diffracted; they spread out in passing through a hole. Light may also be diffracted. When light is passed through a hole, not too large compared to its wavelength, and allowed to fall upon a screen, the screen pattern consists of a series of dark and bright rings. It will not consist of a single spot of light. This experiment, as well as interference effects produced by light, show that light is *propagated* as a wave motion. See Fig. 3.1 (page 36) and Fig. 8.7.

Although the electromagnetic wave theory of light is successful in explaining the results dealing with the propagation of light, many phenomena can be explained only by attributing *mechanical* (particle) properties to light. It is necessary, for example, to endow light with momentum, a characteristic property of matter in motion. These phenomena, a few of which will be discussed, are associated with interactions of radiation with matter.

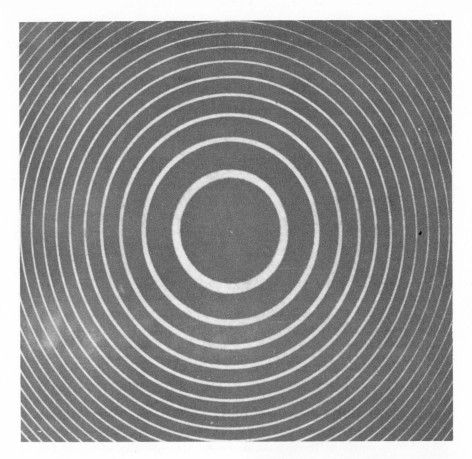

(a)

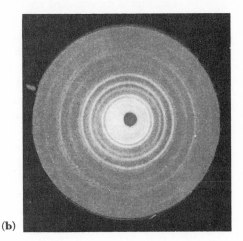

(b)

Fig. 8.7. *Diffraction patterns showing the wave nature of electromagnetic waves: (a) visible light; (b) x rays through a silver foil.*

(1) Light or other electromagnetic radiation falling upon a body exerts a pressure in the same direction as the motion of the radiation. The

pressure produced by a gas is attributed to the collisions of its molecules with a body. Similarly, the radiation pressure may be attributed to "atoms of light."* The "atom of light" was named the **photon** in 1926 by the chemist Gilbert N. Lewis, who wrote, "I therefore take the liberty of proposing for this hypothetical new atom, which is not light but plays an essential part in every process of radiation, the name photon."

(2) In the late 19th century, many scientists were involved in the study of the distribution of the wavelengths and the intensities (the energies) of the light waves emitted by hot bodies, such as a hot tungsten filament. Science, at that time, recognized the quantization of matter and of electricity, but radiant energy was believed to be continuous. That is, the electromagnetic wave theory assumed that the energy of a radiation may be *any* value, from infinitely small to infinitely large. But all arguments based on this assumption failed miserably to account for the energy distribution found experimentally. To obtain complete agreement with experiment, Max Planck, in 1900, found it necessary to invent what is now known as the *quantum theory*. Namely, in interactions between radiation and matter, radiant energy behaves as if it is composed of "atoms" or "quanta." Further, the energy of a quantum, E, is given by

$$E = h\nu = \frac{hc}{\lambda}$$

where ν is the frequency of the radiation absorbed or emitted, and h is a constant, 6.625×10^{-27} erg sec per particle, known as Planck's constant. Finally, only a whole number of quanta may be absorbed or emitted by a body. As previously mentioned, the "quantum" has been renamed the "photon."

In terms of the quantum theory, the intensity of an electromagnetic radiation is determined by the number of photons striking a unit area in unit time.

(3) When light falls upon a metal, electrons (**photoelectrons**) are ejected from its surface. Classical physics predicts that as the intensity of light of a given frequency (**monochromatic light**) is increased, the kinetic energy of the ejected electron should increase. However, experiments show that the maximum kinetic energy of the ejected electrons is *independent* of the intensity, and is dependent only on the frequency of the monochromatic light. These results, summarized in Fig. 8.8a and b, were explained by Einstein in terms of the quantum theory of radiation: the energies of all photons for a given frequency, ν, are identical. Each photon has the energy $h\nu$. For each photon absorbed, one electron is ejected. Then, the energy, E_s, required to remove the electron from the surface plus the kinetic energy of the ejected electron must equal the energy of the photon,

$$h\nu = \tfrac{1}{2}mv^2 + E_s$$

Here, m is the mass of the electron, and v is its measured maximum

* Although this explanation is simpler, Maxwell's wave theory also predicts the existence of a radiation pressure.

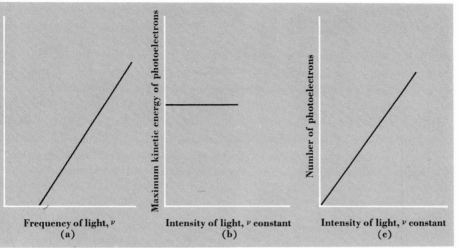

Fig. 8.8 (a) A plot of the maximum kinetic energy of photoelectrons and the frequency of the incident light. The slope of the line is equal to h, Planck's constant. (b) A plot of the maximum kinetic energy of photoelectrons and the intensity of the light for a given frequency. (c) A plot of the number of photoelectrons and the intensity of the light for a given frequency.

velocity. Hence, increasing the intensity of the light increases the number of photons and *not the energy* of an individual photon. Then, the kinetic energy of ejected electrons should remain constant but the number of electrons ejected should increase. This conclusion is in perfect agreement with experimental results. Further, the previous equation rewritten as

$$\tfrac{1}{2}mv^2 = h\nu - E_s$$

predicts that a simple linear relation should exist between the energy of the liberated electron and the frequency of the light. As the frequency of the light is increased, $h\nu$ increases and the energy of the photoelectron should increase. Also, notice that h, a constant, is the slope of the line. Very significantly, then, the equation predicts that the slope of the line relating the energy of the photoelectron and ν should be the same for all metallic surfaces. These predictions have been verified; see Fig. 8.8.

Thus, while the wave character of radiation (electromagnetic waves) is verified by experiments involving diffraction and interference phenomena, the particle character of radiation is verified by experiments involving energy exchanges between radiation and matter. It is nonsense to visualize a beam of light as either a stream of photons or as a wave-train (except for educational convenience).

8.5 SPECTRA OF ELEMENTS

A spectroscope is an instrument for analyzing the composition of light. When a beam of parallel rays of light enters the face of a triangular glass

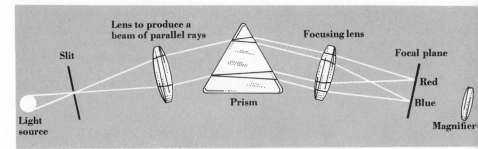

Fig. 8.9. *The dispersion of light composed of two wavelengths by a prism is illustrated. The focusing lens and magnifier constitute a telescope.*

prism, it is dispersed into its component wavelengths. This dispersion of light is the basis of the spectroscope. The essential parts of a spectroscope are illustrated in Fig. 8.9.

Solids, liquids, and dense gases become incandescent at high temperatures. If the light is examined with a spectroscope, it will consist of a **continuous band of colors** as observed in a rainbow. An incandescent substance thus emits a **continuous spectrum.**

When the light emitted from a source is analyzed, the spectrum obtained is called an **emission spectrum.** On the other hand, the spectrum obtained *after light from some source has passed through a substance* is known as an **absorption spectrum.**

When the pressure of a gas in a discharge tube is reduced to about 0.1–10 torr, the gas, as in a neon sign, glows brightly. If the light is examined with a spectroscope, a **line spectrum** is observed. A rainbow will not appear; rather, several isolated colored lines appear, as illustrated in Figs. 8.10 and 8.11. If the light from a flame in which a volatile salt is placed is examined in a spectroscope, again, a line spectrum is observed. Very significantly, the line spectrum of an element is characteristic of that element regardless of its source. Sodium and its compounds, for example, always yield the same sodium line spectrum, differing from that of all other elements. It is thus the *atoms* of the element that emit the line spectrum. The study of the spectra of elements is therefore an important source of information in the determination of the structure of atoms.

The colored lines in the spectra of all elements are observed to come closer and closer to each other at the longer wavelengths. This convergence suggests that the wavelengths (or frequencies) of the lines might be expressible in terms of a mathematical function that approaches a limit.

Fig. 8.10. *The emission spectrum of hydrogen in the visible range. (Note: 4101 should read 4102.)* **Fig. 8.11.** *The emission spectrum of helium in the visible range. [See color plate following page 164; used, by permission, from "Chemistry" by M. J. Sienko and R. A. Plane (2nd ed.) Copyright: 1961, McGraw-Hill, New York.]*

The hydrogen spectrum, for example, can be represented by a relation *involving whole numbers,*

$$\nu = 3.289 \times 10^{15} \ \text{sec}^{-1} \left(\frac{1}{n_1^2} - \frac{1}{n_2^2} \right) \tag{1}$$

where ν is the frequency of the line in sec^{-1}, and $3.289 \times 10^{15} \ \text{sec}^{-1}$ is a constant for hydrogen, known as the *Rydberg constant.*[*] n_1 is a dimensionless integer and n_2 is another dimensionless integer greater than n_1. Thus when $n_1 = 1$, n_2 may be any integer greater than 1 and each value of n_2 yields a frequency, ν, corresponding to a line in the spectrum of hydrogen. When $n_1 = 2$, n_2 is any integer greater than 2, etc.

The energy of a photon, E, is given by

$$E = h\nu = \frac{hc}{\lambda} \tag{2}$$

This means the radiant energy emitted or absorbed as radiation of frequency ν by a number of identical atoms can be only in integral multiples of $h\nu$. Thus each spectral line corresponds to photons possessing a definite energy. For example, the 4102 A line in the spectrum of hydrogen corresponds to 4.842×10^{-12} ergs per atom,

$$E = h\frac{c}{\lambda} = 6.625 \times 10^{-27} \frac{\text{erg sec}}{\text{atom}} \times \frac{2.998 \times 10^{10} \frac{\text{cm}}{\text{sec}} \, 10^8 \frac{\text{A}}{\text{cm}}}{4102 \, \text{A}}$$

$$= 4.842 \times 10^{-12} \frac{\text{erg}}{\text{atom}}$$

The atoms therefore emit or absorb only photons of definite characteristic energies.

8.6 QUANTIZATION OF THE ENERGY OF AN ELECTRON ASSOCIATED WITH A NUCLEUS

An atom consists of a positively charged nucleus surrounded by electrons within a volume roughly 10^{-8} cm in radius. The arrangement of these electrons, we further believe, determines the physical and chemical properties of the elements.

What prevents the electrons from being attracted into the nucleus? All attempts to answer this question on the basis of classical physics fail. Let us consider the simplest of atomic systems, the hydrogen atom. If the electron were stationary, the coulombic attractive force[†] would cause it to fall into the nucleus. Rutherford then suggested that the electron revolves about the proton (nucleus) in a manner analogous to the revolution of the moon about the earth. The coulombic attractive force acting on the electron keeps it in circular motion and equals the force with which the electron tends to pull away from its orbit and move in a straight line.

---

[*] Named for Johannes Robert Rydberg, who discovered this empirical relation in 1890 after a study of a large mass of data.

[†] See Appendix I (page 784).

The fact, however, that the bodies involved in the hydrogen atom are charged introduces another factor. The Maxwell electromagnetic theory of light predicts that the revolving electron will emit radiant energy. Sideways, the revolving electron looks like an oscillating charge, as in a radio antenna sending out radiation. The revolving electron should lose energy, resulting in a gradual decrease in its kinetic energy, and should therefore spiral toward the proton, emitting a rainbow of colors and falling finally into the proton. This theory thus incorrectly predicts a *continuous spectrum and a collapsed atom*.

This dilemma was boldly resolved by Niels Bohr in 1913 by applying the concepts of the quantum theory to Rutherford's nuclear theory of the atom:

(1) In his theory of the hydrogen atom, Bohr assumed the electron does revolve with a definite fixed energy, without the emission or absorption of energy. Then, how are we to express the energy of the electron in the normal hydrogen atom? Bohr decided to do this by calculating how much work must be done against the attractive force to remove the electron from its normal position near the proton to a distance so far that the attraction becomes practically zero. The calculation* yields -21.79×10^{-12} erg; *the minus sign is used to tell us that work must be done to move the electron from the region of the proton (the nucleus) to infinity*. So, Bohr pictured a normal hydrogen atom as a stationary† proton and a revolving electron with an energy of -21.79×10^{-12} erg.

(2) We come now to a crucial question. Can the energy of the electron assume some other value? If so, what are these other values? Bohr answered, yes, the energy of the electron may take other values, but *these energy values must be quantized*. We say the *energy of the electron is quantized* like mass, electricity, and radiant energy. Recall (page 161) that the spectrum of hydrogen is expressible by an equation involving the squares of whole numbers. Bohr therefore postulated that the energy of the electron can take only the values given by

$$- \frac{21.79 \times 10^{-12} \text{ erg}}{n^2} \tag{3}$$

in which n is a dimensionless *integer*, known as the **principal quantum number.** We speak of these energy values as "the energy levels" of the electron or of the hydrogen atom. So, the energy levels of the electron (hydrogen atom) are restricted to the values given in Table 8.1. The first energy level, when the principal quantum number of the electron is 1, is known as the "normal" or **"ground" state** of the hydrogen atom; all other energy levels are known as **"excited" states.** A convenient method of representing the ground and excited states of the hydrogen atom, illus-

---

* See Appendix III (page 796).

† The assumption that the proton is infinitely heavy compared to the electron and therefore stationary is approximate. The nucleus does possess a motion that decreases the calculated frequency of the spectral lines of the H atom by about 5 parts in 10,000. (See Appendix III.)

TABLE 8.1   Some Energy Levels of the Hydrogen Atom

Principal quantum number of the electron n	Energy in erg per atom $\dfrac{-21.79 \times 10^{-12}}{n^2}$	Number of the energy level[a]
1	$\dfrac{-21.79 \times 10^{-12}}{1} = -21.79 \times 10^{-12}$	1st
2	$\dfrac{-21.79 \times 10^{-12}}{4} = -5.45 \times 10^{-12}$	2nd
3	$\dfrac{-21.79 \times 10^{-12}}{9} = -2.42 \times 10^{-12}$	3rd
4	$\dfrac{-21.79 \times 10^{-12}}{16} = -1.36 \times 10^{-12}$	4th
5	$\dfrac{-21.79 \times 10^{-12}}{25} = -0.872 \times 10^{-12}$	5th
6	$\dfrac{-21.79 \times 10^{-12}}{36} = -0.605 \times 10^{-12}$	6th
etc.	etc.	etc.

[a] **Bohr referred to these as "stationary states" of the hydrogen atom because the electron does not radiate while at such energy levels.**

trated in Fig. 8.12, shows the energy levels as lines. Such a figure is known as an **energy level diagram.**

(3) Bohr next proposed a mechanism for the absorption and emission of energy. The absorption of radiation will correspond to a transition— "an electron jump"—between any two of the possible energy levels, from a lower to a higher level. The emission of radiation will correspond to a transition between any two of the possible energy levels, but from a higher to a lower level. Thus, in absorption, the energy of the electron is increased and, in emission, the energy of the electron is decreased, but only in accord with the differences between any two energy levels. The energy lost appears as a photon. Since we have restricted (quantized) the energy of the electron, *the hydrogen atom can emit or absorb only photons whose energy is equal to the difference between the two energy levels.* A spectral line thus originates when the electron "drops" from one energy level to a lower level,

$$E \text{ (energy of photon emitted)} = E_{n_2} - E_{n_1} \qquad (4)$$

where E_{n_2} and E_{n_1} are the energy levels with principal quantum numbers n_2 and n_1, n_2 being larger than n_1.

(4) Finally, using Equation (4), Bohr predicted the energy of the photons that should be emitted by the hydrogen atom. For an electron

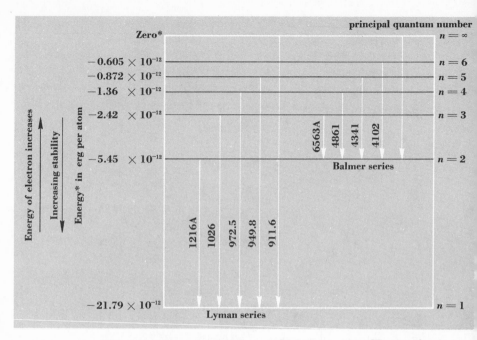

Fig. 8.12. Energy level diagram of the hydrogen atom. Wavelengths are in angstrom units. Compare the predicted lines in the "Balmer series" with the line emission spectrum of hydrogen, Fig. 8.10.

* The reader is reminded that the energy is expressed as the work necessary to separate the electron from the hydrogen atom against the attractive force of the nucleus. Zero energy then means that no work is required to remove the electron when the distance between the proton and the electron is infinite ($n = \infty$).

transition between any two levels (Fig. 8.12), the difference in the energy of the two levels equals the energy of the radiation absorbed or emitted by a hydrogen atom.

EXAMPLE 1   A particle "strikes" a normal hydrogen atom, exciting the electron to its 6th energy level ($n = 6$); this electron then "drops" to its 2nd energy level ($n = 2$). What is the energy of the photon emitted?

ANSWER   According to the Bohr theory, the energy of the photon emitted must be the difference between the higher and the lower energy levels of the electron; hence, from Table 8.1 or Fig. 8.12,

$$E \text{ (energy of the photon)} = E_6 - E_2$$

$$= (-0.605 \times 10^{-12}) \frac{\text{erg}}{\text{atom}} - (-5.45 \times 10^{-12}) \frac{\text{erg}}{\text{atom}}$$

$$= 4.84 \times 10^{-12} \frac{\text{erg}}{\text{atom}}$$

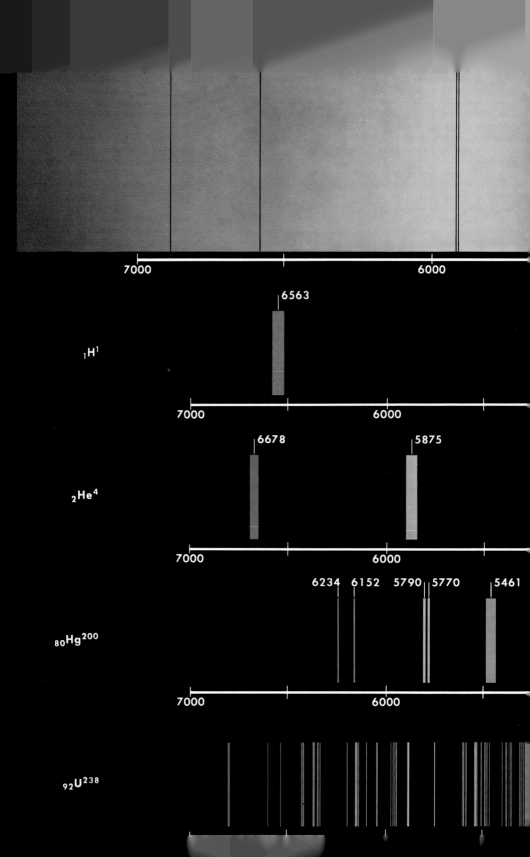

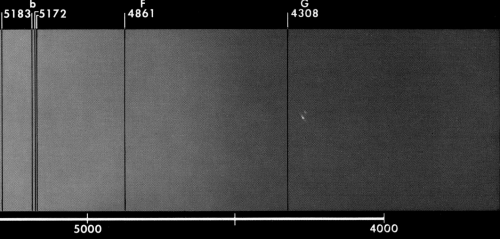

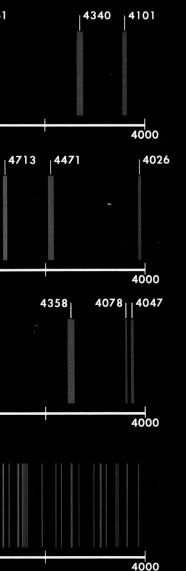

b
5183 5172

F
4861

G
4308

5000   4000

4340   4101

4000

4713   4471   4026

4000

4358   4078   4047

4000

Such diverse and fundamental information on the nature of matter as the composition of distant stars and the structure of atoms and molecules has been obtained by analysis of the light emitted from any incandescent substance.

In the SPECTROSCOPE, such light, passed through a slit and a prism, is broken up into its component wavelengths, which are observed as colored lines, or light of different energies, characteristic of the differences between the various electron energy levels of the atoms. This EMISSION SPECTRUM is CONTINUOUS when the images of the wavelengths are uninterruptedly overlapping; it is a LINE spectrum when only certain specific wavelengths are emitted, as shown here for the elements hydrogen, helium, mercury, and uranium.

On the solar spectrum across the top of this plate appears a series of dark lines — FRAUNHOFER LINES — forming an ABSORPTION SPECTRUM: Some of the light from the intensely hot interior of the sun is absorbed by the cooler gases of its outer layers as the light energies raise the atoms in these layers to higher energy states; bright lines are not, therefore, seen for these changes.

The spectra are calibrated in angstroms (1 A = 10^{-10} m); the letters are arbitrary designations introduced by Fraunhofer for lines important in spectroscopy.

Fig. 8.13. *Comparison of electron and x ray diffraction. Pattern produced by passing (a) x rays through gold foil; (b) an electron beam through gold foil.*

(a)   (b)

This photon corresponds to a radiation of wavelength 4102 A, in perfect agreement with one of the lines (Fig. 8.10) in the spectrum of hydrogen.

It is significant that the "Lyman series" of lines in the ultraviolet range, given in Fig. 8.12, as well as other series of lines, were discovered after Bohr predicted their existence.

The dimensionless integers discovered empirically (Equation 1) are now known as principal quantum numbers (Equation 3). Also, Equation (3) may be shown to be in practically perfect agreement with the empirical Equation (1) as follows. According to the Bohr theory,

$$
\begin{aligned}
E \text{ (energy of the photon)} &= h\nu = E_{n_2} - E_{n_1} \\
&= -\frac{21.79 \times 10^{-12}}{n_2^2} - \left(\frac{-21.79 \times 10^{-12}}{n_1^2} \right) \\
&= 21.79 \times 10^{-12} \frac{\text{erg}}{\text{atom}} \left(\frac{1}{n_1^2} - \frac{1}{n_2^2} \right)
\end{aligned}
\tag{5}
$$

Now, if we multiply Equation (1) by Planck's constant, h, to convert the frequency of the radiated line to its corresponding energy,

$$
\begin{aligned}
E \text{ (energy of the radiated line)} &= h\nu = 6.625 \times 10^{-27} \frac{\text{erg sec}}{\text{atom}} \\
&\quad \times 3.289 \times 10^{15} \text{ sec}^{-1} \left(\frac{1}{n_1^2} - \frac{1}{n_2^2} \right) \\
&= 21.79 \times 10^{-12} \frac{\text{erg}}{\text{atom}} \left(\frac{1}{n_1^2} - \frac{1}{n_2^2} \right)
\end{aligned}
\tag{6}
$$

The agreement between Equations (5) and (6) is indeed remarkable. However, only the general features, and not the quantitative treatment, of the Bohr theory may be extended to atomic systems containing more than one electron.

To recapitulate, the assumptions of the Bohr theory, advanced primarily to explain the origin of spectral lines, are as follows:

(1) Spectral lines are produced by atoms.
(2) The Rutherford (nuclear) model of the atom is acceptable.
(3) The energy of the hydrogen atom is quantized and is determined by the square of an integer, the quantum number n.
(4) In any one energy level, the electron does not radiate or absorb energy.
(5) An electron transition between two energy levels, E_1 and E_2, determines the energy absorbed or emitted by a hydrogen atom.
(6) The Planck equation, $E = h\nu$, is valid for the absorption or the emission of the radiation.
(7) The frequency of the radiation absorbed or radiated is determined only by the energy difference of the two levels between which an electron "jumps" or "drops": $h\nu = E_2 - E_1$.

8.7 MODIFICATION OF THE BOHR THEORY

The extraordinary success of Bohr's celebrated atomic theory in explaining the origin of the spectra of hydrogen-like particles does not, of course, make it correct. In fact, the agreement with experimental results may be regarded as a fluke, and the Bohr theory has been superseded by a radically different theory (page 168).

Thus, the Bohr theory predicts that one and only one spectral line can originate between any two given energy levels. For example (see Fig. 8.12), for the transition, $n = 3 \rightarrow n = 2$, only one line, 6563 A, can be radiated. But if a spectroscope of high resolution is used, *two very slightly different lines*, 6562.8 and 6562.7 A, *are observed* in place of the 6563 A line. This is a typical and not an exceptional characteristic of atomic spectra. When the light source—the atoms emitting radiation—is placed in a strong magnetic field, each spectral line is further split into a number of spectral lines. For example, a magnetic field of about 22×10^3 gauss splits each of the two yellow sodium lines (5889.963 A and 5895.930 A) into 4 lines (each of the two lines increases and decreases approximately one part in 20,000). To account for these additional spectral lines, it was assumed that each principal energy level was subdivided into a number of sublevels, each of which possesses a slightly different energy. Increasing the number of energy levels increases the number of spectral lines that may be radiated. These sublevels were designated by three additional quantum numbers, l, m_l, and m_s.

8.8 MATTER WAVES

To this point, we have been content to accept the electron as a particle, a bit of matter. However, Louis de Broglie in 1924 reasoned that since radiation possesses both wave and mechanical (particle) properties, it is likely that a wave character is associated with a particle, such as an electron, a proton, an atom, a molecule, or a piece of chalk. The wave associated with a particle is called a *matter wave*. Thus, the energy of a photon may be expressed as $h\nu$ or as mc^2 (*see page 118*),

$$E = h\nu = \frac{hc}{\lambda} = mc^2$$

Cancelling c,

$$\frac{h}{\lambda} = mc$$

from which

$$\lambda \ (a \ wave \ property) = \frac{h}{mc} = \frac{h}{\text{momentum} \ (a \ particle \ property)}$$

This equation, valid for a photon, was assumed to be applicable to particles upon substituting the mass of the particle for m and the speed of the particle v for the speed of light,

$$\lambda = \frac{h}{mv}$$

In words, a beam of electrons, each with a speed v and a mass m, will exhibit wave properties, and the wavelength (a wave property) associated with this moving electron beam may be predicted by dividing the momentum (a particle property) of the electron into Planck's constant. For electrons accelerated by a potential difference of 10^4 volts, λ corresponds to about 0.1 A, the approximate wavelength of an x ray. A crystal then should yield the same kind of diffraction pattern with an electron beam as with an x ray beam. The de Broglie hypothesis has been verified by numerous experiments (see Fig. 8.13; similar diffraction patterns are obtained by passing an electron beam or an x ray beam through metallic foils or reflecting them from a metallic surface).

Matter waves possess wave-like characteristics; they are *not*, however, electromagnetic waves. They are *not* radiated into space or emitted by the particle; they are never dissociated from the particle. The speed of a matter wave is not the same as the speed of light, nor is it a constant.

Thus, like electromagnetic radiations, particles of matter exhibit wave properties and particle properties. The electron microscope, now a common laboratory tool (Fig. 1.1, page 6), is an application of the de Broglie concept.

8.9 THE WAVE EQUATION

Erwin Schroedinger in 1926 conceived an equation regarded as one of the greatest products of the human mind; in his honor the equation is known as the **"Schroedinger equation."** This equation, also known as the **"wave equation,"** is the basis of wave mechanics, so called because the equation was discovered by analogy to the properties of waves and by recognizing that particles exhibit wave properties. However, attempts at a logical derivation of the equation by theoretical mathematicians have proven futile; it is therefore accepted as a postulate.

The equation is fundamental; it is, in principle, applicable to the problems that arise when particles, such as electrons, nuclei, atoms, and molecules, are subjected to a force. Wave mechanics is therefore also referred to as "quantum" or "particle" mechanics. Its application to chemical questions is referred to as **"quantum chemistry."**

Wave mechanics was discovered as a solution to the many difficulties associated with the Bohr theory—the concept of an electron revolving in definite paths around the nucleus, the arbitrary introduction of quantum numbers to eliminate discrepancies with experiment and to account for the splitting of spectral lines in magnetic fields. Further, many phenomena were either described incorrectly or could not be explained prior to the discovery of quantum mechanics. For example:

(1) The covalent bond, envisaged as the sharing of electrons between atoms forming the bond (page 211), does not explain how this sharing of electrons leads to stability. Bond stability is, however, explicable in terms of wave mechanics, and the existence of molecules can be predicted from the wave equation (Chapter 11).

(2) The intensities of spectral lines can be calculated *only* with the aid of the wave equation.

We have always *taken for granted* that the equations of motion developed by the great mathematicians of the past centuries are of universal application; that is, that they apply to all bodies, regardless of size. Quantum mechanics, of necessity, contradicts this concept; *it does not depict the structure of the atom in terms that are familiar to us from the behavior of visible bodies.* Nevertheless, it is interesting and significant to note that when the Schroedinger equation is applied to chemical problems, the energy of the chemical system is assumed to be expressible in terms of classical laws. For example, the energy is assumed to be the sum of kinetic and potential energies, and the force between charged particles —electrons and nuclei—is assumed to be given by Coulomb's law. Therefore, quantum mechanics is a part of the evolution of our knowledge, born from and retaining many characteristics of classical mechanics. Schroedinger could not have done his work without the picture that Bohr provided for him.

The Schroedinger equation in one dimension may be written in Cartesian coordinates (x, y, and z) as

$$\frac{\partial^2\psi}{\partial x^2} + \frac{8\pi^2 m}{h^2}(E - P)\psi = 0 \tag{1}$$

where h is Planck's constant, m is the mass of the particle located in space by the coordinates, and E is the total energy of the particle, the sum of its kinetic and potential energy; P is the potential energy of the particle. (This refers to the *work done against a force* in changing the position of a particle. For example, work is done against an electrical attractive force when an electron is moved away from a nucleus. If an electron is not subjected to any force, then $P = 0$.) The Greek letter ψ (*psi*) is a mathematical function expressed in terms of the coordinates of the particle; for example, for the electron in a particular environment in which the electron is not subjected to a force and the motion of the electron is restricted to oscillations in one dimension, x, ψ might be

$$\psi = k \sin\left(a\pi \frac{x}{d}\right) \tag{2}$$

in which k is some constant, a is a whole number (1, 2, 3...), d is the fixed distance over which the electron moves back and forth, and x is the coordinate which may take any value from 0 to d; x locates the electron along the distance 0 to d; ψ is known as a **wave function.** The symbol $\partial^2\psi/\partial x^2$ tells us what mathematical operations we must do upon ψ to solve for E. The reader is familiar with the "operator" $\times$ ("times"), $6 \times 1010 = 6060$. If you are *not* familiar with the "operator" $\partial^2/\partial x^2$ (differential calculus), **do not be concerned.** The *important feature* is that when the P term has been evaluated, a ψ function can be obtained, and the Schroedinger equation can be solved for E.

8.10 THE OSCILLATING ELECTRON

Thus, let us apply the Schroedinger equation to the case in which we allow an electron to move back and forth over a distance d in the absence of any potential field. Since the electron is not subject to any force, $P = 0$, and, since it is moving in one dimension, Equation (1) becomes

$$\frac{\partial^2\psi}{\partial x^2} + \frac{8\pi^2 m}{h^2}(E - 0)\psi = 0 \tag{3}$$

where m is the mass of the electron. The mathematical solution of Equation (3) yields Equation (2) and Equation (4),

$$E_a = \frac{a^2 h^2}{8md^2} \tag{4}$$

That Equations (2) and (4) are solutions of Equation (3) may be proven by (a) substituting Equation (4) for E in Equation (3); (b) operating upon Equation (2), the wave function, in accord with the instructions $\partial^2/\partial x^2$.

If a classmate with some experience in differential calculus carries out these two steps for you he will arrive at

$$- \frac{a^2\pi^2\psi}{d^2} + \frac{8\pi^2 m}{h^2} \frac{a^2 h^2}{8md^2} \psi$$

which, in agreement with Equation (3), does equal zero.

Let us now consider some important consequences of this treatment:

(a) For a fixed distance d, Equation (4) states that the translational motion (kinetic energy) of the electron is *quantized* since a is an integer. If d is, say, 2.5 angstrom units, then the permissible values of the energy* of the electron are given by

$$E_a = \frac{a^2 h^2}{8m(2.5 \times 10^{-8})^2}$$

Thus when $a = 2$,

$$E_2 = \frac{4h^2}{8m(2.5 \times 10^{-8})^2}$$

(b) But for a fixed distance and a definite E value, there is a definite corresponding wave function. Thus, when $a = 2$,

$$\psi_2 = k \sin\left(2\pi \frac{x}{2.5 \times 10^{-8}}\right)^\dagger$$

When $a = 1$,

$$E_1 = \frac{(1)^2 h^2}{8m(2.5 \times 10^{-8})^2}$$

and

$$\psi_1 = k \sin\left(\pi \frac{x}{2.5 \times 10^{-8}}\right)$$

When $a = 3$,

$$E_3 = \frac{(3)^2 h^2}{8m(2.5 \times 10^{-8})^2}$$

and

$$\psi_3 = k \sin\left(3\pi \frac{x}{2.5 \times 10^{-8}}\right)$$

In this way, the wave equation relates the energy of a system E to a wave function ψ. But, *very significantly*, note that for each value of a, the permissible value of E *does not depend upon the location of the particle*. This

* The units for E are

$$\frac{erg^2 \, sec^2 \, g \, cm^2}{particle^2 \, \dfrac{g}{particle} \, cm^2 \, erg \, sec^2} = \frac{ergs}{particle}$$

† The value of k does not matter; it drops out when any significant quantity is calculated.

means E *does not depend upon the value of the coordinate* x. E_3, for example, is independent of the location of the electron; x may take *any* value between 0 and 2.5 angstrom units, but this does not affect E_3.

(c) The integer a is a quantum number. But it *was not* arbitrarily introduced into Equations (2) and (4). It appears naturally during the mathematical solution of Equation (3).

To recapitulate, the wave equation, Equation (1), relates the energy E of a system to a wave function ψ; ψ is a function of the coordinates of the system; the coordinates locate the system in space. As the position of the system in space is altered, the numerical value of ψ changes, but the energy of the system remains constant.

Returning to Equation (4), we see that for a given quantum number, the *energy of the electron decreases as the distance over which it is confined increases.* In other words, the *more delocalized* the path available to the electron, the lower is its energy. Visualize a chain of four carbon atoms over which an electron oscillates. The spectrum and stability of this chain may be associated with the energy of this electron. If the chain of carbon atoms is now extended to six atoms, the confining distance is increased, and the electron is more delocalized. The energy of the electron is thus decreased, and the oscillating electron will make a greater contribution to the stability of the six-carbon atom chain. (Recall that the lower the energy of a system, the greater is its stability.) These quantum mechanical concepts are utilized in explaining the nature of the chemical bond (Chapter 11) and the acidity of compounds (Chapter 18).

8.11 THE HYDROGEN ATOM

Since a solution of the Schroedinger equation has not been obtained in simple form for any system of chemical interest, except for the hydrogen atom, let us continue our discussion in terms of the hydrogen atom, the simplest chemical system. Further, let us ignore the motion of the proton. Then E refers to an energy level of the electron (or the hydrogen atom) and ψ is some function of the coordinates of the electron relative to the stationary proton as the origin. The system of coordinates is arbitrary; spherical coordinates in which r would be the linear distance between the proton and the electron may be used. The potential energy is evaluated in terms of r.*

The mathematical solution† of the wave equation by Paul Dirac reveals the following:

---

* Appendix III (page 796).

† Again, we must emphasize that the *only* assumptions involved are that: (1) the wave equation is applicable; (2) the energy of the hydrogen atom is the sum of the kinetic and potential energies of the electron and of the proton; (3) the law describing the forces between charged macrobodies is applicable to electrons and protons; and (4) relativistic effects are applicable. The mathematical solution, we assure you, is on a firm foundation, as strong as, let us say, Euclidean geometry or anybody else's geometry and the arithmetical procedure known as addition.

(a) The wave functions are characterized by four quantum numbers corresponding to n, l, m_l, and m_s.

(b) Proper (acceptable) wave functions are obtained *only* when the quantum numbers take the following values:

$$n = 1, 2, 3, \ldots$$
$$l = 0, 1, 2, \ldots, n - 1$$
$$m_l = +l, \ldots, 0, \ldots -l$$
$$m_s = +\tfrac{1}{2} \text{ or } -\tfrac{1}{2}$$

For example, when $n = 3$, l can take values of 0, 1, and 2. When $l = 2$, m_l can take values of 2, 1, 0, -1, -2.

(c) The energy of the electron in the hydrogen atom is quantized and may be determined by two to four of the quantum numbers, depending upon the environment of the hydrogen atom.

8.12 ATOMIC ORBITALS; SHELLS AND SUBSHELLS

The wave functions identified by the three quantum numbers n, l, and m_l are called **atomic orbitals.** An orbital is commonly designated by a symbol that gives its l value, or its n and l values. The letters s, p, d, f, g, h, etc., correspond, respectively, to l values of 0, 1, 2, 3, 4, etc. For example, a $3d$ orbital refers to an orbital for which $n = 3$ and $l = 2$. The possible orbitals for $n = 1, 2,$ and 3 are given in Table 8.2.

TABLE 8.2   *The Orbitals for $n = 1, 2,$ and* 3

Quantum numbers

n	l	m_l	Orbital symbol	Shell	Subshells
1	0	0	$1s$	K	$1s$
2	0	0	$2s$		$2s$
2	1	1	$2p$		
2	1	0	$2p$	L	$2p$
2	1	-1	$2p$		
3	0	0	$3s$		$3s$
3	1	1	$3p$		
3	1	0	$3p$		$3p$
3	1	-1	$3p$		
3	2	2	$3d$	M	
3	2	1	$3d$		
3	2	0	$3d$		$3d$
3	2	-1	$3d$		
3	2	-2	$3d$		

The orbitals possessing the same principal quantum number, n, are said to belong to a **shell** or a **principal quantum level,** called **K** when $n = 1$, **L** when $n = 2$, **M** when $n = 3$, etc. The set of orbitals possessing the same n and l values is called a **subshell.** See Table 8.2.

8.13 ENERGY OF AN ORBITAL; DEGENERACY; DISTRIBUTION OF ELECTRONS IN ATOMS

In the absence of a magnetic field, the energy of an orbital is determined by only two quantum numbers, n and l; the energy is independent of m_l and m_s. Therefore, all the orbitals in a given subshell have the same energy. The most stable orbital is the orbital for which the sum of n and l is lowest. The more stable of two orbitals is the one for which the sum of n and l is lower. When two orbitals have the same $(n + l)$ value, the more stable orbital is the one with the lower n value. For example, the $4s$ subshell $(n + l = 4 + 0 = 4)$ is more stable than the $4d$ subshell $(n + l = 4 + 2 = 6)$ and the $3d$ subshell $(n + l = 3 + 2 = 5)$. However, the $3p$ subshell $(n + l = 3 + 1 = 4)$ is more stable than the $4s$ subshell. The order of the energy and stability of the orbitals is given in Fig. 8.14.

Thus, the **K** shell consists of one $1s$ orbital. The **L** shell contains one $2s$ orbital and three $2p$ orbitals of *equal energy,* while the **M** shell contains one $3s$ orbital, three $3p$ orbitals of *equal energy,* and five $3d$ orbitals of *equal energy.* Orbitals or energy levels of equal energy are said to be **"degenerate."** Therefore, s orbitals are nondegenerate, p orbitals are *threefold degenerate,* d orbitals are *fivefold degenerate,* and f orbitals are *sevenfold degenerate. In the presence of* an external *magnetic or electric field,* the degeneracy is "broken"; each p, d, and f orbital may acquire a different energy value, depending upon the values of n, l, m_l, and m_s, as illustrated in Fig. 8.15.

We now ask a crucial question. *How many electrons in the same atom may occupy a given orbital?* For example, how many electrons may occupy a $3d$ orbital in an atom? In the hydrogen atom, the question answers itself because this atom has only one electron. But can the two electrons in a helium atom $(Z = 2)$, or the three electrons in a lithium atom $(Z = 3)$, occupy a given orbital? The answer is provided by the famous hypothesis known as the **Pauli Exclusion Principle***: no two electrons in an atom can have the same four quantum numbers. *The maximum possible number of electrons with a given n value in an atomic system is therefore governed by the number of possible l, m_l, and m_s values.* Thus, there can be only a maximum of two electrons for which $n = 1$:

n	l	m_l	m_s	Number of orbitals	Number of electrons
1	0	0	$+\frac{1}{2}$ $\Big\}$	1	2
1	0	0	$-\frac{1}{2}$		

---

* Wolfgang Pauli discovered this fundamental law in 1925 from a study of atomic spectra.

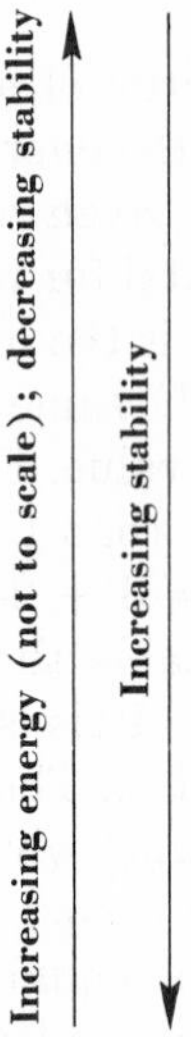

$$6p \quad (6+1)=7$$
$$5d \quad (5+2)=7$$
$$4f \quad (4+3)=7$$
$$6s \quad (6+0)=6$$

$$5p \quad (5+1)=6$$
$$4d \quad (4+2)=6$$
$$5s \quad (5+0)=5$$
$$4p \quad (4+1)=5$$
$$3d \quad (3+2)=5$$
$$4s \quad (4+0)=4$$

$$3p \quad (3+1)=4$$
$$3s \quad (3+0)=3$$

$$2p \quad (2+1)=3$$
$$2s \quad (2+0)=2$$

$$1s \quad (1+0)=1, \text{ the lowest possible energy.}$$
$$(n+l)$$

Fig. 8.14. *The order of the energies and stabilities of atomic orbitals (subshells).*

There can be a maximum of eight electrons for which $n = 2$:

n	l	m_l	m_s	Number of orbitals	Number of electrons
2	0	0	$+\frac{1}{2}$	1	2
2	0	0	$-\frac{1}{2}$		
2	1	-1	$+\frac{1}{2}$	3	6
2	1	-1	$-\frac{1}{2}$		
2	1	0	$+\frac{1}{2}$		
2	1	0	$-\frac{1}{2}$		
2	1	$+1$	$+\frac{1}{2}$		
2	1	$+1$	$-\frac{1}{2}$		

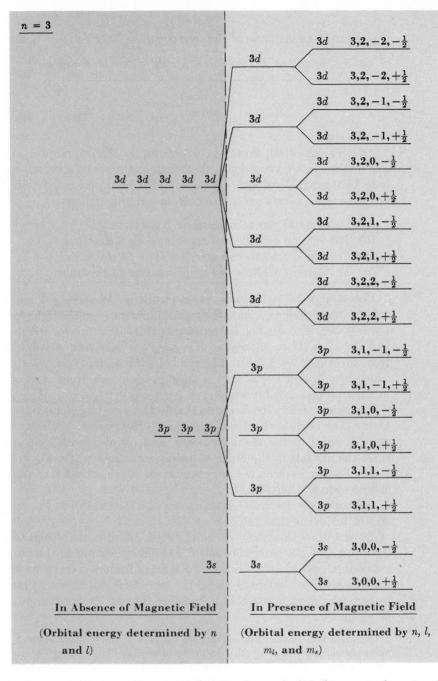

Fig. 8.15. (*Not to scale.*) *Splitting of energy levels in the presence of an external magnetic field. The $n = 3$ (M) shell consisting of three subshells, s, p, and d. In the absence of a magnetic field, the M shell contains five d orbitals of equal energy, three p orbitals of equal energy, and one s orbital. These atomic orbitals, however, may assume different energy values when the atom is in a magnetic field. Observe further that, in the magnetic field, each atomic orbital may be "split" into two different energy levels known as "spin states," one for $m_s = -\frac{1}{2}$ and another for $m_s = +\frac{1}{2}$. The quantum numbers given are, respectively, the values of n, l, m_l, and m_s.*

There can be a maximum of eighteen electrons for which $n = 3$, as shown:

n	Number of orbitals	Number of electrons
3	one s	2
	three p	6
	five d	10

An atomic orbital, however, is defined by three quantum numbers, n, l, and m_l. In a given orbital, the fourth quantum number, m_s, can have only two possible values: $+\frac{1}{2}$ or $-\frac{1}{2}$. Therefore, *an atomic orbital can accommodate a maximum of two electrons*. It then follows:

(a) An s orbital can accommodate 2 electrons.
(b) The three p orbitals can accommodate 6 electrons.
(c) The five d orbitals can accommodate 10 electrons.
(d) The seven f orbitals can accommodate 14 electrons.

The symbol $1s^2$ represents two electrons for which $n = 1$ and $l = 0$; $1s^3$ is an impossible case since the maximum number of electrons for which $l = 0$ is two. The symbol $4p^3$ represents three electrons for which $n = 4$, and $l = 1$; $4p^7$ is an impossible case since the maximum number of electrons for which $l = 1$ is six. The symbol $3d^4$ represents four electrons for which $n = 3$, and $l = 2$; $3d^{11}$ is an impossible case since the maximum number of electrons for which $l = 2$ is ten.

We are now ready to distribute the electrons in the ground states of the atoms. The basis of the distribution is (1) the number of electrons in an atom is equal to the atomic number, and (2) each added electron will enter the orbitals in the order of decreasing stability (see Fig. 8.14*):

$_1$H—the one electron occupies the $1s$ orbital; the electron configuration of hydrogen is, therefore, $1s^1$.

$_2$He with two electrons—both can go into the $1s$ orbital; the configuration of helium is thus $1s^2$.

$_3$Li with three electrons—since the rules prohibit more than two electrons in $1s$, we put two electrons in $1s$ and the third one in the next available orbital, namely, $2s$. The configuration of lithium is therefore $1s^2 \quad 2s^1$.

$_4$Be with four electrons—since, the $2s$ orbital can take two electrons, we put the fourth electron in it, yielding $1s^2 \quad 2s^2$ as the configuration of beryllium.

* Figure 8.14 is based upon calculations confined to the simplest atom, hydrogen, with only one electron. Any other atom has more than one electron. The presence of several electrons creates mathematical problems of great complexity. The differences result from the fact that each electron is not only attracted by the nucleus but is also repelled by all the other electrons. But an approximate description similar to that used for a one-electron atom is still useful. Even though the actual wave functions are different from those for an electron in a hydrogen atom, they are nevertheless sufficiently similar so that there is no ambiguity in using the same orbitals. The electronic structures of atoms with more than one electron can thus be described in terms of the hydrogen orbitals. As a matter of fact, the order given in Fig. 8.14 closely parallels the order of stability obtained from empirical properties of the elements.

$_5$B with five electrons—four can go into the $1s$ and $2s$; the fifth is put in the next available subshell, $2p$. The configuration of boron is therefore $1s^2 \quad 2s^2 \quad 2p^1$.

$_6$C, six electrons—since the $2p$ subshell can take six electrons, we put the sixth electron in $2p$ and the configuration of carbon is $1s^2 \quad 2s^2 \quad 2p^2$. The same argument yields the following configurations:

$_7$N	$1s^2$	$2s^2$	$2p^3$	$_8$O	$1s^2 \quad 2s^2 \quad 2p^4$	
$_9$F	$1s^2$	$2s^2$	$2p^5$	$_{10}$Ne	$1s^2 \quad 2s^2 \quad 2p^6$	

This "closes" the $2p$ subshell.

$_{11}$Na, 11 electrons—since the $2p$ subshell is closed, the eleventh electron is put in the next available subshell, $3s$, yielding $1s^2 \quad 2s^2 \quad 2p^6 \quad 3s^1$ for sodium.

$_{12}$Mg, 12 electrons—$1s^2 \quad 2s^2 \quad 2p^6 \quad 3s^2$.

$_{13}$Al, 13 electrons—$1s^2 \quad 2s^2 \quad 2p^6 \quad 3s^2 \quad 3p^1$.

Since the $3p$ subshell can take six electrons, the following configurations are obtained for the elements $_{14}$Si and $_{18}$Ar:

$$_{14}\text{Si} \quad 1s^2 \quad 2s^2 \quad 2p^6 \quad 3s^2 \quad 3p^2$$
$$_{18}\text{Ar} \quad 1s^2 \quad 2s^2 \quad 2p^6 \quad 3s^2 \quad 3p^6$$

For $_{19}$K and $_{20}$Ca, the next available subshell, $4s$, is used, yielding the configurations

$$_{19}\text{K} \quad 1s^2 \quad 2s^2 \quad 2p^6 \quad 3s^2 \quad 3p^6 \quad 4s^1$$
$$_{20}\text{Ca} \quad 1s^2 \quad 2s^2 \quad 2p^6 \quad 3s^2 \quad 3p^6 \quad 4s^2$$

The next available subshell is the $3d$, which can take ten electrons. Hence, for the elements $_{21}$Sc, $_{25}$Mn, and $_{30}$Zn the configurations are

$$_{21}\text{Sc} \quad 1s^2 \quad 2s^2 \quad 2p^6 \quad 3s^2 \quad 3p^6 \quad 4s^2 \quad 3d^1$$
$$_{25}\text{Mn} \quad 1s^2 \quad 2s^2 \quad 2p^6 \quad 3s^2 \quad 3p^6 \quad 4s^2 \quad 3d^5$$
$$_{30}\text{Zn} \quad 1s^2 \quad 2s^2 \quad 2p^6 \quad 3s^2 \quad 3p^6 \quad 4s^2 \quad 3d^{10}$$

Electronic configurations may be assigned to the remaining elements by similar reasoning.

Since electrons in the closed shells or subshells can generally be ignored, let us now use our predicted electron configurations to construct a periodic table on the basis of a similarity of the electrons in the highest subshells (see Fig. 8.16). Thus, N, P, As, Sb, Bi appear in the same column because their highest energy sublevels are similar, s^2p^3. The positions of most of the elements agree with the empirical periodic table. Helium, however, is incorrectly placed. Its electron configuration, $1s^2$, would place it in Group IIA rather than in Group 0. The other two elements (71, 103) whose positions would not be in agreement with the empirical periodic table are also designated as $+$.

Note the ambiguous positions of $_{21}$Sc, $_{39}$Y, $_{57}$La, and $_{89}$Ac in Fig. 8.16. Chemists usually include these elements with the inner transition elements because they exhibit chemical properties common to the lanthanide and actinide series. The spectroscopist, using spectral evidence, does not so classify them. The apparently ambiguous position of hydrogen should also be noted.

Periodic table (Fig. 8.16)

	IA	IIA	IIIA	IVA	VA	VIA	VIIA	0	IIIB	IVB	VB	VIB	VIIB
Period	s^1	s^2	s^2p^1	s^2p^2	s^2p^3	s^2p^4	s^2p^5	s^2p^6	s^2d^1	s^2d^2	s^2d^3	s^2d^4	s^2d^5
1	1 H $1s^1$						1 H $1s^1$	2 He $1s^2{}_+$					
2 — K [He]	3 Li $2s^1$	4 Be	5 B $2p^1$	6 C	7 N	8 O	9 F	10 Ne					
3 — KL [Ne]	11 Na $3s^1$	12 Mg	13 Al $3p^1$	14 Si	15 P	16 S	17 Cl	18 Ar					
4 — KL3$s^2$3p^6 [Ar]	19 K $4s^1$	20 Ca							21 Sc $3d^1$	22 Ti	23 V	24 Cr• s^1d^5	25 Mn
KLM [Ar]3d^{10}			31 Ga $4p^1$	32 Ge	33 As	34 Se	35 Br	36 Kr					
5 — KLM4$s^2$4p^6 [Kr]	37 Rb $5s^1$	38 Sr							39 Y $4d^1$	40 Zr	41 Nb• s^1d^4	42 Mo• s^1d^5	43 Tc• s^1d^6
KLM4$s^2$4$p^6$4d^{10} [Kr]4d^{10}			49 In $5p^1$	50 Sn	51 Sb	52 Te	53 I	54 Xe					
6 — KLM4$s^2$4p^6d^{10}5$s^2$5p^6 [Xe]	55 Cs $6s^1$	56 Ba							57 La• $5d^1$				
KLMN5$s^2$5p^6 [Xe]4f^{14}										72 Hf $5d^2$	73 Ta	74 W	75 Re
KLMN5$s^2$5$p^6$5d^{10} [Xe]4f^{14}5d^{10}			81 Tl $6p^1$	82 Pb	83 Bi	84 Po	85 At	86 Rn					
7 — KLMN5$s^2$5$p^6$5d^{10}6$s^2$6p^6 [Rn]	87 Fr $7s^1$	88 Ra							89 Ac• $6d^1$				
KLMN5$s^2$5$p^6$5d^{10}5f^{14}6$s^2$6p^6 [Rn]5f^{14}										104			

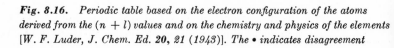

TRANSITIO...
Electron enter...

NOBLE GASES

REPRESENTATIVE ELEMENTS
Electron enters an s or p subshell

Fig. 8.16. *Periodic table based on the electron configuration of the atoms derived from the $(n + l)$ values and on the chemistry and physics of the elements* [W. F. Luder, *J. Chem. Ed.* **20**, 21 (1943)]. *The • indicates disagreement*

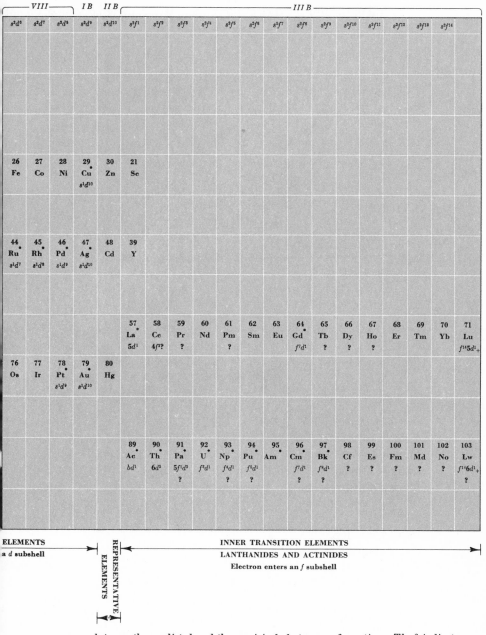

	VIII		IB	IIB	IIIB														
s^2d^6	s^2d^7	s^2d^8	s^2d^9	s^2d^{10}	s^2f^1	s^2f^2	s^2f^3	s^2f^4	s^2f^5	s^2f^6	s^2f^7	s^2f^8	s^2f^9	s^2f^{10}	s^2f^{11}	s^2f^{12}	s^2f^{13}	s^2f^{14}	
26 Fe	27 Co	28 Ni	29 Cu s^1d^{10}	30 Zn	21 Sc														
44 Ru s^1d^7	45 Rh s^1d^8	46 Pd s^1d^9	47 Ag s^1d^{10}	48 Cd	39 Y														
					57 La $5d^1$	58 Ce $4f^2$?	59 Pr ?	60 Nd	61 Pm ?	62 Sm	63 Eu	64 Gd f^7d^1	65 Tb ?	66 Dy ?	67 Ho ?	68 Er	69 Tm	70 Yb	71 Lu $f^{14}5d^1$+
76 Os	77 Ir	78 Pt s^1d^9	79 Au s^1d^{10}	80 Hg															
					89 Ac $6d^1$	90 Th $6d^2$	91 Pa $5f^2d^1$?	92 U f^3d^1	93 Np f^4d^1 ?	94 Pu f^5d^1 ?	95 Am	96 Cm f^7d^1	97 Bk f^8d^1	98 Cf ?	99 Es ?	100 Fm ?	101 Md ?	102 No ?	103 Lw $f^{14}6d^1$+ ?

ELEMENTS
a *d* subshell

REPRESENTATIVE ELEMENTS

INNER TRANSITION ELEMENTS
LANTHANIDES AND ACTINIDES
Electron enters an *f* subshell

between the predicted and the empirical electron configurations. The ? indicates that the empirical electron configuration is not definitely known. The + indicates the elements whose predicted electron configurations would place them incorrectly in the periodic table.

Several of the predicted electron configurations, designated as ●, do not agree with the empirically assigned configurations. The accepted configurations for these elements are also given in Fig. 8.16. The (?) in Fig. 8.16 indicates that the electron configuration is not definitely known despite intense studies of the properties and spectra of these elements.

Observe also that each of the noble ("inert") gases, except helium, has an s^2p^6 electron configuration; *this is then a comparatively stable arrangement.*

8.14 THE PHYSICAL SIGNIFICANCE OF "PSI SQUARE"

The solution of the Schroedinger equation for the ground state of the hydrogen atom yields the wave function

$$\psi_{1s} = c_1 e^{-c_2 r}$$

in which c_1 and c_2 are constants,* and the energy

$$E_1 = -21.79 \times 10^{-12} \frac{\text{erg}}{\text{atom}}$$

Changing the value of the coordinate of the given ψ *does not* alter the energy of the hydrogen atom. Thus, the quantity $E_1 = -21.79 \times 10^{-12}$ erg remains constant as r in ψ_{1s} is varied from zero to infinity.

We come now to the heart of the "new mechanics." Newtonian mechanics assigns a definite energy and a definite position to each body; astronomers have been doing this correctly for centuries, joined recently by space scientists. A space engineer, for example, can state the position—one definite set of values for x, y, and z—and at the same time the velocity (or the momentum or the energy) of his satellite.† In wave mechanics, we cannot assign a definite energy and a definite position to a particle. Rather, a *definite energy* is associated *not with one set of coordinates* but with a wave function, an expression containing the coordinates; r in the above wave function for a given fixed energy may take any value from zero to infinity.

Although there are differing opinions among scientists as to the precise significance of ψ, it is generally agreed that ψ^2, or the function D defined as $4\pi r^2 \psi^2$, is related to the distribution of electrons in atoms and molecules.

EXAMPLE 2 **The solution of the Schroedinger equation for the ground state, $n = 1$, $l = 0$, $m_l = 0$, of the hydrogen atom yields**

$$\psi_{1s} = c_1 e^{-c_2 r}$$

$$E_1 = -21.79 \times 10^{-12} \frac{\text{erg}}{\text{atom}}$$

* The letter e represents 2.718 . . . , called the Napier constant, after the mathematician, John Napier. See Appendix II (page 792).

† Provided it is not hit by a missile under the control of another engineer.

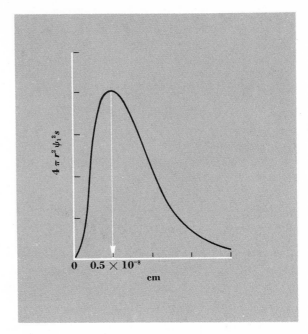

Fig. 8.17. *A plot of $4\pi r^2\psi_{1s}^2$ vs. r, the linear distance between the proton and the electron of the hydrogen atom; $4\pi r^2\psi_{1s}^2$ takes the value of zero when r = 0 and when r = ∞ (recall that $e^{-\infty} = 0$).*

and

$$D_1 = 4\pi r^2\,\psi_{1s}^2 = 4\pi r^2 c_1{}^2 e^{-2c_2 r} \qquad (5)$$

When the energy of the electron in the hydrogen atom is -21.79×10^{-12} erg, what is its position relative to the proton?

ANSWER   This question is unanswerable for two reasons. First, it is *scientifically unanswerable* because it concerns a presently unascertainable quantity; spectral data yield measures of the energy of the electron, but information about the trajectory of the electron in the atom is not obtainable from these or other data. Second, in Equation (5), *r*, the linear distance between the proton and the electron, can take *any value* between zero and infinity so that a point position for the electron cannot be fixed (see Fig. 8.17).

It is evident that we cannot speak of a position of the electron whose energy is -21.79×10^{-12} erg. Nor can we, in the manner in which it is possible to make a precise landing of a space vehicle on a moving celestial body, predict the trajectory of the electron in the hydrogen atom. *Quantum mechanics thus concludes that the Bohr concept of definite electron trajectories in the hydrogen atom is untenable.*

However, we can say the electron is distributed between the nucleus and infinity. Hence ψ^2 and D are commonly referred to as "distribution functions."

How is the electron distributed? No answer to this question is known; there are, however, various opposing personal opinions advanced by scientists. Schroedinger's interpretation of the physical significance of

Fig. 8.18. *The electron cloud of the hydrogen atom in the ground state (1s orbital) according to the predictions of wave mechanics, when $n = 1$, $l = 0$, and $m_l = 0$; this should be visualized as a 3-dimensional cloud surrounding the nucleus of the hydrogen atom [H. E. White, Phys. Rev. 37, 1416 (1931)].*

"psi square," for example, differs from the Max Born interpretation. We will not become embroiled in these arguments; rather *we will postulate* (after Schroedinger) that the electron may be visualized as a 3-dimensional cloud, "an electron cloud," about the proton. The **cloud (electron) density** at any point r in space is given by $4\pi r^2 \psi^2$; the electron density then

Fig. 8.19. *A plot of the wave functions, ψ_{1s} and ψ_{3s}, for the hydrogen atom as a function of r, the linear distance between the proton and the electron of the hydrogen atom, showing ψ_{1s} has no nodes while ψ_{3s} has two nodes.*

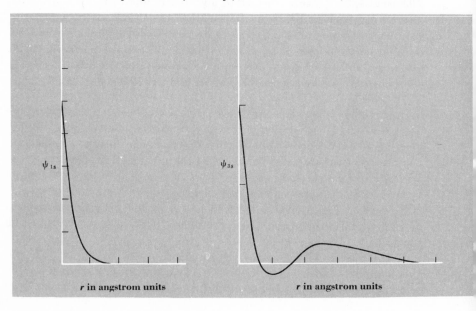

will correspond to Fig. 8.17. The electron density is practically zero near the nucleus, increases to a maximum at about 0.5×10^{-8} cm, and becomes practically zero at about 10^{-8} cm, as represented in Fig. 8.18. The outer diameter of the electron cloud is not exactly definable (see also Fig. 8.20). Note that the concept of an electron as a distinct particle in motion does not enter this interpretation of psi square. Rather, we may portray the electron cloud as possessing a shape and a size depending upon its energy.

An alternate interpretation (after Born)* relates ψ^2 or D to *the* **probability** *of finding an electron in a unit of volume in space.* Thus, the probability of finding the 1s electron (see Fig. 8.17) is practically zero near the nucleus, increases to a maximum at about 0.5×10^{-8} cm, and becomes practically zero at about 10^{-8} cm. In the cloud diagrams, the probability of finding the electron is related to the density of the cloud.

8.15 THE SIGN OF A WAVE FUNCTION

A property of a wave function (as illustrated in Problem 41, page 201) is its algebraic sign; ψ may have positive $(+)$ or negative $(-)$ values (**not to be confused with the sign of a charged body**), depending upon the value of the coordinates. *Squaring the wave function* guarantees that the electron density (or the probability) will be a positive quantity everywhere in space. Consequently, the change in the (algebraic) sign of ψ_{2s} signals a point where ψ_{2s} or ψ_{2s}^2 is zero. The point where this occurs is called **a node.** In Fig. 8.19, ψ_{1s} and ψ_{3s} are plotted as functions of r; ψ_{1s} has no nodes, while ψ_{3s} has two nodes.

8.16 REPRESENTATIONS OF THE SHAPES OF ATOMIC ORBITALS

The wave functions identified by the three quantum numbers n, l, and m_l are called *atomic orbitals.* Figure 8.20 represents the shapes of several orbitals. Observe the profound changes that occur in the shape of the orbital (electron cloud) as the l value changes for a given n value. Observe also that the electron density is independent of the angle only for the $s(l = 0)$ states of the hydrogen atom. That is, at any fixed distance from the nucleus, the electron density is identical for any angle between $0°$ and $360°$. The s orbitals are therefore said to be spherically symmetrical.

Representations of the electronic angular distribution, as given in Fig. 8.21 for s, p, and d orbitals, are also very useful; these show the distribution as a function of angle along a fixed direction. The electron density outside these regions is (practically) zero. The angular distribution is independent of the specific nature of an atom; there is then one angular distribution for s electrons, three for p electrons, and five for d electrons,

---

* Opinions are still much divided. See the philosophical views of Louis de Broglie, "The Current Interpretation of Wave Mechanics: A Critical Study," American Elsevier Publ. Co., New York, 1965, and of David Bohm, "Causality and Chance in Modern Physics," Routledge and Kegan Paul Ltd., London, 1957.

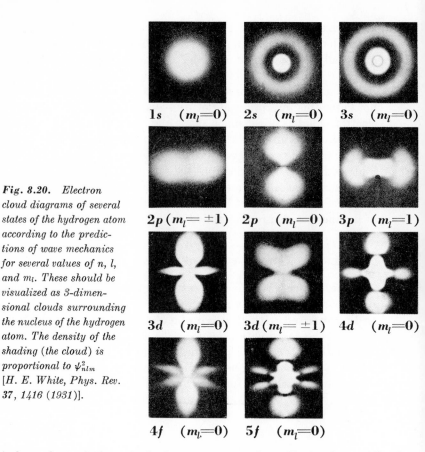

Fig. 8.20. *Electron cloud diagrams of several states of the hydrogen atom according to the predictions of wave mechanics for several values of n, l, and m_l. These should be visualized as 3-dimensional clouds surrounding the nucleus of the hydrogen atom. The density of the shading (the cloud) is proportional to ψ_{nlm}^2* [H. E. White, Phys. Rev. **37**, 1416 (1931)].

1s $(m_l=0)$ 2s $(m_l=0)$ 3s $(m_l=0)$

2p $(m_l=\pm1)$ 2p $(m_l=0)$ 3p $(m_l=1)$

3d $(m_l=0)$ 3d $(m_l=\pm1)$ 4d $(m_l=0)$

4f $(m_l=0)$ 5f $(m_l=0)$

independent of the principal quantum number. *Notice that unlike the s orbitals, the p and d orbitals have preferred directions in space.*

One of the five d orbitals (d_{z^2}) is p-like in character. The other four d orbitals resemble four-leaf clovers. Picture one "clover" $(d_{x^2-y^2})$ along the x and y axes; rotate the "clover" 45 degrees without tilting and you produce the d_{xy} orbital. Picture another "clover" (d_{yz}) upright between the y and z axes. Rotate this "clover" 90 degrees so that it now faces you; you are looking at the d_{xz} orbital.

The algebraic sign of the wave function within a region is also indicated in Fig. 8.21. The sign of the wave function is essential in the explanation of bond stability (Chapter 11). The geometry of molecules is explicable (Chapter 24) by the spatial distribution of the orbitals involved in chemical combinations.

We must, however, emphasize that, although it is useful to indicate the positive and negative regions of the wave functions, *the algebraic sign has no physical significance.* Physical significance is attached only to ψ^2.

The shapes of orbitals (electron cloud diagrams) and Fig. 8.21, we emphasize, are *pictorial representations* of the mathematical solutions of the Schroedinger equation. *They do not represent reality;* the shapes are not pictures of electric charges or of matter. Also, in wave mechanics, the electron may be regarded as neither particle nor wave. It is an indescrib-

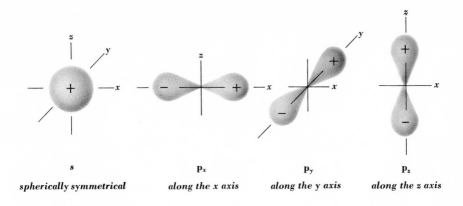

s	p_x	p_y	p_z
spherically symmetrical	*along the x axis*	*along the y axis*	*along the z axis*

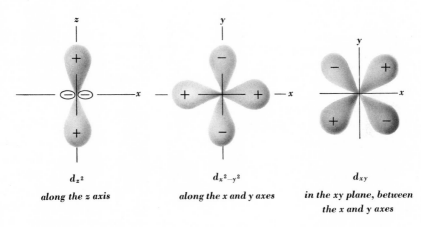

d_{z^2}	$d_{x^2-y^2}$	d_{xy}
along the z axis	*along the x and y axes*	*in the xy plane, between the x and y axes*

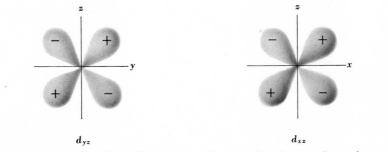

d_{yz}	d_{xz}
in the yz plane, between the y and z axes	*in the xz plane, between the x and z axes*

Fig. 8.21. *The angular distribution* of the s, the three p, and the five d electrons (orbitals). The algebraic sign of the wave function is also given. The nucleus resides at the origin of the axes.*

* Only the square of the angular part of the wave function which depends on the quantum numbers l and m_l is here represented. Hence, the angular distribution is independent of n. These representations are also referred to as boundary surface diagrams. It is equally correct to represent the angular distribution of orbitals with line diagrams.

able entity whose properties are (presently) best elucidated by the Schroedinger equation. Attempts to visualize the nature of the electron "during" the transition from one energy level to another are dismissed as nonsense and futile. The Schroedinger equation will be with us until a scientist gives us another set of rules that will solve problems in a simpler manner and suggest experiments inconceivable under present rules.

We should add that when the equation is applied to a macrosystem, for example a 1-gram weight attached to a frictionless string and set in motion by a definite force, the equation predicts the system will behave exactly as expected from its known properties; the wave mechanical predictions regarding the 1-gram bob are in exact agreement with the classical (Newtonian) mechanical predictions. As Dirac recently wrote "Quantum mechanics works so well that nobody can afford to disagree with it."

8.17 ELECTRON REVOLUTION AND SPIN

In wave mechanics, although the trajectory of the electron is not described, it is useful for educational purposes and for some theoretical calculations to associate the l and m_s quantum numbers with some kind of movement of the electron in an atom.

The l quantum number may be associated with the motion of the electron around the proton of the hydrogen atom, while the m_s quantum number may be associated with the concept that the electron spins like a top about its own axis. The values $+\frac{1}{2}$ and $-\frac{1}{2}$ are interpreted to mean that the spin is oriented in one of two possible ways, clockwise or counterclockwise. The "electron-spin" hypothesis was formulated in 1925 by George Uhlenbeck and Samuel Goudsmit to account for the splitting of spectral lines in a magnetic field. (But we again remind the reader that the "spinning" of the electron is not a real physical phenomenon.)

It is frequently advantageous to express the ground state of an atom in terms of the orbitals. A dash or a circle is used to represent an orbital, an arrow to represent an electron, arbitrarily pointing down ($\downarrow$) to represent one spin orientation and up ($\uparrow$) to represent the other spin orientation. Thus, the electron configurations of $_{11}$Na, $_{12}$Mg, and $_{30}$Zn are expressible as

$_{11}$Na $\underset{1s}{\downarrow\uparrow}$ $\underset{2s}{\downarrow\uparrow}$ $\underset{}{\downarrow\uparrow}$ $\underset{2p}{\downarrow\uparrow}$ $\underset{}{\downarrow\uparrow}$ $\underset{}{\downarrow}$

$_{12}$Mg $\underset{1s}{\downarrow\uparrow}$ $\underset{2s}{\downarrow\uparrow}$ $\underset{}{\downarrow\uparrow}$ $\underset{2p}{\downarrow\uparrow}$ $\underset{}{\downarrow\uparrow}$ $\underset{3s}{\downarrow\uparrow}$

$_{30}$Zn $\underset{1s}{\downarrow\uparrow}$ $\underset{2s}{\downarrow\uparrow}$ $\underset{}{\downarrow\uparrow}$ $\underset{2p}{\downarrow\uparrow}$ $\underset{}{\downarrow\uparrow}$ $\underset{3s}{\downarrow\uparrow}$ $\underset{}{\downarrow\uparrow}$ $\underset{3p}{\downarrow\uparrow}$ $\underset{}{\downarrow\uparrow}$ $\underset{}{\downarrow\uparrow}$ $\underset{}{\downarrow\uparrow}$ $\underset{3d}{\downarrow\uparrow}$ $\underset{}{\downarrow\uparrow}$ $\underset{}{\downarrow\uparrow}$ $\underset{4s}{\downarrow\uparrow}$

8.18 PARAMAGNETISM

Atomic sodium, atomic hydrogen, molecular oxygen, and iron are attracted into magnetic fields. They are typical **paramagnetic** substances; they *possess permanent magnetic moments.*

Hans Oersted in 1820 showed that an electric current flowing through a

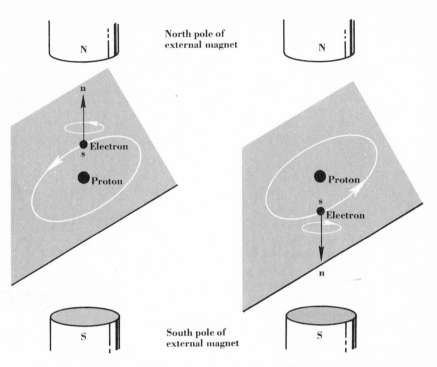

Fig. 8.22. *The spinning electron in motion around the proton behaves like a*

magnet represented as $\uparrow$ *. Two orientations of this elementary magnet may*

occur in a magnetic field: one with the north pole of the electron pointing toward the north pole of the external magnet, and the second with the north pole of the electron pointing toward the south pole of the external magnet.

wire (electrons under the influence of a potential difference) produces a magnetic field around the wire. Magnetic fields are thus produced by the motion of charged particles. Then a single spinning electron, in motion around the nucleus, should behave like a current flowing in a closed circuit of zero resistance and therefore *should act as if it were a small bar magnet with a characteristic permanent magnetic moment.* The magnetism of an isolated atom thus results from two kinds of motion: the orbital motion of the electron around the nucleus, and the spin of the electron around its axis, as illustrated for the hydrogen atom in Fig. 8.22. If a beam of hydrogen atoms, $H\frac{\downarrow}{1s}$, is directed through a strongly inhomogeneous magnetic field,* *the deflection of the atoms will depend on the relative orientation of the magnetic field and the magnet (the electron in the hydrogen atom).* But *only two spin orientations* are permitted for one electron corresponding to the

* The intensity of the magnetic field is not the same for all points in the space around the magnet.

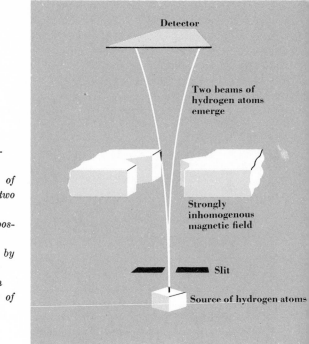

Detector

Two beams of
hydrogen atoms
emerge

Strongly
inhomogenous
magnetic field

Slit

Source of hydrogen atoms

Fig. 8.23. *The Stern-Gerlach experiment; separation of a beam of hydrogen atoms into two distinct beams corresponding to the two possible spin orientations. The force experienced by the spinning electron is related to its orientation and the inhomogeneity of the magnetic field.*

m_s quantum numbers $+\frac{1}{2}$ or $-\frac{1}{2}$. These orientations are arbitrarily "pictured" as $\underset{\text{n}}{\overset{\text{s}}{\downarrow}}$ or $\underset{\text{s}}{\overset{\text{n}}{\uparrow}}$. Thus the atoms with spins $\underset{\text{n}}{\overset{\text{s}}{\downarrow}}$ will be deflected in one direction, and those atoms with spins $\underset{\text{s}}{\overset{\text{n}}{\uparrow}}$ will be deflected in the opposite direction. The initial beam of hydrogen atoms should therefore emerge from the magnetic field as *two separate beams*. The actual experiment, Fig. 8.23, shows that a beam of monatomic hydrogen is split into two and only two parts. Thus *paramagnetism, a property of substances with permanent magnetic moments, is associated with* **unpaired electrons** *in an atom, ion, or molecule*. These permanent micromagnets are attracted into a magnetic field and align with the field, similarly to the magnetic needle of a compass.

The first experiment of this type was performed in 1921 by Otto Stern and Walther Gerlach, using silver (vapor) atoms. A silver atom contains one unpaired electron, as predicted by its electron configuration,

$$_{47}\text{Ag} \quad \text{KLM} \quad \underset{4s}{\uparrow\downarrow} \quad \underset{4p}{\uparrow\downarrow\ \uparrow\downarrow\ \uparrow\downarrow} \quad \underset{4d}{\uparrow\downarrow\ \uparrow\downarrow\ \uparrow\downarrow\ \uparrow\downarrow\ \uparrow\downarrow} \quad \underset{5s}{\uparrow}$$

It is evident that the filled orbitals make no contribution to paramagnetic properties. Also, in silver, there is no question of the order of occupancy of the five $4d$ orbitals since 10 electrons are available. If, however, as in the case of $_{25}\text{Mn}$, 5 electrons are available for the five $3d$

orbitals, the order of occupancy is significant:

$_{25}$Mn   KL $\underset{3s}{\downarrow\uparrow}$ $\underset{}{\downarrow\uparrow}$ $\underset{3p}{\downarrow\uparrow}$ $\downarrow\uparrow$ $\underset{}{\downarrow\uparrow}$ $\underset{3d}{\downarrow\uparrow}$ $\downarrow$ $\underline{}$ $\underline{}$ $\underset{4s}{\downarrow\uparrow}$

or

$_{25}$Mn   KL $\underset{3s}{\downarrow\uparrow}$ $\underset{}{\downarrow\uparrow}$ $\underset{3p}{\downarrow\uparrow}$ $\downarrow\uparrow$ $\underset{}{\downarrow}$ $\underset{3d}{\downarrow}$ $\downarrow$ $\downarrow$ $\downarrow$ $\underset{4s}{\downarrow\uparrow}$

Experimentally, the magnetic moment of Mn corresponds to five, not one, unpaired electrons. This illustrates an empirical rule, the **Hund rule,*** which correctly predicts the number of unpaired electrons in the ground states of atoms, ions, and molecules: *electrons remain unpaired with parallel spins in orbitals of equal energy until each such orbital has at least one electron in it.* For example, the order of occupancy of three 2p orbitals is

$_5$B   K $\underset{2s}{\downarrow\uparrow}$ $\underset{}{\downarrow}$ $\underset{2p}{\underline{}}$ $\underline{}$ $_8$O   K $\underset{2s}{\downarrow\uparrow}$ $\underset{}{\downarrow\uparrow}$ $\underset{2p}{\downarrow}$ $\downarrow$

$_6$C   K $\underset{2s}{\downarrow\uparrow}$ $\underset{}{\downarrow}$ $\underset{2p}{\downarrow}$ $\underline{}$ $_9$F   K $\underset{2s}{\downarrow\uparrow}$ $\underset{}{\downarrow\uparrow}$ $\underset{2p}{\downarrow\uparrow}$ $\downarrow$

$_7$N   K $\underset{2s}{\downarrow\uparrow}$ $\underset{}{\downarrow}$ $\underset{2p}{\downarrow}$ $\downarrow$ $_{10}$Ne   K $\underset{2s}{\downarrow\uparrow}$ $\underset{}{\downarrow\uparrow}$ $\underset{2p}{\downarrow\uparrow}$ $\downarrow\uparrow$

The measured magnetic moment of the isolated atoms in each case is related to the number of unpaired electron spins.†

The Hund rule is most likely associated with repulsion effects between electrons. In carbon atoms, for example, repulsion is greater when the two p electrons are in the same orbital compared to the arrangement when they are in separate orbitals. This leads to another empirical rule, which states that unusual stability is associated with half-filled orbitals‡ of equal energy. Completed orbitals of equal energy, characteristic of the noble gases, however, are of greater stability.

8.19   ATOMIC STRUCTURE AND PERIODIC PROPERTIES OF ATOMS

In this section, we turn from abstruse theories to a consideration of some measurable properties of atoms, and their relation to the positions of the elements in the Periodic Table.

Size of Atoms and Ions.   In agreement with the wave mechanical conclusion, the radius of an atom or an ion is not a definite, physically measurable quantity. Electron and x ray diffraction experiments yield definite information about internuclear distances, called "interatomic" distances in molecules and "interionic" distances in ionic solids. Interatomic distances are also known as **bond lengths.** If enough assumptions are made, a radius can be assigned to each atom or ion, whose addition for a pair of atoms or ions would equal the measured internuclear distance.

* Named in honor of Friedrich Hund for his work with atomic and molecular spectra.

† It is possible, however, for an atom with unpaired electrons to possess a zero magnetic moment, due to cancellation of the moment arising from the electron spin by the moment produced by the movement of the electron around the nucleus.

‡ The s orbitals excepted.

Following the monumental work of Sir William H. Bragg and his son, Sir Lawrence Bragg (page 36), it became evident through the work of Maurice Huggins and Linus Pauling that the radius of an atom or an ion is a function of its environment, that is, the electrical nature of the neighboring atoms in molecules and the geometric arrangement of the ions in crystals. An extreme example is the hydrogen atom, which must be assigned one value when it combines with itself, a second value when it combines with elements of the second period, a third value when it combines with elements of the third period, etc. Most ionic radii, however, may be treated as fairly constant. Among the ionic solids, the alkali halides, lithium iodide, LiI, for example, constitute the major exceptions.

Notwithstanding, it is advantageous for many purposes to assign a radius to each atom, called the "**covalent radius**," and to each ion, called the "**crystal (ionic) radius**."

The variation in the size of atoms and ions within a period and a group is illustrated for the representative elements in Table 8.3.

Within a given period, the atomic radius decreases with increasing atomic number due to the effect of increasing the nuclear charge without the introduction of another shell (principal quantum level). The irregularity at nitrogen may be associated with the stability of the half-filled p orbitals (page 189). Within a given family, however, the atomic radius increases with atomic number because of the addition of another principal quantum level. Several notable exceptions occur in which the atomic radius within a family increases only very slightly or actually decreases with increasing atomic number; for example, $_{13}$Al 1.25 A and $_{31}$Ga 1.25 A; $_{46}$Pd 1.28 A and $_{78}$Pt 1.29 A; $_{40}$Zr 1.45 A and $_{72}$Hf 1.44 A. This results from the presence of the intervening transition elements and, in particular, the inner transition elements, in which the added electrons generally enter an inner principal quantum level without alteration in the outer principal quantum level. We would then expect the added electrons virtually to nullify the electrostatic attraction effect of the increased nuclear charge, maintaining thereby an approximately constant atomic size for each transition series. Actually, however, small but significant decreases occur in each of these series.* Hence, the size increase characteristic of families generally does not appear after these transition series.

Variations in the crystal radius are also regular. It increases downward in a group. However, it decreases across a period for **isoelectronic ions,** ions possessing the same electron configuration, illustrated by Li$^+$ $1s^2$, Be^{2+} $1s^2$, and by N^{3-} $1s^2 2s^2 2p^6$, O^{2-} $1s^2 2s^2 2p^6$, F$^-$ $1s^2 2s^2 2p^6$, Na$^+$ $1s^2 2s^2 2p^6$, Mg^{2+} $1s^2 2s^2 2p^6$, Al^{3+} $1s^2 2s^2 2p^6$.

Although wave mechanics negates the concept of a definite size, we can arbitrarily define the radius as the distance from the nucleus corresponding to the maximum density of electronic charge. This distance is related to the principal quantum number of the orbitals with the highest n value—3 for Na to Cl, 6 for Cs, 2 for N^{3-}, Na$^+$, and Al^{3+}, 3 for Cl$^-$, 5 for Cs$^+$—and is inversely proportional to the nuclear charge. The electrons

* This shrinkage has become known as the **lanthanide contraction.**

TABLE 8.3   *Covalent and Crystal (Ionic) Radii*[a] *in Angstrom Units*

$_1$H 0.28–0.38							$_2$He (0.93)
$_3$Li 1.33	$_4$Be 0.90	$_5$B 0.80	$_6$C 0.77	$_7$N 0.73	$_8$O 0.74	$_9$F 0.71	
$_3$Li$^+$ 0.60	$_4$Be^{2+} 0.31						$_1$H$^-$ 2.08
$_{11}$Na 1.54	$_{12}$Mg 1.36	$_{13}$Al 1.25	$_{14}$Si 1.15	$_{15}$P 1.1	$_{16}$S 1.02	$_{17}$Cl 0.99	
$_{11}$Na$^+$ 0.95	$_{12}$Mg^{2+} 0.65	$_{13}$Al^{3+} 0.50		$_7$N^{3-} 1.71	$_8$O^{2-} 1.40	$_9$F$^-$ 1.36	$_{10}$Ne (1.12)
$_{19}$K 1.96					$_{35}$Br 1.14		
$_{19}$K$^+$ 1.33	$_{20}$Ca^{2+} 0.99				$_{16}$S^{2-} 1.84	$_{17}$Cl$^-$ 1.81	$_{18}$Ar (1.54)
	$_{29}$Cu$^+$ 0.96	$_{30}$Zn^{2+} 0.74					
$_{37}$Rb 2.16					$_{53}$I 1.33		
$_{37}$Rb$^+$ 1.48	$_{38}$Sr^{2+} 1.13				$_{34}$Se^{2-} 1.98	$_{35}$Br$^-$ 1.95	$_{36}$Kr (1.69)
	$_{47}$Ag$^+$ 1.26	$_{48}$Cd^{2+} 0.97					
$_{55}$Cs 2.35							
$_{55}$Cs$^+$ 1.69	$_{56}$Ba^{2+} 1.35				$_{52}$Te^{2-} 2.21	$_{53}$I$^-$ 2.16	$_{54}$Xe (1.90)
	$_{79}$Au$^+$ 1.37	$_{80}$Hg^{2+} 1.10					

[a] **Covalent radii (taken mostly from** *Table of Interatomic Distances,* **London Chemical Society, Special Publications, 1958) are applicable only to "single-bonded" atoms in mainly covalent molecules. Crystal (ionic) radii are from the publications of Linus Pauling.**

occupying the orbitals with smaller values of n, however, partially neutralize the nuclear field.* This "screening effect" reduces the nuclear charge to a so-called "effective nuclear charge." Thus, across a period, the maximum n value remains constant but the effective nuclear charge increases; the electrons are more strongly attracted and the radius decreases. In the transition series, the addition of the electrons to the $3d$ orbitals and to the $4f$ orbitals almost cancels the increase in nuclear charge, resulting in a small decrease in radius. Down a group, the maximum value of n and the nuclear charge increase; however, in going, for example, from $_3$Li to $_{55}$Cs, the screening effect largely cancels the increase in charge and the radius increases.

Ionization Energy. The minimum energy required to remove an electron from a gaseous atom in its ground state, is called the first **ionization energy** or the first **ionization potential;** the second ionization energy refers to the removal of a second electron from the positive ion. The process is illustrated by the equations

$$He(g) - 1e^- \rightarrow He^+(g) \qquad \Delta H = +567 \ \text{kcal/mole}$$
$$He^+(g) - 1e^- \rightarrow He^{2+}(g) \qquad \Delta H = +1254 \ \text{kcal/mole}$$

in which e^- represents an electron.

The ionization energy (potential) can be measured in a discharge tube containing the gas or vapor under low pressure. Initially, the current flow through the tube is practically zero; as the voltage between the cathode and anode is increased, a well-defined voltage is reached at which the gas is ionized; at this voltage, the electrons have acquired sufficient energy for impact of an electron upon an atom to produce ionization. This event is signaled by a sudden very large increase in the current flow through the tube. This well-defined value of the voltage is known as the ionization potential or the ionization energy, commonly expressed in units of volts or electron volts, convertible (page 744) to ergs per atom. One electron volt is equivalent to 3.83×10^{-20} cal per atom, or 23.1 kcal per mole. With hydrogen atoms, for example, a very large increase in current flow occurs when the voltage is 13.60 volts; the ionization energy of the hydrogen atom is then said to be 13.60 volts or 13.60 electron volts.

Among the representative elements, the first ionization energy increases with the completion of an s orbital, decreases upon the addition of an electron to the p orbital, and then increases across the period with an irregularity at p^3:

				H				He	
				$1s$				$1s^2$	
				314				567	kcal/mole

Li	Be	B	C	N	O	F	Ne	
$2s^1$	$2s^2$	$2s^22p^1$	$2s^22p^2$	$2s^22p^3$	$2s^22p^4$	$2s^22p^5$	$2s^22p^6$	
124	215	191	260	335	314	402	497	kcal/mole

* The inner electrons do not prevent the nucleus from attracting the outer electrons, but merely add their own repulsive effect.

The high ionization energy of nitrogen is most likely due to the stability of the half-filled p orbitals. Within a group, the ionization energy decreases downward, with some exceptions:

$_3$Li	124	kcal/mole	$_5$B	191	kcal/mole
$_{11}$Na	118	kcal/mole	$_{13}$Al	138	kcal/mole
$_{19}$K	100	kcal/mole	$_{31}$Ga	138	kcal/mole
$_{37}$Rb	96.3	kcal/mole	$_{49}$In	133	kcal/mole
$_{55}$Cs	89.7	kcal/mole	$_{81}$Tl	141	kcal/mole

This neat pattern, however, is somewhat upset by the transition elements. We will therefore content ourselves with the broad generalization that the first ionization energy increases across a period and decreases down a group.

Among the representative elements, metallic character—malleability, good conduction of heat and electricity, tendency to produce positive ions—decreases rapidly across a period, excepting period 1, and increases downward within a group. This gradation of metallic properties is related to the trends in ionization energy; *the smaller the ionization energy, the greater the metallic character.*

Differences in the chemistry of elements which, though unrelated, possess completed orbitals—for example, Be($2s^2$) and He($1s^2$), may be attributed to differences in ionization energy and the energy required to move—"to promote"—an electron to the next available orbital. Thus, the chemical properties of Be are associated with the relatively little energy required to promote one electron from $1s^2 2s^2$ to $1s^2 2s^1 2p^1$, while the relative chemical inertness of He is related to the great amount of energy that would be needed to disrupt its $1s^2$ configuration. Extremely significant is the observation that the promotion of an electron in an "inert" gas requires an electron jump to an orbital with a higher principal quantum number. The energy required to excite He $1s^2$ to He $1s^1 2s^1$ is higher by a factor of roughly 10^4 than the energy required to excite Be $1s^2 2s^2$ to Be $1s^2 2s^1 2p^1$. Helium therefore behaves as an inert gas, while Be behaves as an alkaline earth element (Group IIA).

The success of the $(n + l)$ rule for obtaining the electron configuration of a neutral element in its ground state is largely fortuitous. For example, the configuration $_{21}$Sc KL $3s^2 3p^6 3d^1 4s^2$ is correct but, since the $4s(4 + 0)$ is calculated to be more stable than the $3d(3 + 2)$, the rule predicts the configuration KL $3s^2 3p^6 3d^0 4s^2$ for Sc$^+$; hence, Sc$^+$ should not be paramagnetic. Experimentally, Sc$^+$ is paramagnetic; its magnetic moment corresponds to two unpaired electrons. The ionization of Sc thus involves the removal of an electron from the $4s$, not the $3d$, orbital, yielding Sc$^+$ KL $3s^2 3p^6 3d^1 4s^1$; thus for the Sc$^+$ ion, the $3d^1 4s^1$ state is more stable than the $3d^2 4s^0$ or $3d^0 4s^2$ state. The configuration of Sc^{2+} is KL $3s^2 3p^6 3d^1$. Thus in the first transition elements, ionization occurs by the loss of the $4s$ electrons first; in some cases, the second $4s$ electron may drop to the $3d$ subshell. For example, the ionization of $_{27}$Co, KL $3s^2 3p^6 3d^7 4s^2$, yields $_{27}$Co$^+$ with a $3d^8 4s^0$ configuration. On the other hand, the formation of $_{39}$Y$^+$, KLM $4s^2 4p^6 5s^2 4d^0$, involves the removal of the electron from the $4d$ subshell. This means that, in an atom with an atomic number higher than 2, the energy of one atomic orbital is actually dependent in a complicated manner on the number of electrons in all the other atomic orbitals. The forces involved, nucleus-electron attraction and repulsion between electrons, cannot be described or evaluated in a simple manner. It is therefore futile to predict which electron is lost in the ionization of the transition elements.

Electron Affinity. Neutral atoms with incomplete orbitals generally have an attraction for electrons. The energy change accompanying the addition of an electron to a gaseous atom in its ground state is called the **electron affinity,** exemplified by the equations

$$Cl(g) + 1e^- \rightarrow Cl^-(g) \qquad \Delta H = -88.2 \text{ kcal/mole}$$
$$O(g) + 1e^- \rightarrow O^-(g) \qquad \Delta H = -53.8 \text{ kcal/mole}$$
$$O^-(g) + 1e^- \rightarrow O^{2-}(g) \qquad \Delta H = +210 \quad \text{kcal/mole}$$

We should expect the attraction to be greatest for the smallest atom within a given family and a given period. The electron affinity is difficult to measure,* and meager available data indicate that it is unwise to generalize on the expected relationship between size and electron affinity of atoms†:

$_1$H					$_2$He
-17.2					0 or + ?
$_3$Li	$_6$C	$_7$N	$_8$O	$_9$F	$_{10}$Ne
-12.5	-48 ± 20	$+16$	-53.8	-83.5	0 or + ?
$_{11}$Na				$_{17}$Cl	
$+28$				-88.2	
$_{19}$K				$_{35}$Br	
$+16$				-81.6	
				$_{53}$I	
				-74.6	

Problems

1. Quantization. Is it possible to select a weight that cannot be counterpoised (within the errors of observation) by a quantity of pennies? Of hydrogen? Explain.

2. Atomic structure. (a) In 1895, P. Lenard detected electrons outside a thin glass tube in which they were produced, and concluded that the atoms in the glass must have a very open structure. Explain the results of this experiment in terms of the presently accepted theory of matter. (b) Describe the fundamental differences among the Dalton, Thomson, Rutherford-Bohr, and Schroedinger models of the atom.

3. Line spectra. (a) Referring to Equation (1) on page 161, is it possible to detect a line in the spectrum of atomic hydrogen corresponding to a transition

---

* Electron affinities have been measured by a study of the equilibrium constant for the reaction $X(g) + 1e^- \rightleftharpoons X^-(g)$ as a function of temperature.

† ΔH values in kcal per mole [from H. O. Pritchard, *Chem. Rev.* **52**, 554 (1953)].

$n = 3.5 \to n = 2$? (b) Use this equation to calculate the energy in ergs per atom of the spectral line in the visible spectrum of hydrogen corresponding to the transition $n = 3 \to n = 2$. Check your answer against Fig. 8.12 (page 164).

4. Nuclear atom. (a) For a given set of conditions, how should the number of alpha particles deflected through a given angle (i) vary (increase or decrease) with the kinetic energy of the particle, and (ii) be related (directly or inversely) to the number of unit positive charges on the nucleus of the atom? (b) How should the angle of deflection vary (increase or decrease) with the closeness of the alpha particle to the nucleus?

5. Nuclear composition. (a) What is the nuclear composition of the isotope of oxygen with each of the following atomic (**isotopic**) weights: 15.01, 15.995, 16.999, and 17.999? (b) Complete the following table by substituting a numerical value where an x appears, and a symbol where an E appears:

Isotope	Mass number	Z	N
$_x\text{Fe}^{54}$	x	x	x
$_x\text{E}^x$	130	x	74
$_x\text{Os}^x$	184	x	x
$_x\text{E}^x$	x	50	62
$_x\text{E}^x$	180	74	x
$_x\text{C}^x$	x	x	6
$_x\text{N}^x$	14	x	x

6. Bohr atom. (a) If the energy of the electron of the He^+ ion could assume any value, what type of emission spectrum would you predict for the helium ion? (b) How much work in kcal per mole (g-atom) is required to remove the electron in the hydrogen atom from the energy level, $n = 3$, to infinity? (c) In a "collision," a high velocity electron transfers energy to a hydrogen atom, causing the transition $n = 1$ to $n = 5$; then, spontaneously, the transitions $n = 5$ to $n = 2$, and $n = 2$ to the ground state, occur. How many photons are emitted by the atom and what is the energy of each photon?

Answer. (b) 34.9 kcal/mole.

7. Bohr atom. (a) Explain the statement, "Since H is the simplest atom, it should have the simplest spectrum of all neutral atoms." (b) Calculate the energy of the hydrogen atom when the principal quantum number of the electron is 9. What does the minus sign signify? (c) In a discharge tube, hydrogen is subjected to collisions with electrons having a maximum kinetic energy of 20.5×10^{-12} erg per electron. On the basis of the original Bohr theory (Fig. 8.12, page 164), what is the number of lines in the spectrum emitted by the H atoms?

Answer. (c) 6 lines.

8. n and l. (a) Account for the fact that in many elements single spectral lines become slightly separated into double or triple lines under high resolution. (b) Give the n and l value for each of the following electrons: $1s$, $4s$, $2p$, and $5d$.

9. n, l, m_l, m_s. Determine the number of possible energy levels that an electron, for which $n = 4$, may occupy when the atom is in a strong magnetic field. What is the maximum number of electrons that may have a principal quantum number of 4 in a given atom?

10. $(n + l)$ rule. (a) Use the $(n + l)$ rule to predict the electron configuration of $_{48}\text{Cd}$ in the ground state. Check your answer in Fig. 8.16 (page 178). (b) What are the numbers of s, p, and d electrons in $_{28}\text{Ni}$?

11. Paramagnetism. (a) Molecular oxygen is attracted into magnetic fields. The two nuclei in a molecule of oxygen are surrounded by 16 electrons. Are any of these electrons unpaired? If so, what must be the minimum number of unpaired electrons in molecular oxygen? (b) Which of the following isolated particles possess paramagnetic properties?

(i) $_{29}$Cu K L ↓↑   ↓↑ ↓↑ ↓↑   ↓↑ ↓↑ ↓↑ ↓↑ ↓↑   ↓
               3s   3p   3d   4s

(ii) $_{29}$Cu$^+$ K L ↓↑   ↓↑ ↓↑ ↓↑   ↓↑ ↓↑ ↓↑ ↓↑ ↓↑   —
               3s   3p   3d   4s

(iii) $_{29}$Cu^{2+} K L ↓↑   ↓↑ ↓↑ ↓↑   ↓↑ ↓↑ ↓↑ ↓↑ ↓   —
               3s   3p   3d   4s

(iv) $_{25}$Mn^{4+} K L ↓↑   ↓↑ ↓↑ ↓↑   ↓ ↓ ↓   —
               3s   3p   3d   4s

(c) Calculate the number of unpaired electrons in (i) $_{23}$V, (ii) $_{23}$V$^+$, (iii) $_{23}$V^{3+}, (iv) $_{23}$ V^{5+}. Assume that the 4s are removed before the 3d electrons in the ionization process.

Answer. (c) (ii) 4.

12. Wave mechanics. (a) An ion does not contain a 2s electron, although it contains 1s and 2p electrons; does this particle have a 2s orbital? (b) Is the electron density for the hydrogen atom in the 1s state zero at 10 atomic diameters from the nucleus? Explain your answer. (c) Is the electron density of a 2p electron at the point on the x axis 1/2 atomic diameter from the nucleus comparatively high or low?

13. ψ^2 interpretations. In a lecture delivered in honor of the 400th anniversary of the birth of Galileo Galilei, Norwood Hanson, Professor of Philosophy at Yale University, stated in reference to Schroedinger's wave function, "Such expressions cannot be 'cashed' into observational currency, not without much philosophical advocacy of one rendition as against others." Translate this for a classmate majoring in the liberal arts.

14. Delocalization. The compound represented as

H$_5$C$_6$—C═C—C$_6$H$_5$
       | |
      H H

absorbs light of wavelength 3190 A, while the compound represented as

H$_5$C$_6$—C═C—C═C—C═C—C$_6$H$_5$
       | | | | | |
      H H H H H H

absorbs at 3770 A. An article in the *Journal of Chemical Education* **39**, 599 (1962) explains this difference in light absorption with the language, ". . . by assuming that delocalization . . . spreads the electron system through the molecule so that it behaves as a single oscillating unit . . . ." (a) In which compound is the electron system more delocalized? (b) In which compound will the delocalized electron system make a greater contribution to the stability of the compound? (c) Explain the difference in light absorption.

15. Orbital degeneracy. The following diagrams (i), (ii), and (iii) represent the five 3d orbitals of an atom or an ion in magnetic fields of different strength. Designate the strength of the magnetic field (comparatively strong, comparatively weak, or zero) corresponding to each of the diagrams:

Energy ↑

↓↑ ↓ ↓ ↓ ↓   ─── ── ── ──

                   ↓↑

                   ↓↑   ↓↑ ↓↑ ↓↑

                   ↓↑

           (i)   *(ii)*   *(iii)*

16. Ionic Radii. The assigned covalent radii of the atoms from C to Si, and the crystal radii of their ions with neon-like structures, are as follows:

C	N	O	F	Na	Mg	Al	Si
0.77	0.74	0.74	0.71	1.54	1.36	1.25	1.14

C^{4-}	N^{3-}	O^{2-}	F^-	Na^+	Mg^{2+}	Al^{3+}	Si^{4+}
2.60	1.71	1.40	1.36	0.95	0.65	0.50	0.41

Explain the variation in atomic size, and the relation between the size of each ion and of its parent atom.

17. Size. (a) Pick from the following list the element with (*i*) the largest atom, (*ii*) the smallest atom, (*iii*) the highest first ionization energy, (*iv*) the highest electrical conductivity; (b) pick the ion with (*i*) the largest radius, (*ii*) the smallest radius:

$$_3Li \quad _3Li^+ \quad _4Be^{2+} \quad _6C \quad _7N^{3-} \quad _8O \quad _9F \quad _9F^- \quad _{10}Ne \quad _{11}Na \quad _{18}Ar$$

Additional problems

18. Electronic charge. *Millikan oil-drop experiment.* In an apparatus (Fig. 8.24) the velocity of rise of a positively charged oil drop in an electric field is measured. With the electric field turned off, its velocity of fall under the action of gravity is measured. From these data, the charge on the drop may be calculated. Some typical results are

Oil drop number	Measured charge on drop (in coulombs)
1	11.2×10^{-19}
2	1.60×10^{-19}
3	24.0×10^{-19}
4	1.59×10^{-19}
5	6.31×10^{-19}

(*i*) What is the electronic charge, and.(*ii*) the charge on each drop in units of the electronic charge? (*iii*) Is this calculated elementary charge independent of assumptions regarding the nature of electricity? (*iv*) This method of calculating the electronic charge is analogous to what method of calculating atomic weights?

Answer. (*i*) 1.60×10^{-19} coul; (*ii*) 7, 1, 15, 1, 4.

19. Electronic charge. Stoney calculated the magnitude of the electronic charge from the following ideas: during electrolysis, a univalent hydrogen ion picks up one electron at the cathode, becoming a hydrogen atom. Then, to liberate $\mathfrak{N}$ atoms or one gram-atom of hydrogen, $\mathfrak{N}$ electrons are required. Let e be the charge associated with one electron; then the quantity of electricity required to liberate 1.0 g of hydrogen is $\mathfrak{N}e$. But this quantity of electricity is easily

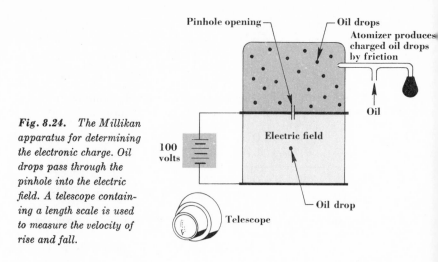

Fig. 8.24. *The Millikan apparatus for determining the electronic charge. Oil drops pass through the pinhole into the electric field. A telescope containing a length scale is used to measure the velocity of rise and fall.*

Pinhole opening

Oil drops

Atomizer produces charged oil drops by friction

Oil

Electric field

100 volts

Oil drop

Telescope

---

measurable, 9.7×10^4 coul. Calculate "the natural unit of electricity" from this information.

Answer. 1.6×10^{-19} coul.

20. Cathode ray. Explain the results of the following experiments carried out by Jean Perrin (*i*), and Sir William Crookes (*ii*):

(*i*) A metal cylinder, open end facing the cathode of a cathode ray tube, was connected to a positively charged electroscope. The leaves of the electroscope collapsed.

(*ii*) A cathode ray is focused on a spot of the glass tube away from the anode. The spot becomes hot.

21. e/m. See Fig. 8.25. (a) The force acting on a particle in an electric field is $F_1 = eE$, where e is the charge on the particle in esu units, and E is field strength in volts per unit length. The force acting on a particle in a magnetic field is $F_2 = evH = mv^2/r$, where v is the velocity of the particle, H is the field strength, m is the mass of the particle, and r is the radius of the circle described by the particle in the magnetic field. An electron beam (cathode ray) is deflected by an electric field, 10^3 volts per cm; the beam is then restored to its original position by a magnetic field, 10^3 gauss, so that $F_1 = F_2$. Calculate the velocity of the electrons. Some required units follow: a particle with a charge of one electromagnetic unit, emu, and a velocity of one cm per sec in a magnetic field of one gauss experiences a force of one dyne, or 1 dyne = emu $\times$ cm $\times$ sec^{-1} $\times$ gauss; 3.00×10^{10} esu = 1 emu; 1 emu = 10 coulombs; 1 joule = 1 volt-coulomb.

(b) An electron beam with a velocity of 4.22×10^8 cm/sec undergoes a deflection equivalent to a radius of 2.11 cm in a magnetic field of 11.4 gauss. Calculate the ratio of the charge of the cathode ray to its mass. See part (a) for some of the required units.

Answer. (a) 10^8 cm/sec.

22. Electronic mass. From mass spectrographic measurements, the ratio of the mass of a hydrogen atom to that of an electron is 1.84×10^3. Calculate (a) the atomic weight of the electron, (b) the mass of an electron.

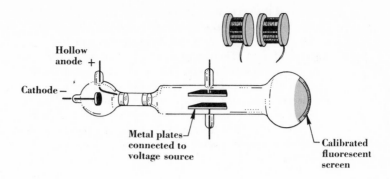

Fig. 8.25. *Sir J. J. Thomson's tube for measuring e/m. The electron beam may be deflected by the plates inside the tube. The magnetic field may be applied with the coils placed over the tube just to the right of the plates. (Lent to Science Museum, London, by the late Lord Kelvin.)*

23. Nuclear atom. (a) When an alpha particle strikes an electron in an atom, what should occur? (Think of this encounter as you would a massive high velocity body striking a relatively puny body.) (b) A fine stream consisting of 8×10^5 alpha particles impinges upon a gold film, 1.0 cm², thickness 4.0×10^{-4} mm; 100 alpha particles are detected in the region between $\phi = 180°$ and 92°; see Fig. 8.4 (page 153). When the experiment is repeated with identical conditions except that the thickness is increased to 5.0×10^{-4} mm, 124 alpha particles are detected. Use these results to argue against the hypothesis that these deflections are caused by a surface reflection (similar to the action of a wall upon a hand-ball).

24. Nuclear atom. The radius of the $_{78}Pt^{195}$ atom is 1.39 A. From electron scattering experiments, the radius of a nucleus in centimeters is given by $1.4 \times 10^{-13} \sqrt[3]{A}$; A is the mass number. Calculate (*i*) the density of the electron cloud about the nucleus in g per cm³, assuming a uniform spherical distribution; (*ii*) the density of the nucleus in g per cm³, assuming a uniform spherical distribution; (*iii*) the electric potential, V, in volts at the surface of a Pt^{195} nucleus. Assuming the nucleus is spherical and behaves like a point charge, then V is given by the ratio of the nuclear charge (in esu units) to the radius of the nucleus (in cm). An esu/cm is equal to 300 volts.

Answer. (*i*) 6.32×10^{-3} g/cm³; (*ii*) 1.5×10^{14} g/cm³; (*iii*) 1.4×10^7 volts.

25. Nuclear atom. Explain the density, greater than 8×10^4 g per cm³, of a "white dwarf" star.

26. Nuclear atom. The first estimate of the size of a nucleus was made by Rutherford, Geiger, and Marsden by calculating the distance of closest approach of an alpha particle to a nucleus. A "head-on collision" or a deflection of 180° will correspond to the closest approach; for such an event, the velocity of the alpha particle must, at some point, be zero. At this distance, the initial kinetic energy of the particle must equal the potential energy,[*]

$$\tfrac{1}{2}mv^2 = \frac{Ze \cdot Z'e}{d}$$

[*] The equation assumes the validity of Coulomb's law.

where m is the mass of an alpha particle, Z its atomic number, v its initial velocity, 2.0×10^9 cm/sec, d the closest distance the particle may approach the nucleus, e the electronic charge, 4.8×10^{-10} electrostatic unit (esu), and Z' the atomic number of gold. The diameter of the nucleus of a gold atom must be smaller than what distance? A required unit is $esu^2 = dyne\ cm^2$.

27. Quantum theory. Predict the minimum energy that an electron in a discharge tube must possess so that, upon collision with a mercury atom, it causes the appearance of the mercury line, $\lambda = 2537 \times 10^{-8}$ cm. This prediction was verified in 1913 by the experiment of James Franck and Gustav Herz, in which electrons of precisely known energy were passed through mercury vapor at low pressure.

Answer. 7.829×10^{-12} erg.

28. Bohr atom. An accelerated particle, mass 5.0×10^{-24} g, possessing a kinetic energy of 21.5×10^{-12} erg, "collides" with a normal hydrogen atom, causing its electron to "jump" to the energy level for which $n = 6$. What is the velocity of the particle after the collision?

29. Bohr atom. (a) Explain the statement, "If we observed the 4861 A line radiated by a few hydrogen atoms, the line would appear only intermittently." (b) Are photons a constituent of hydrogen atoms?

30. Bohr atom. A **positronium atom** is an atomic system consisting of one positron (Chapter 28) and one electron. If nuclear motion is neglected, would the Bohr theory predict identical or dissimilar spectra for light hydrogen, $_1H^1$, deuterium, $_1H^2$, and the positronium atom? Experimentally, they differ.

31. Stability of atom. Given 3 charged spheres at rest at the distances shown:

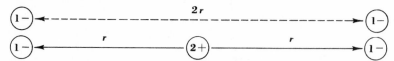

Calculate (a) the repulsion force between the 2 negative spheres, (b) the force of attraction of the positive sphere for each negative sphere. Which force is greater? Assuming the validity of Coulomb's law at atomic distances, what statement can you make about the stabilization of the Rutherford atom by electrostatic forces only?

32. 4s vs. 3d. (a) The electron configuration of $_{20}Ca$ is KL $3s^2 3p^6 4s^2$. Imagine that a proton is added to the nucleus. What is the chemical symbol of the ion produced? What is the electron configuration of this ion? (b) Experimentally, the magnetic moment of Mn^+ in the gaseous state corresponds to six unpaired electrons. Write the electron configuration of $_{25}Mn^+$.

33. X ray spectra lines. Use the oversimplified x ray energy level diagram below to determine the maximum number of "K spectral lines," "L spectral lines," and "M spectral lines."

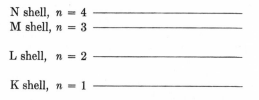

34. Orbitals. Explain the fact that the lowest energy level for the hydrogen atom appears double in a magnetic field, but single otherwise.

35. Electron spin. In the Stern-Gerlach experiment, should the deflection—the separation of the two emerging beams—increase or decrease as (*i*) the magnetic field strength is increased, (*ii*) the velocity of the initial beam is increased?

36. Electron spin. In a Stern-Gerlach experiment, gold vapor splits into two beams. Is this in agreement with its assigned electron configuration?

37. Paramagnetism. A tube (whose reaction to a magnetic field is undetectable), when loaded with a solution of an organic substance of high molecular weight, is repelled from a magnetic field. Can you definitely conclude that the solution does not contain particles with unpaired electrons? Explain your answer.

38. Electron spin. Pick the ion having 5 unpaired electrons: (*i*) Ti^{4+}, (*ii*) Co^{2+}, (*iii*) Fe^{3+}. (Assume that the 4s are removed before the 3d electrons in the ionization process.)

39. Wave mechanics. (a) Did anyone prove that particles of atomic and subatomic dimensions obey Newton's laws of motion? (b) Has anyone proved that an electron is a point charge? (c) Has anyone ever observed light waves with or without the aid of instruments? (d) Pick the correct statement: orbital shapes (patterns of electron distribution) are (*i*) established by experiment, (*ii*) calculated from theory. (e) In studying the trajectory of an ordinary moving pendulum, is it possible to observe the exact position and the frequency of the oscillation at any instant?

40. Wave mechanics. Explain the following statements:

(*i*) Wave mechanics rules out mathematical functions that fix a particle of known energy at a given point.

(*ii*) The distribution of electron density has angular dependence for all except electrons in the s states.

(*iii*) In Newtonian mechanics, the trajectory of a particle is described; in wave mechanics the trajectory is not described.

(*iv*) The electron density at the same point in space for two electrons in an atomic system with similar n, l, m_l, and m_s values is zero.

41. Wave mechanics. Use the following results for the hydrogen atom in the 2s state to plot $4\pi r^2 \psi_{2s}^2$ (*y* axis) vs. r (*x* axis):

r	ψ_{2s}		ψ_{2s}^2		$4\pi r^2 \psi_{2s}^2$	
0	5.2	$\times 10^{11}$	27	$\times 10^{22}$	0	
0.5×10^{-8} cm	1.7	$\times 10^{11}$	2.9	$\times 10^{22}$	9.1	$\times 10^6$
1.0×10^{-8}	0.10	$\times 10^{11}$	0.010	$\times 10^{22}$	0.13	$\times 10^6$
1.5×10^{-8}	-0.52	$\times 10^{11}$	0.27	$\times 10^{22}$	7.8	$\times 10^6$
2.0×10^{-8}	-0.65	$\times 10^{11}$	0.42	$\times 10^{22}$	21	$\times 10^6$
3.0×10^{-8}	-0.58	$\times 10^{11}$	0.34	$\times 10^{22}$	38	$\times 10^6$
5.0×10^{-8}	-0.18	$\times 10^{11}$	0.032	$\times 10^{22}$	10	$\times 10^6$
10.0×10^{-8}	-0.0037	$\times 10^{11}$	0.00001	$\times 10^{22}$	0.018	$\times 10^6$
∞	0		0		0	

Correlate your plot with the electron density diagram for the 2s electron, Fig. 8.20 (page 184).

42. Wave mechanics. The bob (mass point) of a pendulum is set in motion. Following Galileo Galilei's method of instrumentation, we also can use our eyes (observation of an object by the detection of reflected light) to establish a definite relationship between the displacement of the bob from the equilibrium position and time. It is also known that light requires about 10^{-8} second to be reflected or re-emitted. This means that the bob must remain in a given position for at least 10^{-8} second to ascertain that position. Now, let us increase the oscillation of the bob to 10^9 vibrations per second. This means that in 10^{-8} second, the *bob will undergo 10 vibrations* (10^9 vib/sec $\times$ 10^{-8} sec = 10 vib). Can you now establish a definite relationship between the displacement of the bob and time? Can you use a snapshot to establish such a relationship? What information, if any, may be obtained from a snapshot?

43. ψ^2 interpretations. Which interpretation, electron density or probability density, tacitly assumes that the electron is a point charge? Explain.

44. Trajectory. Do electrons travel around the nucleus in definite orbits? Justify your answer.

45. Schroedinger equation. (*This problem is intended only for students with experience in differential calculus.*) For an electron confined to a fixed distance d in one dimension, undergoing an oscillatory translational motion, and not subjected to a force (except when it collides with the barriers at the ends), the wave equation becomes

$$\frac{d^2\psi}{dx^2} + \frac{8\pi^2 m}{h^2}(E)\psi = 0 \tag{1}$$

Let

$$\beta^2 = \frac{8\pi^2 m}{h^2}E \tag{2}$$

Then

$$\frac{d^2\psi}{dx^2} + \beta^2\psi = 0 \tag{3}$$

Show that Equation (3) is satisfied when

(i) $\psi = k\sin\beta x$

(ii) $\psi = k\sin\beta x$ and $\beta = \dfrac{\pi}{d}$

(iii) $\psi = k\sin\beta x$ and $\beta = \dfrac{a\pi}{d}$ where $a = 1, 2, 3, \ldots$ (4)

Show that if

$$\beta = \frac{a\pi}{d}$$

then

$$E = \frac{a^2 h^2}{8md^2} \tag{5}$$

Show finally that Equations (4) and (5) satisfy Equation (1).

46. Radii. Explain the following data: the decrease in the radius for the seven elements, Li to F, is 0.63 A, while the decrease for the fifteen elements, La to Lu, is only 0.13 A.

47. Size. In 1953 Maurice Huggins derived an equation relating the bond length (interatomic distance) r_{AB} to the electrical character of the covalent bond through its effect on the bond energy ΔH_{AB} (in kcal/mole),

$$r_{AB} = r_A^* + r_B^* - \tfrac{1}{2}\log\Delta H_{AB}$$

in which r_A^* and r_B^* are the constant radii assigned to atoms A and B in angstrom units. From the data, $r_C^* = 1.22$, $r_F^* = 1.11$, and $\Delta H_{CF} = 137$ kcal/mole, calculate the C—F bond length in CF_4. The accepted experimental value is 1.36 A $\pm$ 0.02. Note: answer will come out in A units; no dimensional analysis is required.

48. Size. From the Pauling values for crystal radii (page 191), calculate the Na^+–Cl^- interionic distance in a sodium chloride crystal, and the Mg^{2+}–S^{2-} interionic distance in a magnesium sulfide crystal. The accepted experimental values are 2.82 and 2.54, respectively. Calculate the error in percent.

Answer. 2%.

49. Size. (a) Assuming atoms are in virtual contact and geometrically arranged in the same manner (constant number of atoms per unit cell), what statement can you make about the variation of atomic volume, ml per mole, within a period and a group? Would you expect perfect agreement, good agreement, or no agreement with the experimentally determined atomic volumes?

50. Isoelectronic particles. (a) Roughly estimate an atomic radius for argon atoms from the radii of isoelectronic ions (page 191); additional radii required are Ca^{2+} 0.99 A, Sc^{3+} 0.81A. (b) What would have to be the charge and electron configuration of a potassium ion for it to be isoelectronic with Na^+? What can you say about the size of this ion compared to K^+ and Na^+?

51. Ionization energy. (a) Which factor, the radius or the nuclear charge, is more significant in determining the ionization energy of the elements in a family? (b) What is the minimum velocity an electron must acquire to ionize a He atom upon collision?

Answer. (b) 3.44 $\times$ 10^6 cm/sec.

52. Ionization energy. (a) The electron configuration of $_{22}Ti$, as obtained from the $(n + l)$ rule, is $KL8$-$4s^2 3d^2$. The number of unpaired electrons in $Ti^{2+}(g)$ is two. Write the electron configuration of $Ti^{2+}(g)$. (b) Should you use the electron in the energy level $n = 1$, $n = 2$, or $n = 3$ (page 163) to predict the ionization energy of hydrogen? Justify your answer, calculate the ionization energy, and compare with the experimental value, 314 kcal/mole.

53. Ionization energy. (i) Plot the ionization energy for the alkali family as a function of the period number (x axis). (ii) Each transition and inner transition series may be considered a family in the sense we consider, for example, the halogens as a family. What would be the shape of the curve obtained in (i) if the transition and inner transition series behaved as families with respect to atomic radius?

54. Ionization energy. The ionization of molecular oxygen, $O_2 \rightarrow O_2^+ +$ electron, requires 282 kcal per mole, and with platinum hexafluoride vapor, PtF_6, oxygen forms the compound dioxygenyl hexafluoroplatinate(V), $O_2^+(PtF_6)^-$. The ionization energy of the "inert" gas xenon, $Xe \rightarrow Xe^+ +$ electron, is 280 kcal per mole. Would you undertake the preparation of the corresponding compound, $Xe^+ (PtF_6)^-$? Explain your answer.

55. Ionization energy. (a) Correlate the general trends in the ionization energy of the elements in period 2 and in Group IA with the size and nuclear charge of the atoms. (b) Plot the first ionization energy (y axis) vs. atomic number (x axis) for period 2 (page 192) and for the transition elements on the same scale:

$_{21}Sc$	$_{22}Ti$	$_{23}V$	$_{24}Cr$	$_{25}Mn$	$_{26}Fe$	$_{27}Co$	$_{28}Ni$	$_{29}Cu$
154	157	155	156	171	181	181	176	178 kcal/mole

What conclusion(s) would you draw from these data?

56. Promotion energy. (a) Pick the promotion requiring the smaller amount of energy:

(*i*)   Mg KL $3s^2 \rightarrow$ Mg KL $3s^1\ 3p^1$
(*ii*)   Ar KL $3s^2\ 3p^6 \rightarrow$ Ar KL $3s^2\ 3p^5\ 4s^1$

(b) What generally acceptable statement can you make about the energy requirements to ionize an electron and to promote an electron to the next available orbital for the noble (inert) gases compared to the other elements?

57. Electron affinity. (a) Correlate size, ionization energy, and electron affinity of atoms for the representative elements within a period and within a group. How do these correlations generally agree with experimental results? (b) Calculate the heat of the reaction of $O + 2e^- \rightarrow O^{2-}$; how would you account for the endothermicity of this reaction?

58. History. (a) Write an essay on the hypothesis of the Milesian School (~ 600 B.C.), "There is but one basic stuff out of which all physical beings are made."

59. Nature of matter. The Roman Lucretius concluded, "Yet things that are the tiniest will be composed of infinite parts just the same." The famous theoretical physicist Dirac wrote in 1947, "In a classical explanation of the constitution of matter, one would assume it to be made up of a large number of small constituent parts and one would postulate laws for the behavior of these parts from which the laws of the matter in bulk could be deduced. This would not complete the explanation, however, since the question of the structure and stability of the constituent parts is left untouched. To go into this question, it becomes necessary to postulate that each constituent part is itself made up of smaller parts, in terms of which its behavior is to be explained. There is clearly no end to this procedure, so that one can never arrive at the ultimate structure of matter on these lines." Explain these statements in your own words.

9

Types
of
chemical
bonds

UNDER TERRESTRIAL CONDITIONS, most elements rarely exist as isolated atoms. Instead, the atoms of most elements exist in a bonded state. For example oxygen, nitrogen, hydrogen, and the halogens are diatomic molecules. Carbon in the form of diamond or graphite, and red phosphorus, are macromolecules composed of a myriad of bonded atoms. Yellow rhombic sulfur and white phosphorus exist as molecules whose formulas are S_8 and P_4, respectively. Most metallic elements, such as copper and sodium, are crystals composed of innumerable bonded atoms.

Isolated atoms can be produced. At high temperatures, in electric arcs, in discharge tubes at low pressure, or by ultraviolet irradiation, many molecules can be atomized. When metallic elements are vaporized, they are converted mostly to individual atoms. These methods of atomization are endothermic processes. The bonded rather than the unbonded state is evidently more stable in most cases.

How do atoms combine and what are the forces that bind them? These questions are fundamental in the study of chemistry, since chemical change is essentially an alteration of chemical bonds. Of the three types of attractive force—gravitational, magnetic, and electrostatic—only the latter is strong enough to account for observed bond energies. An important clue to the understanding of the driving force for chemical bonding was the discovery of the noble gases and their comparatively inert chemical behavior. The relationship between the bonding of atoms and the electronic configuration of noble gases was proposed in 1916 independently by W. Kossel and Gilbert N. Lewis, and extended in 1919 by

Irving Langmuir. It was suggested that *atoms interact by changing the number of their electrons so as to acquire the electronic structure of (become isoelectronic with) a noble gas.* With the exception of helium, which has a $1s^2$ electronic configuration, each noble gas has eight electrons with an s^2p^6 distribution in its highest principal energy level (page 180). The need for eight electrons gives the name **octet rule** to this concept. There are, however, many exceptions to the octet rule—even compounds of the noble gases have been synthesized.

9.1 LEWIS SYMBOLS

In the following discussion, Lewis symbols are used to represent the atoms. Such symbols comprise the letter designation of the element, dots to represent the *valence* electrons, and, if necessary, the ionic charge. The **valence electrons** are those in the highest principal energy level. They are the electrons usually involved in bonding. For the representative elements, the number of valence electrons is given by the Group number of the element in the Periodic Table. For example, the Lewis symbol for boron is $\dot{\text{B}}\cdot$, since boron has the electron configuration $1s^2 2s^2 2p^1$ and is a Group IIIA element. The letter B is called the **kernel**, and stands for the nucleus and the inner electrons—in this case, the $1s^2$ electrons. This symbolism is very useful for the representative elements, but difficulties arise when Lewis symbols are used for the transition elements. Bonding of the transition elements can involve electrons in more than one principal energy level; hence, the classification "valence electron" is indefinite.

9.2 IONIC BOND

Let us now consider the kind of bond that results when sodium chloride is formed from its elements. Sodium, atomic number 11, has the "neon electronic core" plus one electron. Were a sodium atom to lose one electron, it would become isoelectronic with neon. As indicated by its relatively low ionization energy (page 193), a sodium atom can lose its electron to become a sodium ion, a cation with a charge of $+1$. The chlorine atom, atomic number 17, needs one more electron in order to become isoelectronic with argon. As indicated by its high electron affinity (page 194), chlorine readily accepts an electron to give a negative ion, an anion whose charge is -1. Now imagine a *hypothetical* process in which gaseous sodium atoms react with gaseous chlorine atoms to form isolated, gaseous sodium chloride molecules. On contact, a sodium atom would be expected to transfer an electron to a chlorine atom, forming a molecule of Na^+Cl^-. Although it is a **concerted process,** * the formation of the sodium chloride molecule can be represented as the sum of three

---

* A **concerted process** is one that happens all at once; there are no discernible separate steps.

separate equations,

(1)	$Na(g) \leftrightarrows Na^+(g) + e^-$	$\Delta H = +118$ kcal/mole
(2)	$Cl(g) + e^- \leftrightarrows Cl^-(g)$	$\Delta H = -88$ kcal/mole
(3)	$Na^+(g) + Cl^-(g) \leftrightarrows Na^+Cl^-(g)$	$\Delta H = -119$ kcal/mole

$$Na(g) + Cl(g) \leftrightarrows Na^+Cl^-(g) \qquad \Delta H = -89 \text{ kcal/mole}$$

The first equation represents the ionization of sodium, and its ΔH value is the ionization energy of Na. The second equation shows the formation of a chloride ion, and its ΔH value is the electron affinity of Cl. The third equation represents the mutual approach of the separated ions to form the molecule. The energy change in the third equation stems from the electrostatic attraction of the ions. The energy of the over-all reaction is the sum of the energies of the individual steps (Hess's law). The net effect of electron transfer, the sum of Equations (1) and (2), is endothermic. It is the contribution of the third equation, the electrostatic attraction leading to bond formation, that makes the over-all reaction exothermic, indicating that the molecule is more stable than the separated atoms.

When atoms react by electron transfer, the number of electrons gained and lost must be equal; the resulting compound is neutral. Illustrations of this principle are given below.

$\dot{C}a\cdot + 2H\cdot \rightarrow Ca^{2+} + 2H:^-$		(CaH_2) calcium hydride
$2Li\cdot + \cdot\ddot{O}: \rightarrow 2Li^+ + :\ddot{O}:^{2-}$		(Li_2O) lithium oxide
$\cdot\dot{A}l\cdot + 3\cdot\ddot{F}: \rightarrow Al^{3+} + 3:\ddot{F}:^-$		(AlF_3) aluminum fluoride
$3\dot{M}g\cdot + 2\cdot\dot{N}: \rightarrow 3Mg^{2+} + 2:\ddot{N}:^{3-}$		(Mg_3N_2) magnesium nitride

The number of electrons lost or gained by an atom is equal to its **valence.** Atoms that tend to lose electrons are said to be **electropositive,** those that tend to gain electrons to be **electronegative.** The loss of electrons is called **oxidation,** and the gain of electrons is called **reduction.** By definition, the formation of an ionic bond from elements must involve an oxidation-reduction (**redox**) reaction. The more electropositive element is oxidized, and the more electronegative one is reduced.

9.3 ENERGETICS OF FORMATION OF IONIC SOLIDS; BORN-HABER CYCLE

Sodium chloride is not usually made from its elements; if we wish to prepare it in this manner, we mix solid sodium metal and chlorine gas (not gaseous sodium and chlorine atoms). We obtain solid crystals (no individual gaseous molecules). Consequently, although the previous discussion of the energy of sodium chloride formation is useful in indicating the magnitude of some of the hypothetical steps, it is incomplete. The enthalpy change of the reaction

$$Na(c) + \tfrac{1}{2}Cl_2(g) \rightarrow Na^+Cl^-(c)$$

corresponds to the *heat of formation* of solid sodium chloride. The heat of formation is the heat of the reaction for forming a compound from its elemental components. Again, this reaction is probably concerted, but by using Hess's law we can nevertheless break it down into five hypothetical steps represented by five equations:

Heat of sublimation	$Na(c) \rightleftharpoons Na(g)$	$\Delta H =$	$+26.0$ kcal/mole
Ionization energy	$Na(g) - e^- \rightleftharpoons Na^+(g)$	$\Delta H =$	$+118.0$ kcal/mole
$\tfrac{1}{2}$Bond energy of Cl_2	$\tfrac{1}{2}Cl_2(g) \rightleftharpoons Cl(g)$	$\Delta H =$	$+28.6$ kcal/mole
Electron affinity	$Cl(g) + e^- \rightleftharpoons Cl^-(g)$	$\Delta H =$	-88.2 kcal/mole
Lattice energy*	$Na^+(g) + Cl^-(g) \rightleftharpoons NaCl(c)$	$\Delta H =$	-182.6 kcal/mole

Heat of formation	$Na(c) + \tfrac{1}{2}Cl_2(g) \rightleftharpoons NaCl(c)$	$\Delta H =$	-98.2 kcal/mole

This analysis of the heat of formation of ionic solids is called the Born-Haber cycle. The formation of crystalline sodium chloride is therefore an exothermic reaction. In practice, when a piece of sodium metal is plunged into a jar of chlorine gas, it burns, giving off heat and light. The heats of formation, heats of sublimation, ionization energies, and bond energies generally are readily determined experimentally. Direct measurement of electron affinities is difficult, and accurate measurements have been made only for the halogens (page 194). Lattice energies have been calculated for many crystals, using Coulomb's inverse-square law (page 784), and agree within a few percent with those calculated from the Born-Haber treatment. Lattice energies measured experimentally for a few halides are in good agreement with calculated values.

The Born-Haber treatment also permits analysis of the stability of ionic compounds, exemplified by MgO. Magnesium has a high heat of sublimation, and oxygen has a high heat of dissociation. The formation of both the Mg^{2+} and O^{2-} ions is endothermic. Four of the steps in the cycle are endothermic, yet the heat of formation is negative (cf. Problem 15, p. 236). The crystal lattice formation is necessarily very exothermic in order to more than counterbalance the four endothermic steps. This is not surprising, however, since the ions have relatively small ionic radii and high charges. A discussion of factors affecting crystal lattice energy is found in Chapter 20.

* The lattice energy of an ionic solid is the energy released when one mole of crystal is produced from isolated ions.

In order to simplify the model used to describe the ionic crystalline state, an ion is considered to be an incompressible sphere having a well-defined surface. The oppositely charged ions arrange themselves in a **crystal lattice,** so as to achieve the lowest possible energy. Minimal energy prevails when the oppositely charged ions are as close as possible, and the like-charged ions are at maximum distance from each other. The best way to satisfy these requirements is for the crystal lattice to be comprised of alternating $+$ and $-$ ions, in all three dimensions. Each ion is surrounded by a certain number of ions of the opposite sign; this number is the **coordination number** of the ion. In an AB type of salt, the coordination numbers of the two ions are identical because electrical neutrality must be maintained. For a salt such as CaF_2, the coordination number of Ca^{2+} is twice that of F^-.

The structure of an ionic crystal is determined largely by the dimensions of the larger ion; with few exceptions this is the anion. The anions tend to be close-packed and the cations fit into the remaining spaces or holes. There are three main ways for anions to be close-packed while maintaining charge neutrality. In the *cubic* arrangement (Fig. 3.9, page 43), *eight* anions surround the cation. In the *octahedral* arrangement (Fig. 3.11, page 44), *six* anions surround the cation. In the *tetrahedral* arrangement (Fig. 3.10, page 44), *four* anions surround the cation. These coordinations, which are associated with each type of array, are summarized in Table 9.1. Since the largest coordination number (8) is observed for the cubic arrangement, this array must have the largest hole. The smallest coordination number (4) is observed for the tetrahedral arrangement, and therefore this array has the smallest hole. The octahedral arrangement has the medium size hole.

The structure achieved by a given ionic solid has a maximum number of anions in contact with the cation so as to maximize the electrostatic attraction. However, the anions can only "touch" (see footnote, page 40) each other: any closer approach would result in repulsive forces. Even in this position repulsive forces are present but, for the sake of simplicity, are assumed to be equal to zero. Each array has a limiting structure in which the anions touch the cation and just touch each other, as shown for the octahedron (Fig. 9.1a). The figure is simplified by removing two anions, the ones above and below the cation. If a smaller cation, B^+,

TABLE **9.1**   *Limiting Values for the Radius Ratio*

Coordination number	Type of array	Limiting values of r^+/r^-
8	Cubic	Above 0.732
6	Octahedral	0.414 to 0.732
4	Tetrahedral	0.225 to 0.414

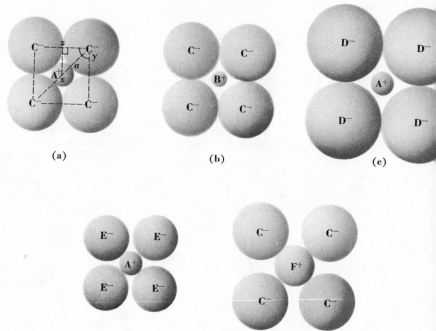

Fig. 9.1. *Octahedral close-packing of different sized ions*

were in the hole (Fig. 9.1b) or larger anions, D^-, surrounded the cation (Fig. 9.1c), some attractive force would be lost and repulsive forces would predominate. A more stable system would result if the centers of the anion and cation came closer together, which can happen only if the coordination number is reduced from 6 to 4. Hence, a tetrahedral array is more favorable than the octahedral array, as pictured in Fig. 9.1b and c. Alternatively, if smaller anions, E^-, were placed around the cation (Fig. 9.1d) or a larger cation, F^+, were inserted between the anions (Fig. 9.1e), it might be possible to place eight rather than six anions around the cation to give a cubic arrangement and thereby increase the attractive forces.

Evidently the attained array and the resulting coordination number depend not only on the need for electrical neutrality but also on the *relative sizes of the ions*. The limiting structure for each arrangement is expressed in terms of the **radius ratio** of the ions involved,

$$\text{radius ratio} = \frac{\text{radius of smaller ion}}{\text{radius of larger ion}}$$

Since the radius of the cation, r^+, is usually smaller than the radius of the anion, r^-, the radius ratio is usually written as r^+/r^-. The lower limit radius ratio can be calculated, with the aid of Fig. 9.1a. Since xyz is a right isosceles triangle, the angle zyx is 45°. One side, yz, is the ionic radius, r^-, of the C^- ion. The hypotenuse, xy, is equal to r^- plus xa, the radius, r^+, of the A^+ ion. Therefore, since cosine = adjacent/hypotenuse,

$$zy = xy \cos 45°$$

and, since $\cos 45° = 0.707$,

$$r^- = (r^+ + r^-)\ 0.707$$
$$0.293\ r^- = 0.707\ r^+$$
$$0.414 = r^+/r^-$$

The lower limiting values, shown in Table 9.1, can be calculated for each type of coordination. Prediction of coordination numbers from radius ratios is generally correct. However, when the ratio is close to the limit for a given coordination number, the prediction becomes uncertain.

A salient fact becomes apparent from the preceding discussion. In an ionic solid, no one positive ion is the exclusive, permanent partner of any one negative ion. Hence, we cannot refer to an individual molecule in the solid state. The entire crystal becomes a macromolecule. The formula NaCl for *solid* sodium chloride actually represents the empirical formula, since it merely gives the ratio of Na^+ to Cl^- ions.

Ionic solids such as sodium chloride can be vaporized at sufficiently high temperatures. In the vapor state the crystalline aggregate disappears, and the cations and anions form individual molecules composed of a single Na^+ and a single Cl^- ion. Some Na_2Cl_2 molecules are also detected.

9.5 COVALENT BOND

Electron transfer leading to an ionic bond most often occurs when an atom with a low ionization energy reacts with an atom of high electron affinity. What happens when two atoms, both of which require electrons to become isoelectronic with a noble gas, react? The simplest example of such a situation is the combination of two hydrogen atoms to form an H_2 molecule. Each hydrogen atom needs one electron to become isoelectronic with a helium atom, so that a transfer of electrons cannot satisfy the requirements of both. Instead, the hydrogen atoms *mutually share their electrons.* The shared pair belongs to both; each hydrogen atom can be considered to have gained an electron, and to have acquired the helium structure,

$$H\cdot + H\cdot \leftrightharpoons H\!:\!H \qquad \Delta H = -104 \text{ kcal/mole}$$

Such a sharing of a pair of electrons results in a **covalent bond,** the presence of which is usually depicted by a dash, $H\!-\!H$, or a pair of dots, $H\!:\!H$. Once the covalent bond has formed, the two bonding electrons are attracted by two nuclei instead of one, and the bonded state is therefore more stable than the nonbonded state.

The number of covalent bonds formed by an atom is termed its **covalency.** Some of the values for the more common elements are as follows: hydrogen and the halogens, 1; oxygen and sulfur, 2; nitrogen, and phosphorus, 3; carbon and silicon, 4. In each case cited, the covalency is equal to the number of electrons the atom needs to become isoelectronic with a noble gas. **Structural formulas,** in which a dash indicates a covalent bond, are given for a few typical compounds of these common elements,

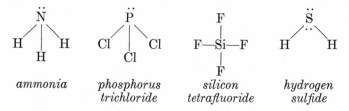

| ammonia | phosphorus trichloride | silicon tetrafluoride | hydrogen sulfide |

Remembering the covalencies of these common elements greatly simplifies the writing of a structural or an electronic formula when given only the molecular formula.

EXAMPLE 1   **Write the structural formula for CH₄O.**

ANSWER   **The only structure that satisfies the octet rule and the covalency requirements of C = 4, O = 2, and H = 1, is**

methyl
alcohol

If all four H atoms were bonded to carbon, the O atom would remain without an octet, and if two H atoms were bonded to the O atom, the carbon atom would remain without an octet.

9.6 **MULTIPLE BONDS**

To satisfy their covalency requirements, two atoms must often share more than one pair of electrons. This leads to the concept of **multiple bonds.** The sharing of two pairs of electrons leads to a **double bond;** the sharing of three pairs of electrons leads to a **triple bond.** Bond multiplicity of more than three is not known. Examples of multiply bonded molecules are phosgene, $COCl_2$, which contains a double bond; N_2 and HCN, each of which contains a triple bond; and CO_2, in which carbon has two double bonds:

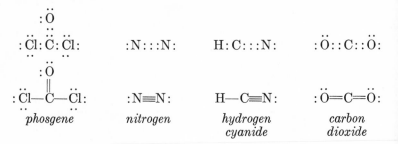

| phosgene | nitrogen | hydrogen cyanide | carbon dioxide |

In general, within a given group in the Periodic Table, the ability to form multiple bonds, while maintaining an octet of electrons, diminishes with increasing size of the atom. With few exceptions, such as S, only atoms in the second period, for example, C, N, and O, can have a multiple bond and an octet of electrons; we find such groups as

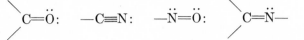

The number of compounds in which sulfur forms multiple bonds are few, and the bonds are much weaker than their oxygen analogs.

Molecular nitrogen possesses a triple bond, but in a molecule of white phosphorus, P_4 (Fig. 3.10), each phosphorus atom lies at the corner of a tetrahedron, has an unshared pair of electrons, and forms a single bond with three other atoms. As another example, carbon dioxide has two double bonds, while the silicon analog, SiO_2, is characterized by single bonds (Fig. 9.2). Each silicon atom is tetrahedrally surrounded by four oxygen atoms, and each oxygen atom is bonded to two silicon atoms. An important feature of such a structure is the absence of a definite molecule. No one silicon atom belongs to any two oxygen atoms. The entire crystal of silicon dioxide is a giant molecule or macromolecule. SiO_2 is therefore an empirical formula, not a molecular formula.

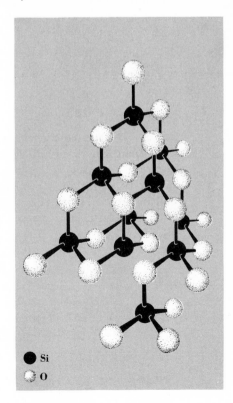

Fig. 9.2. *Silicon dioxide.*

● Si

○ O

9.8 PROPERTIES OF IONIC AND COVALENT COMPOUNDS

By what criteria are compounds classified as ionic or covalent? The distinction is often made on the basis of physical properties. In order to discuss the physical properties of *covalent* substances, it is necessary to classify them into two types:

(a) The **molecular covalent** type, exemplified by CO_2, I_2, P_4, and Cl_2, consists of distinguishable molecules. The atoms in the molecules are held together by strong covalent bonds, but the forces between the molecules themselves are very weak. As a result of weak intermolecular forces, the molecules are easily separated. Hence, molecular covalent compounds are often gases or liquids, or solids that sublime easily or have relatively low melting points and boiling points. It is rare to find a molecular compound that melts above 300°C or boils above 500°C.

(b) The **macromolecular** species is exemplified by silicon dioxide (Fig. 9.2) and diamond (Fig. 9.3).* These substances are large, 3-dimensional aggregates of covalently bonded atoms. The attractive forces between the atoms are very strong. They are therefore invariably solids with very high melting and boiling points. Thus, silicon dioxide (quartz) melts at about 1710°C and boils at 2230°C, and diamond melts at 3500°C and boils at 4200°C.

The property that most clearly identifies an ionic compound is the ability to conduct an electric current when molten. The compound must be molten so that the ions can move; the solid is a poor conductor because the ions are relatively immobile. Ionic compounds are solids, usually with high melting points and boiling points, both above about 500°C. This property is a result of the large amount of heat energy that must be supplied to overcome the strong interionic attractive force. However, the melting and boiling points of ionic compounds are not so high as those of macromolecular covalent solids. For example, NaCl melts at 800.4°C and boils at 1413°C, and NaOH melts at 318.4°C and boils at 1390°C.

9.9 POLAR COVALENT BONDS; ELECTRONEGATIVITY

Equal sharing of a pair of electrons occurs in homodiatomic molecules such as H:H, and between identical atoms, with identical neighbors, as illustrated by the two C atoms in ethane, H_3C—CH_3. But if the two bonded atoms are dissimilar as in H:Cl, or are identical but not in identical surroundings as the two C atoms in H_3C—CCl_3, the sharing is unequal; one atom is likely to attract electrons more strongly than the other. The atom which more strongly attracts electrons develops a fraction of negative charge; the other atom develops a fraction of positive charge. These **fractional charges** are designated as δ^+ and δ^-, not to be confused with unit charges. For example, since a Cl atom is more electron-attracting than an H atom, hydrogen chloride is depicted as

$$\overset{\delta^+}{H}-\overset{\delta^-}{Cl}$$

* See page 225 for Fig. 9.3.

Such covalent bonds are said to be **polar,** as distinguished from the Cl—Cl or H—H bonds, which are called **nonpolar.** The limiting case of unequal sharing of a pair of electrons is the ionic bond in such compounds as CsF, NaCl, or CaF_2; one atom has usurped the pair and the fractional (partial) charges become integers of electronic charge. Thus, the *nonpolar covalent bond and the ionic bond are extremes for the distribution of a pair of electrons between two nuclei.* Between these extremes are the many polar covalent bonds.

The relative tendency of a bonded atom in a molecule to attract electrons is expressed by the term **electronegativity.** Electronegativity is believed to depend on the interplay of electron affinity and ionization energy of the atom. One set of values of electronegativities is based on an average of these two properties of atoms. The values given in Table 9.2 were calculated from bond energy data, using a number of arbitrary assumptions. Although one value has been assigned in Table 9.2, it is now recognized that the electronegativity of a bonded atom is also a function of the bonding state of the atom. For example, the electronegativities of the same element when single-bonded and when double-bonded are different. These values should therefore be used to indicate mainly the magnitude of the differences in electronegativity and not for accurate calculation. *Electronegativities increase as one proceeds from left to right in a Period* and, with a number of exceptions, *from the bottom to the top of a Group.* It is noteworthy that fluorine and oxygen are the most electronegative of the elements. Approximately, it can be stated that, for two bonding atoms, a difference of about 1.7 in electronegativities engenders an ionic bond, a difference of less than 1.7 results in a polar covalent bond, and no difference results in a nonpolar bond.*

9.10 EXCEPTIONS TO THE OCTET RULE

Although the octet rule is a useful generalization, it is not wise to become too dogmatic in its application. Some molecules and ions have atoms with less than an octet associated with them, and some have atoms which exceed the octet.

(a) **Atoms with Less Than an Octet of Electrons.** When an atom with fewer than four outermost electrons forms a covalent bond using each of these electrons, it will apparently have less than an octet of electrons. Boron, ·B:, the first member of Group IIIA, and beryllium Be:, the first member of Group IIA, are typical examples. When boron reacts with fluorine, the most electronegative element, it forms boron trifluoride, BF_3, a covalent molecule (b.p. = −101°C). The energy required to remove three electrons from a B atom evidently prohibits the formation of a B^{3+} ion under ordinary conditions. Hence, boron atoms only share electrons. In the molecule BF_3, typical of all

---

* Exceptions exist. The hydrides, MH_x, of the alkali metals and of Ca, Sr, and Ba in Group IIA are ionic solids. However, the difference in electronegativity of hydrogen and electronegativity of each of these metals is less than 1.7.

TABLE 9.2 *Electronegativities of the Representative Elements Showing Relation to the Periodic Table*

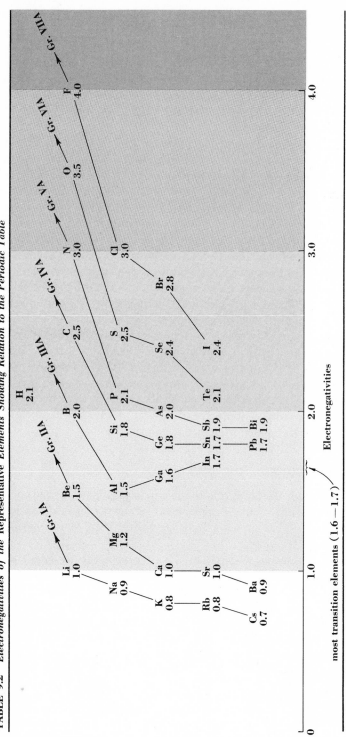

boron halides,

$$\cdot \text{B} \cdot + 3 : \overset{\cdot\cdot}{\underset{\cdot}{\text{F}}} : \rightarrow : \overset{\cdot\cdot}{\underset{\cdot\cdot}{\text{F}}} : \overset{:\overset{\cdot\cdot}{\text{F}}:}{\underset{\cdot\cdot}{\text{B}}} : \overset{\cdot\cdot}{\underset{\cdot\cdot}{\text{F}}} :$$

boron apparently has only six electrons. However, the tendency to acquire an octet predisposes BF₃ to further reaction (this type of reactivity is discussed on page 220).

Although beryllium forms an ionic compound with fluorine, BeF₂, with the less electronegative chlorine atom it forms a covalent molecule, BeCl₂, in which it has only four electrons,

$$\overset{\cdot}{\text{Be}} \cdot + 2 : \overset{\cdot\cdot}{\underset{\cdot}{\text{F}}} : \rightarrow \text{Be}^{2+} + 2 : \overset{\cdot\cdot}{\underset{\cdot\cdot}{\text{F}}} : ^{-}$$

$$\overset{\cdot}{\text{Be}} \cdot + 2 : \overset{\cdot\cdot}{\underset{\cdot}{\text{Cl}}} : \rightarrow : \overset{\cdot\cdot}{\underset{\cdot\cdot}{\text{Cl}}} : \text{Be} : \overset{\cdot\cdot}{\underset{\cdot\cdot}{\text{Cl}}} :$$

(b) Free Radicals. Nitric oxide, NO, is another example of a molecule possessing an atom with less than eight electrons. A possible electronic structure of the molecule

$$: \overset{\cdot}{\text{N}} : : \overset{\cdot\cdot}{\underset{\cdot\cdot}{\text{O}}} :$$

shows the oxygen atom surrounded by eight and the nitrogen atom surrounded by seven electrons. Molecules in which one or more electrons are unpaired are known as **free radicals.** Free radicals are characterized by two properties; they are paramagnetic and colored. Thus, nitrogen dioxide

$$: \overset{\cdot\cdot}{\underset{\cdot\cdot}{\text{O}}} : \overset{\cdot}{\text{N}} : : \overset{\cdot\cdot}{\underset{\cdot\cdot}{\text{O}}} :$$

is a brown gas, and chlorine dioxide

$$: \overset{\cdot\cdot}{\underset{\cdot\cdot}{\text{O}}} : \overset{\cdot}{\underset{\cdot\cdot}{\text{Cl}}} : \overset{\cdot\cdot}{\underset{\cdot\cdot}{\text{O}}} :$$

is a yellow gas; NO is colorless in the gaseous state, blue in the liquid state.

Although an electronic structure consistent with the octet rule can be written for O₂, experiment shows that O₂ has a permanent magnetic moment corresponding to two unpaired electrons. Consequently, molecular oxygen must be a free radical with an unpaired electron on each atom,

$$: \overset{\cdot\cdot}{\text{O}} : : \overset{\cdot\cdot}{\text{O}} : \qquad\qquad : \overset{\cdot\cdot}{\underset{\cdot}{\text{O}}} : \overset{\cdot\cdot}{\underset{\cdot}{\text{O}}} :$$

a possible structure   *a free radical structure*
for O₂   *for O₂*

We shall see (page 269) that neither of these structures accurately represents the O₂ molecule.

Two free radical molecules form a covalent bond by pairing the unpaired electrons, a process known as **dimerization,**

$$\text{H}_3\text{C} \cdot + \cdot \text{CH}_3 \rightarrow \text{H}_3\text{C} : \text{CH}_3$$
dimerization of free radicals

Most free radicals tend to dimerize rather than remain in the odd electron state; NO, NO_2, O_2, and ClO_2 are among the few exceptions. NO_2 dimerizes if the temperature is lowered,

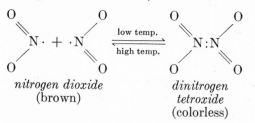

nitrogen dioxide
(brown)

dinitrogen
tetroxide
(colorless)

The dimerization is reversed when the temperature is increased.

(c) **Atoms with More Than Eight Outer Electrons.** The electron octet is never exceeded by atoms in the second period of the Periodic Table. No stable molecules are known in which the atoms Li, Be, B, C, N, O, and F are surrounded by more than eight outer electrons. It is possible, however, for certain atoms in the higher periods to possess more than eight outer electrons. Stable molecules and ions such as $SiF_6{}^{2-}$, PCl_5, SF_6, and ICl_3 are known. Their structural formulas have the P and I atoms surrounded by ten electrons and the Si and S atoms by twelve electrons,

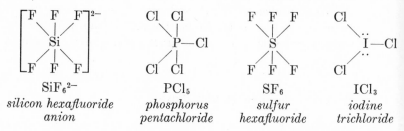

$SiF_6{}^{2-}$
silicon hexafluoride
anion

PCl_5
phosphorus
pentachloride

SF_6
sulfur
hexafluoride

ICl_3
iodine
trichloride

(d) **Ions of Transition Elements and Ions of Certain Representative Elements.** The ions of many transition elements are not isoelectronic with noble gases. Table 9.3 lists some typical transition elements and their ions, and the configuration of the nearest noble gas. Scandium (Sc), the first of the transition elements in Period IV, loses

TABLE 9.3 *Electronic Configuration of Typical Transition Elements and Ions*

Element	Ion	Noble gas
Sc (Ne core,$3s^2,3p^6,3d^1,4s^2$)	Sc^{3+} (Ne core,$3s^2,3p^6$)	Ar (Ne core,$3s^2,3p^6$)
Cr (Ne core,$3s^2,3p^6,3d^5,4s^1$)	Cr^{3+} (Ne core,$3s^2,3p^6,3d^3$)	Ar (Ne core,$3s^2,3p^6$)
Mn (Ne core,$3s^2,3p^6,3d^5,4s^2$)	Mn^{2+} (Ne core,$3s^2,3p^6,3d^5$)	Ar (Ne core,$3s^2,3p^6$)
Fe (Ne core,$3s^2,3p^6,3d^6,4s^2$)	Fe^{3+} (Ne core,$3s^2,3p^6,3d^5$)	Ar (Ne core,$3s^2,3p^6$)
Cu (Ne core,$3s^2,3p^6,3d^{10},4s^1$)	Cu^{1+} (Ne core,$3s^2,3p^6,3d^{10}$)	Kr (Ar core,$3d^{10},4s^2,4p^6$)
Zn (Ne core,$3s^2,3p^6,3d^{10},4s^2$)	Zn^{2+} (Ne core,$3s^2,3p^6,3d^{10}$)	Kr (Ar core,$3d^{10},4s^2,4p^6$)

three electrons to give the ion Sc^{3+}, which is isoelectronic with argon. The ensuing elements, however, form stable ions not isoelectronic with argon or with krypton.

Several of the heavy atoms in Groups IIIA to VA of the Periodic Table form cations that do not have a noble gas configuration. A few examples are shown in the tabulation.

Element	Group	Ion	Typical salt
Tin		Sn^{2+}	
(KLM $4s^2 4p^6 4d^{10} 5s^2 5p^2$)	IV	(KLM $4s^2 4p^6 4d^{10} 5s^2$)	SnF_2
Antimony		Sb^{3+}	
(KLM $4s^2 4p^6 4d^{10} 5s^2 5p^3$)	V	(isoelectronic with Sn^{2+})	$Sb_2(SO_4)_3$
Thallium		Tl^+	
(KLMN $5s^2 5p^6 5d^{10} 6s^2 6p^1$)	III	(KLMN $5s^2 5p^6 5d^{10} 6s^2$)	TlF
Lead		Pb^{2+}	
(KLMN $5s^2 5p^6 5d^{10} 6s^2 6p^2$)	IV	(isoelectronic with Tl^+)	PbF_2
Bismuth		Bi^{3+}	
(KLMN $5s^2 5p^6 5d^{10} 6s^2 6p^3$)	V	(isoelectronic with Tl^+)	BiF_3

The highest principal energy level of each of the ions shown above has only two electrons, which fill the outermost s orbital. These two s electrons are frequently called the **inert pair.** The term *inert pair* refers to the reluctance of a pair of s electrons to be lost or to participate in covalent bond formation. The inertness is noticeable (a) when the s electrons are in the fifth or a higher principal energy level, and (b) when their loss does not afford a species with a noble gas configuration.

(e) **Compounds of Noble Gases.** The apparently inert chemical behavior of the noble gases gave the original and sustaining support to the significance of the stable electronic octet. However, in 1962 even this support was weakened by the reported synthesis of compounds of the noble gases. Shortly before, it was demonstrated that oxygen reacts with platinum(VI) hexafluoride, a deep red vapor at ordinary temperatures, to give an ionic solid, dioxygenyl hexafluoroplatinate(V), $(O_2)^+(PtF_6)^-$. Since the first ionization energy of O_2, 281.3 kcal/mole, is practically the same as that of xenon, it seemed reasonable to attempt the reaction with xenon. The PtF_6 vapor, mixed with an equimolar amount of xenon, immediately formed a yellow solid. In this reaction, xenon transfers an electron to PtF_6,

$$:\overset{..}{\underset{..}{Xe}}: \;+\; PtF_6 \;\rightarrow\; [:\overset{..}{\underset{..}{Xe}}\cdot]^+[PtF_6]^-$$

colorless   red in   yellow solid
gas   vapor state

Also, xenon tetrafluoride, XeF_4, a yellow crystalline solid, was prepared by direct interaction of xenon and fluorine,

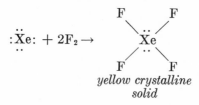

yellow crystalline solid

In XeF_4, xenon has twelve outer electrons. The dike was broken; in a short time, XeF_2, XeF_6, $XeOF_4$, XeF_4, KrF_2, and several others were synthesized.

9.11 COORDINATE COVALENT BOND

In the example given for the formation of a covalent bond (page 211), each atom contributes one electron. This equality of electron donation is not universal in covalent bonding. Covalent bonds can also be formed by having *one* atom contribute *both* electrons. The reaction between boron trifluoride and ammonia is illustrative,

$$\underset{\substack{|\\F}}{\overset{\substack{F\\|}}{F-B}} + \underset{\substack{|\\H}}{\overset{\substack{H\\|}}{:N-H}} \rightleftharpoons \underset{\substack{|\\F}}{\overset{\substack{F\\|}}{F-B}}:\underset{\substack{|\\H}}{\overset{\substack{H\\|}}{N-H}}$$

The N atom in NH_3 contributes both electrons and is called the *donor* atom. The B atom in BF_3 brings no electrons to the "marriage," and is therefore called the *acceptor* atom. Bonds formed between donor and acceptor atoms are called **coordinate covalent.** It should be emphasized, however, that *once a coordinate covalent bond is formed, it is indistinguishable from the covalent bond;* the N—B bond is *covalent.*

9.12 FORMAL CHARGE AND OXIDATION NUMBER

(a) **Formal Charge.** In coordinate covalent bonding, the *donor atom* suffers some *loss* of negative charge because of displacement of the electron cloud toward the acceptor atom. Coincidentally, the acceptor atom gains some negative charge by virtue of this displacement. If we assume *by convention*, that this electronic displacement is just sufficient to distribute the shared electrons equally between the two atoms, then it is possible to assign integral charge values to the two atoms. These values are called **formal charges.** Formal charges must be distinguished from the ionic charges assigned to electrically independent species like Ba^{2+} and F^-. When two molecules combine by coordinate covalent bonding, the donor atom acquires a $+1$ unit of formal charge and the acceptor atom acquires a -1 unit of formal charge for each coordinate covalent bond formed. Thus, the product in the last equation, $H_3N—BF_3$, has a

$+1$ formal charge on the N atom, and a -1 formal charge on the B atom. To indicate these charges, the molecule is frequently written

$$H_3\overset{+}{N}{-}\overset{-}{B}F_3$$

The chemical reactivity and physical properties of a molecule are influenced by the electronic displacements as indicated by the assignment of formal charges. Hence, it is necessary to be able to assign formal charges by examining electronic structures of molecules. The convention for calculating formal charges arbitrarily divides shared electrons equally between bonded atoms. Hence, for each of its bonds, an atom is assigned one electron. This number of electrons added to the number of unshared electrons gives the total allotment which is subtracted from the number of valence electrons to give the formal charge. Since the number of valence electrons is the same as the Group number in the Periodic Table, we can say that

formal charge = Group number in Periodic Table (valence electrons) minus (number of bonds plus number of unshared electrons)

The calculation of formal charge is given in the tabulation for nitric acid, whose electronic structure is distorted to show the assignment of electrons.

Group number − (number of bonds + number of unshared electrons) = $\dfrac{formal}{charge}$

For H	1	− (	1	+	0	) =	0
O$^\alpha$	6	− (	2	+	4	) =	0
O$^\beta$	6	− (	1	+	6	) =	−1
O$^\gamma$	6	− (	2	+	4	) =	0
N	5	− (	4	+	0	) =	+1
						Total formal charge =	0

Notice that the N atom in nitric acid has four covalent bonds. Its normal covalency of three is thus exceeded by one and, as a result, it has a formal charge of $+1$. Likewise, O$^\beta$ has only one covalent bond, one less than its normal covalency. As a result, it has a formal charge of -1. Invariably, *for an atom with an* **octet** *of electrons, a negative charge results when the covalency is less than normal* and, conversely, *a positive charge results when the covalency is more than normal.* The sum of formal charges of all atoms in a molecule must be equal to zero. For an ion, the sum of formal charges equals the charge of the ion. For example, NH_4 must be an ion with a charge of $+1$, since the N atom has a formal charge of $+1$ and the H atoms have zero formal charge.

EXAMPLE 2 **Which of the following structures are ions? Determine their charges.**

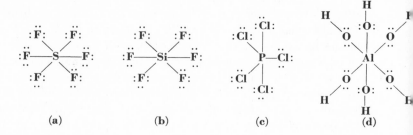

(a)   (b)   (c)   (d)

ANSWER

(a) Formal charge of S $= 6 - (6 + 0) = 0$
  Formal charge of F $= 7 - (1 + 6) = 0$; SF$_6$ is a molecule.
(b) Formal charge of Si $= 4 - (6 + 0) = -2$
  Formal charge of F $= 7 - (1 + 6) = 0$; SiF$_6$ is an ion; charge $= -2$.
(c) Formal charge of P $= 5 - (5 + 0) = 0$
  Formal charge of Cl $= 7 - (1 + 6) = 0$; PCl$_5$ is a molecule.
(d) Formal charge of Al $= 3 - (6 + 0) = -3$
  Formal charge of O $= 6 - (2 + 4) = 0$
  Formal charge of H $= 1 - (1 + 0) = 0$; Al(OH)$_6$ is an ion; charge $= -3$.

(b) Oxidation Number. In calculating formal charge, we assumed that the electron density resulting from the shared pair of electrons was midway between the bonded atoms. From the discussion of polar bonds (page 214) we know this need not be the case. Therefore if we assume arbitrarily that the electronic displacement occurs as if there were ionization, that is, *both electrons are assigned to the more electronegative atom,* then both atoms may be characterized by *another* set of integral charge values. These values are called **oxidation numbers,** and are said to represent the **oxidation state** of the element. A difference in electronegativity is always presumed for a bond between unlike elements. The convention for evaluating oxidation number arbitrarily assigns both electrons of a covalent bond to the more electronegative atom. Again, the allotted number of bonded electrons and the number of unshared electrons are subtracted from the number of valence electrons. When dealing with a representative element, the number of valence electrons is the same as the Group number of the atom in the Periodic Table,

oxidation number = number of valence electrons (Group number)
minus (number of assigned bonded electrons
plus number of unshared electrons)

Nitric acid is again used as an illustration, so that the reader can compare this method to the one used for obtaining formal charge. Since oxygen is more electronegative than nitrogen, the pair of electrons is allotted to the oxygen atoms, as indicated by the arrows. The distorted electronic structure shows the resulting allotment of electrons:

$$\overset{\beta}{\underset{}{\overset{..}{\underset{..}{:O:}}}}$$

$$\overset{\alpha}{H}\!\!\overset{..}{\underset{..}{-O}}\!\!-\!\!N\!\!=\!\!\overset{..}{\underset{..}{O}}:^{\gamma}$$

$$\overset{\beta}{\overset{..}{:O:}}$$

$$\overset{\alpha}{H}\ \overset{..}{\underset{..}{:O:}}\ N\ \overset{..}{::}\overset{..}{\underset{..}{O}}:^{\gamma}$$

$$\text{Group number} - (\text{allotted shared electrons} + \text{unshared electrons}) = \frac{\text{oxidation}}{\text{number}}$$

For H	1	$-$ (	**0**	$+$	**0**	) $=$	1
O^{α}	6	$-$ (	4	$+$	4	) $=$	-2
O^{β}	6	$-$ (	2	$+$	6	) $=$	-2
O^{γ}	6	$-$ (	4	$+$	4	) $=$	-2
N	5	$-$ (	0	$+$	0	) $=$	$+5$

Total oxidation number $=$	0

The sum of the individual oxidation numbers equals the actual charge on the substance: zero for molecules, and an integer for ions. Recall that this is also true for the sum of the formal charges.

EXAMPLE 3 **Calculate the oxidation number of each atom in the thiosulfate ion, $S_2O_3{}^{2-}$, whose electronic structure is**

$$\left[\ \overset{:S:}{\underset{:O:}{:O-S-O:}}\ \right]^{2-}$$

ANSWER **Oxygen is more electronegative than sulfur, so all electrons shared by these atoms are allotted to oxygen. Since the S atoms have the same electronegativity, the electrons are presumed to be equally shared, and one electron is allotted to each S atom. Thus, we have**

$$\left[\ \overset{:S:}{\underset{:O:}{:O:\ S\ :O:}}\ \right]^{2-}$$

S, central: $6 - (1 + 0) = +5$

S, outer : $6 - (1 + 6) = -1$

O, each : $6 - (2 + 6) = -2$

Note that the sum of the oxidation numbers of all the atoms equals the charge on the ion, $3(-2) + 5 + (-1) = -2$.

This method of calculating oxidation numbers requires a prior knowledge of Lewis electronic structures. Such structures are especially troublesome to write for molecules and ions containing transition elements. Fortunately, operational rules can be used to deduce oxidation numbers from molecular formulas without having to write electronic structures. These rules, however, are derived from the method just discussed.

Rule (1). The order of decreasing electronegativities of the more prominent of the most electronegative atoms is

$$F\ (-1) > O\ (-2) > Cl\ (-1) > N\ (-3) > Br\ (-1) > S\ (-2)$$
$$> I\ (-1) > C\ (-4) > P\ (-3) > H\ (-1)$$

Each value shown in parentheses is the oxidation number for the element when it is bonded to a *less electronegative atom*. The less electronegative atom is then assigned an oxidation number so that the total of the oxidation numbers of all atoms is equal to the charge on the substance. This rule is illustrated as follows (the number below the symbol for the atom representing the oxidation number):

H_2O	CaH_2	$SiF_6{}^{2-}$	H_2S	SO_2	OF_2	NH_3	NCl_3
$+1\ -2$	$+2\ -1$	$+4\ -1$	$+1\ -2$	$+4\ -2$	$+2\ -1$	$-3\ +1$	$+3\ -1$

NI_3		CH_4	CO_2		$MnO_4{}^-$	$Cr_2O_7{}^{2-}$	$S_2O_3{}^{2-}$
$-3\ +1$		$-4\ +1$	$+4\ -2$		$+7\ -2$	$+6\ -2$	$+2\ -2$

The detailed calculation of the oxidation number of the dichromate ion, $Cr_2O_7{}^{2-}$, is shown below. The charge on the ion is

$$(2 \times \text{oxidation number of Cr}) + (7 \times \text{oxidation number of O}) = -2$$

Let x = oxidation number of Cr. Since -2 is the oxidation number of O when bonded to a less electronegative atom, then

$$2x + 7(-2) = -2$$
$$x = +6$$

Similarly, for $S_2O_3{}^{2-}$, let x = oxidation number of S. Then

$$2x + 3(-2) = -2$$
$$x = +2$$

Note that the value obtained for the S atoms in thiosulfate ion, $S_2O_3{}^{2-}$, is the average of the values obtained for the individual S atoms by the method of allotting electrons, as done in Example 3 (page 223). Such average values are always obtained when the rules are used for molecules or ions having at least two atoms of the same element with different oxidation numbers.

Rule (2). Whenever an H atom is bonded to a more electronegative atom, it has an oxidation number of $+1$. This rule is especially useful in calculating the oxidation numbers of carbon atoms in organic molecules, as shown below.

Methyl alcohol H_3COH	O = -2; H = $+1$; therefore, C = -2
Formaldehyde H_2CO	O = -2; H = $+1$		C = 0
Formic acid $HCO(OH)$	O = -2; H = $+1$		C = $+2$

Rule (3). When two like atoms are bonded to each other and not bonded to *more* electronegative atoms, there is an increase in the oxidation numbers, listed in Rule (1), by a unit of *one* for each bond between the atoms. Thus, we find the following values:

Chlorine	$:\ddot{C}l\!-\!\ddot{C}l:$	$Cl = -1 + 1 = 0$
Hydrogen peroxide	$H\!-\!\ddot{O}\!-\!\ddot{O}\!-\!H$	$O = -2 + 1 = -1$
Hydrazine	$H_2\ddot{N}\!-\!\ddot{N}H_2$	$N = -3 + 1 = -2$
Nitrogen	$:N\!\equiv\!N:$	$N = -3 + 3 = 0$
Ethane	$H_3C\!-\!CH_3$	$C = -4 + 1 = -3$
Ethylene	$H_2C\!=\!CH_2$	$C = -4 + 2 = -2$
Acetylene	$H\!-\!C\!\equiv\!C\!-\!H$	$C = -4 + 3 = -1$

In the case of diamond (Fig. 9.3), each C atom is singly bonded to *four* other C atoms. Therefore, four positive units are added to -4, the listed value for carbon, to give an oxidation number of zero for the carbon atoms in diamond. In fact, *whenever an atom is found in its elementary state, its oxidation number is zero*, for example, Cl_2, N_2, and C.

Rule (4). In salts, each ion is treated separately, as shown for ammonium sulfate, $(NH_4)_2SO_4$,

$$\underset{-3\ \ +1}{NH_4^+} \quad \underset{+6\ \ -2}{SO_4^{2-}}$$

The total of the oxidation numbers of all atoms in the salt must equal zero. *The oxidation number for monatomic ions such as* K^+, Ca^{2+}, Al^{3+}, Cl^-, *and* S^{2-} *is the ionic charge.*

Oxidation number should not be confused with covalency. Covalency represents the number of bonds an atom forms when it has no formal charge. Covalency has no charge associated with it, whereas oxidation number has. For example, carbon has a covalency of four. On the other

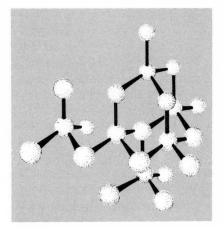

Fig. 9.3. *Structure of diamond.*

hand, the oxidation number of carbon can vary from -4 in CH_4 to $+4$ in CO_2, with all intermediate values, as shown in the previous discussion. In sucrose, which is common cane sugar, $C_{12}H_{22}O_{11}$, carbon has an oxidation number of zero.

In summary, the assignment of electrons for calculating the oxidation number recognizes the ionic character of the bond, whereas the method for assigning formal charge recognizes the covalent character of the bond. Since most bonds formed by sharing electrons are somewhere between purely covalent and purely ionic, neither assigned charge is real. However, both concepts have utility in the further study of chemistry.

(c) **Oxidation Number and Redox Reactions.** The concept of oxidation number is useful in recognizing the occurrence of a redox reaction involving covalently bonded atoms. The terms *oxidation* and *reduction* have been defined in terms of transfer of electrons (page 207). However, in reactions of covalent molecules, or polyatomic ions, the concept of oxidation-reduction is much more nebulous. For example, does oxidation-reduction occur in the following reactions?

$$2H_2 + O_2 \rightarrow 2H_2O$$
$$ 0 0 {+1} \; {-2}$$

$$CH_4 + Cl_2 \rightarrow CH_3Cl + HCl$$
$${-4} \; {+1} 0 {-2} \; {+1} \; {-1} {+1} \; {-1}$$

The answer is in the affirmative, since in both reactions there is a change in oxidation number of certain atoms as shown. For reactions involving alterations in covalent bonds, we define *reduction* as *reduction in oxidation number*, and *oxidation* as *increase in oxidation number*. Thus, in the above reactions, hydrogen is oxidized and oxygen is reduced, and methane, CH_4, is oxidized and chlorine is reduced. When a compound contains an atom that undergoes a change in oxidation number, the *compound* is said to be reduced or oxidized. For this reason we say that methane in the above reaction is oxidized. Hydrogen, which was oxidized, can be said to have reduced the oxygen, and is therefore called the **reducing agent** or **reductant.** The oxygen, which was reduced, can be said to have oxidized the hydrogen, and is therefore called the **oxidizing agent** or **oxidant.** In general, in any redox reaction, (a) the substance containing the atom which shows a *decrease in oxidation number* is the *oxidant*, and (b) the substance containing the atom which shows an *increase in oxidation number* is the *reductant*.

In some reactions the same substance can be the oxidant and the reductant. Such a reaction, typified by the hydrolysis (reaction with water) of nitrogen dioxide, NO_2, is called an **auto-oxidation,** or a **disproportionation,**

$$2NO_2 + H_2O \rightarrow H O N O_2 + H O N O$$
$${+4} \; {-2} {+1} \; {-2} {+1} \; {-2} \; {+5} \; {-2} {+1} \; {-2} \; {+3} \; {-2}$$

$$\text{\textit{nitrogen}} \qquad\qquad \text{\textit{nitric}} \qquad \text{\textit{nitrous}}$$
$$\text{\textit{dioxide}} \qquad\qquad\quad \text{\textit{acid}} \qquad\quad \text{\textit{acid}}$$

Thus, one molecule of NO_2 is oxidized to nitric acid, $HONO_2$, and one molecule of NO_2 is reduced to nitrous acid, $HONO$.

9.13 WRITING LEWIS STRUCTURES

The previous discussion stresses the necessity of being able to write Lewis structures. This need will be paramount when the subject of molecular geometry is discussed in Chapter 24. Although it is impossible to give foolproof rules for writing Lewis structures from molecular formulas, some helpful guides can be offered.

1. Guide for Writing the Sequential Arrangement of Atoms. The formulas of many molecules and ions take the form AB_x or B_xA. In most cases, the sequential arrangement of atoms, the so-called **skeleton,** has x atoms of B attached to and surrounding the **central atom,** A, as in the sulfate (SO_4^{2-}) ion

$$\left[\begin{array}{c} O \\ | \\ O-S-O \\ | \\ O \end{array} \right]^{2-}$$

or as in H_2O, $H-O-H$. The symbol B might stand for a group of atoms, such as OH, as in $Al(OH)_6^{3-}$ (page 222). Some formulas take the form AB_xD_y. In general, these molecules have x B atoms or groups and y D atoms or groups bonded to atom A. Thus, SO_2Cl_2 has the skeleton

Cl—S—Cl   *sulfuryl chloride*

At this stage of the discussion we are not concerned with the actual angles made by the groups attached to the central atom. (The subject of molecular geometry is discussed in detail in Chapter 24.) In this book, molecular formulas are usually written so as to show the proper groupings of atoms as they are arranged in the molecule. Thus, the formula for sulfuric acid is written $(HO)_2SO_2$, rather than H_2SO_4, to show that two atoms of oxygen and two OH groups are attached to the S atom,

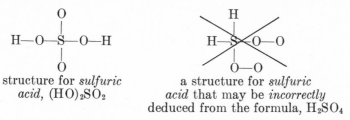

structure for *sulfuric*   a structure for *sulfuric*
acid, $(HO)_2SO_2$ acid that may be *incorrectly*
         deduced from the formula, H_2SO_4

Other examples of the use and interpretation of such *condensed formulas* are

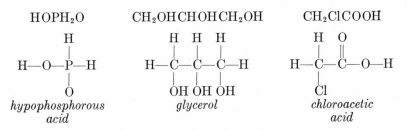

HOPH$_2$O   CH$_2$OHCHOHCH$_2$OH   CH$_2$ClCOOH

hypophosphorous acid   *glycerol*   *chloroacetic acid*

In the structure B$_z$A or AB$_z$, *A will be the central atom if it has a higher covalency or is capable of having a higher oxidation number than B.* Otherwise, we may have an exceptional structure in which one of the B atoms is central. For example, since oxygen has a smaller covalency than nitrogen, the skeleton for nitrous oxide, N$_2$O, is N—N—O rather than N—O—N.

Structures of the type A$_z$B$_y$ pose a problem. One can make a judicious guess by writing a symmetrical skeleton. Thus, for N$_2$O$_3$, N$_2$O$_4$, and N$_2$O$_5$, we have the following symmetrical skeletons (shown with the correct bonding):

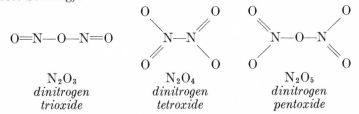

O=N—O—N=O

N$_2$O$_3$
dinitrogen trioxide

N$_2$O$_4$
dinitrogen tetroxide

N$_2$O$_5$
dinitrogen pentoxide

However, this type of reasoning can occasionally lead to incorrect structures, as evidenced by the unsymmetrical structure for the thiosulfate ion, S$_2$O$_3^{2-}$ (page 223).

2. The Number of Electrons in the Lewis Structure. These rules hold for species containing *only* representative elements. The number of electrons in the Lewis structure for

(a) a neutral molecule = the sum of the *valence* electrons of the component atoms; for example, the number of electrons is 8 for NH$_3$, 20 for F$_2$O, and 17 for NO$_2$;

(b) a negative ion = the sum of the valence electrons of the component atoms plus the negative charge; the number of electrons is 8 for OH$^-$, 24 for CO$_3^{2-}$, and 32 for SO$_4^{2-}$;

(c) a positive ion = the sum of the valence electrons of the component atoms minus the positive charge; thus, the ammonium ion, NH$_4^+$, has 8 electrons.

A substance with an *odd* number of electrons must be a *free radical* (page 217).

3. Recognizing the Presence of Multiple Bonds. This discussion assumes the octet rule.

(a) For molecules or ions having *only single bonds*, the number of bonds is *one less* than the number of atoms. Thus, H$_2$O has two single bonds, NH$_3$ has three single bonds, and CH$_4$ has four single bonds.

Molecule or ion	Needed electrons	Actual electrons	Deficiency	Structure
CO	14	$4 + 6 = 10$	4	$:C\equiv O:$
SO_2	20	$6 + (2 \times 6) = 18$	2	$:\ddot{O}-\ddot{S}=\ddot{O}:$
$COCl_2$	26	$4 + 6 + (2 \times 7) = 24$	2	$:\ddot{Cl}-\overset{\overset{\displaystyle :\ddot{O}}{\|}}{C}-\ddot{Cl}:$
$CO_3{}^{2-}$	26	$4 + (3 \times 6) + 2 = 24$	2	$\left[\;\overset{\overset{\displaystyle \ddot{O}:}{\|}}{\underset{:\ddot{O}\diagup\;\;\diagdown\ddot{O}:}{C}}\;\right]^{2-}$

(b) If a *molecule* without H atoms has *only single bonds,* the sum of the valence electrons will be 8 for each atom, less 2 for each single bond. This fact is illustrated in the following typical compounds:

Cl_2 (chlorine)   is diatomic and has 14 electrons
OF_2 (oxygen difluoride)   is triatomic and has 20 electrons
NF_3 (nitrogen trifluoride) is tetratomic and has 26 electrons
CCl_4 (carbon tetrachloride) is pentatomic and has 32 electrons

Molecules with only single bonds are said to be **saturated.**

(c) A hydrogen atom requires a duet rather than an octet of electrons. Therefore, a saturated, hydrogen-bearing molecule must have 2 electrons for each H atom, 8 electrons for each of the other atoms, less 2 for each single bond.

(d) *When the number of valence electrons is fewer than the required number for a saturated molecule, multiple bonding occurs.* One multiple bond is needed for each deficiency of 2 electrons. A triple bond or two double bonds remedies a deficiency of 4 electrons. Illustrations are given in the tabulation above.

(e) In some cases, the deficiency can be remedied by having a cyclic (ring) structure. Each ring in the molecule makes up for the absence of 2 electrons. An example of a cyclic molecule is S_8, the stable form of elementary sulfur,

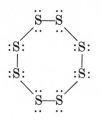

Ring formation is *rare* among the compounds encountered in this text. Therefore, *do not write ring structures unless the molecule is specified as being cyclic.*

(f) When the number of valence electrons *exceeds* the number a molecule requires to follow the octet rule, *the excess electrons are assigned to the central atom.* For example, bromine trifluoride, BrF_3, has twenty-eight (7×4) valence electrons. Only twenty-six $[(4 \times 8) - 6]$ electrons are required to satisfy the octet requirement for each atom. The extra two electrons are given to the Br atom, which has ten electrons,

4. Selection of Best of Several Possible Electronic Structures. Even when the correct skeleton has been chosen and the correct number of single and multiple bonds has been determined, it may happen that more than one electronic structure can be written. In such cases, *always give preference to the structure that obeys the octet rule.* If more than one structure follows the octet rule, then *give preference to the one that meets the covalency requirements.* The structure that meets the covalency requirements will invariably be the one without formal charge. Therefore, the structure having zero formal charge on all its atoms is preferred to the structure whose atoms have formal charge. For example, more than one electronic structure can be written for CO_2,

$$:\overset{..}{O}{=}C{=}\overset{..}{O}: \qquad \overset{+}{:}O{\equiv}C{-}\overset{..}{\underset{..}{O}}{:}^{-}$$
$$\text{(a)} \qquad\qquad\quad \text{(b)}$$

Both are in accord with the octet rule. However, structure (a) is preferred because it follows the covalency requirement of 4 for carbon and 2 for oxygen, and, as a consequence, has no formal charge. Structure (b) does not follow the covalency requirement for oxygen, and consequently has atoms with formal charge.

EXAMPLE 4 **Suggest a plausible structure for (a) disulfur dichloride, S_2Cl_2, and (b) carbon suboxide, C_3O_2 (noncyclic).**

ANSWER (a) S_2Cl_2 **has 26 valence electrons. Since it has 3 bonds, it needs 26 valence electrons $[(4 \times 8) - 6]$ to be saturated. The molecule has the requisite number and therefore has only single bonds. Sulfur has a higher covalency than chlorine, and therefore is the central atom. If we assume a symmetrical skeleton, the Lewis structure is**

$$:\overset{..}{\underset{..}{Cl}} \qquad \overset{..}{S}$$
$$\diagdown\overset{..}{\underset{..}{S}}\diagup\diagdown\overset{..}{\underset{..}{Cl}}:$$

disulfur dichloride

(b) Carbon has a higher covalency than oxygen and should be the central atom. If we assume a symmetrical arrangement of atoms, the skeleton should be O—C—C—C—O; C_3O_2 has 24 valence electrons and so lacks 8 electrons of being *saturated*. This deficiency is best accommodated by four double bonds so that the covalency requirement of each atom is satisfied. Therefore, the Lewis structure is

$$:\overset{..}{O}=C=C=C=\overset{..}{O}:$$
carbon suboxide

9.14 PERIODICITY OF BONDING, VALENCE, AND OXIDATION NUMBER

If a representative atom is to form a *monoatomic anion* (transition elements seldom form anions) that is isoelectronic with the noble gas of next higher atomic number, then the *anionic charge* must be the Group number (G) minus 8 or (G − 8). Thus, sulfur (Group VIA) would become S^{2-}, and nitrogen (Group VA) would become N^{3-}. Certain periodic trends of anion formation are discernible:

(a) *The ability of an element to participate in ionic bonding by forming an anion decreases as the group number decreases.* Thus, there are more ionic fluorides (G = 7) than nitrides (G = 5). This trend is a consequence of the fact that fluorine must gain only one electron to form F^-, whereas nitrogen must gain three electrons to form N^{3-}. It becomes increasingly difficult to acquire successive numbers of electrons.

(b) *The ability of elements, within a given group, to form anions, decreases with increasing atomic weight.* Thus, there are more ionic fluorides than chlorides, bromides, or iodides.

If an atom is to form a *cation* that is isoelectronic with the noble gas of the nearest lower atomic number, then the cationic charge must be numerically equal to the Group number (G). The most favorable circumstances for the existence of cations is in combination as anhydrous salts (free from water) with polyatomic anions, such as perchlorate, ClO_4^-; nitrate, NO_3^-; sulfate, SO_4^{2-}; carbonate, CO_3^{2-}; and phosphate, PO_4^{3-}. If an element does not form a salt-like compound with these anions, then the element cannot sustain a cationic state, and it will *share* rather than *lose* electrons. The ability of an element to support a positive charge depends on the **charge density of the cation.** The definition of the cationic charge density is

$$\text{cationic charge density} = \frac{\text{magnitude of positive charge}}{\text{volume of the cation*}}$$

Table 9.4 gives periodic trends in the charge densities of real and imaginary cations. The values given in this table are *relative* charge densities, the value for Fr^+, the ion of least charge density, being taken as 1.

Small values, such as those of Group IA, indicate stable cations; large

* Volumes of those cations that are imaginary are derived from quantum mechanical calculations.

TABLE 9.4 *Relative Real and Hypothethical Cationic Charge Densities of the Elements*

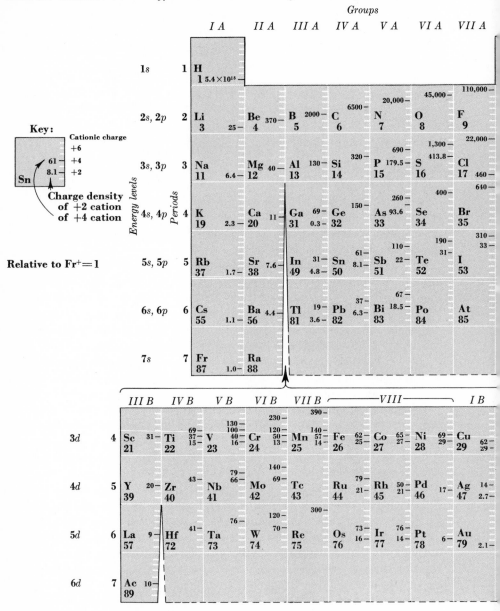

values such as those for C^{4+}, H^+, and N^{5+} indicate imaginary cations. Unfortunately, an unequivocal relationship cannot be drawn between the magnitude of the cationic charge density of an element and the element's tendency to form ionic salts. We have already seen (page 208) that the crystal lattice energy is an important factor in determining the heat of formation of a crystalline salt. Thus, we find that although aluminum has the fairly high cationic charge density of 130, it nevertheless forms a stable sulfate salt. The formation of aluminum sulfate is accounted for mainly because of the large crystal lattice energy arising from the strong electrostatic attraction between the Al^{3+} and SO_4^{2-} ions. Some useful but approximate generalizations, nevertheless, can be made:

(a) Elements form ionic compounds in those cationic states with charge densities of 50 or less. These elements also form ionic compounds (salts) with the halogen atoms.

(b) Elements with cationic charge densities ranging from 50 to about 100 form ionic and covalent bonds.

(c) Elements with values above 100 form mainly, but not exclusively, covalent bonds.

Certain definite trends are discernible from this table. These trends are helpful in organizing and generalizing the known chemistry of many elements:

(a) As we proceed down a group, the cationic charge density decreases and hence the likelihood of finding a cationic state increases. Thus, there are more ionic compounds of thallium (Tl) than of aluminum (Al).

(b) Among the Group A elements, the drop in cationic charge density is most pronounced on proceeding from the second to the third Period. For this reason the chemistry of the elements in the second Period is atypical of their group. Thus, we find that although all the alkali metals (Group IA) form cations, a tendency toward covalent bonding is sometimes observed for lithium. For example, when combined with carbon, as in ethyllithium, CH_3CH_2Li, lithium forms bonds with some covalent character. Unlike the other members of their respective groups, beryllium (Group IIA) rarely forms Be^{2+}, and boron (Group IIIA) never forms B^{3+}.

(c) For any element, the lower the charge state, the lower the cationic charge density and the more likely it is that the cation exists. Therefore, metals are more likely to form ionic compounds in their lower valence states than in their higher ones. (Compare the ionic species $PbCl_2$, m.p. 501°C, with the covalent species $PbCl_4$, m.p. −15°C, in terms of cationic charge densities.)

Another important trend related to periodicity is apparent in Groups IIIA, IVA, and VA, each of which has elements with more than one valence state. It is observed that, within a group, the higher valence state is more stable for the lighter elements, and the lower valence state becomes progressively more stable as the atomic weight increases. Thus, we find that in their stable compounds, carbon and silicon are found only in the tetravalent state. Divalence is observed for germanium, but its tetravalent state is more stable. Thus, although germanium dichloride can be prepared, it is readily converted to the tetrachloride by an auto-oxidation reaction,

$$2GeCl_2 \rightarrow Ge + GeCl_4 \quad \text{(at 75°C)}$$

Tin and lead are much more stable in the divalent than in the tetravalent state, as evidenced by the spontaneous decomposition of lead tetrachloride,

$$PbCl_4 \rightarrow PbCl_2 + Cl_2$$

In Group IIIA, we find that Tl^+ is more stable than Tl^{3+}, whereas Al is found only in the trivalent state. In Group VA, Bi^{3+} is more stable than Bi^{5+}. The changes in order of stability are most noticeable in going from Period 4 to Period 5. It is in Period 5 that the "inert pair $(5s^2)$ effect" becomes apparent. The effect of the "inert pair" is most noticeable in Period 6.

Even though an atom may not actually transfer electrons to form a cation, it can nevertheless acquire a positive oxidation state. For representative elements and for transition elements in Groups IIB, IIIB, IVB, VB, VIB, and VIIB, the maximum attainable oxidation state is equal to the Group number, G. Thus, carbon, in Group IVA, has a maximum oxidation number of $+4$, as in CO_2; nitrogen in Group VA has a maximum oxidation number of $+5$, as in nitric acid, $HONO_2$; and chromium in Group VIB has a maximum oxidation number of $+6$, as in the chromate ion, CrO_4^{2-}. This generalization does not hold for fluorine (Group VIIA), whose maximum oxidation number is 0, as in F_2, or for oxygen (Group VIA), whose maximum oxidation state is $+2$, as found only in OF_2.

Again, as was observed for valence, within a representative group the higher oxidation states are more stable for the lighter elements, but the lower oxidation states are more stable for the heavier atoms. For example, among the Group VA elements, it is observed that $HON^{III}O$ is easily *oxidized* to $HON^{V}O_2$, whereas arsenic acid, $(HO)_3As^{V}O$, is readily *reduced* to arsenious acid, $HOAs^{III}O$. The Roman numeral superscripts indicate the oxidation states.

9.15 EPILOGUE

Our discussion of the nature and stability of compounds has significance only within the familiar reference frame of temperature and pressure. At temperatures in the range 10^3 to 10^8 °C, the population of molecules becomes smaller and smaller, and atoms and ions become the important species. Some "typical" species existing in this temperature range are N, O, CaH, AlCl, Al_2C_2, $(LiF)_3$, Na_2Cl^+, and $NaCl_2^-$. At high pressures, 10^5 to 10^6 atmospheres, most substances become metallic (page 701); wood and chalk $(CaCO_3)$, for example, become metallic conductors under pressures of about 10^5 atmospheres. At high temperatures, elements in the gaseous state can be stripped of electrons to give a material called **plasma.**

Problems

1. Bond type. Write an electronic structure for the binary compound formed from each pair of listed elements. Indicate the type of bond formed and explain your choice. (a) H, Te; (b) Ba, Cl; (c) Cs, N; (d) Be, Br; (e) Bi, F; (f) K, S; (g) Al, O; (h) H, Ca; (i) N, I; (j) S, Cl.

2. Coordination number; ionic radii. Determine the coordination number of both cation and anion in the following compounds (the ionic radii are given): (a) CsCl; (b) CsI; (c) CaS.

$$Ionic\ radii\ (A)$$

$Cs^+ = 1.69$	$Ca^{2+} = 0.99$
$Cl^- = 1.81$	$I^- = 2.16$
$S^{2-} = 1.84$	

3. Covalency. Write electronic structures, consistent with the octet and covalency rules, for the following molecules: (a) CH_2Cl_2; (b) CH_4O; (c) H_4N_2; (d) C_2H_6O (two possibilities); (e) H_3NO; (f) CH_5N; (g) C_2H_7N (two possibilities); (h) Si_2H_6; (i) H_2O_2.

4. Multiple bonding. Write suitable electronic structures, consistent with the octet rule and the covalency rules, for the following molecules, all of which possess at least one multiple bond: (a) CS_2; (b) NOCl; (c) HNCO; (d) C_3H_6; (e) $COCl_2$; (f) H_2CO; (g) HCOOH; (h) N_2F_2; (i) $(H_2N)_2CO$; (j) H_2C_2O.

5. Properties of molecules. Compare the physical properties of (a) NaH and HCl; (b) $BeCl_2$ and $BaCl_2$; (c) SiF_4 and SiO_2.

6. Electronegativities. (a) Indicate the fractional charge, if any, on the atoms in each of the following bonds [consult table of electronegativities (Table 9.2, page 216)]: B—Cl; C—Cl; N—Cl; O—Cl; F—Cl. (b) List three plausible covalent bonds between dissimilar atoms which would show no polarity.

7. Free radicals. Tetramethyl lead, $(CH_3)_4Pb$, is a liquid, b.p. 110°C. When heated, it decomposes, leaving lead and mainly ethane, CH_3CH_3. (a) Write an electronic structural formula for $(CH_3)_4Pb$. (b) Write an equation for each of the two reactions that accounts for the products.

8. Coordinate covalent bond. (a) What must be the essential feature of each of two reacting species to form a coordinate covalent bond? (b) Use electronic structures to show how each of the following substances is formed through formation of a coordinate bond: AlH_4^-; BCl_4^-; H_3O^+; NH_4^+; $CH_3NH_2BF_3$.

9. Oxidation number. Evaluate the oxidation number of the italicized atom in (a) $(O_2P—O—PO_2)_2$, i.e., P_4O_{10}; (b) $HPO(OH)_2$; (c) $H_2C{=}O$; (d) $XeOF_3$;

(e) $TiO^{2+}(SO_4)^{2-}$; (f) $NH_4(VO_3)$; (g) O_2^+; (h) $CH_3\overset{\displaystyle H}{\underset{\displaystyle |}{C}}{=}O$.

10. Formal charge and oxidation number. (a) Write structural formulas for $(HO)_2SO_2$, sulfuric acid; NH_3BF_3; HOClO, chlorous acid. (b) Locate all formal charges. (c) Determine the oxidation numbers of those atoms having a formal charge. (d) Are formal charges and oxidation numbers identical?

11. Charge densities. Aluminum chloride dissolves in water with violent evolution of heat. Explain in terms of the calculated charge density of Al^{3+}.

12. Bond type. (a) Select A and B from among the elements of atomic number 1–9. Write electronic structures and indicate the type of bond formed in each compound (disregard molecules with multiple bonds):

(*i*) 3 compounds of formula AB_3 or A_3B
(*ii*) 5 compounds of formula AB_2 or A_2B
(*iii*) 4 compounds of formula AB
(*iv*) 2 compounds of formula AB_4 or A_4B
(*v*) 2 compounds of formula A_2B_3 or A_3B_2

(b) Indicate which compounds do not fit the octet rule. (c) Which compounds are likely to have a macromolecular covalent structure?

13. Properties of molecules. Carborundum or silicon carbide, SiC, has no multiple bonds. (*i*) Suggest a structural formula consistent with the octet and covalency rules; (*ii*) predict its melting point. Check your predictions by consulting *The Handbook of Chemistry and Physics*.

14. Free radicals. (a) Write electronic structures for O^{2-}; OH^-; H_2O_2; HO_2^-; O_2^{2-}; O_2^-. (b) Which of these, if any, is a free radical?

15. Born–Haber cycle. Calculate the lattice energy of MgO from the following data in kcal/mole:

			ΔH
Electron affinity	$O(g) + 2e^-$	$\rightarrow O^{2-}(g)$	$+ 156$
Dissociation bond energy	$O_2(g)$	$\rightarrow 2O(g)$	$+ 119.1$
Heat of sublimation	$Mg(c)$	$\rightarrow Mg(g)$	$+ 36.5$
Ionization energy	$Mg(g) - 2e^-$	$\rightarrow Mg^{2+}(g)$	$+ 523$
Heat of formation	$Mg(c) + \frac{1}{2}O_2(g) \rightarrow MgO(c)$		$- 143.7$

Answer. -919 kcal/mole.

16. Heat of Formation. (a) From the ΔH values given on page 208, find the heat of the reaction

$$Na(c) + \tfrac{1}{2}Cl_2(g) \rightarrow Na^+Cl^-(g)$$

(b) Why is crystalline rather than gaseous NaCl formed when sodium metal and chlorine gas react?

17. Formal charge and oxidation number. (a) Write a Lewis structure for hydrazoic acid, HN_3, whose skeleton is H—N—N—N. Make certain the structure obeys the octet rule. (b) Locate all formal charges. (c) Calculate the oxidation number for each atom. (d) Account for the fact that, for the middle N atom, the oxidation number and formal charge are identical.

18. Mixed bonding types. Write electronic structures for the following ionic compounds, consistent with the octet rule: (a) calcium carbide, CaC_2; (b) barium peroxide, BaO_2; (c) potassium amide, KNH_2; (d) potassium magnesium fluoride, $KMgF_3$; (e) potassium ethide, KC_2H_5.

19. Charge densities. Calculate the charge density (charge per unit volume) of Mg^{2+} and K^+ from their ionic radii, 0.65 A and 1.33 A, respectively.

Answer. 1.74, 0.102 charge units per A^3.

10

Hydrocarbons and their derivatives

10.1 BONDING OF CARBON

Carbon ($1s^2 2s^2 2p^2$) could become isoelectronic with helium ($1s^2$) by losing four electrons to become the C^{4+} ion, $\cdot \dot{C}: \rightarrow C^{4+} + 4e^-$. No compounds containing the C^{4+} ion are known to date. The non-existence of the C^{4+} ion is attributable mainly to two related factors:

(1) The extremely high ionization energy required to remove the four valence electrons from carbon. The successive values in kcal/mole are: 253, 552, 1104, and 1472, for a total of 3381 kcal/mole.

(2) The intolerably high charge density that this hypothetical cation would have to support (Table 9.4, page 232).

To become isoelectronic with neon, a carbon atom would have to gain four electrons and become C^{4-}. This process is rare; only two ionic-type compounds with a C^{4-} ion are known, Be_2C and Al_4C_3. In these two compounds, the lattice energy is sufficiently large to outweigh the large amount of energy required to add four electrons to carbon, and to remove the necessary number of electrons from the metal.

Instead of transferring electrons, carbon usually shares electrons, forming covalent bonds. This process is illustrated by the formation of methane and carbon tetrachloride from the elements,

$$4H\cdot + \cdot\dot{C}: \rightarrow \begin{matrix} H \\ H:\overset{\displaystyle\cdot\cdot}{\underset{\displaystyle\cdot\cdot}{C}}:H \\ H \end{matrix}$$

methane

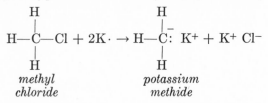

$$4:\overset{\cdot\cdot}{Cl}\cdot + \cdot\overset{\cdot}{C}:\rightarrow :\overset{\cdot\cdot}{Cl}:\overset{:\overset{\cdot\cdot}{Cl}:}{\underset{:\overset{\cdot\cdot}{Cl}:}{C}}:\overset{\cdot\cdot}{Cl}:$$

carbon tetrachloride

These representations are called *Lewis (electron dot) formulas.*

There are molecules in which a carbon atom can participate in both ionic and covalent bonding. When methyl chloride, CH_3Cl, reacts with potassium, potassium methide, CH_3K, is formed,

$$\underset{\underset{H}{|}}{\overset{\overset{H}{|}}{H-C-Cl}} + 2K\cdot \rightarrow \underset{\underset{H}{|}}{\overset{\overset{H}{|}}{H-C:}}\ K^+ + K^+\ Cl^-$$

methyl   *potassium*
chloride   *methide*

Potassium methide is a crystalline, ionic solid, in which there are three covalent C—H bonds, and one ionic bond between the $[:CH_3]^-$ anion and the K^+ cation. Such carbon anions, called **carbanions,** are almost invariably bonded only to the highly electropositive elements of Group IA or IIA. With the less electropositive metallic elements, carbon forms a covalent bond. For example, dimethylmercury, $H_3C-Hg-CH_3$, is a typical covalent molecule (b.p. 96°).

The cationic analog of CH_3^- is CH_3^+. Such a species, called a **carbonium ion,** has only a sextet of electrons about the carbon atom and, as expected, reacts readily in order to complete the octet. Only a very few carbonium ion salts have been isolated. However, carbonium ions are formed as very short-lived intermediates during the course of certain organic reactions (page 689).

Of particular significance is the fact that carbon atoms form covalent bonds with each other to give unbranched chains, branched chains, and cyclic compounds, as exemplified by the following structural formulas,

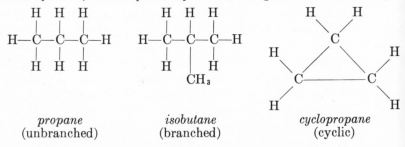

propane   *isobutane*   *cyclopropane*
(unbranched)   (branched)   (cyclic)

Molecules with hundreds of carbon atoms are known. For this reason, there is a myriad of carbon compounds, which explains the need for a separate branch of chemistry, **organic chemistry.** The chemistry of elements other than carbon is called **inorganic chemistry.** To be classified as **organic,** a compound should have at least one C—H or C—C bond. Certain compounds—such as carbon disulfide, CS_2, carbon tetrachloride, CCl_4, phosgene, $COCl_2$, and urea, $(H_2N)_2C=O$, are studied in organic chemistry although they do not possess a C—H or C—C bond. These compounds lie in the fringe region between organic and inorganic chemistry.

Practically all elements have been incorporated into organic molecules. The nonmetallic elements such as oxygen, nitrogen, sulfur, the halogens, phosphorus, silicon, and boron are most frequently covalently bonded to carbon. However, metallic elements also occur in organic molecules. The bond between carbon and metal atoms may have considerable ionic character, as in sodium methide, $[H_3C]^-Na^+$, or the bond may be covalent as in dimethylmercury, $(H_3C)_2Hg$. However, in most cases the bond is polar, with the positive center displaced toward the metal atom and the negative center displaced toward the carbon atom, for example,

$$\overset{\delta^-}{\underset{/}{\overset{\textstyle \diagdown}{{-}C}}}\overset{\delta^+}{{-}}\text{metal atom}$$

10.2   ALKANE HYDROCARBONS

Those organic compounds containing only carbon and hydrogen atoms are called **hydrocarbons.** The noncyclic or so-called *open-chain* compounds are known as **aliphatic hydrocarbons.** A subdivision of the aliphatic hydrocarbons comprises the *alkanes*, which are saturated; that is, they have no multiple bonds. The relationship between the contents of carbon and hydrogen atoms is expressed by the **general formula** C_nH_{2n+2}, where n is a whole number. The formulas for the first ten members of the alkane series are shown in Table 10.1, with their boiling and melting points. **Condensed formulas** are used in which the H atoms and CH_2 groups are grouped together instead of being shown individually. Note that each member of this class of compounds differs from its immediate neighbor by an increment of CH_2. A series of similar compounds in which the formulas change systematically by a unit of CH_2 is called a **homologous series.** Such series are numerous in organic chemistry. Members of homologous series have similarities in chemical properties, and show a systematic change in physical properties.

The boiling points, and in most cases the melting points, increase with increasing molecular weight. The first four alkanes are gases at standard conditions. *n*-Pentane is a liquid under ordinary conditions. *n*-Tetradecane, $C_{14}H_{30}$, has a melting point of 5.9°C, and *n*-octadecane, $C_{18}H_{38}$, is solid at room temperature. Low melting solid alkanes are constituents of petroleum jelly. Higher members of the series that are solid at room temperature comprise paraffin wax and asphalt tar.

The alkanes occur naturally in **petroleum.** The chemist takes advantage of differences in boiling point to separate the mixture into components by *distillation* (page 587). The petroleum industry generally is interested in isolating distillation fractions of mixtures of compounds with narrow ranges of carbon content, rather than pure alkanes. The important fractions are natural gas, C_1–C_2;* liquefied petroleum gas

* These symbols indicate the number of carbon atoms in the compounds in each fraction.

TABLE 10.1 *Names and Physical Properties of Normal[a] Alkanes, C_nH_{2n+2}*

Name	Molecular formula	Condensed formula	Boiling point (°C)	Melting point (°C)
Methane	CH_4	CH_4	−161.5	−182.5
Ethane	C_2H_6	CH_3CH_3	− 88.6	−183.3
Propane	C_3H_8	$CH_3CH_2CH_3$	− 42.1	−187.7
n-Butane[b]	C_4H_{10}	$CH_3CH_2CH_2CH_3$	− 0.5	−138.4
n-Pentane	C_5H_{12}	$CH_3(CH_2)_3CH_3$	36.1	−129.7
n-Hexane	C_6H_{14}	$CH_3(CH_2)_4CH_3$	68.7	− 95.3
n-Heptane	C_7H_{16}	$CH_3(CH_2)_5CH_3$	98.4	− 90.6
n-Octane	C_8H_{18}	$CH_3(CH_2)_6CH_3$	125.7	− 56.8
n-Nonane	C_9H_{20}	$CH_3(CH_2)_7CH_3$	150.8	− 53.5
n-Decane	$C_{10}H_{22}$	$CH_3(CH_2)_8CH_3$	174.1	− 29.7

[a] The term "normal" is explained on page 242.   [b] The symbol n denotes normal.

(LPG), C_3–C_4; petroleum ether, C_5–C_6; gasoline, C_7–C_9; kerosene, C_{12}–C_{14}; and diesel and fuel oils, C_{16}–C_{18}. The very high-boiling lubricating oils and the solid paraffin waxes and asphalt tar do not distill, and hence are recovered from the distillation residue.

Chemically, the alkanes are characterized by their inertness. For this reason they are also called **paraffins,** from the Latin *parum affinis,* meaning "of little affinity." They do not react with bases such as sodium hydroxide, or with acids; even concentrated sulfuric acid leaves them unchanged. The very active alkali metals, lithium, sodium, and potassium, are stored under liquid alkanes such as kerosene. Under ordinary conditions, the alkanes are inert toward oxygen, chlorine, and bromine. However, at elevated temperatures, alkanes burn in the presence of oxygen to form carbon dioxide and water. The reaction, typified by the combustion of propane,

$$C_3H_8 + 5O_2 \rightarrow 3CO_2 + 4H_2O \qquad \Delta H = -483 \text{ kcal/mole}$$

is highly exothermic. For this reason, alkanes are used as fuels. The heat evolved from such reactions is known as the **heat of combustion.**

Methane is the major constituent of natural gas, widely used for heating and cooking. Propane and butane are used as liquefied petroleum gas [LPG ("bottled gases")] in areas where natural gas is not distributed by pipeline. Octane is a constituent of gasoline. Kerosene and diesel and fuel oils are also important sources of power and heat.

Although the alkanes do not normally react with chlorine and bromine, in the presence of strong sunlight or ultraviolet radiation a reaction occurs in which a hydrogen atom is displaced by a halogen atom,

$$CH_4 + Cl_2 \xrightarrow{\text{light}} CH_3Cl + HCl$$

The progression from any member (homolog) of a homologous series to the next higher member is equivalent to replacing an H atom by a CH_3 group. This procedure represents the net addition of a CH_2 increment. The following sequence shows this progression from methane to ethane (but is not meant to represent an actual chemical reaction),

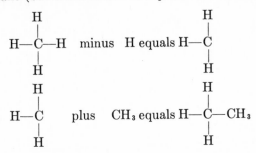

In methane, all four C—H bonds are equivalent; thus, it makes no difference which H is removed. Therefore only one kind of ethane is possible. The same procedure can be used in going from ethane to propane,

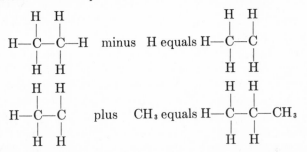

The structural formula of ethane, as drawn, suggests that there might be more than one way of removing an H atom, so that more than one kind of propane is possible. A few of these possibilities are

$$H-\underset{\underset{\displaystyle H}{|}}{\overset{\overset{\displaystyle H}{|}}{C}}-\underset{\underset{\displaystyle CH_3}{|}}{\overset{\overset{\displaystyle H}{|}}{C}}-H \equiv H-\underset{\underset{\displaystyle H}{|}}{\overset{\overset{\displaystyle H}{|}}{C}}-\underset{\underset{\displaystyle H}{|}}{\overset{\overset{\displaystyle CH_3}{|}}{C}}-H \equiv H-\underset{\underset{\displaystyle H}{|}}{\overset{\overset{\displaystyle H}{|}}{C}}-\underset{\underset{\displaystyle H}{|}}{\overset{\overset{\displaystyle H}{|}}{C}}-CH_3$$

Actually, these are all identical structures; the symbol $\equiv$ means identical. There is only one kind of propane molecule. All six C—H bonds in ethane are equivalent, so that it makes no difference which H is removed and replaced by a CH_3 group. A misconception of the nonequivalence of H atoms in ethane could arise because we have used a planar formula to represent the structure of a molecule; the molecule is actually three-dimensional. The geometry of carbon molecules is discussed later (page 274). To obviate these misconceptions, remember that (a) all H atoms on the same carbon are equivalent, and it makes no difference which one is replaced by another group, and (b) in a symmetrical molecule, the two halves are identical. Thus in ethane, a typical symmetrical molecule, the CH_3 group at one end is equivalent to the same group at the other end.

Let us now use this procedure to progress from propane to butane, as shown below. The three H atoms on the first carbon, C_1, and the three H atoms on C_3 are equivalent. These six equivalent H atoms are enclosed by the dotted lines,

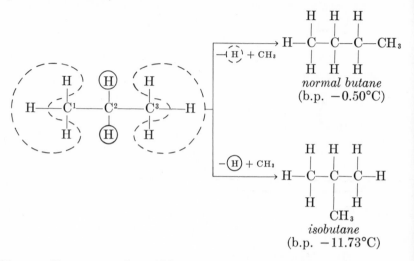

normal butane
(b.p. $-0.50°C$)

isobutane
(b.p. $-11.73°C$)

The two H atoms on the middle carbon, C_2, are equivalent to each other, but are positionally different from the other six. Replacing one of these H atoms (encircled in the above diagram) by a CH_3 group should give a different butane molecule. Two different molecules with the formula C_4H_{10} are known, normal or n-butane and isobutane. The two molecules are called **isomers.** We say that there are two isomers for the structure C_4H_{10}; one isomer is n-butane, the other isomer is isobutane. The existence of two or more compounds with the same molecular formula is called **isomerism.** Isomers have different chemical and physical properties, as exemplified by the boiling points of the two butanes. The two butanes are called *structural isomers,* because they differ from one another in the sequence of atoms in the molecule. (Another type of isomerism is discussed on page 662.) The isomer with the carbon atoms arranged in a continuous sequence (no branching) is called *normal,* and designated by n-, as in n-butane. The prefix *iso-* indicates a specific kind of branching* in the carbon skeleton of the molecule.

Let us next consider the problem of writing the structural formulas for the isomers of pentane, C_5H_{12}. One way of solving this problem is to

---

* Specifically, *iso* is used when all carbon atoms are arranged in a continuous sequence, except for one carbon which is branched from the second carbon in the chain. Thus

$$CH_3—CH—CH_2—CH_2—CH_3$$
$$|$$
$$CH_3$$

is called isohexane.

start with the butanes and decide how many ways there are of replacing an H atom by a CH_3 group. In *n*-butane there are two different kinds of hydrogen atom, as shown below. The six H atoms enclosed by broken lines on C_1 and C_4 are equivalent. The two H atoms on C_2 are equivalent to the two on C_3, and these are enclosed by solid line boxes. Substituting a CH_3 group for one of the six equivalent terminal H atoms gives *n*-pentane. When the exchange involves one of the four equivalent H atoms in the boxes, isopentane results,

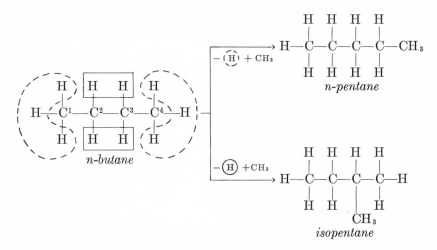

In isobutane, the H atoms on each of the three CH_3 groups are equivalent. Replacing any of these nine H atoms by a CH_3 group gives the same isopentane. However, when the encircled H atom on the center carbon atom is replaced, a third isomer, *neopentane*, results,

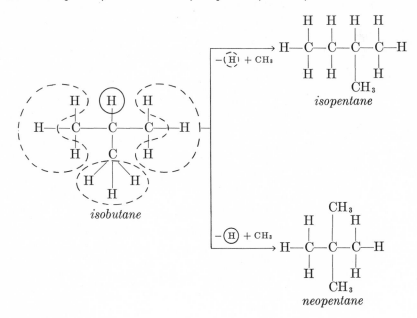

There is a more direct and novel method of approaching the question of alkane isomerism. Alkane isomers arise because of the different ways of bonding a given number of carbon atoms to each other through branching. The number of C—C bonds is one less than the number of carbon atoms in the molecular formula. Thus, in C_5H_{12}, there are four C—C bonds. We can consider a C—C bond as a straight line. The question to be answered in order to get the correct number of isomers is, "How many ways can four lines be connected that differ in branching?"* There are three ways,

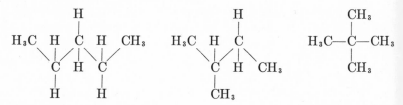

All that remains is to place a carbon atom at the end of each line and to insert the requisite number of H atoms,

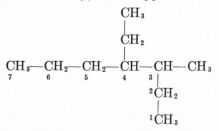

10.4 NOMENCLATURE OF ALKANES

The isomers of pentane and butane have been given **common** or **trivial** names. However, as the number of carbon atoms in a molecule increases, the possibilities for isomerism increase. For example, there are 9 isomers for heptane, and 18 for octane. It would be obviously foolhardy to attempt to give each isomer an unambiguous trivial name. Chemists have developed a method of nomenclature that assigns a systematic, unique name to each possible compound. The system presently used, called the IUPAC system, an abbreviation for the International Union of Pure and Applied Chemistry, will be applied to the naming of

$$
\begin{array}{c}
CH_3 \\
| \\
CH_2 \\
| \\
CH_3-\underset{7}{CH_2}-\underset{6}{CH_2}-\underset{5}{CH_2}-\underset{4}{CH}-\underset{3}{CH}-CH_3 \\
\quad\quad\quad\quad\quad\quad\quad\quad | \\
\quad\quad\quad\quad\quad\quad\quad\quad {}^2CH_2 \\
\quad\quad\quad\quad\quad\quad\quad\quad | \\
\quad\quad\quad\quad\quad\quad\quad\quad {}^1CH_3
\end{array}
$$

Rule 1: Selecting and Naming the Longest Chain. Name the compound as a **derivative** of the alkane represented by the longest chain or continuous sequence of carbon atoms. In the above compound, the

---

* The tetravalence of carbon limits the number of branches from any given point to a maximum of four.

longest chain contains 7 carbons as numbered. The compound is therefore named as a heptane, and is considered to be a *derivative* of this parent compound. The name must end in the suffix *-ane* to indicate that the compound is a member of the alk*ane* series. Except for the first four members of the alkane series, the prefix of the name denotes the number of carbon atoms in the chain. Thus, for example, *hept* indicates 7 carbons. (Table 10.1, page 240, gives names of the first ten parent compounds.)

Rule 2: Numbering the Longest Carbon Chain. Number the carbon atoms in the longest chain, as illustrated, so that the branching groups are on the lower- rather than the higher-numbered carbon atoms.

Rule 3: Locating the Branching Groups. The location of the branching hydrocarbon groups is indicated by the number of the carbon atom of the parent chain to which they are attached. Thus, in our illustrative compound, we find a CH_3 group on C-3 and a CH_3CH_2 group on C-4.

Rule 4: Naming the Branched Groups. Each branched group is named according to the number of carbons in its longest chain. To name the group, replace the suffix *-ane* by *-yl*. Thus, CH_3 is called meth*yl* since it stems from meth*ane*, and CH_3CH_2 is named eth*yl* from eth*ane*.

Rule 5: Arranging the Names of the Branched Groups. The names of these groups are prefixed alphabetically with the number of the carbon atom to which each group is attached. Thus, the name of the illustrative compound is *4-ethyl-3-methylheptane*.

The rules of punctuation are: (*i*) words are run together; (*ii*) a dash is used to separate a number from a word; and (*iii*) a comma is used to separate numbers.

The following examples further illustrate the method:

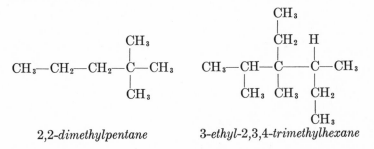

2,2-*dimethylpentane*   3-*ethyl-2,3,4-trimethylhexane*

Note the repetition of numbers when a group appears twice on the same carbon, and the use of *di-* and *tri-* to indicate the number of times the group appears as a branch.

10.5   ALKENES AND ALKYNES; UNSATURATED HYDROCARBONS

Carbon atoms can form multiple bonds with each other. For example, the gaseous compound ethylene (boiling point, $-104°C$) has the molecular formula, C_2H_4. The molecule C_2H_4 has 12 valence electrons. Were it to be saturated, it would need 14 valence electrons (see page 229). Hence, C_2H_4 lacks two electrons of being saturated, and therefore must have a double bond. The necessity for a double bond can also be seen by assembling four hydrogen and two carbon atoms,

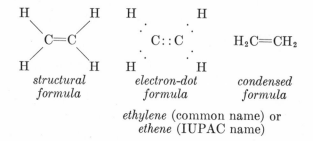

To satisfy the octet rule and the covalency requirements, the carbon
atoms must be joined by a double bond. Several ways of writing the
structure of ethylene are

$$
\begin{matrix}
\text{H} & & \text{H} \\
\diagdown & & \diagup \\
& \text{C}{=}\text{C} & \\
\diagup & & \diagdown \\
\text{H} & & \text{H}
\end{matrix}
\qquad
\text{C}::\text{C}
\qquad
\text{H}_2\text{C}{=}\text{CH}_2
$$

structural   *electron-dot*   *condensed*
formula   *formula*   *formula*

ethylene (common name) or
ethene (IUPAC name)

Hydrocarbons, like ethylene, that possess one carbon-to-carbon double
bond (C=C) belong to the **alkene** homologous series. The suffix *-en*
indicates the presence of the C=C bond. Since the alkenes have two less
H atoms than the corresponding alkanes, their general formula is C_nH_{2n}

The presence of a double bond increases the opportunities for isomerism. Thus, although there is only one *n*-butane, there are two structurally
isomeric *n-butenes*,

$$
\text{H}_2\text{C}{=}\text{CHCH}_2\text{CH}_3 \qquad \text{H}_3\text{CCH}{=}\text{CHCH}_3
$$
1-*butene*   2-*butene*

The location of the double bond is indicated by the lower-numbered
carbon participating in the multiple bond.

Carbons can also be joined by a triple bond. The simplest example is
acetylene, C_2H_2 (boiling point, $-84°C$),

$$
\text{H}{-}\text{C}{\equiv}\text{C}{-}\text{H} \qquad \text{H}:\text{C}:::\text{C}:\text{H}
$$

It is the first member of the **alkyne** homologous series, whose general formula is C_nH_{2n-2}. The ending *-yne* indicates the presence of the $-C{\equiv}C-$
bond. Thus, whereas *acetylene* is the common name, *ethyne* is the IUPAC
name.

10.6   ADDITION REACTION OF UNSATURATED HYDROCARBONS

Both alkenes and alkynes have in common an important type of chemical property. Ethene, a typical alkene, reacts with chlorine readily at
room temperature (even in the dark and in an inert solvent such as carbon

tetrachloride),

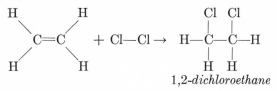

1,2-*dichloroethane*

As a result of this reaction, the double bond becomes a single bond, the
Cl—Cl bond is broken, and two new C—Cl bonds are formed. A reaction
of this type is called an **addition reaction.** Alkynes add two moles of
halogen, as exemplified by the addition of bromine to propyne,

$$H—C≡C—CH_3 + \quad 2Br_2 \quad → \quad H—\overset{\overset{\displaystyle Br}{|}}{\underset{\underset{\displaystyle Br}{|}}{C}}—\overset{\overset{\displaystyle Br}{|}}{\underset{\underset{\displaystyle Br}{|}}{C}}—CH_3$$

propyne   1,1,2,2-*tetrabromopropane*
(colorless) (red-brown)   (colorless)

Addition reactions are typical of most molecules with multiple bonds and
for this reason such molecules are said to be **unsaturated.** Saturated
molecules such as the alkanes do not have multiple bonds and so do not
undergo the addition reaction. The decolorization of the red-brown solution of bromine (see above equation), usually in a solvent such as carbon
tetrachloride, is used as a test for alkenes and alkynes.

Other reagents that add to multiple bonds include:

(a) *Hydrogen in the presence of platinum, palladium, or nickel,*

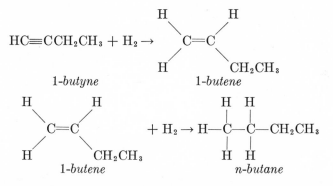

(b) *Anhydrous* (free of water) *hydrogen halides,* such as hydrogen
chloride, HCl (this reagent should not be confused with aqueous HCl,
hydrochloric acid),

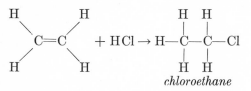

chloroethane

(c) *Water* in the presence of dilute sulfuric acid. The product is an alcohol,

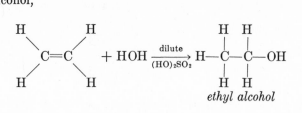

ethyl alcohol

The addition of water to ethylene can be *reversed* by heating ethyl alcohol in concentrated sulfuric acid,

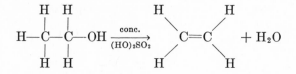

This is a useful method for making ethylene on a laboratory scale. The removal of water from alcohols is the usual method for making alkenes. This type of reaction is commonly called an **elimination.**

10.7 CYCLOALKANES AND CYCLOALKENES

Carbon atoms may also be arranged in rings. Hydrocarbons containing rings of carbon atoms linked together by single bonds are known as **cyclo-alkanes.** Since the minimum number of carbon atoms needed to form a ring is 3, the lowest member of this series is cyclopropane,

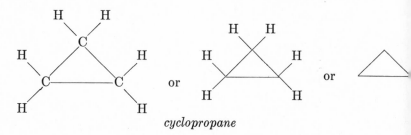

cyclopropane

Note that the chemist frequently simplifies the writing of these structures by omitting the C atoms and even by omitting the H atoms as shown. To name this group of hydrocarbons, *cyclo-* is prefixed to the name of the alkane with the corresponding number of carbons. The nomenclature is indicated by the names of the next three members of the series,

cyclobutane   cyclopentane   cyclohexane

The cycloalkanes have the general formula C_nH_{2n}, and therefore are isomeric with the alkenes. For example, cyclopropane (C_3H_6) and propene, $CH_3CH=CH_2$ (i.e., C_3H_6), are isomers. These two classes of hydrocarbon are, however, chemically distinguishable. With the exception of cyclopropane, the cycloalkanes behave as saturated molecules. Thus, they do not undergo addition reactions.

Cyclic compounds can also possess double bonds. A typical example is cyclohexene, C_6H_{10},

cyclohexene

Cyclohexene is a typical unsaturated molecule. For example, it decolorizes a solution of Br_2 in CCl_4. It also adds H_2 in the presence of platinum to give cyclohexane,

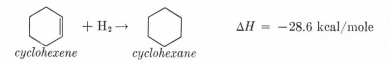

$$\Delta H = -28.6 \text{ kcal/mole}$$

cyclohexene   *cyclohexane*

The ΔH of this type of reaction is called the **heat of hydrogenation**.

10.8 DIENES; BENZENE AND AROMATIC COMPOUNDS

Molecules can have more than one double bond. Thus a group of hydrocarbons having two double bonds is known. They are called the **dienes.** One of the more important dienes is 1,3-butadiene,

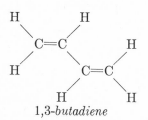

1,3-*butadiene*

It serves as starting material for preparing a variety of polymers (see Chapter 29).

Of particular interest is the cyclic triene called benzene. Benzene is a volatile liquid (b.p. 80°C), first isolated in 1825 by Michael Faraday by the destructive distillation* of coal. Its molecular formula is C_6H_6, and

---

* Destructive distillation is a distillation in which vaporization is accompanied by decomposition.

the structure suggested by August Kekulé in 1865 is

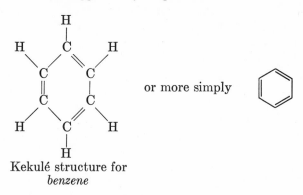

or more simply

Kekulé structure for
benzene

This ring system is an integral unit of a very large number of hydrocarbons with the general formula C_nH_{2n-6}, which are referred to as **arenes** or as benzenoid or aromatic* compounds. Coal tar, a distillate from soft coal, is a source of many arenes, some of which are given below (the simplified structure is used)

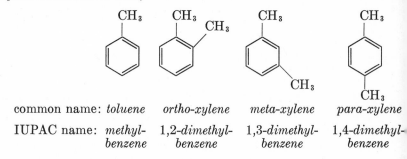

common name: *toluene*   *ortho-xylene*   *meta-xylene*   *para-xylene*

IUPAC name: *methyl-*   *1,2-dimethyl-*   *1,3-dimethyl-*   *1,4-dimethyl-*
          benzene   *benzene*   *benzene*   *benzene*

Note the use of the prefixes *ortho-*, *meta-*, and *para-* to indicate the 1,2-, 1,3-, and 1,4-disubstituted benzene derivatives, respectively. There is a wide range of aromatic hydrocarbons with fused benzene rings—rings with two carbon atoms in common—as in naphthalene, $C_{10}H_8$, a white solid (m.p. 80°C) (used as a moth repellent),

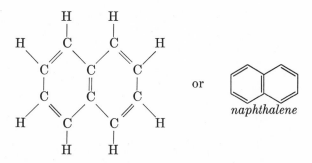

or

naphthalene

---

* This class of compounds is called aromatic because many of their derivatives have pleasant odors. Many of the arenes are toxic, some are carcinogenic—and therefore should not be inhaled.

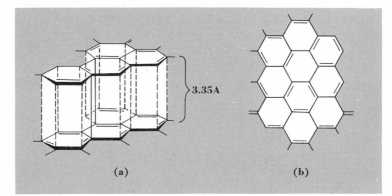

Fig. 10.1. *Graphite structure.* (a) *Continuous layers of fused benzene-like rings.* (b) *A portion of one layer.*

Graphite is an elementary form of carbon. It is a soft, black solid that conducts a current and vaporizes at 4347°C. It is a macromolecular-type substance composed of layers of *fused benzene rings*. The separation of layers is 3.35 A (Fig. 10.1a). Figure 10.1b shows a portion of the fused benzene ring layers. In later chapters we will interpret the properties of graphite in terms of this structure.

Aromatic hydrocarbons are used extensively in the manufacture of plastics, drugs, dyes, insecticides, explosives, and a host of other useful materials. A few examples of compounds derived from aromatic hydrocarbons are

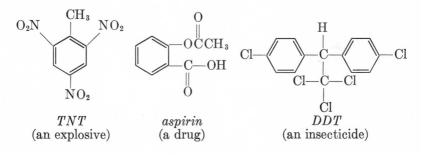

TNT
(an explosive)

aspirin
(a drug)

DDT
(an insecticide)

The chemical reactions of benzene are not typical of an unsaturated compound. For example, it does not undergo catalytic hydrogenation at atmospheric pressure and at room temperature, as do the alkenes and alkynes. It can be converted to cyclohexane, but only under more severe conditions—for example, in the presence of Ni at 150°C, and under 10 atmospheres pressure of H_2. This conversion with hydrogen to cyclohexane, although sluggish, is nevertheless chemical proof for the cyclic structure of benzene. Benzene also gives a negative test for unsaturation; it does not react with Br_2 in CCl_4. It does react with Br_2 in the presence of a catalyst at elevated temperatures. However, the reaction is *not* an addition. Instead, an H atom is replaced by a Br atom,

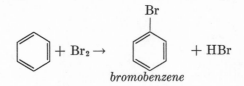

bromobenzene

Benzene evidently resists addition to its double bonds. This behavior of benzene and other aromatic compounds has led to the idea that there is a stability inherent in this ring of six carbon atoms with three alternating double bonds. The explanation for this stability is discussed in the next chapter (page 288), in terms of modern concepts of chemical bonding as applied to the structure of benzene.

10.9 FUNCTIONAL GROUP DERIVATIVES

The H atom of a hydrocarbon can be replaced by another atom or group of atoms not of the hydrocarbon variety. The resulting compounds are called hydrocarbon **derivatives,** and the atom or group is known as a **functional group.** Throughout this book, frequent reference to hydrocarbon derivatives will be made. The more common functional groups are listed in Table 10.2. The symbol **R** is used to represent an alkyl group.* The chemistry of these derivatives is characteristic mainly of the functional group.

We will consider the chemistry of alcohols, and thus see how alcohols, ethers, aldehydes, ketones, carboxylic acids, and esters are interrelated. The simplest alcohol is methyl alcohol, or methanol, CH_3OH (b.p. 64.7°C). It is commonly called wood alcohol, since it was formerly made by the destructive distillation of wood. The present-day industrial synthesis involves the addition of H_2 to the multiple bond of carbon monoxide at high temperatures and pressures,

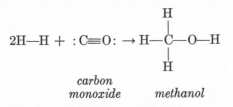

carbon
monoxide   *methanol*

The next homolog is ethyl alcohol, or ethanol, C_2H_5OH (b.p. 79°C). It is sometimes called grain alcohol, since it is made by fermentation of the sugars that occur in a variety of grains. A more important method of industrial preparation is the addition of H_2O to ethylene (page 248). As seen from the names methanol and ethanol, the IUPAC method for naming uses the suffix *-ol* in place of the terminal *-e* in the name of the parent alkane. When more than one isomer is possible, a number is used to indicate the position of the OH group on the chain. Much of the reactivity

* **Ar** stands for an arene group.

TABLE 10.2   *Common Functional Groups in Organic Compounds*

Group	General formula	General name	Example Formula	Example Name
—Cl	R—Cl	Chloride	CH_3Cl	Methyl chloride (chloromethane)
—Br	R—Br	Bromide	CH_3Br	Methyl bromide (bromomethane)
—OH	R—OH	Alcohol	CH_3CH_2OH	Ethyl alcohol (ethanol)
	Ar—OH	Phenol	C_6H_5OH	Phenol
—O—	R—O—R	Ether	$CH_3CH_2OCH_2CH_3$	Diethyl ether
—NH₂	RNH_2	Amine	$CH_3CH_2CH_2NH_2$	n-Propylamine
—N (O, O)	RNO_2	Nitro compound	$C_6H_5NO_2$	Nitrobenzene
—C=O, H	R—C=O, H	Aldehyde	$CH_3CH_2C=O$, H	Propionaldehyde
			$C_6H_5C=O$, H	Benzaldehyde
—C=O, R	R—C=O, R	Ketone	$CH_3—C(=O)—C_2H_5$	Methyl ethyl ketone
—C=O, OH	R—C=O, OH	Carboxylic acid	$CH_3—C(=O)—OH$	Acetic acid
—C(=O)—OR'	R—C(=O)—OR'	Ester	$CH_3—C(=O)—OC_2H_5$	Ethyl acetate
—C(=O)—NH₂	R—C(=O)—NH₂	Amide	$CH_3—C(=O)—NH_2$	Acetamide
—C(=O)—Cl	R—C(=O)—Cl	Acid chloride	$CH_3—C(=O)—Cl$	Acetyl chloride

of alcohols, ROH, is due to the presence of the OH group. For example, ethanol reacts with sodium to yield hydrogen and sodium ethoxide,

$$Na \cdot + H:\overset{..}{\underset{..}{O}}—\overset{\overset{H}{|}}{\underset{\underset{H}{|}}{C}}—\overset{\overset{H}{|}}{\underset{\underset{H}{|}}{C}}—H \rightarrow \tfrac{1}{2}H_2 + Na^+ \left[:\overset{..}{\underset{..}{O}}—\overset{\overset{H}{|}}{\underset{\underset{H}{|}}{C}}—\overset{\overset{H}{|}}{\underset{\underset{H}{|}}{C}}—H \right]^-$$

ethanol   *sodium ethoxide*

$$\text{Na}\cdot + \text{H}:\overset{..}{\underset{..}{\text{O}}}-\text{H} \rightarrow \tfrac{1}{2}\text{H}_2 + \text{Na}^+ \left[:\overset{..}{\underset{..}{\text{O}}}-\text{H} \right]^-$$
sodium hydroxide

In this respect, ethanol behaves like water. In fact, in order to understand some of the chemistry, it is advantageous to consider alcohols as alkyl derivatives of water, H—O—H. Note that the H atoms on carbon, like those in an alkane, are not displaced by sodium.

We have already mentioned (page 248) that when heated with concentrated sulfuric acid, alcohols lose water *intramolecularly*, to give alkenes. At lower temperatures, and with a higher ratio of alcohol to sulfuric acid, an ether is the main product, as a result of an *intermolecular* elimination of water,

$$\underset{\substack{\text{an alcohol}}}{\text{ROH}} + \text{HOR} \xrightarrow[\text{(HO)}_2\text{SO}_2]{\text{conc.}} \underset{\substack{\text{an ether}}}{\text{R—O—R}} + \text{H—O—H}$$

$$\text{CH}_3\text{CH}_2\text{OH} + \text{HOCH}_2\text{CH}_3 \xrightarrow[\text{(HO)}_2\text{SO}_2]{\text{conc.}} \underset{\substack{\text{diethyl ether}}}{\text{CH}_3\text{CH}_2\text{OCH}_2\text{CH}_3} + \text{H}_2\text{O}$$

This is the method for preparing diethyl ether; the compound, commonly called "ether," is used as a general anesthetic.

If the OH group of the alcohol is attached to a carbon bearing two H atoms, the alcohol can be oxidized by reagents such as potassium permanganate, KMnO_4, and potassium dichromate, $\text{K}_2\text{Cr}_2\text{O}_7$, to an aldehyde,

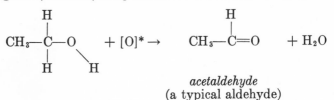

acetaldehyde
(a typical aldehyde)

If only one H atom is attached to the carbon atom with the OH group, the alcohol is oxidized to a ketone,

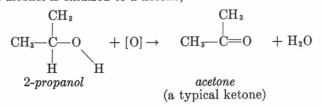

acetone
(a typical ketone)

An alcohol with no H atoms on the carbon bearing the OH group resists oxidation under the usual conditions,

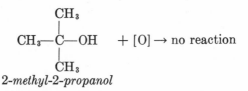

* To simplify writing the above equations, [O] is used to indicate the oxidant. (The writing and balancing of redox reactions is discussed on page 367.)

Oxidation is a useful method for the synthesis of ketones, since ketones withstand further oxidation. It has only limited utility for the preparation of aldehydes, since the aldehyde obtained is readily oxidized further to a carboxylic acid,

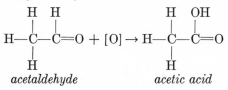

$$\underset{\textit{acetaldehyde}}{H-\overset{\displaystyle H}{\underset{\displaystyle H}{C}}-\overset{\displaystyle H}{C}=O} + [O] \rightarrow \underset{\textit{acetic acid}}{H-\overset{\displaystyle H}{\underset{\displaystyle H}{C}}-\overset{\displaystyle OH}{C}=O}$$

Thus we find the sequence of increasing oxidation states for carbon in methane derivatives to be

$$\underset{-4}{CH_4} \rightarrow \underset{-2}{H_3C-OH} \rightarrow \underset{\underset{\textit{formaldehyde}}{0}}{H_2C=O} \rightarrow \underset{\underset{\underset{\textit{acid}}{\textit{formic}}}{+2}}{H-\overset{\displaystyle OH}{C}=O} \rightarrow \underset{+4}{O=C=O}$$

The oxidation of appropriate alcohols to aldehydes or ketones can be reversed. Thus, aldehydes and ketones add hydrogen in the presence of platinum to give the corresponding alcohol,

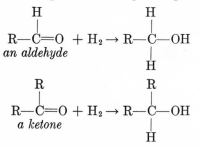

$$\underset{\textit{an aldehyde}}{R-\overset{\displaystyle H}{C}=O} + H_2 \rightarrow R-\overset{\displaystyle H}{\underset{\displaystyle H}{C}}-OH$$

$$\underset{\textit{a ketone}}{R-\overset{\displaystyle R}{C}=O} + H_2 \rightarrow R-\overset{\displaystyle R}{\underset{\displaystyle H}{C}}-OH$$

The C=O group, called the **carbonyl group,** has a multiple bond, and it is therefore not surprising that aldehydes and ketones behave as unsaturated molecules and undergo the addition reaction.*

When a carboxylic acid and an alcohol are heated in the presence of concentrated sulfuric acid, an ester is formed, the reaction being called **esterification,**

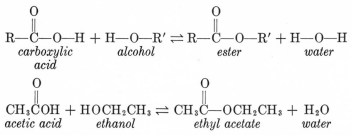

$$\underset{\underset{\textit{acid}}{\textit{carboxylic}}}{R-\overset{\displaystyle O}{\overset{\|}{C}}-O-H} + \underset{\textit{alcohol}}{H-O-R'} \rightleftharpoons \underset{\textit{ester}}{R-\overset{\displaystyle O}{\overset{\|}{C}}-O-R'} + \underset{\textit{water}}{H-O-H}$$

$$\underset{\textit{acetic acid}}{CH_3\overset{\displaystyle O}{\overset{\|}{C}}OH} + \underset{\textit{ethanol}}{HOCH_2CH_3} \rightleftharpoons \underset{\textit{ethyl acetate}}{CH_3\overset{\displaystyle O}{\overset{\|}{C}}-OCH_2CH_3} + \underset{\textit{water}}{H_2O}$$

Esters also react with water to yield the constituent alcohol and carboxylic acid (ester hydrolysis).

* The reagents that add to the carbonyl group are not generally the same kind that add to carbon-to-carbon multiple bonds. Thus, although H_2 adds to the carbonyl group, the halogens, the hydrogen halides, and water do not.

Hydrolysis of esters in aqueous alkali, such as a water solution of sodium hydroxide, NaOH, is known as **saponification** (conversion to soap) because soaps, which are salts of long-chain carboxylic acids, are made by this method from fats or fatty oils. Fats are solid esters while fatty oils are liquid esters of carboxylic acids. These esters are derived from a common alcohol, glycerol, $HOCH_2CHOHCH_2OH$, and therefore are known as **glycerides,**

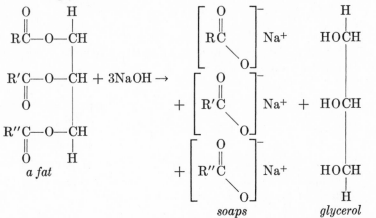

Fats contain largely the saturated carboxylic acids; in greatest abundance are palmitic acid, $CH_3(CH_2)_{14}COOH$, and stearic acid, $CH_3(CH_2)_{16}COOH$. On the other hand, the fatty oils contain carboxylic acids with at least one C=C bond.

10.10 SUMMARY

Table 10.3 summarizes the hydrocarbon homologous series referred to in this chapter.

TABLE 10.3 *Hydrocarbon Homologous Series*

Name	*General formula*	*Typical example*	*Formula*	*Chemical behavior*
Alkane	C_nH_{2n+2}	**Eth**ane	$H_3C—CH_3$	**Saturated**
Alkene	C_nH_{2n}	**Eth**ene	$H_2C=CH_2$	**Unsaturated**
Alkyne	C_nH_{2n-2}	**Eth**yne	$H—C\equiv C—H$	**Unsaturated**
Alkadiene	C_nH_{2n-2}	**1,3-Buta**diene	$H_2C=CH—CH=CH_2$	**Unsaturated**
*Cyclo*alkane	C_nH_{2n}	*Cyclo*hexane		**Saturated**
*Cyclo*alkene	C_nH_{2n-2}	*Cyclo*hexene		**Unsaturated**
Benzenoid	C_nH_{2n-6}	**Benzene**		**Aromatic**

1. Homologous series. Given the compounds (a) C_4H_{10}, (b) C_4H_8, and (c) C_4H_6. Write the general formula for these hydrocarbons and name all the homologous series (when more than one is possible) to which they belong (see Table 10.3, page 256). Write a structural formula consistent with each series.

2. Nomenclature. Give the IUPAC name for

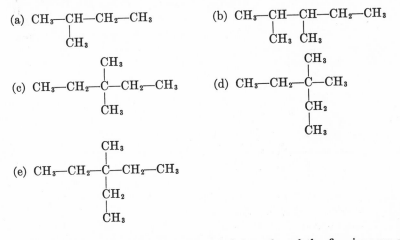

3. Alkane isomerism. Draw the structural formulas of the five isomers of C_6H_{14}, and name each by the IUPAC system.

4. Alkene isomerism. Give the structural formulas for the three structural isomers of the alkene, C_4H_8.

5. Homologous series isomerism. Give the structural formulas for three isomers with the formula C_3H_4, and name the homologous series to which each isomer belongs.

6. Functional group isomerism. (a) Draw the structural formulas and give the IUPAC names for the four *alcohols* with the molecular formula $C_4H_{10}O$. (b) Write the structural formulas for the three ethers with the molecular formula $C_4H_{10}O$. (c) Since alcohols and ethers are isomers, give a simple chemical test to distinguish the two classes of compounds.

7. Oxidation of alcohols and aldehydes. There are four isomeric alcohols with the molecular formula C_4H_9OH. (a) Which isomer does not undergo oxidation? (b) Which isomer is oxidized to a ketone? Name and draw the structure of the ketone. (c) Two isomers are oxidized to aldehydes. Give the equations for these reactions. (d) Give the structures of the carboxylic acids resulting from the oxidation of the aldehydes found in part (c).

8. Ether formation. (a) Give the equation for the conversion of methanol to the corresponding ether. Name the ether formed. (b) How many ethers are possible when a mixture of CH_3OH and CH_3CH_2OH is reacted with concentrated sulfuric acid? (c) Would you use the method in part (b) to synthesize methyl ethyl ether, $CH_3OCH_2CH_3$? Explain.

Additional problems

9. Elimination reaction. (a) How many alkenes can be formed when 2-butanol, $CH_3CHOHCH_2CH_3$, is heated with concentrated sulfuric acid? (b) Write equations for the reactions and name the alkenes.

10. Benzene isomerism. Write the structural formulas for the four aromatic isomers with the molecular formula C_7H_7Cl. When applicable, indicate which is *ortho*, *meta*, and *para*.

11. Addition reactions. With the aid of equations show that two products are possible when HI adds to propene. Name the products.

12. Substitution in alkanes. (a) Write the two possible monochloro substitution products arising from the reaction of isobutane (2-methylpropane) with Cl_2 in sunlight. (b) The major product is 2-chloro-2-methylpropane. What conclusion can you draw about the reactivity of the two different kinds of hydrogen in isobutane toward chlorination? (c) Give an equation for the preparation of the compound in part (b) by an addition reaction.

13. Esterification. Use structural formulas to complete the equations

$$CH_3CH_2COOH + CH_3OH \rightarrow$$
$$CH_3COOH + CH_3CH_2CH_2OH \rightarrow$$
$$HCOOH + CH_3CH_2OH \rightarrow$$

14. Heat of hydrogenation. Compute the heat of hydrogenation of ethylene from the following *heats of combustion* (all ΔH values are in kcal/mole): ethane = -372.8; ethylene = -337.3; hydrogen = -68.3.

Answer. -32.8 kcal/mole.

15. Unsaturation and redox. (a) Write an equation for the reaction of ethylene with (*i*) hydrogen, (*ii*) bromine. (b) With the aid of oxidation numbers show that these are both redox reactions. (c) In each reaction, indicate the oxidizing and reducing agents. (d) Is the addition of H_2O to ethylene a redox reaction? Explain.

11

The
covalent
bond

11.1   INTRODUCTION

In the preceding chapter, we said that chemical bonding involves electrostatic forces. It is easy to comprehend the role of an electrostatic force in electrovalent compounds, since ions are present. On the other hand, a covalent molecule like H_2 is not ionic, yet it is also held together by electrostatic forces. What is the origin of the electrostatic force in the covalent bond? This question has been the concern of some of the greatest thinkers in chemistry, dating back to the early 19th century and extending to the present. Chemists have progressed from the early, primitive picture of hooks holding the atoms together in a molecule to the present wave mechanical electronic model. In years to come, more precise models may be introduced. Nevertheless, our present model, crude as it is even for simple molecules, greatly aids our comprehension of the subject.

Any model for covalent bonding must predict the dissociation energy of a molecule and the interatomic distances. The dissociation energy is the energy needed to sever the bonds between atoms. Conversely, it is also the energy released when atoms become bonded to form the molecule. It is a composite of electron-electron and nucleus-nucleus repulsions and electron-nucleus attractions. The attractions must necessarily overshadow the repulsions; otherwise, the molecule would not be more stable than the individual atoms. When the Schroedinger equation is solved for the H_2 molecule, the agreement of the energy and bond distance with the observed values is very good. Solutions of Schroedinger's equation are, however, very difficult unless simplifications are made. For instance, the nuclei are considered to remain in fixed relative positions; their slight

259

vibrations are ignored. Only valence electrons are taken into account. The inner electrons are lumped together with the nucleus and the resulting kernel is assumed to have the net charge localized in its center.

There are two methods of approximating a solution to the Schroedinger equation from which the dissociation energy of a substance is obtained. The Valence Bond method (VB) was introduced in 1927 by Walther Heitler and Fritz London, and extended by John Slater and Linus Pauling. The Molecular Orbital method (MO) was developed around 1932 by F. Hund, Robert Mulliken, Erich Hückel, and Sir J. Lennard-Jones.

11.2 MOLECULAR ORBITAL METHOD

(a) **Linear Combination of Atomic Orbitals.** In the wave mechanical picture, the covalent bond in a binary molecule is derived from the fusion or overlap of two atomic orbitals, one belonging to each of the atoms. This overlap engenders a new electron cloud, called a molecular orbital, which embraces both atoms. Figure 11.1 depicts the formation of the molecular orbital of an H_2 molecule by the overlap of the $1s$ orbitals of the two H· atoms. Notice that the Pauli exclusion principle requires that the spin of the electron of one H atom be opposite to the spin of the electron of the other H atom. The two electrons in a molecular orbital attract the positively charged nuclei, bringing them to the optimum bond distance. The optimum bond distance is such that the electron-nucleus attraction balances the nucleus-nucleus and electron-electron repulsions. To minimize electron-electron repulsion, the two electrons in the molecular orbital, at any given instant, are *most probably* as far from each other as possible while still remaining in the proximity of the nuclei.

General analysis of the mathematical procedure is helpful in understanding the source of the bonding energy. Each atomic orbital is described by a wave function, ψ (page 170). It is assumed that the molecular orbital wave function, Ψ, is a linear combination (addition or subtraction) of the wave functions of the individual atomic orbitals. This procedure, called the "Linear Combination of Atomic Orbitals (LCAO) method" can be expressed for addition by Equation (1) for the interaction of two identical atoms, A and B,

$$\Psi_{MO} = \psi_A + \psi_B \tag{1}$$

Fig. 11.1. *Schematic representation of overlap of (a) atomic orbitals of two H atoms to form (b) molecular orbital of an H_2 molecule. Arrows indicate electron spin.*

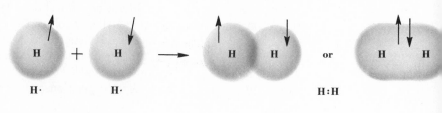

Equation (1) is squared to give Equation (2) because it is the square of the wave function (page 180) that is related to the distribution of electrons,

$$\Psi_{MO}^2 = \psi_A^2 + 2\psi_A\psi_B + \psi_B^2 \tag{2}$$

The term Ψ_{MO}^2 is related to the charge density between the two atoms, A and B. The greater the value of Ψ_{MO}^2, the greater is the charge density between the nuclei of the atoms. We might compare the bonding process between atoms A and B to the joining of two bricks. The term ψ_A^2 in Equation (2) is related to the probability of finding an electron about atom A if atom B were not present, and the term ψ_B^2 has the same connotation for atom B. Adding just these two terms would mean that the molecular orbital would have about the same energy as the isolated unbonded atoms. It would be analogous to placing two bricks alongside each other; for structural purposes they might almost as well be apart, since there is no cement to hold them together. However, because of the term $2\psi_A\psi_B$ the value of Ψ_{MO}^2 is *greater* than the sum of $\psi_A^2 + \psi_B^2$. This is interpreted to mean that there is a greater charge density between the bonded atoms than there is between the nonbonded atoms. We might say that the term $2\psi_A\psi_B$ is the "cement" that causes the bonded state to be more stable than the unbonded state. This term exists because of the interaction or overlap of the atomic orbitals. The magnitude of this term depends on the extent of the overlap. *The more the atomic orbitals can overlap the greater is the charge density between the nuclei, and the more stable is the bond.* The bonding electrons no longer belong one to each nucleus. They each belong to both nuclei; they are said to be *delocalized* with respect to the individual atoms. The significance of the interaction term, $2\psi_A\psi_B$, is further shown by comparing the plot of the electron charge density of the individual atomic orbitals, ψ_A^2 and ψ_B^2, as indicated in Fig. 11.2 by the dotted line, and the electron charge density of the bonding molecular orbital, Ψ_{MO}^2, as indicated by the solid line. Points H and H represent the nuclei separated by the appropriate bond distance. The plot for the individual atomic orbitals shows only a slight electron charge density between the nuclei, and therefore there is no bonding. The plot for the Ψ_{MO}^2 shows a high electron charge density between the nuclei. It is this concentration of charge that binds the atoms together.

We are now in a position to visualize the electrostatic nature of the covalent bond. The bond is made up of two positive nuclei separated by a high density of negative charge, as shown in Fig. 11.3a. Such a charge array is similar to the alternating Na^+ and Cl^- ions in crystalline NaCl (Fig. 11.3b). There are basic differences, however, between the two. The alternation and attraction of the Na^+ and Cl^- ions extends 3-dimensionally throughout the entire crystal. In the case of the covalent bond the attraction resides within the molecule and does not extend intermolecularly. For this reason, the intramolecular force of attraction is strong, but the intermolecular force of attraction is weak.

(b) Bonding and Antibonding Orbitals. The linear combination

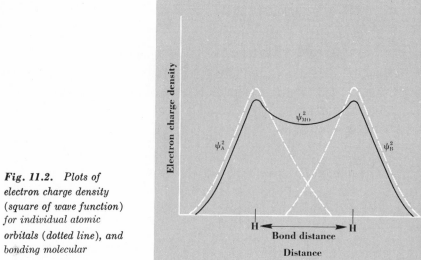

Fig. 11.2. *Plots of electron charge density (square of wave function) for individual atomic orbitals (dotted line), and bonding molecular orbital (solid line).*

of atomic orbitals can be effected by a subtraction as well as by an addition, as shown in Equation (3). Squaring Equation (3) gives Equation (4),

$$\Psi_{MO}^* = \psi_A - \psi_B \tag{3}$$
$$\Psi_{MO}^{*2} = \psi_A^2 - 2\psi_A\psi_B + \psi_B^2 \tag{4}$$

The interaction term in Equation (4) is *negative*. Therefore, Ψ_{MO}^{*2} is less than $\psi_A^2 + \psi_B^2$, which is interpreted to mean that there is less charge density between the interacting atoms than between the noninteracting atoms. Hence, the energy of the molecular orbital represented by Ψ_{MO}^* is greater than the sum of the energies of the component atoms, and the resulting bond is less stable. This situation is shown in Fig. 11.4, in which Ψ_{MO}^{*2} is represented by the solid line, and the electron charge density of the separate atomic orbitals is shown by the dotted line. Points H and H again represent the nuclei separated by the appropriate bond distance. The solid line touches the x axis midway between H and H. At this node

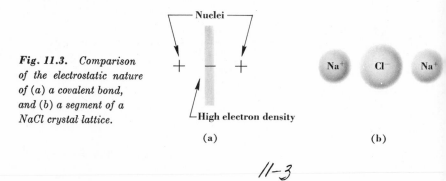

Fig. 11.3. *Comparison of the electrostatic nature of (a) a covalent bond, and (b) a segment of a NaCl crystal lattice.*

11–3

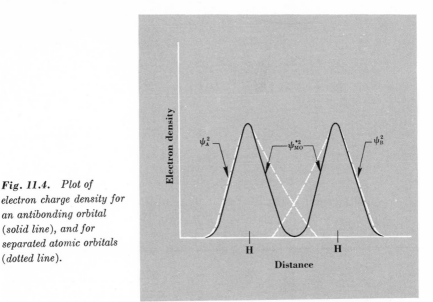

Fig. 11.4. Plot of electron charge density for an antibonding orbital (solid line), and for separated atomic orbitals (dotted line).

point the electron charge density is zero. Note that the electron density between the nuclei in this molecular orbital is actually less than the electron density between the nuclei of the noninteracting atomic orbitals. In the state described by Ψ_{MO}^*, electrons are rarely found between the nuclei. The nuclei repel each other and, consequently, this comparatively high-energy molecular orbital is said to be **antibonding.** Since the interaction of two atomic orbitals can be mathematically described equally well by addition or by subtraction of their wave functions, the following generalization can be made: *Whenever two atomic orbitals interact, there is a conservation of orbitals, so that two molecular orbitals result, one bonding, Ψ_{MO}, and one antibonding, Ψ_{MO}^*.* The energy of the bonding orbital is lower than the energy of the atomic oribtals by an amount, $-E_{MO}$, whereas the energy of the antibonding orbital is greater by approximately

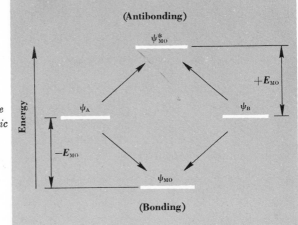

Fig. 11.5. An energy level diagram showing the combination of two atomic orbitals to form two molecular orbitals, one bonding and one antibonding.

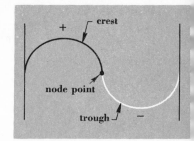

Fig. 11.6. *Standing wave showing crest (+) and trough (−).*

the same amount, $+E_{MO}$, as represented schematically in Fig. 11.5. The magnitude of E_{MO} varies, depending on the wave function of the atomic orbital used. Thus, the value of E_{MO} for H_2 is not the same as the value of E_{MO} for F_2, because the wave functions of the atomic orbitals used by the H and F atoms are different.

(c) **Types of Overlap of Atomic Orbitals; Sigma and Pi Bonds.** Recall that signs + and − are assigned to atomic orbitals (page 183). We can interpret bonding and antibonding molecular orbitals in terms of the signs of the interacting atomic orbitals. Let us consider an atomic orbital as a wave having a crest and a trough (Fig. 11.6). If two waves interact so that the crest (+ sign) of one coincides with the crest (+ sign) of the other, the new wave is reinforced. The new wave resulting from this type of *in-phase* interaction is akin to the formation of a bonding molecular orbital. Since the signs of an atomic orbital are assigned in the same way as are those of the wave in Fig. 11.6, we can say that *a bonding molecular orbital results from overlap of atomic orbitals with the same sign.*

Schematic representations for bonding molecular orbitals are shown in Fig. 11.7 from (a) overlap of two *s* atomic orbitals, (b) **head-to-head**

Fig. 11.7. *Schematic representation of types of sigma bond: (a) $\sigma(s)$; (b) $\sigma(ps)$; (c) $\sigma(p)$. The dot represents the nuclei and + and − represent the signs of the orbitals or parts thereof.*

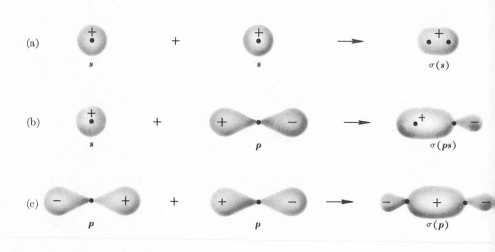

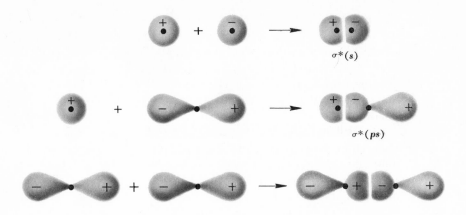

Fig. 11.8. *Schematic representation of types of antibonding (σ^*) orbitals: (a) $\sigma^*(s)$; (b) $\sigma^*(ps)$; (c) $\sigma^*(p)$.*

overlap of an *s* and a *p* atomic orbital, and (c) head-to-head overlap of two *p* atomic orbitals. The three molecular orbitals represented in Fig. 11.7 have a symmetrical charge distribution about a line joining the nuclei, the so-called **bond axis.** Such bonds are referred to as **sigma** (σ) **bonds.** They are more specifically designated $\sigma(s)$, $\sigma(ps)$, and $\sigma(p)$, depending on the types of atomic orbitals from which they are formed. If two waves interact so that the crest ($+$ sign) of one coincides with the trough ($-$ sign) of the other, the new wave is greatly weakened. The new wave resulting from this type of *out-of-phase* interaction is akin to an antibonding molecular orbital. We can therefore say that an antibonding molecular orbital results from overlap of atomic orbitals with unlike signs, as shown in Fig. 11.8. These orbitals are designated σ^*.

Two *p* orbitals may also overlap *laterally* (side-to-side) to form a **pi** (π) **bond** (Fig. 11.9a). The bonding π molecular orbital consists of two electron charge clouds concentrated above (the positive portion) and below

Fig. 11.9. *Types of π bond: (a) pi (π) bond; (b) anti-pi bond (π^*).*

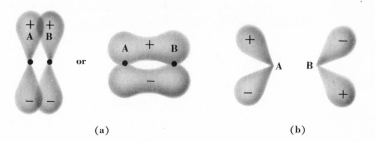

(a)   (b)

(the negative portion) the axis joining the A—B nuclei.* The shape of the antibonding molecular orbital is shown in Fig. 11.9b. *A strong π bond can result only when the individual p orbitals are parallel.* Thus, a π bond can result from overlap of two p_y or two p_z orbitals, but not from a p_y and a p_z. The electron cloud of a π bond is concentrated in either the x, y, or z plane, and so does not exhibit the cylindrical charge symmetry of the σ bond.

(d) **Molecular Orbital Energy Levels.** Can we set up a series of molecular orbitals from which we can predict the electronic structure of a molecule as we set up a series of atomic orbitals from which we were able to predict the electronic structure of atoms (page 174)? The molecular orbital method does this by making use of relative energy levels of bonding and antibonding molecular orbitals. The energy levels are obtained from spectral data. For simplicity, the following application of the MO method is restricted to the description of bonding in diatomic molecules.

Figure 11.10 is an energy level diagram showing MO energy levels which arise from combination of atomic orbitals of the first and second Periods. Note that an *antibonding* molecular orbital such as the $1\sigma^*$ formed from a *lower-energy* atomic orbital has a *lower* energy than a *bonding* molecular orbital such as $\sigma(2s)$ formed from a *higher-energy* atomic orbital. The π molecular orbital (MO) arising from overlap of the $2p_y$ atomic orbitals has the same energy as the π MO resulting from overlap of the $2p_z$ orbitals. Although the two π molecular orbitals, π_y and π_z, have the same energy, they are not identical, since their spatial orientation is different. The π_y orbital is oriented along the y axis, and the π_z along the z axis. The same equality of energy is found for the antibonding π_y^* and π_z^* molecular orbitals.

How do we use these molecular orbital energy levels to get the electronic structure of the diatomic molecules? We start with the two nuclei and then distribute the total number of electrons into molecular orbitals, applying the same principles used for the distribution of electrons into atomic orbitals (page 176). Thus, the molecular orbitals are filled in the order of increasing energy. A molecular orbital, whether bonding or antibonding, takes a maximum of two electrons, provided the electrons have opposite spins (Pauli's exclusion principle). Hund's rule (page 189) is applicable to degenerate molecular orbitals. As a first approximation, the total energy of a molecule is the sum of the energy of each electron in each molecular orbital. *In order for bonding of atoms to occur, there must be an excess of bonding over antibonding electrons.*

Figure 11.11 shows the electron configuration of molecules and ions formed from combinations of H and He atoms. The ion, H_2^+, has one electron which enters the σ1s molecular orbital, the one of lowest energy, as indicated in Fig. 11.11. One might therefore predict that the bonding of H^+ and $H\cdot$ to give H_2^+ should be exothermic, and that H_2^+ should have

---

* A π bond is never formed between two atoms unless accompanied by a σ bond. It is the σ bond that largely supplies the electron density along the axis joining the atoms.

some stability. This prediction has been validated experimentally. The H₂ molecule has two electrons which fill $\sigma 1s$. The bond energy of H_2 is predicted to be about twice that of H_2^+. Experimentally, the bond energy is 60 kcal/mole for H_2^+, and 104 kcal/mole for H_2.

Addition of a third electron to H_2 produces the H_2^- ion. The electron structure of H_2^- is obtained by adding the third electron to the antibonding $\sigma 1s$ molecular orbital. Consequently, compared to H_2, there is a loss in bonding energy. The H_2^- ion may be expected to be somewhat less stable than the H_2^+ ion because of the increased electron repulsion. The molecule HeH is isoelectronic with the H_2^- ion. One would predict that the compound HeH should be more stable than the isolated He and H

Fig. 11.10. *Energy diagram showing MO energy levels that arise by combination of the atomic orbitals of the first ten elements.*

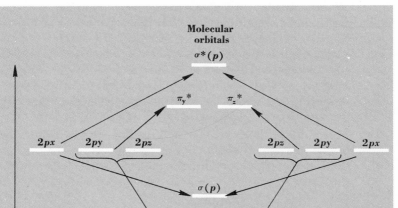

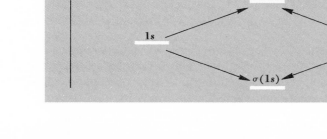

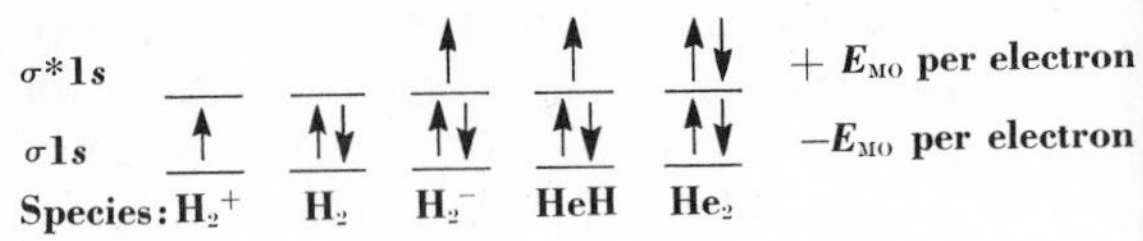

Fig. 11.11. *Electron configuration of molecules and ions formed from hydrogen and helium atoms.*

σ^*1s			↑	↑	↑↓	$+\,E_{MO}$ per electron
$\sigma 1s$	↑	↑↓	↑↓	↑↓	↑↓	$-\,E_{MO}$ per electron
Species:	$H_2{}^+$	H_2	$H_2{}^-$	HeH	He_2	

atoms; such a molecule is known in the vapor phase. A remarkable feature of the MO theory is the extension of our understanding of covalent bonding so that we can predict the existence of a molecule such as HeH. The simple shared pair concept enunciated in the preceding chapter could never accommodate such a molecule. In recent years, chemists have used MO theory successfully to predict the existence and stability of hitherto unknown substances.

The molecule He_2, if it existed, would contain four electrons. The fourth electron fills the antibonding σ^*1s molecular orbital. Now the numbers of electrons in bonding and in antibonding molecular orbitals are equal. Consequently, there is no bonding energy, and we predict that the He_2 molecule does not exist. This prediction is borne out—He_2 has never been detected. We can generalize by saying that for representative elements, *electrons in filled energy levels ("inner shell" electrons) make no contribution to the bonding energy of a molecule.* In some cases (page 271) these electrons are considered likely to remain in atomic orbitals. *Only molecular orbitals formed from atomic orbitals of valence electrons* can make a contribution to bond energy. This generalization does not hold for the transition elements, whose bonding usually involves electrons in more than one energy level.

As examples of molecules formed from the second Period elements, we will consider Li_2, N_2 and O_2.

Li_2

We bring together two lithium nuclei to give an Li^{3+}—Li^{3+} skeleton. Six electrons are added to the molecular orbitals following the sequence shown in Fig. 11.10. The four "inner shell" $1s$ electrons (two from each atom) fill the $\sigma 1s$ and σ^*1s molecular orbitals and hence contribute nothing to the bond energy. The two $2s$ electrons enter the $\sigma 2s$ bonding molecular orbital and, therefore, Li_2 should be stable. The molecule has been detected in the vapor state of lithium. It should be emphasized that MO theory does not predict that Li_2 is the most stable state in which lithium can be found at ordinary temperatures. We know it is not; the solid crystalline state is far more stable. This latter fact can also be explained with the aid of a wave mechanical model (see page 703). The construction of the MO configuration of Li_2 is

$$Li(1s^2,2s^1) + Li(1s^2,2s^1) \rightarrow Li_2[(\sigma 1s)^2(\sigma^*1s)^2(\sigma 2s)^2]$$

The MO's of the inner electrons are not involved in bonding and need not be explicitly indicated. These MO's are designated by the letter of the shell of the atomic orbitals from which they are fabricated. The Li_2 configuration is therefore represented as $[KK(\sigma 2s)^2]$.

N₂

The nuclear skeleton, N^{7+}—N^{7+}, of N_2 requires fourteen electrons. Again, the four "inner shell" $1s$ electrons fill the $\sigma 1s$ and $\sigma^* 1s$ molecular orbitals and hence contribute nothing to the bond energy. The four $2s^2$ electrons fill the bonding $\sigma 2s$ and the antibonding $\sigma^* 2s$ molecular orbitals. The antibonding effect of the two electrons in the $\sigma^* 2s$ molecular orbital cancels the bonding effect of the two electrons in the $\sigma 2s$ molecular orbital. These four electrons make no contribution to the bond energy and therefore are called **nonbonding electrons.** The unshared pairs of electrons on each N atom in the structure shown below are the nonbonding electrons. The six remaining electrons enter as pairs into the $\pi 2p_y$, $\pi 2p_z$ and $\sigma 2p_x$ molecular orbitals, each of which is bonding. Consequently, a molecule of N_2 has one sigma and two pi bonds,

nonbonding electrons

The electronic configuration of N_2 is

$$[KK(\sigma 2s)^2(\sigma^* 2s)^2(\pi 2p)^4(\sigma 2p)^2]$$

O₂

Sixteen electrons must be added to the O^{8+}—O^{8+} skeleton to get the electronic configuration of an O_2 molecule. The distribution of the first fourteen electrons into the molecular orbitals is the same as that used to build up the N_2 molecule. In accordance with Hund's rule, one of the two remaining electrons enters the $\pi^* 2p_y$, and the other electron enters the $\pi^* 2p_z$. The electronic structure for O_2 is

$$[KK(\sigma 2s)^2(\sigma^* 2s)^2(\pi 2p)^4(\sigma 2p)^2(\pi^* 2p)^2]$$

Thus the theory predicts that an oxygen molecule is a diradical (page 217).

The four electrons filling the $\sigma 2s$ and $\sigma^* 2s$ molecular orbitals of O_2 are nonbonding. The six electrons filling the $\pi 2p_y$, $\pi 2p_z$, and $\sigma 2p_x$ are all bonding. However, one third of their bonding effect is canceled by the two electrons in the antibonding $\pi^* 2p$ molecular orbitals. The bond energy of a molecule of O_2 is therefore the net effect of two bonding molecular orbitals. From this analysis of the bonding in an oxygen molecule, it is evident that neither electronic structure shown for O_2 (page 217) is accurate. Structure (a) emphasizes the double bond character, but overlooks the diradical properties. Structure (b) emphasizes the diradical character, but denies the double bond character.

Figure 11.10 can be used to describe the electronic structure of a diatomic molecule composed of two different atoms. The energy levels of the atomic orbitals of each atom may not coincide, as they do for like atoms, but the distribution of the relative energy levels of the molecular orbitals does not change. For example, carbon monoxide has a total of 14 electrons. Its electron configuration is therefore isoelectronic with nitrogen. We would write for CO,

$$KK(\sigma 2s)^2(\sigma *2s)^2(\pi 2p)^4(\sigma 2p)^2$$

11.3 VALENCE BOND APPROACH

The Valence Bond method is a quantum mechanical expression of the Lewis concept of the shared electron pair. It considers the bond to be formed from the interaction of atomic orbitals as the atoms approach each other. There can be one electron in each atomic orbital, or two electrons in one atomic orbital and none in the other. The two electrons must have opposite spins. As the atomic orbitals begin to overlap, the two electrons come under the influence of the two nuclei, and are *localized* between these nuclei. The nuclei are attracted by the electrons and approach each other until the bond distance is reached. When the orbitals overlap, the electrons become indistinguishable; one can no longer say which electron came with which atom. In the VB as in the MO approach, bonds are called sigma or pi. The VB and MO theories are used throughout the book, and the student will have ample opportunity to compare and evaluate them.

11.4 HYBRIDIZATION OF ATOMIC ORBITALS

We now consider bonding in molecules with more than two atoms. Methane, CH_4, will serve as the example. Any theory of bonding must be consistent with the observed chemical and physical properties of the molecule. Therefore, let us summarize some of the properties of methane:

(a) All four C—H bonds are identical; they have the same bond length (1.093 A) and bond energy (99.3 kcal/mole). Substitution of a Cl atom for any H atom gives only one kind of methyl chloride molecule, CH_3Cl.

(b) All H—C—H bond angles are alike; they are 109°. The bond angle is the angle between the lines (axes) joining the atoms.

We will use the molecular orbital approach to conceptualize the bonding in CH_4. The carbon atom must provide *four* atomic orbitals, one for each bond. These four atomic orbitals are the $2s$, $2p_x$, $2p_y$, and $2p_z$. Each H atom provides a $1s$ atomic orbital. Hence, we have a total of eight atomic orbitals, four from the carbon atom and one from each of four H atoms, with which to construct our molecular orbitals. Eight atomic orbitals engender eight molecular orbitals: four bonding and four antibonding. Figure 11.12a shows the energy level distribution for the molecular orbitals formed from these atomic orbitals. There are eight electrons that must be placed in these molecular orbitals, as shown by the use of Lewis symbols,

$$\cdot \overset{\cdot}{C} \cdot + 4H \cdot = \text{methane}$$

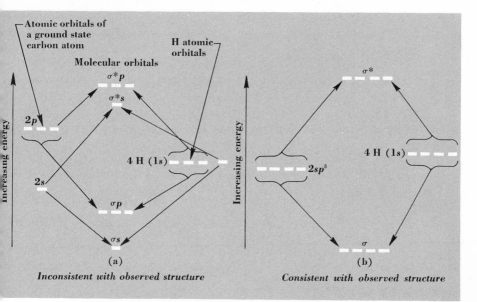

Fig. 11.12. *Molecular orbital energy diagrams for CH_4 formed from four H 1s atomic orbitals and (a) the valence atomic orbitals of carbon, (b) hybridized sp^3 atomic orbitals of carbon.*

Note that the two electrons in the inner shell of carbon are not involved in the bonding and so remain in the 1s atomic orbital. Eight electrons can be placed in the four bonding molecular orbitals, two electrons in each molecular orbital. There are no electrons in antibonding molecular orbitals, and so this model can be used to predict that methane should be a stable molecule. However, there is one serious defect in this picture. One of the molecular orbitals, the one arising from the 2s atomic orbital, has a lower energy than the other three. This bonding situation does not actually exist in methane; all four molecular orbitals should be degenerate, since all four C—H bonds are equivalent.

Four degenerate molecular orbitals can arise only if carbon uses four degenerate atomic orbitals. It is assumed that the four equivalent atomic orbitals used by carbon are fabricated by blending of the 2s and the three 2p orbitals. This blending is called **hybridization.** Figure 11.12b shows the energy levels of the molecular orbitals of CH_4 arising from a carbon atom in the hybridized state. Since these four hybrid orbitals have $\frac{3}{4}$ the character of p orbitals and $\frac{1}{4}$ the character of an s orbital, they are called sp^3 hybrid orbitals. Hybridization involves a redistribution of the ground state atomic orbitals; it does not result in an increase or decrease in the number of orbitals. Mathematically, we take the wave functions of the unhybridized atomic orbitals and *mix* them by a linear combination (addition and subtraction) to give new wave functions. These new wave functions are assigned to the hybrid atomic orbitals. Hybridization, then, is actually a mathematical process and not a real physical phenomenon.

Hybridization and molecular orbital formation have been presented *arbitrarily* as a two-step process. Actually, an isolated carbon atom has the ground state electronic distribution. The degenerate molecular orbitals form under the influence of the approaching H atoms. The initial formation of hybridized atomic orbitals, and steps leading to their formation, have been hypothesized in order to facilitate the application of quantum mechanical equations to the problem. However, these steps are not necessarily traversed by the atom. Any suggestion of a way that a ground state is transformed into a hybridized state is conjectural. In practice methane is not made from isolated carbon and hydrogen atoms. The quantum mechanical models do not necessarily explain the actual chemical formation of a molecule. They are used to picture the bonding and to predict the bond energies and bond distances.

The Valence Bond theory also uses the concept of hybridization to explain the four equivalent bonds in CH_4. The four valence electrons of carbon are distributed among the hybridized orbitals in accord with Hund's rule, so that the electronic configuration of carbon in the sp^3 hybridized state is

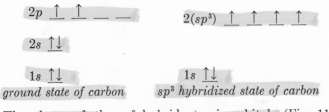

The shape of the sp^3 hybrid atomic orbitals (Fig. 11.13) is like a *p* orbital, except that the two lobes are of unequal size. The atomic nucleus is near a node point. In order to simplify the use of orbital pictures for molecules, the small lobes are frequently omitted. Each sp^3 hybrid orbital overlaps with the 1s orbital of an H atom to form a σ bond. In fact, *bonds formed from hybrid atomic orbitals fabricated from s and p atomic orbitals will* (with very few exceptions) *form sigma bonds*.

Since a pair of electrons in one sigma bond repels the pair of electrons in each of the other sigma bonds, the theory predicts that the four sigma bonds formed from the sp^3 hybrid atomic orbitals should be separated from each other in space as much as possible. To best satisfy this need the axis of each sp^3 orbital should be directed toward the corner of a

Fig. 11.13. *Shape of an sp^3 hybrid atomic orbital. This is also the shape of all hybrid orbitals made up from s and p orbitals, the so-called s-p type hybrid orbitals.*

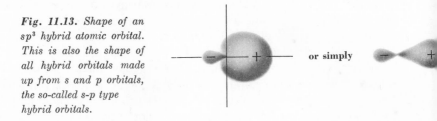

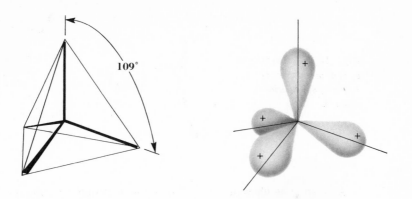

Fig. 11.14. Shape and spatial orientation of tetrahedral, sp^3 hybrid orbitals.

tetrahedron, and the bond angle should be 109° (Fig. 11.14). The observed bond angle is 109° and the success of this prediction strengthens the chemist's belief in the concept of hybridization. Because of this geometry, sp^3 orbitals are called **tetrahedral hybrid orbitals.**

The concept of hybridization is also used to account for the three equivalent B—F bonds in boron trifluoride (page 217). Each B—F bond length is 1.29 A, and the bond energy is 154 kcal/mole. All four atoms lie in the same plane. The structure has a boron atom in the center of an equilateral triangle and a fluorine atom at each of the three corners. The F—B—F bond angle is 120°

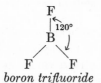

boron trifluoride

The three necessary equivalent atomic orbitals are assumed to result from a blending of the 2s and *two* of the 2p atomic orbitals of boron. The new hybrid orbitals are called sp^2:

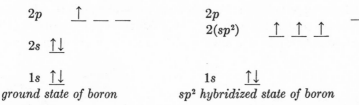

The observed geometry of the molecule is in accord with the prediction that the spatial orientation of the hybrid orbitals permits the maximum bond angle. The sp^2 hybrid orbitals always have this triangular, coplanar orientation (Fig. 11.15) and hence are called **trigonal hybrid orbitals.**

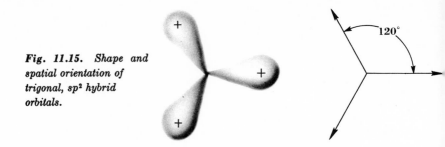

Fig. 11.15. *Shape and spatial orientation of trigonal, sp² hybrid orbitals.*

A third type of hybridization of s and p atomic orbitals is suggested to explain the bonding of beryllium. For example, beryllium chloride, BeCl, is a white solid, m.p. 405°C, which readily sublimes. In the gaseous state it is a linear molecule, Cl—Be—Cl; all three atoms lie on a straight line. Each Be—Cl bond has the same bond length and energy, and so they are equivalent. It is necessary, therefore, for the Be atom to provide two degenerate atomic orbitals to form the two equivalent sigma bonds. It is assumed that the two atomic orbitals which hybridize are the 2s and one of the 2p orbitals. These two hybrid orbitals are designated sp:

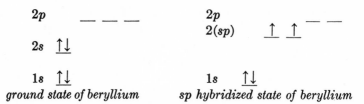

ground state of beryllium   sp hybridized state of beryllium

Since there are only two covalent bonds to the Be atom, and no lone pairs, the maximum angle separating the axes of the two hybrid atomic orbitals should be 180° (Fig. 11.16), which *is* the observed value. Because of this spatial orientation, the sp hybrid orbitals are also called **digonal hybrid orbitals.**

Table 11.1 summarizes the properties of the hybrid orbitals formed from s and p atomic orbitals, the so-called s-p type hybrids.

The bond angle can be used as a criterion for the type of atomic orbital used in bonding. For example, in ammonia, NH₃, the three N—H bonds are equivalent, and the H—N—H bond angle is 107°. This is very close to the tetrahedral angle of 109°, and so the N atom in ammonia is

Fig. 11.16. *Shape and spatial orientation of digonal, sp hybrid orbitals.*

TABLE 11.1   *Properties of s-p Type Hybrid Atomic Orbitals*

Type	Name	s Character	p Character	Bond angle	Geometric arrangement	Type of bond formed
sp	Digonal	$\frac{1}{2}$	$\frac{1}{2}$	180°	Linear	Sigma
sp^2	Trigonal	$\frac{1}{3}$	$\frac{2}{3}$	120°	Coplanar triangular	Sigma
sp^3	Tetrahedral	$\frac{1}{4}$	$\frac{3}{4}$	109°	Tetrahedral	Sigma

presumed to use sp^3 hybrid orbitals:

$2p$ ↑ ↑ ↑ $2(sp^3)$ ↑↓ ↑ ↑ ↑

$2s$ ↑↓

$1s$ ↑↓ $1s$ ↑↓
ground state of nitrogen   *sp^3 hybridized nitrogen, as in* NH_3

We see that a hybrid orbital can also accommodate an unshared (lone) pair of electrons. It is noteworthy that the N atom has available three degenerate $2p$ orbitals with which to form three equivalent N—H bonds. Nevertheless, it is presumed that the N atom uses hybrid orbitals. Were the nitrogen atom to use p orbitals to form the three sigma bonds with the H atoms, the bond angle would be approximately 90°, as shown in Fig. 11.17. This is so because each p orbital is oriented along one of the three

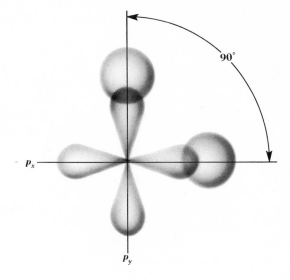

Fig. 11.17. Orbital representation of two σ bonds, each formed from a p orbital to show 90° bond angle.

Cartesian axes, the x, y, and z axes, and the angle between any two of these axes is 90°. (An explanation of the bonding for nitrogen in the ammonia molecule is discussed in more detail on page 642, Chapter 24.

The two equivalent H—O bonds in water form an angle of 105°. This value is much closer to the tetrahedral value of 109° than it is to the 90 angle expected if p orbitals were used to form the two sigma bonds:

$$2p \quad \uparrow\downarrow \; \uparrow \; \uparrow \qquad\qquad 2(sp^3) \quad \uparrow\downarrow \; \uparrow\downarrow \; \uparrow \; \uparrow$$

$$2s \quad \uparrow\downarrow$$

$$1s \quad \uparrow\downarrow \qquad\qquad\qquad 1s \quad \uparrow\downarrow$$

ground state of oxygen   *sp³ hybridized oxygen, as in H_2O*

In this respect, oxygen behaves like nitrogen in that it utilizes hybrid orbitals rather than p orbitals to form sigma bonds. In general, Be, B, C N, and O use hybrid atomic orbitals to form sigma bonds and also to house lone pairs of electrons, when present.

11.5   MULTIPLY BONDED ORGANIC MOLECULES

We have seen that the triple bond in N_2 and CO consists of a sigma and two pi bonds. We will always find that *no more than one bond between two atoms can be a σ bond,* and that *all bonds in excess of one must be π bonds* Thus, single bonds are σ bonds, double bonds are composed of one σ and one π bond, and triple bonds are composed of one σ bond and two π bonds

Of special interest are the multiply bonded carbon molecules, as typified by ethylene and acetylene. The geometry of these two molecules is the clue to the hybridization of the carbon atoms. Ethylene is a planar molecule in which the H—C—H and H—C—C bond angles are approximately 120°:

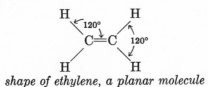

shape of ethylene, a planar molecule

Such geometry implies sp^2 hybridization for each carbon atom. The energy levels of the atomic orbitals of the sp^2 hybridized carbon atom are shown in Fig. 11.18c. The spatial arrangement of the sp^2 and p orbitals i shown in Fig. 11.19a.

The joining of two such units with 4 H atoms is shown in Fig. 11.19b Two of the three sp^2 hybrid orbitals of each carbon atom overlap with the $1s$ orbital of each of four H atoms. The third sp^2 hybrid orbital overlaps with the sp^2 hybrid orbital of the other carbon atom. This array of sigma bonds, called the **skeleton** of the molecule, is coplanar (Fig. 11.19c) The p_z orbitals remaining on the adjacent carbon atoms overlap to form a

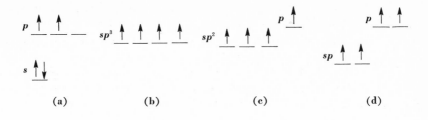

Fig. 11.18. *Electronic structures exhibited by carbon: (a) ground state; (b) sp³ hybridized; (c) sp² hybridized; (d) sp hybridized.*

π bond. The π bond is perpendicular to the skeleton of the molecule (Fig. 11.19d). The two carbon atoms and the four hydrogen atoms provide a total of 12 valence electrons. Ten of these electrons are used for the five σ bonds. The remaining two electrons comprise the π bond.

According to molecular orbital theory, since 12 atomic orbitals are involved in bonding (8 from the two C atoms and 4 from the four H atoms), twelve molecular orbitals result; six are bonding and six are anti-bonding. Five of the bonding and five of the antibonding orbitals are sigma. The remaining two are a π and a π^* molecular orbital. The twelve valence electrons are then used to fill the five σ- and the one π-bonding molecular orbitals.

Although devoid of electrons in the ground state molecule, the π^* anti-bonding molecular orbital nevertheless plays an important role in the chemistry of multiply bonded compounds. This is especially true when compounds with multiple bonds are irradiated with ultraviolet light. An electron in the π molecular orbital absorbs a certain quantum of radiation from the ultraviolet spectrum and goes to a higher energy level. A so-called "excited" molecule results. This higher energy level is in most cases the antibonding, π^* molecular orbital.

$$\begin{array}{ccc} \pi^*_{\text{MO}}\underline{\hspace{1.5cm}} & & \pi^*_{\text{MO}}\underline{\downarrow} \\ & +\text{ energy } (h\nu) \rightarrow & \\ \pi_{\text{MO}}\underline{\uparrow\downarrow} & & \pi_{\text{MO}}\underline{\uparrow} \\ \textit{ground state} & & \textit{excited state} \end{array}$$

Acetylene is the simplest member of the alkyne series (page 246). The four atoms in acetylene, C_2H_2, lie on a straight line,

$$\text{H—C} \equiv \text{C—H}$$
acetylene,
a linear molecule

A linear geometry indicates that each carbon is using sp hybrid orbitals. The energy levels of an sp hybridized carbon atom are shown in Fig. 11.18d. Figure 11.20a shows the assembly of two H atoms, each with a $1s$ atomic orbital, and two C atoms, each with two sp hybrid orbitals and a p_y and p_z orbital. Each carbon atom forms two σ bonds; one by over-lapping an sp hybrid orbital with the other carbon atom, and the second by overlapping an *sp* orbital with the *s* orbital of a hydrogen atom. Each carbon atom has a p_y and p_z orbital, each with one electron. The p_y orbitals overlap laterally to form a π bond in the *y* plane, and the p_z orbitals interact similarly to form a π bond in the *z* plane. Therefore, the triple bond comprises one σ and two π bonds. The planes of the two π bonds are at right angles to each other and to the C—C σ-bond axis. It is believed, however, that these two π bonds coalesce into a cylindrical

Fig. 11.19. *Orbital representation of ethylene: (a) sp² hybrid orbitals and a p$_z$ orbital; (b) assembly of two such units plus four H 1s orbitals; (c) skeleton; (d) representation of π bond. Black dots represent electrons.*

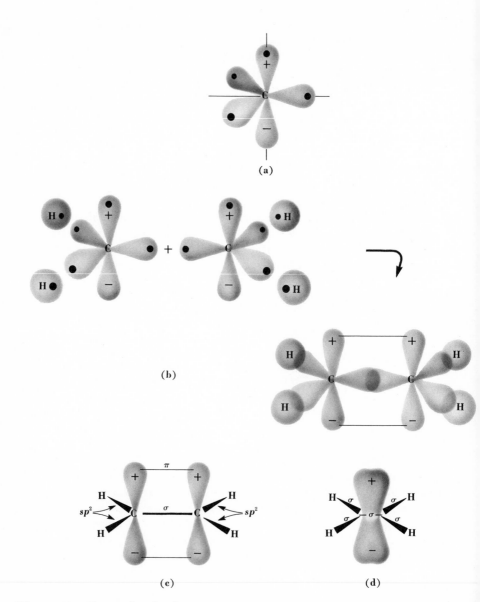

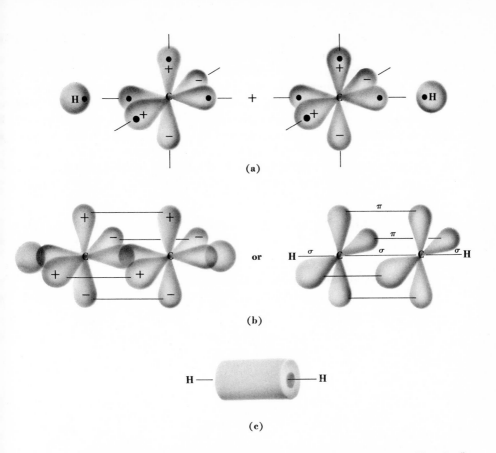

Fig. 11.20. *Orbital representation of acetylene: (a) assembly of 2H and 2C atoms; (b) schematic representation showing σ-bond skeleton and π bonds; (c) representation of the acetylene-type π bond.*

shape (Fig. 11.20b), called an acetylenic π bond. The acetylenic π bond is nevertheless counted as two bonds.

Carbon dioxide is an example of a molecule with two double bonds to the same carbon. It is a linear molecule in which both O=C bonds are equivalent:

$$:\ddot{O}\!=\!\!C\!=\!\ddot{O}:$$
$$\underset{180°}{\diagdown\diagup}$$

shape of a CO₂ molecule

Linearity means the O—C—O bond angle is 180°, a fact indicating that the carbon uses *sp* hybridized orbitals to form a sigma bond to each O atom (Fig. 11.21a). The carbon atom also has two *p* orbitals, each of which overlaps laterally with a *p* orbital of an adjacent oxygen atom to give two π bonds. Each π bond holds a pair of electrons, one from each atom, and therefore the octet requirement for carbon is satisfied. The π bonds are in planes perpendicular to each other but, since they do not involve the same two atoms, do not coalesce. If we assume the lone pairs of electrons on each oxygen atom to be housed in individual *hybrid* orbitals, then the oxygen atoms are both sp^2 hybridized.

For the three molecules just discussed, the geometry was used to indicate the kind of hybridization that should be assumed for the carbon atom. However, it would be preferable if the type of hybridization could be deduced from the electronic structure, thus making it unnecessary to remember or to seek information on the geometry of each molecule. This prediction can be accomplished by utilizing the **hybrid orbital number** rule. The hybrid orbital number is the number of hybrid orbitals used by an atom, and is defined as

hybrid orbital number = coordination number (number of σ bonds) + number of pairs of unshared electrons

Values of 4, 3, and 2 indicate, respectively, sp^3, sp^2, and sp hybridization. The coordination number is the number of atoms bonded to the atom being considered, and so is equal to the number of sigma bonds to that

Fig. 11.21. (a) *Orbital representation of the construction of a molecule of* CO_2. (b) *Schematic orbital representation of a CO_2 molecule.*

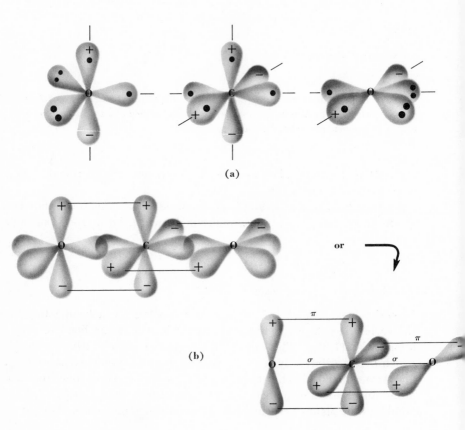

(a)

(b)

or

atom. The basis for this rule is the assumption that *it is necessary to provide a hybrid orbital for each unshared and sigma-bonded pair of electrons.* Exceptions to this rule may occur for certain compounds of elements in the higher periods of the Periodic Table. It is observed that the tendency to use unhybridized p orbitals rather than hybridized orbitals increases within a Group of the Periodic Table as the size of the element increases. (Some of these exceptions will be discussed in Chapter 23.)

EXAMPLE 1   **Use the hybrid orbital number rule to predict the bonding of**

(a) **a carbanion such as $H_3C:^-$**

(b) **a carbonium ion such as H_3C^+**

(c) **a free radical such as $H_3C\cdot$**

ANSWER

(a) **The hybrid orbital number for the C atom in $H_3C:^-$ is $3 + 1 = 4$; therefore the C atom uses sp^3 hybridized atomic orbitals.**

(b) **The hybrid orbital number for the C atom in H_3C^+ is $3 + 0 = 3$; therefore the C atom is sp^2 hybridized.**

(c) **In applying the hybrid orbital number rule, an unpaired electron is *not* counted. This is so since, unlike an unshared *pair* of electrons, a *lone electron* is in a p orbital rather than in a hybrid orbital. Hence the structure for $H_3C\cdot$ and H_3C^+ are alike, except that for $H_3C\cdot$ the remaining p orbital, instead of being empty, has one electron.**

11.6   **HYBRIDIZATION OF ATOMS WITH MORE THAN AN OCTET OF ELECTRONS**

Elements in Groups IV, V, VI, and VII of the third and higher periods form compounds in which the total number of bonding and lone-pair electrons exceeds eight. The number is occasionally ten, as in phosphorus pentachloride, PCl_5, and sulfur tetrafluoride, $:SF_4$, and more often twelve as in sulfur hexafluoride, SF_6, and bromine pentafluoride, $:BrF_5$. In iodine heptafluoride, IF_7, the central atom has fourteen electrons.

(a) **Six Pairs of Electrons on the Central Atom.**   To accommodate six pairs of electrons, either lone or bonding, an atom must have available

Fig. 11.22.   Electronic arrangement of outermost principal energy level of sulfur: (a) ground state, (b) hybridized sp^3d^2 state.

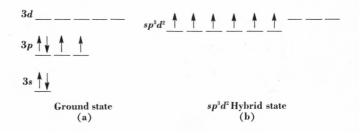

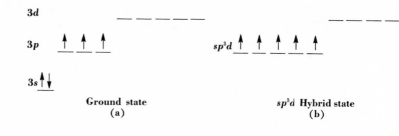

Ground state
(a)

sp^3d Hybrid state
(b)

Fig. 11.23. *Electronic arrangement of outermost principal energy level of phosphorus: (a) ground state, (b) hybridized sp^3d state.*

six atomic orbitals. Its outermost s and p orbitals total only four. According to the Valence Bond theory, the deficiency is met by hybridization of these four orbitals with two d orbitals of the same principal quantum number. In this way, six equivalent sp^3d^2 hybrid orbitals become available to accommodate the six pairs of electrons. Thus, the sulfur atom in SF_6 acquires six orbitals by hybridizing its one $3s$, three $3p$, and two $3d$ orbitals (Fig. 11.22).* Each orbital points to the corner of an octahedron (Fig. 24.3, page 643), and hence the sp^3d^2 hybrid orbitals are called **octahedral.** The angle between any pair of bonds is 90°.

(b) Five Pairs of Electrons on the Central Atom. Since five orbitals are needed to accommodate the five pairs of electrons, the Valence Bond theory suggests that one d orbital hybridizes with the one s and three p orbitals of the same principal quantum number to give five sp^3d hybrid orbitals. Thus, the phosphorus atom in gaseous PCl_5 uses the $3s$, three $3p$, and one $3d$ orbital to form the five sp^3d hybrid orbitals (Fig. 11.23). The PCl_5 molecule is a **trigonal bipyramid** (Fig. 11.24). Three Cl atoms lie at the corners of an equilateral triangle, while a fourth Cl atom lies above and a fifth below the center of the triangle. This type of geome-

* According to Molecular Orbital theory, the two additional orbitals used are antibonding rather than d orbitals. This discussion is restricted to the more entrenched Valence Bond theory, not because it is superior, but because it is more easily understood.

Fig. 11.24. *Spatial arrangement of trigonal bipyramid, sp^3d hybrid orbitals.*

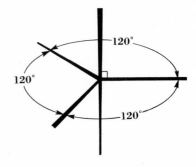

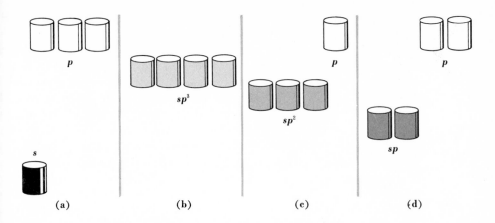

Fig. 11.25. *Hybridization analogy: (a) ground state, (b) sp^3, (c) sp^2, (d) sp.*

try indicates that the five bonds are not equivalent. In this respect the sp^3d hybrid orbitals differ from the hybrid orbitals previously discussed, all of which engender equivalent bonds. (This question is discussed in more detail in Chapter 24.)

11.7 RELATIVE ENERGY LEVELS OF THE s-p TYPE OF HYBRID ORBITAL

A crude analogy to the concept of hybridization is the mixing of a can of black with cans of white paint. The s orbital is represented by the can of black paint, and the p orbitals are represented by three cans of white paint. The hybrid orbitals will have different shades of gray, depending on the number of white cans mixed with the black. This mixing is shown in Fig. 11.25. Notice that the fewer the cans of white paint that are mixed, the darker the shade of gray. We can interpret these shades of gray in terms of relative energy levels of the hybrid orbitals. Since the s orbital (can of black paint) is at a lower energy level than the p orbital (can of white paint), the darker the shade of gray the lower is the energy level of the corresponding hybrid orbital. Hence, the sequence of relative energy levels of the s-p type of orbital is

$$s < sp < sp^2 < sp^3 < p$$
$\leftarrow$ lower energy   higher energy $\rightarrow$

We usually say that for a given atom *the more s character* (or less p character) *in an atomic orbital, the lower is the energy of the orbital.*

11.8 LOCALIZED MOLECULAR ORBITALS

We now consider in more detail the models for chemical bonding that are forthcoming from the Valence Bond and Molecular Orbital theories.

The Valence Bond theory depicts the pair of electrons of a covalent bond as belonging only to the two bonded atoms. The electrons are said to be localized in the bond resulting from overlap of atomic orbitals. For most molecules the Valence Bond model can be easily transcribed into a Lewis structure. Thus, in the structural formula for methane, each dash between the carbon atom and a hydrogen atom stands for a localized pair of electrons. Even in a π bond, such as in ethylene, the pair of electrons is assumed to be localized between the two carbon atoms. The Molecular Orbital model arises from considering electrons as being in molecular orbitals at certain energy levels. These energy levels pertain to the entire molecule, and the electrons cannot be said to belong to only one atom or a pair of atoms. This model cannot be transposed into the simple, convenient Lewis symbolism, and this has been a drawback to the widespread use of molecular orbital models. To overcome this drawback, the Molecular Orbital theory can be modified so that we can say, for example, that the pair of electrons in a C—H bond of methane can be localized in a molecular orbital encompassing only the C atom and the particular H atom. Such a **localized molecular orbital** is said to be two-centered rather than multicentered. These two-centered molecular orbitals are similar to the localized bonds of the Valence Bond theory. All sigma bonds and isolated π bonds can be assumed to be localized two-centered molecular orbitals.

Many of the properties of a compound such as methane can be accounted for in terms of the localized bond. These include the geometry, chemical reactivity, bond energy, bond length, heats of formation, and heats of combustion. Most of these properties pertain to the molecule in its ground state. However, the properties of the molecule in the excited state cannot be adequately explained in terms of the "localized bond" picture. For example, if we wish to predict the ionization energy for methane,

$$CH_4 \rightarrow CH_4{}^+ + e^-$$

we must use the concept of multicenter molecular orbitals. In this case, the electron is being removed from the entire molecule and not from any one isolated bond. (We shall have more to say about localized vs. multicentered molecular orbitals in Section 11.10b, page 288.)

11.9 PROPERTIES OF COVALENT BONDS

Chemical bonds are characterized by their length and energy. The bond angle, a property of atoms with more than one bond, is discussed in a later chapter. Bond length (page 189) and bond energy (page 115) have been discussed previously. In this section we are concerned with the structural features that change the normal values. *Any structural feature that shortens the distance between two atoms increases the energy needed to dissociate the atoms.* This happens because the closer the atoms are, the more their orbitals overlap. The generalization is substantiated by the observed

TABLE 11.2   *Multiple Bond Covalent Radii (in Angstroms)*

Element	Single-bond radius	Double-bond radius	Triple-bond radius
C	0.77	0.665	0.60
N	0.73	0.60	0.55
O	0.74	0.55	
S	1.02	0.94	

distances and energies of the bonds between the two carbon atoms in ethane, ethylene, and acetylene:

	H_3C-CH_3	$H_2C=CH_2$	$HC\equiv CH$
Bond distance (in A)	1.54	1.33	1.20
Bond energy (in kcal/mole)	83	143	194

These values also show that the *distance between two atoms decreases when the number of bonds between the atoms increases.*

Just as we assigned a single-bond covalent radius to an atom (page 190), so we can assign a multiple-bond covalent radius to an atom. By halving the C=C bond distance in ethylene, the C≡C bond distance in acetylene, the N=N bond distance in azomethane, $CH_3-N=N-CH_3$, and the N≡N bond distance in N_2, the multiple-bond covalent radii shown in Table 11.2 are obtained.

The double-bond radius for oxygen is obtained from the C=O bond distance in formaldehyde, $H_2C=O$; this distance is 1.21 A. If 0.665 A is assumed to be the portion due to the carbon radius, 0.55 A is the value assumed for the double-bond radius for oxygen.

The wave mechanical model of the covalent bond offers a reasonable explanation for the observed shortening of multiple-bond lengths. Multiple bonding results in a greater electron density between the bonding nuclei. The nuclei are shielded more effectively from each other and can approach more closely.

Bond polarity may also cause contraction of bond length. For example, the length of the polar Si—F bond, calculated from Table 8.3 (page 191), by adding r_{Si} and r_F is 1.86 A. However, the measured bond length in SiF_4 is 1.54 A. When a similar comparison is made of the calculated and observed lengths of a bond between atoms of *similar* electronegativity, the correspondence is very good. Thus, in the **interhalogen** compound, bromine chloride, Br—Cl, the calculated bond length is 2.13 A; the observed length 2.14 A.

Coincidental with the contraction of a bond length is an increase in bond energy. The closer the atoms approach each other, the more effectively can their atomic orbitals overlap and the stronger is the bond. Hence, we find that *an increase in polarity of a covalent bond always strengthens the bond.* *

11.10 RESONANCE AND DELOCALIZED p ELECTRONS

(a) **Resonance Concept.** Let us write an electronic structure for dinitrogen oxide (nitrous oxide), N_2O (page 228). (This compound, often called laughing gas and used widely as a propellant gas in whipped cream "bombs," is still used occasionally as an anesthetic in dentistry.) There are two reasonable Lewis electronic structures for N_2O, both of which fit the octet rule and have the required skeleton (Fig. 11.26a and a'). Which structure, *if any*, is correct? This question might be resolved by comparing the calculated bond lengths, which should differ for the two structures, with the observed bond lengths. The bond lengths can be calculated from the single-bond and double-bond covalent radii. For example, the calculated $N=O$ bond length, 1.15 A (Fig. 11.26a), is the sum of the double-bond covalent radii for N and O (0.60 + 0.55), as given in Table 11.2. The calculated bond lengths are shown below the respective bonds in each structure in Fig. 11.26a and a'. The measured values (Fig. 11.26b) do not correspond to either set of bond lengths. These values indicate that *neither structure (a) nor (a') is correct.* The actual N-to-N bond length is less than an $N=N$ bond length but more than the $N\equiv N$ bond length. Similarly, the N-to-O bond length is more than the $N=O$ bond length but less than the $N-O$ bond length. The experimental data are interpreted in the Valence Bond theory by using the concept of **resonance.**

According to the resonance concept, the structure of a molecule such as N_2O *cannot* be accurately depicted by a Lewis structure. Even though the Lewis structures written (Fig. 11.26a and a') for N_2O are incorrect, nevertheless, taken together they indicate much about the structure of the actual molecule. For example, although the bond between the N and O atoms in the actual molecule is not a double bond as suggested in Fig. 11.26a, or a single bond as suggested in Fig. 11.26a', its bonding quality is somewhat between a double and a single bond. Therefore, these incorrect Lewis structures that we write are called **contributing** or **resonance structures,** and the actual molecule, which cannot be represented with a

* The reader should not form the impression that, since the ionic bond is the extreme case of a polar bond, ionic bonds are stronger than polar covalent bonds. The above generalization holds only when bonds arise from overlap of atomic orbitals.

Fig. 11.26. Possible electronic structures for N_2O showing (a and a') expected bond lengths, and (b) actual bond distances. Formal charges are shown.

Lewis formula, is said to be a **hybrid** of the contributing structures. The term "hybrid" has the biological connotation, indicating a species that is a "cross" between two other species. It should be emphasized that, in chemistry, the term hybrid is meant to be a *real* species that is a cross between several (not necessarily two) *fictitious, unreal, imaginary, mythical, nonexisting* species as represented by Lewis formulas.

A double-headed arrow, ↔, is always written between the contributing structures to indicate resonance. There are important restrictions on the kind of contributing structures one can write:

(a) *The relative positions of all atoms in the molecule must remain the same—only the positions of the electrons may be altered.*

(b) *There must be the same number of pairs of electrons in all contributing structures.* For example, $:\overset{..}{\text{O}}::\overset{..}{\text{O}}:$ and $:\overset{..}{\underset{.}{\text{O}}}:\overset{..}{\underset{.}{\text{O}}}:$ are not contributing structures of oxygen.

EXAMPLE 2 **Write contributing structures for (a) nitrate ion, NO_3^-, and (b) benzene, C_6H_6. Show all formal charges for NO_3^-.**

ANSWER

(a)

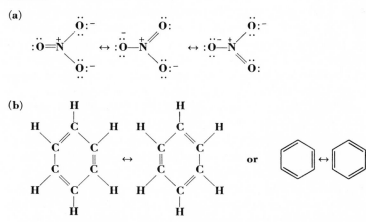

(b)

Observe that the three contributing structures for the nitrate ion look equivalent. In each structure the N atom has a single bond to each of two O atoms, and a double bond to a third oxygen atom. The three written structures, taken together, have a different connotation than has any single one. Any one of the contributing structures implies, *incorrectly*, two N—O bond distances of the same length and one shorter N=O bond distance. Actually, all three nitrogen-oxygen bond distances are found to be the same. This experimental fact is consistent with the interpretation that all three oxygen atoms are indistinguishable from each other. No one oxygen atom can be said to be the one that is doubly bonded to the nitrogen atom. Instead, *each O atom participates in a double bond*—a fact *represented by writing the three resonance structures.*

The same equivalence of resonance structures exists for benzene (Example 2b). Again, by drawing both contributing structures, we imply that none of the double bonds is fixed between a given pair of adjacent carbon atoms.

(b) Extended π Bonding. Evidently substances such as N_2O, NO_3^-, and benzene cannot be adequately represented by drawing individual valence bond (Lewis) structures, since such structures require the localization of bonding electrons between a given pair of adjacent atoms. Writing several contributing structures, none of which is correct, is an attempt to circumvent this difficulty. However, when the Molecular Orbital theory is used to describe the electronic structure of a molecule, this problem does not arise. Although the MO picture considers electrons as belonging to the entire molecule, it is usually expedient to assume that electrons in σ bonds and isolated π bonds are localized between the bonding atoms.

Let us now consider the validity of the "localized molecular orbital" concept as applied to a molecule like benzene, C_6H_6, which cannot be depicted by a Lewis structure. The nuclei of all twelve atoms comprising the benzene molecule lie in one plane, hence benzene is a planar molecule. Each C—C—C and H—C—C bond angle is 120°, and each carbon-to-carbon bond length is 1.40 A (Fig. 11.27a). This type of geometry indicates that each C atom is using sp^2 hybridized atomic orbitals to form three localized σ bonds for the carbon-hydrogen skeleton (Fig. 11.27b). Each carbon atom utilizes three of its four valence electrons to fabricate its three σ bonds. The fourth valence electron must reside in the remaining p orbital. Each carbon atom has such a p orbital, and the six p orbitals are parallel and adjacent to each other (Fig. 11.27c). How do these p orbitals interact? If we were to apply the Valence Bond theory or the localized Molecular Orbital theory to write Lewis structures, we would say that the p orbitals overlap in pairs to form three localized (two-centered) π bonds. Thus, the p orbitals of carbon atoms 1 and 2, atoms 3 and 4, and atoms 5 and 6 could overlap to give the structure shown in Fig. 11.27d'. Then again, the p orbitals of carbon atoms 2 and 3, atoms 4 and 5, and atoms 6 and 1 could overlap to give the structure shown in Fig. 11.27d''. Structures d' and d'' represent the mythical contributing structures written for benzene in Example 2. We know these structures to be incorrect, because they imply that the bond in benzene should alternate-in length between 1.34 A for a C=C bond and 1.54 A for a C—C bond. Experimentally all the carbon-to-carbon bond distances are 1.40 A (Fig. 11.27a). This interpretation of the interaction of the p orbitals must therefore be incorrect. The error was made when we insisted that a given p orbital had to overlap with one or the other of its neighboring p orbitals. Actually, *a given p orbital can overlap at the same time with each parallel p orbital adjacent to it* (Fig. 11.27e). It is therefore wrong to say that the six p electrons of a benzene molecule are localized in pairs in each of three π bonds. Instead, *the six electrons are delocalized in an extended, cyclic π bond encompassing all six carbons.* Hence, for a molecule like benzene, the

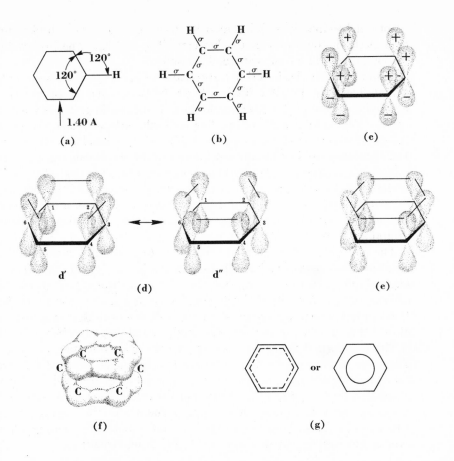

Fig. 11.27. *Molecular orbital representation for benzene: (a) structure showing geometry; (b) σ-bonded skeleton; (c) p orbitals; (d) overlap of p orbitals for
two contributing structures (d′ and d″); (e) cyclic overlap of p orbitals; (f)
extended π bond; (g) shorthand notation.*

localized picture of bonding is accurate for the σ bonding, but inaccurate
for the π bonding. The electron distribution has the shape of a pair of
doughnuts, one above and the other below the σ-bonded carbon skeleton.
Since the electron density is somewhat greater at the carbon atoms and
somewhat less between the carbons, the doughnuts are depicted with
lumps at the carbon atoms (Fig. 11.27f).

This model for the bonding in benzene predicts that the bonding is
uniform between any pair of carbon atoms, and hence each carbon-to-
carbon bond should have the same length. The model also predicts the
C-to-C bond length to be less than a C—C bond length and more than a
C=C bond length, in agreement with experiment. Since the benzene molecule has no definite single or double bonds as conceived by the Lewis

theory of bonding, it is represented by drawing a continuous broken line or a circle in the center of the hexagon (Fig. 11.27g). The broken line (or circle) stands for the extended π bond.

It should be emphasized that the *extended π bond is not a single molecular orbital*. The six p atomic orbitals interact by lateral overlap to give *six π molecular orbitals*, three bonding and three antibonding. The six p electrons of benzene fill the three bonding molecular orbitals, each of which is delocalized over all six carbon atoms. The charge cloud (shown in Fig. 11.27f) actually represents the most stable of the three bonding molecular orbitals. The most stable bonding molecular orbital arises when the p orbitals interact so that all + lobes are on the same side of the σ-bonded carbon skeleton. In fact, electron cloud representations for a delocalized, extended π bond usually depict the most stable π-bonding molecular orbital.

The nitrate ion, NO_3^-, which cannot be represented by a single Lewis structure, also has an extended (delocalized) π bond. Each O—N—O bond angle is 120°, a fact indicating that the N atom utilizes sp^2 hybrid atomic orbitals to form the σ-bonded skeleton. The nitrogen atom has a p orbital that can act as a pivot for overlapping with a p orbital of each oxygen atom* (Fig. 11.28a) to give an extended π bond (Fig. 11.28b).

The σ-bonded skeleton and the lone pairs of electrons on each oxygen atom account for 18 of the 24 valence electrons of the NO_3^- ion. Therefore, the remaining six electrons must be present in the delocalized, extended π bond. Note that Fig. 11.28b does not provide a good bookkeeping of electrons, an unfortunate defect not encountered when contributing structures are used. We should expect to find extended π bonding whenever a molecule can be depicted by contributing structures.

* The hybrid orbital number rule applied to a contributing structure for NO_3^- (Example 2, page 287) predicts that the O atoms singly bonded to the N atom should use sp^3 hybrid orbitals, whereas the oxygen atom doubly bonded to the N atom should use sp^2 hybrid orbitals. However, to provide p orbitals for extended π bonding, both oxygen atoms have the lower hybrid orbital number. The rules for predicting when such a change can be expected are given by H. Meislich, in *Journal of Chemical Education* **40**, 401 (1963).

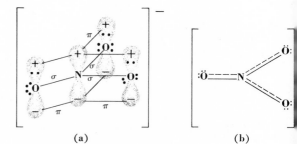

Fig. 11.28. Extended π bonding in nitrate ion.

(a)   (b)

The culmination of delocalized, extended π bonding is observed in graphite (Fig. 10.1, page 251). In graphite, p electrons are delocalized over an entire layer of fused benzene rings. The broken lines joining layers actually represent head-to-head overlap of the "upper doughnut" of one layer, and the "bottom doughnut" of the layer above. The distance (3.35 A) between layers of fused benzene rings, is, however, large enough to prevent extensive overlap between the "doughnuts." Hence, these broken lines represent a kind of weak bonding force rather than *actual* covalent bonds. We know that the layered structure is not rigid. Graphite is used as a lubricant, and therefore the layers must be able to slip by each other easily. Easy slippage would not be possible if strong bonds existed between layers.

11.11 DELOCALIZATION OR RESONANCE ENERGY

Electrons in an extended π bond are free to move anywhere within the region of the charge cloud. Since the delocalized electrons can move in a larger volume, *the repulsive forces between them are weakened.* As a result, the real molecule with delocalized p electrons has less energy than the fictitious molecule with localized p electrons, and therefore is more stable:

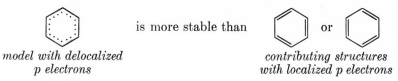

model with delocalized   is more stable than   or   *contributing structures*
p electrons   *with localized p electrons*

The difference in energy between the localized and delocalized model is called delocalization (resonance) energy.

One method for arriving at the resonance (delocalization) energy of benzene is based on heats of hydrogenation. Other methods use heats of combustion (Problem 10, page 293) and heats of formation. The conversion of cyclohexene to cyclohexane with hydrogen (hydrogenation) (page 249) liberates 28.6 kcal/mole. If we assume that a contributing structure of benzene correctly depicts this molecule, then benzene should be considered to have three double bonds. Hence, benzene might be expected to liberate three times as much heat, or 85.8 kcal/mole, when hydrogenated. The observed heat of hydrogenation is only 49.8 kcal/mole. Benzene, therefore, actually has 36 kcal/mole (85.8 − 49.8) *less* energy than expected if it were a typical compound with three double bonds; this value is identified as the resonance energy of benzene. *The more extensive the delocalization of p electrons, the greater is the resonance energy and the more stable is the molecule.* We can now explain the aromatic character of benzene. Benzene does not normally undergo addition reactions because addition would have to destroy the highly stable, cyclic, extended π bond. Substitution reactions do not destroy the stable bonding system in benzene and hence are favored over addition reactions.

Graphite is a more stable form of carbon than is diamond. This fact is in part attributable to the large delocalization energy inherent in graphite with its massive extended π-bond system, not observed in the localized σ bonding typical of diamond.

Problems

1. Definitions. Define and illustrate each of the following terms: (a) bonding molecular orbital, (b) antibonding molecular orbital, (c) resonance, (d) hybridization, (e) delocalization energy.

2. Molecular orbital designation. (a) Give the molecular orbital designation, as was done for O_2 (page 269), for (i) Be_2; (ii) F_2; (iii) He_2^+; (iv) HeH^+; (v) LiH (as a covalent molecule); (vi) Ne_2. (b) Which of these substances is/are unlikely to exist? Explain.

3. Molecular orbital theory. (a) Give the molecular orbital designation for B_2, as was done for O_2 (page 269). (b) Should B_2 be paramagnetic?

4. Hybridization. Show the distribution of the valence electrons in the orbitals, just prior to bonding with an H atom, of (a) an sp^2 hybridized N atom, (b) an sp^3 hybridized B atom, (c) an sp^2 hybridized O atom, (d) an sp hybridized N atom, (e) an sp hybridized Cl atom, (f) an sp^3d^2 hybridized Si atom.

5. Hybrid orbital number rule. Apply the hybrid orbital number rule (to N, C, and O atoms) to predict the molecular orbital structure of

carbon monoxide, $:C{\equiv}O:$

formaldehyde, $H_2C{=}\overset{..}{O}:$

hydrogen cyanide, $H{-}C{\equiv}N:$

allene, $H_2C{=}C{=}CH_2$

6. Bond lengths. (a) From the data in the table on page 191, calculate the lengths of the following sets of bonds: (i) O—F, O—Cl, O—Br, O—I; (ii) C—C, C—N, C—O, C—F. (b) What change is observed in the calculated bond length of A—B as (i) B increases in atomic weight within a family, (ii) B increases in atomic number within a period? Explain.

7. Multiple bond lengths. Compare the bond lengths and predict the relative bond stabilities for

(a) $-C{\equiv}C-$, $:N{\equiv}N:$; (b) $C{=}O$, $C{=}S$; (c) $-N{=}O$, $-N{=}\overset{|}{C}-$

8. Resonance. (a) Write two contributing structures consistent with the octet rule for hydrazoic acid, HN_3, for which the sequence of bonded atoms is HNNN. (b) Locate all formal charges in each structure. (c) Which if any is the correct structure of the molecule? Explain. (d) Predict the two N-to-N bond distances for HN_3 relative to a single, double, and triple bond distance.

9. Extended π bonding and resonance. (a) Write the contributing structures of (i) ozone, O_3;

(ii) carbonate ion, $\left[O{-}\overset{\overset{\textstyle O}{\|}}{C}{-}O \right]^{2-}$; (iii) formate ion, $H{-}\overset{\overset{\textstyle O}{\|}}{C}{-}O^-$; (iv) diazomethane, H_2CNN. (b) Write structures representing extended π bonding in compounds (i), (ii), (iii).

10. Delocalization energy. Calculate the delocalization energy of benzene from the following data: (a) the heat of combustion $\Delta H = -781.0$ kcal/mole; (b) if benzene had typical single and double bonds, the heat of combustion would be the sum of the following contributions: C—H, 53.3; C—C, 50.2; and C=C, 118.8.

      Answer. 45.8 kcal/mole (other methods give the value of 36.0 kcal/mole).

11. Molecular orbital theory. Explain why the first ionization energy of nitric oxide is less than that of carbon monoxide.

12. Orbital overlap. Explain why a lateral (sidewise) overlap of an *s* and a *p* orbital is nonbonding, whereas a head-to-head overlap can be bonding or anti-bonding. Draw a schematic representation of each type of overlap.

13. Extended π bonding. Account for the fact that the B—F bond distance in BF_3 is shorter than in BF_4^-.

12

Intermolecular
forces

SINCE LIQUID AND solid substances can be vaporized without chemical decomposition, the forces holding molecules together in the aggregated states must be weaker than the chemical bonding forces between atoms and between ions. These **intermolecular forces** are particularly weak for molecular covalent substances of low melting point and boiling point. In this chapter we describe the nature of these electrostatic intermolecular forces, known as **van der Waals forces.**

12.1 DIPOLE-DIPOLE INTERACTION

We have seen that certain covalent bonds are polar. Because of the polarity of individual bonds, the entire molecule *may* have separated centers of positive and negative charge. Such a molecule constitutes a dipole (page 784). A crude illustration of a dipolar molecule is

$$\boxed{\quad - \quad + \quad}$$

The dipole is symbolized by ⇸, where the arrow points toward the negative pole. Polar molecules possess a dipole moment, μ, which is the product of the magnitude of electronic charge, q, and the distance, d, between the centers of opposite charge,

$$\mu = q \times d$$

The charge and distance are, respectively, of the order of 10^{-10} e.s.u. and 10^{-8} cm, so that the dipole moments are about 10^{-18} e.s.u.-cm/molecule. The unit, 1×10^{-18} e.s.u.-cm/molecule is named the debye (D), in honor of Peter Debye, who pioneered in this field of study.

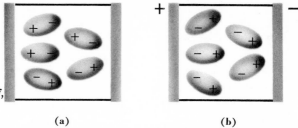

Fig. 12.1. *Orientation of polar molecules in an electric field: (a) field off, (b) field on.*

(a)   (b)

As a consequence of the dipole moment, polar molecules tend to be oriented in an electric field with the positive ends directed toward the negative electric pole and the negative ends toward the positive pole (Fig. 12.1). The orientation is far from perfect because of the kinetic energy of the molecules. Measurements based on these orientations are used to calculate dipole moments. It was the discovery that molecules were polar that led to the supposition that individual bonds are polar.

It is reasonable that such polar molecules should attract each other, so that the positive pole of one molecule is close to the negative pole of another molecule, as shown in Fig. 12.2a. This is known as a **dipole-dipole** attraction. The attraction is inversely proportional to the distance between the molecules raised to the seventh power, $F \propto 1/r^7$. Consequently, because molecules in the gaseous state under normal pressures are far apart, dipole-dipole attraction is very small. As the pressure on the gas increases and the temperature decreases, the molecules approach each other with diminished kinetic energy permitting the dipole-dipole interaction to promote liquefaction and eventually solidification.

The extent of dipole-dipole interaction is one of the factors that determine the melting and boiling points of polar substances. Other factors such as molecular weight and molecular shape being equal, a substance with no dipole moment will have a lower boiling point and melting point than a polar molecule. Thus, the nonpolar molecules N_2 and O_2 have boiling points of $-196°C$ and $-183°C$, respectively, whereas the somewhat polar molecule NO ($\mu = 0.070$ D) boils at $-151°C$.

12.2 ION-DIPOLE ATTRACTIONS

Polar molecules are attracted to ions. The negative pole is attracted to cations; the positive pole is attracted to anions. This type of attraction,

Fig 12.2. *(a) Dipole-dipole attraction; (b) exemplified by HCl.*

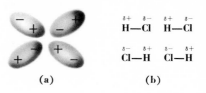

$$\overset{\delta+}{H}\text{—}\overset{\delta-}{Cl} \quad \overset{\delta+}{H}\text{—}\overset{\delta-}{Cl}$$

$$\overset{\delta-}{Cl}\text{—}\overset{\delta+}{H} \quad \overset{\delta-}{Cl}\text{—}\overset{\delta+}{H}$$

(a)   (b)

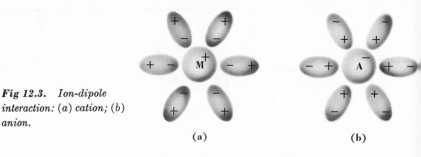

Fig 12.3. *Ion-dipole interaction: (a) cation; (b) anion.*

(a)   (b)

shown in Fig. 12.3, is called **ion-dipole** interaction. Ion-dipole interactions are involved in solution processes (Chapter 15).

12.3 HYDROGEN BONDING

The presence of an attractive force between certain molecules, which is greater than that expected from dipole-dipole interaction, is evidenced by comparing the boiling points of binary covalent hydrides in Fig. 12.4. The Group IV hydrides, CH_4, SiH_4, and SnH_4, are nonpolar and tetrahedral. As the atomic weight of the central atom increases, there is a regular increase in boiling point. In the absence of dipole-dipole interaction and major differences in shape, this direct relationship between boiling point and molecular weight is typical. Even in the case of the polar hydrides,

Fig. 12.4. Comparison of boiling points of binary covalent hydrides.

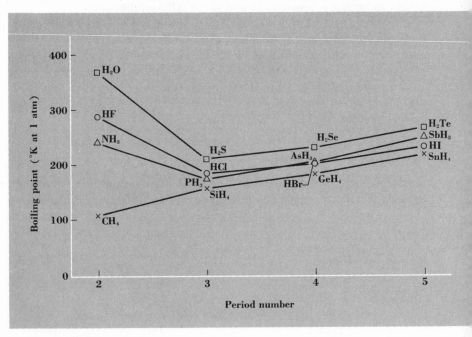

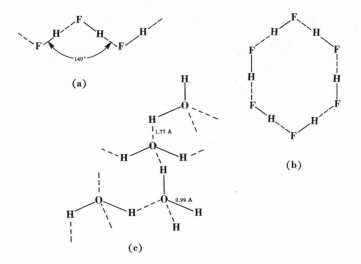

(a)

(b)

(c)

Fig. 12.5. *Hydrogen-bonded structure for (a) H—F (linear); (b) (HF)₆ (cyclic); and (c) ice (cross-linked); broken lines indicate H bond.*

those of Group V, VI, and VII, this straight-line relationship prevails except for the hydrides of the first members of these groups. NH_3, H_2O, and HF are more polar than the other hydrides in their respective groups, because N, O, and F are the most electronegative elements. Nevertheless, the large deviations from the straight-line relationship indicate that a force stronger than a dipole-dipole interaction prevails for H_2O, HF, and NH_3.

These three polar molecules have one structural feature in common: each has at least one hydrogen atom covalently bonded to a highly electronegative atom with at least one unshared pair of electrons. Thus, the O, F, and N atoms attract the somewhat positive H atom of another molecule,

$$\overset{\delta^-}{:}X\overset{\delta^+}{—}H\text{- - -}\overset{\delta^-}{:}X\overset{\delta^+}{—}H$$
hydrogen bonding

The hydrogen atom increases the intermolecular attraction by bridging the two molecules. Since the very small hydrogen atom is the bridge between the two electronegative atoms, the interacting molecules can approach sufficiently close to each other to produce an attraction strong enough to be considered a *bond*, rather than just another dipole-dipole attraction. This unique type of bond is called the **hydrogen bond.** The energy of the hydrogen bond, which varies from 3 to 10 kcal/mole, depends as a first approximation on the electronegativity of the X atom, and hence usually decreases in the order F > O > N ≈ Cl.

One of the strongest hydrogen bonds is observed in hydrogen fluoride, whose formula should be written $(HF)_x$, since it exists as linear or cyclic aggregates, as shown in Fig. 12.5a and b.

The hydrogen difluoride ion, HF_2^-, possesses the strongest known hydrogen bond. It can be shown experimentally that the H atom is midway between the two F atoms; hence, the ion consists of two fluoride ions shielded from each other by a proton,

$$[F- - -H- - -F]^- \quad \text{or} \quad [F^- \oplus F^-]^-$$
$$\textit{structure of } HF_2^-$$

If it is true that the hydrogen bond in $(HF)_x$ is stronger than the hydrogen bond in water, how can we account for the observation that water (b.p. 100°C, molecular weight 18) has a much higher boiling point than hydrogen fluoride (b.p. 19.4°C, molecular weight 20)? The answer comes from considering the geometry of the two hydrogen-bonded systems. In the case of hydrogen fluoride, any one F atom can be surrounded by only two hydrogen atoms, and so can participate in only one hydrogen bond. This limitation leads to linear (Fig. 12.5a) or cyclic (Fig. 12.5b) arrays. In ice, the oxygen atom is surrounded tetrahedrally by four hydrogen atoms, and so participates in two hydrogen bonds (Fig. 12.5c). The presence of two hydrogen bonds per H_2O molecule increases the attraction between the individual H_2O molecules. The unusually high melting point of 0°C for a molecule with a molecular weight of 18 g/mole is accounted for by the cross-linked nature of the hydrogen bonds. Since cross-linked hydrogen bonds persist to some extent in the liquid state, water also has an inordinately high boiling point. As ice melts, the hydrogen bonding becomes more random and the molecules at first are able to move closer together. The density of water increases, therefore, from 0°C to 4°C, at which temperature it is at the maximum. Above 4°C, the increase in kinetic energy of the molecules is sufficient to cause the molecules to begin to disperse, and the density steadily decreases with increasing temperature.

Hydrogen bonding also occurs between unlike molecules. For example, the very large solubility of ammonia, NH_3, and ammonium salts in water is principally due to this phenomenon. Recent studies have shown that hydrogen bonding is not restricted to strongly electronegative elements like F, O, N, and Cl. Whenever a molecule with an H atom attached to an element more electronegative than hydrogen comes in contact with a substance possessing an atom with an unshared pair of electrons, hydrogen bonding can occur,

$$\overset{\delta^-}{A}—\overset{\delta^+}{H} + \; :B \rightarrow \overset{\delta^-}{A}—\overset{\delta^+}{H}- - -:B$$

12.4 LONDON FORCES

All gases, *including the noble elements and nonpolar molecules* such as O_2, N_2, and F_2 can be liquefied. Apparently there is some attractive force, even among these nonpolar molecules and atoms. Since these substances have

Substance	*He*	*H₂*	*Ne*	*N₂*	*O₂*	*Ar*	*F₂*	*Kr*
No. of electrons:	2	2	10	14	16	18	18	36
B.P. (°C):	−269	−253	−246	−196	−183	−186	−186	−152

very low boiling points, the attractive forces are relatively weak, certainly weaker in most cases than dipole-dipole, ion-dipole, or hydrogen-bond forces. These weak forces are called **London forces** after Fritz London, who developed a theoretical explanation of them in 1928.

According to quantum mechanical theory, the electrons in a molecule may be regarded as in constant motion. The term Ψ^2 for a given molecular orbital represents an *average* charge density. Hence, at any instant, there may be an imbalance of charge distribution in the molecule. Thus, a nonpolar molecule may be momentarily *self-polarized* because of the unbalanced charge distribution (page 530). This polarized molecule induces a dipole moment in a neighboring molecule. *These induced dipoles then cause the nonpolar molecules to be mutually attracted.*

The data in Table 12.1 for noble gases and nonpolar molecules containing fewer than 20 electrons reveal a superficial correlation between the boiling point and the number of electrons. The boiling point increases as the number of electrons increases. The London forces apparently are roughly proportional in strength to the number of electrons per molecule. It is also true that for more complicated nonpolar molecules of similar structure, the boiling point increases with increasing molecular weight, as shown in the alkane series (Table 10.1, page 240). As more carbon and hydrogen atoms, and consequently more electrons, are included in the molecule, the London forces evidently become stronger and the boiling points increase.

In general, for similarly constituted molecules, as size increases, polarizability increases and boiling point increases.

12.5 LONDON FORCES AND MOLECULAR SHAPE

The correlation of boiling point and melting point with molecular weight is considerably influenced by the shape of the molecule. A comparison of the boiling and melting points of the isomers, *n*-pentane and neopentane, reveals this dependence. Both isomers have the same kind and number of atoms and therefore the same number of electrons, yet the boiling points differ by as much as 27°. A molecule of *n*-pentane may be regarded as a zigzag chain (Fig. 12.6a), a molecule of neopentane as a sphere (Fig. 12.6b). For *n*-pentane, the approach between the two molecules can occur over the entire length of the chain whereas, for neopentane, the approach can occur only at a tangential point. The lateral, side-to-side approach of two *n*-pentane molecules involves more contact, which increases the

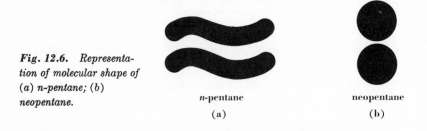

Fig. 12.6. Representation of molecular shape of (a) n-pentane; (b) neopentane.

n-pentane
(a)

neopentane
(b)

London forces, and therefore the boiling point of *n*-pentane is higher:

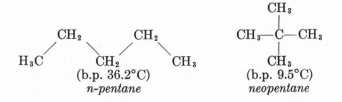

(b.p. 36.2°C)
n-pentane

(b.p. 9.5°C)
neopentane

12.6 VAN DER WAALS RADII

There is a limit to the proximity of approach of molecules. The separation of adjacent molecules corresponds to the distance at which the intermolecular attractive force is balanced by the repulsive force originating between the outer portions of the electron clouds. The distance of this closest approach may be ascertained from x ray diffraction measurements made on the solid. For example, the distance between two nonbonded bromine atoms in adjacent molecules of solid bromine is 3.90 A, as compared to the Br—Br bond distance of 2.28 A,

$$\text{Br—Br} \cdots \text{Br—Br}$$
2.28 A   3.90 A   2.28 A

One-half of 3.90 A is assigned as the **van der Waals radius** for a bromine atom. The intermolecular distances of most solid homoatomic substances have been measured; the van der Waals radii are listed in Table 12.2. The additivity principle that was assumed for covalent bond radii (page 189) is likewise assumed for van der Waals radii. Thus the optimum approach of a C atom in one molecule and a Br atom in an adjacent molecule is 3.95 A [2.0 (C) + 1.95 (Br)].

TABLE **12.2** *Periodic Arrangement of van der Waals Radii (in Angstroms)*

H 1.2				
C 2.0	N 1.5	O 1.4	F 1.35
	P 1.9	S 1.85	Cl 1.80
	As 2.0	Se 2.00	Br 1.95
	Sb 2.2	Te 2.20	I 2.15

1. Dipole moment. Account for the following order of dipole moments observed for the hydrogen halides: HF, 1.9 D; HCl, 1.03 D; HBr, 0.74 D; HI, 0.38 D.

2. Hydrogen bonding. Suggest a structure for H_3F_3, a component of liquid hydrogen fluoride.

3. Hydrogen bonding. Account for the following facts. (a) Although ethyl alcohol, C_2H_5OH (b.p. 80°C), has a larger molecular weight than water (b.p. 100°C), it has a lower boiling point. (b) Salts of the HCl_2^- anion are known. (c) Mixing 50 ml each of water and ethyl alcohol gives a solution whose volume is less than 100 ml.

4. Van der Waals radii. (a) Calculate the closeness of approach of (*i*) two molecules of Cl_2; (*ii*) two molecules of I_2; (*iii*) a molecule of I_2 and one of Cl_2; (*iv*) two molecules of HF, as shown: H—F F—H, H—F H—F, and F—H H—F. (b) What conclusion can you draw about the approach of the same homodiatomic molecules such as Cl_2 and the size of the atom? (c) What effect would hydrogen bonding have on the proximity of the H—F H—F type of approach?

5. Intermolecular attraction. Select the compound in each of the following pairs of molecules which should have the higher boiling point: (a) O_2 or H_2S; (b) Ar or Xe; (c) H_2S or HCl; (d) CH_3CH_2OH or CH_3OCH_3; (e) $CH_3CH_2CH_2CH_2OH$

or its isomer, CH_3—$\overset{\displaystyle OH}{\underset{\displaystyle CH_3}{\overset{|}{\underset{|}{C}}}}$—$CH_3$; (f) CH_3—$\overset{}{\underset{\displaystyle CH_3}{\overset{}{\underset{|}{N}}}}$—$CH_3$ or its isomer, $CH_3CH_2CH_2NH_2$.

Explain your choice.

6. Hydrogen bonding. Carboxylic acids, $R\overset{\displaystyle O}{\overset{\|}{C}}$—OH, have a strong tendency to form dimers (structures made up of two individual molecules). Draw a likely structure for the dimer.

13

Solutions

13.1 INTRODUCTION

A **solution** is a *mixture of two or more substances dispersed as molecules* rather than as larger aggregates. The intermediate zone between solutions and coarse suspensions embraces the colloidal dispersions (page 63–65); although we will not be explicitly concerned with them in this chapter, most of what we say will apply to colloids as well as to "true" solutions. Two important classes of solutions will be omitted: gaseous mixtures, such as air, and ionic solutions, in which some of the constituent particles are electrically charged. Because of the special properties and great importance of ionic solutions, Chapter 15 has been reserved for them.

13.2 LIQUID SOLUTIONS

The word "solution" suggests a liquid to most of us, and liquid solutions are indeed the most important and interesting ones. The molecules in a liquid are in intimate contact, so that the properties of each component in a liquid solution are considerably influenced by the presence of the others. For example, the energy of a molecule is affected by the nature of the molecules surrounding it; as a result, heat is usually absorbed or emitted when a solution is formed. In some cases, there is actually a chemical reaction between the components, so that the molecules present in solution are quite different from the molecules of the pure components; the clearest examples are found among the ionic solutions. There is a twilight zone in which it is not clear whether the formation of the solution should be described as a physical change—a mere mixing—or as a chemical change. Sometimes a liquid solution can be prepared from gases alone ($HCl + H_2O$) or from solids alone ($Na + K$), but usually at least one component is a liquid, when it is pure under the conditions of the experiment. When one component is a gas or a solid and the other is a liquid, the former is called the **solute** and the latter the **solvent;** when both are liquids, and one is much more abundant than the other, the major component is considered the solvent and the minor component the solute. Of course, there may be several solutes—a solution need not have only two components.

A **dilute solution** is one which contains only a small quantity of solute (or solutes) relative to the quantity of solvent. A **concentrated solution** contains a large proportion of solute. These terms are no more precise than the words "large" and "small"—as many a student has learned when he used "dilute hydrochloric acid" and found that it was 20 or 30 times more concentrated than the acid he was supposed to use.

13.3 SATURATION: GASES IN LIQUIDS

Consider a gas being dissolved in a liquid, with the entire gas-liquid system enclosed (Fig. 13.1a). The gas molecules are moving about in all directions. Molecules frequently strike the surface of the liquid; they may merely bounce off, but there is a chance that a gas molecule will be captured and will diffuse into the body of the liquid. Conversely, a molecule already in the liquid may happen to reach the surface with enough kinetic energy to escape and become part of the gas again. At a fixed temperature (and thus fixed average kinetic energy), the rate at which gas molecules enter the liquid depends on the number of collisions with the liquid surface, and thus on the pressure of the gas; the rate at which gas molecules leave the liquid depends on the number already dissolved. When the rate of escape of gas from the solution equals the rate of dissolving, the composition of the solution remains constant; no more of the gas dissolves. We say that **equilibrium** has been attained. The processes of capture and escape are still taking place, but their rates are equal, and there is no further net change in the pressure of the vapor or the composition of the solution. The solution is said to be **saturated.**

If the pressure of the gas is increased (Fig. 13.1b), the number of collisions with the surface is increased, and the rate of capture of gas molecules by the liquid therefore increases. The quantity of dissolved gas

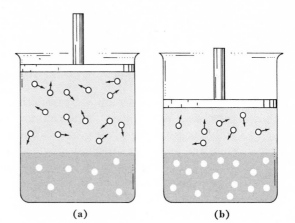

Fig. 13.1. Dissolving of a gas in a liquid at (a) low pressure, (b) higher pressure.

(a)   (b)

	0°C	25°C	50°C
N_2	0.00294	0.00175	0.00122
O_2	0.00694	0.00393	0.00266
H_2	0.000192	0.000154	0.000129
CO_2	0.335	0.145	0.076
SO_2	22.83	9.41	

thus increases until the rate of escape has built up to equality with the new rate of capture. Thus, the **solubility** *of a gas in a liquid*—the quantity of gas that dissolves in a given quantity of liquid to form a saturated solution—*increases with rising pressure.* A carbonated beverage must be kept under pressure; when the cap or cork is removed, the pressure drops, the solubility of the gas decreases, and the beverage fizzes.

Raising the temperature nearly always decreases the solubility of a gas in a liquid. Although higher temperature results in more frequent collisions of gas molecules with the liquid surface, the principal effect of raising the temperature is that a larger fraction of the dissolved molecules have the kinetic energy needed in order to escape from the liquid. This is what we expect; the vapor pressure (page 53) of a pure liquid increases with increasing temperature, and the pressure required to keep a gas in equilibrium with a solution of it may be regarded as the vapor pressure of the solute over that solution. When *the temperature rises,* the vapor pressure of a given solution rises, or *the solubility under a given pressure decreases.*

Table 13.1 gives the solubilities of some common gases in water, as the weight in grams of the gas which can be dissolved in 100 grams of water when the total pressure of gas and water vapor is one atmosphere. This is the usual manner of expressing solubility, although any of the measures of composition to be described later (page 311) can be used. The very large solubility of SO_2 is noteworthy; this is believed to be one of the cases in which dissolving is accompanied by a chemical reaction,

$$SO_2 + H_2O \leftrightharpoons (HO)_2SO \ (sulfurous \ acid)$$

13.4   SATURATION: SOLIDS IN LIQUIDS OR LIQUIDS IN LIQUIDS

A solid dissolves in a liquid by essentially the same process by which a gas dissolves, except that we should picture the solute molecules not as colliding with the solvent, but as diffusing away from the surface of the solid and becoming surrounded by—and, to some extent, attached to—the solvent molecules. When some of the solute has gone into solution, some solute molecules will be recaptured by the solid from the solution, and the rate of this redeposition will increase as the solution becomes more concentrated. If enough solid is present, the solution will attain a composition at which dissolving and deposition are equal in rate. At this point, the solution is saturated.

The rates of dissolving and of deposition are both proportional to the surface area of the solid; if the rates are equal and the area is doubled, both rates are doubled, so that they are still equal, and the solubility is independent of the surface area. (However, very fine subdivision of a solid, finer than about 10^{-5} cm in diameter, increases the solubility.) At this point, we should note the distinction between *solubility* and *rate of dissolving*. A finely divided solid dissolves much more rapidly than large lumps—the solution becomes saturated sooner—but that does not mean that the total amount which can be dissolved is greater. Similarly, stirring accelerates the dissolving process, but, once the solution is saturated, you can stir your arm off without dissolving another milligram.

Many pairs of liquids are completely **miscible**—that is, they dissolve in each other in all proportions. Examples are water and acetic acid, water and glycerol, benzene and toluene. In such cases, there is no such thing as a saturated solution. Other pairs of liquids, however, are only partially miscible: each dissolves in the other to some extent, giving two saturated solutions. Even so-called "immiscible" liquids—water and carbon tetrachloride, for example—usually have a measurable solubility in each other. A familiar example of partial miscibility is water and diethyl ether, $(C_2H_5)_2O$; when these two liquids are shaken together at 25°C, two layers are obtained: 94.1% water and 5.9% ether (by weight) in the bottom layer, 1.3% water and 98.7% ether in the top layer.

The distinction among liquid solutions of a gas, of a liquid, or of a solid is, in a sense, meaningless; a solution of, say, water and ethanol, with given temperature and composition, is the same whether it was made from the two liquids, from ice and liquid ethanol, from steam and ethanol vapor, or from steam and frozen ethanol. In the case of a saturated solution, however, there is an important distinction—not as to how the solution was made, but as to what is present at equilibrium. When a solution is saturated, it is in equilibrium with a pure component, or with another solution, and we must be told the nature of this second phase before we know what is meant by saying that the solution is saturated, or that the solubility of a component is so much. Ice can be in equilibrium with an ethanol-water solution; such a solution is a saturated solution of ice in ethanol. An entirely different solution of the same two components may be in equilibrium with a gaseous solution of water and ethanol vapors, in which the partial pressures have certain values; such a solution may logically be called a saturated solution of gaseous water in ethanol, or of gaseous ethanol in water.

13.5 DEPENDENCE OF SOLUBILITY ON TEMPERATURE AND PRESSURE

We observed in Section 13.3 that, at constant pressure, the solubility of a gas in a liquid decreases with increasing temperature. The solubility of a solid in a liquid may change with temperature in either direction, as illustrated by the following solubilities in water, in g solute per 100 g H_2O

Temperature (°C)	20	40	60	80
Sucrose ($C_{12}H_{22}O_{11}$)	204	238	287	362
Lithium carbonate (Li_2CO_3)	1.33	1.17	1.01	0.85

The typical behavior is that of sucrose; the solubility of a solid in a liqui usually increases with increasing temperature. We may think of dissolvin as analogous to melting; we know that raising the temperature cause melting and, similarly, it causes more solid to dissolve.

This is not the whole story, however. Two things happen when a soli dissolves: solute molecules are pulled apart, as in melting (or even as i evaporation), which requires an input of heat; solute molecules becom associated with solvent molecules, with a resultant output of heat. Fo most solutions of solids in liquids, the "melting" effect predominates When a gas dissolves in a liquid, only the association effect is presen (as in condensation), and heat is given out. The change of solubility witl temperature can be predicted if we know whether heat is given out o absorbed when the solution is formed.* When 1 mole of Li_2CO_3 is dissolvec in 220 moles of water, 3060 cal of heat are given out; when 1 mole of SO is dissolved in 2000 moles of water, 8554 cal of heat are given out. In botl these cases, the solubility decreases with increasing temperature. How ever, when 1 mole of sucrose is dissolved in a large quantity of water 1320 cal of heat is absorbed. In this case, the solubility increases witl increasing temperature. The rule is general: *if heat is given out on dissolvinε one component in the other, the solubility decreases with increasing tempera ture; if heat is absorbed, the solubility increases with increasing temperature*

In most cases of partial miscibility between liquids, raising the tempera- ture increases the mutual solubility until, at some temperature, they become completely miscible. When water and isobutyl alcohol

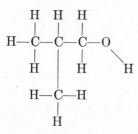

are shaken together at 25°C, the two layers in equilibrium with each other contain 16.8% water and 83.2% alcohol (by weight) in one layer, and 91.8% water and 8.2% alcohol in the other layer. As the temperature is raised, the solubility of each liquid in the other increases until, at

* Strictly speaking, the heat effect in question is that associated with the addition of solute to a nearly saturated solution. There are rare instances in which heat is emitted on forming the dilute solution and absorbed on adding solute to a concen- trated solution (for example, NaOH in H_2O), or conversely.

132.8°C, the two layers become identical in composition; above this temperature, the two liquids are completely miscible. There are instances, however, in which the solubility of one liquid in another decreases with increasing temperature; an example is water and triethylamine, $(C_2H_5)_3N$, which are completely miscible below 18.5°C, but only partially miscible at higher temperatures.

In contrast to the effect of pressure on gases, the solubilities of solids and liquids are affected very little by moderate changes of pressure. The solubility of sodium chloride, NaCl, in water is multiplied by only 1.025 when the pressure is increased from 1 to 1000 atmospheres. The effects are not always that small; the solubility of naphthalene, $C_{10}H_8$, in tetrachloroethane, $C_2H_2Cl_4$, is multiplied by 0.596 when 1000 atmospheres pressure is applied.

13.6 SUPERSATURATION

Suppose that we prepare a solution of a solid in a liquid at a high temperature, and then cool the solution. In most cases, the solubility decreases on cooling, and the solution may, at some temperature, become saturated. If we expect a crystal to appear at or just below the temperature of saturation, we may be disappointed. It is often possible to cool the solution far below this temperature without the appearance of solid. The solution existing under these conditions contains a larger percentage of solute than a saturated solution at the same temperature; it is said to be **supersaturated.** One who has learned that a saturated solution contains the largest possible proportion of solute, at a given temperature, may feel that a solution in which this proportion is exceeded is somehow freakish. But there is nothing wrong with a supersaturated solution, any more than with a book standing on end; in each case, there exists another situation which is more stable, namely, saturated solution plus excess solid, or the book lying flat. Just as the book needs a push in order to reach its more stable position, the supersaturated solution may not disgorge its excess solute without a little encouragement. Supersaturation can be observed in any kind of solution, provided a finite solubility exists, but the phenomenon is most commonly observed when one component is a crystalline solid.

It is not easy to initiate the growth of a crystal. The embryonic crystal must be formed by several molecules or ions that come together in the correct configuration and stay that way long enough for other particles to deposit on them. Such an event is not impossible, but remains improbable until the solution is considerably supersaturated. Supersaturation is much more likely to be relieved by deposition of solute molecules on a dust particle, the container wall, or any other solid present. The best crystallization nucleus, of course, is a fragment of the solute itself, or of something else with a similar crystal structure. When such a "seed" is introduced, crystals usually form very rapidly, leaving a saturated solution.

When a solid or a liquid dissolves in a liquid, the molecules of each kind must lose some of their like neighbors, obtaining in exchange neighbors of the other kind. When the solute is a gas, its molecules have no near neighbors, but they lose something else by dissolving: their freedom to move about. The stronger the attractive forces between unlike molecules, the greater the solubility. For a component that is, when pure, a solid or liquid, strong forces between its molecules will inhibit its solubility unless the molecules of the other component can exert a comparable attraction.

It is a time-honored, although ambiguous, maxim among chemists that "like dissolves like," and this is as we should expect; forces between similar molecules are comparable to those between identical molecules, condition under which the new molecules can replace the previously neighboring molecules with impunity. The most important kind of similarity is the presence or absence, in the molecule, of local concentrations of electric charge. The water molecule, for example, is highly polar. Water molecules, in the solid or the liquid, hang firmly together (see page 297). If another molecule is to break into this happy arrangement, it, too, must have positive and negative charges to attract the opposite charges in the water molecule. Examples of such **polar molecules** are

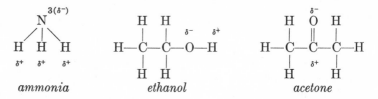

ammonia   *ethanol*   *acetone*

Ammonia is a gas so soluble that, under ordinary conditions, nearly 700 volumes will dissolve in 1 volume of water; the other two compounds are liquids completely miscible with water. On the other hand, 2,2,4-trimethylpentane (isoöctane), a typical constituent of gasoline, has no strong dissymmetries in its electric charge distribution; its structure is

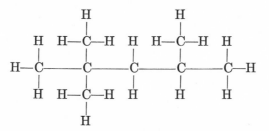

The C—H bond is only slightly polar. It should not surprise us that water and gasoline are not appreciably miscible. But gasoline is a very good solvent for oils, greases, and waxes, which also have nearly nonpolar molecules; neither substance has very strong intermolecular forces in these cases. Typical components of grease are the glycerides (page 256).

Their molecules have large hydrocarbon portions similar in chemical constitution to hydrocarbons like isoöctane.

The most striking examples of the relation between charge distribution and solubility will be considered in Chapter 15, where we shall see that such highly polar liquids as H_2O and NH_3 (which boils at $-33°C$) can hold ions (charged particles) in solution, a feat that gasoline could never hope to imitate.

13.8 DETERGENCY

There is no reason why a single molecule cannot have a part that is polar, or even charged—and therefore has a strong affinity for water—and another part consisting of a long hydrocarbon chain. Such a molecule or ion—the most important examples are ions—should be somewhat soluble both in oil and in water. More important, it can facilitate the dispersion of oil into water, or of water into oil. A salt containing such ions may be useful as a **detergent,** or cleansing agent, because of its ability to bring the oily, greasy components of dirt into colloidal dispersion in water.

Molecules at the surface of a phase have higher energy than molecules deeper within the phase (see page 48). When two immiscible liquids, or a liquid and a solid that does not dissolve in it, are in contact, the area of contact counts as liquid surface. Work must therefore be done to create additional surface area. The work required, per unit increase in area, is called the **interfacial tension.** When one phase is a gas, the interfacial tension becomes the ordinary surface tension.

Detergent ions find an especially congenial environment at the interface between oil and water, for they can have their hydrocarbon ends in the oil and their ionic ends in the water—the best of both worlds (Fig. 13.2).

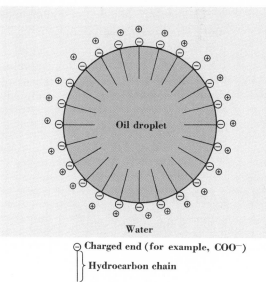

Fig. 13.2.   Detergent ions at an oil-water interface.

⊖ Charged end (for example, COO^-)
} Hydrocarbon chain

The oil and water molecules are likewise attracted to the corresponding ends of the detergent ions, the interfacial tension being thereby greatly reduced. It thus becomes possible to detach oil or grease from a soiled surface and bring it into a finely divided state, dispersed throughout the water, with the surface of each globule protected by a layer of detergent ions.

The most common detergents have either $-COO^-$ or $-OSO_3^-$ as their ionic parts. Three examples are shown below.

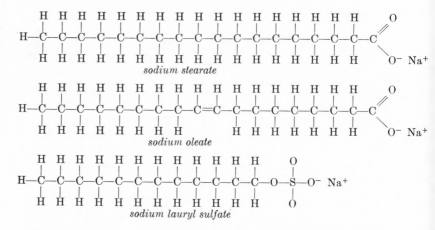

sodium stearate

sodium oleate

sodium lauryl sulfate

The word "soap" is used technically to refer to any salt in which the negative ion contains the carboxylate group, $-COO^-$, and a long hydrocarbon chain, about C_{15-17}. Thus, sodium stearate and sodium oleate are soaps, but sodium lauryl sulfate is not; it is a nonsoap detergent or synthetic detergent ("syndet"). Carboxylate salts of metals other than the alkali metals are usually only slightly soluble in water and therefore not useful as detergents, but are nevertheless called "soaps." Some of them find industrial application as lubricants. However, insoluble soaps are more often nuisances. Natural waters usually contain Ca^{2+}, Mg^{2+}, Fe^{2+}, and perhaps other ions. Such water is described as "hard," and these positive ions react with, for example, the stearate ion, forming nearly insoluble salts. The result is that soap is wasted—the first portion is consumed in reacting with the troublesome metal ions—and the insoluble soap clings to the fabric, the sides of the bathtub, or whatever other surface is available. The greatest advantage of the synthetic detergents is the solubility of their Ca^{2+}, Mg^{2+}, etc. salts; they are much better than soaps for use with hard water.

13.9 **SOLID SOLUTIONS**

A solid solution is usually prepared by mixing the liquids and freezing the liquid solution. Although solid solutions are not at all uncommon, the number of pairs of substances that show appreciable miscibility as solids is much less than the number of pairs that mix in the liquid state. The regular arrangement of molecules in a crystal will tolerate only those re-placements that resemble the solvent molecules in their type of inter-molecular forces, and have nearly the correct size and shape to fit in without causing serious distortion of the lattice. Solid solutions are most frequently found among metals; all metals are made of spherical ions and free electrons, with essentially the same type of bond (page 702) holding them together, and ions of similar size should be able to replace each other. Thus, copper and nickel form crystals with the same structure, and the radii of the atoms (half the internuclear distances) are not too different: 1.278 and 1.246 A, respectively. These two metals are completely miscible in the solid state. The same is true of silver and gold, with radii of 1.444 and 1.442 A, respectively. But copper and silver are only partially misci-ble. Another large class of solid solutions consists of ionic crystals, where ions of similar size, shape, and charge can replace each other indiscrimi-nately. Examples are K_2SO_4 and $(NH_4)_2SO_4$; $FeCO_3$ and $MnCO_3$. The radii of the positive ions are K^+, 1.33 A; NH_4^+, 1.48 A; Fe^{2+}, 0.76 A; Mn^{2+}, 0.80 A. In $CaCO_3$, on the other hand, only a small amount of Mg^{2+} (0.65 A) can replace Ca^{2+} (0.99 A).

The solid solutions described in the last paragraph are called **substitu-tional,** because each solute particle replaces a solvent particle at its proper lattice position. Another kind of solid solution is the **interstitial,** where small atoms fit into the crevices between large ones without chang-ing the arrangement of the large atoms, except perhaps for some disten-sion of the lattice. Many metals, notably palladium, can absorb hydrogen, which is believed to be present as interstitial H atoms. At 30°C and 24.8 torr pressure, 1 gram of palladium can absorb 60.8 cm³ of hydrogen (meas-ured at standard temperature and pressure).

13.10 MEASURES OF COMPOSITION FOR SOLUTIONS

In discussing solutions, we must be able to specify their compositions—that is, the relative amounts of the several components. Composition is expressed in a number of ways. Let us assume that we have a solution of two components, A and B. We adopt the following notation:

w_A, w_B = mass ("weight") in grams of A or B in the solution
n_A, n_B = number of moles of A or B
V_A, V_B = volume of pure A or B, in liters
V = total volume of the solution, in liters

The most important measures of composition for liquid solutions are the following.

(a) **Weight fraction** (more properly "mass fraction") of B is

$$w_B/(w_A + w_B)$$

Weight percentage is, of course, 100 times the weight fraction. These are the simplest and perhaps most useful measures; nothing need be known about the components except their masses, which are easily determine experimentally, and which always add up to the mass of the solution.

(b) **Weight ratio** is w_B/w_A; more commonly, $100\ w_B/w_A$ is given. Solubilities are often tabulated in terms of this measure, which must not be confused with weight percentage.

(c) **Volume fraction** of B is V_B/V, the volume of pure B divided by the volume of the solution. It should be noted that, in general, $V \neq V_A + V_B$; there is often an appreciable change in volume when two substances form a solution. Volume fraction (or percentage) is confined to liquid liquid solutions, and is more commonly used in commerce than in scientific work. The "proof number" of an ethanol-water solution is twice the volume percentage of the ethanol; 100 proof whiskey contains a quantity of ethanol that would occupy, if pure, half the volume of the whiskey.

(d) **Mole fraction** of B, denoted by X_B, is the ratio of the number of moles of B to the total number of moles,

$$X_B = \frac{n_B}{n_A + n_B}$$

Let $\mathfrak{N}$ be Avogadro's number; then $\mathfrak{N}n_A$ and $\mathfrak{N}n_B$ are the numbers of molecules of A and of B, respectively, in the solution, and

$$X_B = \frac{\mathfrak{N}n_B}{\mathfrak{N}n_A + \mathfrak{N}n_B}$$

A mole fraction is a number fraction—the mole fraction of B is the fraction of all the molecules in the solution that are B molecules. It is obvious from the definition that $X_A + X_B = 1$ or, for more than two components, $X_A + X_B + X_C + \cdots = 1$.

(e) **Molality** of B is

$$m_B = \frac{n_B}{(w_A/1000)} = \frac{\text{moles B}}{\cancel{g\ A} \times \frac{1\ \text{kg A}}{1000\ \cancel{g\ A}}} = \frac{\text{moles B}}{\text{kg A}}$$

that is, the number of moles of B dissolved in one kilogram (1000 grams) of A; w_A is in grams, and $w_A/1000$ is the number of kilograms of A in the solution.

(f) **Molarity** or **concentration** of B is n_B/V, with V in liters; it is the *number of moles of B per liter of solution*. The molarity of B is represented by [B], M_B, or c_B. When we know the molarity of a solution, we can measure out a certain volume of it and calculate the number of moles of B in that volume. Against this virtue must be set the disadvantage, not shared by molality or mole fraction, that the molarity changes on a mere change of temperature, because of the thermal expansion or contraction of the solution.

The following statements are equivalent: the molarity of B is 0.1; the molarity of the solution with respect to B is 0.1; the solution is $0.1M$ (0.1 molar) with respect to B. The same forms of language are used in specifying molality.

It is customary to refer to the molality or molarity of a solution with respect to the solute (B), not the solvent. These measures of composition are most useful for dilute solutions.

EXAMPLE 1 A solution of 20.0% ethanol, C_2H_5OH, and 80.0% water, by weight, has density 0.966 g/ml at 25°C. Find (a) the mole fraction, (b) the molality, (c) the molarity of ethanol in this solution.

ANSWER The molecular weights are 18.016 g/mole for water and 46.07 g/mole for ethanol. We fix our attention on a definite but arbitrary quantity of solution, say 100 grams. In this 100 g of solution, there are 20.0 g ethanol and 80.0 g water; the numbers of moles of the components are

$$n_{water} = \frac{80.0 \text{ g}}{18.02 \frac{\text{g}}{\text{mole}}} = 4.44 \text{ moles}$$

$$n_{ethanol} = \frac{20.0 \text{ g}}{46.1 \frac{\text{g}}{\text{mole}}} = 0.434 \text{ mole}$$

The volume of the 100 g of solution (needed only in calculating the molarity) is

$$\frac{100.0 \text{ g}}{0.966 \frac{\text{g}}{\text{ml}}} = 103.5 \text{ ml} = 0.1035 \text{ liter}$$

(a) $$X_{ethanol} = \frac{0.434}{4.44 + 0.434} = \frac{0.434}{4.87} = 0.891$$

(b) $$m_{ethanol} = \frac{0.434 \text{ mole } C_2H_5OH}{0.080 \text{ kg } H_2O} = 5.43 \frac{\text{mole}}{\text{kg}}$$

(c) $$[C_2H_5OH] = \frac{0.434 \text{ mole}}{0.1035 \text{ liter}} = 4.19 \frac{\text{mole}}{\text{liter}}$$

A solution of known molarity can be prepared without knowing its density or the weight of solvent used, with the aid of a **volumetric flask** (Fig. 13.3). The solute must be available in a state of high purity, in order that a known mass will correspond to a definite number of moles. An accurately measured mass of solute (usually a solid) is dissolved in the solvent, and the solution is transferred completely (with rinsing) to the flask; or, if the solute flows freely and dissolves easily, it may be introduced directly into the flask through a dry funnel with a wide aperture. Solvent is then added to slightly below the mark on the neck. When the solute is entirely dissolved and the solution well mixed, solvent is added carefully to the mark, and the solution mixed again. We now have a known volume of solution containing a known number of moles of solute, and can easily calculate the molarity. If we need to know the molality, weight percentage, or some other measure of composition, we will need the density of the solution.

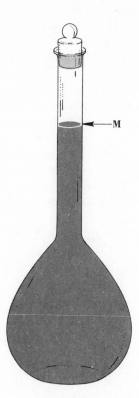

Fig. 13.3. *Volumetric flask. The capacity, up to the mark M, is accurately known.*

EXAMPLE 2   (a) A solution was prepared by dissolving 86.53 g of sodium carbonate, Na_2CO_3, in water in a 1000-ml volumetric flask at 20°C, adding water to the mark, and mixing. Find the molarity of the solution. (b) The density of the solution, at 20°C, is 1.0816 g/ml. Find its molality.

ANSWER   (a) The molecular weight of Na_2CO_3 is 105.99 g/mole. The number of moles used is

$$\frac{86.53 \text{ g}}{105.99 \dfrac{g}{mole}} = 0.8164 \text{ mole}$$

The volume of the solution is 1.000 liter; the molarity is therefore 0.8164 mole/liter.

(b) The mass of 1 liter of solution is

$$1.0816 \frac{g}{ml} \times 1000 \frac{ml}{liter} = 1081.6 \frac{g}{liter}$$

We know that this quantity of solution contains 86.53 g Na_2CO_3, and it must therefore contain 995.1 g H_2O:

$$1081.6 - 86.53 = 995.1 \text{ g } H_2O$$

There is 0.8164 mole Na_2CO_3 in 995.1 g H_2O; in 1000 g H_2O, there is

$$0.8164 \text{ mole} \times \frac{1000}{995.1} = 0.8203 \text{ mole}$$

The molality is 0.8203.

Vapor pressures of solutions

13.11 GENERAL REMARKS

We saw in Chapter 3 that a solid or liquid, placed in an enclosed space, evaporates to some extent. As the partial pressure of the vapor increases, the rate of return of vapor molecules to the solid or liquid increases, until finally the rate of evaporation equals the rate of condensation, and equilibrium is attained. The partial pressure of the vapor at equilibrium is the **vapor pressure** of the substance. The vapor pressure increases rapidly with temperature, but is independent of the size of the container—as long as some of the solid or liquid is present—and, to a good approximation, is independent of the presence of foreign gases.

Many substances have no appreciable vapor pressure at ordinary temperatures—most metals and most salts, for example. However, their vapor pressures can be measured at high temperatures, and there is every reason to believe that, on cooling, the vapor pressure becomes smaller and smaller without ever becoming exactly zero. Indeed, vapor pressures can be calculated from other data when they are too small to be measured directly. Therefore, we shall not hesitate to speak of the vapor pressure of a substance, however minute it may be; a "nonvolatile" substance will mean one having a vapor pressure that can be neglected in comparison to other pressures.

13.12 RAOULT'S LAW

Each component of a solid or liquid solution has a certain vapor pressure, which is *less than the vapor pressure of the pure substance* at the same temperature. The other component apparently occupies part of the surface, and thus decreases the rate at which molecules pass into the vapor. In order to obtain quantitative information about the vapor pressures of solutions, one may prepare a series of solutions of two components, measure the total vapor pressure of each solution at a fixed temperature, and then analyze samples of the vapor to obtain the partial pressure (page 20) of each component. The vapor pressures are then plotted against one of the measures of composition given on page 312. The most interesting graphs are obtained when mole fraction (X) is chosen. Examples of such graphs are given in Figs. 13.4, 13.5, and 13.6. When the mole fraction of component A is zero, its vapor pressure is, of course, zero; when the mole fraction is 1, its vapor pressure p_A is that of the pure substance (p_A^0).

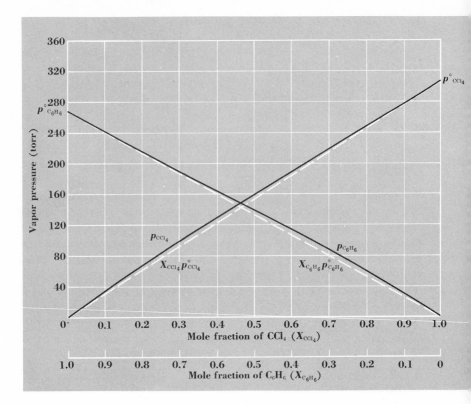

Fig. 13.4. *Vapor pressures of benzene-carbon tetrachloride solutions at 49.99°C. $p°_{C_6H_6}$ and $p°_{CCl_4}$ are the vapor pressures of pure benzene and pure carbon tetrachloride, respectively. The solid curves represent the experimental values; the dashed lines represent the vapor pressures predicted by Raoult's law.*

In between, the vapor pressure of each component rises with increasing mole fraction. In Fig. 13.4, the experimental values of p_{CCl_4} are close to the dashed straight line, which is a plot of $X_{CCl_4}p^0_{CCl_4}$—the value which p_{CCl_4} would have if it were directly proportional to the mole fraction X_{CCl_4} of CCl_4—and $p_{C_6H_6}$ is close to the dashed line which represents $X_{C_6H_6}p^0_{C_6H_6}$.

There are many liquid solutions in which *the partial vapor pressure of each component is nearly equal to the mole fraction of that component times the vapor pressure of the pure component,*

$$p_A = X_A p^0_A$$

This relation was first pointed out by François Marie Raoult in 1886, and is called **Raoult's law.** It is a good approximation for solutions in which the different molecules are very similar in size and polarity. It seems that, in such cases, the fraction of the surface occupied by A molecules is X_A— the same as the number fraction of A molecules in the bulk of the solution —and the rate of escape of A molecules into the vapor is only X_A times as large as in pure A, while the rate of return is unaffected. A solution in which both (or all) components have vapor pressures as given by Raoult's law is called an **ideal solution.** (An "ideal" solution has nothing to do with an "ideal" gas, except that each is described by an especially simple law.) Probably there are no exactly ideal solutions, but many solutions are nearly ideal. C_6H_6 and CCl_4 are an example of a pair of liquids that form a slightly but perceptibly nonideal solution.

13.13 DEVIATIONS FROM RAOULT'S LAW

When the attraction between different molecules is weaker than between identical molecules, the molecules of each kind can escape from the solution more easily than from the pure substance, and the vapor pressures are therefore greater than one would predict from Raoult's law; the solution is said to exhibit **positive deviation** from Raoult's law. When the attraction is stronger between different than between identical molecules —a less common situation—the molecules are held more firmly in the

Fig. 13.5. *Vapor pressures of water-ethanol solutions at 20°C. The solid curves represent the experimental vapor pressures; the solid white lines represent the vapor pressures predicted by Raoult's law; the dashed white lines represent the vapor pressures predicted by Henry's law (Section 13.15).*

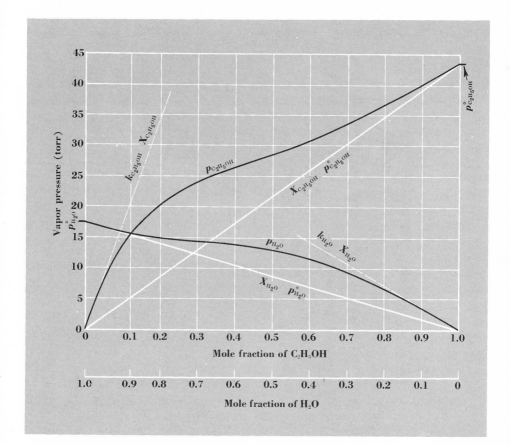

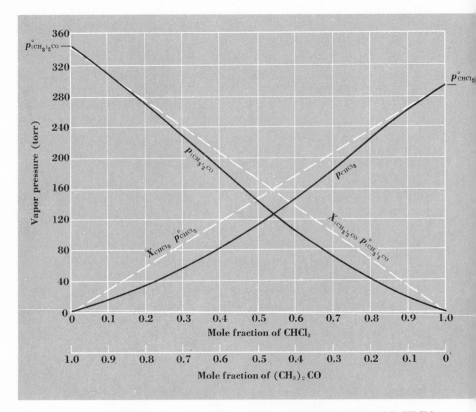

Fig. 13.6. *Vapor pressures of acetone-chloroform* $[(CH_3)_2CO\text{-}CHCl_3]$ *solutions at 35.17°C. The solid curves represent the experimental vapor pressures; the dashed lines represent the vapor pressures predicted by Raoult's law.*

solution than in the pure substances, the vapor pressures are lower than predicted, and the solution exhibits **negative deviation** from Raoult's law. Figures 13.4, 13.5, and 13.6 illustrate, respectively, slight positive deviation, strong positive deviation, and strong negative deviation.

13.14 ACTIVITY

The measured ratio of the vapor pressure of dissolved A to that of pure A, p_A/p_A^0, is called the **activity** of A in the solution—more specifically, the activity of A referred to the pure substance—and is represented by a_A. We are assuming that the vapor of A can be treated as an ideal gas, a decent approximation for pressures up to a few atmospheres; when the vapor cannot be considered ideal, the activity must be defined in a way too abstruse for this book. For each component of an *ideal* solution, $p_A/p_A^0 = X_A$, the mole fraction of A. In this case, activity is the same as mole fraction: $a_A = X_A$. The **activity coefficient** is defined by

$$\gamma_A = \frac{a_A}{X_A} = \frac{p_A}{X_A p_A^0}$$

If the solution is ideal, $\gamma_A = 1$. The activity coefficient is the ratio of the actual vapor pressure to the vapor pressure predicted by Raoult's law. When $\gamma_A > 1$, the deviations from Raoult's law are positive; when $\gamma_A < 1$, the deviations are negative.

We should note that the activity of a pure solid or liquid is necessarily equal to 1.

EXAMPLE 3 **From the data in Fig. 13.5, find (a) the vapor pressure, (b) the activity, and (c) the activity coefficient of each component in a water-ethanol solution in which the mole fraction of ethanol is 0.40.**

ANSWER (a) **By inspection of the graph, we see that** $p_{\text{ethanol}} = 26$ **torr,** $p_{\text{water}} = 14$ **torr.**

(b) **The vapor pressures of the pure components can be read at the ends of the graph:** $p_{\text{ethanol}}^0 = 44$ **torr,** $p_{\text{water}}^0 = 17.5$ **torr. Then the activities are**

$$a_{\text{ethanol}} = \frac{p_{\text{ethanol}}}{p_{\text{ethanol}}^0} = \frac{26}{44} = 0.59$$

$$a_{\text{water}} = \frac{14}{17.5} = 0.80$$

(c) **The activity coefficients are**

$$\gamma_{\text{ethanol}} = \frac{a_{\text{ethanol}}}{X_{\text{ethanol}}} = \frac{0.59}{0.40} = 1.5$$

$$\gamma_{\text{water}} = \frac{a_{\text{water}}}{X_{\text{water}}} = \frac{0.80}{0.60} = 1.3$$

An important generalization is well illustrated by water in Fig. 13.5. In the solutions containing only a little ethanol, the vapor pressure of water is close to the Raoult's law line, so that the activity of the water is nearly equal to its mole fraction, although the solution is far from ideal. This behavior is general; *the vapor pressure and activity of the* **solvent** *in any dilute solution are given approximately by Raoult's law.* The activity coefficient of the solvent in a dilute solution is therefore close to 1. How dilute the solution must be depends on the identity of the solvent and solute, and on how good an approximation we demand; no general rule can be laid down.

13.15 HENRY'S LAW

Another property of these solutions can be seen by inspection of the graphs, especially Fig. 13.5. *In a dilute solution, the vapor pressure of the* **solute** *is approximately proportional to its mole fraction,*

$$p_B \approx k_B X_B$$

This statement is **Henry's law***; as with Raoult's law for the solvent, the

* After William Henry (1774–1836), an Englishman, not the American, Joseph Henry (1799–1878).

range of validity of this approximation varies from one case to another. In an ideal solution, Henry's law and Raoult's law become the same, for in such a solution, $p_B = p_B^0 X_B$ always. When the solution is not ideal, there are two different proportionality constants, depending on whether the solution is mostly B or mostly A. When it is mostly B, Raoult's law applies: $p_B \approx p_B^0 X_B$. When it is mostly A, the curve has a different slope: $p_B \approx k_B X_B$. The proportionality constant k_B varies with temperature, of course, and depends on the identity of the solvent—the vapor pressure of ethanol over a dilute aqueous solution may be quite different from that with the same mole fraction of ethanol in another solvent.

EXAMPLE 4 Use Fig. 13.5 to find the Henry's law constant k_{water} for a dilute solution of water in ethanol.

ANSWER The rightmost part of the curve for water—corresponding to a solution that is nearly all ethanol—is approximately fitted by the dashed line, which has the equation $p_{water} = kX_{water}$. The slope of this dotted line is k_{water}. The slope is measured by dividing any convenient ordinate (p) on the straight line by the corresponding abscissa (X_{water}); we find $k_{water} = 38$ torr.

In a dilute solution, the molarity [B] and the molality m_B of a solute are approximately proportional to its mole fraction (Problem 11, page 331),

$$[B] \approx A_1 X_B$$
$$m_B \approx A_2 X_B$$

where A_1 and A_2 are constants that depend on the identity of the solvent. It follows, then, that *the vapor pressure of the solute in a dilute solution is also approximately proportional to its molarity or molality,*

$$p_B \approx k_B X_B \approx (k_B/A_1)[B] \approx (k_B/A_2)m_B$$

Henry's law may thus be stated in terms of molarity or molality, as well as mole fraction, a fact that will be of interest in connection with chemical equilibrium.

When a solution of B, with mole fraction X_B, is in equilibrium with B vapor, having partial pressure p_B, we may say that (1) p_B is the vapor pressure of B in equilibrium with the solution, or (2) the solution is saturated with gaseous B, and the solubility of B is X_B when the pressure of the gas is p_B. The first point of view assumes that we started with the solution and let some of it evaporate; the second, that we started with solvent and dissolved some gaseous B in it. Henry's law, therefore, often is regarded as giving the solubility of a gas, under given applied pressure, in a liquid,

$$X_B = \frac{p_B}{k_B}$$

This was, indeed, Henry's own interpretation of the law. The restriction of Henry's law to dilute solutions requires that it be applied only to gases that are not very soluble: O_2 or N_2 in water, for example, but not NH_3 or HCl in water.

13.16 VAPOR PRESSURE AND EQUILIBRIUM

The reason we are so much interested in vapor pressures is that the vapor pressure of any substance, pure or in solution, is a measure of what may be called its "escaping tendency." Let us perform this experiment: we place two beakers, one containing water, the other ethanol, in an enclosed space held at constant temperature (Fig. 13.7). Water molecules escape from the left beaker into the space above. Some of these molecules collide with the ethanol surface in the right beaker and are captured. The water vapor is now depleted, and more water evaporates in an attempt to restore the equilibrium pressure. Thus, there is a transfer of water from the left to the right beaker and, similarly, a transfer of ethanol from the right to the left beaker; the vapor of each liquid condenses in the other, and we obtain two solutions. As long as the left solution is richer in water than the right, the equilibrium vapor pressure of water appropriate to the left solution is greater than the vapor pressure corresponding to the right solution. The partial pressure of water vapor in the space above the solutions is somewhere between these two vapor pressures. Water evaporates from the left solution because the pressure of water vapor is less than the pressure of water vapor that would be in equilibrium with that solution; water condenses in the right beaker because the pressure of water vapor is too high. This process continues until the solutions become identical in composition. A similar transfer of ethanol from the right to the left beaker has been taking place at the same time. *In order for the two solutions to be in equilibrium, the vapor pressure of each component must be the same for one solution as for the other.*

The same principle applies to any two phases: they are in equilibrium if, and only if, the vapor pressure of each component common to the two phases is the same for the two phases. A substance always *tends* to go

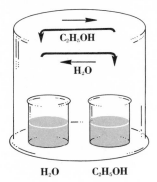

Fig. 13.7. Transfer of vapor between liquid solutions.

from the place where its vapor pressure is higher to the place where it is lower, regardless of whether the transfer takes place through the vapor or in some other way, of whether vapor is actually present, and of whether the vapor pressure is high enough to be measured. But to say that a substance "tends" to do something is not to say that the rate of the process is measurably greater than zero. If one beaker in Fig. 13.7 had contained sodium chloride, this compound would have stayed right there, because its vapor pressure is practically zero at room temperature, and its transfer by way of the vapor is too slow to be observed. We should say that there will not, in any case, be net transfer of a substance from a phase in which its vapor pressure is lower to one in which it is higher, and will avoid any general commitment on the question of whether the reverse process actually occurs.

13.17 DELIQUESCENCE

There is always some water vapor in the air; we specify how much by giving its partial pressure or the relative humidity (page 55). An aqueous solution, exposed to moist air, may either lose or gain water. If the pressure of water vapor in equilibrium with the solution is greater than the pressure of water vapor in the surrounding atmosphere, water will evaporate from the solution; if the pressure of water vapor in the surrounding atmosphere is greater than the equilibrium water vapor pressure of the solution, water vapor from the air will condense in the solution. This evaporation or condensation will continue until the concentration of the solution has been so adjusted that its water vapor pressure is equal to the pressure of atmospheric water vapor.

If the humidity is low enough, the solution loses water by evaporation, and may become saturated before its vapor pressure has been brought down to equilibrium with the air. Unless the solution becomes supersaturated, its concentration can increase no further and, as evaporation progresses, the quantity of solution is lessened by loss of water, while the quantity of precipitated solute increases. If, on the other hand, the vapor pressure of the saturated solution is less than the pressure of water vapor in the air, water will condense in the saturated solution until all the solute has been dissolved. A piece of solute (we assume that it is a solid) will, in the latter case, turn into a puddle of solution on mere exposure to the air; all that is necessary is that a minute amount of water should condense on the solid, forming a saturated solution at which water will then condense until the solid is dissolved. A solid that behaves in this way is said to be **deliquescent.** A familiar example is sodium hydroxide, NaOH; the vapor pressure of its saturated solution* at 20°C is 0.61 torr. The vapor pressure of water at 20°C is 17.5 torr; water from the air will condense in the saturated NaOH solution whenever the relative humidity is greater than $0.61/17.5 = 0.035$ or 3.5%.

* The solid in equilibrium with this saturated solution is not NaOH, but the hydrate NaOH (H_2O).

Gases very soluble in water, such as NH_3 and HCl, also show deliquescence. If the partial pressures of the gas and of water vapor are high enough, they can form droplets of liquid solution, which we describe as fog, mist, or fumes.

Colligative properties of solutions

13.18   VAPOR PRESSURE DEPRESSION

We have seen that, in any dilute solution, the vapor pressure of the solvent A is approximately equal to the mole fraction of A times the vapor pressure of pure A (Raoult's law): $p_A \approx X_A p_A^0$. Let us assume that there is only one solute, B. Then

$$X_A = 1 - X_B$$
$$p_A \approx (1 - X_B)p_A^0$$

or

$$p_A^0 - p_A \approx X_B p_A^0 = \frac{n_B}{n_A + n_B} p_A^0$$

where n_A and n_B are the numbers of moles of the two components. If the solution is dilute, n_B is much less than n_A, and we can simplify this equation to

$$p_A^0 - p_A \approx \frac{n_B}{n_A} p_A^0$$

The quantity $p_A^0 - p_A$ is the **vapor pressure depression** caused by the addition of the solute to the solvent. Any property of a solution that is approximately proportional to the number of moles (or molecules) of solute per unit quantity of solvent, independently of the identity of the solute, is called a **colligative property**; vapor pressure depression is an example of such a property.

EXAMPLE 5   **By how much is the vapor pressure of 100 g of water depressed when 2.00 g of sucrose ($C_{12}H_{22}O_{11}$) are dissolved in it at 25°C?**

ANSWER   **We first find the numbers of moles of the two substances (the molecular weight of sucrose is 342.3 g/mole):**

$$n_{water} = \frac{100 \text{ g}}{18.0 \frac{\text{g}}{\text{mole}}} = 5.55 \text{ moles}$$

$$n_{sucrose} = \frac{2.00 \text{ g}}{342 \frac{\text{g}}{\text{mole}}} = 0.00584 \text{ mole}$$

The vapor pressure of pure water at 25°C is 23.8 torr $= p_{water}^0$ (page 800). Then

$$p_{water}^0 - p_{water} = \frac{0.00584 \text{ mole}}{5.55 \text{ moles}} \times 23.8 \text{ torr} = 0.0250 \text{ torr}$$

Two other colligative properties can be understood with the aid of Fig. 13.8. The solid lines reproduce the pressure-temperature phase diagram for a typical substance (call it A), as shown in Fig. 3.25 (page 63). The curve ST gives the vapor pressure of the solid as a function of temperature; TU gives the vapor pressure of the liquid; TW gives the melting point of the solid as a function of pressure. F and B represent the freezing and boiling points of pure A under one atmosphere pressure. Now, let us add a solute (call it C), that has a negligible vapor pressure, to the solvent A. The vapor pressure of solid A is unaffected—the solid is still pure A—but the vapor pressure of the liquid is lowered by the presence of the solute. The dotted curve $T'U'$ represents the vapor pressure of A in equilibrium with the solution. The temperature, t'_b, at which this vapor pressure becomes equal to one atmosphere is the boiling point of the solution (point B'). As we see, t'_b is greater than t_b, the boiling point of pure A. The boiling-point elevation is approximately proportional to the mole fraction of C,

$$t'_b - t_b \approx K'_b \frac{n_C}{n_A + n_C} \approx K'_b \frac{n_C}{n_A}$$

Fig. 13.8. *Phase diagram for pure solvent (solid curves) and solution (dashed curves).*

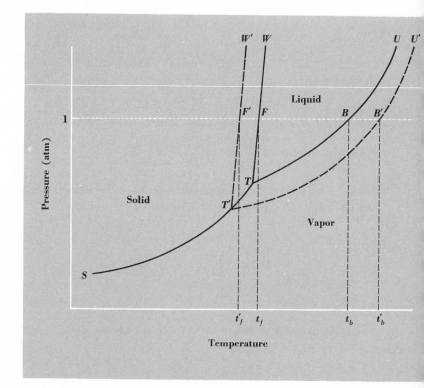

The last step assumes that the solution is dilute enough so that $n_A + n_C \approx n_A$. K_b' is a constant.

Similarly, the triple point T has been moved to T', and the solid-liquid equilibrium curve now extends up from T' instead of T. The freezing point (t_f') is lower than it was (t_f) for the pure solvent. The depression of the freezing point $(t_f - t_f')$ is, like the boiling-point elevation, a colligative property.

By convention, these two properties are calculated from the molality, rather than the mole fraction,

$$t_b' - t_b \approx K_b m_C$$
$$t_f - t_f' \approx K_f m_C$$

Using the molality is equivalent to choosing n_A as that number of moles of solvent which weighs 1000 g; then n_C is the number of moles of solute in 1000 g solvent, and $n_C = m_C$. The proportionality constants K_b and K_f, called the boiling-point elevation constant and the freezing-point depression constant, respectively, are characteristic of the solvent. Constants for some common solvents are listed in Table 13.2.

TABLE 13.2   *Boiling-Point Elevation and Freezing-Point Depression Constants*

Solvent	Boiling point (°C) at 1 atm	K_b $\left(\dfrac{deg\ kg}{mole}\right)$	Freezing point (°C)	K_f $\left(\dfrac{deg\ kg}{mole}\right)$
Acetic acid (CH₃COOH)	118.1	3.07	16.6	3.90
Benzene (C₆H₆)	80.1	2.53	5.51	4.90
Carbon tetrachloride (CCl₄)	76.8	5.03	− 22.8	31.8
Ethanol (C₂H₅OH)	78.5	1.22	−117.3	1.99
Water	100	0.512	0	1.86

EXAMPLE 6   **Find the freezing and boiling points of the water-sucrose solution described in Example 5 (2.00 g sucrose in 100 g water).**

ANSWER   **This solution has 0.00584 mole sucrose dissolved in 100 g water. It therefore contains 0.0584 mole sucrose per 1000 g water, and this is its molality; $m = 0.0584$ mole/kg. Then the freezing-point depression is**

$$t_f - t_f' = K_f m = 1.86 \frac{deg\ kg}{mole} \times 0.0584 \frac{mole}{kg} = 0.109°$$

and the freezing point is

$$0° - 0.109° = -0.109°C$$

The boiling-point elevation is

$$t_b' - t_b = K_b m = 0.512 \, \frac{\text{deg kg}}{\text{mole}} \times 0.0584 \, \frac{\text{mole}}{\text{kg}} = 0.0299°\text{C}$$

and the boiling point is

$$100° + 0.0299° = 100.0299°\text{C}$$

When the solution contains two or more solutes, the molality to be used in calculating the colligative properties is the total molality of all solutes,

$$t_b' - t_b \approx K_b(m_C + m_D + \cdots)$$
$$t_f - t_f' \approx K_f(m_C + m_D + \cdots)$$

A liquid solution boils when its total vapor pressure is equal to the applied pressure (unless it becomes superheated, page 59). If the solute is nonvolatile, the total vapor pressure is the vapor pressure of the solvent. If the solute C is volatile, then $P = p_A + p_C$, and we must interpret B' (Fig. 13.8) as the temperature at which the contribution (p_A) of the solvent alone to the vapor pressure of the solution becomes one atmosphere. But this temperature is no longer the boiling point of the solution, and is much more difficult to measure. Thus, boiling-point elevation is usually considered only in connection with nonvolatile solutes.

Fig. 13.9. *Freezing points (F.P.) of trichloroacetic acid-benzene* *(CCl₃COOH-C₆H₆) solutions. E, eutectic point.*

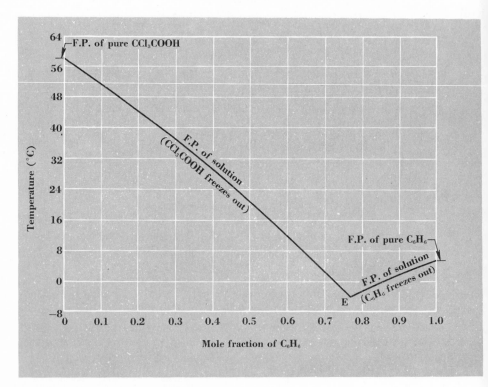

Freezing-point depression is unaffected by volatility of the solute, but we must be sure that the solid which is in equilibrium with the solution is the pure solvent, and not a solid solution, a compound of solute and solvent, or pure solute. In the absence of solid solutions, the freezing point is always depressed in very dilute solutions, but, if the solution is too concentrated, the solute may precipitate before the solvent when the temperature is lowered. A typical example of the behavior of the freezing point over the entire range of possible compositions is shown in Fig. 13.9 for solutions of trichloroacetic acid, CCl_3COOH, and benzene, C_6H_6. Pure trichloroacetic acid freezes at 58.0°C, and pure benzene at 5.4°C. The freezing point of each liquid is depressed by addition of the other. When a solution containing less than 76.5 mole % benzene is cooled, the solid that separates first is trichloroacetic acid; we may say that the solvent freezes or, equally well, that the solution becomes saturated with trichloroacetic acid. When a solution containing 76.5 to 100 mole % benzene is cooled, the solid that separates is pure benzene. There is one special composition, 76.5 mole % benzene (point E), which becomes saturated with respect to the two components simultaneously; no solid appears until the temperature has fallen to −4.0°C, and the two solids precipitate when an attempt is made to cool below this temperature. A solution with this unique composition is called a **eutectic mixture,** and its freezing point is called the **eutectic point.**

3.20 OSMOTIC PRESSURE

This colligative property can be understood with the aid of three facts. First, it is often possible to find a membrane—a partition—allowing one kind of particle, but not another, to pass through. Such a membrane is said to be **semipermeable.** Cellophane, parchment paper, and the walls of living cells are permeable to water and other small molecules, but not to larger molecules. Second, the vapor pressure of a liquid depends to some extent on the pressure applied to the liquid. For example, the vapor pressure of water at 25°C is multiplied by 1.00074 when the pressure on the liquid is increased by one atmosphere. To measure the vapor pressure of a liquid under high pressure, one must apply the pressure by way of a gas, and measure the partial pressure of the vapor in its mixture with the gas. If the pressure is applied by a solid piston, no vapor is present, but we can still think of the liquid as having a certain escaping tendency, specified by the pressure of the vapor that would be in equilibrium with it if a gas were introduced. Third, as we already know, the vapor pressure of a pure solvent is greater than the vapor pressure of the same solvent in a solution, provided solvent and solution are at the same temperature and under the same applied pressure.

In the apparatus of Fig. 13.10, the membrane is permeable only to solvent molecules. More solvent will pass through the membrane into the solution than from the solution into the pure solvent. We can stop this transfer by applying to the piston a certain excess pressure π, the osmotic

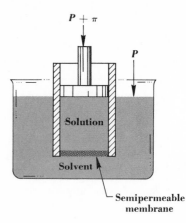

Fig. 13.10. *Apparatus for measuring osmotic pressure. P is the atmospheric pressure; π is the excess pressure (the osmotic pressure) applied to the solution.*

pressure of the solution. The osmotic pressure is the excess pressure that must be applied to the solution to make the vapor pressure of the solvent in the solution equal to the vapor pressure of the pure solvent. For dilute solutions, π is given by the equation

$$\pi \approx [B]RT$$

where [B] is the molarity of the solute (moles/liter), R is the gas constant (0.08206 liter atm/deg mole), and T is the absolute temperature. When there are several solutes, [B] is to be interpreted as the sum of their concentrations.

13.21 DETERMINATION OF MOLECULAR WEIGHTS

The strongest reason for interest in colligative properties is that they provide a means of measuring the number of moles of solute present, n; if we also know the mass of the solute, w, we can calculate its molecular weight, w/n. Freezing-point depression is the easiest of the properties to measure experimentally, except with solutes of very high molecular weight (Chapter 29), for which osmotic pressure is more useful.

EXAMPLE 7   **The freezing point of pure benzene was measured as 5.49°C. With the same benzene and equipment, the freezing point of a solution containing 0.100 g naphthalene in 10.0 g benzene was found to be 5.10°C. The density of the solution was 0.79 g/ml. Find (a) the molecular weight of naphthalene; (b) the boiling point of a solution containing 3.21% (by weight) naphthalene in ethanol; (c) the osmotic pressure at 25°C of the solution in (b).**

ANSWER   (a) **The freezing-point depression is**

$$t_f - t_f' = 5.49 - 5.10 = 0.39°$$
$$t_f - t_f' = K_f m$$
$$K_f = 4.90 \frac{\text{deg kg}}{\text{mole}} \text{ (Table 13.2, page 325)}$$

The molality of naphthalene is

$$m = \frac{t_f - t_f'}{K_f} = \frac{0.39 \text{ deg}}{4.90 \frac{\text{deg kg}}{\text{mole}}} = 0.080 \frac{\text{mole}}{\text{kg}}$$

The weight of naphthalene per kilogram of benzene is

$$w = \frac{0.100 \text{ g naphthalene}}{10.0 \text{ g benzene}} \times 1000 \frac{\text{g}}{\text{kg}} = 10.0 \frac{\text{g}}{\text{kg}}$$

The molecular weight is therefore

$$\frac{w}{m} = \frac{10.0 \frac{\text{g}}{\text{kg}}}{0.080 \frac{\text{mole}}{\text{kg}}} = 125 \frac{\text{g}}{\text{mole}}$$

$$\left(\text{actual value, } 128 \frac{\text{g}}{\text{mole}} \right).$$

(b) From the statement of the problem, 100 g of solution contains 3.21 g naphthalene and 96.79 g ethanol. The weight of naphthalene per kilogram of ethanol is

$$\frac{3.21 \text{ g naphthalene}}{96.79 \text{ g ethanol}} \times 1000 \frac{\text{g}}{\text{kg}} = 33.2 \frac{\text{g}}{\text{kg}}$$

$$m = \frac{33.2 \frac{\text{g}}{\text{kg}}}{125 \frac{\text{g}}{\text{mole}}} = 0.266 \frac{\text{mole}}{\text{kg}}$$

From Table 13.2 (page 325),

$$K_{b \text{ ethanol}} = 1.22 \frac{\text{deg kg}}{\text{mole}}; \qquad t_b = 78.5°C$$

Then

$$t_b' - t_b = K_b m = 1.22 \frac{\text{deg kg}}{\text{mole}} \times 0.263 \frac{\text{mole}}{\text{kg}} = 0.321°$$

and

$$t_b' = 0.321° + 78.5° = 78.8°C$$

(c) The volume of 100 g of solution is

$$\frac{100 \text{ g}}{0.79 \frac{\text{g}}{\text{ml}}} = 127 \text{ ml} = 0.127 \text{ liter}$$

and this quantity of solution contains 3.21 g naphthalene. Therefore, the molarity is

$$c = \frac{3.21 \text{ g}}{125 \frac{\text{g}}{\text{mole}} \times 0.127 \text{ liter}} = 0.202 \frac{\text{mole}}{\text{liter}}$$

The osmotic pressure is

$$\pi = cRT = 0.202 \; \frac{\text{mole}}{\text{liter}} \times 0.08206 \frac{\text{liter atm}}{\text{deg mole}} \times 298°\text{K} = 4.9 \text{ atm}$$

(**Why are only two significant figures used?**)

Problems

1. Molarity. Solutions were prepared by dissolving 50.00 g of each of the following solutes in water, and adding water to the mark in a 500-ml volumetric flask. Find the molarity of each solution: (a) NaCl; (b) K_2SO_4; (c) glucose, $C_6H_{12}O_6$.

Answer. (a) 1.71 mole/liter.

2. Composition measures. A solution is 16% NH_3 and 84% H_2O by mass. Its density is 0.936 g/ml. Find (a) the mole fraction, (b) the molality, and (c) the molarity of NH_3 in this solution.

Answer. (c) 8.8 moles/liter.

3. Raoult's law. Urea, $(NH_2)_2CO$, has practically no vapor pressure at ordinary temperatures. The vapor pressure of pure water at 30°C is 31.824 torr. A solution contains 50.0 g urea and 1000 g H_2O. Find the vapor pressure of this solution at 30°C.

Answer. 31.354 torr.

4. Raoult's law. At 25°C, the vapor pressure of liquid n-butane, C_4H_{10}, is 1823 torr; the vapor pressure of liquid n-pentane, C_5H_{12}, is 521 torr. Assume that solutions of these two compounds are ideal. (a) Find the total vapor pressure at 25°C of a liquid solution containing 10% n-butane and 90% n-pentane, by weight. (b) Find the mole fraction of n-butane in a butane-pentane solution having a total vapor pressure of 760 torr at 25°C.

5. Activity. In a solution of water and acetone, $(CH_3)_2CO$, the mole fraction of acetone is 0.420. The vapor pressures of water and acetone in equilibrium with this solution at 25°C are 23 torr and 164 torr, respectively. The vapor pressure of pure acetone at 25°C is 229 torr; of pure water, 23.76 torr. Find (a) the activity of each component in this solution, and (b) the activity coefficient of each component. (c) Are deviations from Raoult's law positive or negative?

Answer. (a) 0.97, 0.716; (b) 1.67, 1.71.

6. Henry's law. In an aqueous solution of ethanol, C_2H_5OH, the mole fraction of ethanol is 0.0417. The vapor pressure of ethanol over this solution is 6.7 torr at 20°C. (a) Estimate the Henry's law constant $k_{ethanol}$ from these data. (b) Use Henry's law to predict the vapor pressure of ethanol at 20°C over a solution in which its mole fraction is 0.089. (The actual pressure is 12.6 torr.)

7. Colligative properties. A solution contains 1.00% glycerol, $C_3H_5(OH)_3$, and 99.00% water by weight. The vapor pressure of water at 25°C is 23.756 torr. Assume that glycerol is nonvolatile, that the solid which separates on freezing is pure ice, and that the solution has the same density as pure water. Find (a) the vapor pressure of the solution at 25°C; (b) the freezing point of the solution; (c) the boiling point of the solution at 1 atm pressure; (d) the osmotic pressure of the solution at 25°, with a membrane permeable to water but not to glycerol.

Answer. (a) 23.709 torr; (b) −0.20°; (c) 100.056°; (d) 2.66 atm.

8. Determination of molecular weight. An aqueous solution contains 0.20 g of an unknown solute and 50.0 g H_2O. It freezes at −0.075°C. Find (a) the molecular weight of the solute, (b) the boiling point of the solution.

9. Solubility and molecular structure. In each of the following pairs, select the compound that you would expect to be more soluble in water; explain (you may wish to refer to the table of electronegativities on page 216):

(a) C_2H_5F and C_2H_5I

(b) C_3H_7OH and C_3H_7SH

(c)

    and

(d) NO and H_2NNH_2

(e) NH_3 and AsH_3

10. Molarity. What mass of each of the following compounds should be weighed out in order to prepare a 0.500 molar solution with the aid of a 1000-ml volumetric flask? (a) $AgNO_3$; (b) $MgSO_4(H_2O)_7$; (c) acetamide, H_3CCONH_2.

11. Composition measures. Let B be the solute, and A the solvent, in a solution. Express (a) the molality m_B in terms of the mole fraction $[X_B = n_B/(n_A + n_B)]$ and the molecular weights M_A and M_B; (b) the molarity [B] in terms of X_B, M_A, M_B, and d, the density of the solution. (Suggestion: first express m_B and [B] in terms of n_A, n_B, M_A, M_B, and, if necessary, d.) (c) Show that m_B and [B] are both proportional to X_B in solutions that are sufficiently dilute (X_B much less than 1, and d nearly equal to the density of pure A).

$$\text{Answer. (a) } \frac{1000\,X_B}{M_A(1 - X_B)}; \text{ (b) } \frac{1000\,dX_B}{M_A + X_B(M_B - M_A)}.$$

12. Composition measures. Two aqueous solutions of methanol, CH_3OH, have mole fractions of methanol 0.0100 and 0.0200. Their densities are 0.996 and 0.994 g/ml, respectively. Using the results of the preceding problem, find (a) the molalities, and (b) the molarities, of methanol in these two solutions. Find (c) the ratio of the molality in the second solution to the molality in the first, and (d) the corresponding ratio of molarities. Compare these ratios with the ratio (2:1) of the mole fractions.

13. Composition measures. The molarity of NH_3 in an aqueous solution is 11.8 moles/liter. The density of the solution is 0.916 g/ml. Find (a) the molality, (b) the weight fraction, and (c) the mole fraction of NH_3 in this solution.

Answer. (a) 16.5 moles/kg; (b) 0.219; (c) 0.229.

14. Composition measures. An aqueous solution of hydrofluoric acid, HF, is 5.55 molal with respect to HF, and has density 1.040 g/ml at 0°C. Find (a) the mole fraction, (b) the weight fraction, and (c) the molarity of HF in this solution.

15. Composition measures. What volume of the solution in the preceding problem contains 5.0 g of HF?

Answer. 45 ml.

16. Change of molarity with temperature. The coefficient of expansion of H_2O near 20°C is 2.1×10^{-4} per degree; this means that the volume of a sample of H_2O is multiplied by 1.00021 when the temperature is raised 1°C. A certain aqueous solution is $0.1000M$ at 15°C. Find its molarity at 25°C, assuming the coefficient of expansion of this solution to be the same as that of pure water.

17. Composition measures. A bottle of concentrated hydrochloric acid has the following information on the label: "Assay 38% HCl. Specific gravity 1.18." Find (a) the molarity of HCl in this solution; (b) the volume of the concentrated acid that must be used in order to prepare 100 ml of $3.0M$ solution by dilution with water.

Answer. (a) 12 moles/liter; (b) 25 ml.

18. Solubility and temperature. The solubility of sodium chlorate, $NaClO_3$, in water is 89 g/100 g H_2O at 10°C, and 172 g/100 g H_2O at 70°C. A solution was prepared by dissolving $NaClO_3$ in 200 ml H_2O (how many grams is this?) until no more would dissolve at 70°, and the solution was then cooled to 10°. How many grams of $NaClO_3$ precipitated? Assume that no water evaporated, and that there was no supersaturation.

Answer. 166 g.

19. Solubility and temperature. Saturated solutions of $CdBr_2$ in water contain 37.9% $CdBr_2$ at 0°C, and 62.3% $CdBr_2$ at 80°C. A solution made from 50 g $CdBr_2$ and 50 g H_2O was cooled from 80° to 0°. What mass of $CdBr_2$ precipitated? Make the same assumptions as in the preceding problem.

20. Volume change on mixing. At 25°C, the density of ethanol (C_2H_5OH) is 0.785 g/ml; the density of water is 0.997 g/ml; the density of a 50.0% (by mass) solution of ethanol in water is 0.910 g/ml. Find the ratio of the volume of this solution to the total volume of the pure components from which it was made.

Answer. 0.965.

21. Composition measures. Find (a) the mole fraction, (b) the volume fraction, and (c) the molarity of ethanol in a 50.0% (by mass) solution of ethanol in water at 25°C. Use data in the preceding problem.

22. Density of solution. At 25°C, the density of chloroform, $CHCl_3$, is 1.48 g/ml; the density of acetone, $(CH_3)_2CO$, is 0.785 g/ml. Assuming no volume change on mixing, find the density of a solution prepared by mixing 56.3 g chloroform and 43.7 g acetone.

Answer. 1.07 g/ml; actual density, 1.068 g/ml.

23. Raoult's law. The vapor pressures of carbon disulfide, CS_2, and ethyl acetate, $CH_3COOC_2H_5$, at 27°C are 390 torr and 100 torr, respectively. Find the total vapor pressure at 27°C of a solution prepared by mixing 10.0 g CS_2 and 30.0 g $CH_3COOC_2H_5$. Assume that Raoult's law is applicable.

Answer. 181 torr.

24. Activity. In a solution prepared by mixing 2.0 moles chloroform, $CHCl_3$, and 3.0 moles diethyl ether, $(C_2H_5)_2O$, the vapor pressures of the components at 17°C are $p_{CHCl_3} = 34$ torr, $p_{(C_2H_5)_2O} = 196$ torr. The vapor pressures of the pure liquids at 17°C are $p^0_{CHCl_3} = 143$ torr, $p^0_{(C_2H_5)_2O} = 397$ torr. (a) Find the activities of chloroform and of ether in this solution. (b) Find their activity coefficients. (c) What can you say about the force of attraction between a chloroform molecule and an ether molecule, as compared to the force between two chloroform molecules or between two ether molecules?

Answer. (a) 0.24, 0.49; (b) 0.60, 0.82.

25. Activity. The vapor pressure of mercury at 324°C is 408 torr. In an amalgam (solution) containing equal numbers of atoms of Hg and Pb, the activity coefficient of Hg is 1.39 at 324°C. Find the vapor pressure of Hg in equilibrium with this amalgam.

26. Gas solubility. Find the solubility of H_2 in H_2O at 25°C under a total pressure of 5.0 atmospheres, in (a) g H_2 per 100 g H_2O, (b) volume of H_2 (measured at 5.0 atm) per unit volume of H_2O. (Refer to Table 13.1, page 304.)

Answer. (a) 0.00077 g H_2/100 g H_2O; (b) 0.019 ml H_2/ml H_2O.

27. Deliquescence. The vapor pressure of water in equilibrium with a saturated solution of potassium acetate, $KC_2H_3O_2$, is 3.5 torr at 20°C. Find the highest relative humidity at which potassium acetate can be kept as a solid exposed to the open air at 20°C.

28. Determination of molecular weight. A solution of 8.00 g acetic acid in 100 g benzene freezes at 2.10°C. A solution of 8.00 g acetic acid in 100 g water freezes at −2.50°C. Find the molecular weight of acetic acid from each of these data. What can you conclude about the state of the acetic acid molecules dissolved in each of these solvents? How are these results related to the properties of the water and benzene molecules?

Answer. 115 g/mole in benzene, 60 g/mole in water.

29. Freezing-point depression. The two most commonly used antifreezes are methanol, CH_3OH, and ethylene glycol, $(CH_2OH)_2$. Estimate the weight of each of these solutes that must be added to one kilogram of water in order to prevent the water from freezing at −10°C.

30. Boiling-point elevation. Separate solutions of two nonvolatile solutes, B and C, in the same solvent A were prepared. The molecular weight of B is 50. The boiling points of the solvent and the solutions were as follows:

Solute	Weight of solute (per 100 g A)	Boiling point
None		70.00°
B	1.00 g	70.40°
C	0.50 g	70.30°

Find (a) the boiling-point elevation constant of A, (b) the molecular weight of C.

Answer. (a) 2.0° kg/mole; (b) 33 g/mole.

31. Determination of molecular weight. A certain nonvolatile hydrocarbon (a compound of C and H only) contains 5.66% H by weight. 1.00 g of this hydrocarbon was dissolved in 50 g benzene; the resulting solution boiled 0.285° higher than pure benzene. Find the molecular weight and the molecular formula of the hydrocarbon.

32. Osmotic pressure. An aqueous solution containing 10 g starch per liter gave an osmotic pressure of 20 torr at 25°C. (a) Find the molecular weight of the starch. (Because not all the starch molecules are identical, the result will be an average.) (b) What is the freezing point of the solution? Would it be easy to find the molecular weight of the starch by measuring the freezing-point depression?

Answer. (a) 9.3×10^3 g/mole; (b) −0.002°.

33. Freezing-point depression. The eutectic point of the system $NaCl–H_2O$ (the temperature at which ice freezes out of a solution saturated with NaCl) is −21°C. The eutectic point of the system $CaCl_2(H_2O)_6–H_2O$ is −55°C. Which salt would you recommend for melting the ice on roads in a cold climate? Why?

34. Osmotic pressure. (a) An aqueous solution containing 2.00 g oxyhemoglobin (a protein) per liter shows an osmotic pressure of 7.6 mm H_2O (0.56 torr) at 27°C. Find the molecular weight of the oxyhemoglobin. (b) Estimate the freezing-point depression of this solution. (c) Which method, osmotic pressure or freezing-point depression, would you recommend for determining molecular weights of proteins?

14
Chemical equilibrium

―――――

14.1 INTRODUCTION

Consider a mixture of hydrogen and iodine, in a closed vessel, at a temperature such that both are gases. They will react to form hydrogen iodide, also a gas,

$$H_2 + I_2 \rightarrow 2HI \tag{1}$$

If we had started with pure HI at the same temperature, it would have decomposed to give hydrogen and iodine,

$$2HI \rightarrow H_2 + I_2 \tag{2}$$

Now, the HI that is formed in reaction (1) acts like any other HI: as soon as some of it has been formed, the decomposition (reaction 2) sets in. The H_2 and I_2 formed in reaction (2) will react to give HI, as in reaction (1). Thus, in any mixture of the three gases H_2, I_2, and HI, reactions (1) and (2) will both take place. This fact is expressed by saying that reaction (1) or (2) is **reversible,** and writing it with a double arrow,

$$H_2 + I_2 \rightleftharpoons 2HI$$

or

$$2HI \rightleftharpoons H_2 + I_2$$

If reaction (1) is faster than reaction (2), there is a net formation of HI, so that its concentration increases with time, while the concentrations of H_2 and I_2 decrease. As we will see in Chapter 23, the rate of a reaction usually increases as the concentrations of reactants increase, and decreases as they decrease. In the present case, the falling concentrations of H_2 and I_2 result in a slowing of reaction (1), while the rising concentration of HI

334

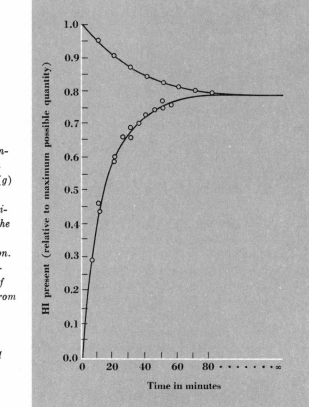

Fig. 14.1. *Experimental data on the reaction* $H_2(g) + I_2(g) \rightleftharpoons 2HI(g)$ *at the boiling point of sulfur, 445°C. The horizontal axis represents the time elapsed from the beginning of the reaction. The vertical axis represents the composition of the reaction mixture, from pure HI at the top to* $H_2 + I_2$ *at the bottom.* [*After M. Bodenstein, Z. phys. Chem.* **13**, *111* (*1894*)]

speeds up reaction (2). If reaction (2) is faster, the loss of HI will slow it down, and the gain of H_2 and I_2 will speed up reaction (1). Thus, the faster reaction becomes slower, and the slower becomes faster. A state of **equilibrium** will eventually be reached when the two reactions, forward and reverse, are occurring at the same rate; from then on, there will be *no further net change* in the composition of the reaction mixture, unless some external disturbance is imposed, such as a change in temperature or volume of the container, or the addition or removal of one of the substances involved in the reaction. The concept of equilibrium is the same here as for a saturated solution; in that case, the two processes of dissolving and coming out of solution were equal in rate at equilibrium. Now we are concerned with two chemical reactions, one the reverse of the other, which proceed at the same rate when the various concentrations have adjusted themselves to the proper values.

The reaction $H_2 + I_2 \rightleftharpoons 2HI$ was one of the first gas reactions studied in detail with respect to rate and equilibrium. Some of the original experimental data, published by Max Bodenstein in 1894, are shown in Fig. 14.1. In some experiments, he started with various quantities of pure HI, and the quantity initially present is taken as one unit. In other experiments, he started with equal numbers of moles of H_2 and I_2; the quantity of HI that would be formed by complete combination of these starting materials is again called one unit. The vertical axis gives the fraction of this maximum quantity of HI that was present when the sealed tube was opened and its contents analyzed; the length of time (in minutes) that the reaction had been in progress is shown on the horizontal axis. The two curves show clearly that the proportions of the three substances approach the same final values, whether one starts with HI (*upper curve*) or with H_2 and I_2 (*lower curve*).

In this particular case, equilibrium is attained in an hour or two; in other reactions, it may take a tiny fraction of a second, and there are many reactions that would be nowhere close to equilibrium after a million years. Some reactions settle down to equilibrium after formation of only minute amounts of the products; in other reactions, only minute amounts of the reactants remain unreacted at equilibrium. Sometimes, as in the HI reaction, appreciable quantities of both reactants and products are present in the equilibrium mixture. One method of predicting the conditions at which equilibrium will be attained is to write an expression for the rate of the forward reaction as a function of concentrations, and a similar expression for the rate of the reverse reaction; at equilibrium, these two expressions must be equal, and a condition is thus imposed on the concentrations. The difficulty with this approach is that, as we will see in Chapter 23, the rate law for a reaction can be ascertained only by arduous experimentation, not merely by inspection of the chemical equation. The problem of predicting the equilibrium state can, fortunately, be solved in another way requiring no knowledge of rates. The condition for equilibrium can be written (except for one number, which must be measured experimentally) at once on inspection of the equation for the reaction. This method ignores rates, and starts from the assertion that *a system in equilibrium can do no work*, that, indeed, work must be done on the system to displace it from equilibrium. The derivation is beyond the scope of this book; we shall content ourselves with the results.

14.2 EQUILIBRIUM IN GASES

Let the ideal gases A, B, C, and D undergo, at constant temperature, the reaction

$$aA + bB \leftrightharpoons cC + dD$$

where a, b, c, and d are the stoichiometric coefficients (small integers or simple fractions). We define the **reaction quotient in terms of pressures** as

$$Q_p = \frac{p_C{}^c p_D{}^d}{p_A{}^a p_B{}^b}$$

where p_A, . . . , p_D are the partial pressures of the gases in the reaction mixture. The **Law of Chemical Equilibrium** states that, at each temperature, there is associated with this reaction a number K_p, called the **equilibrium constant in terms of pressures**, such that at equilibrium, $Q_p = K_p$. When $Q_p < K_p$, the partial pressures of C and D are smaller than they would be at equilibrium, for given values of p_A and p_B. Alternatively, we may say that the partial pressures of A and B are greater than they would be at equilibrium, for given values of p_C and p_D. The only possible direction of the reaction, under these conditions, is the direction that makes p_C and p_D larger, and—since A and B are consumed when C and D are formed—makes p_A and p_B smaller. This process is described by saying that the reaction "goes from left to right." Similarly, when $Q_p > K_p$, the partial pressures of C and D are too great, or the partial pressures of A and B are too small; in this case, the only possible direction of the reaction is from right to left—the formation of more A and B at the expense of C and D. In general, the reaction can proceed in the direction making Q_p *more nearly* equal to K_p. We have not said that the reaction will take place in that direction; there may be no reaction at all, or there may be an imperceptibly slow reaction. All we know is that the reaction will not go in the other direction.

The law of chemical equilibrium, as we have stated it, is strictly true only for ideal gases—gases for which $PV = nRT$ exactly. In reality, there are no ideal gases. However, the law is a fairly good approximation for real gases under ordinary conditions, and the modifications needed to allow for nonideality are difficult. Therefore, we shall treat all gases in this chapter as if they were ideal, and keep in mind that the results thus obtained are not reliable at high pressure or low temperature.

14.3   **THE SULFUR DIOXIDE–SULFUR TRIOXIDE EQUILIBRIUM**

Another example of a reversible gas reaction is

$$2SO_2(g) + O_2(g) \leftrightharpoons 2SO_3(g)$$

This reaction is the crucial step in the most common process for making sulfuric acid, $(HO)_2SO_2$. The reaction is extremely slow under ordinary conditions, but proceeds quite rapidly above 500°C in the presence of a catalyst, such as platinum or divanadium pentoxide (V_2O_5). Table 14.1 shows a few data from an extensive series of experiments by Max Bodenstein and Wilhelm Pohl (1905), in which the equilibrium constant of this reaction was measured. A mixture of SO_2, O_2, and in some cases N_2, in the molar ratio shown and at a total pressure of 1.00 atmosphere, was passed through a tube containing platinum sponge, heated to 1000°K. Various rates of flow were used, to ensure that the gas was passing through slowly enough to allow time for attainment of equilibrium; if the same output composition is obtained at the different rates, we are confident that the mixture remained in the tube for a sufficient time. The outcoming gas was analyzed for SO_2, SO_3, and O_2. The equilibrium condition in this case is

$$\frac{p_{SO_3}^2}{p_{SO_2}^2 p_{O_2}} = K_p$$

TABLE 14.1 *Determination of the Equilibrium Constant of* $2SO_2(g) + O_2(g) \leftrightharpoons 2SO_3(g)$ *at $1000°K$*

Rate of flow (cm³/min)	Initial molar ratio			Final partial pressures (atm)			$\dfrac{p_{SO_3}^2}{p_{SO_2}^2 p_{O_2}} = Q_p$
	SO_2	O_2	N_2	SO_3	SO_2	O_2	
5.4	1.24	1	0	0.338	0.309	0.353	3.39
25.3	2.28	1	0	0.364	0.457	0.180	3.52
27.4	2.44	1	0	0.357	0.484	0.165	3.29
22.4	3.36	1	0	0.331	0.559	0.101	3.47
53.4	2.62	1	3.76	0.128	0.248	0.080	3.33

The reaction quotient is roughly constant, as it should be at equilibrium; the rate of flow, the initial ratio of reactants, and the presence or absence of an indifferent gas (N_2) can be changed without drastic effect on Q_p. Thus, it appears that equilibrium has been attained.

14.4 CHANGE OF K WITH FORM OF EQUATION

Instead of writing

$$2SO_2 + O_2 \leftrightharpoons 2SO_3$$

with the equilibrium condition

$$\frac{p_{SO_3}^2}{p_{SO_2}^2 p_{O_2}} = K_p$$

we could write, no less correctly,

$$4SO_2 + 2O_2 \leftrightharpoons 4SO_3$$

Let us represent by K_p' the equilibrium constant for the reaction written in this form; the equilibrium condition then becomes

$$\frac{p_{SO_3}^4}{p_{SO_2}^4 p_{O_2}^2} = K_p'$$

Obviously, $K_p' = K_p^2$. When the chemical equation is multiplied through by a constant n, the equilibrium constant is raised to the nth power. Thus, for

$$SO_2 + \tfrac{1}{2}O_2 \leftrightharpoons SO_3$$

the equilibrium condition is

$$\frac{p_{SO_3}}{p_{SO_2} p_{O_2}^{1/2}} = K_p''$$

and

$$K_p'' = K_p^{1/2} = \sqrt{K_p}$$

If the reaction is written backward

$$2SO_3 \rightleftharpoons 2SO_2 + O_2$$

the equilibrium condition becomes

$$\frac{p_{SO_2}^2 p_{O_2}}{p_{SO_3}^2} = K_p''' = \frac{1}{K_p}$$

Reversing the chemical equation changes the equilibrium constant to its reciprocal. To speak of "the equilibrium constant for the formation of SO_3 from SO_2 and O_2" is ambiguous—one should write the chemical equation. It is also necessary to agree on the units in which the partial pressures are to be expressed. Atmospheres are usual and will be used consistently here, but torr (millimeters of mercury) and kilograms per square centimeter are sometimes seen.

14.5 COMBINATION OF EQUILIBRIA

It is possible to find the equilibrium constant for a reaction when the constants for certain other reactions are known. One may be interested, for example, in the reaction

$$SO_2(g) + CO_2(g) \rightleftharpoons SO_3(g) + CO(g) \tag{3}$$

but may find that data on it are not readily available. However, the equilibrium constants for the reactions

$$2SO_2(g) + O_2(g) \rightleftharpoons 2SO_3(g) \tag{4}$$

and

$$2CO_2(g) \rightleftharpoons 2CO(g) + O_2(g) \tag{5}$$

are well known. We can write for them the equilibrium conditions

$$\frac{p_{SO_3}^2}{p_{SO_2}^2 p_{O_2}} = K_4$$

and

$$\frac{p_{CO}^2 p_{O_2}}{p_{CO_2}^2} = K_5$$

respectively. (The constants are labeled by the same numbers as the equations. To avoid cumbersome notation, we omit the subscript p in this section.) In a mixture of all five gases—SO_2, SO_3, CO, CO_2, and O_2—these two conditions must be satisfied simultaneously at equilibrium. If we multiply the left side of one equation by the left side of the other, and similarly multiply the right sides together, we obtain another equation,

$$\frac{p_{SO_3}^2}{p_{SO_2}^2 p_{O_2}} \times \frac{p_{CO}^2 p_{O_2}}{p_{CO_2}^2} = K_4 K_5$$

or

$$\frac{p_{SO_3}^2 p_{CO}^2}{p_{SO_2}^2 p_{CO_2}^2} = K_4 K_5 \tag{6}$$

But the equilibrium condition for Equation (3) is

$$\frac{p_{SO_3} p_{CO}}{p_{SO_2} p_{CO_2}} = K_3 \tag{7}$$

On comparing Equations (6) and (7), we see that

$$K_3 = (K_4 K_5)^{1/2}$$

Of course, K_3 is the same whether or not O_2 is present.

The procedure can be simplified if we observe that, when two reactions are added to obtain a third reaction, their equilibrium constants are multiplied to give the equilibrium constant of the third reaction. Thus, we may add reactions (4) and (5),

$$2SO_2(g) + O_2(g) \leftrightharpoons 2SO_3(g) \tag{4}$$

$$\underline{\hspace{1.5cm} 2CO_2(g) \leftrightharpoons 2CO(g) + O_2(g)} \tag{5}$$

$$2SO_2(g) + 2CO_2(g) \leftrightharpoons 2SO_3(g) + 2CO(g) \tag{8}$$

Without writing out the equilibrium conditions, we can see, from the way the reaction quotient is constructed, that $K_4 K_5 = K_8$. That $K_8 = K_3{}^2$ is obvious from the rule (page 338) about multiplying the equation through by a constant. In general, when a number of reactions are added, their equilibrium constants are multiplied together to give the equilibrium constant of the over-all reaction—care being taken, of course, to use the equilibrium constants for the reactions as they are actually written, with all reversals, doublings, halvings, etc., taken into account. The process is similar to the calculation of a heat of reaction with the aid of Hess's law (page 114), except that equilibrium constants are multiplied together, while heats of reaction are added. Changing the sign of ΔH, when the equation is reversed, corresponds to taking the reciprocal of K. Multiplying ΔH by 2, when each term in the equation is doubled, corresponds to squaring K.

14.6 THE EQUILIBRIUM CONDITION IN TERMS OF CONCENTRATIONS

The composition of a gas mixture can be expressed as well by molar concentrations (moles per liter) as by partial pressures. For the reaction

$$2SO_2 + O_2 \leftrightharpoons 2SO_3$$

the equilibrium condition in terms of concentrations is

$$\frac{[SO_3]^2}{[SO_2]^2[O_2]} = K_c$$

The relation between partial pressure p_A and concentration [A] is

$$p_A = \frac{n_A RT}{V} = [A]RT$$

In order to have p_A in atmospheres, R must be 0.08206 liter atm/deg mole. The equilibrium condition for the reaction $2SO_2 + O_2 \leftrightarrows 2SO_3$ is, in terms of pressures,

$$\frac{p_{SO_3}^2}{p_{SO_2}^2 p_{O_2}} = K_p$$

Substituting for each pressure gives

$$\frac{[SO_3]^2 (RT)^2}{[SO_2]^2 (RT)^2 [O_2](RT)} = K_p$$

$$\frac{[SO_3]^2}{[SO_2]^2 [O_2](RT)} = K_p$$

$$= \frac{K_c}{RT}$$

or

$$K_c = K_p RT$$

for the specific reaction considered here. In general,

$$K_c = K_p (RT)^m$$

where the power m may be positive, negative, or zero. The value of m ($+1$ in the example chosen) can be ascertained by the procedure illustrated: substitute $[A]RT$ for p_A and simplify the expression.

14.7 PRINCIPLE OF LE CHÂTELIER

The composition of a mixture at equilibrium depends, in general, on the quantities of the reacting substances that are initially brought together, on the volume of the container in which they are placed, and on the temperature. The only one of these factors affecting the actual value of the equilibrium constant is the temperature. However, a change in volume, or the addition or removal of matter, may also require a change in the proportions of the reacting substances in order that the equilibrium condition shall continue to be satisfied under the new conditions. Before we study quantitative calculations on equilibrium mixtures, we shall develop some useful rules enabling us to predict qualitatively the direction in which the composition of an equilibrium mixture will change.

(a) **Change of Quantity.** If a mixture of SO_2, O_2, and SO_3 is in equilibrium and more O_2 is added, the initial effect is to make $p_{SO_3}^2 / p_{SO_2}^2 p_{O_2}$ smaller than K_p, because the denominator has become larger. If equilibrium is to be restored, the numerator must increase, or the denominator must decrease, or both. Actually, both will happen: SO_3 can be produced only by consuming SO_2 and O_2. When SO_3 is thus produced at the expense of SO_2 and O_2, the reaction $2SO_2 + O_2 \leftrightarrows 2SO_3$ is said to *shift to the right*. Similarly, adding SO_2 causes a shift to the right; adding SO_3 causes a shift to the left (formation of more SO_2 and O_2). The general rule is that *increasing the concentration (or partial pressure) of one substance in an equilibrium mixture causes the reaction to take place in that direction which* *consumes some of the material added.* Similarly, decreasing the concentration of a substance causes the production of more of that substance.

(b) Change of Volume. Another way in which we can disturb an equilibrium mixture of gases is to change the volume of the container. We recall that, for each component, $p = nRT/V$, where n is the number of moles of that component present. Thus, for the reaction $2SO_2 + O_2 \rightleftharpoons 2SO_3$,

$$Q_p = \frac{(n_{SO_3}RT/V)^2}{(n_{SO_2}RT/V)^2 (n_{O_2}RT/V)} = \frac{n_{SO_3}^2}{n_{SO_2}^2 n_{O_2}} \cdot \frac{V}{RT}$$

Increasing the volume, in this case, makes $Q_p > K_p$, and the numbers of moles must change to restore equilibrium. To decrease Q_p, more SO_2 and O_2 must form, at the expense of SO_3. Decreasing the volume, conversely, results in the formation of more SO_3. The rule is that *increasing the volume favors that reaction which produces more moles of gas.* $2SO_2 + O_2$ is 3 moles of gas, $2SO_3$ is 2 moles of gas, and the equilibrium $2SO_2 + O_2 \rightleftharpoons 2SO_3$ is therefore shifted to the left when the volume increases, to the right when it decreases.

(c) Change of Temperature. An equilibrium constant is constant only as long as the temperature does not change. A change in temperature results in a change, often quite large, in the equilibrium constant. *Increasing the temperature causes reaction to occur in that direction which results in absorption of heat; decreasing the temperature causes reaction to occur in that direction which results in emission of heat.* In the formation of SO_3, heat is given out,

$$2SO_2 + O_2 \rightarrow 2SO_3 \qquad \Delta H = -47 \text{ kcal}$$

Therefore, raising the temperature decreases K_p, shifting the equilibrium to the left; lowering the temperature increases K_p. However, the rate of attainment of equilibrium is increased by raising the temperature, regardless of the effect that temperature has on the final state of equilibrium. An increase in temperature speeds up both the formation and the decomposition of SO_3, but speeds up the decomposition more than the formation, so that less SO_3 is present when the two rates become equal.

The rules given in the last three paragraphs are summarized by **Le Châtelier's Principle***: *when a disturbance is imposed on a system in equilibrium, the equilibrium shifts in such a way as to undo, in part, the effect of the disturbance.* Adding a reactant results in partial consumption of that reactant; decreasing the volume (and thus increasing the total pressure) favors the formation of those substances which would, at a given pressure and temperature, occupy a smaller volume (and thus exert a smaller pressure in a given volume); raising the temperature results in a reaction which absorbs heat and makes the rise in temperature, for a given quantity of heat added, less than it would otherwise be.

We saw some illustrations of Le Châtelier's principle when we studied

---

* After Henry Le Châtelier (1850–1936), who formulated the principle in 1888. Essentially the same principle was recognized by F. Braun in 1886, as a result of his work on solubility.

solubility. If heat is absorbed in the process, solute + solvent → solution, raising the temperature shifts the equilibrium to the right—that is, increases the solubility—whereas, if heat is given out, raising the temperature shifts the equilibrium to the left. If the solute is a gas, decreasing the volume of the container increases the pressure and forces more gas into solution; that is, the equilibrium, gas + solvent ⇌ solution, has been shifted to the right: from the side on which gas appears (the left) to the side on which no gas appears.

14.8 EQUILIBRIUM AND CATALYSIS

One thing that does *not* cause a shift in equilibrium is the addition or removal of a catalyst (page 624). We have noted that a system in equilibrium can do no work; on the other hand, it is always possible, in principle if not in practice, to obtain work from a system as it passes from a state of disequilibrium to a state of equilibrium. Suppose that equilibrium is established in the absence of a catalyst, and the catalyst is then introduced. If a reaction occurred as a result of this addition, we could obtain work from the reaction, perhaps by the electrical means to be discussed in Chapter 16. Then, on removal of the catalyst, the equilibrium would shift back to where it was before, and more work could be obtained. The catalyst would (by definition) be essentially unchanged, ready to be reintroduced and thus to start the cycle all over again. This is too good to be true; we would have a perpetual-motion machine. A catalyst changes the rate of approach to equilibrium, but must affect the rates of the forward and reverse reactions in the same way, so that the composition of the *equilibrium mixture* is *unchanged* by its presence.

14.9 HETEROGENEOUS EQUILIBRIUM

When chemical equilibrium is established in one phase—a mixture of gases, a liquid solution—we have a case of **homogeneous equilibrium.** When more than one phase is involved—gas and solid, for example, or liquid and solid—the equilibrium is said to be **heterogeneous.** A saturated solution in equilibrium with solute is a familiar instance of heterogeneous equilibrium. For the present we shall concern ourselves with gas-solid reactions.

We have studied the formation of HI from H_2 and I_2, at a temperature at which I_2 is a gas. At room temperature, on the other hand, I_2 is a solid, although its vapor pressure is high enough that the violet color can be seen in an enclosed space above solid iodine. At 25°C, the vapor pressure of I_2 is 4.04×10^{-4} atm. The equilibrium constant of the reaction

$$H_2(g) + I_2(g) \rightleftharpoons 2HI(g)$$

is 871 (with pressures in atm) at 25°C,

$$\frac{p_{HI}^2}{p_{H_2}p_{I_2}} = 871$$

But now, as long as solid I_2 is present, $p_{I_2} = 4.04 \times 10^{-4}$ atm; it can have no other value at 25°C, provided that equilibrium is established. The equilibrium condition can be rewritten

$$\frac{p_{HI}^2}{p_{H_2}} = 871 p_{I_2} = 871 \times 4.04 \times 10^{-4} = 0.352$$

and this equation may be regarded as the equilibrium condition for the reaction

$$H_2(g) + I_2(c) \leftrightharpoons 2HI(g)$$

We say that, for this reaction, $K_p = 0.352$ at 25°C. The constant pressure of $I_2(g)$ has been incorporated into the equilibrium constant to give a new constant, just as constant as the old one, provided that the temperature is fixed and solid is present to maintain the equilibrium vapor pressure. Whenever a reaction involves pure solids or pure liquids, their vapor pressures are handled in this way, and they do not appear in the reaction quotient. The vapor pressures need not be known; if we measure p_{H_2} and p_{HI} at equilibrium, in the presence of $I_2(c)$, K_p for the solid-gas reaction can be calculated immediately.

The same rule applies even when the vapor pressure is too small to be measured. Steam will oxidize red-hot iron, forming magnetite (Fe_3O_4) and hydrogen. The reaction also proceeds in the other direction if we start with H_2 and Fe_3O_4,

$$4H_2O(g) + 3Fe(c) \leftrightharpoons 4H_2(g) + Fe_3O_4(c) \tag{9}$$

When the equilibrium (9) is established, minute amounts of Fe and Fe_3O_4 are present in the gas phase—one atom or molecule once in a while—and these vapors must be in equilibrium with H_2 and H_2O. For the gas equilibrium, we can write the equation

$$4H_2O(g) + 3Fe(g) \leftrightharpoons 4H_2(g) + Fe_3O_4(g) \tag{10}$$

The equilibrium condition for this reaction is

$$\frac{p_{H_2}^4 p_{Fe_3O_4}}{p_{H_2O}^4 p_{Fe}^3} = K_p' \tag{11}$$

Since Fe and Fe_3O_4 do not form solid solutions with each other, we are dealing here with two pure solids. Equation (11) can be written

$$\frac{p_{H_2}^4}{p_{H_2O}^4} = K_p' \left(\frac{p_{Fe}^3}{p_{Fe_3O_4}} \right) = K_p \tag{12}$$

K_p is as good a constant as K_p'.

Table 14.2 shows data, published in 1904 by G. Preuner, that provide an experimental test of Equation (12). Fe and Fe_3O_4 were in a container heated to 900°C; various amounts of hydrogen were introduced, and the total pressure ($p_{H_2} + p_{H_2O}$) was observed until it became constant. p_{H_2O} at 900°C was held constant at a known value as the reaction occurred, by having the reaction tube connected to a reservoir containing liquid water at a constant (but adjustable) temperature near room tem-

p_{H_2} (torr)	p_{H_2O} (torr)	$p_{H_2}^4/p_{H_2O}^4 = K_p$
14.2	10.0	4.06
30.6	21.5	4.06
54.1	35.4	5.48
69.4	46.6	4.93

perature. Thus, p_{H_2O} was always equal to the vapor pressure of water at the reservoir temperature.

A few of Preuner's graphs are shown in Fig. 14.2. The vertical axis shows the total pressure of H_2 and H_2O; this should become constant at equilibrium, since p_{H_2O} is constant. The horizontal axis represents time, 10 minutes for each interval. He did something that should always be done in equilibrium measurements: he approached equilibrium from both directions, adding sometimes excess H_2, sometimes excess H_2O. Thus, he could be confident that the reaction had not stopped far short of equilibrium in either direction, as it would, for example, if one of the solids had become coated with a layer of the other, effectively removing it from the reaction mixture.

The application of Le Châtelier's principle to heterogeneous reactions deserves a few remarks. In reaction (9),

$$4H_2O(g) + 3Fe(c) \leftrightharpoons 4H_2(g) + Fe_3O_4(c)$$

the reaction quotient depends on the ratio p_{H_2}/p_{H_2O}, which is unaffected by a change in the volume of the container; such a change will multiply p_{H_2} and p_{H_2O} by the same factor. If the numbers of moles of gas on the two sides of the equation are not the same, however, the volume of the container has a pronounced effect. For the reaction

$$H_2(g) + I_2(c) \leftrightharpoons 2HI(g)$$

the equilibrium condition is

$$\frac{p_{HI}^2}{p_{H_2}} = K_p$$

Dividing the volume by 2 doubles p_{HI} and p_{H_2}, and thus multiplies p_{HI}^2/p_{H_2} by 2. To make this reaction quotient again equal to K_p, p_{HI} must decrease and p_{H_2} increase; that is, the equilibrium shifts to the left. In general, a decrease in volume favors the side having fewer moles of gas. This is the side corresponding to smaller volume, for the volume of a solid or liquid is practically zero as compared to the volume of a gas.

Adding or subtracting a solid has no effect, as long as some of each solid involved in the reaction is still present. The vapor pressure of a pure substance is independent of the quantity present. Changing the quantity

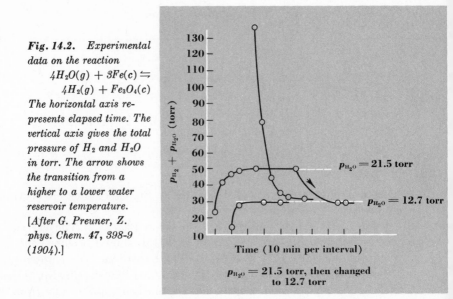

Fig. 14.2. *Experimental data on the reaction*
$$4H_2O(g) + 3Fe(c) \leftrightharpoons 4H_2(g) + Fe_3O_4(c)$$
The horizontal axis represents elapsed time. The vertical axis gives the total pressure of H_2 and H_2O in torr. The arrow shows the transition from a higher to a lower water reservoir temperature. [*After G. Preuner, Z. phys. Chem.* **47**, *398-9 (1904).*]

$p_{H_2O} = 21.5$ torr

$p_{H_2O} = 12.7$ torr

$p_{H_2} + p_{H_2O}$ (torr)

Time (10 min per interval)

$p_{H_2O} = 21.5$ torr, then changed to 12.7 torr

of a gas, however, shifts the equilibrium in the direction that counteracts the change, just as in an all-gas reaction.

The principles in this section are applicable to any reaction involving *pure solids or liquids*; these substances *are ignored in writing the equilibrium condition*. When liquid solutions or, less commonly, solid solutions are involved, the situation is more complicated, as we shall see in the next section.

14.10   EQUILIBRIUM IN SOLUTIONS

One of the first reactions to be studied in detail was the formation of an ester and water from an alcohol and an acid,

$$C_2H_5OH(l) + CH_3COOH(l) \leftrightharpoons CH_3COOC_2H_5(l) + H_2O(l)$$

ethanol   *acetic acid*   *ethyl acetate*

(an alcohol)   (an ester)

The four liquids form one solution over a wide range of compositions. If the liquids are in equilibrium, their vapors must also be in equilibrium. Otherwise, there would be a reaction among the vapors, changing their partial pressures away from the equilibrium vapor pressures. Some components would then evaporate from the liquid, and others would condense in the liquid; the composition of the liquid solution would thus change, contradicting the assumption that it was in equilibrium. For the reaction

$$C_2H_5OH(g) + CH_3COOH(g) \leftrightharpoons CH_3COOC_2H_5(g) + H_2O(g) \qquad (13)$$

the equilibrium condition is

$$\frac{p_{ester}p_{water}}{p_{ethanol}p_{acid}} = K_p \qquad (14)$$

The vapor pressures of the components of a liquid solution may be unknown or too small to be measured. It is therefore better to discuss solution equilibria in terms of quantities referring to the liquid itself, rather than to its vapor. Three such quantities are commonly used: (a) the activity, (b) the mole fraction, and (c) the molarity of each component.

(a) **Activity.** By definition (page 318),

$$a_{ester} = \frac{p_{ester}}{p^0_{ester}} = \frac{\text{vapor pressure in solution}}{\text{vapor pressure when pure}}$$

and similarly for the other three components of the solution. Equation (14) thus becomes

$$\frac{a_{ester}a_{water}}{a_{ethanol}a_{acid}} \times \frac{p^0_{ester}p^0_{water}}{p^0_{ethanol}p^0_{acid}} = K_p$$

Let

$$K_p\left(\frac{p^0_{ethanol}p^0_{acid}}{p^0_{ester}p^0_{water}}\right) = K_x$$

Then

$$\frac{a_{ester}a_{water}}{a_{ethanol}a_{acid}} = K_x \tag{15}$$

K_x is as good a constant as K_p, because the vapor pressures (p^0) of the pure substances are constant at any one temperature. Equation (15) is exactly satisfied at equilibrium. The exactness of the law of chemical equilibrium in terms of activities is the principal reason for defining these quantities. Data on vapor pressures and activities are often unavailable, however, especially for solutions with many components, and we must therefore be satisfied with useful approximations, to which we now turn.

(b) **Mole Fraction.** Suppose that the liquid solution is approximately ideal. According to Raoult's law (page 316), in an ideal solution,

$$X_{ester} = \frac{p_{ester}}{p^0_{ester}} = a_{ester}$$

where X_{ester} is the mole fraction of the ester in the solution, with similar equations for the other substances. Equation (15) can then be written

$$\frac{X_{ester}X_{water}}{X_{ethanol}X_{acid}} = K_x \tag{16}$$

An experimental test of Equation (16) is shown in Table 14.3, based on work done by Marcellin Berthelot and Péan de Saint-Gilles in 1862. They did not calculate equilibrium constants—for the law of chemical equilibrium was first stated two years later, by the Norwegians Cato Guldberg and Peter Waage—but give data from which K_x can be calculated. Their procedure was to seal the reactants in glass tubes and keep them at 100°C until equilibrium was attained, about 4 days. Acetic acid was then determined by titration (page 555), and the quantities of the other substances

TABLE 14.3 *Determination of the Equilibrium Constant of*
$C_2H_5OH(l) + CH_3COOH(l) \leftrightharpoons CH_3COOC_2H_5(l) + H_2O(l)$ *at* $100°C$

Initial relative number of moles		Final relative numbers of moles				
C_2H_5OH	CH_3COOH	C_2H_5OH	CH_3COOH	$CH_3COOC_2H_5$	H_2O	Q_x
1	1	0.335	0.335	0.665	0.665	3.94
1	2.9	0.12	2.02	0.88	0.88	3.19
2	1	1.172	0.172	0.828	0.828	3.40

could be calculated in a way to be studied later. The last column gives the reaction quotient in terms of mole fractions,

$$Q_x = \frac{X_{\text{ester}}X_{\text{water}}}{X_{\text{ethanol}}X_{\text{acid}}}$$

At equilibrium, Q_x should have the same value, K_x, for all the solutions; if we remember that chemistry was still a young science in 1862, the results are not bad.

(c) **Molarity (Concentration).** A dilute solution is one in which the quantity of every component except one—the solvent—is very small in comparison to the quantity of solvent. This is, of course, not a precise definition, and to try to make it more precise would be useless; what we consider "small" depends on the specific case in hand. We saw (page 319) that in a sufficiently dilute solution, the vapor pressure of each solute B is approximately proportional to its molarity: $p_B = k'_B[B]$ (Henry's law). Here, k'_B is a constant for a given solute, solvent, and temperature. We could just as well refer to molality or mole fraction instead of molarity, but it is customary to use molarity in discussing equilibrium in dilute solutions.

As an example, we consider the ethanol-acetic acid reaction discussed earlier, with the condition that water is the predominant constituent of the solution. In this case, we may regard ethanol, acetic acid, and ethyl acetate as solutes in a dilute solution.* The vapor pressure of each solute is given by Henry's law,

$$p_{\text{ethanol}} = k'_{\text{ethanol}}[C_2H_5OH]$$
$$p_{\text{acid}} = k'_{\text{acid}}[CH_3COOH]$$
$$p_{\text{ester}} = k'_{\text{ester}}[CH_3COOC_2H_5]$$

* To signify that this point of view is adopted, we write the reaction as

$$C_2H_5OH(aq) + CH_3COOH(aq) \leftrightharpoons CH_3COOC_2H_5(aq) + H_2O$$

The symbol *aq* means that the substance is a solute in a dilute aqueous solution.

The vapor pressure of water, the solvent, is given by Raoult's law,

$$p_{\text{water}} = p^0_{\text{water}} X_{\text{water}}$$

The equilibrium condition, in terms of partial pressures, was given in Equation (14),

$$\frac{p_{\text{ester}} p_{\text{water}}}{p_{\text{ethanol}} p_{\text{acid}}} = K_p$$

Substitution by Henry's and Raoult's laws gives

$$\frac{[\text{CH}_3\text{COOC}_2\text{H}_5] X_{\text{water}}}{[\text{C}_2\text{H}_5\text{OH}][\text{CH}_3\text{COOH}]} \times \frac{k'_{\text{ester}} p^0_{\text{water}}}{k'_{\text{ethanol}} k'_{\text{acid}}} = K_p$$

or

$$\frac{[\text{CH}_3\text{COOC}_2\text{H}_5] X_{\text{water}}}{[\text{C}_2\text{H}_5\text{OH}][\text{CH}_3\text{COOH}]} = K_c$$

where

$$K_c = K_p \frac{k'_{\text{ethanol}} k'_{\text{acid}}}{k'_{\text{ester}} p^0_{\text{water}}}$$

Since X_{water} is practically 1, we can simply write

$$\frac{[\text{CH}_3\text{COOC}_2\text{H}_5]}{[\text{C}_2\text{H}_5\text{OH}][\text{CH}_3\text{COOH}]} = K_c$$

K_c is as constant as K_p, but only as long as the solvent is water. If we were to add some seemingly innocuous solute—sodium chloride, sugar, acetone, for example—in large amount, the nature of the solvent would be changed, and we would no longer be justified in using the K_c that was applicable when the solution was mostly water.

We thus have a simple rule for writing the equilibrium condition for a reaction in dilute solution: *the molarity of each product is written in the numerator, and the molarity of each reactant in the denominator, each molarity raised to the appropriate power, except that the solvent is omitted.* We must not forget, however, that the value of the equilibrium constant depends on the nature of the solvent, and that the accuracy of the equilibrium condition is limited to the accuracy of Henry's law. When gases are also involved in the reaction, their partial pressures appear in the reaction quotient.

The principle of Le Châtelier is the same for solution reactions as for the other cases we have studied, but one point should be noted. If one of the reacting substances is a pure solid (or, less commonly, a pure liquid that does not mix with the solution), its quantity does not matter, as long as some of it is present. The situation here is the same as for solid-gas reactions. The equilibrium condition for the reaction

$$\text{AgCl}(c) \leftrightharpoons \text{Ag}^+ + \text{Cl}^-$$

is $[Ag^+][Cl^-] = K_c$; adding or removing solid AgCl has no effect on the product $[Ag^+][Cl^-]$, and therefore causes no shift in the equilibrium.

14.11 THE DISTRIBUTION LAW (OR LAW OF PARTITION)

A relatively simple process—it can hardly be called a chemical reaction—is the transfer of a solute between two immiscible (or slightly miscible) solvents. For example, ammonia dissolves in water and in chloroform, $CHCl_3$, but these two liquids are practically immiscible. If a solution of NH_3 in chloroform is shaken with water, or conversely, NH_3 molecules can be transferred from one liquid phase to the other,

$$NH_3(in\ CHCl_3) \rightleftharpoons NH_3(aq)$$

The solute is said to be **extracted** by one solvent from the other. If the solutions are dilute, the equilibrium condition is

$$\frac{[NH_3]_{H_2O}}{[NH_3]_{CHCl_3}} = K_c$$

where $[NH_3]_{H_2O}$ is the molarity of ammonia in the aqueous layer, and $[NH_3]_{CHCl_3}$ is the molarity in the chloroform layer. The equilibrium constant K_c is called the **distribution coefficient** of ammonia between water and chloroform. At 18°C, $K_c = 27.5$. We can obtain an idea of what is meant by a "dilute solution" in this case by observing that the reaction quotient is 26.5 when the aqueous solution is $1M$, 21.7 when it is $4M$, as compared to 27.5 for a very dilute solution—the only case in which the equilibrium condition holds exactly.

When the solute has a finite solubility in each solvent, the distribution coefficient is the ratio of the solubilities in the two solvents (to the approximation that the saturated solutions are "dilute"). If pure solute is in equilibrium with both solutions, they must be in equilibrium with each other; otherwise, solute would be transferred from one solution to the other, and the first would become unsaturated and the second supersaturated, contrary to the assumption that equilibrium was established. Numerator and denominator in the reaction quotient are then the solubilities in the respective solvents, and their ratio is the distribution coefficient. When the solute is completely miscible with both solvents—acetic acid with water and benzene, for example—a distribution coefficient still exists, but cannot be related to solubilities.

EXAMPLE 1   100 ml of $0.0100M$ solution of NH_3 in chloroform was shaken with 10.0 ml of water until distribution equilibrium was attained at 18°C. Find the number of moles of NH_3 remaining in the chloroform layer after extraction.

ANSWER   The chloroform layer originally contained

$$\frac{100\ \text{ml}}{1000\ \dfrac{\text{ml}}{\text{liter}}} \times 0.0100\ \frac{\text{mole}}{\text{liter}} = 0.00100\ \text{mole}\ NH_3$$

Let x be the number of moles of NH_3 remaining in the chloroform layer after extraction; the number of moles extracted by the water must be $0.00100 - x$. The molarity of NH_3 in the aqueous layer is then

$$\frac{(0.00100 - x) \text{ mole}}{0.0100 \text{ liter}} = 0.100 - 100x \frac{\text{mole}}{\text{liter}} = [NH_3]_{H_2O}$$

The molarity in the chloroform layer is

$$\frac{x \text{ mole}}{0.100 \text{ liter}} = 10.0x \frac{\text{mole}}{\text{liter}} = [NH_3]_{CHCl_3}$$

(We assume that the volumes of the two liquid phases are unaffected by the transfer of NH_3.) The equilibrium condition is

$$\frac{[NH_3]_{H_2O}}{[NH_3]_{CHCl_3}} = 27.5$$

or

$$\frac{0.100 - 100x}{10.0x} = 27.5$$

$$0.100 - 100x = 275x$$

$$x = 2.67 \times 10^{-4} \text{ mole}$$

When the molecular weight of the solute is the same in the two solvents, as here, the concentrations can be expressed in grams (or any other mass unit) per milliliter (or any other volume unit) and the distribution coefficient will be unaffected, as long as the same units are used in numerator and denominator.

14.12 EQUILIBRIUM CALCULATIONS

The most important calculation involving equilibria is, of course, the calculation of the equilibrium constant. When the values at equilibrium of all the partial pressures, mole fractions, or molarities are known, this calculation involves merely a substitution of the numbers into the reaction quotient. More commonly, however, what we know is the initial quantity of each reactant or product, and the final quantity of some one substance. Conversely, we may know the equilibrium constant at some fixed temperature, and wish to find the equilibrium quantities of the reacting substances when the initial quantities are given. Methods of performing such calculations as these are the subject of this section.

In the reaction

$$2SO_2 + O_2 \rightleftharpoons 2SO_3$$

the equation tells us that, for every mole of O_2 consumed, 2 moles of SO_2 must also be consumed, and 2 moles of SO_3 must be produced. Conversely, if the reaction goes from right to left, 2 moles of SO_2 and 1 mole of O_2 must be produced for every 2 moles of SO_3 consumed. We can start with any amounts; let us introduce 3.00 moles SO_3, with no SO_2 or O_2, into a container of fixed volume. We do not know how much of the SO_3 will have been consumed when equilibrium is attained, nor do we know how much SO_2 and O_2 will have been formed, but we do know the ratios of these quantities. The balanced equation says that 1 mole of SO_3 gives 1 mole of SO_2 and $\frac{1}{2}$ mole of O_2. Let x be the number of moles of O_2 produced; then $2x$ is the number of moles of SO_2 produced, and $2x$ is the number of moles of SO_3 consumed. The numbers of moles present at equilibrium are SO_2, $2x$; O_2, x; SO_3, $3.00 - 2x$:

	$2SO_2$	$+ O_2$	$\rightleftharpoons 2SO_3$
Initial moles	0	0	3.00
Change	$2x$	x	$2x$
Final moles	$0 + 2x$	$0 + x$	$3.00 - 2x$

Suppose that we find, by experiment, that the quantity of O_2 present at equilibrium is 0.95 mole. Then $x = 0.95$; the numbers of moles of the other gases are $2x = 1.90$ moles for SO_2, $3.00 - 2x = 1.10$ moles for SO_3. If we also know the volume V of the container and the temperature T, we can calculate the partial pressure p of each gas by the equation $p = nRT/V$. For $V = 8.00$ liters and $T = 1105°K$, the partial pressure of O_2 is

$$p_{O_2} = \frac{0.95RT}{V} = \frac{0.95 \text{ mole} \times \left(0.08206 \frac{\text{liter atm}}{\text{deg mole}}\right) \times 1105 \text{ deg}}{8.00 \text{ liter}}$$

$$= 10.8 \text{ atm}$$

Similarly,

$$p_{SO_2} = 1.90RT/V = 21.6 \text{ atm}$$
$$p_{SO_3} = 1.10RT/V = 12.5 \text{ atm}$$

Then

$$K_p = \frac{p_{SO_3}^2}{p_{SO_2}^2 p_{O_2}} = \frac{12.5^2}{21.6^2 \times 10.8} = 0.0310$$

When the volume of the container in a gas reaction (or the volume of the solution in a dilute-solution reaction) is fixed, one can dispense with knowledge of this volume by knowing the initial partial pressures (or molarities), rather than numbers of moles. Assume that the partial pressures of the gases are, initially, SO_2, 0; O_2, 0; SO_3, 2.00 atm. Since, for each gas, $p = nRT/V$, and T and V are constant, changes in the p's must stand in the same ratio as changes in the n's. Thus, if x moles of O_2 are formed, $2x$ moles of SO_3 must be consumed. The partial pressure of O_2 is $y = xRT/V$. The partial pressure of SO_3 decreases by $2y$, to $2.00 - 2y$ atm. Similarly, $2x$ moles of SO_2 are formed, and $p_{SO_2} = 2y$. The equilibrium condition is then

$$\frac{p_{SO_3}^2}{p_{SO_2}^2 p_{O_2}} = \frac{(2.00 - 2y)^2}{(2y)^2(y)} = K_p$$

EXAMPLE 2   At 801°K, the equilibrium constant for the reaction

$$2SO_2(g) + O_2(g) \rightleftharpoons 2SO_3(g)$$

is $K_p = 982$, with pressures in atmospheres. A mixture of SO_2, O_2, and SO_3 was prepared in which the initial partial pressures at 801°K were 2.00 atm for O_2 and 1.00 atm for SO_3. No SO_2 was present. A catalyst was then introduced into the mixture, and the reaction allowed to come to equilibrium at constant temperature and volume. Find the final partial pressure of each gas.

ANSWER   We see at once that the reaction must go from right to left. (Why?) The final partial pressures may be represented as

$$
\begin{array}{ccccc}
2SO_2 & + & O_2 & \rightleftharpoons & 2SO_3 \\
(0 + 2x) & & (2 + x) & & (1 - 2x) \text{ atm}
\end{array}
$$

If x is the increase in partial pressure of O_2, the changes in the partial pressures of SO_2 and SO_3 must be $+2x$ and $-2x$, respectively. The equilibrium condition is

$$\frac{p_{SO_3}^2}{p_{SO_2}^2 p_{O_2}} = K_p$$

$$\frac{(1 - 2x)^2}{(2x)^2(2 + x)} = 982 \tag{17}$$

This is a cubic equation; to avoid having to solve it by trial and error, we seek some reasonable approximation. Because 982 is a large number, the denominator must be much less than 1, as it can be only if x is small. Let us assume that $2x \ll 1$. (The symbol $\ll$ means "is much less than," with the implication that the smaller quantity can be neglected.) Equation (17) then becomes

$$\frac{1}{(2x)^2(2)} = 982 \tag{18}$$

If the value of $2x$ obtained in solving Equation (18) is in fact negligible as compared to 1, we can be confident that we have found the value of x which satisfies Equation (17); on being substituted into the equations, such a small x must give to the left member of Equation (17) practically the same value that it gives to the left member of Equation (18). Solving Equation (18),

$$(2x)^2 = \frac{1}{2 \times 982} = 5.09 \times 10^{-4}$$

$$2x = \pm 0.0226$$

$$x = \pm 0.0113$$

The negative root must be rejected, for it would make the partial pressure of SO_2 negative. Then

$$p_{SO_2} = 2x = 0.023 \text{ atm}$$

$$p_{O_2} = 2 + x = 2.01 \text{ atm}$$

$$p_{SO_3} = 1 - 2x = 0.98 \text{ atm}$$

Whether 0.023 can be neglected in comparison to 1 depends on what accuracy we demand. The ideal gas law is in error by roughly 1% at ordinary conditions (less at the high temperature of this problem), and there is therefore not much point in pushing beyond 1 or 2% accuracy an equilibrium calculation based on the assumption that the gases are ideal. In the example above, accurate solution of the cubic equation gives $x = 0.0110$; p_{SO_2} is thus changed to 0.022 atm, and the other pressures are essentially unaltered.

EXAMPLE 3   **In one of their experiments, Berthelot and Saint-Gilles mixed ethanol, acetic acid, and water in the ratio of 1.00 mole, 1.00 mole, and 7.50 moles. They reported that, at equilibrium, 25% of the acetic acid had been consumed. Use this result to calculate the equilibrium constant K_x for the reaction**

$$C_2H_5OH + CH_3COOH \leftrightharpoons CH_3COOC_2H_5 + H_2O$$

ANSWER   **We can fix our attention on any specific quantity of solution; we consider that quantity which contained, initially, one mole of ethanol and one mole of acetic acid. At equilibrium, 25% of the acid, or 0.25 mole, had been consumed; therefore, 0.25 mole of ethanol must also have been consumed, while 0.25 mole each of the ester and of water had been formed:**

	Ethanol	Acid	Ester	Water
Moles present initially	**1.00**	**1.00**	**0**	**7.5**
Moles present at equilibrium	**0.75**	**0.75**	**0.25**	**7.75**
Mole fraction at equilibrium	**$\dfrac{0.75}{9.50}$**	**$\dfrac{0.75}{9.50}$**	**$\dfrac{0.25}{9.50}$**	**$\dfrac{7.75}{9.50}$**

and

$$K_x = \frac{X_{ester}X_{water}}{X_{ethanol}X_{acid}} = \frac{(0.25)(7.75)}{(0.75)(0.75)} = 3.44$$

(Observe that the total number of moles, 9.50, drops out in this special case.)

Problems

1. Form of equilibrium condition.   Write the equilibrium condition for each of the following reactions:

(a) $\qquad\qquad CO(g) + \tfrac{1}{2}O_2(g) \leftrightharpoons CO_2(g)$
(b) $\qquad\qquad 2Cl_2(g) + 2H_2O(g) \leftrightharpoons 4HCl(g) + O_2(g)$
(c) $\qquad\qquad C(c) + CO_2(g) \leftrightharpoons 2CO(g)$
(d) $\qquad\qquad NH_4HS(c) \leftrightharpoons NH_3(g) + H_2S(g)$
(e) $\quad C_6H_5COOH(l) + C_2H_5OH(l) \leftrightharpoons C_6H_5COOC_2H_5(l) + H_2O(l)$
$\qquad$ (Assume that the solution is ideal but not dilute)
(f) $\qquad\quad H_2C_4H_2O_4(aq) + H_2O(l) \leftrightharpoons H_2C_4H_4O_5(aq)$

2. Principle of Le Châtelier. For the reaction

$$2Cl_2(g) + 2H_2O(g) \rightleftharpoons 4HCl(g) + O_2(g) \qquad \Delta H = +27 \text{ kcal}$$

The four gases Cl_2, H_2O, HCl, and O_2 are mixed and the reaction is allowed to come to equilibrium. State and explain the effect (increase, decrease, no change) of the operation in the left column (below) on the equilibrium value of the quantity in the right column. Each operation is to be considered separately. Temperature and volume are constant except when the contrary is stated.

(a) Increasing the volume of the container	Number of moles of H_2O
(b) Adding O_2	Number of moles of H_2O
(c) Adding O_2	Number of moles of O_2
(d) Adding O_2	Number of moles of HCl
(e) Decreasing the volume of the container	Number of moles of Cl_2
(f) Decreasing the volume of the container	Partial pressure of Cl_2
(g) Decreasing the volume of the container	K_p
(h) Raising the temperature	K_p
(i) Raising the temperature	Number of moles of HCl
(j) Adding He	Number of moles of HCl
(k) Adding catalyst	Number of moles of HCl

3. Combination of equilibria. Given the following equilibrium constants at 1476°K:

$$CO(g) + \tfrac{1}{2}O_2(g) \rightleftharpoons CO_2(g) \qquad K_p = 2.5 \ \times 10^5$$
$$C(\text{graphite}) + CO_2(g) \rightleftharpoons 2CO(g) \qquad K_p = 1.67 \times 10^3$$

Find K_p for the reaction

$$C(\text{graphite}) + O_2 \rightleftharpoons CO_2(g)$$

at 1476°K.

Answer. 1.04×10^{14}.

4. Calculation of equilibrium constant. At 503°K, 3.00 moles NO, 2.00 moles Cl_2, and 5.00 moles ClNO were introduced into a 25.0 liter container. When the reaction

$$2NO(g) + Cl_2(g) \rightleftharpoons 2ClNO(g)$$

had come to equilibrium, there were 6.12 moles of ClNO in the container. Find (a) the number of moles of Cl_2 present at equilibrium; (b) K_p for the reaction.

5. Gas equilibrium. 1.00 mole H_2O was placed in an otherwise empty, closed container of the fixed volume 100 liters. The container was heated to 2642°K, at which temperature the equilibrium constant for the reaction

$$2H_2O(g) \rightleftharpoons 2H_2(g) + O_2(g)$$

is $K_p = 4.21 \times 10^{-5}$. Find (a) K_c (in terms of molar concentrations) for this reaction; (b) the number of moles of O_2 present in the container at 2642°K.

Answer. (a) 1.94×10^{-7}; (b) 1.68×10^{-2} mole.

6. Solid-gas equilibrium. At 24°C, the equilibrium constant K_p for the reaction

$$NH_4HS(c) \rightleftharpoons NH_3(g) + H_2S(g)$$

is 0.094. (a) Solid NH_4HS was introduced into an otherwise empty container and allowed to come to equilibrium with its gaseous decomposition products at 24°C. Find the total pressure of the gas mixture at equilibrium. (b) Find the equilibrium partial pressure of H_2S in a similar experiment in which NH_4HS was introduced into a container of fixed volume which also contained NH_3 at an initial pressure of 0.50 atm.

7. Dilute-solution equilibrium. The following equilibrium is established in the presence of water and a certain enzyme:

$$H_2C_4H_2O_4(aq) + H_2O \rightleftharpoons H_2C_4H_4O_5(aq)$$
fumaric acid   malic acid

One liter of solution was prepared from water and 0.100 mole of pure malic acid. At equilibrium, the solution contained 0.022 mole of fumaric acid, in addition to some unchanged malic acid. Find the equilibrium constant K_c for the reaction, treating the solution as dilute.

Answer. 3.5.

8. Distribution law. When an aqueous solution of Br_2 is shaken with CCl_4 (a liquid immiscible with H_2O) at 25°C until equilibrium is attained, the final ratio of the molarity of Br_2 in the aqueous solution to the molarity of Br_2 in the CCl_4 solution is 0.035. Find the volume of CCl_4 that must be shaken with 25 ml of an aqueous solution of Br_2 in order to extract 90% of the Br_2 from the aqueous layer.

Additional problems

9. Combination of equilibria. Given the following equilibrium constants at 1362°K:

$$H_2(g) + \tfrac{1}{2}S_2(g) \rightleftharpoons H_2S(g) \qquad\qquad K_p = 0.80$$
$$H_2(g) + Br_2(g) \rightleftharpoons 2HBr(g) \qquad\qquad K_p = 7.2 \times 10^4$$

Find K_p for the reaction

$$Br_2(g) + H_2S(g) \rightleftharpoons 2HBr(g) + \tfrac{1}{2}S_2(g)$$

10. Calculation of equilibrium constant. CO_2 was passed over graphite at 1323°K. The emerging gas stream consisted of 0.74 mole % CO_2 and 99.26 mole % CO. The total pressure was 2.00 atm throughout. Find K_p for the reaction

$$C(\text{graphite}) + CO_2(g) \rightleftharpoons 2CO(g)$$

Answer. 2.7 × 10².

11. Gas equilibrium. The equilibrium constant K_p of the reaction

$$H_2(g) + I_2(g) \rightleftharpoons 2HI(g)$$

is 66.5 at 633°K and 50.7 at 713°K. (a) Is ΔH for this reaction positive or negative? (b) What is K_c for the reaction at 633°K? (c) Find K_p for the reaction

$$\tfrac{1}{2}H_2(g) + \tfrac{1}{2}I_2(g) \rightleftharpoons HI(g)$$

at 633°K. (d) Pure HI is placed in a container of constant volume and heated to 713°K. What fraction of the HI is decomposed to H_2 and I_2 at equilibrium? Is any superfluous information given in (d)?

Answer. (b) 66.5; (c) 8.15; (d) 0.219.

12. Gas equilibrium. At 1557.8°K, the equilibrium constant of the reaction

$$Br_2(g) \rightleftharpoons 2Br(g)$$

is $K_p = 0.133$. Find the percentage of Br_2 that is dissociated into atoms when 0.010 mole of Br_2 is confined in a 1.0-liter container and heated to 1557.8°K.

13. Gas equilibrium. At 1170°K, the equilibrium constant of the reaction

$$2SO_2(g) + O_2(g) \rightleftharpoons 2SO_3(g)$$

is $K_p = 0.128$. SO_2 and O_2 were mixed in a container of fixed volume so that their partial pressures at 1170°K were, initially, 1.00 atm for SO_2 and 0.50 atm for O_2. Find the partial pressure of SO_3 at equilibrium. (Suggestion: use a systematic procedure of trial and error or successive approximations.)

Answer. 0.19 atm.

14. Heterogeneous equilibrium. The equilibrium constant for the reaction

$$H_2(g) + Br_2(l) \rightleftharpoons 2HBr(g)$$

is $K_p = 4.5 \times 10^{18}$ at 25°C. The vapor pressure of liquid Br_2 at this temperature is 0.28 atm. Assume that the gases do not dissolve in the liquid. (a) Find K_p at 25°C for the reaction

$$H_2(g) + Br_2(g) \rightleftharpoons 2HBr(g)$$

(b) How will the equilibrium in (a) be shifted by a decrease in the volume of the container if (i) liquid Br_2 is absent, (ii) liquid Br_2 is present? Explain why the effect is different in the two cases.

15. Solid-gas equilibrium. At −10°C, the solid compound $Br_2(H_2O)_{10}$ is in equilibrium with gaseous bromine and ice. The partial pressures of the two gases in equilibrium with a mixture of $Br_2(H_2O)_{10}$ and ice are 0.30 atm for Br_2, 0.00262 atm for water vapor. Find the equilibrium constant K_p for the reaction

(a) $Br_2(H_2O)_{10}(c) \rightleftharpoons Br_2(g) + 10H_2O(g)$

and the reaction

(b) $Br_2(H_2O)_{10}(c) \rightleftharpoons Br_2(g) + 10H_2O(c)$

Answer. (a) 4.6×10^{-27}; (b) 0.30.

16. Solid-gas equilibrium. Calculate K_p for the reaction

$$4H_2O(g) + 3Fe(c) \rightleftharpoons 4H_2(g) + Fe_3O_4(c)$$

from the data in Fig. 14.2. Use both values of p_{H_2O}.

17. Solution equilibrium. When 1.00 mole benzoic acid, C_6H_5COOH, and 3.00 moles ethanol, C_2H_5OH, are mixed and kept at 200°C (under sufficient pressure to prevent vaporization) until equilibrium is attained, it is found that 87% of the acid is consumed by the reaction

$$C_6H_5COOH(l) + C_2H_5OH(l) \rightleftharpoons C_6H_5COOC_2H_5(l) + H_2O(l)$$

(a) Find the equilibrium constant K_x for this reaction. (b) Find the percentage of the acid that would be consumed if 1.00 mole benzoic acid and 4.00 moles ethanol were mixed and treated in the same way.

18. Distribution law. The solubility of I_2 in H_2O is 0.029 g/100 ml at 20°C; its solubility in diethyl ether, $(C_2H_5)_2O$, is 21 g/100 ml at 20°C. Assume that water and ether are immiscible. (a) Find the distribution coefficient of I_2 between water (numerator) and ether (denominator). Is it necessary to convert the solubilities to other units before making this calculation? Why or why not? (b) 50 ml of a saturated aqueous solution of I_2 was extracted with 20 ml of ether. Find the weight of I_2 remaining in the aqueous layer. (c) 50 ml of a saturated aqueous solution of I_2 was extracted with two consecutive 10-ml portions of ether. Find the weight of I_2 remaining in the aqueous layer. (d) Which method of extraction, (b) or (c), is to be recommended?

Answer. (a) 0.0014; (b) 5.0×10^{-5} g; (c) 6.8×10^{-7} g

15
Ionic
solutions

15.1 ELECTRICAL CONDUCTANCE

As long ago as the eighteenth century, certain aqueous solutions were found to have a special property not shared by the pure solutes, by water, or by most other liquids: these solutions easily conduct electricity. Solutes that show this property are of the kinds known as acids, bases, and salts. The first rough measurements of the conductivities of such solutions were made by Henry Cavendish in 1777: he compared the lengths of different solutions through which the discharge of a battery of Leyden jars gave equal shocks. More recent data, obtained by more accurate and less heroic methods, on the conductivities (page 379) of solutions, in comparison to other conductors and insulators, are shown in Table 15.1.

The solutions are rather poor conductors in comparison to the metals, although far from being in the same category as the insulators. It is

TABLE 15.1 *Conductivities at Room Temperature (in ohm^{-1} cm^{-1})*

Metals		Aqueous solutions		Insulators	
Ag	6.1×10^5	0.1M HCl	3.5×10^{-2}	H_2O (pure)	6×10^{-8}
Cu	5.8×10^5	0.1M KCl	1.1×10^{-2}	Maple wood	3×10^{-11}
Fe	1.0×10^5	0.1M NaCl	9.2×10^{-3}	Glass	10^{-14}
Hg	1.0×10^4	0.1M CH$_3$COOH	4.7×10^{-4}	Hard rubber	10^{-15}
C^a	1.2×10^3	0.1M NH$_3$	3.1×10^{-4}		

^{a} **Graphite. Carbon is not a metal, but the electrical properties of graphite are similar to those of metals.**

noteworthy that the conductivity of a solution increases sharply with increasing temperature, whereas the conductivity of a metal decreases as the temperature increases.

There is another striking difference between the solutions and the metals in behavior as conductors. When a current is passed through a copper wire, the copper is entirely unaffected by this process. The same wire can carry a current for years or decades. Of course, the wire will become hot, and may melt if too large a current passes through, but such an effect is attributable to the heat and not directly to the electricity. On the other hand, when a direct current* is passed through a solution of, say, NaCl, gases are evolved at the electrodes (the metallic conductors in contact with the solution), and the chemical composition of the solution near the electrodes changes. It seems that the mere passage of an electric current into, and out of, such a conducting solution must be accompanied by a chemical reaction—gas evolution is a common, but not universal, feature of these reactions. Such a pair of reactions (one at each electrode), caused by electricity, is called **electrolysis.** A conductor in which a current is accompanied by electrolysis is called an **electrolytic conductor;** a solute that can be dissolved in a suitable solvent (usually water) to give an electrically conducting solution is an **electrolyte.** Many electrolytes conduct not only when dissolved, but also when melted.

15.2   **COLLIGATIVE PROPERTIES OF SOLUTIONS OF ELECTROLYTES**

Another peculiarity of solutions of electrolytes was discovered in 1884 by François Marie Raoult, of vapor-pressure fame. He observed that the freezing-point depression in an aqueous solution of NaCl is almost twice what one would expect from the molality of the solution. The atomic weights of Na and Cl are 23.0 and 35.5, respectively; the molecular weight of NaCl clearly cannot be less than 58.5 g/mole. If we dissolve 58.5 g of NaCl in 1000 g of water, the solution is 1.00 molal, and we expect it to freeze approximately 1.86° below the freezing point of pure water (page 325). The actual freezing point is $-3.37°C$. In the case of zinc chloride, $ZnCl_2$, the freezing-point depression is nearly three times as great as we would calculate from its formula weight. The more dilute the solution, the more nearly is the depression equal to twice or three times the calculated value. The ratio of the observed to the calculated value of the freezing-point depression is called the **van't Hoff factor,** and is represented by i. Table 15.2 illustrates how i depends on molality for several typical electrolytes.

Similar magnifications are found for the other colligative properties: boiling-point elevation, vapor-pressure depression, and osmotic pressure are all multiplied by the same integral factor in dilute solutions of an electrolyte. The conclusion is inescapable: what is present in the solution

* With an alternating current, the reaction that occurs in each half-cycle is undone in the next half-cycle, unless the frequency is so low that gas can escape before the current reverses.

TABLE 15.2 *Freezing-Point Depressions of Aqueous Solutions of Electrolytes*

Molality (m) $\left(\dfrac{moles}{kg\ H_2O}\right)$	Calculated freezing-point depression (°C) (1.86m)	van't Hoff factor $\left(i = \dfrac{(t_f - t'_f)_{measured}}{(t_f - t'_f)_{calculated}}\right)$		
		NaCl	ZnCl₂	MgSO₄
0.00100	0.00186	1.97		1.82
0.0100	0.0186	1.94	2.77	1.53
0.100	0.186	1.87	2.66	1.21
1.00	1.86	1.81	2.80	1.09

is not NaCl molecules, or ZnCl₂ molecules, but individual Na and Cl particles, or Zn and Cl particles. In a MgSO₄ solution, however, the colligative properties are multiplied by 2, not by 6, so that this substance must dissociate not into Mg, S, and four O's, but into two fragments—probably Mg and SO₄, since the SO₄ group turns up in many compounds and is undoubtedly a stable entity.

15.3 ELECTRONIC CONDUCTION

It has been known since the discovery of the electron that an electric current in a metal is a flow of electrons. In a metal, the inner electrons of each atom remain with their own nucleus, but one or more outer electrons from each atom are shared by all the atoms (page 705), and these **conduction electrons** are free to move through the metal under the influence of an electric field. The nuclei do not migrate in this process. Every electron leaving the metal at one end is replaced by an identical electron entering at the other end. This type of conduction is called **electronic (metallic) conduction,** and it can continue indefinitely without producing observable change in the metal.

15.4 IONIC CONDUCTION

The remarkable properties of solutions of electrolytes can be understood if the solute is assumed to be present in the form of charged particles— **ions.** When an electric field is applied to a liquid containing ions, the positive ions will move toward the electrode with a negative charge, and the negative ions will move toward the electrode with a positive charge (Fig. 15.1). Such a motion of charges constitutes an electric current. In a metal, the only mobile charged particles are negative electrons, but, in the solution, both positive and negative ions are present. The motion of a positive charge in one direction fulfills the same purpose in conducting a current as the motion of a negative charge in the other direction. We

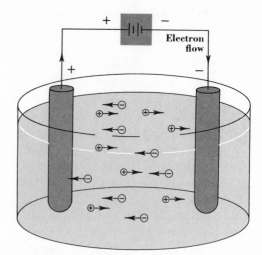

Fig. 15.1. *The motion of ions in an electric field.*

say that the metal contains charge carriers of only one sign, while the solution contains carriers of both signs. The temperature dependence of the conductivity of a solution is consistent with this picture; since the viscosity of a liquid decreases with increasing temperature, the ions can more easily make their way through the solution at a higher temperature, and the conductivity should increase with increasing temperature, as it does.

A simple and striking demonstration that ions are present in an electrolytic conductor is provided by a solution of copper(II) dichromate. An aqueous solution of this compound is green. Place such a solution in the bottom of a U-tube, with a colorless electrolytic solution (e.g., NaCl) in each arm, taking care to have as little mixing as possible (Fig. 15.2a). Now pass a direct current through the tube. After a time, a layer of blue-green solution appears on the side of the tube into which electrons are being fed, and a layer of orange solution appears on the side from which electrons are being withdrawn (Fig. 15.2b). The blue-green color is the usual color of copper salts in aqueous solution, and moves in the direction expected of a positive ion; the orange color is characteristic of dichromates ($K_2Cr_2O_7$, for example), and moves in the direction expected of a negative ion. It thus seems clear that the solution of $CuCr_2O_7$ contains positive copper ions and negative dichromate ions. The copper ion is known (page 376) to be doubly charged (Cu^{2+}), and the dichromate ion must therefore be $Cr_2O_7^{2-}$ in order for the solid salt and the solution to be electrically neutral.

When an ion reaches an electrode, its journey ends. In the simplest cases, a negative ion gives up one or more electrons to the electrode to which it moved, and a positive ion accepts one or more electrons from the other electrode. (Other possibilities will be discussed later, page 372.) When, for example, a solution of $CuBr_2$ is electrolyzed by a direct current

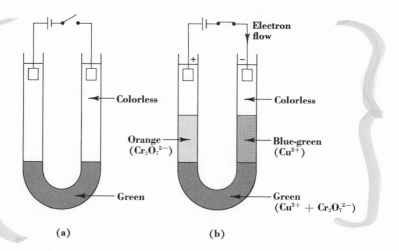

Fig. 15.2. *An experiment demonstrating migration of ions. (a) Before the current has begun to flow, the colored ions are intermingled in the bottom of the tube. (b) After current has flowed for some time, the positive copper ions (blue-green) have moved toward one electrode, and the negative dichromate ions (orange) toward the other.*

between unreactive electrodes such as platinum, copper is deposited on one electrode, while bromine, as a red gas or liquid, appears at the other. These processes are represented, respectively, as

$$Cu^{2+} + 2e^- \rightarrow Cu$$

and

$$2Br^- \rightarrow Br_2 + 2e^-$$

Such a transfer of electrons to or from a chemical species changes it into a new species, and thus constitutes a chemical reaction—specifically, an **oxidation-reduction reaction** (pages 207 and 367). The chemical changes associated with electrolytic conduction are thus consistent with the theory that the solute is present as ions.

It should be emphasized that every part of the solution remains electrically neutral during conduction. We shall see later (page 373) how ion migration and the electrode reactions combine to maintain this neutrality.

15.5 SOLVATION OF IONS

When Svante Arrhenius proposed this **theory of electrolytic dissociation** in 1887, most chemists greeted it with less than enthusiasm. The principal objection was that forces between charged particles are very strong, and it seemed implausible that, in solution, these particles would be separated from each other and free to move independently. An explanation is suggested by the fact that the solvents in which electrolytic conduction is observed—such as water, liquid NH_3, and liquid SO_2—consist of molecules with large dipole moments (page 294). An ion attracts the oppositely charged ends of such solvent molecules almost as strongly as it attracts another ion. The ions are said to be **solvated**, or, when the solvent is water, **hydrated** (page 296). Solvation sometimes involves the formation of covalent bonds between the ion and the adjacent solvent molecules, in addition to simple electrostatic attraction. Solvation is an exothermic process, corresponding to a decrease in energy. The effect of solvation is that the state in which the ions are separated by solvent becomes nearly as low in energy as the state in which they are combined to form neutral molecules or a crystalline ionic solid. For each ionic crystal, there is a certain concentration of its ions (in a given solvent at a given temperature) at which the solution and the crystal are equally stable; this concentration is the solubility (page 304) of the substance, and corresponds to a state of equilibrium in a process such as

$$KCl(c) \leftrightharpoons K^+(aq) + Cl^-(aq)$$

or

$$Ag_2SO_4(c) \leftrightharpoons 2Ag^+(aq) + SO_4^{2-}(aq)$$

15.6 DIELECTRIC CONSTANT

When two charged bodies are immersed in a material medium, the force between them is less than it would be in a vacuum by a factor $1/D$, where D is the **dielectric constant** of the medium (page 784). The reason for the diminution of the force is that described in the last paragraph. If the molecules of the medium are polar and are free to rotate, they are predominantly aligned with their negative ends adjacent to a positively charged body, so that there is a layer of negative charge just outside the positive body; the effect is to cancel part of the charge on the body. Similarly, there is a layer of positive charge just outside a negatively charged body. Even if the molecules are not polar (or are unable to rotate, as in most solids), the dielectric constant is greater than 1, because dipoles are induced in the molecules, such that the end of a molecule adjacent to a positively charged body is negative, and conversely. We may say that the charged bodies are **shielded** from each other by the medium. We expect, therefore, that liquids with high dielectric constants—the same ones that have the most polar molecules—will be the most effective in decreasing the forces between separated ions and will thus be the best solvents for ionic crystals. The best solvent is water, which has the very high dielectric constant 78.5 at 25°; other ionizing solvents, with their dielectric constants, are NH_3, 22 (at $-34°$); HCN, 116; CH_3OH, 33; SO_2, 15.6. Nonpolar (and slightly polar) molecules, on the other hand, have much lower dielectric constants, e.g., benzene, C_6H_6, 2.27; CCl_4, 2.24; CS_2, 2.65; diethyl ether, $(C_2H_5)_2O$, 4.34. Ionic salts seldom have appreciable solubility in these solvents.

More recent support for the Arrhenius theory has come from two sources. The modern theory of atomic and molecular structure suggests that many ions should be quite stable (pages 206–208). For example, sodium has 11 electrons; if it loses one to form Na^+, it has 10 electrons, like Ne. Magnesium attains the neon configuration by losing two electrons. The first ionization energy (page 192) of Na, and the first and second ionization energies of Mg, are comparatively small, so that Na can lose one electron, and Mg can lose two. Similarly, polyatomic ions often have closed-shell structures, with each atom surrounded by an octet of electrons (a duet for H). Examples of such stable ions are

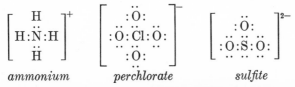

ammonium   perchlorate   sulfite

The other evidence for ionization is provided by x-ray crystallography. Many electrolytes exist in the pure state as crystals in which the ions are arranged in an orderly array, positive and negative alternately (page 209). In such crystals, there is no such thing as a molecule, unless the whole crystal is regarded as one giant molecule. When an ionic crystal dissolves in an ionizing solvent, there is no need for existing molecules to dissociate into ions; the "ionization" really takes place when the crystal is formed from its elements, not when it dissolves. The existence of ions in the crystal makes it seem more reasonable that ions can also exist in solution.

15.8 COVALENT ELECTROLYTES

Ionic crystals are not the only solutes that yield ions in solution. Some covalent molecules react with the solvent to give ions, usually by the transfer of a proton from one molecule to the other. An example is hydrogen chloride, which is a gas under ordinary conditions and consists of covalently bonded molecules. When it is dissolved in water, the reaction

$$HCl + H_2O \rightarrow H_3O^+ + Cl^-$$

produces the **hydronium** or **hydrogen** ion, H_3O^+,* and the chloride ion, Cl^-. Similarly, another gas, ammonia, reacts with water, not by giving it a proton, but by taking one away,

$$NH_3 + H_2O \leftrightharpoons NH_4^+ + OH^-$$

A proton donor, as HCl, is called an **acid**; a proton acceptor, as NH_3, is a **base.** Acids and bases will be discussed in detail in Chapters 17–19.

* One theory is that the proton (H^+) is equidistant from the oxygen ends of three water molecules: $[H(OH_2)_3]^+$. Another theory is that three protons are covalently bonded to an oxygen atom, and each is hydrogen-bonded to the oxygen end of a water molecule: $[OH_3(OH_2)_3]^+$. We shall represent this ion by H^+ or H_3O^+, without claiming that either formula depicts its actual structure.

15.9 NET IONIC EQUATIONS

As soon as we recognize that ions exist in solution as more or less independent chemical species, it becomes natural to write chemical equations
in terms of ions, as we have written them in this and previous chapters.
In order to decide when to write an equation in ionic form, we must
recognize which substances exist primarily as ions—that is, which substances are strong electrolytes (page 383). The custom is to represent
each substance involved in a reaction by the formula corresponding to
the form in which most of it exists. Thus, we write the reaction between
hydrochloric acid and ammonia, in aqueous solution, as

$$H_3O^+ + Cl^- + NH_3 \rightarrow NH_4^+ + Cl^- + H_2O \tag{1}$$

The strong acid HCl is represented as $H_3O^+ + Cl^-$, since it is almost
completely ionized. Ammonium chloride, NH_4Cl, is a strong (completely ionized) salt, and is therefore written as the two distinct species,
$NH_4^+ + Cl^-$. Ammonia and water, on the other hand, are weak electrolytes (page 386) and are represented by their molecular formulas,
NH_3 and H_2O. If the acid were acetic acid, which is weak, the equation
would be

$$CH_3COOH + NH_3 \rightarrow NH_4^+ + CH_3COO^-$$

The weak acid is represented by its molecular formula, CH_3COOH; the
product, ammonium acetate, is a typical strong salt and is written in
terms of ions.

Inspection of Equation (1) shows that a further simplification is possible. Cl^- appears on both sides, which means that it was present initially
and is not changed by the reaction. Any species remaining unchanged
can be omitted from a chemical equation. Equation (1) can therefore be
replaced by

$$H_3O^+ + NH_3 \rightarrow NH_4^+ + H_2O \tag{2}$$

Equation (2) is called a **net ionic equation** because superfluous species
have been omitted, leaving only those that actually participate in the
reaction. We know that negative ions must be present to keep the solution
electrically neutral, but Equation (2) does not tell us what they are, nor
do we necessarily care. The reaction is the same whether the acid is
hydrochloric, nitric, hydrobromic, or perchloric, as long as it is a strong
acid. Only when the solution is evaporated, to obtain a solid product, does
the identity of the acid make a difference; the solid product obtained
will then be NH_4Cl, NH_4NO_3, NH_4Br, or NH_4ClO_4, depending on which
acid is used.

Solids, including ionic crystals, and gases are represented by their
molecular formulas. For example, when solutions of the strong salts KCl
and $AgNO_3$ are mixed, a white precipitate of silver chloride, AgCl, is
formed. We write the formulas of the soluble salts in ionic form, but AgCl,
which is present almost entirely as the solid, is represented as AgCl,

$$K^+ + Cl^- + Ag^+ + NO_3^- \rightarrow AgCl(c) + K^+ + NO_3^-$$

This equation is not yet a net equation. K^+ and NO_3^- appear on both sides and may be omitted,

$$Cl^- + Ag^+ \rightarrow AgCl(c)$$

This form of the equation emphasizes that the only real chemical change is the combination of Ag^+ and Cl^- ions. A reaction involving the other two ions will occur only if the final solution is evaporated; when it becomes sufficiently concentrated, KNO_3 will precipitate,

$$K^+ + NO_3^- \rightarrow KNO_3(c)$$

15.10 BALANCING OXIDATION-REDUCTION EQUATIONS BY THE ION-ELECTRON METHOD

Equations for oxidation-reduction (redox) reactions are often difficult to balance. The method to be described in this section is especially appropriate for reactions involving ions in solution. The principle underlying this method is that the reaction can be resolved, on paper, into two parts, or **half-reactions:** a loss of electrons (**oxidation**) and a gain of electrons (**reduction**). In reality, most oxidation-reduction reactions probably do not proceed in this way, except in an electrolytic or galvanic cell (Chapter 16), where electrons must be lost at the anode and gained at the cathode. (Even then, we do not necessarily know what species are involved in the electrode processes.) The method is essentially a bookkeeping device enabling us to deal with the oxidation and with the reduction separately, and finally to combine the results into a balanced equation.

As an example, we take the reaction

$$Cu(c) + HONO_2(aq) \rightarrow Cu(NO_3)_2(aq) + H_2O + NO(g)$$

which occurs when copper is added to dilute nitric acid. The first step is to write the equation in ionic form. $HONO_2$ (or HNO_3) and $Cu(NO_3)_2$ are strong electrolytes and are represented as ions,

$$Cu + H^+ + NO_3^- \rightarrow Cu^{2+} + 2NO_3^- + H_2O + NO$$

(For simplicity, we will write H^+ instead of H_3O^+ in this section.) Next, we must observe which species are involved in each of the two processes, oxidation and reduction (although it is not yet necessary to decide which process is which). We write a partial equation for oxidation and a partial equation for reduction. Here, it is obvious that Cu becomes Cu^{2+},

$$Cu \rightarrow Cu^{2+} \tag{3}$$

and that NO_3^- somehow becomes NO,

$$NO_3^- \rightarrow NO \tag{4}$$

Equation (3) is almost balanced, but not quite. An equation must have not only the same number of atoms of each kind on each side, but also the same total electric charge on each side. Equation (3) has a charge of 0 on the left and $+2$ on the right. This situation is remedied by adding two electrons (e or e$^-$) to the right side,

$$Cu \rightarrow Cu^{2+} + 2e^- \tag{3'}$$

We have now achieved a balanced **partial equation** for the oxidation of Cu.

Equation (4) is more difficult, for it balances neither electrically nor atomically. We first balance it with respect to the number of atoms. There are three O atoms on the left and one on the right. Where did the other two go? We must not assume that they became O$_2$ gas unless we are told that O$_2$ is a product of the reaction. Here, it is not a product. The only other fate possible for the O atoms is to become part of the water molecules,

$$NO_3^- \rightarrow NO + 2H_2O$$

But now the equation is unbalanced with respect to H. We do not have H$_2$ gas available—it is not given as a reactant—and our source of the needed H must be the H$^+$ (or H$_3$O$^+$) ion,

$$NO_3^- + 4H^+ \rightarrow NO + 2H_2O$$

The equation is now balanced atomically. The net charge is $-1 + 4 = +3$ on the left, and 0 on the right; we add three electrons to the left to balance it electrically,

$$NO_3^- + 4H^+ + 3e^- \rightarrow NO + 2H_2O \quad \textit{(reduction)} \tag{4'}$$

We should observe that the number of electrons appearing in the partial equation is the same as the change in oxidation number (page 222) of the atom undergoing a change in oxidation number. In the oxidation, $Cu \rightarrow Cu^{2+} + 2e^-$, the oxidation number of Cu changes from 0 to $+2$, corresponding to a *loss* of two electrons. In the reduction, the oxidation number of N changes from $+5$ (in NO$_3^-$) to $+2$ (in NO), a change of -3; accordingly, the partial equation shows that NO$_3^-$ *gains* three electrons.

It remains to combine Equations (3') and (4') to obtain a balanced equation for the over-all reaction. We cannot simply add them, for there would then be one electron on the left side, which would have to come from somewhere. *The number of electrons given out in the oxidation must be equal to the number of electrons taken up in the reduction.* In this case, two electrons were lost in the oxidation of one Cu atom, and three electrons were gained in the reduction of one NO$_3^-$ ion. It follows that, for every three Cu atoms oxidized, two NO$_3^-$ ions must be reduced, so that six electrons are lost and six gained. We multiply Equation (3') by 3, Equation (4') by 2, and add,

$$3Cu \rightarrow 3Cu^{2+} + 6e^-$$
$$2NO_3^- + 8H^+ + 6e^- \rightarrow 2NO + 4H_2O$$

$$\overline{3Cu + 2NO_3^- + 8H^+ \rightarrow 3Cu^{2+} + 2NO + 4H_2O} \tag{5}$$

Equation (5) is the final balanced equation for most purposes. If, for some reason, an equation in molecular rather than ionic form is wanted, it can be obtained as follows. First, make the net charge zero on each side of the equation. Here, the net charge on each side is $+6$, and we must add $6NO_3^-$ to each side of the equation,

$$3Cu + 8NO_3^- + 8H^+ \rightarrow 3Cu^{2+} + 6NO_3^- + 2NO + 4H_2O$$

Now combine formulas of oppositely charged ions into molecular formulas,

$$3Cu + 8HONO_2 \rightarrow 3Cu(NO_3)_2 + 2NO + 4H_2O \qquad (5')$$

Equation (5') might be useful if we had to calculate the mass of $Cu(NO_3)_2$ that could be prepared from a given mass of Cu or of $HONO_2$. We can talk about ions and write formulas for them, but it is only an electrically neutral compound that can be isolated and weighed on a balance.

Note the dual role of NO_3^- in this reaction. Some NO_3^- ions are reduced to NO, while others are "spectator ions"—they are needed just to sit there and keep the solution electrically neutral.

If there is an objection to writing H^+ instead of H_3O^+, $8H_2O$ can be added to each side of Equation (5),

$$3Cu + 2NO_3^- + 8H_3O^+ \rightarrow 3Cu^{2+} + 2NO + 12H_2O \qquad (5'')$$

When the equation to be balanced was first given, it was not necessary to show H_2O or H^+ in the equation. If we are told that the reaction occurs in an acidic solution (understood to be aqueous), we know that H_2O is available as a source of oxygen and H^+ as a source of hydrogen. The problem might have been posed as: balance the equation $Cu + NO_3^- \rightarrow Cu^{2+} + NO$ in acid solution. We would then be quite justified in adding H_2O and H^+ as needed to obtain balanced partial equations.

Sometimes it is not obvious whether a certain transformation is an oxidation or a reduction, or some other kind of reaction. If it is neither an oxidation nor a reduction, the partial equation will balance without the introduction of electrons. Take a trivial example,

$$H^+ \rightarrow H_2O$$

After balancing with respect to O and H, this becomes

$$H^+ + H_2O \rightarrow H_2O + H^+$$

which is no reaction at all. Some cases are not so easy:

$$Cr_2O_7^{2-} \rightarrow CrO_4^{2-}$$

The balancing process here yields

$$Cr_2O_7^{2-} + H_2O \rightarrow 2CrO_4^{2-} + 2H^+$$

which balances with respect to both atoms and charge $[-2 = 2(-2) + 2]$, with no gain or loss of electrons. The same conclusions can be arrived at by calculating the oxidation number of H in H^+ and in H_2O ($+1$ in both), and the oxidation number of Cr in $Cr_2O_7^{2-}$ and in CrO_4^{2-} ($+6$ in both);

the absence of a change in oxidation number shows that no oxidation or reduction has occurred.

If the solution is basic, it contains very little H^+, but does contain more or less high concentration of OH^-. We should balance the equation for a reaction in such a solution by using H_2O as the source of *hydrogen* and OH^- as the source of oxygen. Each H_2O will provide one H^+ and leave one OH^- behind; each *two* OH^- ions will provide one O^{2-} and leave H_2O.

As an example, we consider the reaction

$$MnO_4^- + SO_3^{2-} \rightarrow MnO_2(c) + SO_4^{2-}$$

in basic solution. The unbalanced partial equations are

$$MnO_4^- \rightarrow MnO_2 \tag{6}$$

and

$$SO_3^{2-} \rightarrow SO_4^{2-} \tag{7}$$

Equation (6) is short by two O on the right; therefore, we add *four* OH^- to the right,

$$MnO_4^- \rightarrow MnO_2 + 4OH^-$$

Balancing numbers of atoms requires $2H_2O$ on the left,

$$MnO_4^- + 2H_2O \rightarrow MnO_2 + 4OH^-$$

The net charge is -1 on the left and -4 on the right. We add $3e^-$ to the left,

$$MnO_4^- + 2H_2O + 3e^- \rightarrow MnO_2 + 4OH^- \ (reduction) \tag{6'}$$

Equation (7) is balanced similarly. We add $2OH^-$ on the left, which leaves H_2O on the right,

$$SO_3^{2-} + 2OH^- \rightarrow SO_4^{2-} + H_2O$$

For electrical balancing, we add $2e^-$ to the right,

$$SO_3^{2-} + 2OH^- \rightarrow SO_4^{2-} + H_2O + 2e^- \ (oxidation) \tag{7'}$$

Before adding the equations, we must multiply Equation (6') by 2 and Equation (7') by 3:

$$2MnO_4^- + 4H_2O + 6e^- \rightarrow 2MnO_2 + 8OH^-$$
$$3SO_3^{2-} + 6OH^- \rightarrow 3SO_4^{2-} + 3H_2O + 6e^-$$

$$2MnO_4^- + 3SO_3^{2-} + 4H_2O + 6OH^- \rightarrow 2MnO_2 + 3SO_4^{2-} + 3H_2O + 8OH^- \tag{8}$$

Equation (8) admits of some simplification. H_2O and OH^- appear on both sides and should be canceled in part,

$$2MnO_4^- + 3SO_3^{2-} + H_2O \rightarrow 2MnO_2 + 3SO_4^{2-} + 2OH^- \tag{8'}$$

EXAMPLE 1   **Balance the equation**

$$I^- + H_2O_2 \rightarrow I_2(aq) + H_2O$$

in acid solution.

ANSWER

(a) **Write skeleton partial equations,**

$$I^- \rightarrow I_2$$
$$H_2O_2 \rightarrow H_2O$$

(Any other products would have been specified.)

(b) **Balance with respect to atoms,**

$$2I^- \rightarrow I_2$$
$$H_2O_2 \rightarrow 2H_2O \text{ (balanced for O)}$$
$$H_2O_2 + 2H^+ \rightarrow 2H_2O \text{ (balanced for H and O)}$$

(c) **Balance electrically,**

$$2I^- \rightarrow I_2 + 2e^-$$
$$H_2O_2 + 2H^+ + 2e^- \rightarrow 2H_2O$$

(In this case, the number of electrons lost happens to equal the number gained.)

(d) **Add partial equations,**

$$H_2O_2 + 2H^+ + 2I^- \rightarrow I_2 + 2H_2O$$

EXAMPLE 2   **Balance the equation**

$$NaClO + NaBr \rightarrow NaBrO_3 + NaCl$$

in basic solution. Write the balanced equation in ionic and molecular form.

ANSWER

(a) $Na^+ + ClO^- + Na^+ + Br^- \rightarrow Na^+ + BrO_3^- + Na^+ + Cl^-$.

(b) $ClO^- \rightarrow Cl^-$
       $Br^- \rightarrow BrO_3^-$

(c) $ClO^- + H_2O \rightarrow Cl^- + 2OH^-$
       $Br^- + 6OH^- \rightarrow BrO_3^- + 3H_2O$

(d) $ClO^- + H_2O + 2e^- \rightarrow Cl^- + 2OH^-$
       $Br^- + 6OH^- \rightarrow BrO_3^- + 3H_2O + 6e^-$

(e) $3ClO^- + 3H_2O + 6e^- \rightarrow 3Cl^- + 6OH^-$
       $Br^- + 6OH^- \rightarrow BrO_3^- + 3H_2O + 6e^-$

$3ClO^- + Br^- + 3H_2O + 6OH^- \rightarrow 3Cl^- + BrO_3^- + 3H_2O + 6OH^-$

(f) $3ClO^- + Br^- \rightarrow 3Cl^- + BrO_3^-$

(g) $3NaClO + NaBr \rightarrow 3NaCl + NaBrO_3$

15.11 ELECTRODE PROCESSES

We observed (page 363) that the passage of a current through an electrolytic conductor is always accompanied by reactions at the electrodes. At one electrode, electrons are being supplied to the electrolyte, and some molecule or ion must accept them and be **reduced.** The electrode at which this reduction takes place is the **cathode.** At the other electrode electrons in equal number are being removed from the electrolyte, and something is being **oxidized;** this electrode is the **anode.** Reactions of several types are possible at each electrode; the following list covers the most common types, but is not meant to be exhaustive.

Anode Reactions.   Anode reactions include the following:

(a) The metal of which the electrode is made may be oxidized to positive ions,

$$Cu(c) \rightarrow Cu^{2+} + 2e^-$$

(b) A constituent of the solution, neutral or charged, may be oxidized and remain in solution,

$$Fe^{2+} \rightarrow Fe^{3+} + e^-$$

$$C_2H_5OH + 2H_2O \rightarrow \overset{O}{\overset{\|}{CH_3CH}} + 2H_3O^+ + 2e^-$$
$$\textit{acetaldehyde}$$

(c) A negative ion in the solution may become a neutral molecule and escape as a gas,

$$2Cl^- \rightarrow Cl_2(g) + 2e^-$$

(d) A gas in contact with the electrode may be oxidized to a positive ion,

$$H_2(g) + 2H_2O \rightarrow 2H_3O^+ + 2e^-$$

(e) In an aqueous solution, water may be oxidized to gaseous oxygen,

$$6H_2O \rightarrow O_2(g) + 4H_3O^+ + 4e^-$$

Since water is the predominant species in a dilute aqueous solution, reaction (e) is always possible and occurs unless some other reaction is easier.

Cathode Reactions.   (a) A positive ion in the solution may be reduced to the element, which deposits on the electrode. (b) A constituent of the solution may be reduced and remain in solution. (c) A gas in contact with the electrode may be reduced to a negative ion. (The reverses of the anode reactions under (a), (b), and (c) above will serve as illustrations.) (d) In an aqueous solution, water may be reduced to gaseous hydrogen,

$$2H_2O + 2e^- \rightarrow H_2(g) + 2OH^-$$

As with the production of O_2, this reaction is always a possibility.

The equations for the anode reaction and the cathode reaction, in the same solution, can be added to obtain an equation for the over-all reaction. The number of electrons given up by one electrode must be the same as the number of electrons accepted by the other electrode, and each equation may therefore have to be multiplied by a coefficient that will make the numbers of electrons the same in the two equations, just as in the preceding section. If the partial equations are

$$6H_2O \rightarrow O_2 + 4H_3O^+ + 4e^-$$

and

$$2H_2O + 2e^- \rightarrow H_2 + 2OH^-$$

we must double the second, or halve the first, to show that electrons are conserved in the over-all process:

$$6H_2O \rightarrow O_2 + 4H_3O^+ + 4e^- \tag{9}$$
$$4H_2O + 4e^- \rightarrow 2H_2 + 4OH^- \tag{10}$$

$$\overline{10H_2O \rightarrow 2H_2 + O_2 + 4H_3O^+ + 4OH^-}$$

This is the final result if the solutions near the two electrodes do not mix with each other. But, if the entire solution is stirred, H_3O^+ and OH^- ions react to form water,

$$4H_3O^+ + 4OH^- \rightarrow 8H_2O$$

The total process then is

$$2H_2O \rightarrow 2H_2 + O_2$$

merely the decomposition of water into its elements.

Equations (9) and (10) above illustrate the necessity of adding a non-reacting electrolyte, such as Na_2SO_4, to water before decomposing it by electrolysis. A separation of positive and negative charge, in appreciable quantity (more than a few ions), to considerable distances (more than a few molecular diameters), would require an enormous amount of energy. Therefore every measurable sample of a solution must be electrically neutral. Reaction (9) produces positive ions around the anode; they will move away, but cannot cross over to the cathode instantaneously. To preserve electrical neutrality near the anode, there must be negative ions which can move into the anode region to compensate for those H_3O^+ ions which have not moved away. Similarly, positive ions migrate into the vicinity of the cathode to compensate for the charge of the OH^- ions. The process is illustrated schematically in Fig. 15.3, where we have imagined that each section of the solution contained, initially, $6Na^+$ ions and $3SO_4^{2-}$ ions, and that 5 electronic units of charge passed through the circuit, producing $5H_3O^+$ ions and $5OH^-$ ions.

In general, several reactions may take place simultaneously at each electrode. In a $CuCl_2$ solution, for example, the cathode process will be

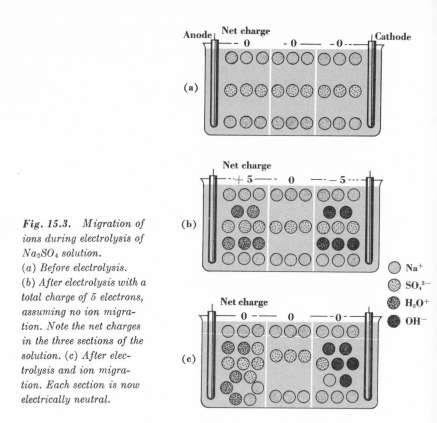

Fig. 15.3. *Migration of ions during electrolysis of Na_2SO_4 solution.*
(a) Before electrolysis.
(b) After electrolysis with a total charge of 5 electrons, assuming no ion migration. Note the net charges in the three sections of the solution. (c) After electrolysis and ion migration. Each section is now electrically neutral.

$\bigcirc$ Na$^+$
$\bigcirc$ SO$_4{}^{2-}$
$\bigcirc$ H$_3$O$^+$
$\bullet$ OH$^-$

some combination of the reactions

$$Cu^{2+} + 2e^- \rightarrow Cu(c)$$

and

$$H_2O + e^- \rightarrow \tfrac{1}{2}H_2(g) + OH^-$$

The decision as to which will predominate cannot always be made without a specific experiment, but some useful rules will be mentioned in Chapter 16.

15.12 ELECTROLYSIS OF FUSED SALTS

When an ionic crystal melts, the liquid is still composed of ions, now having a mobility lacking in the crystal. These ions, like the ions in a liquid solution, can move under the influence of an electric field, and a fused ionic salt is therefore an electrolytic conductor. Solid ionic crystals also have appreciable conductivity, especially at high temperatures, indicating that the ions can migrate to some extent even in the solid.

Electrode reactions impossible in the presence of water become possible when the electrolyte is a fused salt. Thus, the alkali and alkaline earth metals are prepared by the electrolysis of their fused chlorides, chosen because of their abundance and relatively low melting points. The reaction at the anode is

$$Cl^- \rightarrow \tfrac{1}{2}Cl_2(g) + e^-$$

and at the cathode

$$Na^+ + e^- \rightarrow Na(l)$$

in the case of NaCl. If water were present, H_2, not Na, would be the product.* The melting point of NaCl is 801°C, so that Na, which melts at 97.5°C, is produced as a liquid. Aluminum is another metal that cannot be produced by electrolysis of an aqueous solution; only H_2 is liberated at the cathode. It has no inexpensive salts that melt easily and conduct in the liquid state—the chloride consists of covalent molecules, and the oxide melts above 2000°C—but Al_2O_3 dissolves in fused cryolite, Na_3AlF_6, which melts at the reasonable temperature of 1000°C, and the electrolytic reduction of Al_2O_3 in this solvent is a major industry. Chapter 27 discusses such electrometallurgical processes.

5.13 FARADAY'S LAWS

When there is only one reaction at an electrode, there are two simple and significant relations between the quantity of charge passed through the circuit and the quantity of matter produced or consumed by the electrode process. These relations are called **Faraday's laws,** after Michael Faraday, who discovered them in 1832–33. Before stating these laws, we will illustrate them with a familiar reaction, the electrolytic decomposition of water. An electrolyte, usually sulfuric acid, $(HO)_2SO_2$, is added to make the water a conductor, but the sulfate ion (SO_4^{2-} or $O_2SO_2^{2-}$) is very stable and is not oxidized at the anode. The only possible reactions are

$$3H_2O \rightarrow \tfrac{1}{2}O_2(g) + 2H_3O^+ + 2e^-$$

at the anode, and, in acid solution,   ELECTROLYSIS OF WATER.

$$H_3O^+ + e^- \rightarrow \tfrac{1}{2}H_2(g) + H_2O$$

or, in basic solution,

$$H_2O + e^- \rightarrow \tfrac{1}{2}H_2(g) + OH^-$$

at the cathode. Let us pass through the solution the same current for different lengths of time, or different currents for the same time. When the current or the time is doubled, the mass and volume of H_2 and of O_2 are doubled. This result is not very surprising, and had been suggested

* Even with an aqueous solution, Na can be obtained as a product by using Hg as the cathode. Liberation of H_2 at a Hg surface is difficult—the overvoltage (page 426) is large—and the Na dissolves in the Hg rapidly enough to rescue most of it from the water.

by several chemists before Faraday's careful experiments established it beyond doubt. It is an instance of Faraday's **first law:**

(1) *The mass of product produced (or reactant consumed) in a given electrode reaction is proportional to the quantity of charge (current × time) that has passed through the circuit.**

Since the two electrodes are in series, the same current, and therefore the same total charge, must pass through them. We find that the ratio of the mass of H_2 to the mass of O_2 is 2.016:16.00—just the ratio of the molecular weight of H_2 to half the molecular weight of O_2. If another electrolysis apparatus is in series with this one, and the only reaction at the cathode of the second apparatus is the reduction of silver ion to metallic silver (which is plated on the electrode), the formation of 16.00 g of O_2 is associated with the deposition of 215.74 g of Ag; 16 is half the molecular weight of O_2, and 215.74 is twice the atomic weight of Ag. Equally well we may say

1 gram-atom (107.87 g) of Ag is produced by the same quantity of charge that liberates
$\frac{1}{4}$ mole or $\frac{1}{2}$ gram-atom (8.00 g) of O_2 and
$\frac{1}{2}$ mole or 1 gram-atom (1.008 g) of H_2. The same charge will plate out
$\frac{1}{2}$ gram-atom (31.77 g) of Cu† or
$\frac{1}{3}$ gram-atom (8.99 g) of Al; it will liberate
35.453 g ($\frac{1}{2}$ mole or 1 gram-atom) of Cl_2.

These results illustrate Faraday's second law, which is most easily stated if we first adopt a definition: one **faraday** is *the quantity of electric charge that will deposit exactly one gram-atom of silver.* Silver is chosen as the standard element because it lends itself to accurate weighing. Then Faraday's **second law** is

(2) *The mass (in grams) of a product (or reactant) produced (or consumed) in an electrode reaction, when one faraday passes through the circuit, is equal to the atomic or molecular weight of the substance divided by a small integer.*

One faraday is equal to 96,487 coulombs. This quantity is taken as a fundamental unit because the production (or removal) of one gram-atom or one mole of any substance always requires 1, or 2, or 3, etc., faradays, never a fractional part of a faraday. One mole is a definite number of atoms or molecules; the fact that this number of molecules is produced by an integral number of faradays suggests strongly that one molecule is produced by the addition or removal of an integral number of atoms of electricity, or **electrons.** *A faraday is Avogadro's number of electronic charges—one mole of electrons.*

In this section, we will call that quantity of an element or compound produced or consumed by one faraday an **equivalent;** the mass in grams

---

* Charge is measured in *coulombs;* current is measured in *amperes.* One ampere is one coulomb per second.

† This fact constitutes the proof, promised on page 362, that the copper ion is doubly charged.

of this quantity is the **equivalent weight,** and is equal to the molecular or atomic weight divided by the number of electrons transferred per molecule, atom, or ion. With knowledge of chemical formulas, we can determine the number of electrons transferred, if we know the identities of the reactants and products, by writing the partial equation for the electrode reaction. Thus, the partial equation

$$2H_2O + 2e^- \rightarrow H_2 + 2OH^-$$

shows that two electrons are needed to produce one molecule of H_2, so that two faradays are needed for one mole of H_2, or one faraday for $\frac{1}{2}$ mole; the equivalent weight is $\frac{1}{2}$ the molecular weight. For O_2, we see from the partial equation

$$6H_2O \rightarrow O_2 + 4H_3O^+ + 4e^-$$

that four electrons are removed for every molecule of O_2 that is formed, or four faradays for every mole, or one faraday for every $\frac{1}{4}$ mole, and the equivalent weight is $32.00/4 = 8.00$ g. When Cu is deposited on, or removed from, an electrode, the reaction is

$$Cu^{2+} + 2e^- \rightarrow Cu$$

or the reverse; its equivalent weight is therefore $\frac{1}{2}$ its atomic weight. When Fe^{3+} is reduced to Fe at a cathode,

$$Fe^{3+} + 3e^- \rightarrow Fe$$

its equivalent weight is $\frac{1}{3}$ its atomic weight. But another possible cathode reaction is

$$Fe^{3+} + e^- \rightarrow Fe^{2+}$$

Here, the equivalent weight is equal to the atomic weight. We see that the equivalent weight of a species is not simply a property of itself, but depends on the reaction in which it participates. (Chapter 21 discusses other meanings and applications of the idea of equivalent weight.)

When several reactions occur simultaneously at the same electrode, Faraday's laws still apply, in the sense that the total number of equivalents produced or consumed in all the reactions is equal to the number of faradays passed through the circuit. Thus, if 3.177 g of Cu (0.1000 equivalent) is plated on an electrode from a solution containing Cu^{2+}, and at the same time 0.2016 g of H_2 (0.2000 equivalent) is liberated at the same electrode, we know that $0.1000 + 0.2000 = 0.3000$ faraday has passed through.

EXAMPLE 3 **An aqueous solution of gold(III) chloride, $AuCl_3$, was electrolyzed with a current of 0.500 ampere until 1.200 g of Au had been deposited on the cathode. There was no other reaction at the cathode. At another electrode in series with this one, the only reaction was the evolution of O_2. Find (a) the number of moles, (b) the volume at standard conditions, and (c) the mass of**

O_2 liberated; (d) the number of coulombs passed through the circuit; (e) the duration of the electrolysis.

ANSWER   The atomic weight of Au is 197.0 g/g-atom. The cathode reaction is

$$Au^{3+} + 3e^- \rightarrow Au$$

so that the equivalent weight of Au is

$$\frac{197.0 \text{ g/g-atom}}{3 \text{ eq/g-atom}} = 65.67 \frac{\text{g}}{\text{eq}}$$

The number of equivalents deposited is

$$\frac{1.200 \text{ g}}{65.67 \frac{\text{g}}{\text{eq}}} = 0.01827 \text{ eq}$$

This is also the number of faradays that have passed through the circuit. (a) The number of equivalents of O_2 is 0.01827. From the partial equation

$$6H_2O \rightarrow O_2 + 4H_3O^+ + 4e^-$$

we see that one mole of O_2 is 4 equivalents, so that

$$\frac{0.01827 \text{ eq}}{4 \frac{\text{eq}}{\text{mole}}} = 0.00457 \text{ mole}$$

of O_2 is liberated.

(b) $$0.00457 \text{ mole} \times 22.4 \frac{\text{liters}}{\text{mole}} = 0.102 \text{ liter (sc)}$$

(c) $$0.00457 \text{ mole} \times 32.00 \frac{\text{g}}{\text{mole}} = 0.146 \text{ g}$$

(d) $$0.01827 \text{ faraday} \times 9.65 \times 10^4 \frac{\text{coul}}{\text{faraday}} = 1.76 \times 10^3 \text{ coul}$$

(e) The charge (q) in coulombs is the current (I) in amperes times the time (t) in seconds,

$$q = It$$

The current is given as

$$0.500 \text{ amp} = 0.500 \frac{\text{coul}}{\text{sec}}$$

We have found that the charge is

$$1.76 \times 10^3 \text{ coul}$$

Then

$$t = \frac{q}{I} = \frac{1.76 \times 10^3 \text{ coul}}{0.500 \frac{\text{coul}}{\text{sec}}} = 3.52 \times 10^3 \text{ sec}$$

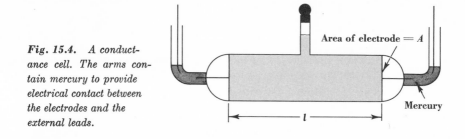

Fig. 15.4. *A conductance cell. The arms contain mercury to provide electrical contact between the electrodes and the external leads.*

Area of electrode $= A$

Mercury

l

15.14 MEASUREMENT OF CONDUCTIVITY

We now return to the topic that engaged our attention at the beginning of the chapter: the fact that a solution of an electrolyte conducts electricity. To measure the **conductivity** (specific conductance) of an electrolytic solution, we measure the resistance R of a sample of the solution with known length and cross-sectional area (Fig. 15.4). The **conductance** is $K = 1/R$; it is proportional to the cross-sectional area A, and inversely proportional to the length l of the conductor;

$$K = \frac{kA}{l}$$

The proportionality constant k is the conductivity. R is measured in ohms, and K is ohm^{-1} (reciprocal ohms, mhos). Since $k = lK/A$, k is in ohm^{-1} cm^{-1} when l is in cm and A in cm^2.

Alternating current, usually with a frequency of the order of 1000 cycles/sec, is always used for conductivity measurements. With direct current, the migration of the ions and the reactions at the electrodes would change the composition of the solution and make it inhomogeneous; the evolution of gas would be especially undesirable, because a layer of gas on the electrode surface would have a very high resistance. With high-frequency alternating current, there is no net chemical reaction, for each half-cycle undoes the reaction of the previous half-cycle.

A conductance cell in which the length and cross section are known accurately is difficult to construct. The conductivities of certain solutions, especially of KCl in water, have been determined with great care, and such a solution can be used to determine l/A for a given cell: $l/A = kR$, where k is the known conductivity of the KCl solution, and R is the measured resistance of the cell when it contains the standard KCl solution. The same cell can then be used to determine the conductivities of other solutions,

$$k = \frac{1}{R}\left(\frac{l}{A}\right)$$

$k = K\left(\dfrac{l}{A}\right)$ K is specific conductor.

where l/A is known, and R is measured with the new solution in the cell.

The conductivity of a solution is the conductance of a cube 1 cm on an edge. The conductivity of a solution of a given electrolyte—say NaCl—depends on the number of ions present in this cubic centimeter, and thus on the molar concentration of the solution. As a first approximation, the conductivity should be proportional to the number of ions in the cube, and therefore proportional to the concentration c of the electrolyte, in moles per liter; in other words, k/c should be approximately constant (at a fixed temperature). The quantity 1000 k/c is called the **equivalent conductance** of the solution, and is represented by Λ (capital lambda); the factor 1000 is introduced because $c/1000$ is the number of moles per cm^3 (1 cm^3 = 1 ml very nearly). The advantage of working with equivalent conductance, rather than conductivity, is that any change of Λ with concentration must be attributed to one (or both) of two effects: the fraction of the electrolyte present as ions must be changing, or the current-carrying efficiency of each ion—essentially, the speed (at given electric field strength) with which it moves through the solution—must be dependent on concentration. Thus, we can focus our attention on these effects without being distracted by the large change in k caused merely by a change in the quantity of electrolyte.

In defining the equivalent conductance of an electrolyte in which the ions are not all singly charged, we represent by c not the molarity, but the number of **equivalents** per liter. An equivalent is not the same here as it was in Section 15.13. An equivalent is defined here as that quantity of the solute which gives, in solution, positive ions with a total charge of one faraday and negative ions with a total charge of one faraday. For NaCl, of course, one equivalent is one mole. For CaCl$_2$, an equivalent is $\frac{1}{2}$ mole, for 1 mole of CaCl$_2$ gives 1 mole of Ca^{2+} ions, having a charge of $+2$ faradays, and 2 moles of Cl$^-$ ions, each mole with a charge of -1 faraday. One mole of Al$_2$(SO$_4$)$_3$ gives 2 moles of Al^{3+} and 3 moles of SO$_4{}^{2-}$, with total charges of $+6$ and -6 faradays, respectively, so that an equivalent of Al$_2$(SO$_4$)$_3$ is $\frac{1}{6}$ of a mole. The **equivalent weight** of an electrolyte in solution is the mass (in grams) of one equivalent, or the *molecular weight divided by the total charge of the positive ions (or the negative ions) appearing in the formula*. The equivalent weight of NaCl is the same as the molecular weight, 58.45 g/eq. The equivalent weight of CaCl$_2$ is $\frac{1}{2}$ the molecular weight,

$$110.99 \frac{\text{g}}{\text{mole}} \times \frac{1 \text{ mole}}{2 \text{ eq}} = 55.50 \frac{\text{g}}{\text{eq}}$$

The equivalent weight of Al$_2$(SO$_4$)$_3$ is

$$342.14 \frac{\text{g}}{\text{mole}} \times \frac{1 \text{ mole}}{6 \text{ eq}} = 57.02 \frac{\text{g}}{\text{eq}}$$

A physical interpretation of Λ is provided by the apparatus in Fig. 15.5. The large electrodes B and D are 1 cm apart; the cross-sectional area, in cm^2, occupied by the solution is therefore numerically equal to the volume

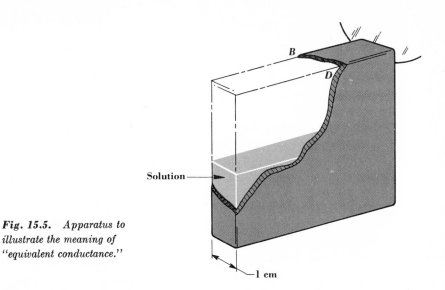

Fig. 15.5. *Apparatus to illustrate the meaning of "equivalent conductance."*

of the solution in cm³. Assume that the solution contains one equivalent of an electrolyte, to which sufficient solvent is added so that the concentration is c eq/liter. The volume of the solution is then

$$\frac{1}{c} \text{ liter}$$

or

$$\frac{1000}{c} \text{ cm}^3$$

and the area it covers is

$$\frac{1000}{c} \text{ cm}^2$$

since the electrodes are 1 cm apart. The conductance of this solution is

$$K \text{ ohm}^{-1} = \frac{kA}{l} = k \text{ ohm}^{-1} \text{ cm}^{-1} \times \frac{1000}{c} \text{ cm}^2 \Big/ 1 \text{ cm}$$

But $1000k/c = \Lambda$, the equivalent conductance of the solution. As water is added or evaporated off, the quantity of dissolved electrolyte between the electrodes does not change. Any change in the conductance must be the result of a change in the fraction ionized or in the speed of the ions.

The reason for expressing concentration in equivalents, rather than moles, per liter is to permit a fair comparison between electrolytes in which the ions have different charges. When *one* Ca^{2+} ion moves a certain distance through a solution, it transports as much charge as *two* Na^+ ions moving the same distance. We should, therefore, dissolve in the apparatus of Fig. 15.5 *half* as many *moles* of $CaCl_2$ as of NaCl—or the *same* number of *equivalents*—if we wish to compare the abilities of these two electrolytes to carry current.

The units of Λ are ohm^{-1} cm^2 eq^{-1},

$$\Lambda = \frac{1000 \text{ cm}^3 \text{ liter}^{-1} \times k \text{ ohm}^{-1} \text{ cm}^{-1}}{c \text{ eq liter}^{-1}} = \frac{1000k}{c} \text{ ohm}^{-1} \text{ cm}^2 \text{ eq}^{-1}$$

15.16 CHANGE OF EQUIVALENT CONDUCTANCE WITH CONCENTRATION

The equivalent conductance of an electrolyte depends quite noticeably on concentration. The variation of Λ with c, for a few typical electrolytes, is shown in Fig. 15.6. We plot Λ against $\sqrt{c}$ because a more nearly straight line is obtained in this way than with c as the independent variable.

How can we account for this change of Λ with concentration? There are two possible causes for a change in Λ: the fraction of the electrolyte present as ions may depend on concentration, or the speed of migration of the ions may depend on concentration. Arrhenius's explanation of this variation was that an equilibrium is established between ions and undissociated molecules; as the concentration increases, the equilibrium is shifted toward neutral molecules, with a consequent loss in the number of ions available for conduction. For example, he assumed that, in a KCl

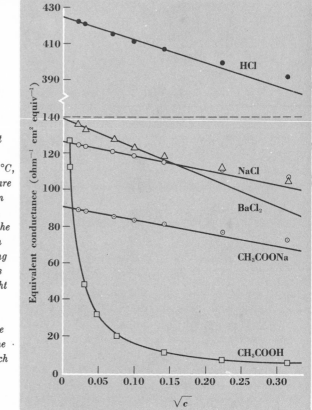

Fig. 15.6. *Equivalent conductances (Λ) of several electrolytes at 25°C, as functions of the square root of the concentration in equivalents per liter. The circles, etc., show the experimental values. In dilute solutions of strong electrolytes, these points are well fitted by straight lines. The dashed line illustrates the constant value of Λ that would be observed for BaCl$_2$ if the ions did not impede each other's migration.*

solution, the equilibrium

$$KCl \rightleftharpoons K^+ + Cl^-$$

is established. If this is indeed the case, an increase in concentration would shift this equilibrium to the left, so that a smaller fraction of the dissolved KCl would be present as ions and available for conduction. Qualitatively, of course, this assumption is in agreement with the facts. It fails, however, to predict the variation of equivalent conductance with even approximate quantitative correctness. If the equilibrium is established, the equilibrium condition

$$\frac{[K^+][Cl^-]}{[KCl]} = K$$

should be satisfied. An apparent equilibrium constant can be calculated from conductance data, but is far from being constant—at 18°C, for example, $K = 2.3$ for a $1M$ solution, and 15.2 for a $0.01M$ solution. Similar variations are found in the values of K calculated from colligative properties.

15.17 STRONG ELECTROLYTES

Most, though not all, of the electrolytes with which these difficulties arise are those that exist as ionic crystals in the solid state. They are also the electrolytes with relatively large equivalent conductances. Such electrolytes are called **strong electrolytes,** and are believed to be present almost entirely as ions in dilute solutions. For strong electrolytes, the graph of Λ vs. $\sqrt{c}$ (Fig. 15.6) becomes nearly a straight line at low concentrations, so that it can be extrapolated with confidence to $c = 0$. The limiting value of Λ obtained by this extrapolation, Λ_0, is called the **equivalent conductance at infinite dilution;** it would be the conductance of one equivalent of the electrolyte, in a layer 1 cm thick, if the ions were so far apart as to have no effect on each other.

The concept of "infinite dilution" may require a little thought before it becomes clear. An "infinitely dilute solution," taken literally, would be pure solvent. What we mean to convey by such a phrase is that the equivalent conductance changes with concentration in a way sufficiently regular so that we have no doubt as to what the equivalent conductance would be if we could measure it at a concentration as low as we please, but still greater than zero. What prevents such a measurement is that the solute eventually becomes an insignificant impurity, its effect overshadowed by other impurities and by the conductance of the solvent itself. Although the equivalent conductance, $1000k/c$, has no meaning when $c = 0$, it does seem to approach a limit as c is taken smaller and smaller— just as $(\sin x)/x$ is meaningless when $x = 0$, but approaches the limit 1 as x approaches 0.

Even if the electrolyte is present entirely as ions, it is reasonable that its equivalent conductance should decrease as the concentration increases. Each ion has neighbors predominantly of the opposite charge; it is at-

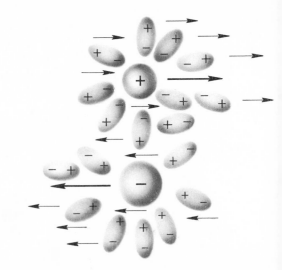

Fig. 15.7. *A schematic diagram of two oppositely charged ions moving in opposite directions through a polar solvent. Each ion is attempting to carry its sheath of solvent molecules with it.*

tracted by these ions moving in the opposite direction, and its progress is thus hindered. What is equally bad, the oppositely charged ions nearby are dragging solvent with them in the wrong direction, enhancing the viscous resistance that any moving particle must overcome (Fig. 15.7). These effects are, of course, greater the greater the concentration.

Not only the conductance, but also the colligative properties of strong electrolytes, show deviations from the values to be expected on the basis of complete ionization. In a one molal solution of either NaCl or $MgSO_4$ in water, there should be 2 moles of ions per kilogram of water, giving a freezing-point depression of $2 \times 1.86 = 3.72°$, but, as Table 15.2 (page 361) shows, the depression is only $1.81 \times 1.86°$ for NaCl, and $1.09 \times 1.86°$ for $MgSO_4$. These diminutions in the colligative properties are also accounted for, at least qualitatively, by the concept of interionic attraction, although the connection is less obvious here than in the case of conductance. In general, the effect of attraction is to make the ions behave as if they were not all there. (See also pages 386 and 392.)

In addition to the ionic salts (including the soluble hydroxides, as NaOH), some acids behave as strong electrolytes in aqueous solution: HCl, HBr, HI, $(HO)_2SO_2$ (sulfuric acid), $HONO_2$ (nitric acid), and $HOClO_3$ (perchloric acid) are the most common of them. A few other compounds that are covalent in the pure state ionize almost completely in solution;

$$Al_2Cl_6(c) + 12H_2O \rightarrow 2Al(H_2O)_6{}^{3+} + 6Cl^-$$

represents a familiar case.

15.18 CONDUCTANCES OF INDIVIDUAL IONS

If our picture of conduction by ions is correct, we may regard a solution as consisting of two distinct, but intermingled, conductors: the positive ions and the negative ions. We can attribute a certain conductance to each of these conductors, and the conductance of the solution is therefore the sum of the conductances of the positive ions and of the negative ions. Recalling the apparatus of Fig. 15.5, with one equivalent of positive ions and one equivalent of negative ions between the electrodes, we may call the contribution of each kind of ion to the conductance the **equivalent ionic conductance,** or simply the **ionic conductance,** of that species. If the solution is sufficiently dilute, the ionic conductance of Na^+ ions, for example, should be the same, regardless of whether the negative ion is Cl^-, Br^-, or SO_4^{2-}. Indeed, Friedrich Kohlrausch found in 1874 that the equivalent conductance of an electrolyte at infinite dilution, Λ_0, could be represented as a sum of two terms, one for each ionic species, and that these ionic conductances have the same values in different electrolytes containing the same ion:

$$\Lambda_{0,NaCl} = \lambda_{0,Na^+} + \lambda_{0,Cl^-}$$

and

$$\Lambda_{0,\frac{1}{2}Na_2SO_4} = \lambda_{0,Na^+} + \lambda_{0,\frac{1}{2}SO_4^{2-}}$$

with the same λ_{0,Na^+} for the two salts. In measuring equivalent conductance, of course we always measure a sum of ionic conductances, but there are methods, not discussed here, by which the relative contributions of the two ions to the total conductance can be ascertained. The ionic conductances at infinite dilution of some familiar ions are given in Table 15.3.

For an ion with multiple charge, we write $\frac{1}{2}Ba^{2+}$, $\frac{1}{2}SO_4^{2-}$, etc., to remind us that the conductance of one equivalent, not one mole, of such an ion is tabulated.

From a table such as this, one can calculate the equivalent conductance at infinite dilution of any strong electrolyte made up of a positive ion and a negative ion included in the table. For Na_2SO_4, for example,

$$\Lambda_0 = 50.11 + 79.8 = 129.9 \text{ ohm}^{-1} \text{ cm}^2 \text{ eq}^{-1}$$

TABLE 15.3 *Ionic Conductances at Infinite Dilution at 25° C (in ohm^{-1} cm^2 eq^{-1})*

Ag^+	61.92	Br^-	78.4
H_3O^+	349.82	CH_3COO^-	40.9
K^+	73.52	Cl^-	76.34
Na^+	50.11	NO_3^-	71.44
NH_4^+	73.4	OH^-	198
$\frac{1}{2}Ba^{2+}$	63.64	$\frac{1}{2}SO_4^{2-}$	79.8
$\frac{1}{2}Ca^{2+}$	59.50		
$\frac{1}{2}Mg^{2+}$	53.06		

15.19 ASSOCIATION IN STRONG ELECTROLYTES

The idea that a solution of a strong electrolyte contains only ions has been quite successful in pointing to explanations of the properties of such a solution, as long as it is very dilute. It is to be expected, however, that ions of opposite charge will collide from time to time, even in a dilute solution, and that such collisions will be "sticky"—once the ions come into contact, with no intervening solvent molecules, their electrostatic attraction for each other will keep them together longer than two uncharged molecules would remain together. This behavior can be described by saying that, at any given moment, some of the ions are present as **ion pairs.*** The ion pair, as long as it exists, does not contribute to conduction, and counts as one particle in the calculation of colligative properties.

The concentration of ion pairs should be related to the concentrations of free ions by the law of chemical equilibrium. For the reaction

$$Na^+ + Cl^- \leftrightharpoons Na^+Cl^-$$
$$\textit{ion pair}$$

for example, we can write the equilibrium condition

$$\frac{[Na^+Cl^-]}{[Na^+][Cl^-]} = K$$

where K is called the **association constant** of NaCl. The association constant of NaCl at 25°C can be estimated as 0.71, which corresponds to an association of 6% of the ions into pairs in a $0.1M$ solution of NaCl in water. Association becomes more important for multiply charged ions, for more concentrated solutions, and in solvents with dielectric constants less than that of water.

Association of ions seems like a return to the original Arrhenius theory of partial dissociation, and so it is in a sense. However, the degree of association is considerably less than Arrhenius assumed, and attraction between ions not in contact is now considered to have a greater effect on the conductance of the solution than association has. There is also a subtle difference in the point of view. Arrhenius assumed that the crystal contained molecules, which dissociated after dissolving; the association theory pictures the effect as a partial pairing of particles which entered the solution as ions.

15.20 WEAK ELECTROLYTES

Acetic acid, on being dissolved in water, yields hydronium ions and acetate ions by the reaction

$$CH_3COOH + H_2O \leftrightharpoons H_3O^+ + CH_3COO^-$$

---

* The distinction between an ion pair and a molecule is not clearly defined; perhaps we can say that the ion pair is ionically bonded and the molecule is covalently bonded (pages 206–212), but the line between the two kinds of bonding is not sharp. The main distinction is their longevity; an ion pair that endures long enough (in gaseous NaCl, for example) is thought of as a molecule.

We should be able to calculate the equivalent conductance of an extremely dilute solution of acetic acid by adding the ionic conductances of H_3O^+ and CH_3COO^- (Table 15.3),

$$\Lambda_0 = 349.82 + 40.9 = 390.7 \text{ ohm}^{-1} \text{ cm}^2 \text{ eq}^{-1}$$

As we can see in Fig. 15.6, however, the equivalent conductance of acetic acid is nowhere near this value, even in the most dilute solutions for which measurements have been made. The most likely explanation is that we have in this case a partial dissociation into ions, just as Arrhenius postulated for all electrolytes. An electrolyte dissociated only to a small extent into ions at equilibrium is known as a **weak electrolyte.** Most acids are of this kind; the exceptions were mentioned on page 384. The most common weak bases* are ammonia, NH_3, and many compounds related to it by the replacement of one or more hydrogen atoms by other atoms or groups of atoms; examples are methylamine, H_3CNH_2, and hydrazine, H_2NNH_2, an important rocket fuel. There are a relatively few **weak salts** which exist, even in dilute solution, predominantly as undissociated molecules: $CdCl_2$, $(CH_3COO)_2Pb$, $HgCl_2$, for example.

15.21 DEGREE OF DISSOCIATION

(a) **From Equivalent Conductance.** The equivalent conductance of completely ionized acetic acid at infinite dilution would be 390.7 ohm^{-1} cm^2 eq^{-1}, as we saw in the last paragraph. The observed equivalent conductance at 25°C of a $0.050M$ solution of acetic acid is 7.358 ohm^{-1} cm^2 eq^{-1}. We may say that the solution is only $7.358/390.7 = 1.88\%$ as good a conductor as it would be if the acid were completely ionized. If we adopt the approximation that each ion carries current as efficiently in the $0.05M$ solution as in an infinitely dilute solution, the number of ions present in the solution is 1.88% of the number that would be present if ionization were complete—in other words, 1.88% of the acetic acid molecules have reacted with water to become H_3O^+ and CH_3COO^- ions, and 98.12% of the acetic acid is still present as neutral molecules. The fraction of a weak electrolyte that is present as ions is called the **degree of dissociation** or **degree of ionization** of the electrolyte; it depends, of course, on the concentration of the solution, the identity of the solvent, and the temperature.

(b) **From Colligative Properties.** The degree of dissociation of a weak electrolyte can also be calculated from the colligative properties of its solution. Taking the freezing-point depression as an example, we recall (from page 325) that the depression Δt is given by $\Delta t = K_f m$, where $K_f = 1.86°$ kg/mole for H_2O, and m is the total molality of all solute particles. Suppose that a solution of a weak acid HA is prepared with molality 0.70 mole/kg H_2O, and that the degree of dissociation of the

---

* Here we are considering only those weak acids and bases which are neutral molecules. See page 446 concerning the acidic and basic properties of ions.

acid is 0.020, or 2.0%. Then the reaction

$$HA + H_2O \rightleftharpoons H_3O^+ + A^-$$

gives $0.020 \times 0.70 = 0.0140$ mole of H_3O^+ and 0.0140 mole of A^- per kilogram of water, and $0.70 - 0.0140$ mole of undissociated HA remains. The total molality of all solute species is

$$m = 0.70 - 0.0140 + 0.0140 + 0.0140$$
$$= 0.714 \frac{\text{mole}}{\text{kg } H_2O}$$

The freezing-point depression then is

$$\Delta t = K_f m = 1.86 \frac{\text{deg kg}}{\text{mole}} \times 0.714 \frac{\text{mole}}{\text{kg}} = 1.33°$$

If there were no dissociation, the depression would be $1.86 \times 0.70 = 1.30°$. Conversely, the degree of dissociation can be calculated from measurements of freezing-point depression.

EXAMPLE 4   The freezing point of a 0.10m aqueous solution of hydrofluoric acid, HF, is $-0.198°C$. Find the degree of dissociation of the acid.

ANSWER   The total molality is

$$m = \frac{\Delta t}{K_f} = \frac{0.198°}{1.86 \text{ deg kg/mole}} = 0.106 \frac{\text{mole}}{\text{kg}}$$

Let α be the degree of dissociation of the acid. Then the molality of H_3O^+ is 0.10α; of F^-, 0.10α; of HF, $0.10 - 0.10\alpha = 0.10(1 - \alpha)$. The total molality is

$$m = m_{HF} + m_{H_3O^+} + m_{F^-}$$
$$= 0.10(1 - \alpha) + 0.10\alpha + 0.10\alpha$$
$$= 0.10(1 + \alpha)$$

Since $m = 0.106$,

$$1 + \alpha = \frac{0.106}{0.10} = 1.06$$
$$\alpha = 0.06 \text{ or } 6\%$$

Because ionization of a weak electrolyte causes only a small change in the freezing-point depression, the degree of dissociation calculated from this or other colligative properties is not very accurate, unless the temperatures are measured with extreme precision. The degree of dissociation of 0.10m HF, calculated from conductance measurements at 0°C, is 9.05%; this figure is more reliable than the 6% obtained from freezing-point depression.

We have made the assumption that ions have the same effect as neutral molecules in depressing the freezing point. This is a good approximation in very dilute solutions, and a poor one in solutions as concentrated as 0.1m. The effect of an ion on the colligative properties of a solution is related, in a complicated way, to its activity coefficient (pages 391, 515–518).

5.22 ACTIVITIES OF ELECTROLYTES

If there is an equilibrium between molecules and ions in a solution of a weak electrolyte, we should be able to apply the law of chemical equilibrium. Let c moles of a weak acid HA be dissolved in water to make a liter of solution. The acid will ionize to give some H_3O^+ and A^-. Let $x = [H_3O^+] = [A^-]$; then $[HA] = c - x$. The law of chemical equilibrium (page 348) requires that

$$\frac{[H_3O^+][A^-]}{[HA]} = K$$

$$\frac{x^2}{c - x} = K$$

or, in terms of the degree of dissociation, $\alpha = \frac{x}{c}$,

$$\frac{c^2\alpha^2}{c(1 - \alpha)} = \frac{c\alpha^2}{1 - \alpha} = K$$

We can calculate α from the equivalent conductance of the solution, and substitute it in the expression for the reaction quotient to see whether a constant is obtained. Some results of an especially careful test of this kind are shown in Table 15.4. The following sample calculation illustrates how K is obtained:

$$c = 2.0000 \times 10^{-2} \text{ mole/liter}$$
$$\alpha = 0.029875$$
$$1 - \alpha = 0.970125$$
$$K = \frac{c\alpha^2}{1 - \alpha} = \frac{2.0000 \times 10^{-2} \times (0.029875)^2}{0.970125}$$
$$= 1.840 \times 10^{-5}$$

The deviations from constancy, although not large, exceed the experimental uncertainty, and follow a definite trend, usually a symptom of

TABLE 15.4 *Reaction Quotient for Ionization of Acetic Acid*

Concentration (c) (mole/liter)	Degree of dissociation (α)	$K = \dfrac{c\alpha^2}{1 - \alpha}$
2.8014×10^{-5}	0.53926	1.768×10^{-5}
2.1844×10^{-4}	0.24767	1.781×10^{-5}
2.41400×10^{-3}	0.082900	1.809×10^{-5}
2.0000×10^{-2}	0.029875	1.840×10^{-5}

some deficiency in the theory. It is found quite generally that the law of chemical equilibrium, expressed in terms of concentrations, applies with only poor accuracy to reactions involving ions. The reason is that the law of chemical equilibrium is strictly correct only when activities, rather than concentrations, are used. We shall now consider how the activity concept can be adapted to electrolytes.

On page 318, we defined the activity of a component B of a solution as the ratio of its vapor pressure, in equilibrium with the solution, to its vapor pressure when pure at the same temperature: $a_B = p_B/p_B{}^0$. Most electrolytes have immeasurably small vapor pressures, although not really zero, so that their activities can, in principle, be defined in this way also. There are, however, two complications; the first complication applies to any solute in a dilute solution, while the second is peculiar to ions.

(1) The vapor pressure of the pure substance, in the definition of activity, properly refers to the pure substance in the same stage of aggregation as the solution—liquid, in our case. For the solvent in a dilute solution, this requirement presents no difficulty. The activity of the solvent compares its vapor pressure—its escaping tendency—over the solution to its vapor pressure in the pure state. The latter state is a standard from which the solvent deviates only slightly in a dilute solution. However, the solute—say iodine, I_2—in a dilute solution is in a state vastly different from that of pure liquid (supercooled) I_2 at the same temperature, and a comparison of their vapor pressures is of no special interest. Therefore, we adopt a definition of the activity of iodine based on Henry's law (page 320), which says that the vapor pressure of the solute is approximately proportional to its molar concentration,

$$p_{I_2} \approx k[I_2]$$

The proportionality becomes better as the solution becomes more dilute. First, we define an activity coefficient γ_{I_2} as the ratio of the actual vapor pressure p_{I_2} to what Henry's law says it should be,

$$\gamma_{I_2} = \frac{p_{I_2}}{k[I_2]}$$

The more dilute the solution, the closer γ_{I_2} is to 1. Now we define the activity of I_2 as the concentration multiplied by the activity coefficient,

$$a_{I_2} = \gamma_{I_2}[I_2] = \frac{p_{I_2}}{k}$$

For a sufficiently dilute solution, the activity so defined is equal to the concentration—another way of stating Henry's law. Hereafter, when we refer to the activity of a solute, it is this "Henry's law activity" that we shall mean. I_2, a nonelectrolyte, was used as an example in order that only one complication should appear at a time.

(2) HCl is one of the few electrolytes having measurable vapor pressures at room temperature. In the solution, H_3O^+ and Cl^- ions are present, with some HCl molecules if the concentration is high. In the gas

phase, there are no ions—only HCl molecules. The following equilibrium between molecules in gas and ions in solution is established:

$$H_3O^+ + Cl^- \rightleftharpoons HCl(g) + H_2O(l)$$

Applying the law of chemical equilibrium, in the form appropriate to a reaction involving a gas and a very dilute solution (page 349), we have

$$\frac{p_{HCl}}{[H_3O^+][Cl^-]} \approx K$$

or

$$p_{HCl} \approx K[H_3O^+][Cl^-]$$

This equation is a kind of modified Henry's law, for it relates the vapor pressure of the solute to its concentration in solution. But here, the pressure is proportional, not to the concentration of a single solute, but to a product of two concentrations. We cannot follow quite the same procedure as in the last paragraph in defining an activity for H_3O^+ or for Cl^-. We can, however, define the product of their activities: the product of the activity coefficients is

$$\gamma_{H_3O^+}\gamma_{Cl^-} = \frac{p_{HCl}}{K[H_3O^+][Cl^-]}$$

which becomes 1 in very dilute solution; the product of the activities is then

$$a_{H_3O^+}a_{Cl^-} = \gamma_{H_3O^+}\gamma_{Cl^-}[H_3O^+][Cl^-] = \frac{p_{HCl}}{K}$$

As with a nonelectrolyte, this product becomes equal to the product of the concentrations when the solution is sufficiently dilute.

This necessity for defining a product of ionic activities, rather than the activity of an individual ionic species, is quite general. When the electrolyte has a more complex formula, the product contains the activity of each ion raised to a power equal to the number of times it appears in the formula. For $CaCl_2$, for example, only the product $a_{Ca^{2+}}a_{Cl^-}^2$ can be measured by any experiment. (This product is referred to as the activity of $CaCl_2$, and is represented by a_{CaCl_2}.) It is possible to give some meaning to the idea of a single-ion activity, but only in terms of imaginary experiments always remaining outside the bounds of possibility. However, many equations are most simply written in terms of ionic activities, and an approximate theoretical calculation of these quantities is possible; we shall, therefore, following common practice, write such symbols as $a_{H_3O^+}$ and a_{Cl^-}, with the understanding that only approximate numerical values can be assigned to them.

15.23 ACTIVITY AND INTERIONIC FORCES

Henry's law, for a nonelectrolyte, expresses the fact that the rate of escape of solute molecules is proportional to the number of molecules present per unit volume—the escaping tendency of each molecule is approximately unaffected by the presence of other solute molecules. This is true, of course, only as long as the solution is dilute, when each solute molecule is far removed from the others. The effect of one solute particle on another should be much stronger when they are electrically charged than when they are neutral. The attractive force between two neutral molecules is weak even when they are close together, and falls off approximately as $1/r^7$ as the distance r between them increases. The attractive or repulsive force between two ions is much stronger at small distances, and is proportional to $1/r^2$ (Coulomb's law), so that it persists at greater distances. Therefore, it should not surprise us to find that electrolytic solutions deviate from Henry's law much more sharply than solutions of neutral molecules.

A mathematical analysis of the effects of electrostatic forces on the activities of ions was carried out in 1923 by Peter Debye and Erich Hückel. The assumption of their theory is that the spatial distribution of ions in a solution is not completely random; rather, the probability of finding a negative ion in the immediate vicinity of a positive ion is somewhat greater than the probability of finding the same negative ion just anywhere in the solution. Similarly, there is a preponderance of positive ions in the vicinity of any negative ion. The situation is described by saying that each ion is surrounded by an **ionic atmosphere** consisting of ions of opposite charge. This terminology has the unfortunate implication that each ion has a whole retinue of oppositely charged ions following it around. Of course, no one ion has such power over the others. There is merely a bias, superimposed on the random motions of the ions, which increases the probability that unlike ions will be found close together, and decreases the probability that like ions will be found close together.

The effect of the oppositely charged ionic atmosphere is that each ion is held more firmly in solution than it would otherwise be. The larger the concentration of ions of all kinds, the more closely each ion will be surrounded by its atmosphere, and the less its escaping tendency will be. We have already noted (pages 383–384) the effect of interionic forces on the equivalent conductance and on the colligative properties of an ionic solution. We are now interested in another effect of interionic forces: the activity coefficient of an ionic species is usually less than 1, and decreases as other ions, of whatever kind, are added. (The quantitative application of the Debye-Hückel theory will be left for Chapter 19, where we shall use it in making estimates of activity coefficients.)

Problems

1. **Freezing-point depression.** A 0.00200 molal aqueous solution of $KCo(NH_3)_2(NO_2)_4$ freezes at $-0.00736°C$. How many moles of ions are present in a solution containing one mole of this compound?

2. Balancing equations. Balance each of the following equations by the ion-electron method. Show the balanced partial equations for oxidation and reduction, and the ionic equation for the over-all reaction.

(a) $\quad\quad\quad\quad Pb(c) + PbO_2(c) \rightarrow Pb^{2+}$ (in acid solution)

(b) $\quad\quad\quad\quad Cl_2(g) + CN^- \rightarrow CNO^-$ (cyanate ion) $+ Cl^-$ (in basic solution)

(c) $\quad\quad\quad\quad Cr_2O_7{}^{2-} + H_2S(aq) \rightarrow Cr^{3+} + S_8(c)$ (in acid solution)

(d) $\quad\quad\quad\quad SO_3{}^{2-} + MnO_4{}^- \rightarrow SO_4{}^{2-} + MnO_4{}^{2-}$ (manganate ion) (in strongly basic solution)

(e) $\quad\quad\quad\quad I_2(c) \rightarrow I^- + IO_3{}^-$ (in basic solution)

(f) $\quad\quad\quad\quad Cu(NH_3)_4{}^{2+} + CN^- \rightarrow Cu(CN)_3{}^{2-} + CNO^- + NH_3$ (in basic solution)

(g) $\quad\quad\quad\quad H_2CO \quad + Ag(NH_3)_2{}^+ \rightarrow HCOO^- + Ag(c) + NH_3$ (in basic
$\quad\quad$ *formaldehyde* $\quad\quad\quad\quad\quad$ *formate* $\quad\quad$ solution)
$\quad\quad\quad\quad\quad\quad\quad\quad\quad\quad\quad\quad\quad\quad$ *ion*

3. Faraday's laws. An aqueous solution of $CuSO_4$ was electrolyzed between inert electrodes for 30.0 minutes. The only cathode reaction was the deposition of 0.231 g of Cu. (a) What was the reaction at the anode? ($SO_4{}^{2-}$ ion is not changed by the electrolysis.) How many (b) moles, (c) grams, (d) liters (sc) of the gaseous product were evolved at the anode? (e) How many coulombs passed through the solution? (f) What was the average current in amperes?

$\quad\quad\quad$ **Answer.** (b) 0.00182 mole; (c) 0.0582 g; (d) 0.0407 liter; (e) 702 coul; (f) 0.390 amp.

4. Equivalent conductance. The conductivity of a $0.100M$ solution of $Ca(NO_3)_2$ is 0.00966 ohm^{-1} cm^{-1} at 18°C. Find its equivalent conductance.

5. Degree of dissociation. (a) Find the equivalent conductance of benzoic acid, C_6H_5COOH, at infinite dilution at 25°C, assuming that it is completely ionized,

$$C_6H_5COOH + H_2O \rightarrow H_3O^+ + C_6H_5COO^-$$

The equivalent conductance of the benzoate ion at infinite dilution is 32.3 ohm^{-1} cm^2 eq^{-1}. (b) The equivalent conductance of $0.10M$ benzoic acid is 8.8 ohm^{-1} cm^2 eq^{-1}. Find the degree of dissociation of the acid in this solution.

$\quad\quad\quad$ **Answer.** (a) 382.1 ohm^{-1} cm^2 eq^{-1}; (b) 0.023.

6. Colligative properties. A $0.202m$ aqueous solution of chloroacetic acid, $CH_2ClCOOH$, freezes at -0.466°C. (a) Find the degree of dissociation of the acid. (b) Estimate the osmotic pressure of the solution at 0°C. (Molarity and molality are approximately equal.)

Additional problems

7. Freezing-point depression. Potassium chlorate, $KClO_3$, is an ionic salt. Estimate the freezing point of a 0.01000 molal aqueous solution of $KClO_3$. The actual freezing point is -0.03556°.

8. Osmotic pressure. Estimate the osmotic pressure of a $0.050M$ aqueous solution of $NaNO_3$ at 15°C.

9. Conductivity and temperature. Would you expect the conductivity of a fused salt to increase or to decrease as the temperature increases? Explain.

10. Balancing equations. Balance each of the following equations by the ion-electron method. Show the balanced partial equations, and the over-all equation in both ionic and molecular form.

(a) $Zn(c) + HONO_2(aq) \rightarrow Zn(NO_3)_2(aq) + NH_4NO_3(aq)$ (in acid solution)

(b) $(COOH)_2(aq,$ weak acid$) + KMnO_4(aq) + (HO)_2SO_2(aq) \rightarrow 2CO_2(g) + MnSO_4(aq) + K_2SO_4(aq)$ (in acid solution)
(Note that $(HO)_2SO_2$ is not oxidized or reduced)

(c) $CoSO_4(aq) + Na_2O_2(c) \rightarrow Co(OH)_3(c) + Na_2SO_4(aq)$ (in basic solution)

(d) $I_2(aq) + Na_2S_2O_3(aq) \rightarrow Na_2S_4O_6(aq) + NaI(aq)$ (in acid or neutral solution)

11. Faraday's laws. Three electrolytic cells are connected in series. In the first, Ag^+ is reduced to Ag. In the second, Zn is oxidized to Zn^{2+}. In the third, Hg_2^{2+} is oxidized to Hg^{2+}. If 1.00 g of Ag is deposited in the first cell, find the weight of Zn that is removed from the anode in the second cell, and the weight of $Hg(NO_3)_2$ that can be recovered from the solution in the third cell.

Answer. 0.303 g Zn, 3.01 g $Hg(NO_3)_2$.

12. Faraday's laws. A current of 0.750 ampere is used for the electrolytic decomposition of water. (a) How long (in hours) will it take to produce 1.00 liter (sc) of O_2? (b) What weight of H_2 will be produced in the same time?

13. Ion migration. Refer to Fig. 15.2b. Cu^{2+} ions have moved up the right arm of the tube; $Cr_2O_7^{2-}$ ions have moved up the left arm. OH^- ions (perhaps also Cl^-) have been produced at the top of the right arm; H_3O^+ ions have been produced at the top of the left arm. However, a sample (of more than a few molecules) taken from any part of the solution must be electrically neutral. Show in a diagram how the Na^+, Cl^-, and other ions migrate from one part of the solution to another, in such a way as to preserve neutrality.

14. Faraday's laws. Rhodium was plated from an aqueous solution containing Rh^{z+} for 2.00 hours with a current of 0.0650 ampere. The rhodium deposit on the cathode weighed 0.1664 g. (a) Find the equivalent weight exhibited by rhodium in this process. (b) What is the charge of the rhodium ion?

15. Faraday's laws. In a chemical plant, fused $NaCl$ is electrolyzed with a current of 100 amperes. How many (a) grams, and (b) pounds, of Na will be produced every 24 hours? How many (c) liters (sc), and (d) cubic feet (sc), of Cl_2 will be produced?

Answer. (a) 2.06×10^3 g; (b) 4.54 lb; (c) 1.00×10^3 liters; (d) 35.3 ft³.

16. Faraday's laws. In the electrolysis of a $CuSO_4$ solution, there were two reactions at the anode,

$$Cu \rightarrow Cu^{2+} + 2e^-$$

and

$$6H_2O \rightarrow O_2 + 4H_3O^+ + 4e^-$$

A current of 1.00 ampere passed for 1.00 hour. The loss in weight of the Cu anode was 0.600 g. (a) Find the current efficiency for the dissolution of Cu (the percentage of the current used in oxidizing Cu to Cu^{2+}). (b) How many moles of O_2 were liberated?

17. Faraday's laws. Chromium is plated from an acidic aqueous solution containing the dichromate ion; the reaction may be represented as

$$Cr_2O_7{}^{2-} + 14H_3O^+ + 12e^- \rightarrow 2Cr + 21H_2O$$

The current efficiency is low, about 15% (that is, 15% of the current is used to produce Cr). (a) What cathode reaction accounts for the remaining 85% of the current? (b) How many grams of Cr can be deposited by a current of 10.0 amperes flowing for 1.00 hour? Assume 15% current efficiency. (c) If the object being plated has a surface area of 100 cm², how thick a coating of Cr will be deposited in 1.00 hour? The density of Cr is 7.20 g/cm³.

Answer. (b) 0.481 g; (c) 6.71×10^{-4} cm.

18. Equivalent conductance. (a) From the data in Table 15.3, find the equivalent conductance of NaOH at infinite dilution at 25°C. (b) Find the conductivity of a $0.200M$ solution of NaOH, assuming that the equivalent conductance at this concentration is 80.0% of the equivalent conductance at infinite dilution.

Answer. (a) 248 ohm⁻¹ cm² eq⁻¹; (b) 0.0397 ohm⁻¹ cm⁻¹.

19. Electrical units. Using the results of the preceding problem, find (a) the resistance at 25°C of a cube of $0.20M$ NaOH solution 1.00 cm on an edge; (b) the resistance of $0.20M$ NaOH solution in a tube 10.0 cm long and 1.00 mm² in cross-sectional area; (c) the current that will flow through the tube in (b) if the potential difference across the tube is 10.0 volts and the electrodes have the same area as the tube; (d) the time required for one coulomb to pass through the tube under the conditions of (c).

20. Equivalent conductance. In pure water at 25°C, $[H_3O^+] = [OH^-] = 1.0 \times 10^{-7}$ mole/liter. Find the conductivity of perfectly pure water at this temperature.

Answer. 5.5×10^{-8} ohm⁻¹ cm⁻¹.

21. Equivalent conductance. The conductivity of a saturated solution of AgCl at 25°C is 1.7×10^{-6} ohm⁻¹ cm⁻¹, after subtraction of the conductivity of the water. Find the solubility, in moles per liter, of AgCl in H_2O at this temperature.

22. Ionic conductance. The equivalent conductance of thallium(I) perchlorate, $TlClO_4$, at infinite dilution at 25°C is 142.7 ohm⁻¹ cm² eq⁻¹. Experiments on the fraction of the current carried by each of the two ions indicate that the individual ionic conductances of Tl^+ and $ClO_4{}^-$ are in the ratio 1.099 to 1. Find the ionic conductances of Tl^+ and $ClO_4{}^-$.

Answer. 74.7, 68.0 ohm⁻¹ cm² eq⁻¹.

23. Degree of dissociation. The equivalent conductance at infinite dilution at 25°C of sodium propionate, C_2H_5COONa, is 85.92 ohm⁻¹ cm² eq⁻¹. (a) Find the equivalent conductance at infinite dilution of the propionate ion. (b) The equivalent conductance of $1.0M$ propionic acid, C_2H_5COOH, is 1.4 ohm⁻¹ cm² eq⁻¹. Find the degree of dissociation of this acid.

24. Strong electrolytes. The equivalent conductance of an aqueous solution of HCl at 25°C is 425.13 ohm⁻¹ cm² eq⁻¹ when the concentration is 2.841×10^{-5} mole/liter, and 418.10 when the concentration is 2.994×10^{-3} mole/liter. (a) From these data, calculate the apparent degree of dissociation of HCl in each of the two solutions. (b) Calculate the apparent values of the equilibrium constant for the reaction $HCl + H_2O \rightleftharpoons H_3O^+ + Cl^-$. (c) What conclusions can you draw from the results of these calculations?

Answer. (a) 0.998, 0.981; (b) 0.011, 0.15.

25. Freezing-point depression. In a 0.1000 molal aqueous solution, formic acid, HCOOH, is 4.2% ionized. Estimate the freezing point of this solution.

26. Association constants. The association constant of sodium bromate, $NaBrO_3$, in water at 25°C is 0.50. Find the percentage of ions paired in (a) 0.0010M and (b) 1.0M solutions of $NaBrO_3$ in water. (c) The association constant of $NaBrO_3$ in a mixed solvent consisting of 55% dioxane

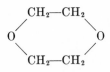

and 45% H_2O is 11.8 at 25°. Explain the difference between the constants in water and in the mixed solvent.

Answer. (a) 0.05%; (b) 27%.

16

Galvanic cells and the driving force of chemical reactions

16.1 INTRODUCTION

We saw in the last chapter that an electric current can cause chemical reactions. The process can be reversed, and electricity obtained from a chemical reaction. This discovery, by Alessandro Volta in 1796, provided for the first time a source of continuous electric current, and thus made possible the great electrical discoveries of the early nineteenth century, including the electrochemical observations that we have described. Today, the electrochemical cell, or battery of cells, has been generally superseded by the generator as a source of electricity. However, cells still have a place as portable sources of relatively small amounts of power. What is more important, from the point of view of chemistry, is that the electrical work that can be obtained from a chemical reaction provides a direct measure of the driving force of the reaction, and, not quite so directly, of its equilibrium constant.

One of the most familiar chemical reactions is the reaction between zinc and a soluble copper salt,

$$Zn(c) + CuSO_4(aq) \rightarrow Cu(c) + ZnSO_4(aq)$$

or, in ionic form,

$$Zn(c) + Cu^{2+} \rightarrow Cu(c) + Zn^{2+}$$

The products in this reaction have lower enthalpy than the reactants; that is, ΔH is negative, or the reaction is exothermic. Merely adding a piece of zinc to a $CuSO_4$ solution results in the liberation of heat, but yields no work, in mechanical or electrical form, aside from a minute amount that the reaction mixture will do if it expands against atmospheric pressure. Of course, the liberated heat can be partially converted to work (as in a steam engine), but this process is notoriously inefficient and does not help us to measure the maximum available work—the quantity in which we are especially interested.

16.2 ELECTRICITY FROM A CHEMICAL REACTION

To see how a reaction can be so harnessed as to produce electrical work directly, we first recall that an oxidation-reduction reaction can be resolved into two partial reactions (page 367),

$$Zn \rightarrow Zn^{2+} + 2e^- \quad (oxidation)$$
$$Cu^{2+} + 2e^- \rightarrow Cu \quad (reduction)$$

If we can arrange for these partial reactions to occur in two physically separated places, then the electrons will have to flow from the place where the oxidation occurs (the **anode**) to the place where the reduction occurs (the **cathode**). This flow of electrons constitutes a current, which can be used to drive a motor and lift a weight, or otherwise to do work.

The most obvious way to separate the partial reactions is to insert the Zn into a solution that does not contain Cu^{2+}—it may contain Zn^{2+}, or it may be plain water—and to insert a piece of Cu (or some unreactive

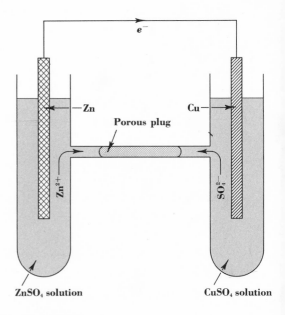

Fig. 16.1. A galvanic cell with liquid junction.

ZnSO$_4$ solution   CuSO$_4$ solution

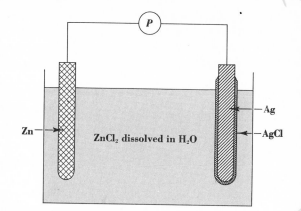

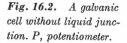

Zn — ZnCl₂ dissolved in H₂O — Ag
— AgCl

Fig. 16.2. A galvanic cell without liquid junction. P, potentiometer.

metal) into a solution containing Cu^{2+} (Fig. 16.1). When this is done, a minute amount of Zn can go into solution as Zn^{2+}, leaving a negative charge on the Zn (because of the electrons left behind) and a positive charge in the solution. These charges stop the process almost immediately; for every Zn^{2+} ion entering the solution, it or another ion will be driven back to the Zn electrode by the attraction of the negative electrode and the repulsion of the positive solution. Similarly, a few Cu^{2+} ions may deposit on the Cu electrode as Cu atoms, but this process will make the electrode positive and the solution negative and will thus stop itself. The deadlock can be broken if we connect the two electrodes by a wire, to allow the electrons from the Zn to flow to the electron-deficient Cu electrode,* and bring the two solutions into contact, to allow the charges of the solutions to be neutralized by a flow of ions between them (Fig. 16.1.) In other words, the circuit must be closed. The solutions should be connected through a narrow tube or a porous plug; we must not allow Cu^{2+} ions to reach the Zn electrode and take electrons from the Zn there, thus bypassing the wire and defeating our purpose. We can now see that the solution in contact with the Zn electrode must contain an electrolyte to make it a conductor—pure water is almost an insulator and would leave an open circuit.

An apparatus in which chemical energy is converted to electrical energy is known as a **galvanic cell**, after Luigi Galvani, whose discovery in 1786 of the effects of electricity on frog muscles prepared the way for Volta's work.

16.3 A GALVANIC CELL WITH ONE SOLUTION

Another galvanic cell, perhaps simpler (though less familiar) than that just described, is shown in Fig. 16.2. Two electrodes are immersed in a

* It may be that both the Cu and the Zn give up positive ions to the solution and become negatively charged, or they may both become positively charged by deposition of positive ions from the solution; no one can be sure. We do know that the Cu is more positive than the Zn, or the Zn is more negative than the Cu.

solution of $ZnCl_2$: one is simply a piece of zinc, and the other is a piece of silver, with a porous coating of silver chloride. Because of the very low solubility of AgCl, the solution contains only a trace of Ag^+ ion.

If the two solids, Zn and AgCl, are brought into contact, the reaction

$$Zn(c) + 2AgCl(c) \rightarrow 2Ag(c) + Zn^{2+} + 2Cl^-$$

will take place very slowly. The slowness results merely from the difficulty of establishing sufficiently intimate contact between two solids. But the reaction has a strong tendency to take place, in the sense that equilibrium is attained only when the reaction has gone nearly to completion. In the apparatus of Fig. 16.2, if there is no wire joining the electrodes, this reaction will occur so slowly that it can be ignored. The only way it can occur is by a reaction between Zn and the minute amount of Ag^+ in the solution,

$$Zn + 2Ag^+ \rightarrow Zn^{2+} + 2Ag$$

followed by dissolution of more AgCl to replenish the Ag^+,

$$AgCl \rightleftharpoons Ag^+ + Cl^-$$

However, when the two electrodes are joined by a conductor, the same reaction can proceed by an alternative route, which is much faster. Zn can enter the solution as Zn^{2+} ion at the left electrode,

$$Zn \rightarrow Zn^{2+} + 2e^-$$

The two electrons left behind on the Zn can travel through the conductor to the right electrode,* where the reaction

$$2e^- + 2AgCl \rightarrow 2Ag + 2Cl^-$$

occurs. The over-all process is

$$Zn + 2AgCl \rightarrow 2Ag + Zn^{2+} + 2Cl^-$$

the same reaction which, although spontaneous, was extremely slow until the circuit was closed. As in the Zn-Cu cell, the cell works because the reactants are kept apart and can react only by sending electrons through an external conductor.

16.4 ELECTRICAL WORK

When one gram-atom of Zn is converted to Zn^{2+} in this reaction, two faradays (page 376) of charge, or $2 \times 9.65 \times 10^4$ coulombs, pass through the external circuit. They can be harnessed to an electric motor, which does mechanical work, or their energy can be dissipated as heat in a resistor. The quantity of work that can be obtained as a given amount of charge passes from one point to another is determined by the **difference**

---

* More precisely, the electrons left on the Zn push other electrons toward the Ag electrode. The electrons that come out at one end of a conductor need not be the same ones that entered at the other end. It is not even meaningful to ask whether they are the same ones.

of potential between the two points. Potential is usually measured in *volts*. If point A is at a higher potential than point B, the work that must be done to transport a positive charge from B to A, against electrostatic forces, is

$$\underset{\text{[in joules]}}{\text{work}} = (\underset{\text{[in volts]}}{\text{potential at } A - \text{potential at } B}) \times \underset{\text{[in coulombs]}}{\text{charge}}$$

Conversely, work is done by a positive charge moving from A to B. For a negative charge, the signs of the work are reversed: the negative charge does work when it goes from a lower to a higher potential. A volt, then, is a joule per coulomb. The potential difference between the two electrodes in a galvanic cell is called the **electromotive force, or e.m.f.,** of the cell. The e.m.f. of the cell in Fig. 16.2 depends on the temperature and the concentration of the $ZnCl_2$ solution; if the temperature is 25°C and the concentration is suitably chosen (about 1.5 moles $ZnCl_2$ per liter), the e.m.f. of this particular cell is 1.00 volt. This means that when one gram-atom of zinc is consumed, and two faradays ($2 \times 9.65 \times 10^4$ coulombs) flow through the circuit, the work this electricity will do is

$$2 \times 9.65 \times 10^4 \text{ coulombs} \times 1.00 \text{ volt} = 1.93 \times 10^5 \text{ joules}$$
$$= 1.93 \times 10^5 \text{ joules} \times \frac{1 \text{ cal}}{4.184 \text{ joules}}$$
$$= 4.61 \times 10^4 \text{ cal}$$

This is the amount of work that can be obtained from the chemical reaction

$$Zn + 2AgCl \rightarrow 2Ag + Zn^{2+} + 2Cl^-$$

when one gram-atom of Zn reacts with two moles of AgCl, and is the most precise and realistic measure of the driving force of the reaction.

The reader may have noted by now that it was not necessary to have $ZnCl_2$ initially present in the solution; all we need is an electrolyte to make the solution a conductor. $ZnCl_2$ will appear as a product of the reaction. However, the e.m.f. depends on the concentrations of Zn^{2+} and Cl^- ions, so that the initial situation is more definite if we start with a known concentration of $ZnCl_2$, instead of just letting some unknown concentration appear when the reaction begins.

16.5 MEASUREMENT OF ELECTROMOTIVE FORCE

Not all the work theoretically available from a chemical reaction can actually be realized as work. Some of this energy appears as heat because of the resistance of the solution and of the wires. Another difficulty is that the electrode reactions cause local changes of concentration in the solution, and these changes are always such as to decrease the e.m.f. Such inefficiency is inevitable in any device that transforms one kind of energy into another. But we are interested not so much in obtaining work from the reaction as in measuring the maximum work that can be obtained, for this is what measures the driving force. To find this *maximum work*, we must measure the potential difference between the electrodes *when no current is flowing through the cell*. The device used for this purpose is called a **potentiometer.**

We shall not describe the details of the potentiometer. We may regard it simply as a galvanic cell, the e.m.f. of which can be varied continuously and read from a dial. The e.m.f. of the potentiometer tries to make a current flow through the cell. There is a chemical reaction that also tries to make a current flow through the cell, and we connect the cell so that these two currents will be in opposite directions. The potentiometer is then adjusted until the current is zero. At this point, the known e.m.f. of the potentiometer is equal to the e.m.f. of the cell.

16.6   FREE ENERGY AND ENTROPY

When a potentiometer is used to measure the e.m.f. of a cell, the measurement is made with no current flowing. There is, therefore, no loss because of resistance, and no creation of local concentration differences. The e.m.f. thus determined is a measure of the ideal maximum amount of work (in joules per coulomb of charge passed through the circuit) that can be obtained from the chemical reaction taking place in the cell. It is called the **reversible e.m.f.,** because the cell process can be reversed by a very small change in the opposing potential. Assume that the concentration of $ZnCl_2$, in the cell of Fig. 16.2, is such that the reversible e.m.f. is exactly one volt. Then the maximum work available when the cell reaction

$$Zn + 2AgCl \rightarrow 2Ag + Zn^{2+} + 2Cl^-$$

occurs is

$$1.00 \text{ volt} \times 9.65 \times 10^4 \frac{\text{coulombs}}{\text{faraday}} \times 2 \frac{\text{faradays}}{\text{gram-atom}}$$
$$= 1.93 \times 10^5 \text{ volt coulombs/gram-atom Zn}$$
$$= 1.93 \times 10^5 \text{ joules/gram-atom Zn}$$

This quantity is *minus* the **free energy change** (ΔF or ΔG) in the chemical reaction written above. The symbol Δ (*delta*) signifies "change": specifically, final value minus initial value. ΔF is the total free energy of 2 gram-atoms Ag, 1 mole Zn^{2+}, and 2 moles Cl^-, minus the total free energy of 1 gram-atom Zn and 2 moles AgCl:

$$\Delta F = 2F_{Ag} + F_{Zn^{2+}} + 2F_{Cl^-} - F_{Zn} - 2F_{AgCl}$$

Here, ΔF is negative, $-193,000$ joules, because the cell has done work, and its ability to do further work has declined. Free energy—"free" in the sense of "available"—is a measure of this ability to do work. The decrease in free energy is not equal to the electrical work actually done when current is drawn from the cell, for the work done is always less than that which might be done, and it is the possibility, not the performance, that is given by the free energy change.

If Zn and AgCl simply react with each other, not in a galvanic cell—or, equivalently, if the current from the cell is passed through a resistor, converting all work to heat—the total heat liberated is minus the enthalpy change ΔH (page 113). For this reaction, $\Delta H = -2.33 \times 10^5$ joules, the negative sign signifying the emission of heat. The maximum work available from the cell is 1.93×10^5 joules. Even in the ideal case of infinitely slow discharge, the available work is not equal to the heat emitted when the reactants merely mix and do no work (other than work against atmospheric pressure). The difference,

$$(2.33 \times 10^5) - (1.93 \times 10^5) = 4.0 \times 10^4 \text{ joules}$$

is the amount of energy that can be obtained only as heat and not as work.

The **entropy change,** ΔS, in a reaction is a measure of the difference between available heat and available work. The definition is

$$\Delta S = \frac{\Delta H - \Delta F}{T} \qquad \Delta F = \Delta H - \Delta S T$$

The presence of T in this equation becomes plausible if we understand that the entropy of a system is a measure of its randomness (or disorder) (page 51). If energy is added to a system, the vigor of molecular motion and hence the opportunities for disordered arrangements increase; therefore the entropy increases. At low temperatures the opportunity for increased disorder is great; therefore a given increase in energy produces a large increase in entropy. At high temperatures (when there is a higher likelihood of disorder) the effect of change in energy on change of entropy becomes small. Thus, for any given value of the difference $\Delta H - \Delta F$, the entropy change, ΔS, will be smaller at higher temperatures, greater at lower temperatures.

The heat emitted when the maximum work is done is

$$\begin{aligned} &\text{(heat emitted when no work is done)} - \text{(maximum work)}\\ =\quad &\qquad\qquad (-\Delta H) \qquad\qquad - \qquad (-\Delta F)\\ =\ &\Delta F - \Delta H\\ =\ &-T\Delta S \end{aligned}$$

For the Zn + AgCl reaction at 25°C,

$$\Delta S = \frac{-2.33 \times 10^5 - (-1.93 \times 10^5) \text{ joules}}{298°}$$

$$= -1.3 \times 10^2 \text{ joules/deg}$$

It is also possible for the maximum work that can be done to be greater than the maximum heat that can be given out; in such a case, heat is absorbed when the reaction occurs slowly enough in a galvanic cell, and ΔS is positive. An example is the reaction

$$Pb(c) + Hg_2Cl_2(c) \rightarrow PbCl_2(c) + 2Hg(l)$$

for which $\Delta H = -9.43 \times 10^4$ joules, and $\Delta F = -1.034 \times 10^5$ joules.

Entropy is one of the most important, and also one of the most subtle, concepts in physical science. A system tends to arrive at the least orderly configuration—the configuration of greatest entropy—simply because there are many more ways to be disorderly than to be orderly. On the other hand, the least orderly configurations have infinitely high energies; in general, an orderly arrangement (as in a crystal) has low energy, while a disorderly arrangement (as in a gas) has high energy. A system at a fixed temperature has only a limited amount of energy available to it, and therefore cannot achieve an indefinitely high entropy at that temperature. A balance is struck between low energy and high entropy: the system tends to arrive at that state in which $E - TS$ is a minimum. When the pressure is kept constant, enthalpy (page 122) plays the role of energy, and *the system tends to arrive at that state in which* $H - TS$ *is a minimum.* The higher the temperature, the more sensitive $H - TS$ is to changes in S, and therefore the more important is the tendency toward maximum entropy; the lower the temperature, the more important is the tendency toward minimum enthalpy. The function $H - TS$ is nothing other than the free energy F. The most stable state of the system, at a fixed temperature and pressure, is the state of minimum F. A process in which ΔF is negative (F decreases) leads to a more stable state, and this process can occur without the application of work; indeed, with sufficient ingenuity, work can be obtained from the process, in an amount not exceeding $-\Delta F$. A process with negative ΔF is described as "spontaneous," but the word is rather unfortunate, for the process may not actually occur at a measurable rate. The reaction

$$2H_2 + O_2 \rightarrow 2H_2O(l)$$

has $\Delta F = -113$ kcal at 25°C and is therefore "spontaneous," but the reaction does not occur at room temperature in the absence of a catalyst. The reverse reaction,

$$2H_2O(l) \rightarrow 2H_2 + O_2$$

has $\Delta F = +113$ kcal, which means that there is no hope of decomposing water to its elements at 25°C unless work, in the amount of at least 113 kcal for every 2 moles H_2O, is done. This information about free energy does not guarantee that water can be decomposed at all. We know that it can be, by electrolysis, and the electrical work required will be somewhat more than 113 kcal per 2 moles because of the inefficiency to be expected in any process.

The free energy change in a reaction is thus a measure of the driving force of the reaction. "Drift" might be a better word than "drive," for molecules behave randomly, not purposefully. The only direction in which the reaction can proceed, at constant temperature and pressure, is the direction of lower free energy, unless work is done on the reacting system. The reversible e.m.f. $\mathcal{E}$ associated with a reaction is really the free energy change in different units, and with the sign reversed. Let n be the number of faradays which pass through the circuit when the reaction occurs as written, and let $\mathfrak{F}$ be the Faraday constant, 9.65×10^4 coulombs/faraday. Then the free energy change is

$$\Delta F = -n\mathfrak{F}\mathcal{E}$$

The minus sign appears because, for a "spontaneous" reaction, ΔF is negative, while $\mathcal{E}$, by convention, is positive. $\mathcal{E}$ is in joules per coulomb (volts); ΔF is in joules or, more often, calories or kilocalories:

$$\Delta F \text{ (joules)} = -n \text{ (faradays)} \times \mathfrak{F}\left(\frac{\text{coulombs}}{\text{faraday}}\right) \times \mathcal{E}\left(\frac{\text{joules}}{\text{coulomb}}\right)$$
$$= -9.65 \times 10^4 \, n\mathcal{E} \text{ joules}$$
$$\Delta F \text{ (cal)} = -n \text{ (faradays)} \times 9.65 \times 10^4 \left(\frac{\text{coulombs}}{\text{faraday}}\right)$$
$$\times \mathcal{E}\left(\frac{\text{joules}}{\text{coulomb}}\right) \times \frac{1 \text{ cal}}{4.184 \text{ joules}}$$
$$= -2.305 \times 10^4 \, n\mathcal{E} \text{ cal}$$

We always think of the e.m.f. of a cell as being given for some definite concentration of each reactant and each product. If an appreciable amount of reaction takes place in a galvanic cell, the concentrations of the species involved in the reaction must change, and the e.m.f. will change with them. However, it is often convenient to speak of "the work done when the reaction

$$\text{Zn} + 2\text{AgCl} \rightarrow 2\text{Ag} + \text{Zn}^{2+} + 2\text{Cl}^-$$

takes place as written" (that is, when one gram-atom of Zn reacts with two moles of AgCl), and to calculate the work by multiplying the e.m.f., for definite concentrations, by the number of coulombs ($2 \times 9.65 \times 10^4$ in this case) associated with the reaction of these numbers of moles. This language may be interpreted in either of two ways:

(1) We imagine that only minute (infinitesimal) quantities of Zn and AgCl are consumed, say ϵ mole and 2ϵ mole, and "the work done when one mole of Zn is consumed" is $1/\epsilon$ times the work done when ϵ mole is consumed.

(2) We imagine that a very large, or infinite, quantity of each reactant and each product is present, so that one or two moles, more or less, does practically nothing to the concentrations—just as the salt concentration in the ocean is not appreciably changed by dumping in another mole (two ounces) of NaCl.

16.7 CELLS WITH LIQUID JUNCTIONS

A galvanic cell is a device in which a chemical reaction can take place only to the extent that electrons are transferred through an external circuit. The arrangement must be such that no reaction can occur until the circuit is closed, so that the tendency of a current to flow—the e.m.f.— is a measure of the tendency of the reaction to proceed. In the Zn-Ag-AgCl

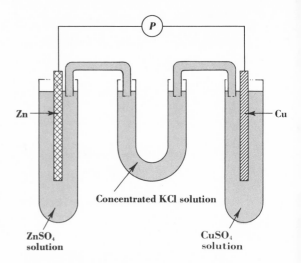

Fig. 16.3. *A galvanic cell with a salt bridge. P, potentiometer.*

ZnSO₄ solution

Concentrated KCl solution

CuSO₄ solution

Zn

Cu

P

cell (Fig. 16.2), this condition was satisfied because of the extreme slowness of the reaction between Zn and the minute quantity of Ag^+ in the solution, and the impossibility of a direct reaction between Zn and AgCl because of their physical separation. The zinc-copper cell that we discussed first, on the other hand, requires two different solutions, with one electrode in each solution (Fig. 16.1). The meeting place of the two solutions ($ZnSO_4$ and $CuSO_4$) is called a **liquid junction.**

The presence of a liquid junction introduces certain complications, which we shall not discuss. These complications are minimized when each solution is in contact with a concentrated solution of a salt in which the positive and negative ions have about the same equivalent conductance (page 385); KCl or NH_4NO_3 is usually chosen. Such a solution, used to join two other solutions in a galvanic cell, is called a **salt bridge.** A Zn-Cu cell, modified by inclusion of a salt bridge, is shown in Fig. 16.3. When the $ZnSO_4$ and $CuSO_4$ solutions have concentrations of 1 mole per liter, the e.m.f. of this cell is about 1.1 volts.

16.8 CONVENTIONAL NOTATION FOR CELLS

One often wishes to describe a galvanic cell without taking the trouble to draw an actual picture of it. We shall use the following notation for this purpose:

The material of one electrode (normally a metal) is listed first, by chemical symbol. Any other substance, not part of the solution, which is in contact with the electrode comes next; then the solution (assumed aqueous unless otherwise specified) is described by giving the formula(s) and concentration(s) of the solute(s). Phase boundaries (between solid and liquid, liquid and gas, or solid and gas) are indicated by |. If there is a second solution, its description is separated from the first by ¦ if the two solutions are in direct contact, or by ‖ if they are joined by a salt bridge. After the solution(s), the second electrode is specified, this time with the metal last.

The cells previously discussed may be represented thus:

Fig. 16.1: $Zn \mid ZnSO_4(\_M) \vdots CuSO_4(\_M) \mid Cu$
Fig. 16.2: $Zn \mid ZnCl_2(\_M) \mid AgCl \mid Ag$
Fig. 16.3: $Zn \mid ZnSO_4(\_M) \parallel CuSO_4(\_M) \mid Cu$

The anode is written on the left, and the cathode on the right, a rule that may be remembered by observing the alphabetical order in each of the following pairs: anode-cathode, oxidation-reduction, left-right. When this rule is obeyed and the left electrode is really the anode, the e.m.f. is positive. If, for any reason, the cell description is reversed, and the left electrode turns out to be the cathode, the sign of the e.m.f. is also reversed. A negative e.m.f. signifies that the cell has been written backward, and that the reaction goes in the direction opposite to that which was assumed.

16.9   THE HYDROGEN HALF-CELL; CONCENTRATION CELLS

An important type of cell is illustrated in Fig. 16.4:

$$Pt \mid H_2(1 \text{ atm}) \mid HCl(0.10M) \mid AgCl \mid Ag$$

Gaseous hydrogen is allowed to bubble over a "platinized platinum" electrode—a Pt electrode coated with finely divided Pt. The Pt serves as a catalyst for the anode reaction

$$\tfrac{1}{2}H_2(g) + H_2O \rightarrow H_3O^+ + e^-$$

The cathode is the same as in Fig. 16.2.

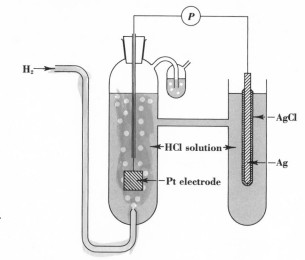

Fig. 16.4. *The cell*
Pt | H₂ | HCl | AgCl | Ag.
P, potentiometer.

The H_2–Pt–H_3O^+ part of this cell is called the "hydrogen electrode" or, more correctly (since an electrode is a piece of metal), the "hydrogen half-cell." It is of special importance because of its use as a standard of comparison for other half-cells (page 414).

A **concentration cell** is a cell in which there is no *net* chemical reaction—merely a transfer of matter from one concentration to another. We give two examples:

(a)   Pt | $H_2(p_1$ atm) | HCl(0.1M) | $H_2(p_2$ atm) | Pt*

This is called an **electrode concentration cell,** for the two halves of the cell differ only in the pressure (and concentration) of H_2. The reactions are

Anode: $H_2(p_1$ atm) $+ 2H_2O \rightarrow 2H_3O^+(0.1M) + 2e^-$
Cathode: $2H_3O^+(0.1M) + 2e^- \rightarrow H_2(p_2$ atm) $+ 2H_2O$

Over-all: $H_2(p_1$ atm) $\rightarrow H_2(p_2$ atm)

The work that the cell can do is just the work that H_2 will do in expanding from p_1 atm to the lower pressure p_2 atm; if p_2 is greater than p_1, we have written the cell backward, and the left electrode will be the cathode. If $p_1 = p_2$, the e.m.f. must be zero—otherwise, we could simply connect the two hydrogen reservoirs together, let the cell deliver current forever, and have a perpetual-motion machine.

(b)   Cu | $CuSO_4(aM)$ | $CuSO_4(bM)$ | Cu

The reactions here are

Anode: Cu $\rightarrow Cu^{2+}(aM) + 2e^-$
Cathode: $Cu^{2+}(bM) + 2e^- \rightarrow$ Cu

Over-all: $Cu^{2+}(bM) \rightarrow Cu^{2+}(aM)$

This cell is an **electrolyte concentration cell.** The e.m.f. is positive if $b > a$, in which case the cell process involves the transfer of Cu^{2+} from a more concentrated solution to a more dilute solution. The reverse process—more dilute to more concentrated—is nonspontaneous. Therefore, the e.m.f. for the cell as written is negative if $b < a$.

16.10   THE SIGN OF AN ELECTRODE

In a galvanic cell, electrons are fed into the anode by the oxidation (loss of electrons) taking place there. The *anode* emits these electrons into the external circuit and is therefore regarded as the *negative* electrode—the source of negative charge. The *cathode* is an electron sink and is therefore called the *positive* electrode.

In an electrolysis cell, the cathode is still the electron sink, but this time we are forcibly feeding electrons into the cathode by connecting it to the

* The pressures p_1 and p_2 are partial pressures if the H_2 is mixed with another gas. In this cell, water vapor will always be present, and we therefore write p rather than P.

negative terminal (the electron source) of a generator or a galvanic cell. Therefore, we think of the *cathode* as the *negative* electrode. Electrons are being sucked out of the anode by the positive terminal of the power source, and the *anode* is therefore considered *positive*.

Oxidation takes place at the anode and reduction at the cathode, in a cell of either type. The only difference is in our decision as to what we will call positive and what we will call negative.

16.11 THE NERNST EQUATION

The e.m.f. of a cell depends on the activity (or pressure) of each species involved in the cell reaction. We shall state without proof the equation relating the e.m.f. of a galvanic cell to these activities. The equation is called the **Nernst equation,** after Walther Nernst, who developed it in 1889 by considering the relation between activity and free energy. The equation is

$$\mathcal{E} = \mathcal{E}^\circ - \frac{2.303RT}{n\mathcal{F}} \log Q$$

standard Pontential–when all products and reactants are at unit concentration

where $\mathcal{E}$ is the e.m.f. of the cell in volts; $\mathcal{E}^\circ$ is a number, which depends on the temperature and on what the cell is; R is the gas constant, 1.987 cal/deg mole or 8.314 joules/deg mole; T is the absolute temperature; $\mathcal{F}$ is Faraday's constant, 9.6487×10^4 coulombs/faraday; n is the number of moles of electrons (faradays) transferred through the external circuit when the cell reaction takes place as written; the logarithm is to base 10; Q is the reaction quotient (page 336) for the reaction as written, and consists of the activity (page 318) of each product in the numerator and of each reactant in the denominator, each raised to a power equal to the coefficient of that species in the equation. For a gas, the partial pressure replaces the activity. When $T = 298.15°K$ ($25°C$), then

$$\frac{2.303RT}{\mathcal{F}} = \frac{2.303 \times 8.314 \frac{\text{joules}}{\text{deg mole}} \times 298.15°}{9.6487 \times 10^4 \frac{\text{coul}}{\text{faraday}}}$$

$$= 0.05915 \frac{\text{joule faraday}}{\text{coul mole}} \text{ or } \frac{\text{volt faraday}}{\text{mole}}$$

Because each faraday of charge corresponds to the production or consumption of one equivalent (page 376) of a product or reactant, we can also think of n as the number of equivalents involved in the reaction as written, in which case we would take the units as

$$\frac{2.303RT}{\mathcal{F}} = 0.05915 \frac{\text{volt eq}}{\text{mole}}$$

At 25°C, the Nernst equation is

$$\mathcal{E} = \mathcal{E}^\circ - \frac{0.05915}{n} \log Q$$

An example will give more meaning to these abstract statements. Take the cell of Fig. 16.2 (page 399),

$$Zn \mid ZnCl_2(aq) \mid AgCl \mid Ag$$

The cell process is

$$Zn(c) + 2AgCl(c) \rightarrow 2Ag(c) + Zn^{2+} + 2Cl^-$$

The number of faradays transferred when the cell reaction occurs as written is $n = 2$, as we can see by writing the two electrode reactions:

$$Zn \rightarrow Zn^{2+} + 2e^-$$
$$2AgCl + 2e^- \rightarrow 2Ag + 2Cl^-$$

The reaction quotient is

$$Q = a_{Zn^{2+}}(a_{Cl^-})^2$$

The solids are omitted (page 344). Then the e.m.f., at 25°C, is

$$\mathcal{E} = \mathcal{E}^\circ - \left(\frac{0.05915}{2}\right) \log (a_{Zn^{2+}}a_{Cl^-}^2)$$

When $a_{Zn^{2+}}a_{Cl^-}^2 = 1$, $\mathcal{E} = \mathcal{E}^\circ$ (since log 1 = 0); this quantity is called the **standard e.m.f.,** and is the e.m.f. of the cell when all activities are equal to 1. We should note that the e.m.f. depends on the product $a_{Zn^{2+}}a_{Cl^-}^2$, which is a product of ion activities of the kind that can be measured (page 391). The e.m.f. of the cell cannot give us $a_{Zn^{2+}}$ or a_{Cl^-} alone.

The cell reaction could have been written, just as correctly,

$$\tfrac{1}{2}Zn + AgCl \rightarrow Ag + \tfrac{1}{2}Zn^{2+} + Cl^-$$

In this case, the electrode processes are

$$\tfrac{1}{2}Zn \rightarrow \tfrac{1}{2}Zn^{2+} + e^-$$
$$AgCl + e^- \rightarrow Ag + Cl^-$$

so that $n = 1$. The reaction quotient for this reaction is

$$Q' = (a_{Zn^{2+}})^{1/2} a_{Cl^-}$$

Clearly, $Q' = Q^{1/2}$, and

$$\log Q' = \log (Q^{1/2}) = \tfrac{1}{2} \log Q$$

The e.m.f. of the cell, with the reaction written in the second form, is

$$\mathcal{E} = \mathcal{E}^\circ - \frac{0.05915}{1} \log Q' = \mathcal{E}^\circ - 0.05915 \times \tfrac{1}{2} \log Q$$

the same as before. Thus, the relation between the e.m.f. and the activities is unaffected by multiplying all the coefficients in the equation by a constant. The change of n just compensates for the power to which Q is raised.

For the purpose of obtaining a better understanding of the Nernst equation, and of learning how it can be used for calculations, we shall, in this section, make the simplifying assumption that activities are equal to concentrations. This approximation is not very good, and we shall see, in the next section, how a cell can be used to determine true activities.

When $Q = 1$, $\log Q = 0$, and $\varepsilon = \varepsilon°$. The physical significance of $\varepsilon°$, then, is that it is the e.m.f. of a cell in which $Q = 1$: a cell in which all activities are equal to 1 (and pressures are 1 atm, if there are gases). When we assume that activities and concentrations are the same, we can interpret $\varepsilon°$ as the e.m.f. of a cell in which the concentration of each solute species—molecule or ion—appearing in the cell reaction is 1 mole per liter.

When $\varepsilon°$ and concentrations are given, the Nernst equation can easily be used to calculate ε for the cell.

EXAMPLE 1 For the cell

$$\text{Sn} \mid \text{SnCl}_2(0.10M) \mid \text{AgCl} \mid \text{Ag}$$

$\varepsilon° = 0.363$ volt at 25°C. Calculate ε.

ANSWER At the anode (left side), the reaction (oxidation) is

$$\text{Sn} \rightarrow \text{Sn}^{2+} + 2e^-$$

At the cathode, the reaction (reduction) is

$$\text{AgCl} + e^- \rightarrow \text{Ag} + \text{Cl}^-$$

The equation for the over-all reaction is obtained by doubling the second partial equation (to obtain $2\text{AgCl} + 2e^- \rightarrow 2\text{Ag} + 2\text{Cl}^-$) and adding,

$$\text{Sn} + 2\text{AgCl} \rightarrow 2\text{Ag} + \text{Sn}^{2+} + 2\text{Cl}^-$$

When this reaction occurs as written (1 mole Sn reacts with 2 moles AgCl), two faradays pass through the circuit, as we can see from the partial equations: $n = 2$. The Nernst equation, in terms of concentrations, is therefore

$$\varepsilon = \varepsilon° - \left(\frac{0.05915}{2}\right) \log\,[\text{Sn}^{2+}][\text{Cl}^-]^2$$

In a $0.10M$ solution of SnCl_2, $[\text{Sn}^{2+}] = 0.10$ and $[\text{Cl}^-] = 0.20$ mole/liter. Therefore

$$\varepsilon = \varepsilon° - \left(\frac{0.05915}{2}\right) \log\,[(0.10)(0.20)^2]$$

$$= 0.363 - \left(\frac{0.05915}{2}\right) \log\,(4 \times 10^{-3})$$

$$= 0.363 + 0.071 = 0.434 \text{ volt}$$

If we had used activities instead of concentrations, we would have obtained $\varepsilon = 0.460$ volt.

EXAMPLE 2   **Find ε for the cell**

$$\text{Cu} \mid \text{CuCl}_2(0.50M) \mid \text{Cl}_2(1.50 \text{ atm}) \mid \text{Pt}$$

given that ε° = +1.012 volts at 25°C.

ANSWER   **The anode reaction is the oxidation of Cu,**

$$\text{Cu} \rightarrow \text{Cu}^{2+} + 2e^-$$

The cathode reaction is the reduction of Cl₂,

$$\text{Cl}_2 + 2e^- \rightarrow 2\text{Cl}^-$$

The over-all cell reaction is

$$\text{Cu} + \text{Cl}_2 \rightarrow \text{Cu}^{2+} + 2\text{Cl}^-$$

and the Nernst equation is

$$\varepsilon = \varepsilon° - \left(\frac{0.05915}{2}\right) \log \left(\frac{[\text{Cu}^{2+}][\text{Cl}^-]^2}{p_{\text{Cl}_2}}\right)$$

Here, $[\text{Cu}^{2+}]$ = 0.50 mole/liter, $[\text{Cl}^-]$ = 1.00 mole/liter, and p_{Cl_2} = 1.50 atm. Thus

$$\varepsilon = \varepsilon° - \left(\frac{0.05915}{2}\right) \log \left(\frac{0.50 \times 1.00^2}{1.50}\right)$$
$$= 1.012 + 0.014 = 1.026 \text{ volts}$$

The direction of the change in e.m.f. resulting from a change of concentration can be predicted, without calculation, by a rule closely related to Le Châtelier's principle (page 342). *Increasing* the concentration of a *product decreases* the tendency of the reaction to occur and therefore *decreases* (algebraically) the e.m.f. *Increasing* the concentration of a *reactant increases* the e.m.f.

16.13   **DETERMINATION OF STANDARD E.M.F. AND ACTIVITY COEFFICIENTS**

For the cell $\text{Zn} \mid \text{ZnCl}_2(aq) \mid \text{AgCl} \mid \text{Ag}$, the Nernst equation at 25°C is

$$\varepsilon = \varepsilon° - \left(\frac{0.05915}{2}\right) \log \left[a_{\text{Zn}^{2+}}(a_{\text{Cl}^-})^2\right]$$

If we write the activities in terms of concentrations and activity coefficients, we have

$$\varepsilon = \varepsilon° - \left(\frac{0.05915}{2}\right) \log \left(\gamma_{\text{Zn}^{2+}}\gamma_{\text{Cl}^-}^2 \ [\text{Zn}^{2+}][\text{Cl}^-]^2\right)$$

or

$$\varepsilon° = \varepsilon + \left(\frac{0.05915}{2}\right) \log \left(\gamma_{\text{Zn}^{2+}}\gamma_{\text{Cl}^-}^2 [\text{Zn}^{2+}][\text{Cl}^-]^2\right)$$

In a very dilute solution, $\gamma_{Zn^{2+}} = 1$ and $\gamma_{Cl^-} = 1$, so that in such a solution,

$$\mathcal{E}° = \mathcal{E} + \left(\frac{0.05915}{2}\right) \log \left([Zn^{2+}][Cl^-]^2\right)$$

The very dilute solution is prepared with known concentrations, and $\mathcal{E}$ is measured with a potentiometer; $\mathcal{E}°$ can then be calculated.* The value of $\mathcal{E}°$ obtained in careful experiments of this kind is 0.9849 volt.

Once we know $\mathcal{E}°$, the cell can be used to determine the product $\gamma_{Zn^{2+}}$ $\times \gamma_{Cl^-}^2$ in more concentrated solutions; we need only measure $\mathcal{E}$ with known concentrations. Some results of such experiments are tabulated on page 518, and compared with the predictions of the Debye-Hückel theory.

As a second example, consider the cell of Fig. 16.3 (page 406),

$$Zn \mid ZnSO_4 \parallel CuSO_4 \mid Cu$$

in which the reaction is

$$Zn + Cu^{2+} \to Zn^{2+} + Cu$$

Here again, $n = 2$ ($Zn \rightleftharpoons Zn^{2+} + 2e^-$). The reaction quotient is

$$Q = \frac{a_{Zn^{2+}}}{a_{Cu^{2+}}}$$

and the e.m.f. is

$$\mathcal{E} = \mathcal{E}° - \left(\frac{0.05915}{2}\right) \log \left(\frac{a_{Zn^{2+}}}{a_{Cu^{2+}}}\right)$$

at 25°C. This expression is not exact, because of the complications resulting from the liquid junction (page 406). When a suitable salt bridge is used, however, the equation is believed to be a good approximation and is generally used, either to estimate the ratios of ionic activities or to find the e.m.f. when these activities are given.

A final example will be the electrode concentration cell

$$Pt \mid H_2(g)(p_1 \text{ atm}) \mid HCl \mid H_2(g)(p_2 \text{ atm}) \mid Pt$$

The net reaction in this cell is

$$H_2(g, p_1 \text{ atm}) \to H_2(g, p_2 \text{ atm})$$

and this process is accompanied by the transfer of two faradays through the circuit. The e.m.f. is

$$\mathcal{E} = \mathcal{E}° - \left(\frac{2.303RT}{2\mathcal{F}}\right) \log \left(\frac{p_2}{p_1}\right)$$
$$= - \left(\frac{0.05915}{2}\right) \log \left(\frac{p_2}{p_1}\right)$$

at 25°C. We saw (page 408) that $\mathcal{E} = 0$ for this cell when $p_1 = p_2$. $\mathcal{E}°$ must therefore be 0, since, when $p_1 = p_2$, $\log (p_2/p_1) = 0$, and $\mathcal{E} = \mathcal{E}°$.

* In practice, the calculation involves an extrapolation to zero concentration.

A galvanic cell always requires two electrodes. Oxidation must occur at one electrode (the anode), and reduction at the other (the cathode). There is no way in which we can measure the potential difference between an electrode and a solution without introducing another electrode; what we always measure, as the e.m.f. of a cell, is a potential difference between two electronic conductors.

However, it is useful, as a bookkeeping device, to think of a cell as consisting of two half-cells, with each half-cell contributing its share to the e.m.f. of the entire cell. A half-cell consists of an electrode and the solution with which it is in contact. If a cell is made of two half-cells containing different solutions, we consider the solutions to be joined by a salt bridge. *It is possible to assign a potential to each half-cell*, such that the e.m.f. of the entire cell is equal to the difference between the half-cell potentials. It is this fact that makes useful the resolution of an e.m.f. into half-cell potentials. Instead of tabulating the standard e.m.f. $\mathcal{E}°$ for every cell, we need tabulate it only for every half-cell, and $\mathcal{E}°$ for any cell that can be made by combining two of these half-cells is obtained immediately by subtraction.

Only the e.m.f. of a complete cell can be measured, and this e.m.f. is a difference of half-cell potentials. Therefore, we can choose any half-cell arbitrarily, call its standard potential zero, and measure the standard potentials of all other half-cells by combining them with this reference half-cell. If we had taken the standard potential of the reference half-cell to be 100 volts instead of 0, all half-cell potentials would be increased by 100 volts, but their differences would be unaffected. *The half-cell always chosen as the reference is* $HCl(aq) \mid H_2 \mid Pt$. The standard potential of another half-cell (C) is defined as the standard e.m.f. of the cell obtained by combining the half-cell C, on the left, with the reference H_2 half-cell on the right. The e.m.f. of the resulting cell is positive if C is really the anode. Therefore, a half-cell has a *positive* potential if it functions as an *anode* when combined with the reference half-cell; a *negative* potential, if it is a *cathode* relative to the reference half-cell. The words "anode" and "cathode" apply strictly to the electrodes (the metallic conductors). However, we shall also refer to the half-cell (electrode + solution) in which oxidation occurs as the anode, and the half-cell in which reduction occurs as the cathode.

For example, the standard e.m.f. of the cell

$$Ag \mid AgCl \mid HCl(aq) \mid H_2 \mid Pt$$

is -0.2221 volt. The negative sign indicates that the electrode on the left is actually the cathode. If we write the cell thus,

$$Pt \mid H_2 \mid HCl(aq) \mid AgCl \mid Ag$$

we would say that the e.m.f. is $+0.2221$ volt—not because the cell has changed, but because our representation of it has been reversed. When we consider a half-cell by itself, we always regard it as an anode, for uniformity. Thus, the half-cell potential of

Ag | AgCl | HCl(aq)

is the same as the e.m.f. of the cell

Ag | AgCl | HCl(aq) | H$_2$ | Pt

and is -0.2221 volt. Whether a given half-cell proves to be the anode or the cathode depends on what the other half-cell is. $\mathcal{E}°$ for a cell is always $\mathcal{E}°$ for the left half-cell minus $\mathcal{E}°$ for the right half-cell,

$$\mathcal{E}°_{cell} = \mathcal{E}°_{left} - \mathcal{E}°_{right}$$

For the cell Ag | AgCl | HCl(aq) | H$_2$ | Pt, $\mathcal{E}°_{right} = 0$ by arbitrary convention, and

$$\mathcal{E}°_{cell} = \mathcal{E}°_{left} - 0 = -0.2221 \text{ volt}$$

Then $\mathcal{E}°_{left} = -0.2221$ volt. If we write the cell as

Pt | H$_2$ | HCl(aq) | AgCl | Ag

$\mathcal{E}°_{left} = 0$ by convention, and

$$\mathcal{E}°_{cell} = 0 - \mathcal{E}°_{right} = +0.2221 \text{ volt}$$

so that $\mathcal{E}°_{right} = -0.2221$ volt, as before.

The cell

Zn | ZnCl$_2$(aq) | AgCl | Ag

may similarly be resolved into two half-cells:

Zn | ZnCl$_2$, and ZnCl$_2$ | AgCl | Ag

The second of these differs from the half-cell HCl | AgCl | Ag only in that the positive ion is Zn^{2+} instead of H$_3$O$^+$. But this difference does not affect $\mathcal{E}°$, for the reaction in this half-cell,

AgCl + e$^-$ → Ag + Cl$^-$

involves only the Cl$^-$ ion; the standard e.m.f. is determined by measurements in very dilute solution, such that activities are equal to concentrations, and at such low concentrations it makes no difference to the Cl$^-$ ion whether Zn^{2+} or H$_3$O$^+$ is the other kind of ion. Thus, the standard potential of the right electrode is still -0.2221 volt. The standard e.m.f. of the entire cell at 25°C (page 413) is 0.9849 volt. As in the last paragraph,

$$0.9849 = \mathcal{E}°_l - \mathcal{E}°_r = \mathcal{E}°_l - (-0.2221)$$

and $\mathcal{E}°_l = +0.7628$ volt for the half-cell Zn | ZnCl$_2$(aq).

The standard potential of the half-cell Cu | Cu^{2+} may be determined by comparing it with any of the three half-cells for which we now know the potentials. If the Zn half-cell is chosen, we prepare the cell

Zn | ZnCl$_2$ ‖ CuSO$_4$ | Cu

using a salt bridge to join the two unlike solutions. (Any soluble salts of Cu^{2+} and Zn^{2+} could be used in place of $CuSO_4$ and $ZnCl_2$.) The reaction of this cell, as written, is

$$Zn + Cu^{2+} \rightarrow Zn^{2+} + Cu$$

At 25°C, $\mathcal{E}°$ for this cell is found by experiment to be $+1.1088$ volts. Then

$$+1.1088 = \mathcal{E}_l° - \mathcal{E}_r° = +0.7628 - \mathcal{E}_r°$$

and $\mathcal{E}_r° = -0.3460$ volt. By experiments of this kind, the standard potential of every possible half-cell can be determined. A list of a relatively few such potentials is given in Table 16.1. When an inert electrode is needed, we have indicated Pt, but other substances, notably graphite, could be used, except when the catalytic activity of platinum is important (as in the reactions involving gases).

The proof that the calculation of an e.m.f. from half-cell potentials is legitimate is left to the reader (Problem 10, page 434).

EXAMPLE 3   **Find $\mathcal{E}°$ at 25°C of the cell**

$Cu \mid CuCl_2(aq) \mid Cl_2(g) \mid Pt$

ANSWER   **First we write the anode and cathode reactions, and the over-all cell process. Beside each half-reaction, we write $\mathcal{E}°$ from the table on page 417:**

		$\mathcal{E}°$ (volts)
Anode:	$Cu \rightarrow Cu^{2+} + 2e^-$	-0.3460
Cathode:	$Cl_2 + 2e^- \rightarrow 2Cl^-$	-1.3583

$$Cu + Cl_2 \rightarrow Cu^{2+} + 2Cl^-$$

Then we calculate $\mathcal{E}°$ for the cell by subtracting the standard e.m.f. for the right half-cell from that for the left half-cell:

$$\mathcal{E}° = -0.3460 - (-1.3583) = +1.0123 \text{ volts}$$

The plus sign indicates that the left electrode is the anode.

Many persons prefer to *reverse the sign* of $\mathcal{E}°$ for the cathode (reduction) half-reaction, and then *add* the $\mathcal{E}°$'s,

$$-0.3460$$
$$+1.3583$$
$$\overline{+1.0123}$$

Obviously, there is no difference between $\mathcal{E}_l° - \mathcal{E}_r°$ and $\mathcal{E}_l° + (-\mathcal{E}_r°)$, but much difficulty results from confusing the two procedures. The best advice is: adopt one convention or the other and stick to it. Either copy the e.m.f. values *directly from the table* and *subtract*, or *reverse the sign* of the *cathode* e.m.f. and *add.*

TABLE 16.1 *Half-Cell Potentials in Aqueous Solution at 25°C (arranged alphabetically by chemical symbols)*

Half-cell	Half-reaction	$\mathcal{E}\,°(volts)$
Ag | Ag$^+$	Ag $\leftrightharpoons$ Ag$^+$ + e$^-$	-0.7996
Ag | AgCl(c) | Cl$^-$	Ag + Cl$^-$ $\leftrightharpoons$ AgCl(c) + e$^-$	-0.2221
Ag | Ag$_2$CrO$_4$(c) | CrO$_4{}^{2-}$	2Ag + CrO$_4{}^{2-}$ $\leftrightharpoons$ Ag$_2$CrO$_4$(c) + 2e$^-$	-0.4463
Ag | AgI(c) | I$^-$	Ag + I$^-$ $\leftrightharpoons$ AgI(c) + e$^-$	$+0.1519$
Ag | NH$_3$(aq), Ag(NH$_3$)$_2{}^+$	Ag + 2NH$_3$(aq) $\leftrightharpoons$ Ag(NH$_3$)$_2{}^+$ + e$^-$	-0.373
Al | Al^{3+}	Al $\leftrightharpoons$ Al^{3+} + 3e$^-$	$+1.67$
Au | Au$^+$	Au $\leftrightharpoons$ Au$^+$ + e$^-$	-1.7
Au | Au^{3+}	Au $\leftrightharpoons$ Au^{3+} + 3e$^-$	-1.42
Au | CN$^-$, Au(CN)$_2{}^-$	Au + 2CN$^-$ $\leftrightharpoons$ Au(CN)$_2{}^-$ + e$^-$	$+0.60$
^{a}Ba | Ba^{2+}	Ba $\leftrightharpoons$ Ba^{2+} + 2e$^-$	$+2.90$
Pt | Br$_2$(l) | Br$^-$	2Br$^-$ $\leftrightharpoons$ Br$_2$(l) + 2e$^-$	-1.0650
^{a}Ca | Ca^{2+}	Ca $\leftrightharpoons$ Ca^{2+} + 2e$^-$	$+2.76$
Cd | Cd^{2+}	Cd $\leftrightharpoons$ Cd^{2+} + 2e$^-$	$+0.4024$
Pt | Cl$_2$(g) | Cl$^-$	2Cl$^-$ $\leftrightharpoons$ Cl$_2$(g) + 2e$^-$	-1.3583
Pt | Cr^{3+}, HCrO$_4{}^-$, H$_3$O$^+$	Cr^{3+} + 11H$_2$O $\leftrightharpoons$ HCrO$_4{}^-$ + 7H$_3$O$^+$ + 3e$^-$	-1.195
Cr | Cr^{3+}	Cr $\leftrightharpoons$ Cr^{3+} + 3e$^-$	$+0.74$
Cu | Cu^{2+}	Cu $\leftrightharpoons$ Cu^{2+} + 2e$^-$	-0.3460
^{a}Pt | F$_2$(g) | F$^-$	2F$^-$ $\leftrightharpoons$ F$_2$(g) + 2e$^-$	-2.85
Fe | Fe^{2+}	Fe $\leftrightharpoons$ Fe^{2+} + 2e$^-$	$+0.441$
Pt | Fe^{2+}, Fe^{3+}	Fe^{2+} $\leftrightharpoons$ Fe^{3+} + e$^-$	-0.7701
Pt | H$_2$(g) | H$_3$O$^+$	H$_2$(g) + 2H$_2$O $\leftrightharpoons$ 2H$_3$O$^+$ + 2e$^-$	0.0000
Pt | H$_2$(g) | OH$^-$	H$_2$(g) + 2OH$^-$ $\leftrightharpoons$ 2H$_2$O + 2e$^-$	$+0.8277$
Hg(l) | Hg$_2{}^{2+}$	2Hg $\leftrightharpoons$ Hg$_2{}^{2+}$ + 2e$^-$	-0.7986
Hg(l) | Hg^{2+}	Hg $\leftrightharpoons$ Hg^{2+} + 2e$^-$	-0.852
Hg(l) | Hg$_2$Cl$_2$(c) | Cl$^-$	2Hg + 2Cl$^-$ $\leftrightharpoons$ Hg$_2$Cl$_2$(c) + 2e$^-$	-0.2677
Pt | I$_2$(c) | I$^-$	2I$^-$ $\leftrightharpoons$ I$_2$(c) + 2e$^-$	-0.5356
^{a}K | K$^+$	K $\leftrightharpoons$ K$^+$ + e$^-$	$+2.9241$
^{a}Li | Li$^+$	Li $\leftrightharpoons$ Li$^+$ + e$^-$	$+2.9595$
Mg | Mg^{2+}	Mg $\leftrightharpoons$ Mg^{2+} + 2e$^-$	$+2.375$
Pt | Mn^{2+}, MnO$_4{}^-$, H$_3$O$^+$	Mn^{2+} + 12H$_2$O $\leftrightharpoons$ MnO$_4{}^-$ + 8H$_3$O$^+$ + 5e$^-$	-1.50
^{a}Na | Na$^+$	Na $\leftrightharpoons$ Na$^+$ + e$^-$	$+2.7132$
Ni | Ni^{2+}	Ni $\leftrightharpoons$ Ni^{2+} + 2e$^-$	$+0.23$
Pt | O$_2$(g) | H$_3$O$^+$	6H$_2$O $\leftrightharpoons$ O$_2$(g) + 4H$_3$O$^+$ + 4e$^-$	-1.229
Pt | O$_2$(g) | OH$^-$	4OH$^-$ $\leftrightharpoons$ O$_2$(g) + 2H$_2$O + 4e$^-$	-0.401
Pb | Pb^{2+}	Pb $\leftrightharpoons$ Pb^{2+} + 2e$^-$	$+0.1263$
Pb | PbSO$_4$(c) | SO$_4{}^{2-}$	Pb + SO$_4{}^{2-}$ $\leftrightharpoons$ PbSO$_4$(c) + 2e$^-$	$+0.336$
Pt | PbSO$_4$(c) | PbO$_2$(c) | H$_3$O$^+$, HOSO$_3{}^-$	PbSO$_4$(c) + 5H$_2$O $\leftrightharpoons$ PbO$_2$(c) + 3H$_3$O$^+$ + HOSO$_3{}^-$ + 2e$^-$	-1.685

(Continued on next page.)

TABLE **16.1** (*Continued*)

Half-cell	Half-reaction	$\varepsilon°$ (*volts*)
Pt | **Pt²⁺**	$Pt \leftrightharpoons Pt^{2+} + 2e^-$	-1.2
Sn | **Sn²⁺**	$Sn \leftrightharpoons Sn^{2+} + 2e^-$	$+0.1406$
Zn | **Zn²⁺**	$Zn \leftrightharpoons Zn^{2+} + 2e^-$	$+0.7628$

ᵃ **These half-cells cannot be prepared because of a vigorous reaction between one**
constituent and water. Their potentials have been determined indirectly.

16.15 CALCULATION OF EQUILIBRIUM CONSTANTS

The Nernst equation, in its general form (page 409), is

$$\varepsilon = \varepsilon° - \left(\frac{2.303RT}{n\mathfrak{F}}\right) \log Q$$

where Q is the reaction quotient, the same function of activities and partial
pressures that appears in the law of chemical equilibrium. Now, if current
is drawn from the cell until the cell reaction has come to equilibrium, the
e.m.f. must become zero, for a system at equilibrium can do no work
(page 336). In other words, no reaction, no e.m.f. *The condition of equilibrium for the cell reaction is, then, $\varepsilon = 0$*, or

$$\varepsilon° - \left(\frac{2.303RT}{n\mathfrak{F}}\right) \log Q = 0$$

or

$$\log Q = \frac{n\mathfrak{F}\varepsilon°}{2.303RT}$$

Define K by

$$\frac{n\mathfrak{F}\varepsilon°}{2.303RT} = \log K$$

Then the condition of equilibrium (when $\varepsilon = 0$) is $Q = K$, which is the
law of chemical equilibrium (page 336). As we see, this law is a consequence of the Nernst equation for any reaction that can take place in a
galvanic cell; a cell, or combination of cells, can be devised for almost any
reaction on paper, but often not in reality.

For example, in the cell

$$Pt \mid H_2(p \text{ atm}) \mid HCl(M \text{ moles/liter}) \mid AgCl(c) \mid Ag(c)$$

the reactions are

$$\tfrac{1}{2}H_2 + H_2O \leftrightharpoons H_3O^+ + e^-$$
$$AgCl + e^- \leftrightharpoons Ag + Cl^-$$

$$\tfrac{1}{2}H_2 + H_2O + AgCl \leftrightharpoons H_3O^+ + Cl^- + Ag$$

The reaction quotient is

$$Q = \frac{a_{H_3O^+}\, a_{Cl^-}}{p_{H_2}^{1/2} X_{H_2O}}$$

where we have omitted the solids and recalled that the activity of H_2O is approximately equal to its mole fraction (Raoult's law, page 319). To determine the equilibrium constant is the same as to determine $\mathcal{E}°$ for the cell. This is done by making the HCl solution so dilute that activities can be replaced by concentrations, and X_{H_2O} by 1; in such a cell,

$$\mathcal{E} = \mathcal{E}° - \left(\frac{2.303RT}{n\mathcal{F}}\right) \log\left(\frac{[H_3O^+][Cl^-]}{p_{H_2}^{1/2}}\right)$$

For this cell, at 25°C, $\mathcal{E}° = 0.2221$ volt and $n = 1$; then

$$\log K = \frac{\mathcal{F}\mathcal{E}°}{2.303RT} = \frac{\mathcal{E}°}{0.05915} = 3.75$$

$$K = 10^{3.75} = 5.6 \times 10^3$$

That is to say, when an aqueous solution of HCl is in contact with solid Ag, solid AgCl, and gaseous H_2, the equilibrium condition is

$$\frac{a_{H_3O^+}\, a_{Cl^-}}{p_{H_2}^{1/2}\, X_{H_2O}} = 5.6 \times 10^3 \approx \frac{[H_3O^+][Cl^-]}{p_{H_2}^{1/2}}$$

The equilibrium constant of any reaction can be determined if we can resolve it into two half-reactions for which the potentials are given in a table. The potential for the reduction half-reaction is subtracted from the potential for the oxidation half-reaction. From the resultant e.m.f. $\mathcal{E}°$, we calculate K as shown above.

EXAMPLE 4   **Find the equilibrium constant at 25°C for the reaction**

$$Ag_2CrO_4(c) \leftrightharpoons 2Ag^+ + CrO_4{}^{2-}$$

ANSWER   **Inspection of those half-reactions in the table involving Ag shows that the following two can be combined to give the desired reaction:**

	$\mathcal{E}°$ (volts)
$Ag \leftrightharpoons Ag^+ + e^-$	-0.7996
$2Ag + CrO_4{}^{2-} \leftrightharpoons Ag_2CrO_4 + 2e^-$	-0.4463

We double the first, reverse the second, and add the half-reactions:

$2Ag \leftrightharpoons 2Ag^+ + 2e^-$	-0.7996
$Ag_2CrO_4 + 2e^- \leftrightharpoons 2Ag + CrO_4{}^{2-}$	$-(-0.4463)$
$AgCrO_4 \leftrightharpoons 2Ag^+ + CrO_4{}^{2-}$	-0.3533

Note that the potential is not affected by doubling the coefficients, or multiplying them by any constant. The potential of the half-reaction written as a reduction is subtracted (or, its sign is changed and it is added) to obtain $\mathcal{E}° = -0.3533$ volt. Here $n = 2$(two electrons appear in each half-reaction).

Then

$$\log K = \frac{2\varepsilon^\circ}{0.05915} = \frac{2(-0.3533)}{0.05915} = -11.94$$

$$K = 10^{-11.94} = 1.15 \times 10^{-12} = (a_{Ag^+})^2 a_{CrO_4^{2-}}$$

EXAMPLE 5 **Find the equilibrium constant at 25°C for the reaction (in aqueous solution)**

$$Zn + Cu^{2+} \leftrightharpoons Zn^{2+} + Cu$$

ANSWER **The half-reactions, with their standard potentials, are**

		ε° (volts)
Oxidation:	$Zn \to Zn^{2+} + 2e^-$	$+0.7628$
Reduction:	$Cu^{2+} + 2e^- \to Cu$	$-(-0.3460)$

Thus $\varepsilon^\circ = 0.7628 - (-0.3460) = +1.1088$ volts, and $n = 2$ (two electrons in each half-reaction). Then

$$\log K = \frac{n\varepsilon^\circ}{0.05915} = \frac{2 \times 1.1088}{0.05915} = 37.5$$

$$K = 10^{37.5} = 3 \times 10^{37}$$

EXAMPLE 6 **Find the equilibrium constant at 25°C for the reaction**

$$2H_2O \leftrightharpoons H_3O^+ + OH^-$$

ANSWER **The two half-reactions suitable in this case are**

	ε° (volts)
$H_2 + 2H_2O \leftrightharpoons 2H_3O^+ + 2e^-$	0.0000
$2H_2O + 2e^- \leftrightharpoons H_2 + 2OH^-$	$-(+0.8277)$
$4H_2O \leftrightharpoons 2H_3O^+ + 2OH^-$	-0.8277

This reaction is double the desired one. We multiply each half-reaction by $\frac{1}{2}$ to make the over-all reaction

$$2H_2O \leftrightharpoons H_3O^+ + OH^-$$

This does not affect the potentials, but makes $n = 1$ instead of 2, so that

$$\log K = \frac{-0.8277}{0.05915} = -14.00$$

$$K = 1.0 \times 10^{-14}$$

This quantity is known as the *ion product of water*, and is probably the most frequently encountered of all equilibrium constants.

16.16 FREE ENERGY AND EQUILIBRIUM

When a chemical reaction is capable of doing work, as in a galvanic cell, there is a decrease in free energy (page 402) when the reaction occurs.

The maximum work available from the reaction, in which $\frac{1}{2}$ mole H_2, 1 mole H_2O, and 1 mole AgCl yield 1 mole HCl and 1 gram-atom Ag, is $-\Delta F$ for the reaction

$$\tfrac{1}{2}H_2 + H_2O + AgCl \rightarrow H_3O^+ + Cl^- + Ag$$

The maximum work is also measured by the reversible e.m.f. of the cell in which this reaction occurs. $\mathcal{E}$ is work in joules per coulomb (volts); $-\Delta F$ is the work available for the number of moles shown in the equation. The relation between these two measures of maximum work is (page 405)

$$-\Delta F = n\mathfrak{F}\mathcal{E}$$

For the reaction above, $n = 1$, but, if the equation were written

$$H_2 + 2H_2O + 2AgCl \rightarrow 2H_3O^+ + 2Cl^- + 2Ag$$

n would be 2, and ΔF would be doubled. ΔF is like ΔH in its dependence on the form chosen for the equation; $\mathcal{E}$, on the other hand, is work *per coulomb* and is unaffected if the equation is doubled, halved, etc. When the equation is reversed, both $\mathcal{E}$ and ΔF change sign.

When all species involved in the reaction are at unit activity, $\mathcal{E} = \mathcal{E}^\circ$ and $\Delta F = \Delta F^\circ$. This special value of ΔF is called the **standard free energy change** for the reaction,

$$-\Delta F^\circ = n\mathfrak{F}\mathcal{E}^\circ$$

Obviously, the equations that we have written in terms of $\mathcal{E}$ and $\mathcal{E}^\circ$ can equally well be written in terms of ΔF and ΔF°. The Nernst equation becomes its historical predecessor, the **van't Hoff equation** (Jacobus Henricus van't Hoff, 1886),

$$\Delta F = \Delta F^\circ + 2.303RT \log Q$$

At equilibrium, the reaction can do no work: $\mathcal{E} = 0$, $\Delta F = 0$. The van't Hoff equation is, in this case,

$$0 = \Delta F^\circ + 2.303RT \log Q$$

or, since $Q = K$ at equilibrium,

$$\Delta F^\circ = -2.303RT \log K$$

When ΔF° is negative ($\mathcal{E}^\circ$ positive), K is greater than 1; when ΔF° is positive ($\mathcal{E}$ negative), K is less than 1.

Equilibrium constants can thus be calculated equally well from $\mathcal{E}^\circ$ values or from ΔF° values, depending on the form in which the data are available. ΔF°'s for several reactions can be combined to yield ΔF° for another reaction, in exactly the same way that ΔH's are combined by Hess's law (page 114).

EXAMPLE 7   **Calculate ΔF° and K for the reaction**

$$\tfrac{1}{2}H_2(g) + H_2O(l) + AgCl(c) \leftrightharpoons H_3O^+(aq) + Cl^-(aq) + Ag(c)$$

given the following $\Delta F°$ values at 25°C:

	$\Delta F°$ (kcal)
$Ag(c) + \frac{1}{2}Cl_2(g) \rightarrow AgCl(c)$	-26.22
$H_2(g) + Cl_2(g) \rightarrow 2HCl(g)$	-45.54
$HCl(g) + H_2O(l) \rightarrow H_3O^+(aq) + Cl^-(aq)$	-8.58

ANSWER   The reactions must be written in such a way that they add up to the desired reaction. We must reverse the first, halve the second, and leave the third as it is:

	$\Delta F°$ (kcal)
$AgCl(c) \rightarrow Ag(c) + \frac{1}{2}Cl_2(g)$	$-(-26.22)$
$\frac{1}{2}H_2(g) + \frac{1}{2}Cl_2(g) \rightarrow HCl(g)$	$\frac{1}{2}(-45.54)$
$HCl(g) + H_2O(l) \rightarrow H_3O^+(aq) + Cl^-(aq)$	-8.58
$\frac{1}{2}H_2(g) + H_2O(l) + AgCl(c) \rightarrow H_3O^+(aq) + Cl^-(aq) + Ag(c)$	-5.13 kcal

Then $\Delta F° = -5.13$ kcal/mole $= -5130$ cal/mole, and

$$\log K = \frac{-\Delta F°}{2.303RT}$$

$$= \frac{5130 \frac{\text{cal}}{\text{mole}}}{2.303 \times 1.987 \frac{\text{cal}}{\text{deg mole}} \times 298°}$$

$$= 3.76$$

$$K = 5.7 \times 10^3$$

16.17   PREDICTING THE DIRECTION OF A REACTION

Often we wish to know whether a reaction can occur when certain chemicals are present in certain amounts. A rigorous way to answer this question is to find the equilibrium constant K for the reaction in question and to calculate the reaction quotient Q for the reaction, using the initial activities, concentrations, or pressures of the species present. Then if $Q < K$, the reaction may go from left to right; if $Q > K$, from right to left.

EXAMPLE 8   A solution contains Ag^+ and CrO_4^{2-} ions, with $[Ag^+] = 10^{-3}$ mole/liter and $[CrO_4^{2-}] = 10^{-4}$ mole/liter. Will solid Ag_2CrO_4 dissolve in or precipitate from this solution? Assume that activities are equal to concentrations.

ANSWER   For the reaction

$$Ag_2CrO_4(c) \leftrightharpoons 2Ag^+ + CrO_4^{2-}$$

we have

$$Q = [Ag^+]^2[CrO_4^{2-}] = (10^{-3})^2(10^{-4}) = 10^{-10}$$

This is greater than $K = 1.15 \times 10^{-12}$ (Example 4), and the reaction will go to the left; in other words, Ag_2CrO_4 will precipitate.

A simpler procedure is often adequate to determine the direction of a reaction. Suppose the reactants and products are all mixed in such quantities that the activity of each species (for a gas, the partial pressure) is 1. Then $Q = 1$. If $K > 1$, the reaction will go to the right; if $K < 1$, to the left. Of course, we do not usually mix chemicals at unit activity, but in a large proportion of cases the concentrations are in the range 0.01 to 10 moles/liter—not vastly removed from 1 mole/liter (or pressures, not too far from 1 atm). Thus, when chemicals are mixed together, the chances are that Q is neither very large nor very small. (Example 8 illustrates an exception.) On the other hand, most equilibrium constants *are* very large or very small, with only an occasional one happening to fall near 1. To decide, therefore, which way a reaction will go, it usually suffices to ascertain whether $K > 1$ or $K < 1$. These cases correspond, respectively, to $\log K > 0$ and $\log K < 0$, and to $\mathcal{E}° > 0$ and $\mathcal{E}° < 0$, as we see from the equation

$$\mathcal{E}° = \left(\frac{2.303RT}{n\mathcal{F}}\right) \log K$$

If $\mathcal{E}° > 0$, the reaction goes from left to right; if $\mathcal{E}° < 0$, it goes from right to left. The rule becomes unreliable when $\mathcal{E}°$ is close to 0—and, of course, it applies only when all concentrations are near 1 mole/liter.

EXAMPLE 9 **Will Fe reduce Fe^{3+} to Fe^{2+}?**

ANSWER **The half-reactions in which we are interested are**

		$\mathcal{E}°$ (volts)
Oxidation:	$Fe \rightarrow Fe^{2+} + 2e^-$	+0.441
Reduction:	$(Fe^{3+} + e^- \rightarrow Fe^{2+}) \times 2$	$-(-0.7701)$

For the over-all reaction

$$Fe + 2Fe^{3+} \rightarrow 3Fe^{2+}$$

the standard e.m.f. is

$$\mathcal{E}° = +0.441 - (-0.7701) = +1.211$$

Since $\mathcal{E}° > 0$, the reaction is possible when activities are near 1. A practical consequence of this result is that a solution of a ferrous (Fe^{2+}) salt can be protected from atmospheric oxidation by keeping solid iron in the bottle; any Fe^{3+} formed will be reduced to Fe^{2+}.

EXAMPLE 10 **Will the permanganate ion, MnO_4^-, liberate O_2 from water in the presence of acid (H_3O^+)?**

ANSWER **The reaction in question is**

$$4MnO_4^- + 12H_3O^+ \rightleftharpoons 4Mn^{2+} + 5O_2 + 18H_2O$$

which is the resultant of the half-reactions

$$\begin{array}{lr} & \mathcal{E}° \text{ (volts)} \\ (6H_2O \leftrightharpoons O_2 + 4H_3O^+ + 4e^-) \times 5 & -1.2229 \\ (MnO_4^- + 8H_3O^+ + 5e^- \leftrightharpoons Mn^{2+} + 12H_2O) \times 4 & -(-1.50) \\ \hline & +0.28 \end{array}$$

For the over-all reaction, $\mathcal{E}°$ is positive, and the reaction is possible. What we mean is not that, if we mix MnO_4^- and H_3O^+ in aqueous solution, at least minute amounts of Mn^{2+} and O_2 will be formed at equilibrium; that much can be said without calculation or reference to data. The significant result of the calculation is that, when the reaction has gone far enough to make each activity (or pressure, for O_2) of the order of 1, equilibrium has not yet been attained. The reaction will continue until there is more Mn^{2+} than MnO_4^-, and a considerable amount of O_2 has accumulated.

We have learned nothing here about the rate of the reaction; in neutral solution, this one is very slow, so that MnO_4^- solutions can be stored, with certain precautions, for several years without measurable change of composition. In acid solution, the reaction is much faster.

EXAMPLE 11 Will O_2 oxidize gold to $Au(CN)_2^-$ in the presence of cyanide ion (CN$^-$) and OH$^-$?

ANSWER The reactions in question are

$$\begin{array}{lr} & \mathcal{E}° \text{ (volts)} \\ (Au + 2CN^- \leftrightharpoons Au(CN)_2^- + e^-) \times 4 & +\quad 0.60 \\ O_2 + 2H_2O + 4e^- \leftrightharpoons 4OH^- & -(-0.401) \\ \hline 4Au + 8CN^- + O_2 + 2H_2O \leftrightharpoons 4Au(CN)_2^- + 4OH^- & +\quad 1.00 \end{array}$$

The reaction goes to the right—a rather surprising result, for Au is notoriously unreactive and does not tarnish in air. The explanation is that the presence of CN$^-$ permits the formation of a complex ion, $Au(CN)_2^-$, which is much more stable than anything that could be formed from Au, O_2, and H_2O alone. The metallurgical application of this effect in the cyanide leaching of gold ores is described in Chapter 27.

16.18 OXIDATION AND REDUCTION POTENTIALS

The potentials in Table 16.1 (page 417) are called **oxidation potentials** because they measure the tendency of a half-reaction to occur, in the direction corresponding to oxidation. The more *positive* the potential the more the electrode tends to behave as an *anode*; the more *negative* the potential, the more it tends to be a *cathode*. The most positive potentials belong to the half-reactions in which the best reducing agents are oxidized, and their oxidized forms are the poorest oxidizing agents. For example, the potential $+2.9241$ volts tells us that potassium is an excel

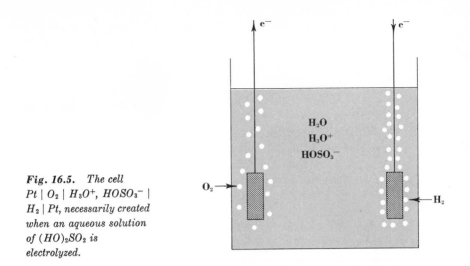

Fig. 16.5. *The cell*
Pt | O₂ | H₃O⁺, HOSO₃⁻ |
H₂ | Pt, necessarily created
when an aqueous solution
of (HO)₂SO₂ is
electrolyzed.

lent reducing agent, because it is easily oxidized to K^+, whereas K^+ is very difficult to reduce to K, so that K^+ is a poor oxidizing agent. Sodium, with an oxidation potential of $+2.7132$ volts, is also a very good reducing agent, but not quite so good as K. At the other extreme, the potential for the half-reaction $2F^- \rightleftharpoons F_2 + 2e^-$ is -2.85 volts, which indicates that F^- is a very poor reducing agent, being oxidized to F_2 only with great difficulty; conversely, F_2 is the best of all oxidizing agents.

Some books give reduction potentials, which are simply the negatives of ours. The easiest way to determine which sign convention is being used is to look for the potential associated with a familiar half-reaction near one of the extremes. For example, if a table gives a positive potential for the half-cell Na | Na⁺, we know that this table lists oxidation potentials, for it is common knowledge that Na is easily oxidized to Na⁺; if the table gives a negative potential, the tabulated values must be reduction potentials.

16.19 DECOMPOSITION POTENTIAL; OVERVOLTAGE AND POLARIZATION

Consider the electrolysis, at Pt electrodes, of water that contains some sulfuric acid to make it a conductor. The reactions are

$$4H_3O^+ + 4e^- \rightarrow 2H_2(g) + 4H_2O \qquad \text{at the cathode}$$

and

$$6H_2O \rightarrow O_2(g) + 4H_3O^+ + 4e^- \qquad \text{at the anode}$$

As soon as current starts to flow, the liberation of O_2 and H_2 converts the apparatus to the galvanic cell

$$Pt \mid O_2 \mid H_3O^+, HOSO_3^- \mid H_2 \mid Pt \qquad \text{(Fig. 16.5)}$$

The e.m.f. of this cell is

$$-1.229 - 0 = -1.2 \text{ volts}$$

if all activities and pressures are 1, and it will not differ greatly from this value in the actual situation. As the negative e.m.f. shows, the anode of this galvanic cell is the right electrode, which we are using as a cathode in the electrolysis, and conversely. The cell is trying to make a current flow in the direction opposite to the current with which we are trying to electrolyze the solution. In order to overcome this back e.m.f., the applied e.m.f. must be at least 1.2 volts. For each coulomb passed, 1.2 joules are used in changing the water to the less stable form of hydrogen and oxygen gases. Only the energy in excess of this value is available for overcoming the electrical resistance of the circuit. If the applied e.m.f. is increased gradually from zero, practically no current will flow until 1.2 volts is attained. Thereafter, the current rises approximately as a straight line, with a slope determined by the resistance of the circuit (Fig. 16.6). The e.m.f. $\mathcal{E}_d$ at which the rise begins is called the **decomposition potential** of the solution.

The decomposition potential must be at least equal to the zero-current e.m.f. (page 402) of the cell whose reaction is opposite to the desired electrolysis reaction. However, it is often necessary to increase the applied e.m.f. considerably above this value in order to cause a reaction at an appreciable rate. The excess potential required is called the **overvoltage,** and depends on the nature of the electrode surface, the current per unit area, and the composition of the solution. Large overvoltages are observed only when gases are products of the reaction. Typical values of overvoltage are zero to one volt.

Even in the absence of overvoltage, the potential necessary to bring about electrolysis at an appreciable rate may be considerably greater

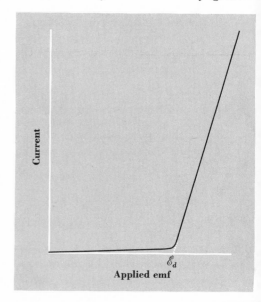

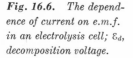

Fig. 16.6. The dependence of current on e.m.f. in an electrolysis cell; $\mathcal{E}_d$, decomposition voltage.

than one would calculate from the $\varepsilon°$ values. These apply to unit activity of every species, and the electrolysis causes non-uniformities in the concentration of the electrolyte, always in such a way as to increase the required potential. For example, the process of deplating Cu from one electrode and plating it on another electrode in the same solution has $\varepsilon° = 0$:

$$Cu \rightarrow Cu^{2+} + 2e^-$$
$$Cu^{2+} + 2e^- \rightarrow Cu$$

Net reaction: none; merely the transfer of Cu from one place to another. In canceling Cu^{2+} from the two sides of the equations, we assumed that the Cu^{2+} ion produced at the anode is fully identical with the Cu^{2+} ion consumed at the cathode. Even if the solution is initially homogeneous, however, the electrode reactions will increase the concentration of Cu^{2+} near the anode and decrease it near the cathode, thus creating the concentration cell

$$Cu \mid Cu^{2+}(c_1) \mid Cu^{2+}(c_2) \mid Cu$$

and the reactions corresponding to this cell are

$$Cu \rightarrow Cu^{2+}(c_1) + 2e^-$$
$$Cu^{2+}(c_2) + 2e^- \rightarrow Cu$$
$$\overline{\phantom{Cu^{2+}(c_2) \rightarrow Cu^{2+}(c_1)}}$$
$$Cu^{2+}(c_2) \rightarrow Cu^{2+}(c_1)$$

The e.m.f. of this concentration cell is

$$\varepsilon = 0 - \frac{0.05915}{2} \log\left(\frac{c_1}{c_2}\right)$$

The electrolysis produces Cu^{2+} on the left (thus increasing c_1), and depletes Cu^{2+} on the right (thus decreasing c_2). The result is that $c_1 > c_2$, and $\varepsilon < 0$. Thus, the process tends to go from right to left, and the cell creates an e.m.f. in opposition to the e.m.f. applied for the purpose of plating and deplating Cu. This effect is called **concentration polarization,** and can often be diminished simply by stirring the solution. The term "polarization" includes any effect (other than ordinary resistance) that raises the decomposition potential above its theoretical minimum value. A galvanic cell from which current is drawn exhibits concentration polarization, and the reader can easily verify (Problem 16, page 435) that the polarization will always diminish the e.m.f. available from the cell.

16.20   **SELECTION OF ELECTRODE PROCESS**

It is usually possible to write a number of reactions that might occur at each electrode when an electric current is passed through a solution. Several of these may actually occur at the same time. A decision as to which one, or ones, will predominate can often be made with the aid of a table of half-cell potentials. We recall that the more positive the potential, the more easily the oxidation takes place; the more negative the potential, the more easily the reduction takes place. Therefore, of all the conceivable anode reactions for which the reactants are present, that with the most positive half-cell potential will predominate. Of all the conceivable cathode reactions for which the reactants are present, that with the most negative potential will predominate. We shall assume here that activities are close enough to 1 so that, for each half-reaction, ε does not differ greatly from $\varepsilon°$. These rules are based on the assumption that there is no overvoltage.

EXAMPLE 12   **An aqueous solution of NiBr$_2$ and HBr is electrolyzed with Cu electrodes. What will be the reaction at each electrode, neglecting overvoltage? Assume that all activities are approximately equal to 1.**

ANSWER   **Conceivable reactions at the anode:**

		$\varepsilon°$ (volts)
(1)	$6H_2O \rightarrow O_2 + 4H_3O^+ + 4e^-$	-1.229
(2)	$Cu \rightarrow Cu^{2+} + 2e^-$	-0.346
(3)	$2Br^- \rightarrow Br_2(l) + 2e^-$	-1.065

Conceivable reactions at the cathode:

(4)	$2H_3O^+ + 2e^- \rightarrow H_2(g) + 2H_2O$	0
(5)	$Ni^{2+} + 2e^- \rightarrow Ni$	$+0.23$

($2H_2O + 2e^- \rightarrow H_2 + 2OH^-$ is excluded in this solution, which contains the strong acid HBr; any OH$^-$ produced would react with H$_3$O$^+$, and the net reaction would be reaction (4) again.)

Reaction (2) will predominate at the anode, because it has the most positive (least negative) potential; reaction (4) will predominate at the cathode, because it has the most negative (least positive) potential.

Taking account of overvoltage may lead to selection of a different reaction. In this example, the overvoltage for evolution of H$_2$ on a nickel surface is high enough so that the principal reaction at the cathode is reaction (5) rather than (4).

The reaction selected in this way is not necessarily the only one that occurs. If the applied e.m.f. is large enough, the more difficult reactions can be brought about at the same time. In the preceding example, reactions (2) and (5) require an e.m.f. of at least $0.346 + 0.23 = 0.58$ volt to overcome the back e.m.f.; reactions (2) and (4) would require $0.346 + 0 = 0.346$ volt. If the applied e.m.f. is greater than 0.58 volt, H$_2$ and Ni may be formed simultaneously at the cathode.

16.21   **THE DRY CELL AND THE STORAGE CELL**

Of the galvanic cells used as sources of power, we shall discuss only the two most familiar: the dry cell and the lead-acid storage battery. Figure

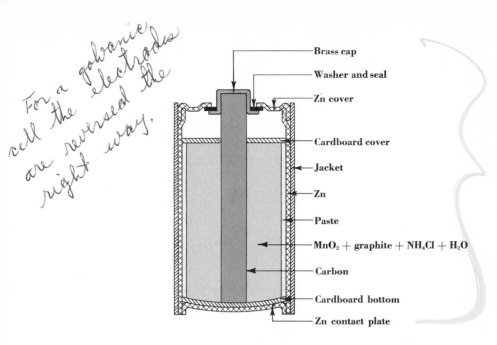

Fig. 16.7. *A dry cell as used in flashlights.*

16.7 shows a typical dry cell. The anode is Zn; the cathode is C, which is chemically inert under ordinary conditions. A paste consisting of graphite, MnO_2, NH_4Cl, and H_2O surrounds the cathode. Adjacent to the Zn is a layer of paste, usually made from wheat flour, containing H_2O, NH_4Cl, and $ZnCl_2$, but not MnO_2. The cell is "dry" only in the sense that it contains paste rather than free liquid; it could not function if water were absent. The electrode reactions are complicated and subject to some controversy. One representation is

Anode: $Zn \rightarrow Zn^{2+} + 2e^-$
Cathode: $2NH_4^+ + 2MnO_2 + 2e^- \rightarrow Mn_2O_3 + 2NH_3(aq) + H_2O$

The lead-acid storage cell, in its charged state, consists of an electrode of spongy lead and an electrode of finely divided solid PbO_2, each material supported by a grid of Pb-Sb alloy (stronger and more resistant to corrosion than pure Pb). The electrolyte is an aqueous solution of sulfuric acid (Fig. 16.8). The reactions, on discharging, are

$$Pb(c) + HOSO_3^- + H_2O \rightarrow PbSO_4(c) + H_3O^+ + 2e^-$$
$$PbO_2(c) + 3H_3O^+ + HOSO_3^- + 2e^- \rightarrow PbSO_4(c) + 5H_2O$$

$$Pb(c) + PbO_2(c) + 2H_3O^+ + 2HOSO_3^- \rightarrow 2PbSO_4(c) + 4H_2O$$

The cell can be recharged by passing current in the reverse direction, with electrons entering at the Pb electrode and leaving at the PbO_2 electrode. On charging, both electrode reactions are simply reversed. Sulfuric acid is consumed in the discharging process, and regenerated on

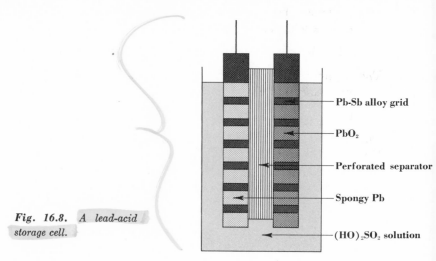

Fig. 16.8. *A lead-acid storage cell.*

- Pb-Sb alloy grid
- PbO$_2$
- Perforated separator
- Spongy Pb
- (HO)$_2$SO$_2$ solution

charging; therefore, the percentage of acid in the solution provides an indication of the degree to which the cell is charged. This percentage is most easily estimated by measuring the density of the solution, for the density increases as the acid content increases. The solution in a charged cell usually contains 30–40% (HO)$_2$SO$_2$, corresponding to a density of 1.2–1.3 g/ml. The e.m.f. of the cell is roughly 2 volts.

A **battery** is a number of galvanic cells connected together, in either series or parallel.

16.22 CORROSION

We may define corrosion as any undesired process in which a metal is converted to one of its compounds. We shall consider primarily the corrosion of iron, the most widely used and one of the more easily corroded metals.

A familiar fact about the corrosion, or rusting, of iron is that both oxygen and water are necessary. Perfectly dry iron does not rust at ordinary temperatures, and iron immersed in water does not rust if the water is free of O$_2$. Furthermore, the presence of acids and salts* in the water greatly accelerates the process of corrosion. These observations suggest that electrochemical processes may be involved in corrosion. The generally accepted theory is that Fe is oxidized to Fe^{2+} by H$_2$O or H$_3$O$^+$,

$$\text{Fe} \rightarrow \text{Fe}^{2+} + 2\text{e}^- \tag{1}$$
$$2\text{H}_3\text{O}^+ + 2\text{e}^- \rightarrow 2\text{H} + 2\text{H}_2\text{O} \tag{2}$$

If the H$_3$O$^+$ concentration is large, so that reactions (1) and (2) are rapid, the next step is 2H $\rightarrow$ H$_2(g)$, and bubbles of H$_2$ appear. In corrosion by

---

* Salts which decrease the concentration of H$_3$O$^+$ (for example, Na$_2$CO$_3$) are exceptional in that they inhibit corrosion.

natural waters, however, dissolved O_2 usually reacts with the H atoms before the atoms pair off to form H_2,

$$2H + \tfrac{1}{2}O_2(aq) \rightarrow H_2O \tag{3}$$

The oxygen and water also react with the Fe^{2+} ions liberated in reaction (1), producing hydrated ferric oxide (rust),

$$4Fe^{2+} + O_2 + (12 + 2x)H_2O \rightarrow 2Fe_2O_3(H_2O)_x + 8H_3O^+ \tag{4}$$

The H_3O^+ consumed in reaction (2) is regenerated in reaction (4), so that H_3O^+ is behaving as a catalyst: it accelerates the reaction without being consumed. CO_2 is nearly always present in natural waters, and increases the H_3O^+ concentration by the reaction $CO_2 + 2H_2O \rightleftharpoons H_3O^+ + HCO_3^-$, thus contributing to corrosion.

It is not necessary that reactions (1) and (2) should occur at the same place on the iron. Electrons liberated by reaction (1) can flow through the iron to another point at which H atoms are formed. Such a process, indeed, is conducive to rapid corrosion, for Fe^{2+} ions can more easily diffuse away from a place where the surface is not coated with H atoms. The corrosion of an iron or steel pipe is greatly accelerated if it is attached to a copper pipe; reaction (1) occurs on the Fe, reaction (2) mostly on the Cu. Any metal less active (a poorer reducing agent) than Fe will behave in the same way as Cu. Even when only Fe is present, some points on the surface ("anodic sites") will be more chemically reactive than others ("cathodic sites"), because of mechanical strain or small variations in composition. Thus, reaction (1) takes place at the anodic sites, which will be corroded, and reaction (2) occurs at the cathodic sites, which will not be corroded. The circuit through the metal must be completed by ionic conduction through the solution, which explains why an electrolyte accelerates corrosion.

If another metal—Zn or Mg, for example—more active than Fe is in contact with the Fe, the more active metal will be oxidized in preference to the Fe, and the Fe in the vicinity will be protected from corrosion. The Fe is said to be made **cathodic;** the active metal is called a "sacrificial anode," for it is allowed to corrode away in order to protect the Fe. The same result can be achieved by imposing a negative electric potential on the iron and a positive potential on other electrodes placed in the water or the ground nearby. These methods are often used to protect water tanks, boilers, ship hulls, and submerged or buried pipes.

The most obvious way to prevent corrosion is to coat the metal with an impervious layer of paint, grease, or another metal. Even this procedure has its pitfalls. When only part of the surface of a piece of Fe is exposed to O_2, the unexposed part, surprisingly, corrodes faster than the exposed part, apparently because the coating of rust formed in the presence of O_2 provides some protection, whereas reaction (1) proceeds without hindrance on the area that is wet but protected from air. If a coating of paint has holes in it, and especially if it does not adhere firmly, corrosion may actually be worse at the half-protected places than it would be if no paint had been applied. Plating with another metal is most helpful when the surface metal is more active (more easily oxidized) than the underlying metal—Zn plated on Fe, for example. Then, if there is a small hole in the coating, the Zn serves as a sacrificial anode and protects the Fe. On the other hand, if the Fe is plated with a metal less active than itself, such as Sn or Cu, a small hole will result in very rapid corrosion, for the Fe will behave as a sacrificial anode and will protect the plating—hardly a desirable result.

Many metals start to corrode by forming a thin, continuous, adherent layer of oxide, which prevents further corrosion. Examples are Al, Co, Cr, and Ni. Such metals are resistant to corrosion under ordinary conditions, even though Al and Cr, for example, are more active than Fe. An especially impervious coating can be produced on many metals, even on Fe, by treating the metal with a strong oxidizing agent, such as concentrated HNO_3 or Pb_3O_4 ("red lead"), or by using it as the anode in an electrolysis, with high current density. The metal is said to become **passive.** Unfortunately, the passivity of Fe is easily destroyed, merely by touching the passive metal with a piece of normal (active) Fe. The resistance of Pt and related elements to electrolytic oxidation is much greater than one would expect from their oxidation potentials; this is also a case of passivity. Passivity is not always desirable, especially not when an attempt is being made to oxidize the metal electrolytically to its ion.

Problems

1. Cell construction. For each of the following reactions, draw a diagram of a galvanic cell in which the reaction occurs. Show the composition of the anode, the cathode, and the solution or solutions. Indicate on your diagram the direction of migration of each kind of ion in the cell, and the direction of flow of electrons in the external circuit.

(a) $2Cr(c) + 3HgCl_2(aq) \rightarrow 2Cr^{3+} + 6Cl^- + 3Hg(l)$
(b) $Ni^{2+} + H_2(g) + 2OH^- \rightarrow Ni(c) + 2H_2O$
(c) $Fe(c) + Hg_2Cl_2(c) \rightarrow Fe^{2+} + 2Hg(l) + 2Cl^-$

2. Calculation of e.m.f. For each of the following cells: (a) write the equation for the cell process; (b) find $\mathcal{E}°$ at 25°C; (c) find $\mathcal{E}$ at 25°C, using the Nernst equation and assuming that activities are equal to concentrations. Explain the significance of any negative answers in (b) and (c).

(i) $Fe \mid FeBr_2(0.10M) \mid Br_2(l) \mid Pt$
(ii) $Ag \mid AgI(c) \mid HI(0.030M) \mid H_2(0.75 \text{ atm}) \mid Pt$
(iii) $Pb \mid PbSO_4(c) \mid (HO)_2SO_2(4.0M) \mid PbSO_4(c) \mid PbO_2(c)$
         (Note that surfuric acid is strong with respect to the first ionization, weak with respect to the second.)

                         Answer. (i) (b) +1.506 v; (c) +1.577v.

3. E.m.f. and equilibrium constant. For each of the following reactions, (a) devise a galvanic cell in which the reaction occurs; (b) find $\mathcal{E}°$ for the cell at 25°C; (c) write the Nernst equation for the cell, assuming that the activity of each solute is equal to its concentration; (d) find the equilibrium constant for the given reaction.

(i) $\qquad$ $\text{Ni} + \text{Sn}^{2+} \rightarrow \text{Ni}^{2+} + \text{Sn}$

(ii) $\quad$ $5\text{Hg}(l) + 2\text{MnO}_4^- + 16\text{H}_3\text{O}^+ \rightarrow 5\text{Hg}^{2+} + 2\text{Mn}^{2+} + 24\text{H}_2\text{O}$

(iii) $\qquad$ $2\text{H}_2(g) + \text{O}_2(g) \rightarrow 2\text{H}_2\text{O}(l)$

$\qquad\qquad$ **Answer.** (i) (b) $+0.09$ v; (d) 1.1×10^3.

4. Direction of reaction. Ascertain, with as little calculation as possible, whether each of the following reactions will go as written or in the reverse direction at 25°C, when all activities and pressures are equal to 1:

(a) $\qquad\qquad$ $2\text{Cr} + 3\text{Cu}^{2+} \rightarrow 2\text{Cr}^{3+} + 3\text{Cu}$

(b) $\qquad\qquad$ $\text{Zn} + \text{Mg}^{2+} \rightarrow \text{Zn}^{2+} + \text{Mg}$

(c) $\qquad\qquad$ $\text{Fe} + \text{Cl}_2(g) \rightarrow \text{Fe}^{2+} + 2\text{Cl}^-$

(d) $\qquad\qquad$ $2\text{Fe}^{2+} + \text{Cl}_2(g) \rightarrow 2\text{Fe}^{3+} + 2\text{Cl}^-$

(e) $\qquad$ $4\text{Ag} + \text{O}_2(g) + 4\text{H}_3\text{O}^+ \rightarrow 4\text{Ag}^+ + 6\text{H}_2\text{O}$

(f) $\quad$ $4\text{Ag} + \text{O}_2(g) + 4\text{H}_3\text{O}^+ + 4\text{Cl}^- \rightarrow 4\text{AgCl}(c) + 6\text{H}_2\text{O}$

5. E.m.f. and work. The e.m.f. of a galvanic cell is 1.30 volts. (a) How much work, in joules, is done by this cell when 10 coulombs of charge pass from one electrode to the other? (b) When a current of 0.10 amp flows, how much power (in watts) is the cell producing (1 watt = 1 joule/sec)? (c) How much work, in joules and in calories, does the cell do when one faraday passes through the circuit? Assume that the e.m.f. of the cell is unaffected by the rate at which current is drawn.

Additional problems

6. Entropy. (a) From information on page 403, calculate the maximum amount of heat (in joules and in calories) absorbed when the reaction

$$\text{Pb}(c) + \text{Hg}_2\text{Cl}_2(c) \rightarrow \text{PbCl}_2(c) + 2\text{Hg}(l)$$

occurs as written (1 gram-atom Pb, etc.) in a galvanic cell. (b) Find the entropy change (in cal/deg) in this reaction at 25°C. (c) How much heat (in calories) is absorbed or liberated when the reaction occurs on simple mixing of the reactants?

$\qquad\qquad$ **Answer.** (a) 9.1×10^3 joules, 2.17×10^3 cal; (b) 7.3 cal/deg;

$\qquad\qquad\qquad$ (c) 2.25×10^4 cal liberated.

7. Form of equation. Compare (a) ΔF, (b) K, and (c) $\mathcal{E}$ for reaction (i) with the corresponding quantity for (ii) and for (iii):

(i) $\qquad$ $\text{Zn} + 2\text{Ag}^+ \rightarrow \text{Zn}^{2+} + 2\text{Ag}$

(ii) $\qquad$ $\tfrac{1}{2}\text{Zn} + \text{Ag}^+ \rightarrow \tfrac{1}{2}\text{Zn}^{2+} + \text{Ag}$

(iii) $\qquad$ $\text{Zn}^{2+} + 2\text{Ag} \rightarrow \text{Zn} + 2\text{Ag}^+$

Explain the differing ways in which these three quantities are affected when the equation is written differently.

8. Cell reaction and standard e.m.f. For each of the following cells $(i-v)$, (a) write the equations for the anode and cathode processes, assuming that the left electrode is the anode; (b) write the equation for the over-all cell process; (c) find the standard e.m.f. $\mathcal{E}°$ at 25°C; (d) state whether the cell reaction will actually occur as written in (b) or in the reverse direction when all the activities are equal to 1.

(i)   Pt | Br₂(l) | HBr(aq) | H₂(g) | Pt
(ii)   Al | AlCl₃(aq) || CdSO₄(aq) | Cd
(iii) Pt | Pb(NO₃)₂(aq) || FeCl₂(aq), FeCl₃(aq) | Pt
(iv)   Mg | MgCl₂(aq) | Hg₂Cl₂(c) | Hg(l)
(v)   Pt | I₂(c) | KI(aq) | AgI(c) | Ag

Answer. (c) (i) −1.065 v; (ii) +1.27 v.

9. Nernst equation. (a) Write the Nernst equation for the cell

$$\text{Pt} \mid H_2(g)(P_1 \text{ atm}) \mid \text{HCl}(aq) \mid H_2(g)(P_2 \text{ atm}) \mid \text{Pt}$$

at an arbitrary temperature T. (b) How much work is done by this cell when *one mole* of H_2 is transferred from the anode (pressure P_1) to the cathode (pressure P_2)? (c) (Calculus required.) When one mole of an ideal gas expands from the volume V_1 to the volume V_2 in a cylinder fitted with a piston, the work done by the gas is

$$w = \int_{V_1}^{V_2} P \, dV$$

Show that

$$w = 2.303 \, RT \log (P_1/P_2)$$

(d) If the maximum work done by one mole of H_2 when it "expands" in the cell were not equal to the maximum work done by one mole of H_2 when it expands in the cylinder, it would be possible to combine the cylinder and cell to obtain a perpetual-motion machine of the *second kind*: one which does not create energy, but extracts heat from its surroundings and does an equivalent amount of work. Explain. (Note that, for the idealized case we are considering here—an infinitely slow process, no friction—the work merely changes sign when the gas is compressed or the cell is run backward.) (e) The **second law of thermodynamics** asserts that perpetual motion of the second kind is impossible. Show how the results of this problem establish the correctness of the Nernst equation for the particular cell considered here.

10. Half-cell potentials. Figure 16.9 shows three cells in series. When current flows through this circuit, a reaction occurs at electrode A in cell 1, and the reverse reaction occurs, to the same extent, at electrode A in cell 3. Similarly, the reactions at electrodes B and C in cell 2 are equal and opposite to the reactions at electrodes B and C in cells 1 and 3. (a) The net e.m.f. of this arrangement of cells must be zero ($\mathcal{E}_1 + \mathcal{E}_2 + \mathcal{E}_3 = 0$); otherwise, a perpetual-motion machine could be constructed. Explain. (b) Choose A as the reference half-cell. This means that, by definition, $\mathcal{E}_C = \mathcal{E}_3$ and $\mathcal{E}_B = -\mathcal{E}_1$. Show that $\mathcal{E}_2 = \mathcal{E}_B - \mathcal{E}_C$. You have now proved the validity of expressing the e.m.f. of a cell as the difference of two half-

Fig. 16.9. Three cells with resultant e.m.f. equal to zero

cell potentials, each of which is really the e.m.f. of a cell containing the reference half-cell.

11. Irreversible e.m.f. Cell (iii) of Problem 2 is a partially charged storage cell. If current is drawn from the cell, will the potential across the terminals be equal to, greater than, or less than the $\mathcal{E}$ that was calculated? Will the e.m.f. needed to charge the cell be equal to, greater than, or less than $\mathcal{E}$? Give at least two causes for any differences between $\mathcal{E}$ and these potentials.

12. Equilibrium constant. Find the equilibrium constant at 25°C for each of the following reactions:

(a) $\qquad 2H_2O + 2Ag + 4NH_3(aq) \rightleftharpoons H_2(g) + 2OH^- + 2Ag(NH_3)_2^+$

(b) $\qquad\qquad 2H_2O + 2Ag \rightleftharpoons H_2(g) + 2OH^- + 2Ag^+$

(c) $\qquad\qquad\qquad Ag(NH_3)_2^+ \rightleftharpoons Ag^+ + 2NH_3(aq)$

Use the results of (a) and (b) in answering (c). (Review combination of equilibria, page 339.)

$\qquad\qquad$ **Answer.** (a) 2.5×10^{-41}; (b) 9.5×10^{-56}; (c) 6.1×10^{-8}.

13. Equilibrium constant. Find the equilibrium constant at 25°C of each of the reactions in Problem 4.

$\qquad\qquad\qquad$ **Answer.** (a) 2×10^{110}; (b) 3.1×10^{-55}.

14. Equilibrium constant. From the results of parts (e) and (f) of the preceding problem, find the equilibrium constant (see page 339) for the reaction $AgCl(c) \rightleftharpoons Ag^+ + Cl^-$.

15. Decomposition potential. The following solutions are electrolyzed at 25°C. In each case, (a) predict the reaction that will predominate at the anode and at the cathode; (b) find the minimum voltage necessary to bring about these reactions. Assume that all activities and pressures of species mentioned are 1.

(i) $AgNO_3 + HONO_2$ solution with Ag electrodes. (Assume that NO_3^- ion is chemically inert.)

(ii) NaCl solution with graphite electrodes. (Assume that C is chemically inert.)

(iii) $FeSO_4$ solution with Pt electrodes. (Assume that SO_4^{2-} and Pt are chemically inert.)

$\qquad\qquad\qquad$ **Answer.** (iii) (b) 1.21 v.

16. Polarization. Show that, when current is drawn from the cell

$$Zn \mid ZnCl_2(1M) \parallel CuSO_4(1M) \mid Cu$$

concentration gradients are produced such as to decrease the e.m.f. of the cell below its zero-current value.

17. Dry cell. Why is the dry cell so designed that Zn and MnO_2 do not come into contact? What reaction might occur if they were in contact? How would this reaction affect the usefulness of the cell?

18. Dry cell. The total charge that can be delivered by a six-inch dry cell, before its e.m.f. drops too low, is usually about 35 ampere-hours. (One ampere-hour is the charge which passes through a circuit when one ampere flows for one hour.) Find the weight of Zn consumed when 35 ampere-hours of charge are drawn from the cell.

19. Fuel cells. A fuel cell may be defined as a galvanic cell to which the reactants are supplied continuously, and from which the products are removed continuously (as distinguished from, for example, a dry cell, in which the zinc, MnO_2, etc., are initially present and are not replenished during use). One type of fuel cell uses H_2 and O_2 as the reactants, an aqueous solution of KOH as the electrolyte, and specially treated porous carbon as the electrodes. (a) Write the partial equations for the anode and cathode reactions in this cell, and the equation for the over-all reaction. (b) Find the standard e.m.f. $\mathcal{E}°$ of the cell at 25°C. (c) Assume that the available e.m.f. is 75% of the value found in (b). How many joules of work can be obtained when one mole of H_2 is consumed? (d) What volume of H_2 (at standard conditions) is needed to produce 1 kilowatt-hour? (1 KWH = 3.600×10^6 joules.)

Answer. (b) 1.229 v; (c) 1.78×10^5 joules; (d) 4.5×10^2 liters

20. Storage cell. A galvanic cell must be so constructed that not all the reactants can come into contact and react directly. (a) How is this rule violated in the design of the lead-acid storage cell? (b) What reaction, resulting from this violation, helps to account for the fact that a charged storage cell slowly discharges itself on standing idle?

21. Corrosion. Would you recommend plating Fe, to protect it from corrosion, with each of the following metals: Au; Cr; Ba; Pb? Why or why not? (Ignore the cost of the metal in making your decision.)

22. Corrosion. A magnesium bar weighing 20 pounds is attached to a buried iron pipe by way of a copper wire, to protect the pipe from corrosion. An average current of 0.30 amp flows between the bar and the pipe. (a) What reaction occurs at the surface of the bar? Of the pipe? In which direction do electrons flow through the copper wire? (b) How many years will it take for the Mg bar to be entirely consumed? (See page 788 for the number of seconds in a year.) (c) What reaction(s) will occur if the bar is not replaced after the time calculated in (b)?

Answer. (b) 7.6 years

23. Corrosion. Which of the following methods of storing used steel wool is best? Which is most conducive to rusting? Explain. (a) Keep it immersed in plain tap water. (b) Keep it immersed in soapy water (a basic solution). (c) Just leave it in the sink.

Acid - produces H^+ in solution

Base - produces OH^- in solution

$$NH_3 + H_2O \rightarrow NH_4 + [OH]$$

17.1 NOMENCLATURE OF OXYACIDS AND THEIR ANIONS

There are two main classes of acids, binary acids and oxyacids. The nomenclature of binary acids has been treated (page 100).

Oxyacids have the general formula $(HO)_mXO_n$. They possess at least *one* OH group attached to a central atom but need not always have a lone oxygen atom.

The naming of the oxyacids is complicated by the fact that the central element may exist in different oxidation states and there may be an acid corresponding to each state. When only one oxidation state exists, the suffix **-ic** is added to the root name of the element followed by the word **acid.** This method is illustrated by the name carbon**ic acid**, $(HO)_2CO$, given to the water solution of carbon dioxide. When two oxyacids are known for a given central element, the one with the higher oxidation number (page 222) has the suffix **-ic,** the other the suffix **-ous:**

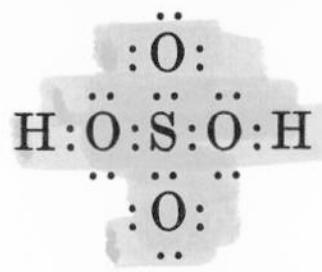

$$
\begin{array}{c}
:\!\overset{..}{O}\!: \\
H\!:\!\overset{..}{O}\!:\!\overset{..}{S}\!:\!\overset{..}{O}\!:\!H \\
:\!\overset{..}{O}\!:
\end{array}
\qquad \text{oxidation number of S} = +6, \text{ sulfur\textbf{ic} acid}
$$

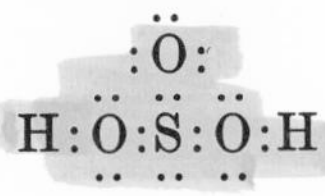

$$
\begin{array}{c}
:\!\overset{..}{O}\!: \\
H\!:\!\overset{..}{O}\!:\!\overset{..}{S}\!:\!\overset{..}{O}\!:\!H
\end{array}
\qquad \text{oxidation number of S} = +4, \text{ sulfur\textbf{ous} acid}
$$

If an element has three oxidation states, the acid corresponding to the lowest state is designated by bracketing the root with the prefix **hypo-** and the suffix **-ous** (the H atom is assumed to have an oxidation number of +1):

$$
\begin{array}{c}
\text{H} \\
\text{H:\ddot{O}:P:\ddot{O}:} \\
\text{H}
\end{array}
$$

oxidation number of P = +1, **hypo**phosphor**ous acid**

$$
\begin{array}{c}
\text{H} \\
\text{H:\ddot{O}:P:\ddot{O}:H} \\
\text{:\ddot{O}:}
\end{array}
$$

oxidation number of P = +3, phosphor**ous acid**

$$
\begin{array}{c}
\text{H} \\
\text{:\ddot{O}:} \\
\text{H:\ddot{O}:P:\ddot{O}:H} \\
\text{:\ddot{O}:}
\end{array}
$$

oxidation number of P = +5, phosphor**ic acid**

When four oxyacids are known, each with the central atom in a different oxidation state, the acid with the atom in the highest state is designated by the prefix **per-** and suffix **-ic**. This method is illustrated with the oxyacids of chlorine:

$$ \text{H:\ddot{O}:\ddot{Cl}:} $$

oxidation number of Cl = +1, **hypo**chlor**ous acid**

$$ \text{H:\ddot{O}:\ddot{Cl}:\ddot{O}:} $$

oxidation number of Cl = +3, chlor**ous acid**

$$
\begin{array}{c}
\text{:\ddot{O}:} \\
\text{H:\ddot{O}:\ddot{Cl}:\ddot{O}:}
\end{array}
$$

oxidation number of Cl = +5, chlor**ic acid**

$$
\begin{array}{c}
\text{:\ddot{O}:} \\
\text{H:\ddot{O}:\ddot{Cl}:\ddot{O}:} \\
\text{:\ddot{O}:}
\end{array}
$$

oxidation number of Cl = +7, **per**chlor**ic acid**

Oxyacids in the same oxidation state may differ in water content, and the prefixes **ortho, pyro,** and **meta** are used in order of decreasing hydration.

Prefix	Meaning	Examples	Names
Ortho	**Contains most water possible**	H_3PO_4, $(HO)_3PO$	**Orthophosphoric acid**
		H_3BO_3, $B(OH)_3$	**Orthoboric acid**
Pyro	**Intermediate water content; an acid that appears to be formed by the removal of 1 H_2O molecule from 2 acid molecules**	$H_2S_2O_7$, $HO-\overset{\overset{O}{\|}}{\underset{\underset{O}{\|}}{S}}-O-\overset{\overset{O}{\|}}{\underset{\underset{O}{\|}}{S}}-OH$	**Pyrosulfuric acid**
		$H_4P_2O_7$, $\overset{HO}{\underset{HO}{>}}P\overset{O}{<}O-P\overset{O}{<}\overset{OH}{\underset{OH}{}}$	**Pyrophosphoric acid**
Meta	**Contains least water possible**	HPO_3, $HOPO_2$	**Metaphosphoric acid**
		HBO_2, $HOBO$	**Metaboric acid**

The anions of oxyacids are named by changing the suffixes **-ous** and **-ic** to **-ite** and **-ate,** respectively. More than one anion may be derived from an acid $(HO)_mXO_n$ when m is greater than 1, because it is possible for the molecule to lose more than one hydrogen atom. These anions are differentiated by indicating the number of hydrogen atoms. For example, $(HO)_2PO_2^-$ is named **di**hydrogen phosphate and $HOPO_3^{2-}$ is named **mono**hydrogen phosphate, although in practice the prefix **mono-** is frequently omitted. When no more than one H atom can be present in the anion, the prefix **bi-** is often used; $HOSO_3^-$ and $HOCO_2^-$ are commonly called **bi**sulfate and **bi**carbonate, respectively.

17.2 EARLY DEFINITIONS

Acidic and basic solutions were first defined in terms of several easily recognizable chemical and physical properties. Thus, solutions were called acidic if they had a sour taste, changed the color of indicators (turned blue litmus red), and reacted with active metals to release hydrogen. Solutions were called basic if they felt slippery, tasted bitter, and changed red litmus to blue. Acidic and basic solutions were said to neutralize each other to produce water and a salt. With time, structural features that might account for the observed behavior received attention. Svante Arrhenius, in 1887, made the first attempt to give a structural definition of acids and bases. It was based on the knowledge that (1) pure molecular acids, such as anhydrous sulfuric acid and 100% (glacial) acetic acid, are nonelectrolytes, yet their aqueous solutions conduct a current, and (2) substances recognized as acids possess at least one hydrogen atom. Arrhenius reasoned that a pure acid, such as HCl, is a neutral molecule that dissolves in water to give H^+ and Cl^-; the acidic solution is known as hydrochloric acid. The abundance of the H^+ ion was thought to impart the familiar acidic properties to the solution.

Since all bases at the time of Arrhenius were known to possess the hydroxyl group, OH, and to conduct a current when dissolved in water, he assumed that a base is a substance that dissociates in water to give an OH^- ion and a cation: $NaOH \rightarrow Na^+ + OH^-$. The characteristic behavior of a base was attributed to the abundance of the OH^- ion.

Equilibria were thought to exist between the molecules and the ions in solution. For a strongly electrolytic acid such as hydrochloric acid, and a strongly electrolytic base such as sodium hydroxide, the values of the constants for the equilibria are large numbers. Consequently, for dilute solutions, ionization is practically complete, as indicated by the relative lengths of the arrows in the equations,

$$HCl \rightleftharpoons H^+ + Cl^- \qquad K > 10^2$$
$$NaOH \rightleftharpoons Na^+ + OH^- \qquad K > 10^2$$

For a weakly electrolytic acid such as acetic acid, $CH_3COOH,^*$ and a

---

* The CH_3CO group is abbreviated Ac, standing for *acetyl*. Therefore acetic acid is often written AcOH.

weakly electrolytic base such as ammonia, the equilibrium constants are small and ionization is very incomplete,

$$CH_3COOH \rightleftharpoons H^+ + CH_3COO^- \qquad K \approx 10^{-5}$$
$$NH_3 \cdot H_2O \rightleftharpoons NH_4^+ + OH^- \qquad K \approx 10^{-5}$$

In terms of the Arrhenius theory, we would define an acid-base reaction as one occurring specifically between H^+ and OH^- to form water, coincident with the formation of a salt,

$$in\ water: \quad \underbrace{H^+ + Cl^-}_{acid} + \underbrace{Na^+ + OH^-}_{base} \rightarrow H_2O + \underbrace{Na^+ + Cl^-}_{salt}$$

17.3 BRÖNSTED-LOWRY CONCEPT OF ACID-BASE REACTIONS

One limitation of Arrhenius's definition is its failure to deal with acid-base reactions that occur without the intervention of water. Hydrogen chloride and ammonia do not ionize in benzene, yet react to form ammonium chloride, the same salt obtained from an aqueous solution. Also, one would not expect an H^+ ion to maintain its identity in water because of its exceedingly large cationic charge density (5.4×10^{15}), as indicated in Table 9.4 (page 232). It would be strongly attracted to any molecule or ion having a free pair of electrons. It could exist in an isolated state, as in an electric discharge tube, but certainly not in the regions of high electron density surrounding the oxygen atoms of water molecules.

A major improvement on Arrhenius's definition of acids and bases came in 1923 when J. N. Brönsted and M. Lowry independently proposed a more general theory. Their theory states that *an acid-base reaction involves a proton transfer; the acid is the proton donor and the base is the proton acceptor.* The loss of a proton is often called **protolysis** and the transfer is called a **protolytic reaction.** This theory emphasizes the interdependence of an acid and a base; one cannot react without the other. The stronger the acid, the more readily it donates a proton; the stronger the base, the more readily it accepts a proton.

(a) Conjugate Acid-Base Pairs. In aqueous solution an acid, HA, ionizes by transferring its proton to water, the base,

$$\underset{base_1}{\overset{H}{\underset{H}{\diagdown}} :O: } + \underset{acid_2}{H:A} \rightleftharpoons \left[\underset{}{\overset{H}{\underset{H}{\diagdown}} :O:H} \right]^+ + \underset{base_2}{:A^-} \tag{1}$$

The hydronium ion is further hydrated, but for simplicity it will be written as H_3O^+. In some equations it will be further simplified by writing H^+. In the reverse reaction, H_3O^+ is the acid that donates a proton to A^-, the base. The reaction of an acid and a base *always* leads to the formation of a new acid and a new base. The product acid, H_3O^+, arises when the reactant base, H_2O, accepts a proton; H_3O^+ and H_2O are said to comprise a **conjugate acid-base pair.** Similarly, the product base, A^-, results when the reactant acid, HA, loses a proton; HA and A^- also comprise a conjugate acid-base pair. One conjugate acid-base pair in the reaction is designated by the subscript 1 and the other pair by the subscript 2, as demonstrated in Equations (1) above and (2),

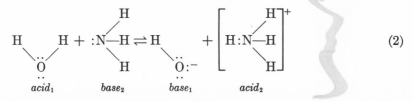

$$\tag{2}$$

$$\underset{acid_1}{} \qquad \underset{base_2}{} \qquad \underset{base_1}{} \qquad \underset{acid_2}{}$$

In the reaction of ammonia, $:NH_3$, with water, Equation (2), NH_3 is the base and water is the acid. The ammonium ion is the conjugate acid of NH_3, and hydroxide ion, OH^-, is the conjugate base of H_2O. In the reaction between NH_3 and HCl in benzene, hydrogen chloride, the acid, donates a proton to ammonia, the base. This produces chloride ion, the conjugate base of HCl, and ammonium ion, the conjugate acid of NH_3,

$$\underset{base_1}{H_3N:} + \underset{acid_2}{HCl} \overset{\text{in benzene}}{\underset{\longleftarrow}{\longrightarrow}} \underset{acid_1}{[H_3N:H]^+} \underset{base_2}{Cl^-} \downarrow$$

Electronic structures have been used in the preceding equations to reveal an important structural feature: *the base in each case has an unshared pair of electrons that can form a coordinate covalent bond with the transferred proton.* For this reason, the base gains in positive charge when it is converted to its conjugate acid, for example,

$$NH_3 \overset{H^+}{\rightarrow} NH_4^+$$
$$OH^- \overset{H^+}{\rightarrow} H_2O$$
$$O^{-2} \overset{H^+}{\rightarrow} OH^-$$

The reverse is true of the acid.

There is an interdependent relationship between the strengths of a given conjugate pair. In general, *the stronger an acid, the weaker its conjugate base; the stronger a base, the weaker its conjugate acid.* Thus, from observing the relative positions of the equilibria of Equations (3) and (4),

$$\underset{\substack{acid_1 \\ (stronger)}}{HCl} + \underset{\substack{base_2 \\ (stronger)}}{H_2O} \rightleftharpoons \underset{\substack{acid_2 \\ (weaker)}}{H_3O^+} + \underset{\substack{base_1 \\ (weaker)}}{Cl^-} \qquad K \approx 10^2 \tag{3}$$

$$\underset{\substack{acid_1 \\ (weaker)}}{CH_3COOH} + \underset{\substack{base_2 \\ (weaker)}}{H_2O} \underset{\longleftarrow}{\rightharpoonup} \underset{\substack{acid_2 \\ (stronger)}}{H_3O^+} + \underset{\substack{base_1 \\ (stronger)}}{CH_3COO^-} \qquad K \approx 10^{-5} \tag{4}$$

it is evident that hydrochloric acid is a stronger acid than acetic acid. From the relative extent of the reverse reactions, it is evident that acetate ion, CH_3COO^-, is a stronger base than Cl^-, because of its greater tendency to accept a proton from H_3O^+.

In every acid-base reaction, the two existing bases—as H_2O and Cl^- in Equation (3)—are always competing for the proton. The stronger base prevails and is thereby converted to its conjugate acid. The weaker base fails to acquire the proton and thus remains unchanged. Consequently *the equilibrium favors the formation of the weaker base*. Thus in Equation (3), Cl^- is a weaker base than H_2O, which must also mean that HCl is a stronger acid than H_3O^+. Also, in Equation (4), CH_3COO^- is a stronger base than water, which means that H_3O^+ is a stronger acid than CH_3COOH. We see that acid-base reactions "run downhill" *to favor the formation of the weaker base and weaker acid*. (It is noteworthy that a similar relationship prevails in electron transfer reactions of oxidant-reductant pairs. Thus, fluorine, the strongest oxidant, has the strongest tendency to accept electrons, while F^- ion has the least tendency to lose electrons, and is the weakest reductant known. The equilibrium of a redox reaction also tends to favor the weaker oxidant and reductant.)

(b) Relative Acidity and Basicity. *Strengths of acids must be compared toward the same base;* the base of choice is water. Dilute aqueous solutions of strong acids, those with $K > 2$, ionize practically completely so that the only acid present is H_3O^+:

$$HCl \qquad + H_2O \rightarrow \quad H_3O^+ \; + Cl^-$$
hydrochloric acid
$$HONO_2 \qquad + H_2O \rightarrow \quad H_3O^+ \; + NO_3^-$$
nitric acid
$$HOClO_3 \qquad + H_2O \rightarrow \quad H_3O^+ \; + ClO_4^-$$
perchloric acid

strong acids of different   *only acid*
strength; ($K > 2$) all   *present*
stronger than H_3O^+

H_3O^+ is the strongest acid that can exist in water. Consequently, under these conditions all such acids are equally strong. Water is a strong enough base to "level out" or obscure differences in acid strength. As we will discuss later in the chapter, this **"leveling effect"** can be overcome by using a weaker base than water.

Since weak acids ionize incompletely, equilibrium is established and an equilibrium constant, K_a, can be calculated (page 389),

$$HA + H_2O = H_3O^+ + A^-$$
$$K_a = \frac{[H_3O^+][A^-]}{[HA]}$$

The magnitude of K_a, the ionization constant, is a measure of acidity—the larger the value for K_a, the stronger is the acid. Thus, acetic acid, $K_a = 1.8 \times 10^{-5}$, is more acidic than hydrocyanic acid, $K_a = 7.2 \times 10^{-10}$. To avoid the use of exponential expressions, a new term, pK_a, is defined, such that $pK_a = -\log K_a$.

EXAMPLE 1   **Find the pK_a for (a) acetic acid, and (b) hydrocyanic acid. (See page 791 for use of logs.)**

ANSWER

(a) **For acetic acid:**

$$pK_a = -\log(1.8 \times 10^{-5})$$
$$= -(\log 1.8 + \log 10^{-5})$$
$$= -(0.25 - 5)$$
$$= 4.8$$

(b) **For hydrocyanic acid:**

$$pK_a = -\log(7.2 \times 10^{-10})$$
$$= -(\log 7.2 + \log 10^{-10})$$
$$= -(0.86 - 10.00)$$
$$= 9.1$$

The weaker acid thus has the larger pK_a value.

The same principles apply for comparing basicities. The bases, B: and OH⁻ compete for the proton,

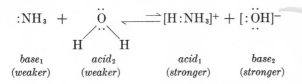

$$B: + \quad \underset{H \quad \quad H}{\overset{..}{O}} \quad \rightleftharpoons [B:H]^+ + [:\overset{..}{\underset{..}{O}}H]^-$$

When the base, B:, is a molecule (has no charge) it is invariably a weaker base than OH⁻. Hence, the equilibrium does *not* favor the formation of OH⁻ ions. The weak ionization of the neutral base, ammonia, illustrates this point,

$$:NH_3 + \quad \underset{H \quad \quad H}{\overset{..}{O}} \quad \rightleftharpoons [H:NH_3]^+ + [:\overset{..}{\underset{..}{O}}H]^-$$

base₁	*acid₂*	*acid₁*	*base₂*
(weaker)	*(weaker)*	*(stronger)*	*(stronger)*

The expression for the equilibrium constant is

$$K_b = \frac{[NH_4^+][OH^-]}{[NH_3]} = 1.8 \times 10^{-5}$$

17.4   AMPHOTERISM; AUTOPROTOLYSIS (SELF-IONIZATION)

Water behaves either as an acid or as a base:

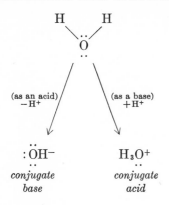

(as an acid)
−H⁺

(as a base)
+H⁺

:ÖH⁻
conjugate base

H₃O⁺
conjugate acid

17.4   Amphoterism; autoprotolysis (self-ionization)

It is an example of a group of substances that are said to be **amphiproti**
or **amphoteric**. A substance with an H atom attached to a fairly strongl
electronegative atom with an unshared pair of electrons may be amphi
protic; examples are $:NH_3$ and $C_2H_5\ddot{O}H$. Since water possesses dua
acid-base behavior, it undergoes **self-ionization (autoprotolysis)**:

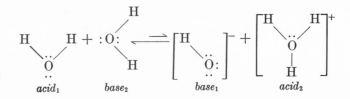

Any water solution with an equal concentration of OH^- and H_3O^+ ion
is said to be **neutral**. If an excess of OH^- is present, as in a solution c
sodium hydroxide, the solution is **basic** (alkaline); if an excess of H_3O^+ i
present, as in a solution of hydrochloric acid, the solution is **acidic**. *
substance that engenders an excess of OH^- is a *base*. A substance tha
produces an excess of H_3O^+ is an *acid*. A substance that has no effect o
either concentration is *neutral*.

Self-ionization is exhibited by many pure liquids; for example, in pur
liquid ammonia,

$$:NH_3 + :NH_3 \rightleftharpoons :\overset{..}{N}H_2^- + [HNH_3]^+$$
$$\underset{acid_1}{} \quad \underset{base_2}{} \quad \underset{\substack{base_1 \\ (amide\ ion)}}{} \quad \underset{\substack{acid_2 \\ (ammonium\ ion)}}{}$$

in pure liquid sulfuric acid,

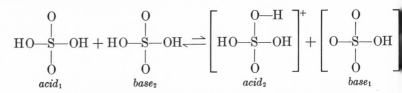

in pure liquid hydrogen fluoride,

$$HF + HF \rightleftharpoons H_2F^+ + F^-$$
$$\underset{acid_1}{} \ \underset{base_2}{} \quad \underset{acid_2}{} \ \underset{base_1}{}$$

We can generalize by saying that when a liquid undergoes self-ionizatio
its conjugate acid and its conjugate base are formed (Equation 5 below
The equilibrium constant for the autoprotolysis of water is

$$K_w = [H_3O^+][OH^-]$$
$$= 1.0 \times 10^{-14} \ (at\ 25°C)$$
$$= 9.6 \times 10^{-14} \ (at\ 60°C)$$
$$pK_w = 14 \ (at\ 25°C)$$

17.5 TYPES OF PROTOLYTIC REACTION

Before the introduction of the Brönsted-Lowry theory, many reactions actually involving transfer of a proton were thought to be unique, and were given specific names. Several typical protolytic reactions are listed in Table 17.1 to emphasize their similarity.

(a) **Neutralization.** The reaction between an acid and a base was called neutralization (page 439) even before the days of Arrhenius. In dilute aqueous solutions of strong acids, the only acid present to react with the OH^- ion is H_3O^+. Hence, in terms of the Bronsted-Lowry theory, neutralization is the reaction between H_3O^+ and OH^-, as shown in reaction 4 in Table 17.1. The term neutralization has been extended to include all protolytic reactions between the conjugate acid and conjugate base of the same substance. Hence reaction 4', Table 17.1, represents a neutralization reaction between NH_4^+, the conjugate acid of NH_3, and amide ion, NH_2^-, the conjugate base of the same molecule.

In general, *neutralization is the reverse of an autoprotolysis:*

$$\xleftarrow{\text{autoprotolysis}}$$

$$\underset{\substack{\textit{conjugate acid} \\ \textit{of HX}}}{H_2X^+} \quad + \quad \underset{\substack{\textit{conjugate base} \\ \textit{of HX}}}{X^-} \quad \rightleftharpoons 2HX \tag{5}$$

$$\textbf{neutralization} \rightarrow$$

(b) **Polyprotic Acids and Polyprotic Bases.** Some acids, such as $(HO)_2SO_2$, H_2S, and $(HO)_3PO$, have more than one proton that can be donated to a base. When such **polyprotic acids,** as exemplified by the **diprotic** acid H_2S, dissolve in water, they release their protons in sequence:

$$H_2S + H_2O \xrightleftharpoons{} H_3O^+ + HS^- \qquad K_{a1} = 6.3 \times 10^{-8}$$
$$HS^- + H_2O \xrightleftharpoons{} H_3O^+ + S^{2-} \qquad K_{a2} = 10^{-14}$$

The values for the ionization constants reveal that HS^- is a much weaker acid than H_2S. This is understandable since the hydrosulfide ion, HS^-, has a negative charge and so is more likely to resist losing another proton to form the sulfide ion, S^{2-}. Conversely, the sulfide ion has a double negative charge and therefore is more likely to attract a proton than is the singly charged base, HS^-; the sulfide ion is a much stronger base than HS^-.

In oxyacids, only protons bonded to oxygen are donated to water. Thus, hypophosphorous acid is monoprotic, and phosphorous acid is diprotic:

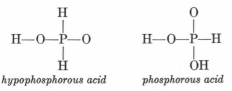

hypophosphorous acid   phosphorous acid

Clearly, the H atoms bonded to phosphorus do not dissociate.

There are also basic compounds that can accept more than one proton

TABLE 17.1   *Types of Acid-Base (Protolytic) Reaction*

Type	$Acid_1$	+	$Base_2$	→	$Acid_2$	+	$Base_1$
(1) Ionization of neutral acid	HCN +		H_2O	→	H_3O^+	+	CN^-
(2) Ionization of neutral base	H_2O +		NH_3	→	NH_4^+	+	OH^-
(3) Autoprotolysis (self-ionization) of water	H_2O +		H_2O	→	H_3O^+	+	OH^-
(4) Neutralization in water	H_3O^+ +		OH^-	→	H_2O	+	H_2O
(4') Neutralization in liquid ammonia	NH_4^+ +		NH_2^-	→	NH_3	+	NH_3
(5) Ionization of conjugate base of a diprotic acid	HS^- +		H_2O	→	H_3O^+	+	S^{2-}
(6) Ionization of conjugate acid of a diprotic base	H_2O +	$H_2NNH_3^+$	→	$H_3NNH_3^{2+}$	+	OH^-
(7) Hydrolysis of an anion	H_2O +		CN^-	→	HCN	+	OH^-
(8) Hydrolysis of a cation	NH_4^+ +		H_2O	→	H_3O^+	+	NH_3
(9) Hydrolysis of hydrated cation	$Fe(H_2O)_6^{3+}$ +	H_2O	→	H_3O^+	+	$Fe(OH)(H_2O)_5^2$

in a stepwise process. For example, each nitrogen atom in hydrazine $\overset{\cdots\,\cdots}{H_2NNH_2}$, has an unshared pair of electrons available for bonding with a proton. As is typical of all such **polyprotic bases,** the ionization constant for the second step is much smaller than that for the first step:

$$H_2\overset{\cdots}{N}-\overset{\cdots}{N}H_2 + H_2O \rightleftharpoons \left[\begin{array}{c} H \\ H_2\overset{\cdots}{N}-\overset{\cdots}{N}H_2 \end{array}\right]^+ + OH^- \qquad pK_{b1} = 6.04$$

$$\left[\begin{array}{c} H \\ \overset{.}{H}_2\overset{\cdots}{N}-\overset{\cdots}{N}H_2 \end{array}\right]^+ + H_2O \rightleftharpoons \left[\begin{array}{c} H\ \ H \\ H_2\overset{\cdots}{N}-\overset{\cdots}{N}H_2 \end{array}\right]^{++} + OH^- \qquad pK_{b2} = 15$$

This is to be expected, because the $H_2N-NH_3^+$ already has a positive charge and resists accepting a second proton.

   (c) **Reactions of Anions with Water.**   An aqueous solution containing the conjugate base of a weak acid is basic, as exemplified by a solution of sodium cyanide ($Na^+ + CN^-$). Cyanide ion is sufficiently basic to remove a proton from water,

$$\underset{base_1}{CN^-} + \underset{acid_2}{H_2O} \rightleftharpoons \underset{acid_1}{HCN} + \underset{base_2}{OH^-}$$

The equilibrium constant* for this reaction with water (hydrolysis) is

$$K_{b*} = \frac{[HCN][OH^-]}{[CN^-]} \tag{6}$$

The strength of the basic anion as measured by the magnitude of K_b is related to the strength of its conjugate acid and therefore to K_a. We illustrate the general relationship by considering HCN and CN^-. The equation for the ionization of HCN is

$$HCN + H_2O \rightleftharpoons H_3O^+ + CN^-$$

and the equilibrium constant, K_a, for this reaction is

$$K_a = \frac{[H_3O^+][CN^-]}{[HCN]} \tag{7}$$

If we multiply Equations (6) and (7), we get

$$K_a \cdot K_b = \frac{[H_3O^+][CN^-]}{[HCN]} \cdot \frac{[HCN][OH^-]}{[CN^-]} = [H_3O^+][OH^-]$$

Since $[H_3O^+][OH^-] = K_w$ (page 444),   *Ionic Product of H_2O*

$$K_a \cdot K_b = K_w$$

At 25°C, $K_w = 1.0 \times 10^{-14}$; therefore, at this temperature,

$$K_a \cdot K_b = 1.0 \times 10^{-14}$$

$\frac{[H_3O^+]}{=} \frac{[OH^-]}{10^{-7}}$ K is constant as long as temp remains constant

and, in p units,

$$pK_a + pK_b = pK_w = 14$$

The equation $K_a \cdot K_b = K_w$ permits quantitative predictions to be made concerning the extent of reaction of anions with water; these are discussed in Chapter 19. The following are some qualitative conclusions:

(1) The conjugate base of an acid, such as perchloric acid, which is much stronger than water, hydrolyzes very slightly, if at all. For example, ClO_4^-, Cl^-, SO_4^{2-}, and NO_3^- do not hydrolyze measurably.

(2) The conjugate base of an acid, such as nitrous acid, $pK_a = 3.29$, which is moderately stronger than water ($pK_w = 14$), undergoes a degree of hydrolysis until a state of equilibrium is reached. Examples of such ions are NO_2^- and $HOPO_3^{2-}$ (hydrogen phosphate).

(3) The conjugate base of an acid, such as $HOPO_3^{2-}$, $pK_a = 12$, which is approximately equal in strength to water, hydrolyzes almost completely. Examples of such ions are PO_4^{3-} and S^{2-}.

(4) The conjugate base of an acid much weaker than water hydrolyzes completely. Another way of stating this fourth conclusion is that any base stronger than OH^- reacts with water so that OH^- remains as the only base. This situation is another manifestation of the "leveling effect."

* These constants are also referred to as "hydrolysis" constants, K_h.

Since ammonia, hydrogen, and methane all have pK_a values greater than 30, their conjugate bases are all converted by water to the OH^- ion:

$$:NH_2^- \quad + H_2O \rightarrow NH_3 + \quad OH^- \quad \text{(as from sodium amide, NaNH}_2\text{)}$$

$$:H^- \quad + H_2O \rightarrow H_2 \quad + \quad OH^- \quad \text{(as from calcium hydride, CaH}_2\text{)}$$

$$H_3C:^- \quad + H_2O \rightarrow CH_4 + \quad OH^- \quad \text{(as from sodium methide, NaCH}_3\text{)}$$

$$\underset{base_1}{} \qquad \underset{acid_2}{} \quad \underset{acid_1}{} \quad \underset{base_2}{}$$

(strong bases of different strength; all stronger than OH⁻)   *(only base present)*

The conjugate base of a weak diprotic acid is capable of behaving either as an acid or as a base, as exemplified by HS^-,

$$\underset{base}{HS^-} + H_2O \rightleftharpoons H_2S + OH^-$$

$$\underset{acid}{HS^-} + H_2O \rightleftharpoons S^{2-} + H_3O^+$$

The HS^- ion is amphoteric.

(d) **Reactions of Cations with Water.** Conjugate acids of weak bases, such as ammonium ion, NH_4^+, are strong enough to donate a proton to water,

$$NH_4^+ + H_2O \rightleftharpoons NH_3 + H_3O^+$$

and

$$K_a = \frac{[H_3O^+][NH_3]}{[NH_4^+]}$$

Since

$$K_a = \frac{K_w}{K_b} \quad \text{and} \quad K_b = 1.8 \times 10^{-5}$$

then

$$K_a = \frac{10^{-14}}{1.8 \times 10^{-5}} = 5.6 \times 10^{-10}$$

Salts of trivalent cations, such as aluminum sulfate, $Al_2(SO_4)_3$, and chromic nitrate, $Cr(NO_3)_3$, give acidic water solutions. Because of their high cationic charge density, Al^{3+} and Cr^{3+} form covalent bonds with six water molecules,

$$M^{3+} + 6H_2O \rightarrow$$ 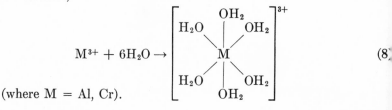   (8)

(where M = Al, Cr).

These hydrated ions act as acids. $Al(H_2O)_6^{3+}$ is a triprotic acid; the end product is hydrated aluminum hydroxide, which forms as a gelatinous precipitate when an aqueous solution of aluminum sulfate is allowed to stand,

$$Al(H_2O)_6^{3+} + H_2O \leftrightharpoons H_3O^+ + Al(OH)(H_2O)_5^{2+}$$
$$Al(OH)(H_2O)_5^{2+} + H_2O \leftrightharpoons H_3O^+ + Al(OH)_2(H_2O)_4^+$$
$$Al(OH)_2(H_2O)_4^+ + H_2O \leftrightharpoons H_3O^+ + Al(OH)_3(H_2O)_3$$

$$\underset{acid_1}{} \qquad \underset{base_2}{} \quad \underset{acid_2}{} \qquad \underset{\substack{(hydrated\ aluminum \\ hydroxide) \\ base_1}}{}$$

This precipitate has good adsorptive properties, and therefore Al(III) salts are used for water purification in the coagulation process.

Divalent cations not having noble gas configurations may also form acidic hydrated cations. For example, an aqueous solution of $Zn(NO_3)_2$ is acidic because of the presence of $Zn(H_2O)_4^{2+}$. On the other hand, an aqueous solution of $Ca(NO_3)_2$ is neutral; Ca^{2+} has a noble gas configuration and does not form a hydrated cation by bonding with the oxygen atom of water molecules.

When a strong base such as OH^- is added to hydrated aluminum hydroxide, the precipitate dissolves. Since each of the three water molecules is capable of donating a proton, the addition of hydroxide ion, OH^-, (as NaOH) converts the hydroxide to the aluminate ion, $Al(OH)_4(H_2O)_2^-$,

$$Al(OH)_3(H_2O)_3 + OH^- \rightarrow Al(OH)_4(H_2O)_2^- + H_2O$$

Since $Al(OH)_3(H_2O)_3$ also dissolves in acid,

$$Al(OH)_3(H_2O)_3 + 3H_3O^+ \rightarrow Al(H_2O)_6^{3+} + 3H_2O$$

it is an example of an amphiprotic or amphoteric substance. It is noteworthy that $Fe(H_2O)_6^{3+}$ is a triprotic acid; on standing in water it forms ferric hydroxide, $Fe(OH)_3(H_2O)_3$. Yet it does not dissolve in alkali hydroxides. Therefore, it does not follow that all acidic hydrated cations must form amphoteric hydroxides.

17.6 PROTOLYSIS IN NONAQUEOUS MEDIA

(a) **Extremely Weak Acids.** Numerous compounds containing hydrogen do not dissociate in water because they are too weakly acidic. They may dissociate, however, in the presence of a stronger base, such as sodium hydroxide,

$$HA + OH^- \rightarrow A^- + H_2O$$

One technique for detecting protolysis of a very weak acid by an anionic base uses deuterium labeling. For example, chloroform, Cl_3CH, is converted to Cl_3CD in the presence of "heavy water," D_2O, and OD^-. It is logical to assume that the exchange of protium (H) for deuterium (D) must first involve the formation of the carbanion, $[Cl_3C:]^-$,

$$Cl_3C:H + :\overset{..}{O}D^- \rightarrow [Cl_3C:]^- + H:\overset{..}{\underset{..}{O}}:D$$

$acid_1$ $base_2$ $base_1$ $acid_2$

(a carbanion)

The carbanion then reacts with D_2O to give $Cl_3C:D$,

$$[Cl_3C:]^- + D:\overset{..}{\underset{..}{O}}:D \rightarrow Cl_3C:D + [:\overset{..}{\underset{..}{O}}:D]^-$$

$base_1$ $acid_2$ $acid_1$ $base_2$

The carbanion reacts with the solvent, DOD, rather than with HOD because there is an abundance of DOD molecules and very few HOD molecules.

There are many potential acids too weak to react with even a base as strong as OH^-. To use a stronger base, one cannot employ water as the solvent, since the strongest base that can exist in water is the hydroxide ion (page 448). Amide ion, NH_2^-, is a stronger base than hydroxide ion and may be used in a solvent with which it does not react, such as liquid ammonia, to test for the protolysis of very weak acids. Sodium amide is prepared by reacting (in the presence of a trace of a ferric (FeIII) salt) sodium with liquid ammonia,

$$2Na\cdot + 2:NH_3 \rightarrow 2Na^+ + 2\overset{..}{N}H_2^- + H_2$$

Acetylene, $H-C\equiv C-H$, reacts with $NaNH_2$ in liquid NH_3,

$$H-C\equiv C-H + :\overset{..}{N}H_2^- \rightarrow H-C\equiv C:^- + H:\overset{..}{N}H_2$$

$acid_1$ $base_2$ $base_1$ $acid_2$

acetylene

When the ammonia is allowed to evaporate, the residue is found to be sodium acetylide, $H-C\equiv C:^-Na^+$, a typical ionic solid. When the experiment is performed with ethylene, $H_2C=CH_2$, in place of acetylene, the residue remaining is sodium amide. Evidently ethylene is less acidic than acetylene, since it does not react appreciably with NH_2^-.

(b) Extremely Weak Bases. To study bases too weak to react with water, a solvent is required that is a much stronger acid than water. The solvent often used for this purpose is concentrated sulfuric acid. The extent of the reaction can be calculated by measuring the freezing point of the concentrated sulfuric acid solution. Thus, sulfuric acid solutions of diethyl ether, $C_2H_5OC_2H_5$, and acetic acid, CH_3COOH, dissociate as shown:

$$C_2H_5\overset{..}{\underset{..}{O}}C_2H_5 + HOSO_2OH \rightleftharpoons \left[C_2H_5\overset{\overset{H}{|}}{\underset{..}{O}}C_2H_5 \right]^+ + OSO_2OH^-$$

$$\underset{base_1}{\overset{\overset{O}{||}}{CH_3C}-OH} + \underset{acid_2}{HOSO_2OH} \rightleftharpoons \underset{acid_1}{\left[CH_3-\overset{\overset{OH}{|||}}{C}{\cdots}OH \right]^+} + \underset{base_2}{OSO_2OH^-}$$

Nitric acid dissociates in sulfuric acid. Here is dramatic evidence of the relativity of acid-base behavior; nitric acid, a strong acid in water, behaves as a base toward the stronger acid, $(HO)_2SO_2$,

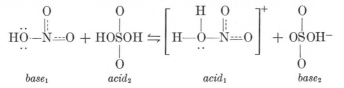

The conjugate acid, $H_2ONO_2^+$, reacts further so that the over-all reaction is

$$HONO_2 + 2(HO)_2SO_2 \rightarrow H_3O^+ + \underset{\substack{nitronium \\ ion}}{NO_2^+} + 2HOSO_3^- \qquad (9)$$

(c) Very Strong Acids. The study of relative strengths of very strong acids is frequently made in 100% (glacial) acetic acid, a solvent that is a much weaker base than water. Typical is the reaction with perchloric acid,

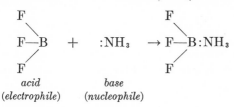

Such studies reveal that the order of acidities of the strong acids is $HClO_4 > H_2SO_4 > HI > HBr > HCl > HNO_3$. This order, however, may not prevail in other solvents.

17.7 LEWIS ACID-BASE CONCEPT

All bases have a lone pair of electrons to share with a proton. The transferred proton is electron-deficient during the process of bonding to the base. A transferred proton is not the only species to form bonds with bases; other electron-deficient substances do likewise, as exemplified by the reaction of boron trifluoride, BF_3, with NH_3.

$$\begin{array}{ccc} \underset{\substack{acid \\ (electrophile)}}{\overset{\displaystyle F}{\underset{\displaystyle F}{\diagup}} F{-}B} & + \quad \underset{\substack{base \\ (nucleophile)}}{:NH_3} & \rightarrow \overset{\displaystyle F}{\underset{\displaystyle F}{\diagup}} F{-}B:NH_3 \end{array}$$

Gilbert N. Lewis recognized the similarity in behavior of boron trifluoride and a transferred proton toward a base, and in 1923 enunciated a definition of acid-base reaction in terms of sharing of an electron pair—*a base donates an electron pair* in covalent bonding *and an acid accepts the pair*. The acid is called an **electrophile,** and the base is called a **nucleophile.** In the base, the atom with the lone pair of electrons is an electron-rich site, and, in the acid, the atom that accepts the pair of electrons to form a covalent bond is an electron-deficient site. The Lewis theory focuses attention on the electron pair rather than on the proton, and in so doing broadens the concept of acidity and abandons the "cult of the proton." The transferred proton of a so-called Brönsted acid is a special case of a Lewis acid.

Lewis bases are necessarily substances with lone pairs of electrons. They can be neutral molecules, such as $:NH_3$, or anions, such as cyanide ion, $:CN^-$ Lewis acids appear in many guises.

17.8 EXAMPLES OF LEWIS ACIDS

(a) **Molecules Possessing an Atom with Fewer Than an Octet of Electrons.** BF_3 falls into this category. A Lewis acid frequently used in organic chemistry is aluminum chloride, $AlCl_3$. The Al atom is electron-deficient, and can form a covalent bond with the electron-rich atom of an ether,

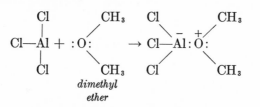

dimethyl ether

The product is shown with formal charges.

(b) **Cations.** Theoretically, every cation is a potential Lewis acid. However, this property is negligible for the alkali metal cations such as Na^+ and K^+, and is weak for the alkaline earth cations such as Ca^{2+}, Sr^{2+}, and Ba^{2+}. Of the alkaline earth group, only Mg^{2+} and Be^{2+} show an appreciable tendency to behave as Lewis acids. Many cations form covalent bonds with Lewis bases. The reaction of the M^{3+} type of ion with water is an example of a Lewis acid-base interaction (Equation 8, page 448). The reaction of Ag^+ and $:NH_3$ is also typical,

$$Ag^+ + 2:NH_3 \rightarrow [H_3N:Ag:NH_3]^+$$
Lewis   *Lewis*
acid   *base*

(c) **Molecules in Which the Central Atom May Acquire More Than an Octet of Electrons.** Silicon tetrafluoride and tin(IV) chloride are typical examples,

$$SiF_4 + 2:\overset{..}{\underset{..}{F}}:^- \rightarrow SiF_6{}^{2-}$$
Lewis   *Lewis*
acid   *base*

$$SnCl_4 + 2:\overset{..}{\underset{..}{Cl}}:^- \rightarrow SnCl_6{}^{2-}$$
Lewis   *Lewis*
acid   *base*

(d) Molecules with a Multiple Bond between Atoms of Dissimilar Electronegativities. An example of such a molecule is carbon dioxide, O=C=O. The oxygen atoms are more electronegative than the carbon atom. As a result, the electron density due to the π electrons is displaced away from the carbon atom, toward the O atoms. The carbon atom is electron-deficient and is apt to form a bond with a Lewis base such as OH⁻,

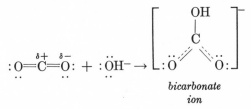

bicarbonate ion

This reaction is discussed in more detail in Chapter 26.

Sulfur dioxide, SO_2, reacts like CO_2 toward OH⁻,

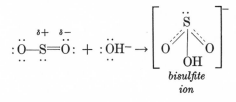

bisulfite ion

(e) Carbonium Ions. Lewis acid-base reactions occur frequently. However, the acid-base aspect of the reaction may be obscure. For example, the reaction of HBr with alkenes is a typical addition reaction (page 246). The reaction can be considered to involve two acid-base reactions. An alkene has a pair of electrons in a π bond and, consequently, behaves as a Lewis base. Thus, ethylene accepts a proton from HBr to give a carbonium ion, the conjugate acid of the alkene,

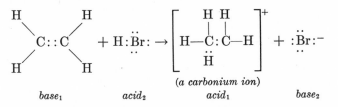

(a carbonium ion)

base₁   acid₂   acid₁   base₂

The carbonium ion has an electron-deficient carbon atom, and hence acts as a Lewis acid. In the second step, the carbonium ion reacts with Br⁻, which is the Lewis base,

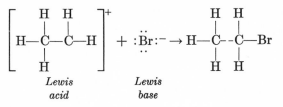

Lewis acid   *Lewis base*

The net reaction is therefore

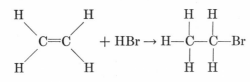

17.9 MECHANISM OF PROTON TRANSFER

A **reaction mechanism** is *the sequence of bond changes that reactants undergo until the products emerge.* Knowing a mechanism helps focus attention on the factors influencing the reaction. Figure 17.1 represents a

Fig. 17.1. *A plausible mechanism for proton transfer involving HCl and H₂O.*

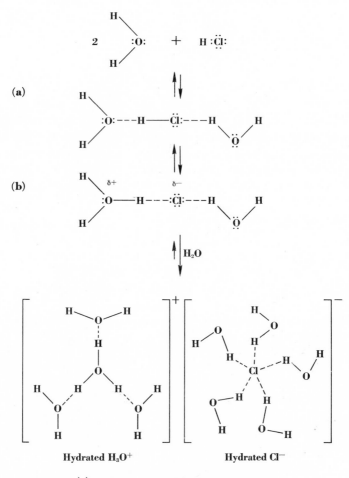

(a)

(b)

(c) each ion solvated by water

plausible mechanism for proton transfer between HCl, a typical acid, and H_2O. We assume the first step is the formation of hydrogen bonds (Fig. 17.1a). These hydrogen bonds must replace those that prevail in the acid itself.

In the next stage, the new O-H bond becomes shorter and stronger concurrently with a lengthening and weakening of the H-Cl bond. This change in bond lengths generates fractional charges on the Cl and O atoms (Fig. 17.1b). These incipient ions attract water molecules by an ion-dipole interaction (page 295), and this solvation of the ions aids in the further weakening of the H-Cl bond. Eventually the solvated ions drift apart. Step (c) emphasizes that, in addition to its basicity, the solvating ability of the solvent is important in influencing the dissociation of an acid. The difference in acidity of various acids is a reflection of the difference in stability of structures (a) and (b). The greater the stability of structure (b), as in the case of HCl, the stronger is the acid. For HF, structure (a) is more stable than structure (b), and HF is a weak acid in water.

17.10 THERMODYNAMICS OF ACID DISSOCIATION

Each stage in the mechanism (Fig. 17.1) is accompanied by a change in enthalpy and entropy, and a knowledge of these changes is necessary to understand the differences in acid strengths. Because of the complexity of the problem, this discussion is confined to binary acids.

The ionization (dissociation) of an acid, HA, in water is represented by

$$HA(aq) \rightleftharpoons H^+(aq) + A^-(aq)$$

The equilibrium constant K_a or the pK_a is related to the standard free energy change,

$$\Delta F° = -2.3RT \log K_a$$

Since $- \log K_a = pK_a$,

$$\Delta F° = 2.3RT\, pK_a$$

in which R is the gas constant, 2.0 cal per mole per degree, and T is the absolute temperature (page 421). $\Delta F°$, the change in free energy accompanying the reaction, is equal to the difference between the free energies of the products and reactants,

$$\Delta F° = F°_{products} - F°_{reactants}$$

The superscript $°$ indicates that all activities are unity. Therefore, if the free energy of the products is less than that of the reactants, $\Delta F°$ is negative. A negative $\Delta F°$ means that $\log K_a$ is positive, and the acid is therefore highly dissociated. Conversely, if $\Delta F°$ is positive, K_a is less than 1, indicating a weak acid.

The free energy change is also given by (page 403)

$$\Delta F° = \Delta H° - T\Delta S°$$

Since a large negative $\Delta F°$ value indicates a strong acid, the more negative the $\Delta H°$ and the more positive the $\Delta S°$ values, the stronger is the acid.

By applying Hess's law, the $\Delta H°$ for the dissociation of an acid may be calculated by addition of the following thermochemical equations, for which $\Delta H°$ values are available:

$H{:}A(g) = H{\cdot}\ (g) + A\cdot(g)$	Bond energy,	$\Delta H°_{BE}$
$H{\cdot}\ (g) - e^- = H^+(g)$	Ionization energy,	$\Delta H°_{IE}$
$H^+(g) = H^+(aq)$	Heat of solution of $H^+(g)$,	$\Delta H°_2$
$A\cdot(g) + e^- = A{:}^-(g)$	Electron affinity,	$\Delta H°_{EA}$
$A{:}^-(g) = A^-(aq)$	Heat of solution of $A^-(g)$,	$\Delta H°_3$
$HA(H_2O)_n = HA(g) + nH_2O$	Reverse of heat of solution of $HA(g)$,	$\Delta H°_1$

$$HA(aq) = H^+(aq) + A^-(aq) \qquad \text{Heat of dissociation,} \qquad \Delta H°_{\text{diss}}$$

The more negative the values for the several enthalpies shown, the more negative is the $\Delta H°$ of dissociation and the stronger the acid. The contribution made by the enthalpy of the last equation, $\Delta H°_1$, and its significance needs elaboration. $\Delta H°_1$ is the *reverse* of the heat of solution of the acid, so that the more negative the heat of solution, the more positive is $\Delta H°_1$. Hence, the more positive is the heat of dissociation, the weaker is the acid. A large negative heat of solution indicates a strong affinity between acid and water molecules. For acids, this affinity is due mainly to hydrogen bonding. Dissociation of the acid destroys these hydrogen bonds, replacing them by hydrogen bonds between water molecules and the ions. Hence, the presence of *strong* hydrogen bonds between acid and water makes dissociation of the acid difficult and tends to make the acid weak. In the case of the other enthalpies, the more negative the values, the more negative is the $\Delta H°$ of dissociation and the stronger is the acid.

Likewise the entropy of dissociation, $\Delta S°_{\text{diss}}$, is the algebraic sum of the $\Delta S°$ values for the reactions. The various $\Delta H°$ and $\Delta S°$ values for HF and HI at 298°K are given in Tables 17.2 and 17.3. Table 17.4 summarizes the predicted values and indicates the fair agreement between the calculated and experimental values for the ionization constants. The thermodynamic data reveal the differences accounting for the relative acidities.

TABLE 17.2 *Enthalpy Changes for Steps in Dissociation of HF and HI*

Acid	$\Delta H°_1$	$\Delta H°_{BE}$	$\Delta H°_{IE}$	$\Delta H°_{EA}$	$\Delta H°_2 +$ $\Delta H°_3$	$\Delta H°_{\text{diss}}$ (calcd.)
HF	+11.5	+134.6	+315.0	−82.0	−381.9	− 2.8
HI	+ 5.5	+ 71.4	+315.0	−75.7	−330.3	−14.1

TABLE 17.3 *Entropy Changes for Steps in Dissociation of HF and HI*

Acid	ΔS_1°	ΔS_{BE}°	$\Delta S_{IE}^\circ + \Delta S_2^\circ$	$\Delta S_{EA}^\circ + \Delta S_3^\circ$	ΔS_{diss}° (calcd.)
HF	$+23$	$+23.8$	-27.4	-40.2	-20.8
HI	$+20$	$+21.2$	-27.4	-17.0	-3.2

Let us consider how reactions from which ΔF° was calculated relate to the relative acid strengths of HI and HF. Two of the enthalpy terms, the ionization energy of hydrogen, ΔH_{IE}°, and the heat of solution of H$^+$, ΔH_2°, are constant. The electron affinity, ΔH_{EA}°, and the heat of solution of the anion, ΔH_3°, are larger for HF, and therefore tend to make HF a stronger acid than HI. The heat of solution of F$^-$ is larger because F$^-$, being a smaller ion than I$^-$, has a higher negative charge density, and therefore more strongly attracts water molecules. Offsetting these factors are the effects of the bond energies and heats of solution of the acids. The stronger H—F bond and the more negative heat of solution of HF(g) tend to make HF the weaker acid. HF is expected to have a more negative heat of solution than HI because the hydrogen bonds between HF and water are stronger than those between HI and water.

With respect to a comparison of ΔS° values, only the $(\Delta S_{EA}^\circ + \Delta S_3^\circ)$ values are significantly different. Recall that the more negative the ΔS° value, the more positive is the ΔF° and the smaller is the K_a. Consequently, the fact that $\Delta S_{EA}^\circ + \Delta S_3^\circ$ for HF is -40.2 cal per mole deg and that the value for HI is -17.0 cal per mole deg indicates that HF is the weaker acid. The difference in entropy for electron transfer to an F or I atom is negligible. Therefore, the significant difference in this composite value must be in *hydration of the ions*. Solvation restricts the freedom of motion of the ions, and brings about a more ordered state with resulting decrease in entropy. Since the F$^-$ ion is more strongly solvated than the I$^-$ ion, its entropy is decreased to a greater degree, tending to make HF a weaker acid. In short, the enthalpy of hydration of F$^-$, which is favorable for dissociation, is practically canceled by the entropy of hydration of F$^-$. The relative weakness of HF is thus attributable mainly to the greater

TABLE 17.4 *Summary of Values for Dissociation of HF and HI in Water at 25°C*

Acid	ΔH°	$-$	$T \Delta S^\circ$	$=$	ΔF°	K_a	Experimental K_a
HF	-2.8		$298(-20.8 \times 10^{-3})$		$+3.2$	10^{-3}	7×10^{-4}
HI	-14.1		$298(-3.2 \times 10^{-3})$		-13.1	10^9	$> 10^7$

strength of the H—F bond and, to a somewhat lesser extent, to the greater heat of solution of the HF molecules.

17.11 INDUSTRIAL APPLICATIONS OF ACID-BASE REACTIONS

(a) **Softening "Temporary" Hard Water.** The hardness of water has been attributed to the presence of certain cations, notably Ca^{2+} and Mg^{2+}, that cause soap to precipitate (page 310). Removal of the interfering cations, a process called **water-softening,** can be effected by acid-base reactions.

In certain hard waters the major anion present is bicarbonate, $HOCO_2^-$. Heating a solution containing Ca^{2+} and $HOCO_2^-$ affords a precipitate of calcium carbonate as the result of a two-step sequence:

$$Step \ (1) \qquad \underset{acid_1}{HOCO_2^-} + \underset{base_2}{HOCO_2^-} \xrightarrow{\text{heat}} \underset{base_1}{CO_3^{2-}} + H_2O + \underset{\substack{\text{or} \\ (HO)_2CO \\ \textit{carbonic acid} \\ acid_2}}{CO_2}$$

$$Step \ (2) \qquad CO_3^{2-} + Ca^{2+} \longrightarrow CaCO_3\downarrow$$

The first step represents the autoprotolysis of the bicarbonate ion. The combination of CO_2 and H_2O can be considered to be the unstable carbonic acid. Heat displaces the equilibrium to the right by decreasing the solubility of CO_2. Water containing sufficient bicarbonate ion to cause precipitation of all interfering cations when heated is called "temporary" hard water.

The formation of calcium carbonate from "temporary" hard water is frequently objectionable, especially when it occurs in hot water boilers and pipes. The deposits of calcium carbonate and other insoluble calcium salts form an adherent scale that lowers the heat conductivity of the boiler tubes and blocks the water passage in the pipes. This may ultimately lead to bursting of the boiler tubes. It is therefore necessary to soften the water before it enters the boiler. The $HOCO_2^-$ ion can be converted to CO_3^{2-} by a base such as hydroxide ion,

$$\underset{acid_1}{HOCO_2^-} + \underset{base_2}{OH^-} \rightarrow \underset{base_1}{CO_3^{2-}} + \underset{acid_2}{H_2O}$$

For large-scale water softening, calcium hydroxide (lime), $Ca(OH)_2$, is used as a cheap source of OH^-. The "temporary" hard water is analyzed to determine the concentration of $HOCO_2^-$. One mole of $Ca(OH)_2$ is added for every two moles of $HOCO_2^-$ present. Any Ca^{2+} ions remaining are removed by adding sodium carbonate (*washing soda*), Na_2CO_3. For softening water in the home, household cleansers are usually reinforced with the basic substances, ammonia and sodium phosphate, Na_3PO_4 (see Problem 4.)

When $HOCO_2^-$ is not the major anion present, the water is said to have "permanent" hardness. In such cases, the Ca^{2+} and Mg^{2+} ions can be converted to insoluble carbonates by adding washing soda, Na_2CO_3, or removed by ion-exchange methods (page 593).

Chemists have developed synthetic detergents, "syndets," with the distinct advantage over soap of not forming precipitates with calcium ion (page 310).

(b) Preparation of Sodium Bicarbonate; the Solvay Process. Another industrial application of acid-base reactions is the very efficient Solvay process for the manufacture of sodium bicarbonate, also called *baking soda*, $NaHOCO_2$. The most abundant source of Na^+ is sodium chloride, and the only source of $HOCO_2^-$ is carbon dioxide. Unfortunately, since CO_2 is a weak acid, $K_1 = 4.47 \times 10^{-7}$, it reacts with water to give a very low concentration of $HOCO_2^-$,

$$CO_2 + H_2O \rightleftharpoons H_3O^+ + HOCO_2^-$$

However, the equilibrium can be shifted to the right by reducing the concentration of H_3O^+. This displacement can be achieved by adding a base. However, we must avoid the removal of the proton from $HOCO_2^-$. The desired results are best attained by mixing ammonia and carbon dioxide in an aqueous solution,

$$CO_2 + H_2O \rightleftharpoons HOCO_2^- + H_3O^+$$
$$NH_3 + H_3O^+ \rightleftharpoons NH_4^+ + H_2O$$

The net reaction is

$$CO_2 + H_2O + NH_3 \rightarrow NH_4^+ + HOCO_2^-$$

A mixture of NH_4^+, $HOCO_2^-$, Na^+, and Cl^- ions could result in the formation of four possible salts, $NaCl$, NH_4Cl, $Na(HOCO_2)$, and $NH_4(HOCO_2)$. These salts are all classified as soluble. However, under the conditions of the reaction, water at 0°C is saturated with NH_3, $NaCl$, and CO_2. Under these circumstances, $Na(HO)CO_2$ is the least soluble of the four salts and precipitates from the solution. Thus the equation for the over-all reaction is

$$Na^+ + Cl^- + NH_3 + CO_2 + H_2O \rightarrow NH_4^+ + Cl^- + NaHOCO_2 \tag{10}$$

The CO_2 is supplied by roasting calcium carbonate: $CaCO_3 \rightarrow CaO + CO_2\uparrow$. The CaO, thus formed, is used to regenerate NH_3 from the ammonium chloride, the by-product in Equation 10,

$$CaO + 2NH_4^+ + 2Cl^- \rightarrow Ca^{2+} + 2Cl^- + 2NH_3\uparrow + H_2O \tag{11}$$

To summarize, we see that the consumed raw materials are $NaCl$ and $CaCO_3$, and the sole by-product is an aqueous solution of calcium chloride (Equation 11). The calcium chloride is used as a drying agent, and for melting ice on highways. Ammonia, the most expensive ingredient, is regenerated.

Solid sodium bicarbonate can be converted to solid sodium carbonate by heating,

$$2NaHOCO_2 \rightarrow Na_2CO_3 + H_2O + CO_2$$

Problems

1. Conjugate acid-base pairs. (a) List the conjugate acids of H_2O, Cl^-, SO_4^{2-}, NH_3, HF. (b) List the conjugate bases of H_2O, HBr, NH_4^+, $(HO)_2PO_2^-$, NH_3, OH^-.

2. Conjugate acid-base pairs. Complete the following protolytic reactions. Indicate the conjugate acid-base pairs. If not shown over the arrow, the solvent is the second reactant.

(a) NH_3 $+ CH_3COOH \longrightarrow$
(b) H^- $+ NH_3$ $\longrightarrow$
(c) O^{2-} $+ H_2O$ $\longrightarrow$
(d) NH_2^- $+ CH_3OH$ $\longrightarrow$
(e) H_3O^+ $+ O^{2-}$ $\overset{H_2O}{\longrightarrow}$
(f) $HCl(g) + H_2SO_4(l)$ $\longrightarrow$

3. Amphiprotism. Write equations to illustrate amphiprotism of (a) $HOCO_2^-$; (b) $(HO)_2PO_2^-$; (c) HF; (d) CH_3OH; (e) $Zn(OH)_2(H_2O)_2$; (f) $Sb(OH)_3$. Designate the conjugate acid-base pairs.

4. Reaction of ions with water. Classify the aqueous solutions of the following salts as acidic, basic, neutral, or doubtful: (a) $NaNO_3$; (b) $NaCN$; (c) NH_4Cl; (d) K_3PO_4; (e) K_2HOPO_3; (f) $FeCl_3$; (g) $BiCl_3$; (h) $CaCl_2$; (i) K_2CO_3; (j) $K_2Al_2(SO_4)_4(H_2O)_{24}$ (alum); (k) $(HONH_3)^+ OAc^-$ (hydroxylammonium acetate).

5. Lewis concept. Categorize the following substances as Lewis acids, bases, or none of these: (a) anhydrous $ZnCl_2$; (b) Cl^-; (c) anhydrous $SnCl_2$; (d) H_2; (e) $B(CH_3)_3$; (f) CH_3OCH_3; (g) CH_3CCH_3; (h) SO_2; (i) SO_3; (j) $(C_6H_5)_3C^+$; (k) $(C_6H_5)_3C:^-$
$$\overset{\parallel}{O}$$

6. Lewis concept. Using structural formulas, formulate and complete the following equations. Specify the electrophile and the nucleophile.
(a)   aluminum hydride + lithium hydride $(Li^+H^-) \rightarrow$
(b)   calcium oxide + sulfur dioxide $\rightarrow$
(c)   sulfur trioxide + sulfide ion $\rightarrow$
(d)   anhydrous zinc sulfate + water $\rightarrow$
(e)   hydride ion + formaldehyde $(H_2C{=}O) \rightarrow$
(f)   boron trifluoride + ethyl ether $(C_2H_5OC_2H_5) \rightarrow$
(g)   cyanide ion + acetone $(CH_3CCH_3) \rightarrow$
$$\overset{\parallel}{O}$$

7. Autoprotolysis. Write equations for the autoprotolysis of the following pure liquids: (a) $(HO)_2SO_2$; (b) CH_3OH; (c) $HONO_2$; (d) $HCOOH$ (formic acid).

8. Neutralization. Write an equation for a neutralization reaction occurring in each of the following pure liquids: (a) ammonia; (b) acetic acid; (c) HF.

9. Polyprotic acids. Write equations (designate conjugate pairs) for the stepwise protolysis in water of (a) H_2S; (b) CO_2; (c) $(HO)_2PO$; (d) $(HO)_3PO$; (e)
$$\overset{|}{\underset{H}{}}$$
PO_4^{-3}; (f) ethylene diammonium ion; $(H_3NCH_2CH_2NH_3)^{+2}$.

10. Protolysis; H-D exchange. (a) Write the equation for the equilibrium established when (i) CH_3COOH is dissolved in D_2O, (ii) CH_3COOD is dissolved in H_2O. (b) How would you prepare DCN? (c) Use equations to formulate the conversion of acetaldehyde, CH_3CHO, to CD_3CHO using OD^- in D_2O.

11. K_a. Discuss the validity of the following statement and illustrate your answer with a definite example. "The K_a does not measure the intrinsic proton-donating power of an acid."

12. Energetics. The data given for HCl are at 298°K. (a) Given the following $\Delta H°$ values in kcal/mole, calculate $\Delta H°_{diss}$: heat of solution of HCl, -4.2; bond energy, $+103.2$; ionization energy, $+315.0$; electron affinity, -87.3; and heat of solution of ions, -348.8. (b) Given the following $\Delta S°$ values in cal/mole deg, calculate the $\Delta S°_{diss}$; entropy of solution, $+18$; bond entropy, $+22.3$; entropy for $H(g) \rightleftharpoons H^+(aq) + e^-$, -27.4; entropy for $Cl(g) + e^- \rightleftharpoons Cl^-(aq)$, -26.3. (c) Calculate $\Delta F°_{diss}$ and K_a. (d) Which steps tend to make HCl a stronger acid than HF, but weaker than HI?

Answer. (a) -13.7; (b) -13.4; (c) -9.5, 10^7.

13. Acid strength. (a) Account for the fact that acetic acid is a weaker acid in ethanol, C_2H_5OH (dielectric constant $= 24.2$), than in water (dielectric constant $= 79$). (b) Account for the fact that NH_4Cl has about the same acidity in both solvents.

14. Nonaqueous solvents. Write equations and account for the fact that (a) acetic acid is a strong acid in liquid NH_3, (b) nitric acid is a weak acid in pure (glacial) acetic acid.

15. Leveling effect. (a) Elaborate on the statement, "The strongest base and acid that can exist in liquid NH_3 are NH_2^- and NH_4^+, respectively." (b) What are the strongest base and acid, respectively, that can exist in pure CH_3OH? (c) Generalize about the strongest acid and base that can exist in any autoprotolytic solvent.

16. Practical protolysis. Write an equation for each of the following practical protolytic reactions:

(a)	$NaHOCO_2(aq) + (HO)_2SO_2$	(*"wet" fire extinguisher*)
(b)	$NaHOCO_2(aq) + K_2Al_2(SO_4)_4(H_2O)_{24}(aq)$	(*baking powder reaction*)
(c)	Calcium hydride + water	(*filling weather balloons*)
(d)	Calcium carbide (Ca^{2+}:$C\equiv C$:$^{2-}$) + water	(*preparation of acetylene*)

17. Neutralization. The heat of reaction at 25°C of NaOH and HCl, or KOH and HNO_3, is -13.82 kcal/mole. That for CH_3COOH and NaOH is -13.52 kcal/mole. Account for the difference in the observed data with the aid of thermochemical equations.

18. Mechanism of protolysis. In terms of Fig. 17.1 (page 454), explain which reaction, forward or reverse, is favored as (a) a solution is made more concentrated; (b) ethanol (dielectric constant $= 24.2$) replaces water (dielectric constant $= 79$) as solvent; (c) an acid with strong internal hydrogen bonding replaces one with no hydrogen bonds.

19. Amphoterism. Mg liberates H_2 from acidic media faster than does Al, but Al liberates H_2 faster from alkaline media. Explain.

18

Hydrides
and
oxides;
Structure
and
basicity

18.1 REACTIVITY OF HYDRIDES

The term **hydride** is used in two ways. It is the *generic* name for all binary hydrogen compounds, and is the *specific* name for the binary hydrogen compounds of the Groups IA and IIA elements, for example lithium hydride and calcium hydride. We will discuss only the hydrides of the representative elements. The hydrides of the transition metals are not included because of the wide variation in types. Most transition metals such as Fe and Co do not form stable hydrides. Some, such as Ni, Pt, and Pd, absorb appreciable amounts of hydrogen gas, but do not give compounds which obey the Law of Definite Proportions. Those hydrides of transition elements that are formed either behave chemically like those of the Group IIA elements, or else are relatively inert.

Not all the representative elements form stable well-defined hydrogen compounds. It is observed, for example, that, except for Groups IA and IIA, *as we proceed down the group, the stability of the hydride decreases.* Thus, we find that *no* appreciable amounts of well-defined hydrogen compounds of gallium (Ga), indium (In), and thallium (Tl) (Group IIIA), lead (Pb) (Group IVA), bismuth (Bi) (Group VA), and polonium (Po) (Group VIA) have as yet been isolated.

We should expect the mode of reaction of hydrides to depend to some extent on the relative electronegativities of hydrogen and the other element. It is evident from Table 9.2 (page 216) that hydrogen is intermediate in electronegativity. Therefore, on the basis of a comparison with hydrogen, we can divide the representative elements into three groups:

(a) Those elements that are less electronegative and, in their hydrides, are positive relative to hydrogen. These are found in the left-hand portion of the Periodic Table.

(b) Those elements that are more electronegative, and, in their hydrides, are negative. These are found in the right-hand portion of the Periodic Table.

(c) Those elements that have approximately the same order of electronegativity, and have little or no fractional (partial) charge in their hydrides. These are found in the center region of the Periodic Table.

The several ways in which hydrides react with water reveal the periodic variations in the bonding and reactivity of these compounds.

(a) **No Reaction.** The hydrides of the elements of Group IVA and Group VA (except for nitrogen) do not react with water. Included in this class of compounds are phosphine, PH_3, and the alkanes, such as CH_4. Generally in this group of compounds the central atom has an octet of electrons, and has an electronegativity close to that of hydrogen.

(b) **Basic Reaction Due to Hydride Ion.** The hydrides of the elements in Group IA and Group IIA (except for Be and possibly Mg) are essentially ionic compounds, and are called "saline" (salt-like) hydrides. These elements all have an electronegativity *much less* than that of hydrogen. The hydride ion is very basic, and reacts with water to produce H_2 and OH^-;

$$\underset{\substack{-1 \\ base_1}}{H:^-} + \underset{\substack{+1 \quad +1 \\ acid_2}}{H-\overset{..}{O}-H} \rightarrow \underset{\substack{0 \quad 0 \\ acid_1}}{H-H} + \underset{\substack{+1 \\ base_2}}{[:\overset{..}{O}-H]^-}$$

oxidation number:

It is noteworthy that the above reaction is also an oxidation-reduction, as deduced from the change in oxidation numbers shown below each H atom in the equation. In this respect, $H:^-$ is a reducing agent. The acceptance of a proton by hydride ion is both an acid-base and a redox reaction.

(c) **Hydrolysis.** Several covalent hydrides react with water to give hydrogen and an oxyacid of the central atom, as typified by the reaction of diborane,

$$\underset{diborane}{\overset{\delta+ \quad \delta-}{B_2H_6}} + 6H_2O \rightarrow 6H_2 + \underset{orthoboric\ acid}{2B(OH)_3}$$

Generally, during this type of hydrolysis, the more electronegative element combines with the hydrogen, and the less electronegative element combines with the OH group. In the above examples, hydrogen is more electronegative and so H_2 is formed. The hydrides that hydrolyze in this manner contain a central element, less electronegative than hydrogen, that cannot exist as a cation in water because of a large cationic charge density (page 232).

(d) **Acidic Reaction.** The hydrogen compounds of the elements in Groups VIA and VIIA dissociate in water to give acidic solutions, as shown for HI and H_2Se,

$$\overset{\delta+\ \delta-}{HI} + H_2O \rightarrow H_3O^+ + I^-$$

$$\overset{\delta+\ \delta-}{H_2Se} + H_2O \rightleftharpoons H_3O^+ + HSe^-$$

In these compounds, the bond is polarized, so that the H atom has a fractional positive charge, as shown in the above equations. However, one should not jump to the *erroneous* conclusion that the more polar the $\overset{\delta+\ \ \delta-}{H-M}$ bond, the more acidic is the binary compound. Were this so, we could expect the more polar H-F molecule to be more acidic than the less polar H-I molecule. HI is actually a much stronger acid than HF. In general, *the acidity of binary compounds, HX, increases on proceeding down a group*, notwithstanding the fact that the electronegativity of the atom, X, decreases:

Compound:	HF	HCl	HBr	HI
K_a:	7×10^{-4}	$\sim 10^7$	$\sim 10^9$	$\sim 10^{10}$

The *acidity of binary compounds increases on proceeding across a period from left to right:*

Compound:	CH_4	NH_3	H_2O	HF
K_a:	10^{-50}	10^{-32}	$2 \times 10^{-16*}$	7×10^{-4}

We can observe this difference in acidity in a very qualitative way, by using sodium, an active metal, as a test reagent. To a rough approximation, the rate of displacement of hydrogen by sodium is an indication of the acidity of the compound. Thus, we find that methane is completely inert toward sodium, ammonia reacts slowly, water reacts violently, and it would be foolhardy to add sodium to liquid hydrogen fluoride. These findings are consistent with the indicated order of acidity.

(e) **Basic Reaction due to a Lone Pair on the Central Atom.** Ammonia is the only hydride that reacts as a base in water by virtue of the lone pair of electrons on the nitrogen atom,

$$H_3N: + H_2O \rightleftharpoons H_3N:H^+ + OH^-$$

* K_a for water $= [H^+][OH^-]/[H_2O] = 10^{-14}/55.5 = 2 \times 10^{-16}$. We must use this form to permit a fair comparison with the other constants, such as K_a for HF $= [H^+][F^-]/[HF]$.

This property falls off sharply as we proceed down the group. Thus, the order of basicity of the hydrides of Group VA elements is

$$NH_3 > PH_3 > AsH_3 > SbH_3$$
decreasing basicity
$$\longrightarrow$$

Ammonia is more basic than water, which in turn is more basic than hydrogen fluoride. Therefore, *basicity due to one or more lone pairs of electrons on the central atom decreases* on proceeding across a period from left to right.

The known hydrides of Group IIIA possess electron-deficient atoms, and so behave as Lewis acids. Of particular interest are their reactions with saline hydrides:

$$AlH_3 \quad + Li^+H^- \rightarrow Li^+ \left[\begin{array}{c} H \\ \cdot\cdot \\ H:\ddot{Al}:H \\ \cdot\cdot \\ H \end{array} \right]^-$$

aluminum	*lithium aluminum*
hydride	*hydride*

$$B_2H_6 \quad + 2Na^+H^- \rightarrow 2Na^+ \left[\begin{array}{c} H \\ \cdot\cdot \\ H:\ddot{B}:H \\ \cdot\cdot \\ H \end{array} \right]^-$$

diborane   *sodium*
borohydride

Sodium borohydride, a typical salt-like compound, is widely used as a reducing agent because it is a source of hydride ions.

18.2   THE PERIODICITY OF PROPERTIES OF THE OXIDES

All elements except some of the noble gases can form oxides; almost all elements form more than one. Since oxygen is the most electronegative of all elements but fluorine, the fractional charge on oxygen in all oxides except OF_2 and O_2F_2 is negative. This fractional charge would be expected to reach its most negative values (approaching -2) in the alkali metal oxides, and its least negative values (approaching 0) in the halogen oxides. As the fractional charge becomes more negative, the structure of the oxide assumes more of the O^{2-} ionic character. As the fractional charge approaches zero, the oxide becomes more covalent. Ionic oxides react with water to give basic hydroxides; these oxides are known as **basic anhydrides,** as typified by calcium oxide, CaO,

$$Ca^{2+}O^{2-} + H_2O \rightarrow \underbrace{Ca^{2+} + 2OH^-}_{base} \tag{1}$$
basic
anhydride

Covalent oxides react with water to give oxyacids; these oxides are known as **acid anhydrides,** as typified by sulfur trioxide, SO_3,

$$SO_3 \quad + H_2O \rightarrow \underbrace{H^+ + HOSO_3^-}_{acid} \tag{2}$$
acid
anhydride

Each case may be considered to be a Lewis base type of attack by the *more negative oxygen* on the *more positive atom of the other compound:*

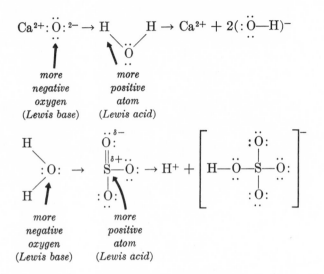

more	more
negative	positive
oxygen	atom
(*Lewis base*)	(*Lewis acid*)

It is to be expected that oxides in which the fractional charge on oxygen is close to that of the oxygen of water will be **amphoteric** as shown for ZnO

$$ZnO + 2H^+ \rightarrow Zn^{2+} + H_2O$$
$$ZnO + 2OH^- + H_2O \rightarrow Zn(OH)_4^{2-}$$

Designations of oxides of different oxidation states of the elements as weakly, moderately, or strongly basic and/or acidic appear in Table 18.1. The following periodic trends are observed.

(a) *The general trend within a period, from left to right, for oxidation states equal to the Group Number, is from basic through amphoteric to acidic oxides.* The trend also holds for the hydroxy compounds as typified by the elements of the third period:

NaOH	Mg(OH)$_2$	Al(OH)$_3$	SiO$_2$(H$_2$O)$_n$	(HO)$_3$PO	(HO)$_2$SO$_2$	HOClO$_3$
strong	weak	amphoteric	very weak	moderate	strong	strongest
base	base		acid	acid	acid	acid

(b) *The general trend within a group, downward, is toward increased basicity and/or decreased acidity of oxides and of hydroxy compounds.* Thus, we find in Group VA:

As(OH)$_3$	Sb(OH)$_3$	Bi(OH)$_3$
(*arsenious acid*)*	amphoteric	weak base
weak acid		

* The structure of arsenious acid is still in doubt. It may be hydrated arsenic(III) oxide, As$_2$O$_3$(H$_2$O)$_n$.

TABLE 18.1 *Basic and/or Acidic Properties of the Oxides of the Elements*

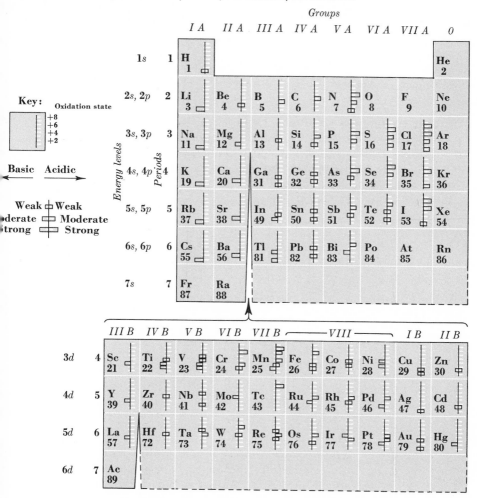

(c) *For any element, the oxide and the hydroxy compound tend to become more acidic the higher the oxidation state of the element,* as illustrated by the chlorine oxyacids:

Acid	Formula	Oxidation number	pK_a
Hypochlorous	HOCl	+1	7.5
Chlorous	HOClO	+3	2
Chloric	HOClO_2	+5	−1
Perchloric	HOClO_3	+7	−11

18.3 STRUCTURE OF OXYANIONS; p-$d\pi$ BONDING

The structure of the oxyanions formed from acid anhydrides is greatly influenced by the size of the central atom. The oxyanions of the second period elements, boron, carbon, and nitrogen,

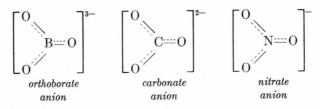

orthoborate *anion*	*carbonate* *anion*	*nitrate* *anion*

have *three* oxygen atoms, each of which participates in extended p-$p\pi$ bonding with the central atom. The ions are planar and have O—M—O bond angles of 120°. Each central atom uses sp^2 hybrid orbitals to form the three sigma bonds. The remaining p orbital is used for the formation of the extended π bond.

The oxyanions of the third period elements, Si, P, S, and Cl,

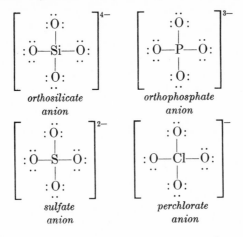

have *four* oxygen atoms bonded to the central atom. Each of these oxyanions has a tetrahedral structure, and hence the central atom utilizes sp^3 hybrid atomic orbitals to form the four sigma bonds, one to each oxygen atom.

There are two main reasons for this difference in structure between oxyanions of the second and third period elements:

(a) The third period elements are larger and can better surround themselves with *four* oxygen atoms.

(b) The third period elements cannot participate in p-$p\pi$ bonding because their bonds to oxygen are too long.*

The third period elements have, in common, the ability to acquire more than an octet of electrons by utilizing available $3d$ atomic orbitals. For this reason, the structures of these oxyanions are best conceived of as possessing an extended π bond involving the central atom and each oxygen atom, as represented for the sulfate ion (Fig. 18.1). Since the sulfur atom must utilize d orbitals for overlap with the p orbital of oxygen, this type

* Sulfur is an exception (page 213).

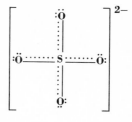

Fig. 18.1. *Structure for sulfate anion, showing delocalized p-dπ bond.*

of bonding is called *p-dπ bonding*. A typical *p-dπ* bond is shown in Fig. 18.2. The 3*d* orbital furnished by the sulfur atom is devoid of electrons, whereas the 2*p* orbital of oxygen has two electrons. Which of the five *d* orbitals are used by the central atom is too complex a question for discussion in this book.

The effectiveness of any kind of π bonding is inversely related to bond distance. Therefore, as the central atom gets larger, its bond to the oxygen atom gets longer and *p-dπ* bonding becomes less effective. The oxygen atom of an OH group does not participate significantly in *p-dπ* bonding; only a lone oxygen atom does.

18.4 RELATIONSHIP OF STRUCTURE TO ACIDITY AND BASICITY

Acidity and basicity are influenced by several factors, so that generalizations about the effect of structural changes must be approximate. *As long as we consider the effect of changing a single factor, generalizations may be used with some confidence.* Examples of closely related acids differing by only one factor are HF and HI (same Group but different Period), H_2O and NH_3 (same Period but different Group), and $(HO)_2SO$ and $(HO)_2SO_2$ (same central atom but different oxidation state). Pairs of acids that are too dissimilar because they vary by more than one factor are HCl and

Fig. 18.2. *Formation of pπ-dπ bond between S and O in SO_4^{2-}.*

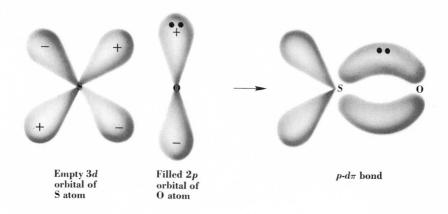

Empty 3*d* orbital of S atom   Filled 2*p* orbital of O atom   *p-dπ* bond

HONO, and $HONO_2$ and $(HO)_2SO$ (different Group, different Period, and different oxidation state).

The generalizations relating periodicity to basicity and acidity offered in the previous sections are based on measured pK values. The theoretical explanation for the observed facts is, however, conjectural. Many factors, several of which become apparent from the discussion of the energetics of the acidity of binary acids (page 455), play a role in determining acidity. Nevertheless it would be useful if at least the effects of electronic structure* could be explained in terms of a single unifying principle. This unifying principle is only a hypothesis and, like fashion in clothing, is subject to change, hopefully not so frequently or so drastically.

Most explanations of acidity of neutral molecules are given in terms of the stability of the products, more specifically in terms of the anion, since the H_3O^+ ion is a common product. This is valid, provided the acids are closely related structurally. Thus, *if a conjugate base is more stable than the conjugate base of a closely related acid, its acid is stronger*. For example, since perchloric acid, $HOClO_3$, is a stronger acid than chloric acid, $HOClO_2$, our theoretical explanation would have to explain the fact that ClO_4^-, the conjugate base of $HOClO_4$, is a more stable anion (less reactive) than ClO_3^-, the conjugate base of $HOClO_2$.

18.5 CHARGE DISPERSAL AND BASICITY

The hypothesis that we will use to explain the effects of electronic structure on basicity might be called the **"Principle of Charge Dispersal."** It states that *dispersal of the electron density from the electron-rich site of a base stabilizes the base and thus decreases its tendency to accept a proton (weakens its basicity)*. As a corollary, the conjugate acid of a stable base tends to lose a proton to revert to the stable structure, and is thus a strong acid. These ideas are summarized for the $HOClO_3$, ClO_4^- conjugate acid-base pair:

Negative charge is widely dispersed
↓
Ion is very stable
↓
Tendency to accept H^+ is very low
↓
Basicity is extremely weak

Tendency to revert to stable anion by losing H^+ is very high
↓
Molecule is unstable
↓
Acidity is very strong

Diffusion of electron density is influenced by the following factors.

---

* Electronic effects influence mainly the $\Delta H°$ of dissociation. But fortunately, if the acids are closely related, *and only then*, the entropies, $\Delta S°$, of dissociation can be presumed to be fairly constant. Therefore, we can assume that the difference in $\Delta H°$ of dissociation of similarly constituted acids is equal to the difference in $\Delta F°$ of dissociation and simply related to differences in K_a values.

(a) Ionic Size. In comparable bases, charge diffusion is greater in the larger ion, or in the molecule with the larger central atom. For the halide ions, we find in going from F^- to I^- that size increases, charge diffusion increases, and basicity decreases. This is consistent with the observed order of acidities of their conjugate acids (page 464). Similar reasoning is used to account for the following orders of decreasing basicity:

$$:NH_3 > :PH_3 > :AsH_3 \text{ and } :\ddot{O}H^- > :\ddot{S}H^- > :\ddot{S}eH^- > :\ddot{T}eH^-$$
$$\longrightarrow basicity\ decreasing$$

The order of acidity of the conjugate acids of these bases is

$$NH_4^+ < PH_4^+ < AsH_4^+ \text{ and } H_2O < H_2S < H_2Se < H_2Te$$
$$\longrightarrow acidity\ increasing$$

This argument is germane only to bases of binary acids and not to bases of oxyacids. *For oxyanions, other factors overshadow the effect of size.*

(b) Available "Surface." Other factors being equal, charge diffusion is greater when more free surface is available. What is meant by "free surface" becomes apparent from the discussion of the relative basicities of methide, CH_3^-; amide, NH_2^-; hydroxide, OH^-; and fluoride, F^- ions. For these anions the charge is the same and the size is approximately the same (it decreases somewhat in proceeding from CH_3^- to F^-) However, in CH_3^-, three hydrogen atoms occupy space around the carbon. atom so that the charge on the carbon atom may be visualized as concentrated into roughly one fourth of the ion surface. This ion, then, has the most concentrated charge and is the most basic. The F^- ion has no H atoms and its entire surface is available; its charge is therefore most diffuse and it is the least basic. The same reasoning can explain the greater basicity of $:NH_3$ as compared to that of $H_2O:$. On this basis, the decreasing order of basicity below is explained:

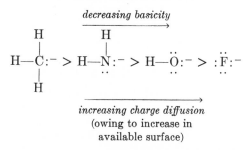

decreasing basicity

increasing charge diffusion
(owing to increase in
available surface)

(c) Extended π Bonding (Resonance). Extended π bonding (resonance) promotes charge dispersal. For example, in the nitrate ion, a typical oxyanion, the charge is dispersed to all three oxygen atoms and *is not just on the oxygen atom from which the proton was removed* (page 287). This charge dispersal or delocalization greatly stabilizes the nitrate ion, causing the ion to be a very weak base, and hence nitric acid to be a very strong acid. *The more lone oxygen atoms bonded to a central atom, the more extended is the π bond, the more delocalized is the charge, and the more stable* *is the anion.* Thus, nitrate ion, having *three* oxygen atoms participating in extended π bonding, is more stable and therefore less basic than nitrite ion, having *two* oxygen atoms participating in extended π bonding:

nitrate ion

nitrite ion

The more lone oxygens bonded to nitrogen,	The fewer lone oxygens bonded to nitrogen,
↓	↓
the more extended the π bonding,	the less extended the π bonding,
↓	↓
the more the dispersal of charge,	the less the dispersal of charge,
↓	↓
the weaker the base.	the stronger the base.

Therefore, nitric acid, $HONO_2$, is a stronger acid than nitrous acid, HONO.

The extended π bond which delocalizes charge can also be of the p-$d\pi$ bond variety, as postulated for the chlorine oxyacids. The oxyanion in which the central atom has the larger oxidation number has the larger number of lone oxygen atoms for participating in extension of the π bond, and therefore is the weaker base:

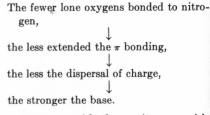

oxidation
number: +7   +5   +3   +1

decreasing charge delocalization →

increasing basicity →

In a given group, as the atomic weight of the central atom increases, the bond distance to oxygen increases, and the effectiveness of p-$d\pi$ bonding decreases. This explains the following order of basicity (M represents the central atom):

increasing order of basicity →

$(HO)_2PO_2^-$ < $(HO)_2AsO_2^-$ < $(HO)_2SbO_2^-$

Has the smallest central atom,	Has the largest central atom,
↓	↓
the smallest M-O bond distance,	the largest M-O bond distance,
↓	↓
the most effective p-$d\pi$ bonding,	the least effective p-$d\pi$ bonding,
↓	↓
the greatest amount of charge dispersal,	the least amount of charge dispersal,
↓	↓
is the weakest base.	is the strongest base.

Because of the familiar conjugate acid-base pair relationship, we find the following order of acidity:

$$(HO)_3PO > (HO)_3AsO > (HO)_3SbO$$

$$\xrightarrow{\hspace{4cm}}$$
decreasing order of acidity

It should be stressed that the concept of charge dispersal through extended π bonding is applicable only to oxyacids, and not to binary acids.

18.6 EFFECT OF ANIONIC CHARGE

We have compared, heretofore, anionic bases of the same charge. We might ask how the charge on an anion affects basicity. Other things being equal, *basicity increases with negative charge.* Thus, oxide ion, O^{2-}, is a stronger base than hydroxide ion, OH^-. Phosphate ion, PO_4^{3-}, is stronger than hydrogen phosphate, $HOPO_3^{2-}$, which is stronger than dihydrogen phosphate, $(HO)_2PO_2^-$. This order is a consequence of the fact that an anion is a stronger base than its conjugate acid. However, it is possible to generalize about similarly constituted bases in which the central atom differs. Thus, orthosilicate, SiO_4^{4-}, is a stronger base than orthophosphate, PO_4^{3-}, which is a stronger base than sulfate, SO_4^{2-}, which is stronger than perchlorate, ClO_4^-. The basicity diminishes as the charge on the anion decreases.

18.7 s CHARACTER AND BASICITY

The basicity of a molecule or anion also depends on the kind of orbital that houses the lone pair of electrons. This point can be illustrated by comparing ammonia, NH_3, and phosphine, PH_3. We have seen that the H—N—H bond angle is 107°, leading to the supposition that the N atom uses sp^3 tetrahedral orbitals. The lone pair of electrons then is in an sp^3 orbital. The H—P—H bond angle in PH_3 is 93.3°. This angle is close to 90°, the expected value if the phosphorus atom uses unhybridized p orbitals for bonding (Fig. 11.17, page 275). The electronic structure for the unhybridized valence orbitals in phosphorus is

$$
\begin{array}{ll}
3p \quad \underline{\uparrow\downarrow}\ \underline{\uparrow\downarrow}\ \underline{\uparrow\downarrow} & \textit{3 bonding pairs} \\
3s \quad \underline{\uparrow\downarrow} & \textit{lone pair}
\end{array}
$$

The lone pair of electrons of phosphorus is in an s orbital. A pair of electrons in an s orbital has a very diffuse electron cloud because the s orbital is spherically disposed around the central atom. On the other hand, a lone pair in an sp^3 hybrid orbital has a concentrated charge density because of the directional quality of the orbital. Such reasoning can be used to interpret the fact that :PH_3 $(K_b = 10^{-23})$ is a much weaker base than :NH_3 $(K_b = 10^{-5})$. This may be summarized as follows.

<table>
<tr><td align="center">: PH₃</td><td align="center">: NH₃</td></tr>
</table>

$: PH_3$ $: NH_3$

Uses unhybridized p orbitals for bonding,   Uses sp^3 hybrid orbitals for bonding,

$\downarrow$ $\downarrow$

has lone pair in s orbital,   has lone pair in sp^3 hybrid orbital,

$\downarrow$ $\downarrow$

has more diffuse electron density,   has less diffuse electron density,

$\downarrow$ $\downarrow$

is the weaker base.   is the stronger base.

We have also seen that acetylene, $H—C{\equiv}C—H$, is a much stronger acid than ethylene, $H_2C{=}CH_2$ (page 450). It has also been demonstrated that ethylene is a stronger acid than ethane, $H_3C—CH_3$:

$$\xrightarrow{\textit{decreasing acidity}}$$
$$H—C{\equiv}C—H > H_2C{=}CH_2 > H_3C—CH_3$$

The order of basicity of the respective conjugate bases is

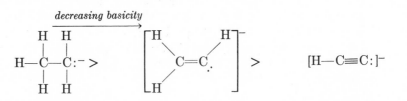

Has sp^3 hybridized carbon,   Has sp^2 hybridized carbon.   Has sp hybridized carbon,

$\downarrow$ $\downarrow$

has least s character,   has most s character,

$\downarrow$ $\downarrow$

is the most basic.   is the least basic.

An essential difference among these three carbanion bases is the state of hybridization of the carbon atom with the lone pair of electrons, as indicated above. It appears that the species with the *most s character* in the orbital housing the lone pair is the *least basic*. It should be recalled (page 283) that an increase in s character of a hybrid orbital is associated with closer proximity to the nucleus, and with a decrease in the energy of the orbital. For a given atom, the lower the energy of the lone pair of electrons, the less available they are for bonding with a proton. Also, the *less* the s character, the *more* directional is the electron cloud and the more *easily* it accepts a proton.

18.8   INDUCTIVE EFFECT AND BASICITY

Introducing different atoms or groups (substituents) on the central atom in place of hydrogen atoms affects dispersal of electron density and alters basicity (and acidity), as illustrated by several substituted ammonia compounds:

Compound	Formula	K_b
Methylamine	$H_3C:NH_2$	5.2×10^{-4}
Ammonia	$H:NH_2$	1.75×10^{-5}
Hydrazine	$H_2N:NH_2$	9.1×10^{-7}
Hydroxylamine	$HO:NH_2$	9.6×10^{-10}

The substituent attracts electrons away from the nitrogen atom or repels electrons toward the nitrogen atom relative to the position of electrons in the $H:N$ bond. This tendency of an atom or a group of atoms to alter electron density about another atom is called an **inductive effect.** If a substituent is more electronegative than an H atom, it will exert an electron-withdrawing inductive effect. Such substituents are the OH, NH_2, and SH groups, and the halogen atoms, F, Cl, Br, and I. The greater the electronegativity of the substituent as compared to the H atom, the greater is the inductive effect. *Electron withdrawal disperses electron density and hence weakens basicity.* For this reason, hydrazine and hydroxylamine are weaker bases than ammonia. Notice, too, that since an oxygen atom is more electronegative than a nitrogen atom, the OH group exerts a more electron-withdrawing inductive effect than does the NH_2 group and, consequently, hydroxylamine is less basic than hydrazine.

Alkyl groups, as typified by the methyl, H_3C, group are unique in that they exert an electron-releasing inductive effect. The shared pair between the carbon atom and the nitrogen atom is closer to the N atom in methylamine than in ammonia. The methyl group increases the electron density about the nitrogen atom and hence methylamine is a stronger base than ammonia. *Electron-releasing groups are base-strengthening.* Both kinds of inductive effect are summarized below with the aid of exaggerated electronic structures:

$H_3C \quad :NH_2$ Electron-releasing inductive effect, base-strengthening

$H \; : \; NH_2$ Standard for comparison

$HO: \quad NH_2$ Electron-withdrawing inductive effect, base-weakening

Acidity is also affected by inductive effects. An electron-withdrawing group increases acidity, as manifested by the fact that chloroform, $HCCl_3$, is more acidic than methane, HCH_3.

18.9 PREPARATION OF ACIDS

(a) **Direct Combination of Elements.** Only binary acids can be synthesized by direct combination of elements. The hydrogen halides and hydrogen sulfide can be prepared by this method. The applicability of this method, however, depends on the stability of the hydride, few of which can survive the temperature needed to promote the reaction. Although HF and HCl are sufficiently stable, the cost of the free halogen makes this method commercially impractical; the halogens are more expensive than their hydrides.

(b) Reaction of Salts with Sulfuric Acid.   A large number of acids are made by reacting their salts with concentrated sulfuric acid. Fortunately, most common acids, such as $HONO_2$, HF, HCl, and CH_3COOH, are volatile. They are easily removed from the reaction mixture so that the equilibrium is driven in the direction of the product,

$$(HO)_2SO_2 + A^- \rightarrow HA\uparrow + HOSO_3^-$$
(concentrated)

(where $\uparrow$ *indicates volatility*). Sulfuric acid is used because it is cheap, strong, stable, and nonvolatile (boils with decomposition at 340°C). This method is not applicable to the preparation of HBr and HI. These compounds are oxidized by concentrated $(HO)_2SO_2$,

$$8HI + (HO)_2SO_2 \rightarrow 4I_2 + H_2S + 4H_2O$$
$$2HBr + (HO)_2SO_2 \rightarrow Br_2 + SO_2 + 2H_2O$$

(c) Acid Anhydride and Water; Preparation of Sulfuric Acid. The reactions of acidic and basic anhydrides with water have been discussed (pages 465).

Phosphoric acid is made by reacting its acid anhydride, P_4O_{10}, with water,

$$P_4O_{10} + 6H_2O \rightarrow 4(HO)_3PO$$

The anhydride is made by burning phosphorus in an ample supply of air.

Sulfuric acid, one of the most important industrial chemicals, is prepared by such a method. The acid anhydride of $(HO)_2SO_2$ is sulfur trioxide, SO_3. Direct oxidation of elementary sulfur affords sulfur dioxide, SO_2, which can be subsequently oxidized in the presence of a vanadium pentoxide (V_2O_5) catalyst to SO_3. The hydration reaction of SO_3 is very exothermic. The heat liberated vaporizes the water, and the steam cloud carries away much of the SO_3 in the form of a sulfuric acid mist. For more effective results, the SO_3 is dissolved in concentrated $(HO)_2SO_2$ to form pyrosulfuric acid, $H_2S_2O_7$, while water is added continuously to maintain a constant concentration of $(HO)_2SO_2$:

$$S_8 + 8O_2(g) \rightarrow 8SO_2(g)$$
$$2SO_2(g) + O_2(g) \rightleftharpoons 2SO_3(g)$$
$$SO_3(g) + (HO)_2SO_2 \rightleftharpoons H_2S_2O_7$$
$$H_2S_2O_7 + H_2O \rightarrow 2(HO)_2SO_2$$

(d) Auto-oxidation of Nonmetallic Oxides; Preparation of Nitric Acid.   Nitrogen dioxide does not yield an oxyacid in which nitrogen has the same oxidation number. Instead, it is auto-oxidized in water to give a mixture of nitric and nitrous acids,

$$\underset{+4}{2NO_2} + 2H_2O \rightarrow H_3O^+ + \underset{+5}{NO_3^-} + \underset{+3}{HONO}$$

Auto-oxidation is typical of oxides of elements in Groups V and VII of the Periodic Table when the element has an even-numbered oxidation state;

the auto-oxidation results in a higher and lower odd-numbered oxidation state. Auto-oxidation in a basic medium results in formation of the oxyanions, as exemplified by the reactions of chlorine dioxide and dichlorine hexoxide:

$$2ClO_2 + 2OH^- \rightarrow ClO_2^- + ClO_3^- + H_2O$$
$$\quad\; +4 \qquad\qquad\quad +3 \qquad +5$$
chlorine
dioxide

$$Cl_2O_6 + 2OH^- \rightarrow ClO_3^- + ClO_4^- + H_2O$$
$$\;\; +6 \qquad\qquad\quad +5 \qquad +7$$
dichlorine
hexoxide

The auto-oxidation of NO_2 is the key step in the industrial preparation of nitric acid. Nitrogen dioxide is made in two steps from ammonia. Ammonia is made from nitrogen and hydrogen in the presence of an iron oxide catalyst at about 600°C and several hundred atmospheres:

$$N_2 + 3H_2 \rightarrow 2NH_3 \qquad\qquad [Haber\ Process]$$
$$4NH_3 + 5O_2 \rightarrow 4NO + 6H_2O \qquad [Ostwald\ Process]$$
$$2NO + O_2 \rightarrow 2NO_2$$
$$2NO_2 + 2H_2O \rightarrow H_3O^+ + NO_3^- + HONO$$

(e) **Hydrolysis of Halides of Nonmetals.** The halides of most nonmetallic elements hydrolyze to give the oxyacid of the element and the corresponding hydrohalogen acid. The oxidation number of the element is retained:

$$BCl_3 + 6H_2O \rightarrow B(OH)_3 \quad + 3H_3O^+ + 3Cl^-$$
$$PBr_3 + 6H_2O \rightarrow (HO)_2PHO + 3H_3O^+ + 3Br^-$$
$$PCl_5 + 9H_2O \rightarrow (HO)_3PO \quad + 5H_3O^+ + 5Cl^-$$

The reaction with PBr_3 is used to prepare hydrobromic acid. In the above examples, the halogen is more electronegative than the central atom. In such cases the reaction usually proceeds as shown. If the halogen is less electronegative, the hydrolysis proceeds as shown for nitrogen triiodide:

$$NI_3 + 3H_2O \rightarrow NH_3 \; + 3HOI$$
$$NH_3 + HOI \rightleftharpoons NH_4^+ + \quad OI^-$$

As the metallic properties of the central atom increase, as is the trend on proceeding down a group, hydrolysis is incomplete and oxyhalides are formed, as shown for antimony(III) chloride:

$$SbCl_3 + 3H_2O \rightleftharpoons SbOCl + 2H_3O^+ + 2Cl^-$$

Problems

1. Preparation of acids. Write equations for the preparation of (a) CH_3COOH (b.p. = 118°C) from sodium acetate; (b) HI from PI_3; (c) permanganic acid, $HOMnO_3$, from its acid anhydride.

2. Amphoterism. (a) Write equations for hypoiodous acid, HOI, dissociating as (*i*) an acid, (*ii*) a base. (b) Account for the fact that HOI can do either, $pK_a = 10.4$, $pK_b = 9.5$.

3. Hydrides. Metallic hydrides, such as MgH_2, give a basic reaction in water; nonmetallic hydrides like HCl are acidic in water. Does it follow that NH_3, which is basic in water, is more like a metallic hydride than is CH_4, which gives no basic reaction? Explain.

4. Hydrides. LiH melts at 689°C. Would you expect liquid LiH to conduct an electric current? Write the equations for the reaction at each electrode. Write the equations for the electrode reactions in the electrolysis of the solution formed by mixing water with LiH. (Assume that the electrodes are Pt in all cases.)

5. Structure and acidity. Arrange the following sets in order of increasing acidity in water. Account for your order. (a) H_2S, H_2Te, H_2Se. (b) SiH_4, HCl, PH_3, H_2S. (c) $HOPO_3^{2-}$, $(HO)_2PO_2^-$, $(HO)_3PO$. (d) $(HO)_2SO_2$, $(HO)_2SeO_2$, $(HO)_2SeO$. (e) CH_4, CH_2Cl_2, $CHCl_3$, CH_3Cl. (f) CH_3F, CH_3Cl, CH_3Br, CH_3I, CH_4.

(g) $Mn(OH)_2$, $Mn(OH)_3$, $(HO)_2MnO_2$, $HOMnO_3$. (h) methyl alcohol, $(CH_3\overset{..}{O}H)$,

$$\overset{\overset{\textstyle \ddot{O}:}{\textstyle \|}}{}$$

methane (CH_4), formic acid, $H—\overset{\overset{\textstyle \ddot O:}{\textstyle \|}}{C}—\overset{..}{\underset{..}{O}}—H$.

6. Structure and basicity. Arrange the following sets in order of increasing basicity in water. Account for your order. (a) HCl, PH_3, H_2S. (b) NH_3, PH_3, AsH_3. (c) H_2O, O^{2-}, OOH^-, OH^-. (d) NO_3^-, NO_2^-, PO_4^{3-}.

7. Structure and acidity. Conjecture as to why (a) the pK_a of NH_3 is 3.5, while (1) the pK_a of nitramide, $H_2N\overset{..}{N}O_2$, is 6.59, and (2) the pK_a of hydrazoic acid, $H—\overset{..}{N}=N=\overset{..}{N}:$, is 4.72; (b) the order of acidity is HOCl > HOOH > HOH.

8. Structure of acids. Arsenious acid, H_3AsO_3, exchanges three protium atoms for deuterium atoms in D_2O. Phosphorous acid, H_3PO_3, exchanges only two protium atoms. Write equations for the exchange reactions, using structural formulas of the acids.

19

Calculations
of
ionic
equilibrium

BECAUSE OF THE great abundance and importance of water, the majority of the reactions encountered by the reader occur in aqueous solutions. Because of the remarkable effectiveness of water as an ionizing solvent, most of these reactions involve ions, often along with neutral molecules or undissolved solids. Ionic reactions usually (not always) come rapidly to equilibrium, and the properties of the solution depend on the concentrations of the species present at equilibrium. For all these reasons, calculations of ionic equilibria deserve careful study.

In the first part of this chapter, we shall, in the interest of simplicity, make the crude approximation that activities and concentrations are identical—that all activity coefficients are 1. Later, we shall see how better calculations can be made by introducing approximate values of the activity coefficients.

Acid-base equilibria

19.1   THE IONIZATION OF WATER

We saw (page 420) how the equilibrium constant (K_w) for the reaction

$$2H_2O \rightleftharpoons H_3O^+ + OH^-$$

can be calculated from the e.m.f.'s of certain galvanic cells. The values obtained at several temperatures are as follows:

Temperature (°C)	K_w	$pK_w = -\log K_w$
0	1.139×10^{-15}	14.9435
25	1.008×10^{-14}	13.9965
50	$5.47 \ \times 10^{-14}$	13.262

Thus, even perfectly pure water contains minute amounts of H_3O^+ and OH^-. Their concentrations must be equal in pure water, for two reasons: (1) In the reaction $2H_2O \rightleftharpoons H_3O^+ + OH^-$, one H_3O^+ ion is formed for every OH^- ion formed, and conversely. (2) The solution must be electrically neutral, which means that the total positive charge equals the total negative charge; when H_3O^+ and OH^- are the only ions present, this requires that $[H_3O^+] = [OH^-]$. The equilibrium concentrations of H_3O^+ and OH^- in pure water at 25°C are found by letting $x = [H_3O^+] = [OH^-]$, and substituting into the equilibrium condition,

$$[H_3O^+][OH^-] = K_w$$
$$x^2 = 1.0 \times 10^{-14}$$
$$x = 1.0 \times 10^{-7}$$

At 50°, however, the concentrations are higher:

$$x^2 = 5.5 \times 10^{-14}$$
$$x = 2.3 \times 10^{-7}$$

If the water contains some source of H_3O^+ or OH^-, other than H_2O itself, we can no longer expect that these two concentrations will be equal. For example, we might make $[H_3O^+] = 0.10$ mole/liter by adding a suitable quantity of acid. Then, at 25°,

$$(0.10)[OH^-] = 1.0 \times 10^{-14}$$
$$[OH^-] = 1.0 \times 10^{-13} \text{ mole/liter}$$

19.2 pH AND pOH

In most aqueous solutions, we are concerned with very small concentrations of H_3O^+ and OH^-. In the preceding chapter, the convenient notation $pK = -\log K$ was introduced. In the same way, we write $pH = -\log [H_3O^+]$, and $pOH = -\log [OH^-]$.* Values for pH and pOH are usually between 0 and 14, but not necessarily; if $[H_3O^+] = 2$ moles/liter, $pH = -\log 2 = -0.3$.

EXAMPLE 1   **Find the pH of a solution in which $[H_3O^+] = 6.38 \times 10^{-6}$ mole/liter.**

ANSWER

$$pH = -\log (6.38 \times 10^{-6})$$
$$= -0.805 + 6 = 5.195 \quad \text{(See page 791.)}$$

* Historically, pH preceded pK. The notation "pH" was introduced in 1909, as an abbreviation of "power of hydrogen."

Note the fact, surprising at first, that the pH in this case is between 5 and 6, not between 6 and 7. The reason is that 6.38×10^{-6} is between 10^{-5} and 10^{-6}, not between 10^{-6} and 10^{-7}.

EXAMPLE 2 Calculate $[H_3O^+]$ for a solution of pH 8.37.

ANSWER

$$[H_3O^+] = 10^{-pH} = 10^{-8.37} = 10^{-9+0.63} = 10^{0.63} \times 10^{-9}$$
$$= 4.3 \times 10^{-9}$$

EXAMPLE 3 A certain solution has pH 3.89 at 0°C. Find pOH and $[OH^-]$.

ANSWER As with other equilibrium constants, we can write $pK_w = -\log K_w$. Since

$$[H_3O^+][OH^-] = K_w$$

then

$$\log [H_3O^+] + \log [OH^-] = \log K_w$$
$$pH + pOH = pK_w = 14.9435$$

at 0°C.

$$pOH = pK_w - pH = 14.94 - 3.89$$
$$= 11.05$$
$$[OH^-] = 10^{-11.05} = 10^{-12+0.95}$$
$$= 8.9 \times 10^{-12} \text{ mole/liter}$$

19.3 ACIDIC, BASIC, AND NEUTRAL SOLUTIONS

An aqueous solution is said to be

acidic   if $[H_3O^+]$ is greater than $[OH^-]$, or pH < pOH;
neutral   if $[H_3O^+] = [OH^-]$, or pH = pOH;
basic   if $[OH^-]$ is greater than $[H_3O^+]$, or pH > pOH.

At 25°, pH = 7.00 for a neutral solution; when pH < 7, the solution is acidic, and when pH > 7, the solution is basic. The number 7 is worth remembering, but one should also remember that it refers to 25°, and that the neutral pH is somewhat different at other temperatures.

EXAMPLE 4 What is the pH of a neutral solution at 50°C?

ANSWER Let $x = pH = pOH$; then

$$pH + pOH = 2x = pK_w = 13.26$$

or

$$x = \tfrac{1}{2} \times 13.26 = 6.63$$

Throughout the remainder of this chapter, you may assume that the temperature is that for which the data are given, usually 25°C.

19.4 IONIZATION OF WEAK ACIDS

We may represent a general acid by HA; it may be either a neutral molecule (as acetic acid, CH_3COOH) or an ion (as ammonium ion, NH_4^+; hydrogen sulfate ion, $HOSO_3^-$). In this section, however, we shall assume that HA is uncharged. The equilibrium constant for the reaction

$$HA + H_2O \rightleftharpoons H_3O^+ + A^-$$

is the ionization constant of HA, as in Chapter 17, and is represented by K_a or K_{HA}. Table 19.1 lists K_a for a number of common acids.

Let c be the number of moles of HA added per liter of solution. The usual problem is to find $[H_3O^+]$ or pH when K_a and c are given. In addition to the equilibrium condition

$$\frac{[H_3O^+][A^-]}{[HA]} = K_a \tag{1}$$

there are two other conditions that must be satisfied:

(a) The solution must be *electrically neutral*. This means that the total number of positive charges is equal to the total number of negative charges. In the present case, there is only one kind of positive ion, H_3O^+; there are two kinds of negative ion, A^- and OH^-. In each liter of solution, then, the number of H_3O^+ ions must equal the total number of A^- and OH^- ions. Equivalently, the number of *moles* of H_3O^+ in a liter must equal the total number of moles of A^- and OH^- in a liter,

$$[H_3O^+] = [A^-] + [OH^-] \tag{2}$$

(b) Some of the HA molecules in the solution lose protons and become A^-. We do not know in advance what percentage of the molecules becomes A^- and what percentage remains HA. However, we may assume that every HA molecule that was put into the solution does one thing or the other; if it is not there as HA, it is there as A^-. We introduced c moles of HA per liter of solution. The total number of moles of HA and A^- present (per liter) at equilibrium must then be c,

$$[HA] + [A^-] = c \tag{3}$$

This equation may be described as the **conservation condition** for the "A" group of atoms.

If the acid is not extremely weak, the solution will be decidedly acidic, which means that $[OH^-] \ll [H_3O^+]$, and Equation (2) can be written

$$[H_3O^+] = [A^-] \tag{2'}$$

We can now let

$$x = [H_3O^+] = [A^-]$$

and Equation (3) gives us

$$[HA] = c - [A^-] = c - x$$

TABLE 19.1 *Ionization Constants of Acids and Bases in Water at 25°C*

Name	Formula	Constant
	Monoprotic acids	K_a
Acetic acid	CH_3COOH	1.75×10^{-5}
Benzoic acid	C_6H_5COOH	6.30×10^{-5}
Bromoacetic acid	$CH_2BrCOOH$	1.38×10^{-3}
Chloroacetic acid	$CH_2ClCOOH$	1.40×10^{-3}
Dichloroacetic acid	$CHCl_2COOH$	$5 \quad \times 10^{-2}$
Formic acid	$HCOOH$	1.76×10^{-4}
Hydrocyanic acid	HCN	$7.2 \quad \times 10^{-10}$
Hydrofluoric acid	HF	$6.7 \quad \times 10^{-4}$
Nitrous acid	$HONO$	$4.5 \quad \times 10^{-4}$
Phenol (carbolic acid)	C_6H_5OH	$1.3 \quad \times 10^{-10}$
Propionic acid	CH_3CH_2COOH	1.34×10^{-5}
Trichloroacetic acid	CCl_3COOH	$2 \quad \times 10^{-1}$

	Polyprotic acids	K_1	K_2	K_3
Carbonic acid[a]	$(HO)_2CO$	4.47×10^{-7}	5.62×10^{-11}	—
Hydrogen sulfide	H_2S	$6.3 \quad \times 10^{-8}$	10^{-14}	—
Malonic acid	$CH_2(COOH)_2$	1.40×10^{-3}	$2.1 \quad \times 10^{-6}$	—
Oxalic acid	$(COOH)_2$	$6.5 \quad \times 10^{-2}$	$5 \quad \times 10^{-5}$	—
Phosphoric acid	$(HO)_3PO$	7.52×10^{-3}	6.22×10^{-8}	4.8×10^{-13}
Phthalic acid	$C_6H_4(COOH)_2$	1.26×10^{-3}	$3.1 \quad \times 10^{-6}$	—
Sulfuric acid	$(HO)_2SO_2$	∞	$1.0 \quad \times 10^{-2}$	—
Sulfurous acid	$(HO)_2SO$	$1.7 \quad \times 10^{-2}$	6.24×10^{-8}	—

	Monoprotic bases	K_b
Ammonia	NH_3	1.76×10^{-5}
Aniline	$C_6H_5NH_2$	3.83×10^{-10}
Dimethylamine	$(CH_3)_2NH$	5.04×10^{-4}
Ethylamine	$CH_3CH_2NH_2$	4.71×10^{-4}
Hydroxylamine	$HONH_2$	10^{-9}
Methylamine	CH_3NH_2	4.40×10^{-4}
Pyridine	C_5H_5N	1.56×10^{-9}
Trimethylamine	$(CH_3)_3N$	6.34×10^{-5}

	Diprotic base	K_1	K_2
Hydrazine	H_2NNH_2	9×10^{-7}	9×10^{-16}

[a] See footnote on page 492.

Substituting into Equation (1), we obtain

$$\frac{x^2}{c - x} = K_a \tag{4}$$

We can arrive at Equation (4) by a somewhat different route, which is often simpler. There are two reactions that occur in the solution:

$$HA + H_2O \rightleftharpoons H_3O^+ + A^- \tag{5}$$
$$2H_2O \rightleftharpoons H_3O^+ + OH^- \tag{6}$$

Reaction (6) produces equal numbers of moles of H_3O^+ and OH^-. We have noticed that, in this acidic solution, $[OH^-] \ll [H_3O^+]$. Another way of saying the same thing is: $[H_3O^+]$ produced by reaction (6) ($= [OH^-]$) is very small in comparison to total $[H_3O^+]$. Most of the H_3O^+ in the solution is produced by the ionization of the acid HA (Reaction 5), not by the ionization of water (Reaction 6)—a result to be expected unless HA is an extremely weak acid, almost as weak as water. Thus, when we say that the solution is markedly acidic, we are also saying that the production of H_3O^+ by Reaction (6) is negligible, and there is only one important reaction: Reaction (5).

In this special, but common, case, where only one reaction need be considered, the calculations can be performed as they were in Section 14.12 (page 351). If we start with c moles/liter of HA, the number of moles/liter of H_3O^+ and A^- must be the same (x), and the remaining number of moles/liter of HA is $c - x$:

$$HA \ + H_2O \rightleftharpoons H_3O^+ + A^-$$

$$c - x \qquad\qquad x \qquad x \qquad \text{moles/liter}$$

$$K_a = \frac{[H_3O^+][A^-]}{[HA]} = \frac{x^2}{c - x}$$

In this chapter, we shall use this simple method when it is clearly applicable. Some problems, however, require that more than one reaction be considered simultaneously, and then it is necessary to write out the equilibrium condition for each reaction, the conservation condition for each molecular fragment conserved in the reactions, and one electrical neutrality condition.

EXAMPLE 5   **Referring to Table 19.1, find the pH of a 0.200M solution of formic acid.**

ANSWER   **Here, $c = 0.200$ mole/liter and $K_a = 1.76 \times 10^{-4}$. Then**

$$\frac{x^2}{0.200 - x} = 1.76 \times 10^{-4}$$

This quadratic equation can be solved without undue labor, but a simplifying approximation is often applicable. The acid is weak, meaning that only a small fraction of it ionizes. We thus expect that x, representing the concentration of each dissociation product (H_3O^+ and A^-), will be much less than c, representing the total concentration of acid, ionized and un-ionized. If this approximation is valid, $0.200 - x$ can be replaced by 0.200 without serious error, and the equation becomes

$$\frac{x^2}{0.200} = 1.76 \times 10^{-4}$$
$$x^2 = 35.2 \times 10^{-6}$$
$$x = 5.93 \times 10^{-3}$$

For most purposes, we may consider 6×10^{-3} negligible in comparison with 0.200. (Accurate solution of the equation gives $x = 5.84 \times 10^{-3}$.) Then

$$pH = - \log x = 3 - \log 5.84$$
$$= 2.23$$

The ionization of a weak acid is commonly described by giving the **degree of ionization** or **degree of dissociation** (represented by α), which is the fraction of the total acid present that ionizes. In terms of concentration,

$$\alpha = \frac{[H_3O^+]}{c} = \frac{x}{c}$$

For the preceding example,

$$\alpha = \frac{5.84 \times 10^{-3}}{0.200} = 2.92 \times 10^{-2} \text{ or } 2.92\%$$

EXAMPLE 6 Find the degree of ionization of acetic acid in a $0.500M$ solution, and the pH of the solution.

ANSWER From Table 19.1, $K_a = 1.75 \times 10^{-5}$. Then, for the reaction

$$CH_3COOH + H_2O \rightleftharpoons H_3O^+ + CH_3COO^-$$

the equilibrium condition is

$$\frac{x^2}{0.500 - x} = 1.75 \times 10^{-5}$$

where $x = [H_3O^+] = [CH_3COO^-]$. If we assume that x is much less than 0.500,

$$\frac{x^2}{0.500} = 1.75 \times 10^{-5}$$
$$x^2 = 8.75 \times 10^{-6}$$
$$x = 2.96 \times 10^{-3} \text{ mole/liter} = [H_3O^+]$$

which is, for our purposes, negligible in comparison to 0.500. Then

$$\alpha = \frac{x}{0.500} = \frac{2.96 \times 10^{-3}}{0.500} = 5.92 \times 10^{-3}$$
$$pH = -\log [H_3O^+] = - \log 2.96 + 3 = 2.529$$

The two following examples will illustrate cases in which the usual simplifying approximations are not applicable.

EXAMPLE 7   Find $[H_3O^+]$ in a $0.50M$ solution of trichloroacetic acid.

ANSWER

Equilibrium: $CCl_3COOH + H_2O \leftrightharpoons H_3O^+ + CCl_3COO^-$

$$\frac{[H_3O^+][CCl_3COO^-]}{[CCl_3COOH]} = 0.2 \tag{7}$$

Electrical neutrality: $[H_3O^+] = [CCl_3COO^-] + [OH^-]$ (8)

Conservation:

$$[CCl_3COOH] + [CCl_3COO^-] = 0.50 \tag{9}$$

This acid is relatively strong, and we are certainly justified in neglecting $[OH^-]$. Thus Equation (8) becomes

$$[H_3O^+] = [CCl_3COO^-] = x$$

Equation (9) gives

$$[CCl_3COOH] = 0.50 - [CCl_3COO^-] = 0.50 - x$$

Equation (7) then is

$$\frac{x^2}{0.50 - x} = 0.2 \tag{10}$$

Let us assume that $x \ll 0.50$. This assumption gives

$$\frac{x^2}{0.50} = 0.2$$

$$x = 0.32$$

Obviously, the assumption was a bad one, for 0.3 is clearly not negligible in comparison to 0.50. Substitution into Equation (10) shows that $x = 0.3$ is not a solution. We must solve Equation (10) as a quadratic equation (page 793). Equation (10) may be rewritten as

$$x^2 + 0.2x - 0.1 = 0$$

$$x = \frac{-0.2 \pm \sqrt{(0.2)^2 - 4(1)(-0.1)}}{2(1)}$$

$$= \frac{-0.2 \pm \sqrt{0.44}}{2}$$

$$= +0.23 \text{ or } -0.43$$

A concentration cannot be negative, and the answer -0.43 must therefore be rejected; then

$$[H_3O^+] = x = 0.2 \text{ mole/liter}$$

(Why is only one significant figure retained?)

EXAMPLE 8   Find the pH of a $1.0 \times 10^{-5}M$ solution of HCN.

ANSWER

Equilibrium: $$HCN + H_2O \rightleftharpoons H_3O^+ + CN^-$$

$$\frac{[H_3O^+][CN^-]}{[HCN]} = 7.2 \times 10^{-10} \tag{11}$$

Electrical neutrality: $$[H_3O^+] = [CN^-] + [OH^-] \tag{12}$$

Conservation: $$[HCN] + [CN^-] = 1.0 \times 10^{-5} \tag{13}$$

When the acid is as weak and as dilute as it is in this problem, we should suspect that the H_3O^+ produced by the ionization of water may be appreciable in comparison to the small amount of H_3O^+ produced by the ionization of HCN. Since [OH⁻] is equal to the concentration of H_3O^+ from the ionization of water, our suspicion is directed at the assumption that $[OH^-] \ll [CN^-]$. However, let us make this approximation and see what happens. Equation (12) becomes

$$[H_3O^+] = [CN^-] = x$$

Equation (13) is then

$$[HCN] = 1.0 \times 10^{-5} - x \approx 1.0 \times 10^{-5}$$

and Equation (11) is

$$\frac{x^2}{1.0 \times 10^{-5}} = 7.2 \times 10^{-10}$$

$$x^2 = 7.2 \times 10^{-15}$$

$$x = 8.5 \times 10^{-8} = [H_3O^+] = [CN^-]$$

The assumption $x \ll 1.0 \times 10^{-5}$ appears to be correct. To check our assumption that $[OH^-] \ll [CN^-]$, we need another equilibrium condition:

$$[H_3O^+][OH^-] = K_w = 1.01 \times 10^{-14} \tag{14}$$

$$[OH^-] = \frac{1.01 \times 10^{-14}}{8.5 \times 10^{-8}} = 1.2 \times 10^{-7}$$

The ratio [OH⁻]/[CN⁻] comes out to be 1.4, so that [OH⁻] is far from negligible and our results are not correct. The alert reader should have noticed something wrong as soon as $[H_3O^+]$ was calculated. We obtained $[H_3O^+] < 10^{-7}$, which, at 25°C, means that the solution is basic—obviously absurd, for we cannot make a basic solution by adding an acid, however weak, to water.

To obtain the correct answer in this case, we let

$$[H_3O^+] = y$$

and, from Equation (14),

$$[OH^-] = K_w/y$$

Then, from Equation (12),

$$[CN^-] = [H_3O^+] - [OH^-]$$

$$= y - \frac{K_w}{y}$$

and, from Equation (13),

$$[HCN] = 10^{-5} - [CN^-] = 10^{-5} - y + \frac{K_w}{y}$$

Substitution into Equation (11) gives

$$\frac{y\left(y - \dfrac{K_w}{y}\right)}{10^{-5} - y + \dfrac{K_w}{y}} = 7.2 \times 10^{-10}$$

This is a cubic equation, but becomes merely quadratic if we recognize that y and K_w/y are much less than 10^{-5}. The solution is

$$y = 1.3 \times 10^{-7} \text{ mole/liter} = [H_3O^+]$$

Finally,

$$\text{pH} = 7 - \log 1.3 = 6.9$$

Thus, the usual approximations work only when the acid is neither too strong nor too weak. If it is too strong, we cannot assume that $[A^-] \ll c$. If it is too weak, or too dilute, or both, we cannot assume that $[A^-] \gg [OH^-]$, and the ionization of water must be taken into account. The latter situation, fortunately, is not encountered very often. Useful rules of thumb are that the assumption $[A^-] \ll c$ is valid when $K/c < 10^{-4}$; the assumption $[A^-] \gg [OH^-]$ is valid when $cK > 10^{-12}$. These rules are based on the stipulation that x can be neglected in comparison to y if $x/y < 0.01$.

19.5 IONIZATION OF WEAK BASES

A base, like an acid, may be a neutral molecule or an ion; in this section, we shall assume that the base is a neutral molecule, and represent it by B. The ionization constant of B is the equilibrium constant of the reaction

$$B + H_2O \rightleftharpoons BH^+ + OH^-$$

for which the equilibrium condition is

$$\frac{[BH^+][OH^-]}{[B]} = K_b \tag{15}$$

As with acids, we require electrical neutrality and conservation of B (which is present in two forms, B and BH$^+$),

$$[BH^+] + [H_3O^+] = [OH^-] \tag{16}$$
$$[B] + [BH^+] = c \tag{17}$$

In a decidedly basic solution, $[H_3O^+] \ll [OH^-]$,

$$[BH^+] = [OH^-] = x \tag{16'}$$
$$[B] = c - x \tag{17'}$$

Then

$$\frac{x^2}{c - x} = K_b \qquad\qquad (15')$$

The only difference from the acid case is that x now represents $[OH^-]$ instead of $[H_3O^+]$.

As with weak acids, we can approach the problem from a simpler point of view. The number of moles of H_3O^+ in the solution is equal to the number of moles of OH^- produced by the ionization of water. This quantity of OH^- is overshadowed by the OH^- produced by the ionization of B. There is, then, only one important reaction in the solution,

$$B + H_2O \rightleftharpoons BH^+ + OH^-$$
$$c - x \qquad\qquad x \qquad x \qquad \text{moles/liter}$$

and we again obtain Equations (16') and (17').

Table 19.1 gives the ionization constants of some common bases.

EXAMPLE 9   **Find the pH of a 0.100M solution of ammonia, NH_3.**

ANSWER

$$NH_3 + H_2O \rightleftharpoons NH_4^+ + OH^-$$
$$\frac{[NH_4^+][OH^-]}{[NH_3]} = K_b = 1.76 \times 10^{-5}$$

Let

$$x = [NH_4^+] = [OH^-]$$

Then

$$\frac{x^2}{0.100 - x} = 1.76 \times 10^{-5}$$

If $x \ll 0.100$,

$$\frac{x^2}{0.100} = 1.76 \times 10^{-5}$$
$$x^2 = 1.76 \times 10^{-6}$$
$$x = 1.33 \times 10^{-3} = [OH^-]$$
$$pOH = 3 - \log 1.33 = 2.88$$
$$pH = 14.00 - pOH = 11.12$$

19.6   CONJUGATE ACID-BASE PAIRS

In Chapter 17, conjugate acid-base pairs were defined: HA is known as the conjugate acid of A^-, and A^- is the conjugate base of HA. A simple relation between the acidic and basic ionization constants in a conjugate pair was established (page 447): $K_a K_b = K_w$, or $pK_a + pK_b = pK_w$. Thus, if we know the ionization constant for an acid or base, we can find the ionization constant for its conjugate base or acid.

EXAMPLE 10   Find K_b and pK_b for the acetate ion, CH_3COO^-.

ANSWER   The ionization constant of CH_3COOH is $K_a = 1.75 \times 10^{-5}$; $K_w = 1.01 \times 10^{-14}$. Then,

$$K_b = \frac{K_w}{K_a}$$

$$= \frac{1.01 \times 10^{-14}}{1.75 \times 10^{-5}} = 5.77 \times 10^{-10}$$

$$pK_b = 10 - \log 5.77 = 9.239$$

19.7   CHARGED ACIDS AND BASES

The ionization constant is usually tabulated for only one member of a conjugate pair. In this book, when one member is uncharged, it is that member for which the ionization constant is tabulated. Thus, we find in Table 19.1 the acidic ionization constants of CH_3COOH and HF, and the basic ionization constants of NH_3 and C_5H_5N (pyridine); we now know how to calculate from this information the basic ionization constants of CH_3COO^- and F^-, and the acidic ionization constants of NH_4^+ and $C_5H_5NH^+$. The only complication presented by charged acids or bases is the presence along with them of oppositely charged ions, which, in the simpler cases, do not participate in any reactions. For example, acetate ion (CH_3COO^-) is always accompanied by a positive ion, most commonly Na^+, which is neither acidic nor basic, but must be taken into account in writing the condition of electrical neutrality. Likewise, ammonium ion (NH_4^+) must be accompanied by a negative ion, such as Cl^- or NO_3^-. These ions, again, are not involved in any reactions, but are needed to preserve electrical neutrality.

EXAMPLE 11   Find the degree of dissociation of pyridinium ion, $C_5H_5NH^+$, in a $0.100M$ solution of pyridinium chloride ("pyridine hydrochloride"), $(C_5H_5NH)^+Cl^-$.

ANSWER   We assume that $(C_5H_5NH)^+Cl^-$ is a strong salt, present in solution as $C_5H_5NH^+$ and Cl^- ions. Then we can say immediately that $[Cl^-] = 0.100$ mole/liter. The acidic ionization constant of $C_5H_5NH^+$, corresponding to the reaction

$$C_5H_5NH^+ + H_2O \rightleftharpoons C_5H_5N + H_3O^+$$

is

$$K_a = \frac{K_w}{K_b}$$

$$= \frac{1.01 \times 10^{-14}}{1.56 \times 10^{-9}}$$

$$= 6.47 \times 10^{-6}$$

The three conditions imposed on the concentrations are:

Equilibrium: $$\frac{[C_5H_5N][H_3O^+]}{[C_5H_5NH^+]} = 6.47 \times 10^{-6} \qquad (18)$$

Electrical neutrality: $\quad [C_5H_5NH^+] + [H_3O^+] = [Cl^-] + [OH^-] \qquad$ **(19)**

Conservation: $\qquad\qquad [C_5H_5NH^+] + [C_5H_5N] = 0.100 \qquad\qquad$ **(20)**

The only new feature is the presence of $[Cl^-]$ in Equation (19). Since $[Cl^-] = 0.100$ and $[OH^-] \ll [H_3O^+]$, we can write Equation (19) as

$$[C_5H_5NH^+] + [H_3O^+] = 0.100$$

or

$$[C_5H_5NH^+] = 0.100 - [H_3O^+] \qquad\qquad \textbf{(19')}$$

Also,

$$[C_5H_5NH^+] = 0.100 - [C_5H_5N] \qquad\qquad \textbf{(20')}$$

Thus,

$$0.100 - [H_3O^+] = 0.100 - [C_5H_5N]$$

so that

$$[H_3O^+] = [C_5H_5N] = x$$

Alternatively, we may recognize that the production of H_3O^+ by the ionization of water is negligible, and there is thus only one important reaction,

$$C_5H_5NH^+ + H_2O \rightleftharpoons H_3O^+ + C_5H_5N$$
$$0.100 - x \qquad\qquad x \qquad x \qquad \text{moles/liter}$$

Equation (18) now becomes

$$\frac{x^2}{0.100 - x} = 6.47 \times 10^{-6}$$

just as with an uncharged acid. If $x \ll 0.100$,

$$\frac{x^2}{0.100} = 6.47 \times 10^{-6}$$
$$x^2 = 0.647 \times 10^{-6}$$
$$x = 8.04 \times 10^{-4} \text{ mole/liter} = [H_3O^+]$$

Then

$$\alpha = \frac{x}{0.100} = 8.04 \times 10^{-3}$$

EXAMPLE 12 Find the pH of a $0.30M$ solution of NaF.

ANSWER We shall leave most of the details to the reader.

$$F^- + H_2O \rightleftharpoons HF + OH^-$$
$$K_b = \frac{K_w}{K_a} = 1.51 \times 10^{-11}$$
$$[OH^-] = [HF] = x$$
$$\frac{x^2}{0.30 - x} = 1.51 \times 10^{-11}$$
$$x^2 = 4.53 \times 10^{-12}$$
$$x = 2.13 \times 10^{-6} = [OH^-]$$
$$pOH = 5.67$$
$$pH = 8.33$$

Let H_2A represent a diprotic acid. The equilibrium constants for the two reactions

$$H_2A + H_2O \leftrightharpoons H_3O^+ + HA^- \tag{21}$$
$$HA^- + H_2O \leftrightharpoons H_3O^+ + A^{2-} \tag{22}$$

are represented by K_1 and K_2, respectively, and are called the first and second ionization constants of H_2A. For a triprotic acid, there is also a third constant K_3. We note that HA^- can act either as an acid, as in reaction (22), or as a base, as in the reaction

$$HA^- + H_2O \leftrightharpoons H_2A + OH^- \tag{23}$$

It is amphiprotic (page 443). Likewise, A^{2-} is a base,

$$A^{2-} + H_2O \leftrightharpoons HA^- + OH^- \tag{24}$$

The equilibrium constants for reactions (23) and (24) are obtained from K_1 and K_2 by the usual relation between the ionization constants of an acid and of its conjugate base:

$$HA^- + H_2O \leftrightharpoons H_2A + OH^- \qquad K_{bHA^-} = \frac{K_w}{K_1}$$

$$A^{2-} + H_2O \rightleftharpoons HA^- + OH^- \qquad K_{bA^{2-}} = \frac{K_w}{K_2}$$

Likewise, for a diprotic base B, there are two ionization constants,

$$B + H_2O \leftrightharpoons BH^+ + OH^- \qquad K_1$$
$$BH^+ + H_2O \leftrightharpoons BH_2^{2+} + OH^- \qquad K_2$$

and, correspondingly, one can calculate from these the acidic ionization constants of BH^+ and BH_2^{2+}. We may observe that A^{2-} is a diprotic base, and BH_2^{2+} is a diprotic acid.

EXAMPLE 13 **Calculate the basic ionization constant of bicarbonate ion, $HOCO_2^-$.**

ANSWER **The conjugate acid of $HOCO_2^-$ (or HCO_3^-) is $(HO)_2CO$ (or H_2CO_3),** *

$$K_{bHCO_3^-} = \frac{K_w}{K_{1H_2CO_3}} = \frac{1.01 \times 10^{-14}}{4.47 \times 10^{-7}} = 2.26 \times 10^{-8}$$

Calculations involving the ionization of polyprotic acids and bases present no great complications, provided that one makes a simplifying

* When CO_2 dissolves in water, a small fraction—less than 1%—reacts to form H_2CO_3,

$$CO_2 + H_2O \leftrightharpoons H_2CO_3$$

Most of the dissolved CO_2 is present as CO_2. However, it is customary to represent dissolved CO_2 by the formula H_2CO_3; $[H_2CO_3]$ means the total concentration of CO_2, H_2CO_3, and possibly a trace of $(HO)_4C$.

assumption. Because the second ionization constant is less than the first—usually much less—we can assume that *the concentration of* A^{2-}, *which is produced in the second ionization, is much less than the concentration of* HA^-, *which is produced in the first ionization.* Calculations involving the first ionization can then be performed as if the acid were monoprotic, and the results of this calculation can then be used to find $[A^{2-}]$. Corresponding remarks apply to ionization of polyprotic bases.

EXAMPLE 14   Find $[H_3O^+]$, $[HOOCCH_2COO^-]$, and $[^-OOCCH_2COO^-]$ in a $0.500M$ solution of malonic acid, $HOOCCH_2COOH$.

ANSWER   Let the acid and its ions be represented by H_2A, HA^-, and A^{2-}. Then the following equations hold:

Equilibrium: $H_2A + H_2O \rightleftharpoons H_3O^+ + HA^-$

$$\frac{[H_3O^+][HA^-]}{[H_2A]} = K_1 = 1.40 \times 10^{-3} \qquad (25)$$

$HA^- + H_2O \rightleftharpoons H_3O^+ + A^{2-}$

$$\frac{[H_3O^+][A^{2-}]}{[HA^-]} = K_2 = 2.1 \times 10^{-6} \qquad (26)$$

Electrical neutrality: $[H_3O^+] = [HA^-] + 2[A^{2-}]$ $\qquad (27)$

Note that, in counting charges, we count each A^{2-} ion twice. It is like counting heads in a room containing some one-headed people and some two-headed people. The number of heads is

   number of one-headed people $+ 2 \times$ (number of two-headed people).

Similarly, the number of negative charges is

   number of singly charged negative ions

$\qquad\qquad\qquad + 2 \times$ (number of doubly charged negative ions).

Conservation: $[H_2A] + [HA^-] + [A^{2-}] = 0.500$ $\qquad (28)$

Here, the conservation condition contains three terms. Each H_2A molecule introduced must still be present in one of three forms: H_2A, HA^-, or A^{2-}, depending on whether it has lost zero, one, or two protons.

   With the approximations that $[A^{2-}] \ll [HA^-]$ and $[OH^-] \ll [H_3O^+]$, Equations (27) and (28) become

$[H_3O^+] = [HA^-] = x$

$[H_2A] = 0.500 - x$

We now see what may not have been obvious initially: that we can start to solve the problem by assuming that only one reaction need be considered,

$H_2A \quad + H_2O \rightleftharpoons H_3O^+ + HA^-$

$0.500 - x \qquad\qquad x \qquad x \qquad$ moles/liter

Equation (25), in terms of x, is

$$\frac{x^2}{0.500 - x} = 1.40 \times 10^{-3}$$

If $x \ll 0.500$,

$$\frac{x^2}{0.500} = 1.40 \times 10^{-3}$$

$$x = 2.65 \times 10^{-2}$$

A more accurate calculation gives $x = 2.58 \times 10^{-2}$. We have now found $[H_3O^+]$ and $[HA^-]$. For $[A^{2-}]$, we substitute these results into Equation (26) and obtain

$$\frac{2.58 \times 10^{-2} [A^{2-}]}{2.58 \times 10^{-2}} = 2.1 \times 10^{-6}$$

$$[A^{2-}] = 2.1 \times 10^{-6}$$

The result $[A^{2-}] = K_2$ will be true in any case in which HA^- is a weak acid and the solution is prepared by dissolving *only* H_2A in water.

There is a source of confusion that should be pointed out here. In a given solution, a given ion or molecule has only one concentration. The misconception sometimes arises that one concentration of H_3O^+ is produced by the reaction

$$H_2A + H_2O \rightleftharpoons H_3O^+ + HA^-$$

and another concentration of H_3O^+ is produced by the reaction

$$HA^- + H_2O \rightleftharpoons H_3O^+ + A^{2-}$$

This is *not* the case. The solution has only *one* value of $[H_3O^+]$, to be used in all the equations in which this concentration appears. After all, an ion has no memory—it knows only what it is, not by what reaction it was produced.

EXAMPLE 15   Find the pH of a $0.25M$ solution of Na_2CO_3, a strong electrolyte.

ANSWER   The solution contains the diprotic base CO_3^{2-},

$$CO_3^{2-} + H_2O \rightleftharpoons HCO_3^- + OH^-$$

$$\frac{[HCO_3^-][OH^-]}{[CO_3^{2-}]} = K_{b1} \tag{29}$$

$$HCO_3^- + H_2O \rightleftharpoons H_2CO_3 + OH^-$$

$$\frac{[H_2CO_3][OH^-]}{[HCO_3^-]} = K_{b2} \tag{30}$$

K_{b2} is the basic ionization constant of HCO_3^-, which is related in a simple way to the acidic ionization constant K_{a1} of its conjugate acid H_2CO_3,

$$K_{b2} = \frac{K_w}{K_{a1}} = \frac{1.01 \times 10^{-14}}{4.47 \times 10^{-7}} = 2.26 \times 10^{-8}$$

Similarly, the basic ionization constant K_{b1} of CO_3^{2-} is related to the acidic ionization constant of HCO_3^-, which is the second ionization constant (K_{a2}) of H_2CO_3,

$$K_{b1} = \frac{K_w}{K_{a2}} = \frac{1.01 \times 10^{-14}}{5.62 \times 10^{-11}} = 1.80 \times 10^{-4}$$

Just as the second ionization constant of a diprotic acid is much less than the first, so here, for the diprotic base CO_3^{2-}, $K_{b2} \ll K_{b1}$. We expect, then, that $[H_2CO_3]$ will be much less than $[HCO_3^-]$. As for the diprotic acid in Example 14, so also for the diprotic base CO_3^{2-} we can confine our attention to the first ionization,

$$CO_3^{2-} + H_2O \rightleftharpoons HCO_3^- + OH^-$$
$$0.25 - x \qquad\qquad x \qquad x \qquad \text{moles/liter}$$

Equation (29) becomes

$$\frac{x^2}{0.25 - x} = 1.80 \times 10^{-4}$$

If $x \ll 0.25$,

$$\frac{x^2}{0.25} = 1.80 \times 10^{-4}$$
$$x = 6.7 \times 10^{-3} = [OH^-]$$
$$pOH = 3 - \log 6.7 = 2.17$$
$$pH = 14.00 - pOH = 11.83$$

19.9 WEAK ACID (OR BASE) IN THE PRESENCE OF STRONG ACID (OR BASE)

If a weak acid is present in a solution that also contains a strong acid, the concentration of H_3O^+ is determined almost entirely by the concentration of the strong acid. The same applies if the acid in which we are interested is present in small concentration relative to other acids in the solution. Corresponding statements are true for bases.

EXAMPLE 16 Find the degree of ionization of CH_3COOH and the concentration of CH_3COO^- in a solution $0.10M$ with respect to HCl and $0.20M$ with respect to CH_3COOH.

ANSWER Since HCl is a strong acid, $[Cl^-] = 0.10$.

Equilibrium:
$$CH_3COOH + H_2O \rightleftharpoons H_3O^+ + CH_3COO^-$$
$$\frac{[H_3O^+][CH_3COO^-]}{[CH_3COOH]} = 1.75 \times 10^{-5} \tag{31}$$

Electrical neutrality: $\qquad [H_3O^+] = [Cl^-] + [CH_3COO^-] + [OH^-]$ (32)
Conservation: $[CH_3COOH] + [CH_3COO^-] = 0.20$ (33)

Because CH_3COOH is a weak acid, $[CH_3COO^-]$ is probably much less than 0.10 mole/liter, while $[OH^-]$ is certainly negligible. Equation (32) is approximately

$$[H_3O^+] = [Cl^-] = 0.10$$

Let $x = [CH_3COO^-]$; then $[CH_3COOH] = 0.20 - x$, and Equation (31) becomes

$$\frac{0.10x}{0.20 - x} = 1.75 \times 10^{-5}$$
$$x = 3.5 \times 10^{-5} \text{ mole/liter} = [CH_3COO^-]$$

The degree of ionization is

$$\alpha = \frac{x}{0.20} = 1.75 \times 10^{-4}$$

It should be noted that the degree of ionization of the weak acid is much decreased by the presence of the strong acid; if the HCl were absent, α would be 9.3×10^{-3} instead of 1.75×10^{-4}. This effect is called the **common ion effect** (in allusion to the H_3O^+ ion, which is common to the two acids), and is an example of Le Châtelier's principle: the equilibrium

$$HA + H_2O \rightleftharpoons H_3O^+ + A^-$$

is shifted to the left by an increase in $[H_3O^+]$.

EXAMPLE 17   **Find the degree of ionization of 0.0500M NH$_3$ in a solution of pH 11.0.**

ANSWER   pOH $= 14.0 - 11.0 = 3.0$; $[OH^-] = 1.0 \times 10^{-3}$.

$$NH_3 + H_2O \rightleftharpoons NH_4^+ + OH^-$$

Let $x = [NH_4^+]$. Then, for conservation,

$$[NH_3] = 0.0500 - [NH_4^+] = 0.0500 - x$$

The equilibrium condition is

$$\frac{[NH_4^+][OH^-]}{[NH_3]} = 1.76 \times 10^{-5}$$

$$\frac{x(10^{-3})}{0.0500 - x} = 1.76 \times 10^{-5}$$

$$x = 8.65 \times 10^{-4}$$

$$\alpha = \frac{x}{0.0500} = 1.73 \times 10^{-2}$$

EXAMPLE 18   **Find the concentration of S^{2-} in a solution 0.10M with respect to H$_2$S and 0.30M with respect to HCl.**

ANSWER   **For the reactions**

$$H_2S + H_2O \rightleftharpoons H_3O^+ + HS^-$$
$$HS^- + H_2O \rightleftharpoons H_3O^+ + S^{2-}$$

we have the equilibrium conditions

$$\frac{[H_3O^+][HS^-]}{[H_2S]} = K_1 = 6.3 \times 10^{-8}$$

$$\frac{[H_3O^+][S^{2-}]}{[HS^-]} = K_2 = 10^{-14}$$

Since $[HS^-]$ does not interest us in this problem, we are free to eliminate it by multiplying the two equations together,

$$\frac{[H_3O^+]^2[S^{2-}]}{[H_2S]} = K_1K_2$$

or

$$[S^{2-}] = \frac{K_1 K_2 [H_2S]}{[H_3O^+]^2}$$

$$= \frac{6.3 \times 10^{-8} \times 10^{-14} \times 0.10}{(0.30)^2}$$

$$= 7 \times 10^{-22} \text{ mole/liter}$$

Note that $[S^{2-}]$ is *not* equal to K_2 in this case. That result (page 494) applied only to the case in which the diprotic acid was the only solute. Here, the solution also contains HCl.

19.10 BUFFER SOLUTIONS

A solution containing an acid and its conjugate base, both moderately weak, is known as a **buffer solution**; such a solution has the property that the addition of acids or bases causes only a relatively small change in pH. The pH of pure water, or of a solution not a buffer solution, is very sensitive to the addition of small quantities of acid or base. Suppose that we want a solution with pH 4.76. Such a solution can be prepared by dissolving 1.74×10^{-5} mole HCl in a liter of water,

$$[H_3O^+] = 1.74 \times 10^{-5}$$
$$pH = 4.76$$

Now, perhaps by accident, 0.10 mole HCl is added per liter of this solution,

$$[H_3O^+] = 0.10 + 1.74 \times 10^{-5} = 0.10 \text{ mole/liter}$$
$$pH = 1.0$$

The pH has been changed drastically.

However, when a strong acid is added to a buffer solution, it reacts with the base (A^-) present in the solution,

$$H_3O^+ + A^- \rightarrow HA + H_2O$$

Similarly, a strong base reacts with the acid (HA) in the solution,

$$OH^- + HA \rightarrow A^- + H_2O$$

In each case, the acid-base ratio is changed, but with only a moderate effect on the pH of the solution. Very little of the H_3O^+ or OH^- added will remain as such. Of course, if the number of moles of H_3O^+ added exceeds the number of moles of A^- in the solution, or if the number of moles of OH^- added exceeds the number of moles of HA in the solution, the buffer is destroyed and there is a large change in pH. The following example illustrates the quantitative treatment of buffer action.

EXAMPLE 19　Calculate the pH of (a) a solution 0.50*M* with respect to CH₃-COOH and 0.50*M* with respect to CH₃COONa; (b) the same solution after 0.10 mole HCl per liter has been added to it. Assume that the volume is unchanged.

Equilibrium: $CH_3COOH + H_2O \leftrightharpoons H_3O^+ + CH_3COO^-$

$$\frac{[H_3O^+][CH_3COO^-]}{[CH_3COOH]} = 1.75 \times 10^{-5} \tag{34}$$

Electrical neutrality: $[Na^+] + [H_3O^+] = [CH_3COO^-] + [OH^-] \tag{35}$

Acetate (CH_3COO^-) has been added in two forms: CH_3COO^- (in CH_3COONa) and CH_3COOH. The amount of each form added is 0.50 mole per liter, and the total quantity of acetate must be constant, however it may be divided between the two forms. Hence the condition:

Conservation: $[CH_3COOH] + [CH_3COO^-] = 0.50 + 0.50 = 1.00 \tag{36}$

$$[Na^+] = 0.50 \tag{37}$$

We make the simplifying assumption that $[H_3O^+]$ and $[OH^-]$ are both negligible as compared to 0.50; this will be true for any solution that is not strongly acidic or basic. Then Equations (35) and (36) become

$$[Na^+] = [CH_3COO^-] = 0.50$$
$$[CH_3COOH] = 0.50$$

We get the same results by writing the equation

$$CH_3COOH + H_2O \leftrightharpoons H_3O^+ + CH_3COO^-$$

$0.50 - x \qquad\qquad x \qquad 0.50 + x \qquad$ moles/liter

and recognizing that $0.50 \pm x \approx 0.50$. Then

$$\frac{[H_3O^+](0.50)}{0.50} = 1.75 \times 10^{-5}$$
$$[H_3O^+] = 1.75 \times 10^{-5}$$
$$pH = 4.76$$

(b) The solution now contains a new ion, Cl^-, with $[Cl^-] = 0.10$ mole/liter. We have also added H_3O^+ in the same amount, but that does not mean that $[H_3O^+]$ has increased by 0.10 mole/liter. On the contrary, most of the H_3O^+ added reacts with the base CH_3COO^- to form CH_3COOH. To find the new value of $[H_3O^+]$, we proceed as before:

Equilibrium:

$$\frac{[H_3O^+][CH_3COO^-]}{[CH_3COOH]} = 1.75 \times 10^{-5} \tag{34}$$

Electrical neutrality:

$$[Na^+] + [H_3O^+] = [CH_3COO^-] + [OH^-] + [Cl^-] \tag{35}$$

Conservation:

$$[CH_3COOH] + [CH_3COO^-] = 1.00 \tag{36}$$
$$[Na^+] = 0.50 \tag{37}$$
$$[Cl^-] = 0.10 \tag{38}$$

If we neglect $[H_3O^+]$ and $[OH^-]$, as in (a), Equation (35′) becomes

$$[Na^+] = [CH_3COO^-] + [Cl^-]$$
$$0.50 = [CH_3COO^-] + 0.10$$
$$[CH_3COO^-] = 0.40$$

Equation (36) gives

$$[CH_3COOH] = 1.00 - 0.40 = 0.60$$

From Equation (34),

$$[H_3O^+] = \frac{0.60}{0.40} \times 1.75 \times 10^{-5}$$
$$= 2.6 \times 10^{-5}$$
$$pH = 4.58$$

The effect of adding the HCl has been to convert 0.10 mole/liter of CH_3COO^- to 0.10 mole/liter of CH_3COOH. $[CH_3COO^-]$ has gone down from 0.50 to 0.40 mole/liter; $[CH_3COOH]$ has gone up from 0.50 to 0.60 mole/liter. Once we understand that this is the result of adding acid, we can solve the problem by writing the single equation

$$CH_3COOH + H_2O \rightleftharpoons H_3O^+ + CH_3COO^-$$
$$0.60 - x \approx 0.60 \qquad\qquad x \qquad 0.40 + x \approx 0.40$$

and, as before,

$$\frac{0.40x}{0.60} = 1.75 \times 10^{-5}$$

If we had added NaOH, the effect would have been to convert CH_3COOH to CH_3COO^-.

The decrease in pH is only 0.18, to be contrasted with a decrease of 3.76 for the unbuffered solution. In the buffer solution, the addition of HCl has multiplied $[H_3O^+]$ by only 1.5; in the unbuffered solution, $[H_3O^+]$ has gone from 1.74×10^{-5} to 0.10, and has thus been multiplied by 5.8×10^3.

Buffer solutions provide another illustration of the common ion effect (page 496). The presence of acetate ion (common to acetic acid and sodium acetate) severely represses the ionization of CH_3COOH. As a result, $[H_3O^+]$ is much less in the solution of CH_3COOH $(0.50M)$ + CH_3COO^- $(0.50M)$ than it would be in a solution $0.50M$ with respect to CH_3COOH and containing no CH_3COO^-. The pH of the buffer solution is 4.76; the pH of a $0.50M$ solution of CH_3COOH is 2.53.

A buffer solution retains its buffering action—its insensitivity to addition of acid or base—as long as the quantity of acid or base added is small compared to the concentrations of the weak acid and its conjugate base in the buffer solution. For maximum buffering capacity, then, one should use a very concentrated solution, but high concentrations may interfere with the use to which the solution is to be put. With a given total concentration, the maximum buffering capacity and minimum sensitivity are attained when the concentrations of the acid and base are initially equal. As we saw in Example 19a, $[H_3O^+] = K_a$, or pH = pK_a, in this case. Similarly, with a base B and its conjugate acid BH^+, the equation

$$\frac{[BH^+][OH^-]}{[B]} = K_b$$

shows that when $[BH^+] = [B]$, then $[OH^-] = K_b$, or pOH = pK_b. If, then, we are told to prepare a buffer solution of given pH, we should seek an acid with p$K_a \approx$ pH, or a base with p$K_b \approx$ pOH = pK_w − pH. We cannot expect to find an available acid for which pK_a = pH exactly, but we choose the one that is closest and adjust the acid-base ratio to make the pH come out right.

EXAMPLE 20   **The following bases, and their conjugate acids (as the chlorides), are available in the laboratory: ammonia, NH_3; pyridine, C_5H_5N; ethylamine, $CH_3CH_2NH_2$. A buffer solution of pH 9.00 is to be prepared, and the total concentration of buffering reagents is to be 0.50 mole/liter. (a) Choose the best base-acid pair. (b) Give the recipe for preparing one liter of the solution. (c) Calculate the pH of the solution after 0.02 mole NaOH has been added per liter.**

ANSWER   (a) **The solution is to have pOH = 14.00 − pH = 5.00. The pK_b values of the three available bases are: NH_3, 4.75; C_5H_5N, 8.81; $CH_3CH_2NH_2$, 3.33. NH_3 has its pK_b closest to 5 and should be chosen.**

(b) $NH_3 + H_2O \rightleftharpoons NH_4^+ + OH^-$

$$\frac{[NH_4^+][OH^-]}{[NH_3]} = K_b$$

$$\frac{[NH_4^+]}{[NH_3]} = \frac{K_b}{[OH^-]} = \frac{1.76 \times 10^{-5}}{1.00 \times 10^{-5}} = 1.76$$

Therefore, NH_4Cl and NH_3 should be added in the molar ratio 1.76:1. To make the sum of the concentrations equal to 0.50 mole/liter, we must have

$$[NH_3] + [NH_4^+] = 0.50$$

Let
$$x = [NH_3]$$

Then
$$1.76x = [NH_4^+]$$
$$x + 1.76x = 0.50$$
$$x = 0.18 \text{ mole/liter} = [NH_3]$$
$$[NH_4^+] = 0.32 \text{ mole/liter}$$

The solution should be prepared by dissolving 0.18 mole NH_3 (3.06 g, or 12 ml of 15M solution) and 0.32 mole NH_4Cl (17.1 g) in H_2O and adding H_2O until the total volume is 1.00 liter.

(c) The effect of adding 0.02 mole Na^+ and 0.02 mole OH^- per liter is to convert 0.02 mole NH_4^+ per liter to NH_3:

$$[NH_3] = 0.18 + 0.02 = 0.20 \text{ mole/liter}$$
$$[NH_4^+] = 0.32 - 0.02 = 0.30 \text{ mole/liter}$$

Then

$$[OH^-] = \frac{K_b[NH_3]}{[NH_4^+]}$$
$$= 1.76 \times 10^{-5} \times \frac{0.20}{0.30}$$
$$= 1.17 \times 10^{-5} \text{ mole/liter}$$
$$pOH = 4.93$$
$$pH = 14.00 - pOH = 9.07$$

19.11   INDICATORS

An indicator is an acid (or base) having a different color from its conjugate base (or acid). Let us represent the acid form of the indicator by HIn and the base form by In^-, without implying that the acid is necessarily uncharged. An example is methyl orange, for which HIn is red and In^- is yellow. The equilibrium condition for the reaction

$$HIn + H_2O \rightleftharpoons H_3O^+ + In^-$$

is

$$\frac{[H_3O^+][In^-]}{[HIn]} = K_i$$

or

$$\frac{[HIn]}{[In^-]} = \frac{[H_3O^+]}{K_i}$$

or

$$\log\left(\frac{[HIn]}{[In^-]}\right) = \log[H_3O^+] - \log K_i$$
$$= pK_i - pH$$

The indicator should be used in such small quantity that $[H_3O^+]$ is determined by the other constitutents of the solution. The ratio $[HIn]/[In^-]$, which determines the color, is then determined by the pH of the solution. With methyl orange, for example, the solution will be red if $[HIn] \gg [In^-]$, yellow if $[In^-] \gg [HIn]$, and varying shades of orange when $[HIn]$ and $[In^-]$ are comparable. As a rough rule, we may assume that gradations of color are detectable when $[HIn]/[In^-]$ is between 0.1 and 10. When this ratio is greater than 10, the solution has the color of HIn, and this color does not change perceptibly if the ratio is made 1000 or 1,000,000 instead of 10 (unless, of course, the indicator accepts another proton, resulting in a second color change). Likewise, if the ratio is less than 0.1, only the In^- color is seen. Suppose, for example, that $K_i = 1.0 \times 10^{-4}$, or $pK_i = 4.0$.

When $[HIn]/[In^-] = 0.1$,

$$pK_i - pH = \log (0.1) = -1$$
$$pH = pK_i + 1 = 5$$

When $[HIn]/[In^-] = 10$,

$$pK_i - pH = \log 10 = 1$$
$$pH = pK_i - 1 = 3$$

Thus, the useful range of this indicator is from 3 to 5. Below 3, nearly all the indicator is in the acid form (HIn); above 5, nearly all the indicator is in the basic form (In⁻). Within this range of about two pH units centered at pK_i, the pH of the solution containing the indicator can be determined by comparing its color with the colors of a series of buffer solutions of known pH's, containing the same indicator at approximately the same concentration. For the indicator with pK_i 4.0, we might prepare buffers of pH 3.0, 3.1, 3.2, . . . , 4.9, 5.0. Then, if the unknown solution containing the indicator has a hue intermediate between the solutions with pH 3.7 and 3.8, we can say that the pH of the unknown solution is between 3.7 and 3.8.

Table 19.2 lists some common indicators, their colors, and the pH ranges in which the colors show perceptible gradations.

TABLE 19.2   *Acid-Base Indicators*

| Indicator | Colors | | pH range |
	Acid	Base	
Methyl violet	Green	Violet	0–2
Methyl orange	Red	Yellow	3–4.5
Methyl red	Red	Yellow	4–6
Bromthymol blue	Yellow	Blue	6–8
Neutral red	Red	Yellow	7–8
Litmus	Red	Blue	5–8
Phenolphthalein	Colorless	Red	8–10
Thymolphthalein	Colorless	Blue	9–10.5
Alizarin yellow	Yellow	Violet	10–12
1,3,5-Trinitrobenzene	Colorless	Red	12–14

EXAMPLE 21   **The pH of a solution is known to be about 4. Select an indicator suitable for more accurate determination of its pH.**

ANSWER   **pH 4 is within the methyl orange range; this indicator is therefore suitable. Methyl red might also be used, but is less desirable because 4 is on the edge of its range.**

19.12 SOLUBILITY PRODUCT

Silver chloride is an ionic salt. It is only slightly soluble in water, but, like other "insoluble" salts, it does have a measurable solubility. The dissolving process may be represented by the equation

$$AgCl(c) \rightleftharpoons Ag^+ + Cl^-$$

The equilibrium condition for this reaction is

$$[Ag^+][Cl^-] = K$$

The solid is omitted from the reaction quotient (page 344). K is called the **solubility product** or **solubility product constant** of AgCl. It is also represented by K_{sp}. When this equilibrium is established, the solution is saturated, and the solubility product thus gives the product of the Ag^+ and Cl^- concentrations in a saturated solution. The individual concentrations may be changed—by adding NaCl or $AgNO_3$, for instance—but *the product, at any one temperature, remains constant.* (We are still assuming that activities are equal to concentrations.) The solubility product principle is usually applied only to slightly soluble salts, because, at high concentrations, the disparity between concentration and activity is so great, and so dependent on the composition of the solution, as to make solubility products useless for calculation. Solubility products of some slightly soluble salts are given in Table 19.3.

Solubility and *solubility product* must not be confused with each other. The solubility of a salt is the quantity present in a unit amount of a saturated solution, expressed in moles per liter, grams per 100 ml, or other units. The solubility depends on what else is in the solution. The solubility *product*, being an equilibrium constant, depends only on temperature. There is a connection, of course, between the solubility and the solubility product; if one is known, the other can be calculated.

EXAMPLE 22 **Find the solubility (in moles/liter) of AgCl at 25°C in (a) pure water; (b) a 0.0100M solution of NaCl.**

ANSWER (a) **The solubility is equal to the concentration of Ag^+ or Cl^-; in the absence of other ions, these two concentrations must be equal. Let s be the solubility in moles/liter;**

$$AgCl(c) \rightleftharpoons Ag^+ + Cl^-$$
$$[Ag^+][Cl^-] = K$$
$$s \cdot s = 1.73 \times 10^{-10}$$
$$s = 1.32 \times 10^{-5} \text{ mole/liter}$$

(b) The number of moles of AgCl that dissolve per liter (the new solubility, s') is equal to the number of moles of Ag^+ in the solution; $s' = [Ag^+]$. Electrical neutrality requires

$$[Na^+] + [Ag^+] + [H_3O^+] = [Cl^-] + [OH^-]$$

and

$$[Na^+] = 0.0100 \text{ mole/liter}$$

TABLE 19.3   *Solubility Products in Water*

Salt	Temperature (°C)	K
AgBr	25	7.7×10^{-13}
AgCl	25	1.73×10^{-10}
Ag_2CrO_4	25	1.15×10^{-12}
AgI	25	1.5×10^{-16}
Ag_2S	25	1.9×10^{-49}
$Al(OH)_3$	25	3.7×10^{-15}
$BaCO_3$	25	8.1×10^{-9}
$BaCrO_4$	18	1.6×10^{-10}
BaF_2	25.8	1.73×10^{-6}
$BaSO_4$	25	1.08×10^{-10}
$CaCO_3$	25	8.7×10^{-9}
CaF_2	26	3.95×10^{-11}
CdS	18	3.6×10^{-29}
CoS	18	3×10^{-26}
CuS	18	8.5×10^{-45}
FeS	25	1.3×10^{-17}
Hg_2Cl_2 [a]	25	2×10^{-18}
HgS	25	2.4×10^{-52}
MgC_2O_4	18	8.57×10^{-5}
MnS	25	7.9×10^{-13}
NiS	18	1.4×10^{-24}
$PbCrO_4$	18	1.77×10^{-14}
PbI_2	25	1.39×10^{-8}
PbS	25	2.3×10^{-27}
$PbSO_4$	18	1.06×10^{-8}
ZnS	25	2.5×10^{-24}

[a] $Hg_2Cl_2(c) \leftrightharpoons Hg_2^{2+} + 2Cl^-$.

Since the solution is neutral, $[H_3O^+] = [OH^-]$. (Even if it were not quite neutral, we could neglect these two concentrations.) Then

$$[Na^+] + [Ag^+] = [Cl^-]$$
$$0.0100 + s' = [Cl^-]$$

Another way to look at the problem is to write the equation for the dissolving process,

$$AgCl(c) \leftrightharpoons Ag^+ + Cl^-$$
$$0 + s' \quad 0.0100 + s'$$

We start with 0 mole of Ag^+ and 0.0100 mole of Cl^- per liter; the dissolving of s' mole of AgCl raises these concentrations to s' and $0.0100 + s'$ mole/liter, respectively. Then, substituting into the equilibrium condition,

$$[Ag^+][Cl^-] = K$$
$$s'(0.0100 + s') = K$$

It is a very good approximation that $s' \ll 0.01$; practically all the Cl^- is contributed by the NaCl. Then

$$0.01s' = K = 1.73 \times 10^{-10}$$
$$s' = 1.73 \times 10^{-8} \text{ mole/liter}$$

We observe that the solubility (s') is much less in the NaCl solution than in pure water (s). This result could have been predicted from Le Châtelier's principle: the equilibrium

$$AgCl(c) \leftrightharpoons Ag^+ + Cl^-$$

is shifted to the left by addition of Cl^- or Ag^+; that is, the solubility of AgCl is decreased. This effect—like the effect of a strong acid in repressing the ionization of a weak acid—is known as the **common ion effect**, because the decrease in solubility is caused by addition of a salt having an ion in common with the slightly soluble salt.

When the salt dissolves to give unequal numbers of positive and negative ions, each concentration must be raised to a power equal to the coefficient of that ion in the equation. For example:

Salt	Reaction	Equilibrium condition
CaF_2	$CaF_2(c) \leftrightharpoons Ca^{2+} + 2F^-$	$[Ca^{2+}][F^-]^2 = K$
Hg_2Cl_2	$Hg_2Cl_2(c) \leftrightharpoons Hg_2^{2+} + 2Cl^-$	$[Hg_2^{2+}][Cl^-]^2 = K$
	(not $2Hg^+$)	
$Al(OH)_3$	$Al(OH)_3(c) \leftrightharpoons Al^{3+} + 3OH^-$	$[Al^{3+}][OH^-]^3 = K$
$Ca_3(PO_4)_2$	$Ca_3(PO_4)_2(c) \leftrightharpoons 3Ca^{2+} + 2PO_4^{3-}$	$[Ca^{2+}]^3[PO_4^{3-}]^2 = K$

EXAMPLE 23 · A solution is saturated with CaF_2. Calculate (a) $[Ca^{2+}]$ when no salt other than CaF_2 is present; (b) $[Ca^{2+}]$ when the solution is $0.10M$ with respect to NaF; (c) $[F^-]$ when the solution is $0.20M$ with respect to $CaCl_2$.

ANSWER $CaF_2(c) \leftrightharpoons Ca^{2+} + 2F^-$

(a) Let $x = [Ca^{2+}]$. Then

$$[F^-] = 2[Ca^{2+}] = 2x$$
$$[Ca^{2+}][F^-]^2 = K$$
$$x(2x)^2 = 3.95 \times 10^{-11}$$
$$4x^3 = 3.95 \times 10^{-11}$$
$$x^3 = 9.88 \times 10^{-12}$$
$$x = 2.15 \times 10^{-4} \text{ mole/liter}$$

(b) Again, we let $x = [Ca^{2+}]$, but now there are two kinds of positive ion. For electrical neutrality,

$$[F^-] = [Na^+] + 2[Ca^{2+}]$$
$$= 0.10 + 2x$$

We may assume that $2x \ll 0.10$, which is equivalent to saying that most o
the F^- in the solution is contributed by the NaF, and very little by the dis
solving of CaF_2. Then

$$[F^-] \approx 0.10 \text{ mole/liter}$$
$$[Ca^{2+}][F^-]^2 = K$$
$$x(0.10)^2 = 3.95 \times 10^{-11}$$
$$x = 3.95 \times 10^{-9} \text{ mole/liter} = [Ca^{2+}]$$

(c) Let $y = [F^-]$. Most of the Ca^{2+} is contributed by the $CaCl_2$: $[Ca^{2+}] \approx 0.2$
mole/liter. Then

$$[Ca^{2+}][F^-]^2 = 3.95 \times 10^{-11}$$
$$(0.20)(y)^2 = 3.95 \times 10^{-11}$$
$$y^2 = 1.98 \times 10^{-10}$$
$$y = 1.4 \times 10^{-5} \text{ mole/liter} = [F^-]$$

EXAMPLE 24   The solubility of thallium(I) iodide, TlI, in water is 6.4×10
g/100 ml at 20°C. Find (a) its solubility product; (b) its solubility, in g/100 m
in $0.050M$ KI solution.

ANSWER   (a) In order to calculate the solubility product, we must first expre
the solubility in terms of molarity (moles per liter). The molecular weight o
TlI is 331.3 g/mole; the molarity of the saturated solution is

$$6.4 \times 10^{-3} \frac{g}{100 \text{ ml}} \times \frac{1000 \text{ ml}}{\text{liter}} \times \frac{1 \text{ mole}}{331.3 \text{ g}} = 1.93 \times 10^{-4} \frac{\text{mole}}{\text{liter}}$$
$$= [Tl^+] = [I^-]$$

The solubility product, for the reaction $TlI(c) \leftrightharpoons Tl^+ + I^-$, is

$$K = [Tl^+][I^-]$$
$$= (1.93 \times 10^{-4})^2$$
$$= 3.72 \times 10^{-8}$$

(b) The solubility *product* (but not the solubility) is the same as it was in par
(a). Here, $[Tl^+] = s$ and $[K^+] = 0.050$ mole/liter. Then, either from the requir
ment of electrical neutrality or by adding up the moles of I^- contributed b
the KI and by the TlI in solution, we conclude that

$$[I^-] = [K^+] + [Tl^+] = 0.050 + s \approx 0.050$$
$$s(0.050) = 3.72 \times 10^{-8}$$
$$s = 7.44 \times 10^{-7} \text{ mole/liter}$$

The solubility in the units specified is

$$7.44 \times 10^{-7} \frac{\text{mole}}{\text{liter}} \times \frac{331.3 \text{ g}}{\text{mole}} \times \frac{0.100 \text{ liter}}{100 \text{ ml}} = 2.5 \times 10^{-5} \frac{\text{g}}{100 \text{ ml}}$$

In an unsaturated or supersaturated solution of, say, TlI, there is n
equilibrium between solid and ions, and we therefore cannot expect t
have $[Tl^+][I^-] = K$. If the solution is unsaturated, $[Tl^+][I^-] < K$; if it
supersaturated, $[Tl^+][I^-] > K$. One use of the solubility product is t

decide whether precipitation is possible when the ions have certain concentrations. We calculate the appropriate product of concentrations (Q, the reaction quotient) and compare it with K. If $Q > K$, the solution is supersaturated, and precipitation is possible (but it may not occur if the solution remains supersaturated); if $Q < K$, the solution is unsaturated, and precipitation is impossible.

EXAMPLE 25 **A solution is prepared by mixing equal volumes of 0.010M MgCl$_2$ and 0.020M Na$_2$C$_2$O$_4$ solutions at 18°C. Is it possible for MgC$_2$O$_4$ to precipitate in the resulting solution?**

ANSWER **The reaction in question is**

$$MgC_2O_4(c) \leftrightharpoons Mg^{2+} + C_2O_4{}^{2-}$$

We ask whether the concentrations of the two ions are large enough for equilibrium to be established in this reaction.

When the solutions are mixed, the volume is doubled (to a very good approximation, though volumes are not strictly additive on mixing), and the concentrations of Mg^{2+} and C$_2$O$_4{}^{2-}$ are half what they were originally: [Mg^{2+}] = 0.005, [C$_2$O$_4{}^{2-}$] = 0.010 mole/liter. Then

$$Q = [Mg^{2+}][C_2O_4{}^{2-}] = 5 \times 10^{-5}$$

which is less than $K = 8.57 \times 10^{-5}$ (Table 19.3). It is impossible for MgC$_2$O$_4$ to precipitate.

EXAMPLE 26 **What is the minimum concentration of S^{2-} which can cause precipitation of CdS from a 0.10M solution of Cd^{2+} at 18°C?**

ANSWER **The minimum concentration is that corresponding to a saturated solution (or, more precisely, to a very slightly supersaturated solution). In a saturated solution,**

$$CdS(c) \leftrightharpoons Cd^{2+} + S^{2-}$$
$$[Cd^{2+}][S^{2-}] = 3.6 \times 10^{-29}$$
$$[S^{2-}] = \frac{3.6 \times 10^{-29}}{0.10} = 3.6 \times 10^{-28} \text{ mole/liter}$$

EXAMPLE 27 **We wish to dissolve enough BaCrO$_4$ in water so that [Ba^{2+}] = 0.10 mole/liter. This result can be accomplished by adding a reagent that reacts with CrO$_4{}^{2-}$. How low must the concentration of CrO$_4{}^{2-}$ be in order for [Ba^{2+}] to be 0.10 mole/liter?**

ANSWER

$$BaCrO_4(c) \leftrightharpoons Ba^{2+} + CrO_4{}^{2-}$$
$$[Ba^{2+}][CrO_4{}^{2-}] = 1.6 \times 10^{-10}$$
$$(0.10)(x) = 1.6 \times 10^{-10}$$
$$x = 1.6 \times 10^{-9} \text{ mole/liter} = [CrO_4{}^{2-}]$$

This is the maximum permissible concentration of CrO$_4{}^{2-}$.

19.13 EFFECT OF pH ON SOLUBILITY

When an acid is weak, the concentration of its anion is affected by the pH of the solution. For example, the reaction

$$HS^- + H_2O \rightleftharpoons H_3O^+ + S^{2-}$$

is shifted to the left by an increase in $[H_3O^+]$. In turn, the solubility of a sulfide is affected by the concentration of S^{2-}. When acid is added to a saturated solution of ZnS, the concentration of S^{2-} is decreased, and the reaction

$$ZnS(c) \rightleftharpoons Zn^{2+} + S^{2-}$$

is shifted to the right, meaning that the solubility of ZnS increases. In general, *the solubility of a salt of a weak acid is increased by addition of a strong acid to the solution.*

The effect is especially pronounced with sulfides, which are salts of the very weak acid HS^-, and this case is of interest because of its importance in qualitative analysis (Chapter 20). If any two of the three concentrations $[H_3O^+]$, $[S^{2-}]$, and $[H_2S]$ are given, the third can be calculated from the equation (Example 18, page 496),

$$\frac{[H_3O^+]^2[S^{2-}]}{[H_2S]} = K_1K_2$$
$$= 6.3 \times 10^{-8} \times 10^{-14} = 6.3 \times 10^{-22}$$

In a solution of H_2S, saturated at one atmosphere pressure and 25°C, $[H_2S] = 0.10$ mole/liter; under these conditions,

$$[H_3O^+]^2[S^{2-}] = 6.3 \times 10^{-23}$$

EXAMPLE 28   **Find $[Zn^{2+}]$ in a saturated solution of ZnS in which $[H_3O^+] = 0.30$ and $[H_2S] = 0.10$ mole/liter at 25°C.**

ANSWER   **First we must calculate $[S^{2-}]$:**

$$[S^{2-}] = \frac{6.3 \times 10^{-23}}{[H_3O^+]^2} = \frac{6.3 \times 10^{-23}}{(0.30)^2} = 7.0 \times 10^{-22} \text{ mole/liter}$$

Then

$$[Zn^{2+}][S^{2-}] = 2.5 \times 10^{-24}$$
$$[Zn^{2+}] = \frac{2.5 \times 10^{-24}}{7.0 \times 10^{-22}} = 3.6 \times 10^{-3} \text{ mole/liter}$$

It should, perhaps, be pointed out again that a given solution has only one concentration of (for example) S^{2-}. The value of $[S^{2-}]$ must be the same in the H_2S equilibrium condition and in the ZnS equilibrium condition.

EXAMPLE 29   **What is the minimum concentration of H_3O^+ in a solution from which PbS will not precipitate, when $[Pb^{2+}] = 0.0050$ and $[H_2S] = 0.10$ mole/liter?**

ANSWER **In a saturated solution of PbS,**

$$PbS(c) \leftrightharpoons Pb^{2+} + S^{2-}$$

$$[Pb^{2+}][S^{2-}] = 2.3 \times 10^{-27}$$

$$[S^{2-}] = \frac{2.3 \times 10^{-27}}{0.0050} = 4.6 \times 10^{-25} \text{ mole/liter}$$

To prevent precipitation, we must make $[S^{2-}]$ slightly smaller than this value. The concentration of $[H_3O^+]$ must be slightly greater than that given by $[H_3O^+]^2[S^{2-}] = 6.3 \times 10^{-23}$:

$$[H_3O^+]^2 = \frac{6.3 \times 10^{-23}}{4.6 \times 10^{-25}} = 1.4 \times 10^2$$

$$[H_3O^+] = 12 \text{ moles/liter}$$

Thus, PbS can be dissolved (or prevented from precipitating) only in very concentrated strong acids.

EXAMPLE 30 A solution has $[Pb^{2+}] = 0.010$ and $[Mn^{2+}] = 0.010$ mole/liter, and is saturated with respect to H_2S. Within what range must $[H_3O^+]$ be in order that PbS will precipitate and MnS will not?

ANSWER The S^{2-} concentration must be between the concentrations given by

$$PbS(c) \leftrightharpoons Pb^{2+} + S^{2-}$$

$$[Pb^{2+}][S^{2-}] = 2.3 \times 10^{-27}$$

$$[S^{2-}] = 2.3 \times 10^{-25}$$

and

$$MnS(c) \leftrightharpoons Mn^{2+} + S^{2-}$$

$$[Mn^{2+}][S^{2-}] = 7.9 \times 10^{-13}$$

$$[S^{2-}] = 7.9 \times 10^{-11} \text{ mole/liter}$$

When $[S^{2-}]$ is in this range, the solution is unsaturated with respect to MnS, since $[S^{2-}]$ is less than the value (7.9×10^{-11} mole/liter) in a solution saturated with MnS. The solution is supersaturated with respect to PbS, since $[S^{2-}]$ is greater than the value (2.3×10^{-25} mole/liter) it would have in a solution saturated with PbS in which $[Pb^{2+}] = 0.010$ mole/liter. We expect, then, that PbS will precipitate and MnS will not. In order for $lS^{2-}]$ to be in the desired range, $[H_3O^+]$ must be between

$$[H_3O^+]^2 = \frac{6.3 \times 10^{-23}}{2.3 \times 10^{-25}} = 2.74 \times 10^2$$

$$[H_3O^+] = 17 \text{ moles/liter}$$

and

$$[H_3O^+]^2 = \frac{6.3 \times 10^{-23}}{7.9 \times 10^{-11}} = 8.0 \times 10^{-13}$$

$$[H_3O^+] = 8.9 \times 10^{-7} \text{ mole/liter}$$

19.14 COMPLEX IONS

A **complex ion** may be defined as an ion composed of several parts, each of which has some independent existence in solution as an ion, molecule or atom. We would not count $SO_4{}^{2-}$ as a complex ion, for S^{6+} and O^{2-}, or other such pairs, do not exist in aqueous solution. A complex ion, in our sense, consists of a positive metal ion, M^{x+} (usually a transition metal) and a number of **ligands,** L, which are uncharged molecules or negative ions. The formula of the complex ion is ML_n, where n is usually 2, 4, or 6. Theories of the structure of these ions are discussed in Chapter 25. Some examples of complex ions are $Ag(NH_3)_2{}^+$, $Ag(S_2O_3)_2{}^{3-}$, $Cu(NH_3)_4{}^{2+}$, $Fe(CN)_6{}^{3-}$, $Fe(CN)_6{}^{4-}$, $Zn(OH)_4{}^{2-}$.

The dissociation of the complex ion $Ag(NH_3)_2{}^+$ may be represented as

$$Ag(NH_3)_2{}^+ \rightleftharpoons Ag^+ + 2NH_3$$

The equilibrium constant for this reaction is called the **dissociation constant** or **instability constant** of $Ag(NH_3)_2{}^+$,

$$\frac{[Ag^+][NH_3]^2}{[Ag(NH_3)_2{}^+]} = K$$

Tables of instability constants are not uncommon, but they are not so widespread as tables of acid or base ionization constants or solubility products. Another useful source of data on complex ions is a table of half cell potentials. In order that the reader may become familiar with the use of such tables, we give some instability constants in this form in Table 19.4, while others are given explicitly in Table 19.5. The calculation of equilibrium constants from half-cell potentials has been described (pages 418–420); the following example reviews the procedure.

EXAMPLE 31   **Find the instability constant of $Ag(NH_3)_2{}^+$ at 25°C.**

ANSWER   **We must find $\varepsilon°$ for the reaction**

$$Ag(NH_3)_2{}^+ \rightleftharpoons Ag^+ + 2NH_3$$

by combining $\varepsilon°$'s for half-reactions which add to the desired reaction:

		$\varepsilon°$ (volts)
Oxidation:	$Ag \rightleftharpoons Ag^+ + e^-$	-0.7996
Reduction:	$Ag(NH_3)_2{}^+ + e^- \rightleftharpoons Ag + 2NH_3$	$-(-0.373)$
	$Ag(NH_3)_2{}^+ \rightleftharpoons Ag^+ + 2NH_3$	-0.427

Now

$$\varepsilon° = \frac{2.303RT}{n\mathfrak{F}} \log K$$

$$= \frac{0.05915}{n} \log K \text{ (at 25°C)}$$

Here,

$$n = 1 \frac{\text{faraday}}{\text{mole}}$$

Standard Half-Cell Potentials for Complex Ions in Water at 25°C

	$\mathcal{E}°$ (volts)
$Ag + 2CN^- \rightleftharpoons Ag(CN)_2^- + e^-$	+0.395
$Ag + 2S_2O_3^{2-} \rightleftharpoons Ag(S_2O_3)_2^{3-} + e^-$	−0.015
$Ag + 2NH_3(aq) \rightleftharpoons Ag(NH_3)_2^+ + e^-$	−0.373
$Ag \rightleftharpoons Ag^+ + e^-$	−0.7996
$Au + 4Br^- \rightleftharpoons AuBr_4^- + 3e^-$	−0.87
$Au + 4Cl^- \rightleftharpoons AuCl_4^- + 3e^-$	−1.00
$Au \rightleftharpoons Au^{3+} + 3e^-$	−1.42
$Hg + 4CN^- \rightleftharpoons Hg(CN)_4^{2-} + 2e^-$	+0.37
$Hg + 4I^- \rightleftharpoons HgI_4^{2-} + 2e^-$	+0.04
$Hg + 4Br^- \rightleftharpoons HgBr_4^{2-} + 2e^-$	−0.21
$Hg + 4Cl^- \rightleftharpoons HgCl_4^{2-} + 2e^-$	−0.38
$Hg \rightleftharpoons Hg^{2+} + 2e^-$	−0.852

ABLE 19.5 Instability Constants of Complex Ions in Water at 25°C

Complex ion	K
$Cd(CN)_4^{2-}$	1.25×10^{-17}
CdI_4^{2-}	3×10^{-7}
$Cd(NH_3)_4^{2+}$	2.57×10^{-7}
$Co(NH_3)_6^{2+}$	10^{-5}
$Co(NH_3)_6^{3+}$	10^{-34}
$Cu(CN)_2^-$	8.7×10^{-17}
$Cu(NH_3)_4^{2+}$	2.14×10^{-13}
$Ni(NH_3)_4^{2+}$	1.12×10^{-8}
$Zn(NH_3)_4^{2+}$	3.47×10^{-10}
$Zn(OH)_4^{2-}$	4.5×10^{-16}

(One faraday passes through the circuit when the reaction occurs as written.)
Then

$$\log K = \frac{n\mathcal{E}°}{0.05915}$$
$$= \frac{1(-0.427)}{0.05915}$$
$$= -7.22$$
$$K = 6.0 \times 10^{-8}$$

19.14 Complex ions

In reality, the dissociation of a complex ion, like the ionization of a polyprotic acid, occurs in steps:

$$Ag(NH_3)_2^+ \leftrightarrows Ag(NH_3)^+ + NH_3$$
$$\frac{[Ag(NH_3)^+][NH_3]}{[Ag(NH_3)_2^+]} = K_1$$

$$Ag(NH_3)^+ \leftrightarrows Ag^+ + NH_3$$
$$\frac{[Ag^+][NH_3]}{[Ag(NH_3)^+]} = K_2$$

The constant calculated above is $K = K_1K_2$. To solve problems involving complex ions, one must, in general, know the equilibrium constants for the individual steps. Such problems can become very complicated, especially when there are not two, but four or six ligands. To avoid undue complication, we shall confine our attention to cases in which two of the three concentrations in an equilibrium condition such as

$$\frac{[Ag^+][NH_3]^2}{[Ag(NH_3)_2^+]} = K \tag{39}$$

can be considered known, and we seek the third. This situation arises whenever the ligand is present in substantial excess; in this case, practically all the metal ion will be present as, for example, $Ag(NH_3)_2^+$, with very little Ag^+ or $Ag(NH_3)^+$, and the ligand concentration will be simply equal to the excess beyond that required to form the complex ion. More formally, suppose that we dissolve c_1 moles $AgNO_3$ and c_2 moles NH_3 in one liter of H_2O. We can write conservation conditions for Ag^+ and for NH_3:

$$[Ag^+] + [Ag(NH_3)^+] + [Ag(NH_3)_2^+] = c_1 \tag{40}$$
$$[NH_3] + [NH_4^+] + [Ag(NH_3)^+] + 2[Ag(NH_3)_2^+] = c_2 \tag{41}$$

[Equation (41) counts moles of NH_3, and each mole of $Ag(NH_3)_2^+$ must be counted twice because it contains two moles of NH_3.] If $[Ag^+]$, $[Ag(NH_3)^+]$, and $[NH_4^+]$ are negligible, these equations reduce to

$$[Ag(NH_3)_2^+] = c_1$$
$$[NH_3] = c_2 - 2[Ag(NH_3)_2^+]$$
$$= c_2 - 2c_1$$

$2c_1$ is the number of moles (per liter) of NH_3 used in forming c_1 moles of $Ag(NH_3)_2^+$, and $c_2 - 2c_1$ is the excess concentration of NH_3.

EXAMPLE 32   A solution is prepared by dissolving 0.20 mole $AgNO_3$ and 0.50 mole NH_3 in H_2O to make 1.00 liter of solution. Find the concentration of Ag^+ in the solution.

ANSWER   The Ag^+ will be almost completely converted to 0.20 mole $Ag(NH_3)_2^+$, and will consume in the process 0.40 mole NH_3. Here, $c_1 = 0.20$ mole/liter, and $c_2 = 0.50$ mole/liter; thus, $[NH_3] = 0.50 - 2(0.20) = 0.10$ mole/liter. The

process may be represented as

$$\text{Ag}^+ \quad + \quad 2\text{NH}_3 \xrightleftharpoons{} \text{Ag}(\text{NH}_3)_2{}^+$$

Initial concentrations	0.20	0.50	0 mole/liter
Moles reacting per liter	$0.20 - x$	$2(0.20 - x)$	
Final concentrations	x	$0.50 - 0.40 + 2x$	$0.20 - x$
		≈ 0.10	≈ 0.20 mole/liter

Then, for the reaction

$$\text{Ag}(\text{NH}_3)_2{}^+ \xrightleftharpoons{} \text{Ag}^+ + 2\text{NH}_3$$

we have the equilibrium condition

$$\frac{[\text{Ag}^+][\text{NH}_3]^2}{[\text{Ag}(\text{NH}_3)_2{}^+]} = 6.0 \times 10^{-8}$$

$$\frac{x(0.10)^2}{0.20} = 6.0 \times 10^{-8}$$

$$x = 1.2 \times 10^{-6} \text{ mole/liter} = [\text{Ag}^+]$$

EXAMPLE 33   A solution is initially $0.50M$ with respect to Ag^+. How many moles per liter of NH_3 must be added to this solution to make $[\text{Ag}^+] = 1.0 \times 10^{-5}$ mole/liter? Assume that the volume of the solution is constant.

ANSWER   The first 1.00 mole/liter of NH_3 added will combine with Ag^+ to form $\text{Ag}(\text{NH}_3)_2{}^+$ with a concentration of 0.50 mole/liter. The concentration (x) of NH_3 in the final solution will be the excess added, beyond 1.00 mole/liter. Then, if $[\text{Ag}^+] = 1.0 \times 10^{-5}$,

$$\frac{[\text{Ag}^+][\text{NH}_3]^2}{[\text{Ag}(\text{NH}_3)_2{}^+]} = 6.0 \times 10^{-8}$$

$$\frac{(1.0 \times 10^{-5})x^2}{0.50} = 6.0 \times 10^{-8}$$

$$x^2 = 3.0 \times 10^{-3}$$

$$x = 5.5 \times 10^{-2} \text{ mole/liter}$$

The number of moles of NH_3 that must be added per liter is $1.00 + x = 1.055$ moles/liter.

19.15   EFFECT OF COMPLEX-ION FORMATION ON SOLUBILITY

When a complex ion is formed, the concentration of the uncomplexed (actually hydrated) metal ion is greatly diminished. The result is that salts of this metal become more soluble, as equilibria of the type $\text{AgCl}(c) \rightleftharpoons \text{Ag}^+ + \text{Cl}^-$ are shifted to the right.

EXAMPLE 34   Calculate the quantity of NH_3 that must be added to dissolve 0.010 mole AgCl in 1.00 liter of water.

ANSWER In the final solution, $[Cl^-] = 0.010$ mole/liter, and $[Ag(NH_3)_2^+] = 0.010$ mole/liter very nearly. In effect, the reaction is

$$AgCl(c) + 2NH_3 \rightarrow Ag(NH_3)_2^+ + Cl^-$$

or, for the numbers of moles in one liter of this solution,

$$0.010AgCl + 0.020NH_3 \rightarrow 0.010Ag(NH_3)_2^+ + 0.010Cl^-$$

First, we must find the maximum permissible concentration of Ag^+:

$$[Ag^+][Cl^-] = 1.73 \times 10^{-10} \text{ (page 504)}$$
$$[Ag^+] = \frac{1.73 \times 10^{-10}}{0.010}$$
$$= 1.73 \times 10^{-8}$$

Then the instability constant of $[Ag(NH_3)_2^+]$ gives $[NH_3]$:

$$\frac{[Ag^+][NH_3]^2}{[Ag(NH_3)_2^+]} = 6.0 \times 10^{-8}$$
$$[NH_3]^2 = \frac{6.0 \times 10^{-8} \times 0.010}{1.73 \times 10^{-8}}$$
$$= 3.47 \times 10^{-2}$$
$$[NH_3] = 0.19 \text{ mole/liter}$$

The total quantity of NH_3 that must be added is 0.020 (to form 0.010 mole of complex ion) + 0.19 (remaining in solution) = 0.21 mole.

EXAMPLE 35 Find the solubility (in moles/liter) of AgBr in a solution in which $[NH_3]$ is held constant at 0.50 mole/liter.

ANSWER AgBr is dissolved by the reaction

$$AgBr(c) + 2NH_3 \rightarrow Ag(NH_3)_2^+ + Br^-$$

The only ions present in appreciable concentration are $Ag(NH_3)_2^+$ and Br^-, and electrical neutrality requires that their concentrations be equal. The concentration of each of these ions is equal to the number of moles of AgBr dissolved per liter—in other words, to the solubility of AgBr in this solution. There are two equilibrium conditions to be satisfied:

$$AgBr(c) \leftrightarrows Ag^+ + Br^-$$
$$[Ag^+][Br^-] = 7.7 \times 10^{-13} \tag{42}$$
$$Ag(NH_3)_2^+ \leftrightarrows Ag^+ + 2NH_3$$
$$\frac{[Ag^+][NH_3]^2}{[Ag(NH_3)_2^+]} = 6.0 \times 10^{-8} \tag{43}$$

We have two equations containing four concentrations. However, one of them ($[NH_3]$) is known, and two others ($[Ag(NH_3)_2^+]$ and $[Br^-]$) are equal. The fourth concentration is $[Ag^+]$, which does not interest us, since very little silver ion is present in this form. On dividing Equation (42) by Equation (43), we eliminate $[Ag^+]$ and obtain

$$\frac{[Br^-][Ag(NH_3)_2^+]}{[NH_3]^2} = \frac{7.7 \times 10^{-13}}{6.0 \times 10^{-8}}$$

$$= 1.28 \times 10^{-5}$$

Let $x = [Ag(NH_3)_2^+] = [Br^-]$ Then

$$\frac{x^2}{(0.50)^2} = 1.28 \times 10^{-5}$$

$$x = 1.8 \times 10^{-3} \text{ mole/liter}$$

This is the solubility.

Calculations using activities

19.16 ACTIVITY COEFFICIENTS

The results thus far obtained in this chapter range from slightly inaccurate to seriously in error. The trouble is that we have used concentrations instead of activities in equilibrium conditions, and, for ions, there is a great difference between the two. The ratio of the activity (a) of an ion to its concentration (c) is the activity coefficient: $\gamma = a/c$. The experimental determination of activity coefficients from measurements on galvanic cells, and the general features of the theory explaining why these coefficients are not equal to 1, were discussed on pages 413 and 392. Here, we will show how activity coefficients can be used to obtain improved results in equilibrium calculations. First, we illustrate the simple case in which the activity coefficients are given in advance; then we shall consider how they are calculated.

EXAMPLE 36 **Find the concentration and activity of H_3O^+ in a $0.2M$ solution of acetic acid (containing also a salt, such as sodium chloride) in which the activity coefficients have the following values: $\gamma_{H_3O^+} = \gamma_{CH_3COO^-} = 0.80$, $\gamma_{CH_3COOH} = 1.00$. The activity of H_2O (approximately its mole fraction) is assumed, as usual, to be 1.**

ANSWER **The equilibrium condition for the reaction**

$$CH_3COOH + H_2O \leftrightarrows H_3O^+ + CH_3COO^-$$

is, in terms of activities,

$$\frac{a_{H_3O^+}a_{CH_3COO^-}}{a_{CH_3COOH}} = K_a$$

$$= 1.75 \times 10^{-5} \text{ (Table 19.1, page 483)}$$

The activity of each species is related to its concentration c by $a = \gamma c$. Then

$$\frac{\gamma_{H_3O^+}\gamma_{CH_3COO^-}}{\gamma_{CH_3COOH}} \times \frac{[H_3O^+][CH_3COO^-]}{[CH_3COOH]} = K_a$$

or

$$\frac{[H_3O^+][CH_3COO^-]}{[CH_3COOH]} = \frac{K_a \gamma_{CH_3COOH}}{\gamma_{H_3O^+} \gamma_{CH_3COO^-}}$$

$$= \frac{1.75 \times 10^{-5} \times 1.00}{0.80 \times 0.80}$$

$$= 2.73 \times 10^{-5}$$

The problem is now the same as it would be if all the activity coefficients were equal to 1, except that the equilibrium constant has a different value. The concentrations are $[H_3O^+] = [CH_3COO^-] = x$, $[CH_3COOH] = 0.20 - x$; then

$$\frac{x^2}{0.20 - x} = 2.73 \times 10^{-5}$$

$$x = 2.32 \times 10^{-3} \text{ mole/liter} = [H_3O^+]$$

$$a_{H_3O^+} = \gamma_{H_3O^+} [H_3O^+]$$

$$= 0.80 \times 2.32 \times 10^{-3}$$

$$= 1.86 \times 10^{-3}$$

The notations "pH" and "pOH" are ambiguous in a context in which activities and concentrations are not assumed to be equal. Previously (page 480), we defined pH $= -\log [H_3O^+]$, pOH $= -\log [OH^-]$. Now, we may use pH and pOH with reference to the activities of the ions: pH $= -\log a_{H_3O^+}$, pOH $= -\log a_{OH^-}$. Thus, the pH of the solution in the previous example is, in the activity sense,

$$pH = -\log (1.86 \times 10^{-3})$$

$$= 2.73$$

Hereafter, we shall use pH and pOH in the activity sense in any case in which activity and concentration are not assumed to be equal.

EXAMPLE 37 Calculate the solubility, in moles/liter, of Ag_2CrO_4, when $\gamma_{Ag^+} = 0.70$ and $\gamma_{CrO_4^{2-}} = 0.50$.

ANSWER Each mole of Ag_2CrO_4 that dissolves gives 2 moles Ag^+ and 1 mole CrO_4^{2-},

$$Ag_2CrO_4(c) \leftrightharpoons 2Ag^+ + CrO_4^{2-}$$

Therefore, the solubility is $s = [CrO_4^{2-}]$, and $[Ag^+] = 2s$. Then

$$(a_{Ag^+})^2 a_{CrO_4^{2-}} = K = 1.15 \times 10^{-12} \text{ (Table 19.3, page 504)}$$

$$(\gamma_{Ag^+})^2 \gamma_{CrO_4^{2-}} [Ag^+]^2 [CrO_4^{2-}] = K$$

$$[Ag^+]^2 [CrO_4^{2-}] = \frac{K \cdot}{(\gamma_{Ag^+})^2 \gamma_{CrO_4^{2-}}}$$

$$= \frac{1.15 \times 10^{-12}}{0.70^2 \times 0.50}$$

$$(2s)^2(s) = 4.69 \times 10^{-12}$$

$$4s^3 = 4.69 \times 10^{-12}$$

$$s = 1.05 \times 10^{-4} \text{ mole/liter}$$

19.17 IONIC STRENGTH

The activity coefficient of a given ion depends, to a useful approximation, not on the identities of the other ions, but only on their concentrations and charges. That is to say, Cl^-, Br^-, NO_3^-, and K^+ all have approximately the same effect on the activity coefficient of Na^+ ions, while SO_4^{2-} ions have a very different effect. The function of concentrations and charges on which activity coefficients depend is known as the **ionic strength,** I, of the solution,

$$I = \tfrac{1}{2}(c_1 z_1^2 + c_2 z_2^2 + c_3 z_3^2 + \cdot \cdot \cdot)$$

where c_1, c_2, . . . are the concentrations (in moles/liter) of the various kinds of ion in the solution, and z_1, z_2, . . . are their charges in electronic units: $z = +2$ for Ca^{2+}, -1 for Cl^-, etc.

EXAMPLE 38   **Calculate the ionic strength of each of the following solutions: (a) 1.0M NaCl; (b) 0.1M $K_3Fe(CN)_6$; (c) 0.5M KCl + 0.5M Na_2SO_4 in one solution.**

ANSWER   (a) **We draw up a table:**

Ion	c	z	cz^2
Na^+	1.0	1	1.0
Cl^-	1.0	-1	1.0
			2.0

and $I = \tfrac{1}{2}(2.0) = 1.0$. **For any uniunivalent electrolyte** ($z_+ = 1, z_- = -1$), I **is equal to the molarity.**

(b) We must recognize that $K_3Fe(CN)_6$ dissolves as $3K^+ + Fe(CN)_6^{3-}$.

Ion	c	z	cz^2
K^+	0.3	$+1$	0.3
$Fe(CN)_6^{3-}$	0.1	-3	0.9
			1.2

$I = 0.6.$

(c) For KCl and Na_2SO_4:

Ion	c	z	cz^2
K^+	0.5	$+1$	0.5
Cl^-	0.5	-1	0.5
Na^+	1.0	$+1$	1.0
SO_4^{2-}	0.5	-2	2.0
			4.0

$I = 2.0.$

19.18 CALCULATION OF ACTIVITY COEFFICIENTS

The ionic strength is a property of the *solution*, and is to be used in calculating the activity coefficient of each ion in the solution. An approximate formula for the activity coefficient γ of an ion with charge z can be derived from the Debye-Hückel theory of ionic interactions,

$$\log \gamma = \frac{-Az^2 \sqrt{I}}{1 + aB \sqrt{I}} \tag{44}$$

A and B are constants depending only on the identity of the solvent and on the temperature; a is characteristic of the individual kind of ion, and is related to its diameter. For a solution in water at 25°C, $A = 0.51$, and $B = 0.33 \times 10^8$ when a is in cm. Most ions have $a \approx 3 \times 10^{-8}$ cm, so that $aB \approx 1$, and Equation (44) becomes approximately

$$\log \gamma = \frac{-0.51z^2 \sqrt{I}}{1 + \sqrt{I}} \tag{45}$$

This is the form we shall use. Table 19.6 shows a few data that give an idea of the amount of error involved in using Equation (45). Combinations of activity coefficients are given because activity coefficients of individual ions cannot actually be measured. Discrepancies as large as 20% can be found in this table, and worse cases are known, but at least the formula gives an approximation to the activity coefficient much better than the approximation $\gamma = 1$.

TABLE 19.6 *Calculated and Measured Activity Coefficients*

| c | KCl $(\gamma_{K^+}\gamma_{Cl^-})^{1/2}$ | | ZnSO$_4$ $(\gamma_{Zn^{2+}}\gamma_{SO_4^{2-}})^{1/2}$ | |
| | Calculated | | Calculated | |
(mole/liter)	(Eq. 45)	Measured	(Eq. 45)	Measured
0.01	0.90	0.90	0.46	0.39
0.02	0.86	0.87	0.36	0.30
0.05	0.81	0.82	0.23	0.20
0.10	0.75	0.77	0.16	0.15
0.20	0.70	0.73	0.109	0.106
0.50	0.62	0.66	0.064	0.067
1.00	0.56	0.62	0.044	0.051

19.19 APPLICATION OF ACTIVITY COEFFICIENTS TO EQUILIBRIUM CALCULATIONS

In order to calculate the activity coefficients of the ions involved in a reaction, we must know the ionic strength, which depends on the concentrations of all the ions in the solution. However, some of the concentrations are not known until the problem is solved. We can escape from this vicious circle by making an estimate of the concentrations in advance, calculating the concentrations by using activity coefficients obtained from this estimate, and then (it seldom is necessary) repeating the calculation with improved activity coefficients based on the calculated concentrations.

As an illustration, we consider the ionization of a weak acid HA, in a solution containing a salt, say $0.50M$ NaCl. Since the acid is weak, we can assume, for the purpose of estimating the ionic strength, that $[H_3O^+]$ and $[A^-]$ are very small. Then the only ions that need be considered are Na^+ and Cl^-; $[Na^+] = [Cl^-] = 0.50$ mole/liter, and

$$I = \tfrac{1}{2}(0.50 \times 1^2 + 0.50 \times 1^2) = 0.50$$

The activity coefficients of the species involved in the reaction

$$HA + H_2O \leftrightharpoons H_3O^+ + A^-$$

are, according to Equation (45),

$$\log \gamma_{HA} = \log \gamma_{H_2O} = 0$$

(since $z = 0$ for a neutral molecule)

$$\gamma_{HA} = \gamma_{H_2O} = 1$$

$$\log \gamma_{H_3O^+} = \log \gamma_{A^-} = \frac{-0.51(1)^2 \sqrt{0.50}}{1 + \sqrt{0.50}} = -0.21$$

$$\gamma_{H_3O^+} = \gamma_{A^-} = 0.62$$

The equilibrium condition, in terms of activities, is

$$\frac{a_{H_3O^+}\, a_{A^-}}{a_{HA}} = K_a$$

or

$$\frac{\gamma_{H_3O^+}\, \gamma_{A^-}[H_3O^+][A^-]}{[HA]} = K_a$$

or

$$\frac{[H_3O^+][A^-]}{[HA]} = \frac{K_a}{\gamma_{H_3O^+}\, \gamma_{A^-}} = \frac{K_a}{(0.62)^2} \tag{46}$$

As we saw in Example 36, the problem can now be solved in the same way as if all activity coefficients were taken equal to 1, except that the equilibrium constant has a different value.

EXAMPLE 39 **Find the degree of ionization of acetic acid in a solution $0.50M$ with respect to acetic acid and $0.30M$ with respect to $CaCl_2$. (Cf. Example 6, page 485.)**

ANSWER **The ionic strength is contributed almost entirely by the CaCl₂,**

$$I = \tfrac{1}{2}(0.30 \times 2^2 + 2 \times 0.30 \times 1^2) = 0.90$$
$$\sqrt{I} = 0.949$$

For H_3O^+ or CH_3COO^-, $z^2 = 1$, and

$$\log \gamma = \frac{-0.51 \sqrt{I}}{1 + \sqrt{I}} = -0.25$$
$$\gamma = 0.56$$

Let $x = [H_3O^+] = [CH_3COO^-]$; then $[CH_3COOH] = 0.50 - x$;

$$\frac{\gamma_{H_3O^+}\gamma_{CH_3COO^-}[H_3O^+][CH_3COO^-]}{[CH_3COOH]} = K_a$$

$$\frac{[H_3O^+][CH_3COO^-]}{[CH_3COOH]} = \frac{K_a}{\gamma_{H_3O^+}\gamma_{CH_3COO^-}}$$

$$= \frac{1.75 \times 10^{-5}}{(0.56)^2} = 5.6 \times 10^{-5}$$

$$\frac{x^2}{0.50 - x} = 5.6 \times 10^{-5}$$

$$x = 5.3 \times 10^{-3} \text{ mole/liter}$$

$$\alpha = \frac{x}{0.50} = 1.1 \times 10^{-2}$$

The result is about twice what we obtained in Example 6, in which we assumed that all activity coefficients are equal to 1. That result was correct for the acetic acid in the absence of a salt, where $I \approx 0$. The increased ionization of an acid or base, or, as we shall see in the next example, the increased solubility of a salt, resulting from the addition of a seemingly innocuous soluble salt, is known as the **salt effect**.

EXAMPLE 40 **Find the solubility (in moles/liter) of CaF_2 in a solution 1.0M with respect to KBr. (Cf. Example 23a, page 505.)**

ANSWER $I = 1.0$, $\sqrt{I} = 1.0$; then

$$\log \gamma_{Ca^{2+}} = \frac{-0.51 \times 2^2 \times 1.0}{1 + 1.0} = -1.02$$

$$\gamma_{Ca^{2+}} = 0.096$$

$$\log \gamma_{F^-} = \frac{-0.51 \times 1^2 \times 1.0}{1 + 1.0} = -0.255$$

$$\gamma_{F^-} = 0.56$$

$$a_{Ca^{2+}}a_{F^-}^2 = K$$

$$\gamma_{Ca^{2+}}\gamma_{F^-}^2[Ca^{2+}][F^-]^2 = K$$

$$[Ca^{2+}][F^-]^2 = \frac{K}{\gamma_{Ca^{2+}}\gamma_{F^-}^2} = \frac{3.95 \times 10^{-11}}{0.096 \times (0.56)^2} = 1.31 \times 10^{-9}$$

The problem is now solved in the familiar way:

$$[Ca^{2+}] = x$$
$$[F^-] = 2x$$
$$4x^3 = 1.31 \times 10^{-9}$$
$$x = 6.9 \times 10^{-4} \text{ mole/liter}$$

The salt effect has increased the solubility by a factor of more than 3.

When the added salt has an ion in common with the slightly soluble salt, the salt effect (which increases solubility) works against the common ion effect (which decreases solubility).

EXAMPLE 41   Find $[Ca^{2+}]$ in a solution saturated with CaF_2 and $0.10M$ with respect to NaF. (Cf. Example 23b.)

ANSWER $I = 0.10$, $\sqrt{I} = 0.316$; then

$$\log \gamma_{Ca^{2+}} = \frac{-0.51 \times 2^2 \times 0.316}{1 + 0.316} = -0.49$$
$$\gamma_{Ca^{2+}} = 0.32$$
$$\log \gamma_{F^-} = \frac{-0.51 \times 1^2 \times 0.316}{1 + 0.316} = -0.122$$
$$\gamma_{F^-} = 0.755$$

Let $[Ca^{2+}] = x$, $[F^-] = 0.10 + 2x \approx 0.10$; then

$$[Ca^{2+}][F^-]^2 = \frac{K}{\gamma_{Ca^{2+}}\gamma_{F^-}^2} = \frac{3.95 \times 10^{-11}}{0.32 \times (0.755)^2} = 2.16 \times 10^{-10}$$
$$x(0.10)^2 = 2.16 \times 10^{-10}$$
$$x = 2.16 \times 10^{-8} \text{ mole/liter}$$

The common ion effect wins, and the solubility (equal to $[Ca^{2+}]$) is much less than in water alone.

EXAMPLE 42   Calculate the product $[H_3O^+][OH^-]$, and the sum pH + pOH (in the activity sense), in a solution at 25°C in which the ionic strength is 0.75.

ANSWER $\sqrt{I} = 0.866$; then

$$\log \gamma_{H_3O^+} = \log \gamma_{OH^-} = \frac{-0.51 \times 1^2 \times 0.866}{1 + 0.866} = -0.237$$
$$\gamma_{H_3O^+} = \gamma_{OH^-} = 0.58$$
$$a_{H_3O^+}a_{OH^-} = K_w$$
$$\gamma_{H_3O^+}\gamma_{OH^-}[H_3O^+][OH^-] = K_w$$
$$[H_3O^+][OH^-] = \frac{K_w}{\gamma_{H_3O^+}\gamma_{OH^-}}$$
$$= \frac{1.01 \times 10^{-14}}{(0.58)^2} = 3.0 \times 10^{-14}$$

(Note that this equation applies only at a certain ionic strength.)

$$pH + pOH = - \log (a_{H_3O^+}a_{OH^-})$$
$$= - \log K_w$$
$$= 14.00$$

EXAMPLE 43   Find the pH (in the activity sense) of a $0.25M$ solution of Na_2CO_3 at 25°C. (Cf. Example 15, page 494.)

ANSWER   The reaction

$$CO_3^{2-} + H_2O \rightleftharpoons HCO_3^- + OH^-$$

consumes a relatively small fraction of the CO_3^{2-} initially present. Therefore, our estimate of the ionic strength is based on the assumption that $[Na^+] = 0.50$ and $[CO_3^{2-}] = 0.25$ mole/liter.

$$I = \tfrac{1}{2}(0.50 \times 1^2 + 0.25 \times 2^2) = 0.75$$
$$\sqrt{I} = 0.866$$
$$\log \gamma_{CO_3^{2-}} = \frac{-0.51 \times 2^2 \times 0.866}{1 + 0.866} = -0.95$$
$$\gamma_{CO_3^{2-}} = 0.112$$

As in the preceding example,

$$\gamma_{HCO_3^-} = \gamma_{OH^-} = 0.58$$

The equilibrium condition is

$$\frac{\gamma_{HCO_3^-}\gamma_{OH^-}}{\gamma_{CO_3^{2-}}} \times \frac{[HCO_3^-][OH^-]}{[CO_3^{2-}]} = K_{b1} = 1.80 \times 10^{-4}$$
$$\frac{[HCO_3^-][OH^-]}{[CO_3^{2-}]} = \frac{K_{b1}\gamma_{CO_3^{2-}}}{\gamma_{HCO_3^-}\gamma_{OH^-}}$$
$$= \frac{1.80 \times 10^{-4} \times 0.112}{(0.58)^2}$$
$$= 6.0 \times 10^{-5}$$
$$\frac{x^2}{0.25 - x} = 6.0 \times 10^{-5}$$
$$x = 3.8 \times 10^{-3} \text{ mole/liter} = [OH^-]$$
$$a_{OH^-} = \gamma_{OH^-}[OH^-]$$
$$= 0.58 \times 3.8 \times 10^{-3}$$
$$= 2.20 \times 10^{-3}$$
$$pOH = - \log a_{OH^-}$$
$$= 2.66$$

From the preceding example, $pH + pOH = 14.00$; then

$$pH = 14.00 - 2.66$$
$$= 11.34$$

Your instructor will tell you whether to calculate activity coefficients in doing Problems 1–39. The answers given for these problems are based on the assumption that all activity coefficients are 1.

When the temperature is not given, take it to be the temperature for which the necessary data are tabulated.

1. Weak acids. Find (a) the degree of ionization, and (b) the pH, of a $0.60M$ solution of HONO.

Answer. (a) 0.027; (b) 1.8.

2. Weak acids. An aqueous solution of a certain monoprotic acid is $0.10M$ and has pH 3.00. Find K_a and pK_a for this acid.

3. Weak bases. Calculate the pH and pOH of a $0.50M$ solution of $(CH_3)_2NH$ in H_2O.

4. Charged bases. Find the pOH and pH of a $0.10M$ solution of KCN at 25°C.

Answer. 2.93, 11.07.

5. Charged acids. Find the pH of a $0.40M$ solution of anilinium chloride, $(C_6H_5NH_3)^+Cl^-$.

6. Polyprotic bases. Find the basic ionization constant of the phthalate ion, $C_6H_4(COO^-)_2$.

Answer. 3.3×10^{-9}.

7. Mixture of acids. A solution is $0.50M$ with respect to HCl and $1.00M$ with respect to HF. Calculate the concentration of F^- in this solution.

8. Buffer solutions. (a) Find the pH of a solution $1.00M$ with respect to NH_3 and $0.80M$ with respect to NH_4Cl. (b) Find the pH of this solution after 0.10 mole HCl per liter has been added to it. (c) A solution of pH 9.34 is prepared by adding NaOH to pure water. Find the pH of this solution after 0.10 mole HCl per liter has been added to it.

Answer. (a) 9.34; (b) 9.24; (c) 1.0.

9. Indicators. Select an indicator suitable for determining the pH of solutions with pH around 7.

10. Solubility product. The solubility of Li_2CO_3 in water is 1.33 g/100 ml solution at 20°C. Calculate its solubility product.

11. Solubility from solubility product. Calculate the concentration of CrO_4^{2-} in a solution saturated with Ag_2CrO_4 and containing (a) no other solute, (b) 0.50 mole $AgNO_3$ per liter.

Answer. (a) 6.6×10^{-5}; (b) 4.6×10^{-12} mole/liter.

12. Precipitation. A $0.0020M$ solution of $AgNO_3$ and a $0.0010M$ solution of NaCl are mixed in equal volumes at 25°C. Is it possible for AgCl to precipitate?

13. Solubility and pH. Find the solubility, in mole/liter, of CdS in a solution in which $[H_2S] = 0.10$ mole/liter and the pH is (a) 2.0, (b) 9.0. Assume that the solubility product of CdS is the same at 18° and at 25°C.

Answer. (a) 5.7×10^{-11} mole/liter.

14. Complex ions. Find the concentration of Ni^{2+} in a solution in which the other equilibrium concentrations are $[NH_3] = 0.10$ mole/liter and $[Ni(NH_3)_4^{2+}] = 0.50$ mole/liter.

Answer. 5.6×10^{-5} mole/liter.

15. Complex ions. A solution was prepared by dissolving 0.010 mole $Cd(NO_3)_2$ and 0.060 mole KCN in water to make 100 ml of solution. Find the concentration of Cd^{2+} in this solution.

16. Ionization of water. What is the pH of pure water at 0°C?

Answer. 7.472.

17. Ionization of water. Fill in the blanks in the following table. Each line (a, b, ... , e) refers to a different solution.

	Temperature (°C)	$[H_3O^+]$	$[OH^-]$	pH	pOH
(a)	25	1.00×10^{-9}	—	—	—
(b)	25	—	—	5.17	—
(c)	0	—	—	7.00	—
(d)	25	—	$2.50 \times 10^-$	—	—
(e)	25	—	—	—	4.82

Answer. (a) 1.01×10^{-5}, 9.00, 5.00; (b) 6.8×10^{-6}, 1.48×10^{-9}, 8.83.

18. Weak acids. Calculate the pH and pOH of a $0.080M$ solution of benzoic acid.

Answer. 2.65, 11.34.

19. Weak acids. Find the pH of a $0.50M$ solution of phenol.

20. Weak acids. Calculate (a) the degree of ionization, and (b) the pH, of chloroacetic acid in a $0.010M$ solution. (Caution: some of the usual approximations may not be valid here.)

Answer. (a) 0.31; (b) 2.51.

21. Charged bases. Calculate the pH of a $1.00M$ solution of HCOONa.

22. Polyprotic acids. Calculate (a) the pH, and (b) the concentration of SO_3^{2-}, in a $0.20M$ solution of $(HO)_2SO$. (Be careful what approximations you make.)

Answer. (a) 1.30; (b) 6.24×10^{-8}.

23. Polyprotic acids. Calculate (a) $[H_3O^+]$, (b) $[(HO)_2PO_2^-]$, (c) $[(HO)PO_3^{2-}]$, and (d) $[PO_4^{3-}]$ in a $0.20M$ solution of phosphoric acid, $(HO)_3PO$ (or H_3PO_4).

24. Mixture of acids. Find the concentration of (a) hydrogen oxalate ion, and (b) oxalate ion, in a solution $0.10M$ with respect to HBr and $0.050M$ with respect to $(COOH)_2$.

Answer. (a) 1.8×10^{-2}; (b) 7.5×10^{-6} mole/liter.

25. Mixture of acids. Find the degree of ionization of $0.30M$ propionic acid in a solution of pH 2.50.

26. Buffer solutions. Find the pH of a solution $0.50M$ with respect to formic acid and $0.20M$ with respect to sodium formate.

27. Buffer solutions. A buffer solution of pH 5.00 is to be prepared from propionic acid and sodium propionate. The concentration of sodium propionate must be 1.00 mole/liter. What should be the concentration of the acid?

Answer. 0.75 mole/liter.

28. Buffer solutions. Assume that all the monoprotic acids listed in Table 19.1, and their sodium salts, are available. (a) Which acid-salt pair should be chosen for a buffer solution of pH 3.80? (b) What should be the molar ratio of acid to salt in this buffer solution?

29. Indicators. A certain indicator has $pK_a = 6.0$. Its acid form is yellow and its base form is blue. What will be the color of the indicator in a solution of pH (a) 4, (b) 6, (c) 6.5, (d) 9?

30. Solubility from solubility product. Find the solubility of $PbSO_4$ in H_2O, in moles/liter and g/100 ml.

31. Solubility product. The solubility of CdC_2O_4 in water is 3.37×10^{-3} g/100 ml at 0°C. Calculate (a) its solubility product; (b) its solubility, in g/100 ml, in $0.050M$ $Cd(NO_3)_2$ solution.

Answer. (a) 2.83×10^{-8}; (b) 1.13×10^{-5} g/100 ml.

32. Solubility from solubility product. Calculate the concentration of Ag^+ in a solution saturated with AgI and $0.15M$ with respect to CaI_2.

33. Precipitation. 50 ml of a $0.0100M$ solution of $BaCl_2$ and 20 ml of a $0.0100M$ solution of NaF were mixed at 25.8°C. (a) Find $[Ba^{2+}]$ and $[F^-]$ in the mixed solution before any reaction occurs. (b) Is it possible for BaF_2 to precipitate?

Answer. (a) 7.14×10^{-3}, 2.86×10^{-3} mole/liter.

34. Solubility and pH. Find the minimum pH at which FeS will precipitate from a solution $0.10M$ with respect to H_2S and $0.020M$ with respect to Fe^{2+}.

Answer. 3.5.

35. Solubility and pH. (a) Find the minimum pH at which PbS will precipitate from a solution $0.10M$ with respect to H_2S and $0.020M$ with respect to Pb^{2+}. (b) In what range should the pH be in order to separate Pb^{2+} and Fe^{2+} by precipitation of one sulfide and not the other? (See the preceding problem.)

36. Complex ions. Calculate the instability constant of (a) $HgBr_4{}^{2-}$, (b) $AuCl_4{}^-$.

Answer. (a) 2×10^{-22}.

37. Complex ions. (a) Calculate the instability constant of $HgCl_4{}^{2-}$. (b) Find the concentration of Hg^{2+} remaining in a $0.10M$ solution of $Hg(NO_3)_2$ after 1.0 mole $NaCl$ per liter has been dissolved in the solution.

Answer. (a) 1×10^{-16}; (b) 8×10^{-17} mole/liter.

38. Complex ions and solubility. What must be the concentration of NH_3 to prevent precipitation of $AgBr$ from a solution $0.020M$ with respect to Br^- and $0.040M$ with respect to $Ag(NH_3)_2{}^+$?

39. Complex ions and solubility. (a) Calculate the instability constant of $Ag(S_2O_3)_2{}^{3-}$. (b) How many moles of sodium thiosulfate, $Na_2S_2O_3$, must be added per liter of solution to dissolve 10g $AgBr$ per liter?

Answer. (a) 5.5×10^{-14}; (b) 0.12 mole/liter.

40. Weak acids. Calculate the concentration of $[H_3O^+]$ in a $0.30M$ solution of propionic acid in which the activity coefficients are 0.75 for each of the ions, and 1.00 for the un-ionized acid.

Answer. 2.66×10^{-3} mole/liter.

41. Weak bases. A certain solution is $0.10M$ with respect to methylamine. Calculate the pOH (in the activity sense) of the solution, assuming the following activity coefficients: $\gamma_{CH_3NH_3{}^+} = \gamma_{OH^-} = 0.65$, $\gamma_{CH_3NH_2} = 1.00$.

42. Solubility. Find the solubility (in moles/liter) of $BaSO_4$ in a solution in which $\gamma_{Ba^{2+}} = \gamma_{SO_4{}^{2-}} = 0.40$.

Answer. 2.6×10^{-5} mole/liter.

43. Ionic strength. Calculate the ionic strength of (a) $0.5M$ KNO_3; (b) $1.0M$ Na_2SO_4; (c) a solution $0.1M$ with respect to $CaBr_2$ and $0.3M$ with respect to HCl.

Answer. (a) 0.5; (b) 3.0.

44. Activity coefficients. Calculate the approximate activity coefficient of each ion in a $0.50M$ solution of $MgCl_2$.

Answer. 0.075, 0.52.

In the following problems, activity coefficients are to be calculated and used.

45. Weak acids. Find the degree of ionization of formic acid in a solution $0.10M$ with respect to HCOOH and $1.00M$ with respect to NaCl.

Answer. 0.073.

46. Buffer solutions. Calculate the pH (in the activity sense) of a buffer solution $0.50M$ with respect to acetic acid and $0.60M$ with respect to sodium acetate.

47. Ionization of water. Calculate the concentration of H_3O^+ in a $0.50M$ solution of KCl at 25°C. Assume that the solution is not acidic or basic.

Answer. 1.63×10^{-7} mole/liter.

48. Solubility. Find the solubility (in moles/liter) of AgI in a $1.00M$ solution of (a) KNO_3; (b) KI.

Answer. (a) 2.2×10^{-8} (b) 4.9×10^{-16} mole/liter.

49. Solubility. Find the solubility (in moles/liter) of PbI_2 in (a) pure water; (b) $0.40M$ $Mg(NO_3)_2$.

20

*Chemistry
of the
common cations
and anions:
Background for
qualitative
inorganic
analysis*

THE SEPARATION AND identification of the components of a mixture comprise a qualitative analysis. The classical "wet" analyses as performed in most general chemistry laboratories have been largely, but not completely, superseded by instrumental methods. Nevertheless, these classical methods serve as traditional illustrations of the application of the principles of ionic equilibrium, and as a framework for presenting the aqueous solution chemistry of cations and anions.

20.1 SOLUBILITY OF SALTS

The separation of ions takes advantage of differences in solubility of salts A review of Section 15.5 (pages 363–364) reveals that two predominant factors control solubility:

(a) The *crystal lattice energy* is needed to convert the ions from the solid state to the gaseous state:

$$M^+X^-(c) \rightarrow M^+(g) + X^-(g) \qquad \Delta H = \text{crystal lattice energy}$$

This process is *endothermic* ($\Delta H > 0$) because energy is required to overcome the strong electrostatic attraction of the ions in the crystal lattice.

(b) The *hydration energy* is released when the separated ions are hydrated:

$$M^+(g) + X^-(g) + H_2O \rightarrow M^+(aq) + X^-(aq)$$
$$\Delta H = \text{hydration energy}$$

This process is *exothermic* ($\Delta H < 0$) because of the electrostatic attraction between the individual ion and the dipolar water molecules. The sum of the heats of the two equations gives the over-all heat of solution:

$$M^+X^-(c) + H_2O \rightarrow M^+(aq) + X^-(aq) \qquad \Delta H = \text{heat of solution}$$

$$\Delta H_{\text{solution}} = \Delta H_{\text{crystal lattice}} + \Delta H_{\text{hydration}} \tag{1}$$

The electrostatic attraction of the ions is *proportional* to the charge on the cation, q_+, and the charge on the anion, q_-, and *inversely proportional* to the square of the distance separating the centers of the ions. Since the ions in the crystal are "touching," the separation distance equals the radius of the cation, r_+, plus the radius of the anion, r_-,

$$\text{crystal lattice energy*} \propto \frac{q_+ \cdot q_-}{(r_+ + r_-)}$$

The hydration energy is also proportional to the charge of the ion and inversely proportional to the size of the ion. The stronger the attraction between the oppositely charged ions in the crystal, the greater is the crystal lattice energy and the less soluble the salt. Alternatively, enhanced attraction between ions and the dipolar water molecule increases the hydration energy and the solubility of the salt. Since both factors are electrostatic in origin, they are affected in the same direction by structural changes in the ions. Thus, replacing the larger Cs^+ ion by the smaller Li^+ ion in a salt increases the attraction both for the anion in the crystal and for the water molecules in the solution. Solubility of a salt, therefore, depends on the balance between these two energies. The ability to predict relative solubilities requires a knowledge of which energy is more influential. It is reasonable to assume that, since attraction between oppositely charged ions is stronger than between ions and dipolar molecules, the electrostatic effects are more pronounced in the crystal than in the solution. When most salts dissolve in water, heat is absorbed. Since in most cases the enthalpy of solution is positive, the crystal lattice energy has a more positive value than the hydration energy has a negative value (Equation 1). Hence, factors increasing the attraction between ions usually decrease solubility and, conversely, factors decreasing attraction between ions increase solubility. Since several structural features influence these energies, it is impossible to make accurate predictions. Nevertheless, certain relationships of ionic structure and solubility permit useful generalizations about solubilities.

(a) **Electrostatic Effects.** These effects on solubility include the following:

(1) Since the electrostatic attraction between ions is directly propor-

---

* Energy = force × distance.

LiF (0.43) → NaF (0.70) → KF → RbF → CsF
 ↓   ↓   ↑   ↑   ↑
LiCl   NaCl   KCl (0.72) RbCl   CsCl
 ↓   ↓   ↑   ↑   ↑
LiBr   NaBr   KBr   RbBr (0.75) CsBr
 ↓   ↓   ↓   ↓   ↑
LiI (0.27) ← NaI ← KI ← RbI ← CsI (0.77)

Fig. 20.1. *Relationship of radius ratio, r_+/r_-, and solubility of alkali metal halide salts. The pertinent radius ratios are given in parentheses. Arrows point in the direction of increasing solubility. One inconsistency is that LiF is less soluble than NaF.*

tional to the charge on the ions, an M^+A^- salt, such as NaCl, is more soluble than an $M^{2+}A^{2-}$ salt, such as $BaSO_4$, which in turn is more soluble than an $M^{3+}A^{3-}$ salt, such as $AlPO_4$.

(2) The crystal lattice energy is influenced by repulsive forces between similarly charged ions as well as by attractive forces between ions of opposite charge. The more the attraction outweighs the repulsion, the less soluble is the salt. Repulsive forces are electrostatic and consequently depend on the distance between the similarly charged ions. This distance is related to the ionic radius. Since both attraction and repulsion are influenced by the sizes of the cation and anion, it is not surprising that the crystal lattice energy and the solubility depend on the radius ratio, r_+/r_-. For a group of related salts, it has been determined that the net attraction is at a maximum when the radius ratio equals approximately 0.75. Therefore the salt in the group, with a radius ratio closest to this value, is the most insoluble. As the value increases or decreases from 0.75, solubility increases. Figure 20.1 shows the relationship of radius ratio to solubility for the alkali metal (Group I) halides.

(3) *Salts of anions showing considerable charge dispersal because of extended π bonding are usually soluble.* This is especially true of univalent anions; perchlorates, chlorates, nitrates, nitrites, and acetates are all more soluble than halides or hydroxides. Even salts of divalent anions with extensive delocalization, such as sulfates, tend to be soluble, notwithstanding the opposing effect of the double charge. When comparing similarly constituted anions with the same central atom in different oxidation states, the anion with the atom in the higher oxidation state, since it has more charge delocalization, has many more highly soluble salts. Sulfates, nitrates, and perchlorates, for example, are usually more soluble than sulfites, nitrites, and chlorates or chlorites, respectively.

(b) Bond Polarization; Fajans' Rules. Molecules are known to polarize their nearby neighbors, thereby generating London forces (page 298). Similar forces also exist, much more strongly, between ions. The nucleus of the cation attracts the electrons of the anion, so that the electron density about the anion is greater in the direction of the cation. The anion has a similar, but weaker, effect on the cation. As a result, the electron density about the cation is somewhat greater in the direction of the anion. A schematic representation of mutual polarization is shown in Fig. 20.2. Kasimir Fajans suggested that covalent bonding is an instance

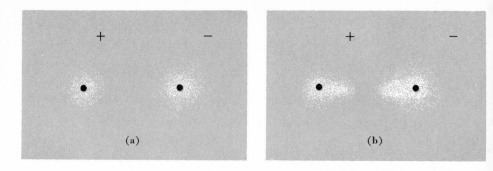

Fig. 20.2. *A representation of polarization between oppositely charged ions;*
(a) nonpolarized ions, (b) mutually polarized ions.

of ionic bonding in which extreme polarization has materially augmented
the electron density between the ions. This view has been supplanted by
the more sophisticated quantum mechanical treatment of covalent bonding. Yet it has merit as a conceptual approach to ionic bonds with some
covalent character.

Polarization increases attraction between the oppositely charged ions in the
crystal and so decreases solubility. An ion can also polarize a water molecule
but, again, we assume this to be a less pronounced effect than polarization
of ions in the crystal. The effect of charge, size, and electronic structure
of ions on polarization has been summarized in Fajans' Rules:

(1) *The smaller and the more highly charged the cation, the more it tends to*
polarize a neighboring anion. For example, Li^+ has a greater polarizing
power than Na^+, so that LiOH is more insoluble than NaOH. Mg^{2+},
which is about the same size as Li^+ but has a double charge, has the
greater polarizing power, so that $Mg(OH)_2$ is more insoluble than
LiOH.

(2) *The larger and the more highly charged the anion, the more readily it is*
polarized. S^{2-} is larger and is more readily polarized than O^{2-}, so that
sulfides are more insoluble than oxides.

(3) *Because of its excess number of electrons, an anion is more readily*
polarized than is a cation. Polarization of a *cation* is significant only
for the larger ones such as Cs^+, and especially for cations like Ag^+,
Hg_2^{2+}, and Pb^{2+}, which are fairly large and lack a noble gas configuration. *The absence of a noble gas configuration enhances the polarizability*
of a cation. Polarizability accounts for the greater insolubility of silver
salts, for example the halides, as compared to sodium salts, although
Ag^+ and Na^+ have the same charge and approximate size.

The effect of bond polarization on solubility should in general be considered only when the anion is a conjugate base of a binary hydride
(I^-, Br^-, S^{2-}, O^{2-}, OH^-, SH^-, and NH_2^-), and not when it is an oxyanion
such as SO_4^{2-}, NO_3^{2-}, CO_3^{2-}, and PO_4^{3-}. The electron density of an
oxyanion is dispersed over all the oxygen atoms as a result of an extended
π bond. The cation is close enough to polarize only one of the several oxy-

gen atoms of the oxyanion. Therefore the distortion of electron density (polarization) about the oxyanion is negligible.

(c) **Effect of Interaction with Water.** Whenever an ion interacts with water, solubility is enhanced. For example, hydrogen bonding accounts for the extreme solubility of ammonium salts (page 298). The dissociation of hydrogen-containing anions, such as bisulfate, $HOSO_3^-$,

$$HOSO_3^- + H_2O \rightleftharpoons H_3O^+ + SO_4^{2-}$$

and $(HO)_2PO_2^-$, tends to increase the solubility of their salts.

20.2 SUMMARY OF SOLUBILITIES OF INORGANIC SALTS

The following is a summary of the solubilities of salts of the more common anions and cations.

(1) Practically all Na^+, K^+, and NH_4^+ salts are soluble.

(2) Nitrates, nitrites, acetates, perchlorates, and chlorates are soluble.

(3) All Cl^-, Br^-, and I^- salts are soluble except those of Ag^+, Pb^{2+}, and Hg_2^{2+} (mercurous), and HgI_2.

(4) Sulfates are soluble except those of Ba^{2+}, Sr^{2+}, and Pb^{2+}. Sulfates of Ca^{2+}, Ag^+, and Hg_2^{2+} are sparingly soluble.

(5) Hydroxides are insoluble with the exception of K^+ and Na^+. Those of Ba^{2+}, Sr^{2+}, and Ca^{2+} are sparingly soluble.

(6) Carbonates (CO_3^{2-}), phosphates (PO_4^{3-}), sulfites (SO_3^{2-}), chromates (CrO_4^{2-}), silicates (SiO_4^{4-}), and many fluorides (F^-) are insoluble except for the NH_4^+, Na^+, and K^+ salts.

(7) Most hydrogen anion salts are soluble, for example bicarbonate (HCO_3^-), bisulfate (HSO_4^-), dihydrogen phosphate ($H_2PO_4^-$), monohydrogen phosphate (HPO_4^{2-}).

(8) Sulfides are insoluble, except for the sulfides of Na^+, K^+, NH_4^+, Ca^{2+}, and Ba^{2+}. The soluble sulfides react extensively with water.

(9) Most oxides are insoluble.

20.3 COLOR

Color is important for the identification of substances and as a signpost indicating the course taken by many reactions. A knowledge of the origin of color and of the color of various substances is essential, therefore, to proper understanding and performance of a qualitative analysis.

Absorption of visible or ultraviolet radiation causes the excitation of an electron from a stable to a less stable orbital. The ground state molecule (or ion) is converted to an excited state molecule (or ion) (page 277). The difference in energy, ΔE, between the excited state, E_2, and the ground state, E_1, equals the energy of the absorbed radiation,

$$E_2 \quad - \quad E_1 \quad = \quad \Delta E$$

excited	*ground*	*energy of*
state	*state*	*absorbed*
		radiation

TABLE 20.1 *Relationship of Absorbed and Observed Color*

Absorbed wavelength (A)	Absorbed color	Observed complementary color
4000–4500	Violet	Yellow
4500–5000	Blue	Orange
5000–5500	Green	Red
5500–6000	Yellow	Violet
6000–6500	Orange	Blue
6500–7000	Red	Green

The energy of the absorbed radiation is inversely proportional to the wavelength, λ; $\Delta E = h \cdot c / \lambda$ (page 158). The longer the wavelength of the absorbed light, the lower is the energy of the electronic excitation. Colorless substances usually absorb in the ultraviolet region. Colored substances absorb in the visible region (4000–7500 A, page 156). Hence, it takes less energy to excite a colored substance than a colorless substance. Color appears when the energy level of the excited state is close to the ground state energy level.

If all visible light is absorbed, the substance appears black. If all but one color is absorbed, the substance will have that color. More frequently, however, only one color is absorbed, in which case the substance has the complementary* color, as shown in Table 20.1. The energy of excitation, ΔE, is smaller as the colors vary from yellow to orange to red to violet to blue to green.

Some substances are more intensely colored than others. For example, a solution containing manganous ion, Mn^{2+}, has a pink color of weak intensity, while a solution of permanganate ion, MnO_4^-, has an intense violet color. Intensity is proportional to the number of molecules or ions being excited per unit time, and is independent of the wavelength of the absorbed energy. Discussion of the factors determining intensity is beyond the scope of this book.

Some of the kinds of inorganic molecule or ion that are predictably colored are given below.

(a) *Ions of transition elements with partly filled d orbitals*: Cations and anions of the representative elements, e.g., Na^+, Ca^{2+}, Pb^{2+}, Al^{3+}, Cl^-, O^{2-}; their complexes, e.g., $Al(OH)_6^{3-}$, BF_4^-; and their oxyanions, e.g., SO_4^{2-}, PO_4^{3-}, ClO_4^-, SiO_4^{4-}, BO_3^{3-}, are generally colorless. The transition metal ions are frequently colored, as are many of their oxyanions, such as chromate, CrO_4^{2-}(yellow), dichromate, $Cr_2O_7^{2-}$(orange), and permanganate, MnO_4^-(purple). The colors of the hydrated cations of the first transition series are given in Table 20.2.

* Complementary colors are two colors that, when combined, produce white or nearly white light.

When no d electrons are present, as in Sc^{3+}, or when all d orbitals are filled, e.g., Cu^+ and Zn^{2+}, the ion is colorless. Only those transition metal ions that have partially filled d orbitals exhibit color.

(b) *Compounds with the same constituent metallic element in two different oxidation states:* A dramatic color change is noticed when Prussian (Turnbull's) blue is formed ($\downarrow$ denotes precipitation):

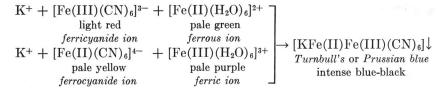

$$K^+ + [Fe(III)(CN)_6]^{3-} + [Fe(II)(H_2O)_6]^{2+}$$

light red — pale green
ferricyanide ion — *ferrous ion*

$$K^+ + [Fe(II)(CN)_6]^{4-} + [Fe(III)(H_2O)_6]^{3+}$$

pale yellow — pale purple
ferrocyanide ion — *ferric ion*

$\rightarrow [KFe(II)Fe(III)(CN)_6]\downarrow$
Turnbull's or *Prussian* blue
intense blue-black

This intensification, or in other cases the appearance, of color is characteristic of compounds having the same constituent element in two different oxidation states. In such cases the atoms of the same element in different oxidation states are interchanging electrons continuously; these electrons are excited by radiation in the visible region.

(c) *Solids with mutually polarized cations and anions:* There are many colored solids, such as yellow AgI and CdS, red HgI_2 and Cu_2O, black BiI_3 and PbS, whose individual ions are normally colorless. The color of these compounds is attributed to mutual polarization of the cation and the monoatomic anion (page 530). Polarized electrons can apparently be excited by visible light. *The more polarized are the electrons, the smaller the energy and the longer the wavelength of the light needed for excitation.* In the examples cited above, the cations Ag^+, Bi^{3+}, Pb^{2+}, and Hg^{2+} are large and lack the noble gas configuration. The anions, if univalent, are very large, such as I^-, or else are divalent, such as O^{2-} and S^{2-}. The colors of the sulfides, listed in Table 20.3, are important for detecting and confirming the presence of cations.

TABLE 20.2 *Colors of the Hydrated Ions of the First Transition Series*[a]

Transmitted color	Ions and number of 3d electrons
Colorless	Sc^{3+} (0), Cu^+ (10), $\underline{Zn^{2+}}$ (10)
Red	Co^{2+} (7), $\underline{Mn^{2+}}$ *(5)
Green	$\underline{Fe^{2+}}$ (6), Ni^{2+} (8), V^{3+} (2)
Purple	Ti^{3+} (1)
Violet	V^{2+} (3), $\underline{Cr^{3+}}$ (3), Mn^{3+} (4), $\underline{Fe^{3+}}$ *(5)
Blue	$\underline{Cr^{2+}}$ (4), $\underline{Co^{3+}}$ (6), $\underline{Cu^{2+}}$ (9)
Yellow	$FeCl^{2+}$

[a] Symbols: * low intensity; <u>underline</u> signifies ion is encountered in analytical schemes.

TABLE 20.3 *Colors of More Common Sulfides*

Color	Sulfide
White	ZnS
Yellow	As_4S_6, CdS, As_2S_5, SnS_2
Orange	Sb_2S_3
Brown	Bi_2S_3
Black	CuS, HgS, PbS, CoS, NiS, FeS, Ag_2S
Pink	MnS

20.4 WASHING PRECIPITATES; PEPTIZATION

Recovered precipitates are coated with solution from which they are isolated. These impurities are removed by stirring the precipitates with water. Some precipitates, especially sulfides, tend to become colloidal on being stirred in water. The conversion of an insoluble solid to a colloidal state is known as **peptization.** The colloidal particles are stabilized by the adsorption of identically charged ions on their surfaces. For example, a colloidal particle of arsenious sulfide, As_4S_6, adsorbs SH^- ions on its surface, and the surface in turn becomes surrounded by a layer of attracted H_3O^+ ions, thus forming a double layer. All colloidal As_4S_6 particles have similarly charged double layers; they therefore repel each other, and coagulation is impeded. If an electrolyte is added during washing, ions of opposite charge are attracted into the double layer of ions, repulsion between particles is overcome, and coagulation is promoted. Thus to prevent peptization, an electrolyte such as NH_4Cl, which does not interfere with the analysis, is frequently added to the wash water.

20.5 QUALITATIVE CATION ANALYSIS

Most systematic procedures of qualitative analysis are based upon a selection from the following twenty-five "cations": Ag^+, Pb^{2+}, Hg(I), Hg(II), Bi(III), Cu^{2+}, Cd^{2+}, As(III), Sb(III), Sn(IV), Fe(II), Fe(III), Al^{3+}, Cr^{3+}, Co^{2+}, Ni^{2+}, Zn^{2+}, Mn^{2+}, Ba^{2+}, Sr^{2+}, Ca^{2+}, Mg^{2+}, K^+, Na^+, and NH_4^+. The detection of each cation in the presence of the others would require twenty-five different reagents, each one being specific for a given ion. It is impractical to seek such a large number of specific reagents. For this reason, in systematic methods of analysis, the unknown mixture is separated into less populated groups of ions, by taking advantage of solubility differences. A small group of cations is converted into insoluble compounds that are separated from the remaining ions by filtration or, more quickly and efficiently, by centrifugation. These groups may be further divided into subgroups, and eventually each individual element is separated. The presence of the element is confirmed by a specific test causing a change in color of the solution, or the appearance of a new phase such as formation of a gas, another liquid, or a solid often having a characteristic color. This subdivision into groups and subgroups prior to identification permits a given reagent to be used to detect more than one element.

(a) **Group Separations in a Systematic Analysis.** (1) *Group I* consists of the three cations, **Ag$^+$**, **Pb^{2+}**, and **Hg$_2^{2+}$** [mercury(I), or mercurous], whose chlorides are insoluble in dilute hydrochloric acid solution.

(2) *Group II* consists of those remaining cations that form sulfides insoluble in 0.3M hydrochloric acid. The interdependence of [H$^+$], [S^{2-}], and [H$_2$S] is expressed (page 496) as

$$\frac{[H^+]^2[S^{2-}]}{[H_2S]} = 6.3 \times 10^{-22}$$

We calculate that when [H$^+$] is 0.3M, the [S^{2-}] in a saturated solution (0.1M) of H$_2$S is almost $10^{-20}M$. A sulfide, MS, will precipitate if $Q > K_{sp}$. Under the above conditions, $Q = [10^{-20}][M^{2+}]$ where [M^{2+}] is usually about $10^{-3}M$, which generally is the concentration of the cation in the solution taken for analysis. It is observed that of the remaining cations, $Q > K_{sp}$ for **Hg^{2+}**, **Pb^{2+}**, **Bi(III)**, **Cu^{2+}**, **Cd^{2+}**, **As(III)**, **Sb(III)**, and **Sn(IV)**. Pb^{2+} ion is included in Group II, since the [Pb^{2+}] remaining *after* precipitation of PbCl$_2$ is sufficient so that $Q > K_{sp}$ for PbS. None of the sulfides of the Group III cations precipitates when [H$^+$] = 0.3M.

The sulfides of As(III), Sb(III), and Sn(IV) are amphoteric; they dissolve in a solution of KOH and thus constitute the subgroup IIB.

(3) *Group III* is composed of the remaining ions forming hydroxides insoluble in a weakly basic solution of ammonia buffered with ammonium ion. These are the trivalent ions **Fe^{3+}**, **Al^{3+}**, and **Cr^{3+}**. Since a source of sulfide ion is generally added to the buffered solution of NH$_3$ and NH$_4^+$, the cations that precipitate as sulfides in basic solution are also included in this group (or in a subgroup). These are the divalent cations **Zn^{2+}**, **Co^{2+}**, **Ni^{2+}**, **Mn^{2+}**, and **Fe^{2+}**.

(4) *Group IV* contains those of the remaining cations that precipitate as insoluble carbonates from a weakly basic solution of ammonia buffered with ammonium ion.

The cations in this group, **Ba^{2+}**, **Sr^{2+}**, and **Ca^{2+}**, are members of the alkaline earth family. The carbonates of these cations can be precipitated from a carbonate solution buffered with NH$_3$ and NH$_4^+$ ion. Mg^{2+}, another member of the alkaline earth family, also forms an insoluble carbonate, but not in the presence of ammonium salts. MgCO$_3$ is 100 times more soluble than the carbonates of Ba^{2+}, Sr^{2+}, and Ca^{2+}, and hence requires a larger concentration of carbonate ion before its solubility product is exceeded. The ammonium ion, however, reduces the concentration of carbonate ion

$$\text{NH}_4^+ + \text{CO}_3^{2-} \rightarrow \text{NH}_3 + \text{HOCO}_2^-$$
$$\quad acid_1 \qquad base_2 \qquad base_1 \qquad acid_2$$

to a level at which MgCO$_3$ cannot precipitate in the presence of reasonable amounts of Mg^{2+}.

(5) *Group V* contains the three remaining cations, Na^+, K^+, and Mg^{2+}, which do not precipitate in the first four groups.

Several of the group separations require the addition of soluble salts. If a sodium or potassium salt is used, the original unknown mixture that may have been free of these cations would become contaminated. Therefore NH_4^+ salts and NH_3 are used exclusively and, consequently, NH_4^+ must be tested for in the original mixture.

(b) Use of Thioacetamide. Thioacetamide, CH_3CSNH_2, is generally used to supply S^{2-} ion, to avoid the direct use of the very toxic, odoriferous H_2S gas. At pH less than 3, thioacetamide hydrolyzes to furnish H_2S,

$$(\text{pH} < 3) \qquad \underset{\textit{thioacetamide}}{CH_3-\overset{\overset{\displaystyle S}{\|}}{C}-NH_2} + H_2O \rightarrow \underset{\textit{acetamide}}{CH_3-\overset{\overset{\displaystyle O}{\|}}{C}-NH_2} + H_2S$$

Further hydrolysis of acetamide to acetate, $CH_3-\overset{\overset{\displaystyle O}{\|}}{C}-O^-$, and NH_4^+ ions under the conditions generally used is inappreciable. At a pH greater than 5, thioacetamide reacts directly with the cation to give a complex which subsequently hydrolyzes to acetamide and the insoluble sulfide,

$$H_2O + CH_3-\underset{\underset{\displaystyle S}{\|}}{C}-NH_2 + M^{2+} \rightarrow \left[CH_3-\underset{\underset{\displaystyle S}{\|}}{C}-NHM \right]^+ + H_3O^+$$

$(\text{pH} \geq 5)$

$$\left[CH_3-\overset{\overset{\displaystyle S}{\|}}{C}-NHM \right]^+ + 2H_2O \rightarrow CH_3-\overset{\overset{\displaystyle O}{\|}}{C}-NH_2 + MS\downarrow + H_3O^+$$

The complexes have colors differing from those of the sulfides, so that unless the hydrolysis of the complex is complete, the characteristic sulfide colors (see Table 20.3, page 534) are not observed. In the pH range 3–5, both pathways are operative.

20.6 CHEMISTRY OF THE CATIONS

(a) Group I and Group II Cations.

Hg_2^{2+}

The mercurous ion, $[Hg:Hg]^{2+}$, forms a white chloride, Hg_2Cl_2, insoluble in hot and cold water. It is auto-oxidized (page 226) in the presence of NH_3 solution to give a characteristic black precipitate composed of black Hg and white mercury(II) amidochloride,

$$2Hg_2Cl_2 + 4NH_3 \rightarrow \underset{(\text{black})}{2Hg\downarrow} + \underset{(\text{white})}{2HgNH_2Cl\downarrow} + 2NH_4^+ + 2Cl^-$$

Ag^+

The silver halides, with the exception of the fluoride, are insoluble in water. Silver chloride is a white precipitate, insoluble in cold or hot water.

Silver bromide has a pale yellow color, and silver iodide a distinct yellow color. The variation in color of the halides is in accord with the direct relationship of size and polarizability of the halide ion. Silver chloride dissolves in an aqueous ammonia solution to give the ammonia complex ion,

$$AgCl + 2NH_3 \rightarrow Ag(NH_3)_2^+ + Cl^-$$

Acidification reverses the reaction,

$$2H^+ + Ag(NH_3)_2^+ + Cl^- \rightarrow AgCl\downarrow + 2NH_4^+$$

Neither silver bromide nor silver iodide dissolves in ammonia. The three insoluble halides, however, dissolve in excess thiosulfate ion or in excess cyanide ion to give the respective complex ions. For example

$$AgBr + 2S_2O_3^{2-} \rightarrow Ag(S_2O_3)_2^{3-} + Br^-$$

$$AgI + 2CN^- \rightarrow Ag(CN)_2^- + I^-$$

Pb²⁺

Among the common insoluble compounds of Pb^{2+} are the fluoride, chloride, bromide, iodide, sulfate, carbonate, hydroxide, chromate, and sulfide. These compounds are white with the exception of the yellow iodide, the yellow chromate, and the black sulfide.

A saturated aqueous solution of $PbCl_2$ at room temperature contains about 7.1 mg Pb^{2+} per ml of solution; it is therefore possible to precipitate PbS from this solution (Problem 16, page 550). Unlike AgCl and Hg_2Cl_2, $PbCl_2$ dissolves in hot water. A saturated solution of $PbCl_2$ is readily converted to $PbCrO_4$ on addition of CrO_4^{2-} as K_2CrO_4,

$$PbCl_2(aq) + CrO_4^{2-} \rightarrow PbCrO_4\downarrow + 2Cl^-$$
$$\text{(yellow)}$$
$$\textit{lead}$$
$$\textit{chromate}$$

Strong acids such as nitric acid dissolve $PbCrO_4$ by converting the chromate ion to the dichromate ion, $Cr_2O_7^{2-}$,

$$2PbCrO_4 + 2H^+ \rightarrow 2Pb^{2+} + Cr_2O_7^{2-} + H_2O$$

On the other hand, weak acids such as CH_3COOH cannot supply sufficient H^+ ions to promote this change.

Nitric acid dissolves lead sulfide, PbS, by oxidizing sulfide ions to sulfur,

$$3PbS + 2NO_3^- + 8H^+ \rightarrow 3Pb^{2+} + 3S + 2NO + 4H_2O \tag{1}$$

Lead sulfate, $PbSO_4$, dissolves in hot sulfuric acid by forming the bisulfate,

$$PbSO_4(c) + (HO)_2SO_2 \rightarrow Pb^{2+} + 2HOSO_3^-$$

and in ammonium acetate by forming acetate complexes, one of which is the triacetate complex,

$$PbSO_4(c) + 3CH_3COO^- \rightarrow Pb(CH_3COO)_3^- + SO_4^{2-}$$

The acetate complexes may be converted to insoluble $PbCrO_4$ by the addition of CrO_4^{2-} ion.

Hg^{2+}

Mercuric ion has an extremely strong affinity for sulfide ion; HgS ($K_{sp} = 10^{-52}$) is the most insoluble sulfide encountered in the analytical procedure. Notwithstanding its extreme insolubility, HgS dissolves in alkali sulfides to give a **thiocomplex ion,**

$$HgS + S^{2-} \rightarrow HgS_2^{2-}$$

Because of the extreme insolubility of HgS, the S^{2-} ion probably reacts directly with the solid HgS rather than with any Hg^{2+} ion that may be in solution. Unlike the other Group II sulfides, *HgS resists dissolution in nitric acid,* but dissolves slowly in hydrochloric acid. Sulfides dissolve in nitric acid because the sulfide ions in equilibrium with the solid sulfide are oxidized to S^0. In the case of HgS, dissolution does not occur because the concentration of S^{2-} ion in solution is insufficient. On the other hand, dissolution occurs in hydrochloric acid because of (a) the formation of a stable chloro complex ion, and (b) the volatility of H_2S,

$$HgS + 2H^+ + 4Cl^- \rightarrow HgCl_4^{2-} + H_2S\uparrow$$

HgS is most rapidly dissolved in aqua regia, a mixture of hydrochloric and nitric acids in the ratio $3:1$ by volume. The combination of the formation of the chloro complex ion and the oxidation of S^{2-} to S^0 promotes the dissolution of the sulfide,

$$2NO_3^- + 3HgS + 12Cl^- + 8H^+ \rightarrow 3HgCl_4^{2-} + 2NO + 3S + 4H_2O$$

When nitric acid acts as an oxidant, it is reduced to a variety of nitrogenous products, depending on its concentration and the nature of the reductant. Concentrated nitric acid produces mainly NO_2 and NO. As the nitric acid concentration decreases and the oxidation potential of the reductant increases, N_2O, N_2, and NH_4^+ are observed in the order shown. For example, Zn or Mg reduces dilute nitric acid to NH_4^+ and N_2. A single nitrogenous reduction product is rarely obtained.

Hg^{2+} in solution is detected by reduction with tin(II) chloride, $SnCl_2$, to white insoluble Hg_2Cl_2, or to black Hg. Most often a gray mixture of Hg_2Cl_2 and Hg results:

$$2HgCl_4^{2-} + Sn^{2+} \rightarrow Hg_2Cl_2\downarrow + SnCl_6^{2-}$$
(white)
mercurous
chloride

followed by

$$Hg_2Cl_2(c) + Sn^{2+} + 4Cl^- \rightarrow 2Hg\downarrow + SnCl_6^{2-}$$
(black)

Cu^{2+}

The common insoluble compounds of Cu^{2+} are CuS (black), CuO (black), $Cu(OH)_2$ (blue), $CuCrO_4$ (red), and the ferrocyanide (red-brown),

$$2Cu^{2+} + Fe(CN)_6^{4-} \rightarrow Cu_2Fe(CN)_6\downarrow$$

The sulfide, CuS, dissolves in hot dilute $HONO_2$ as a result of the reaction shown in Equation (1) (page 537) for PbS.

The hydroxide, $Cu(OH)_2$, does not dissolve in *dilute* sodium hydroxide. It dissolves readily in excess NH_3 to give the deep blue colored tetrammine complex ion,

$$Cu(OH)_2(c) + 4NH_3 \rightarrow Cu(NH_3)_4^{2+} + 2OH^-$$
$$\text{(light blue)} \qquad\qquad \text{(deep blue)}$$

Sufficient Cu^{2+} ion is in equilibrium with the $Cu(NH_3)_4^{2+}$ ion so that addition of H_2S causes CuS to precipitate. Cyanide ion converts the ammonia complex to a cyano complex and reduces $Cu(II)$ to $Cu(I)$, while the CN^- ion is oxidized to the cyanate ion, CNO^-,

$$2Cu(NH_3)_4^{2+} + 7CN^- + H_2O \rightarrow 2Cu(CN)_3^{2-} + CNO^-$$
$$+ 6NH_3 + 2NH_4^+ \quad (3)$$

The equilibrium decomposition of $Cu(CN)_3^{2-}$,

$$Cu(CN)_3^{2-} \rightleftharpoons Cu^+ + 3CN^-$$

does not provide enough Cu^+ ions to produce a precipitate of Cu_2S when H_2S is added. $Cu(CN)_3^{2-}$ is a rare example of a complex ion with a coordination number of three. Most other $Cu(I)$ complexes have a coordination number of two.

The standard oxidation potential for the $Cu^+ \xrightarrow{-e} Cu^{2+}$ half-cell is -0.15 volt, while the value for the $Cu \xrightarrow{-e} Cu^+$ half-cell is -0.52 volt. Consequently, the Cu^+ ion should oxidize another Cu^+ ion to Cu^{2+}, meanwhile being reduced to Cu. The equation for the auto-oxidation is

$$2Cu^+ \rightarrow Cu + Cu^{2+}$$

Hence, $Cu(II)$ is usually more stable than $Cu(I)$. In the cyanide reaction, Equation (3), the $Cu(I)$ state is favored, however, because of the great stability of the cyanide complex. The Cu^{2+} ion can also be reduced if the Cu^+ forms an insoluble compound, as shown,

$$Cu + Cu^{2+} + 2Cl^- \rightarrow 2CuCl\downarrow$$
$$2Cu^{2+} + 4I^- \rightarrow 2CuI\downarrow + I_2$$

The latter reaction is used in the quantitative determination of copper.

Cd^{2+}

The Cd^{2+} ion forms a white insoluble hydroxide and a canary yellow insoluble sulfide. CdS dissolves in nitric acid, but not in KOH solutions, or in solutions containing excess sulfide ion. $Cd(OH)_2$ behaves toward excess hydroxide ion and toward excess ammonia as does $Cu(OH)_2$ (shown above). The tetrammine complex in turn can be converted to a cyano complex,

$$Cd(NH_3)_4{}^{2+} + 4CN^- \rightarrow Cd(CN)_4{}^{2-} + 4NH_3$$

from which cadmium sulfide can be precipitated,

$$Cd(CN)_4{}^{2-} + S^{2-} \rightarrow CdS\downarrow + 4CN^- \quad (in\ NH_3\ solution)$$

Cadmium ion has a strong affinity for chloride ion; a chloro complex is formed in the presence of excess Cl^-,

$$Cd^{2+} + 3Cl^- \rightarrow CdCl_3{}^-$$

When $CdCl_2$ is dissolved in water, an unusual reaction occurs; both anionic and cationic complexes are formed,

$$CdCl_2 + CdCl_2 \rightleftharpoons CdCl_3{}^- + CdCl^+$$

Bi(III)

The aqueous chemistry of Bi(III) is fairly complicated. The free ion, Bi^{3+}, may exist in solutions of low pH, if the solution is acidified with oxyacids such as nitric and sulfuric acids. In excess HCl solutions, Bi(III) exists as chloro complexes such as $BiCl_4{}^-$ and $BiCl_6{}^{3-}$. In solutions of pH around 7, Bi(III) exists as the oxycation, BiO^+, the so-called **bismuthyl ion,** which may also be hydrated, $Bi(OH)_2{}^+$. Many of the bismuthyl compounds are insoluble,

$$BiCl_3 + H_2O \rightarrow \quad BiOCl\downarrow \quad + 2H^+ + 2Cl^-$$
bismuthyl chloride
or
bismuth oxychloride

$$2Bi^{3+} + SO_4{}^{2-} + 2H_2O \rightarrow (BiO)_2SO_4\downarrow + 4H^+$$

Bi(III) forms a white insoluble nonamphoteric hydroxide, in alkali or in NH_3 solution, and a dark brown sulfide, Bi_2S_3, in H_2S. The sulfide can be precipitated from acidified solutions, not in excess of $1M\ H_3O^+$. It dissolves in hot concentrated hydrochloric acid to give H_2S and $BiCl_4{}^-$, and in dilute nitric acid.

In basic media, Bi(III) is reduced by sodium stannite to a black precipitate of Bi,

$$Bi(OH)_3 + [Sn(OH)_3(H_2O)_3]^- \rightarrow Sn(OH)_6{}^{2-} + Bi\downarrow + 3H_2O$$
stannite   stannate
ion   ion

Sodium bismuthate, a yellow solid, often written as $NaBiO_3$, is a strong oxidant, used for the difficult oxidation of Mn^{2+} ion to $MnO_4{}^-$ ion.

As(III)

Because of a high cationic charge density, As^{3+} does not exist in water as a free ion. In basic and neutral solutions it exists mainly as the hydroxy cation, $As(OH)_2{}^+$. In acidic media, it exists as an oxyanion, dihydrogen arsenite, $(HO)_2AsO^-$. Arsenic(III) sulfide, As_2S_3, can be precipitated from solutions of these ions. If arsenic (V) is present, it is reduced by thioacetamide and precipitated as arsenic(III) sulfide even in 0.3M HCl. The sulfide is virtually insoluble in 6M HCl, but dissolves in NH_3, KOH, K_2S, and $(NH_4)_2S$ solutions with the formation of the oxy-, thio-, and oxythio-anions, such as AsO_3^{3-}, AsS_2^-, and $AsOS_2^{3-}$. The complexity and variability of the products make it meaningless to write a definite equation for the reaction. Acidification of these alkaline solutions causes the sulfide to reprecipitate. Nitric acid dissolves the sulfide by oxidation of S^{2-} ion to S and arsenic(III) to arsenic (V),

$$As_2S_3(c) + 10NO_3^- + 8H^+ \rightarrow 2\underset{\substack{dihydrogen \\ arsenate}}{(HO)_2AsO_2^-} + 3S\downarrow + 10NO_2 + 2H_2O$$

Arsenates are detected by conversion to the white insoluble solid, magnesium ammonium arsenate, $MgNH_4AsO_4(H_2O)_6$,

$$AsO_4^{3-} + Mg^{2+} + NH_4^+ + 6H_2O \rightarrow MgNH_4AsO_4(H_2O)_6\downarrow$$

or to the chocolate-brown silver arsenate, Ag_3AsO_4,

$$3Ag^+ + HOAsO_3^{2-} \rightarrow Ag_3AsO_4\downarrow + H^+$$

Arsenic can also be detected by the Marsh test (page 685).

Sb(III)

A high cationic charge density precludes the existence of a free Sb^{3+} ion in solution. In solution, Sb(III) probably exists as hydroxy, thio, and chloro complexes, depending on the pH and the presence of the complexing anion. Some of the ions that do exist are antimonyl, $Sb(OH)_2^+$, antimonite, $Sb(OH)_4^-$, metathioantimonite, SbS_3^{3-}, and tetrachloroantimonite, $SbCl_4^-$. The sulfide, Sb_2S_3, can be precipitated with H_2S or thioacetamide from solutions containing any of these ions. The sulfide also precipitates when the solution of the thioanions is acidified. Unlike As_2S_3, Sb_2S_3 dissolves in 6M HCl mainly because the stable chloro complex $SbCl_4^-$ is formed,

$$Sb_2S_3 + 6H^+ + 8Cl^- \rightarrow 2SbCl_4^- + 3H_2S$$

The sulfide is amphoteric and dissolves in KOH solution, by forming a complex mixture of oxy-, thio-, and oxythioanions. The observation that Sb_2S_3 is amphoteric, while Bi_2S_3 is not, is consistent with the generalization that within a given group in the Periodic Table, basicity increases with increasing atomic number.

Sn(IV)

The usual source of Sn(IV) is $SnCl_4$, which is a covalent substance; anhydrous $SnCl_4$ is a liquid. $SnCl_4$ reacts violently with water, producing hydrated tin(IV) oxide, $SnO_2(H_2O)_4$, and liberating hydrogen chloride,

$$SnCl_4 + 6H_2O \rightarrow SnO_2(H_2O)_4 + 4HCl\uparrow$$

To maintain tin(IV) in a dissolved state, excess HCl is added to the solution, thereby forming hexachlorostannate ions, $SnCl_6^{2-}$. The hydrated oxide is amphoteric and forms the stannate ion, $Sn(OH)_6^{2-}$, in the presence of excess OH^- ions,

$$SnO_2(H_2O)_4 + 2OH^- \rightarrow Sn(OH)_6^{2-} + 2H_2O$$

The yellow sulfide, SnS_2, is precipitated by thioacetamide solution in dilute (less than $1M$) solutions of HCl. Precipitation of SnS_2 is very slow in the presence of oxalate ion, $C_2O_4^{2-}$, because tin(IV) forms a stable oxalato complex, $Sn(C_2O_4)_3^{2-}$,

$$SnCl_6^{2-} + 3C_2O_4^{2-} \rightarrow Sn(C_2O_4)_3^{2-} + 6Cl^-$$

Like Sb_2S_3 and unlike As_2S_3, SnS_2 dissolves in $6M$ HCl solution,

$$SnS_2 + 4H^+ + 6Cl^- \rightarrow SnCl_6^{2-} + 2H_2S$$

But, like Sb_2S_3 and As_2S_3, SnS_2 dissolves in a KOH solution, forming complicated mixtures of oxy- and thioanions.

Tin(IV) can be reduced to tin(II) by metallic tin,

$$Sn + SnCl_6^{2-} \rightarrow 2Sn^{2+} + 6Cl^-$$

or by iron,

$$SnCl_6^{2-} + Fe \rightarrow Sn^{2+} + Fe^{2+} + 6Cl^-$$

Lumps of metallic tin are added to solutions of tin(II) salts to prevent the gradual oxidation of tin(II) by air. The oxidation of tin(II) to tin(IV) by Hg(II) and Hg(I) has been described previously (page 538).

(b) **Group III Cations.** The cations in this group are best discussed by classifying them according to charge; the divalent cations are Mn^{2+}, Fe^{2+}, Co^{2+}, Ni^{2+}, and Zn^{2+}, and the trivalent cations are Al^{3+}, Cr^{3+}, and Fe^{3+}. These cations are complexed with water. Some of the chemistry, important for analysis of the divalent cations, is summarized in Table 20.4. (Note that **ppt** is used as an abbreviation of precipitate.)

With the exception of Zn^{2+}, these divalent cations have partially filled d orbitals and hence are colored; Zn^{2+} and its complex ions and compounds are colorless or white.

In a nitric acid solution, Mn^{2+} is oxidized by potassium chlorate, a strong oxidant, to brown insoluble manganese dioxide, MnO_2,

$$Mn^{2+} + 2ClO_3^- \rightarrow MnO_2\downarrow + 2ClO_2\uparrow$$

and by sodium bismuthate, an even stronger oxidant, to the purple permanganate ion, MnO_4^-. The latter reaction is used as a confirmatory test for Mn(II). While strong oxidants are required to oxidize Mn(II) in acid media, milder oxidants such as hydrogen peroxide readily oxidize Mn(II) in basic media,

$$Mn(OH)_2 + HO_2^- \rightarrow MnO_2\downarrow + OH^- + H_2O$$

TABLE 20.4 *Some Properties of Group III Divalent Cations, M²⁺*

Reagent	Mn^{2+}	Fe^{2+}	Zn^{2+}	Co^{2+}	Ni^{2+}
$S^{2-} + NH_3$	MnS^a	FeS^a	ZnS^a	CoS^a	NiS^a
H_2S, 0.3M HCl	No ppt	No ppt	No ppt	No ppt	No ppt
MS + HCl	Mn^{2+}, H_2S	Fe^{2+}, H_2S	Zn^{2+}, H_2S	Co^{2+}, H_2S^b	Ni^{2+}, H_2S^b
OH^-	$Mn(OH)_2{}^c$	$Fe(OH)_2{}^d$	$Zn(OH)_2$	$Co(OH)_2{}^e$	$Ni(OH)_2$
Color of $M(OH)_2$	White	White	White	Blue or pink	Light green
$M(OH)_2 + OH^-$	$Mn(OH)_2{}^c$	$Fe(OH)_2{}^d$	$Zn(OH)_4{}^{2-}$	$Co(OH)_2{}^e$	$Ni(OH)_2$
$M(OH)_2 + NH_3$	$Mn(OH)_2{}^c$	$Fe(OH)_2{}^d$	$Zn(NH_3)_4{}^{2+}$	$Co(OH)_2$, $Co(NH_3)_6{}^{2+}$	$Ni(NH_3)_6{}^{2+}$
$M^{2+} + (NH_3 + NH_4{}^+)$	No ppt	No ppt	$Zn(NH_3)_4{}^{2+}$	$Co(NH_3)_6{}^{2+}$	$Ni(NH_3)_6{}^{2+}$
Color of ammine complex	—	—	Colorless	Pink	Blue

^{a} See Table 20.2 for colors.

^{b} On standing, NiS and CoS change from readily soluble amorphous forms to insoluble crystalline forms.

^{c} Slowly oxidized by air to brownish $MnO(OH)_2$.

^{d} Slowly oxidized by air to oxides of Fe(III), turning green to black to red.

^{e} Slowly oxidized by air to brownish hydrated Co_2O_3.

In nitric acid, MnO_2 oxidizes H_2O_2 and dissolves as Mn^{2+},

$$MnO_2 + H_2O_2 + 6H^+ \rightarrow Mn^{2+} + 4H_2O$$

This same dependence of oxidation on pH is observed for Fe(II) and Co(II) ions. For example, in acid solutions, Co^{2+} is difficult to oxidize to Co^{3+}; the standard oxidation potential for the $Co^{2+} \xrightarrow{-e} Co^{3+}$ half-cell is -1.82 volts. From among the common oxidants, only F_2, for which the standard oxidation potential $F_2 \xrightarrow{+2e} 2F^-$ is -2.65 volts, is capable of effecting the oxidation. In basic solutions, a mild oxidant such as H_2O_2 can oxidize Co(II) to Co(III),

$$2Co(OH)_2 + H_2O + HO_2{}^- \rightarrow 2Co(OH)_3\downarrow + OH^-$$

The pertinent standard electrode potentials are $Co^{2+} \xrightarrow{-e} Co^{3+}$ in OH^-, $\varepsilon° = -0.17$ volt; $H_2O_2 \xrightarrow{+2e} 2OH^-$, $\varepsilon° = -0.88$ volt.

Fe(II) is also oxidized to Fe(III) more readily by a number of oxidants, including H_2O_2 and oxygen, in basic rather than in acid solutions.

Some of the confirmatory tests used for these cations follow:

Fe^{2+}—After oxidation to Fe^{3+}, thiocyanate ion is added,

$$Fe^{3+} + SCN^- \rightarrow (FeSCN)^{2+}$$
$$\text{(blood red)}$$

Co^{2+}—the addition of potassium nitrite in acetic acid solution produces insoluble yellow potassium hexanitrocobaltate(III),

$$Co^{2+} + 3K^+ + 7NO_2^- + 2CH_3COOH \rightarrow K_3Co(NO_2)_6\downarrow + NO$$
$$\text{yellow}$$
$$+ H_2O + 2CH_3COO^-$$

The addition of thiocyanate ion produces a complex ion imparting a blue color to acetone or alcohol-ether solutions,

$$Co^{2+} + 4SCN^- \rightarrow Co(SCN)_4^{2-}$$

Ni^{2+}—forms a red solid with dimethylglyoxime in a properly buffered solution.

Mn^{2+}—this has been described above.

Zn^{2+}—the formation of the characteristic white zinc sulfide.

Some of the chemistry used for the analysis of the trivalent ions is summarized in Table 20.5.

Fe^{3+} and Cr^{3+} are transition metals with incomplete d orbitals and so are colored. Aluminum is a representative element and its salts and complexes are colorless.

Of these three trivalent cations, only Cr^{3+} can be oxidized. In nitric acid, it is oxidized by $KClO_3$ to the orange-red dichromate ion $Cr_2O_7^{2-}$,

$$6ClO_3^- + 2Cr^{3+} + H_2O \rightarrow Cr_2O_7^{2-} + 6ClO_2 + 2H^+$$

In a basic solution, Cr(III) is oxidized by H_2O_2 to the yellow chromate ion, CrO_4^{2-},

$$2Cr(OH)_3 + 3HO_2^- + OH^- \rightarrow 2CrO_4^{2-} + 5H_2O$$

Again we find that a stronger oxidant is needed in an acid medium than in a basic medium.

(c) **Group IV Cations.** The chemistry of Ba^{2+}, Sr^{2+}, and Ca^{2+} is very similar, so that complete separations are difficult to achieve. This was dramatically revealed by the prolonged painstaking efforts of Pierre and Marie Curie to separate radium, another member of the alkaline earth group, from barium. The cations in this group form few stable complex ions, and undergo few redox reactions. Advantage must be taken, there-

TABLE 20.5   *Properties of Group III Trivalent Cations, M^{3+}*

Reagent	Al^{3+}	Fe^{3+}	Cr^{3+}
H_2S	No ppt	FeS, S	No ppt
OH^-	$Al(OH)_3$	$Fe(OH)_3$	$Cr(OH)_3$
Color of $M(OH)_3$	White	Red-brown	Gray-green
$M(OH)_3 + OH^-$	$Al(OH)_6^{3-}$	$Fe(OH)_3$	$Cr(OH)_6^{3-a}$
NH_3, NH_4^+	$Al(OH)_3$	$Fe(OH)_3$	$Cr(OH)_3{}^b$
S^{2-}, NH_3, NH_4^+	$Al(OH)_3$	FeS, S	$Cr(OH)_3$

[a] Forms slowly.   [b] $Cr(NH_3)_6^{3+}$ forms very slowly.

fore, of marked differences in solubility of certain salts. For example, Ba^{2+} is easiest to separate because its chromate is at least a million times less soluble than strontium and calcium chromates. The yellow barium chromate is precipitated from an acetic acid–acetate ion buffered solution. In acid solutions, chromate ion is in equilibrium with dichromate ion, $Cr_2O_7^{2-}$,

$$2CrO_4^{2-} + H^+ \rightleftharpoons Cr_2O_7^{2-} + H_2O$$
(yellow)   (orange)

At the pH of the buffered solution, the equilibrium concentration of CrO_4^{2-} is sufficient to precipitate *only* $BaCrO_4$.

Strontium sulfate is about 100 times more insoluble than calcium sulfate, and calcium oxalate is about 50 times more insoluble than strontium oxalate. Either of these solubility differences is used for separating Sr^{2+} from Ca^{2+} ions.

The characteristic colors imparted to a flame by these cations can be used as confirmatory tests: the colors are yellowish green for Ba^{2+}, crimson for Sr^{2+}, and orange-red for Ca^{2+}. For the best results in flame tests, the precipitated salts are usually converted to the comparatively volatile chlorides with concentrated hydrochloric acid.

(d) Group V Cations and NH_4^+. The following insoluble salts are most frequently used for the qualitative analysis of Mg^{2+}, K^+, and Na^+.

Mg^{2+} is separated as the white magnesium ammonium phosphate,

$$Mg^{2+} + NH_3 + HOPO_3^{2-} + 6H_2O \rightarrow MgNH_4PO_4(H_2O)_6\downarrow$$

Na^+ is separated as the yellow sodium magnesium uranyl acetate, formed by adding magnesium uranyl acetate, $Mg(UO_2)_3(C_2H_3O_2)_8$, in acetic acid, the so-called sodium reagent,

$$Na^+ + Mg^{2+} + UO_2^{2+} + 9C_2H_3O_2^- + 9H_2O$$
$$\rightarrow NaMg(UO_2)_3(C_2H_3O_2)_9(H_2O)_9$$

K^+ is separated as the yellow dipotassium sodium hexanitrocobaltate(III) by addition of sodium hexanitrocobaltate(III),

$$2K^+ + Na^+ + Co(NO_3)_6^{3-} \rightarrow K_2Na[Co(NO_2)_6]\downarrow$$
(yellow)

Sodium gives a characteristic intense yellow flame test; potassium gives a more fleeting violet flame.

When heated in a solution of NaOH, ammonium salts evolve ammonia gas,

$$NH_4^+ + OH^- \rightarrow NH_3\uparrow + H_2O$$

detectable by its characteristic odor and its action on indicators.

20.7 QUALITATIVE ANALYSIS OF ANIONS

The anions discussed in this section are F^-, Cl^-, Br^-, I^-, S^{2-}, SO_3^{2-}, SO_4^{2-}, CrO_4^{2-}, NO_2^-, NO_3^-, PO_4^{3-}, and CO_3^{2-}. No attempt is made to distinguish between anions in different hydration levels, such as ortho- or metaphosphate ions, or in different stages of protonation, such as $HOSO_3^-$ or SO_4^{2-}.

The anions are classified according to:

(1) Evolution of gas in acid solution
(2) Ability to reduce a solution of acidified potassium permanganate
(3) Ability to oxidize iodide ion
(4) Solubility groups
    (a) the Ba^{2+} group—those ions precipitated with a basic solution containing Ba^{2+} and Ca^{2+}
    (b) the Ag^+ group—those ions precipitated with a solution of Ag^+
    (c) the soluble group—those ions not forming precipitates with Ba^{2+}, Ca^{2+}, or Ag^+

It is imperative to perform the classification tests in the sequence given above. For example, some anions such as PO_4^{3-} and CrO_4^{2-} form precipitates with both Ba^{2+} and Ag^+ and, if these ions were tested for solubility toward Ag^+ before Ba^{2+}, they would be incorrectly placed in the Ag^+ group.

Before beginning a systematic analysis, it is advisable to note the color of the salt and to determine whether the salt is soluble in water.

(a) Color. The color of a salt may be characteristic of the cation and/or the anion. Of those listed, only the Cr(VI) anions are colored; chromate is yellow and dichromate is orange. A solid may be colored even though its ions, when separated, are colorless. This phenomenon, a useful clue in analysis, is a result of polarization.

(b) Solubility in Water; pH of the Solution. The solubility of the salt in water should be estimated roughly. A salt is said to be soluble if at least about 0.3 gram dissolves in 100 ml water. If the salt dissolves, the pH of its solution should be determined. An acidic solution indicates that either an acidic anion or cation is present. The acidic anions are the conjugate bases of the fairly strong polyprotic acids: bisulfate ion, $HOSO_3^-$; bisulfite ion, $HOSO_2^-$; dihydrogen phosphate ion, $(HO)_2PO_2^-$; and dichromate ion, $Cr_2O_7^{2-}$. The basic anions are the conjugate bases of weak acids: SO_3^{2-}, PO_4^{3-}, S^{2-}, and CO_3^{2-}.

(c) Anions That Evolve a Gas with Acid. The four anions that evolve a gas with dilute sulfuric acid or hydrochloric acid are CO_3^{2-}, SO_3^{2-}, S^{2-}, and NO_2^-. They can be distinguished from each other and confirmed by the color and the odor of the evolved gas*:

$$CO_3^{2-} + 2H^+ \rightarrow H_2O + CO_2\uparrow \qquad \text{\textit{colorless, odorless}}$$
$$SO_3^{2-} + 2H^+ \rightarrow H_2O + SO_2\uparrow \qquad \text{\textit{colorless, pungent irritating odor, toxic}}$$
$$S^{2-} + 2H^+ \rightarrow H_2S\uparrow \qquad \text{\textit{colorless, rotten egg odor, toxic}}$$

(1) $NO_2^- + H^+ \rightarrow HONO$
(2) $2HONO \rightarrow 2H^+ + NO_3^- + NO\uparrow$
(3) $2NO + O_2 \rightarrow 2NO_2\uparrow$ *brown, irritating odor, toxic*

* Caution should be exercised in inhaling any toxic gas.

(d) Reductant Anions. The ability of an anion to act as a reductant is generally detected by the decolorization of an acidified solution of permanganate ion, MnO_4^-. The partial equation may be represented as

$$MnO_4^- + 8H^+ + 5e^- \rightarrow \quad Mn^{2+} \quad + 4H_2O$$
(purple)   (pale pink)

The anions giving an immediate positive test are shown in the following *partial* equations:

$$SO_3^{2-} + H_2O \rightarrow SO_4^{2-} + 2H^+ + 2e^-$$
$$S^{2-} \rightarrow S^0 + 2e^-$$
$$2I^- \rightarrow I_2 + 2e^-$$
$$NO_2^- + H_2O \rightarrow NO_3^- + 2H^+ + 2e^-$$

Since bromide and chloride ions react slowly with MnO_4^-, the decisiveness and rapidity of these tests are important factors in grouping the anions.

(e) Oxidant Anions. The ability of an anion to act as an oxidant is determined by the rapid conversion of colorless iodide ion to iodine, detected by its purple color in CCl_4 or by its blue color with starch. The oxidant anions are shown in the following partial equations:

$$Cr_2O_7^{2-} + 14H^+ + 6e^- \rightarrow 2Cr^{3+} + 7H_2O \qquad (acidic)$$
$$NO_2^- + 2H^+ + \quad e^- \rightarrow NO \quad + H_2O$$

Notice that the nitrite ion may act as an oxidant and as a reductant.

(f) Anions Precipitated by Ba^{2+} or Ca^{2+}. The anions in this group are SO_4^{2-}, PO_4^{3-}, F^-, (CrO_4^{2-}), (SO_3^{2-}), and (CO_3^{2-}). The last three anions are in parentheses since they would be detected by other means prior to performing the test for this group and, therefore, are not considered as belonging to this group. An ammoniacal solution of barium chloride and calcium chloride is used as the reagent; the precipitates are $Ba_3(PO_4)_2$, $BaSO_4$, and CaF_2, all of which are white. $BaSO_4$ and, to a lesser extent, CaF_2 are insoluble in dilute HCl; $Ba_3(PO_4)_2$ dissolves,

$$Ba_3(PO_4)_2 + 4H_3O^+ \rightarrow 3Ba^{2+} + 2(HO)_2PO_2^- + 4H_2O$$

The insolubility of barium sulfate in acid solutions characterizes the sulfate ion.

The presence of phosphate ion may be confirmed by the formation of the white insoluble $MgNH_4PO_4$ (page 545).

Fluoride ion is confirmed by taking advantage of the unique ability of hydrogen fluoride to etch glass. Etching is attributed to the conversion of silicon dioxide, a constituent of glass, to volatile silicon tetrafluoride,

$$F^- + (HO)_2SO_2 \rightarrow HF \quad + HOSO_3^-$$
$$4HF + SiO_2 \rightarrow SiF_4\uparrow + 2H_2O$$

(g) Anions Precipitated by Ag^+. The anions in this group, Cl^-, Br^-, I^-, are precipitated by silver ion from a solution acidified with nitric acid:

$$Cl^- + Ag^+ \rightarrow AgCl \quad \textit{white}$$
$$Br^- + Ag^+ \rightarrow AgBr \quad \textit{pale yellow}$$
$$I^- + Ag^+ \rightarrow AgI \quad \textit{yellow}$$

In an excess of aqueous ammonia solution, AgCl completely dissolves to give $Ag(NH_3)_2^+$, AgBr dissolves only partially, and AgI is practically completely insoluble. The white color and solubility of AgCl in aqueous ammonia confirm the presence of chloride ion. The presence of Br^- or I^- is confirmed by oxidizing them, usually with chlorine water, to bromine or iodine in the presence of carbon tetrachloride:

$$Cl_2 + 2Br^- \rightarrow 2Cl^- + Br_2 \quad \textit{brown color in } CCl_4 \textit{ layer}$$
$$Cl_2 + 2I^- \rightarrow 2Cl^- + I_2 \quad \textit{purple color in } CCl_4 \textit{ layer}$$

The halogens are extracted by (page 350), and impart a characteristic color to, the carbon tetrachloride layer.

(h) The Soluble Anions. The anions in this group are NO_3^- and NO_2^-. The NO_2^- ion has been previously detected by its ability to give a characteristic gas in acid solution, and to act as an oxidant and reductant.

The nitrate ion is best characterized by two tests:

(*i*) with copper and concentrated sulfuric acid, a nitrate salt yields a blue solution and a brown gas,

$$\underset{\text{(blue)}}{Cu + 2NO_3^- + 4H^+ \rightarrow Cu^{2+}(aq)} + \underset{\text{(brown)}}{2NO_2\uparrow} + 2H_2O$$

(*ii*) the brown-colored $Fe(NO)^{2+}$ complex ion is formed at the interface of a solution of NO_3^- and Fe^{2+} ions (upper layer) and concentrated H_2SO_4 (bottom layer),

$$3Fe^{2+} + NO_3^- + 4H^+ \rightarrow 3Fe^{3+} + NO + 2H_2O$$
$$\underset{\text{(brown)}}{Fe^{2+} + NO \rightarrow [Fe(NO)]^{2+}}$$

This reaction is the basis of the so-called "brown ring" test.

Problems

1. Solubility and radius ratio. The ionic radii in angstroms of the common alkaline earth metal cations are $Mg^{2+} = 0.75$, $Ca^{2+} = 1.06$, $Sr^{2+} = 1.18$, and $Ba^{2+} = 1.38$. The radius of CO_3^{2-} is 1.62, and the radius of SO_4^{2-} is 1.84. Select the most soluble and most insoluble (a) carbonate; (b) sulfate.

2. Solubility. Account for the following orders of solubility in water: (a) $KCl > BaSO_4 > FePO_4$; (b) oxides > sulfides > selenides; (c) $ZnS > CdS > HgS$; (d) selenates > selenites.

3. Color. Predict which of the following would be colored (give a reason for each answer): (a) Tl^+; (b) Ti^{3+}; (c) Ti^{4+}; (d) Cu^+; (e) PbI_2; (f) CaI_2; (g) AlF_6^{3-}; (h) $K_2Au(AuCl_6)$; (i) Fe_3O_4.

4. Color. (a) Explain the following sequences of colors: (*i*) ZnS—white, CdS—yellow, HgS—black; (*ii*) AsCl$_3$—colorless, AsBr$_3$—yellow, AsI$_3$—red; (*iii*) As$_2$S$_3$—yellow, Sb$_2$S$_3$—orange, Bi$_2$S$_3$—brown-black. (b) Account for the fact that cadmium complexes, such as Cd(NH$_3$)$_4$$^{2+}$ and CdCl$_4$$^{2-}$, are colorless.

5. Cation analysis. Pick the cation that is present.

(a) A precipitate forms with hydrochloric acid and dissolves in excess NH$_3$.

(b) A precipitate forms in a buffered solution of NH$_3$ and NH$_4$$^+$ and dissolves in excess OH$^-$.

(c) A yellow precipitate forms in acidified H$_2$S, and dissolves in potassium hydroxide and in 6N hydrochloric acid.

(d) A precipitate forms in acidified H$_2$S and dissolves in nitric acid to give a colored solution.

(e) No precipitate forms with an H$_2$S solution. A precipitate forms with an NH$_3$ solution, and dissolves in NH$_4$Cl solution.

6. Cation analysis. (a) Labels drop off from each of the following pairs of bottled chemicals. Describe the chemical test you would use to enable you to reaffix the labels correctly. All salts are nitrates. (*i*) Hg$_2$$^{2+}$ and Hg^{2+}; (*ii*) Cu^{2+} and Cd^{2+}; (*iii*) Pb^{2+} and Ag$^+$; (*iv*) Sb(III) and Bi(III); (*v*) Fe^{3+} and Al^{3+}; (*vi*) Ba^{2+} and Ca^{2+}; (*vii*) Co^{2+} and Ni^{2+}; (*viii*) Mn^{2+} and Cr^{3+}; (*ix*) NH$_4$$^+$ and K$^+$. (b) Which pairs could be distinguished on the basis of color?

7. Anion analysis. Give a chemical test to distinguish between the following pairs of sodium salts: (a) sulfite and sulfate; (b) chloride and bromide; (c) fluoride and sulfate; (d) phosphate and chromate; (e) nitrate and nitrite.

8. Anion analysis. Which of the following pairs of anions cannot coexist in an aqueous solution? Give a balanced equation for any reaction that occurs. (a) I$^-$ and Cl$^-$; (b) HOSO$_3$$^-$ and CO$_3$$^{2-}$; (c) (HO)$_2PO_2$$^-$ and SO$_3$$^{2-}$; (d) NO$_2$$^-$ and I$^-$.

Additional problems

9. Anion-cation analysis. Four individual compounds were given to a student as unknowns to be analyzed. He reported them as (1) FeBr$_3$, (2) FeI$_3$, (3) CuI, (4) CoBr$_3$. Which unknown(s) must have been reported incorrectly? Consult the table of standard oxidation potentials (page 417).

10. Anion-cation analysis. A solid mixture contains one or more of the following salts: Pb(NO$_3$)$_2$, Na$_2$CO$_3$, BaCl$_2$, MgSO$_4$, and KAl(SO$_4$)$_2$. The mixture dissolves in water with the evolution of gas. Which substances are present and which are absent? For which salt, if any, is there insufficient evidence to justify a conclusion about its presence? Write ionic equations for all reactions.

11. Mixed anion-cation analysis. A white solid mixture contains some or all of the following salts: Ba(NO$_3$)$_2$, AgNO$_3$, KI, NaHSO$_3$, and MgBr$_2$. The mixture dissolves in water. The water solution bleaches an acidified (acetic acid) solution of KMnO$_4$ concurrently with the formation of a white precipitate. The original water solution imparts a purple color to carbon tetrachloride when Cl$_2$ is added and the mixture shaken. (a) Which salts are present? (b) Which salts are absent? (c) Which salts may or may not be present?

12. Cation analysis. Account for the fact that sodium hydroxide solution is not used to precipitate the hydroxides of Group III.

13. Ionic equilibria of cation analysis. Write ionic equations for all co-existing equilibria in an aqueous solution of the following ions and molecules:

(a) Cd^{2+}, H_2S, HCl; (b) CH_3COOH, CrO_4^{2-}, Ba^{2+}; (c) Mg^{2+}, NH_3, NH_4^+; (d) Zn^{2+}, NH_3, OH^-; (e) Ba^{2+}, CO_3^{2-}, NH_4^+.

14. Calculations; ionic equilibria. (a) Mixed to make one liter of solution are 0.1 mole Fe^{3+}, 0.1 mole NH_4^+, and 0.1 mole NH_3. Will $Fe(OH)_3$ precipitate? K_b for $NH_3 = 10^{-5}$, and K for $Fe(OH)_3 = 10^{-23}$. (b) In part (a), substitute 0.1 mole Mg^{2+} for 0.1 mole Fe^{3+}. K for $Mg(OH)_2 = 5.5 \times 10^{-11}$. Will $Mg(OH)_2$ precipitate?

Answer. (a) yes; (b) no.

15. Calculations. A solution contains $0.1M$ $Cd(CN)_4^{2-}$ and $0.1M$ CN^-. K for $Cd(CN)_4^{2-} = 10^{-17}$. (a) Find $[Cd^{2+}]$. (b) Sulfide ion is added to make $[S^{2-}] = 0.1M$. Will CdS precipitate? K for $CdS = 3.6 \times 10^{-29}$.

16. Calculations. (a) Find $[Pb^{2+}]$ in the presence of $0.1M$ Cl^-. K for $PbCl_2 = 2.4 \times 10^{-4}$. (b) If the filtered solution from part (a) is made $0.32M$ in HCl and $0.1M$ in H_2S, will PbS precipitate? K for $PbS = 10^{-28}$, K_1 for $H_2S = 10^{-7}$, K_2 for $H_2S = 10^{-13}$. (c) Will FeS precipitate from a solution in which $[Fe^{2+}] = 10^{-2}M$, $[H_3O^+] = 0.32M$, and $[H_2S] = 10^{-1}M$? K for $FeS = 3.7 \times 10^{-19}$. (d) What concentration of H_3O^+ will just prevent the precipitation of PbS from a solution in which $Pb^{2+} = 10^{-3}$, and $H_2S = 0.1M$?

Answer. (a) $2.4 \times 10^{-2}M$; (c) no; (d) 10^2 moles/liter.

17. Calculations. What must be the solubility product of a sulfide, MS, so that the sulfide will just not precipitate from a solution in which $[M^{2+}] = 10^{-2}$, $[H_3O^+] = 0.32$, and $[H_2S] = 10^{-1}$? K_1 for $H_2S = 10^{-7}$, K_2 for $H_2S = 10^{-13}$.

21
Quantitative analysis

THE PURPOSE OF this chapter is to apply several of the previously considered principles and concepts to some of the problems involved in the study of quantitative analysis, the determination of the quantities of component substances in a sample.

21.1 GRAVIMETRIC ANALYSIS

In gravimetric methods, the constituent to be determined is separated, as an element or a compound of known composition, from a weighed quantity of the sample. The isolated element or compound, which may be a solid, liquid, or gas, is then weighed. From the known composition of the isolated substance and its weight, the quantity of the desired constituent present in the sample is calculated.

EXAMPLE 1   A 0.2505 g sample of a commercial product is dissolved in water. The solution is acidified with nitric acid. Addition of excess silver nitrate precipitates the chloride in the sample as silver chloride. The solution is heated and stirred to coagulate the precipitate. The precipitate is filtered, washed with dilute nitric acid $(0.01M)$ solution, dried, and weighed. The weight of the precipitate is 0.2060 g. Calculate the percentage of Cl^- in the product. Qualitative analysis shows the Cl^- is present as $MgCl_2$; calculate the percentage of $MgCl_2$ in the product.

ANSWER   The reaction involved is

$$Ag^+ + Cl^- \rightleftharpoons AgCl\downarrow$$

Since one mole of Cl^- (35.45 g) yields one mole of $AgCl$ (143.32 g), the weight of Cl^- required to produce 0.2060 g of silver chloride is (page 102)

$$0.2060 \text{ g AgCl} \frac{35.45 \text{ g Cl}^-}{143.32 \text{ g AgCl}} = 0.05095 \text{ g Cl}^-*$$

Hence, the percentage of Cl^- in the sample is

$$\frac{0.05095 \text{ g Cl}^-}{0.2505 \text{ g sample}} 100 = 20.34\% \text{ Cl}^-$$

Since one mole of $MgCl_2$ (95.21 g) yields two moles of $AgCl$, the weight of $MgCl_2$ required to produce 0.2060 g of silver chloride is

$$0.2060 \text{ g AgCl} \frac{95.21 \text{ g MgCl}_2}{2 \times 143.32 \text{ g AgCl}} = 0.06842 \text{ g MgCl}_2$$

Hence, the percentage of $MgCl_2$ is

$$\frac{0.06842 \text{ g MgCl}_2}{0.2505 \text{ g sample}} 100 = 27.32\% \text{ MgCl}_2$$

It is evident from experience that the completeness of a separation is affected by the solubility of the "insoluble" precipitate.

EXAMPLE 2 Assuming that exactly the stoichiometric quantity† of Ag^+ is added to the sample in a gravimetric determination of Cl^-, calculate the mass in milligrams of the Cl^- *not* precipitated per 100 ml of solution at 25°C. Calculate the negative error if the chloride is precipitated in 400 ml of solution at 25°C. Assume that the activity coefficients of Ag^+ and Cl^- are (*i*) 1.00; (*ii*) 0.65.

ANSWER The solubility of AgCl may be calculated from its solubility product (Table 19.3, page 504):

(*i*) 　　　　　　　　　　　　　　　　　　(*ii*)

$$a_{Ag^+} \cdot a_{Cl^-} = 1.7 \times 10^{-10}$$
$$\text{(at 25°C)}$$
$$[Ag^+]\gamma_{Ag^+}[Cl^-]\gamma_{Cl^-} = 1.7 \times 10^{-10}$$

$$[Ag^+][Cl^-] = 1.7 \times 10^{-10} \qquad [Ag^+][Cl^-] = \frac{1.7 \times 10^{-10}}{\gamma_{Ag^+}\, \gamma_{Cl^-}}$$
$$= \frac{1.7 \times 10^{-10}}{0.65^2}$$
$$= 4.0 \times 10^{-10}$$

Since exactly stoichiometric quantities were used, $[Ag^+] = [Cl^-]$ and letting

* The use of a five place log table is recommended.

† Stoichiometric quantities are the quantities whose molar ratios conform to the empirical formula of the compound formed. For AgCl, the stoichiometric quantities of Ag^+ and Cl^- are in a molar ratio of 1 to 1; for Ag_2SO_4 the molar ratio is 2 of Ag^+ to 1 of SO_4^{2-}.

$x = [Cl^-],$

$$x^2 = 1.7 \times 10^{-10} \qquad\qquad x^2 = 4.0 \times 10^{-10}$$

$$x = 1.3 \times 10^{-5} \frac{mole}{liter} \qquad\qquad x = 2.0 \times 10^{-5} \frac{mole}{liter}$$

The unit millimole/ml (mmole/ml) is equivalent to the unit mole/liter, as there are 10^3 millimoles in one mole and 10^3 ml in one liter. The weight of Cl^- not precipitated per 100 ml solution is therefore

(i) $\qquad 1.3 \times 10^{-5} \dfrac{mmole}{ml} \, 100 \, ml \times 35.45 \, \dfrac{mg}{mmole} = 0.046 \, mg \, Cl^-$

(ii) $\qquad 2.0 \times 10^{-5} \dfrac{mmole}{ml} \, 100 \, ml \times 35.45 \, \dfrac{mg}{mmole} = 0.071 \, mg \, Cl^-$

and the negative error for the precipitation in 400 ml of solution is

(i) $\qquad 1.3 \times 10^{-5} \dfrac{mmole}{ml} \, 400 \, ml \times 35.45 \, \dfrac{mg}{mmole} = 0.18 \, mg \, Cl^-$

(ii) $\qquad 2.0 \times 10^{-5} \dfrac{mmole}{ml} \, 400 \, ml \times 35.45 \, \dfrac{mg}{mmole} = 0.28 \, mg \, Cl^-$

The seriousness of this error will depend upon the accuracy desired. A solid is less soluble in a solution containing one of the ions in equilibrium with the solid than it is in pure water (page 505). An excess of the precipitating agent is therefore always used in quantitative analyses to minimize the loss from solubility.

EXAMPLE 3   What should be the equilibrium concentration of Ag^+ if the loss from solubility is not to exceed 1/1000 of the Cl^- content of a sample? The sample, containing 0.051 g Cl^-, is precipitated from 400 ml of solution and is subsequently washed with 100 ml water at 25°C. Assume the activity coefficients of Ag^+ and Cl^- are (i) 1.00; (ii) 0.65.

ANSWER   To solve this problem, first calculate how many grams or mg of Cl^- we have agreed to leave in solution. This quantity, referred to as the *allowable loss*, corresponds to the quantity of Cl^- in solution when equilibrium is established. From the volume of solvent used, the Cl^- equilibrium concentration is obtained; then, from the latter and the solubility product, the equilibrium concentration of Ag^+ is calculated. The allowable loss in milligrams is

$$0.051 \, g \times 1000 \, \frac{mg}{g} \times \frac{1}{1000} = 0.051 \, mg$$

The AgCl, originally precipitated in 400 ml solution, was also washed with 100 ml water; effectively, then, the 0.051 mg AgCl is dissolved in 500 ml solution. The allowable loss in millimoles per ml becomes

$$\frac{0.051 \, mg}{(400 + 100) \, ml \, 35.5 \, \dfrac{mg}{mmole}} = 2.9 \times 10^{-6} \, \frac{mmole}{ml}$$

The quantity of Cl^- in solution at equilibrium should then be

$$2.9 \times 10^{-6} \frac{\text{mmole}}{\text{ml}};$$

the equilibrium concentration of Ag^+ is therefore

(i)	(ii)
$[Ag^+][Cl^-] = 1.7 \times 10^{-10}$	$[Ag^+]\gamma_{Ag^+}[Cl^-]\gamma_{Cl^-} = 1.7 \times 10^{-10}$
$[Ag^+](2.9 \times 10^{-6}) = 1.7 \times 10^{-10}$	$[Ag^+]\,0.65\,(2.9 \times 10^{-6})\,0.65 = 1.7 \times 10^{-10}$
$[Ag^+] = 5.9 \times 10^{-5}$	$[Ag^+] = 1.4 \times 10^{-4}$

A comparison of Examples 2 and 3 shows that the use of an excess of Ag^+ over the exact stoichiometric quantity decreases the quantity of Cl^- remaining in the solution, thereby increasing the completeness of the precipitation of the Cl^-.

In neutral solutions, Ag^+ also forms insoluble solids with several anions such as nitrite, phosphate, oxalate, carbonate, hydroxide, and chromate. These silver salts, however, dissolve in dilute acid solutions through the formation of a gas or a weakly dissociated product. This decreases the anion concentration to a value not permitting the precipitation of the solid.

EXAMPLE 4 In the chloride analysis, dilute nitric acid is used to prevent the precipitation of acid-soluble silver salts. A chloride sample containing oxalate ions, $C_2O_4^{2-}$, is precipitated in 500 ml of solution at 25°C, such that the equilibrium concentrations of Ag^+ and hydrogen oxalate, $HOC_2O_3^-$, are, respectively, 10^{-3} and 2×10^{-3} mmole/ml. What should be the equilibrium concentration of H^+ to prevent precipitation of silver oxalate, $Ag_2C_2O_4$? The equilibria are

$$Ag_2C_2O_4(c) \rightleftharpoons 2Ag^+ + C_2O_4^{2-} \qquad K_1 = 1.1 \times 10^{-11}$$
$$HOC_2O_3^- \rightleftharpoons H^+ + C_2O_4^{2-} \qquad K_2 = 5.0 \times 10^{-5}$$

and the activity coefficients of the ions are practically 1.0.

ANSWER Two equilibrium conditions in the solution must be satisfied,

$$[Ag^+]^2[C_2O_4^{2-}] = 1.1 \times 10^{-11}$$

and

$$\frac{[H^+][C_2O_4^{2-}]}{[HOC_2O_3^-]} = 5.0 \times 10^{-5}$$

Since the equilibrium concentration of Ag^+ is 10^{-3} mmole/ml, the maximum allowable concentration of $C_2O_4^{2-}$ before precipitation can occur is given by

$$(10^{-3})^2[C_2O_4^{2-}] = 1.1 \times 10^{-11}$$

from which

$$[C_2O_4^{2-}] = 1.1 \times 10^{-5} \frac{\text{mmole}}{\text{ml}}$$

Then the equilibrium concentration of H^+ must be given by

$$\frac{[H^+]1.1 \times 10^{-5}}{2 \times 10^{-3}} = 5.0 \times 10^{-5}$$

from which

$$[H^+] = 9.1 \times 10^{-3}$$

21.2 VOLUMETRIC ANALYSIS; TITRATIONS AND NORMALITY

Another procedure used in quantitative analysis involves the addition of a solution of known composition to a solution of the constituent whose quantity is to be determined. The solution of known concentration is called a **standard solution. Titration** is the process of adding measured volumes of one solution to another solution; the measuring instrument used is the buret (Fig. 21.1), a long tube with volume markings and a stopcock at the bottom.

The aim of a titration is the addition of a quantity of the standard solution **chemically equivalent** *to the quantity of the unknown.* The reaction may be an acid-base reaction, an oxidation-reduction, the precipitation of a slightly soluble salt, or any other reaction which goes practically to completion, without complicating side reactions.

A concentration unit commonly employed in volumetric analyses is **normality,** *the number of equivalents of a substance per liter of solution,* eq/liter, designated by the letter N. The unit milliequivalents per milliliter, meq/ml, is equal to the unit eq/liter, as there are 10^3 milliequivalents in one equivalent and 10^3 ml in one liter,

$$\frac{eq}{liter} \times \frac{10^3 \text{ meq}}{eq} \times \frac{liter}{10^3 \text{ ml}} = \frac{meq}{ml}$$

The number of gram equivalents or simply the number of equivalents, eq, of a substance is its quantity expressed in grams divided by its **equivalent weight** expressed in grams per equivalent (g/eq),

$$\frac{\text{mass of substance (g)}}{\text{equivalent weight (g/eq)}} = \text{equivalents (eq)}$$

Since there are 10^3 milliequivalents in one equivalent and 10^3 milligrams in one gram, the unit milligrams/milliequivalent (mg/meq) is equivalent to the unit g/eq.

In problems involving the normality units, it is advantageous to associate eq/liter with g/eq, and meq/ml with mg/meq.

The **equivalent weight** of a substance is the weight of it that consumes (accepts) or supplies (transfers, loses) one mole of unit charges.

(a) Equivalent Weights of Acids and Bases. Thus, **the equivalent of an acid** is the weight in grams that **transfers** one mole of H^+. Correspondingly, **the equivalent weight of a base** is the weight in grams that **accepts** one mole of H^+. Sodium hydroxide, NaOH, can react

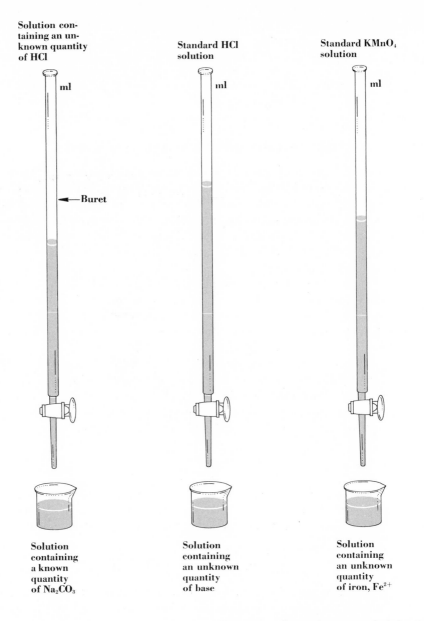

Fig. 21.1. Setups for some typical titrations.

with phosphoric acid, $(HO)_3PO$, for example, in any one of three ways:

$$(HO)_3PO + \quad Na^+ + OH^- \rightarrow \quad Na^+ + (HO)_2PO_2^- + \quad H_2O \quad (1)$$
$$(HO)_3PO + 2(Na^+ + OH^-) \rightarrow 2Na^+ + (HO)PO_3^{2-} + 2H_2O \quad (2)$$
$$(HO)_3PO + 3(Na^+ + OH^-) \rightarrow 3Na^+ + \quad PO_4^{3-} + 3H_2O \quad (3)$$

In reaction (1), since 1 mole of $(HO)_3PO$ transfers 1 mole of H^+, there is 1 equivalent in 1 mole of $(HO)_3PO$; in reaction (2) there are 2 equivalents, and in reaction (3) there are 3 equivalents in 1 mole of $(HO)_3PO$, since 1 mole of the acid transfers, respectively, 2 and 3 moles of H^+. The molecular weight of $(HO)_3PO$ is 98.00; the equivalent weights are therefore

$(HO)_3PO$, Reaction (1):

$$\frac{98.00 \frac{g}{mole}}{1 \frac{eq}{mole}} = 98.00 \frac{g}{eq} = 98.00 \frac{mg}{meq}$$

$(HO)_3PO$, Reaction (2):

$$\frac{98.00 \frac{g}{mole}}{2 \frac{eq}{mole}} = 49.00 \frac{g}{eq} = 49.00 \frac{mg}{meq}$$

$(HO)_3PO$, Reaction (3):

$$\frac{98.00 \frac{g}{mole}}{3 \frac{eq}{mole}} = 32.67 \frac{g}{eq} = 32.67 \frac{mg}{meq}$$

Equivalent weights are evidently not constants; they are a function of the nature of the reaction.

For NaOH in each of the three reactions, (1), (2), and (3), one mole of NaOH accepts one mole of H^+; its equivalent weight is therefore

$$\frac{40.00 \frac{g}{mole}}{1 \frac{eq}{mole}} = 40.00 \frac{g}{eq} = 40.00 \frac{mg}{meq}$$

In the reaction

$$Ca(OH)_2 + 2H^+ \rightarrow Ca^{2+} + 2H_2O$$

there are 2 equivalents in 1 mole of $Ca(OH)_2$, so that its equivalent weight is

$$\frac{74.10 \frac{g}{mole}}{2 \frac{eq}{mole}} = 37.05 \frac{g}{eq}$$

In the reaction of sodium sulfate, Na_2SO_4, with H^+,

$$SO_4^{2-} + H^+ \rightarrow HSO_3^-$$

the equivalent weight of Na_2SO_4 is

$$\frac{142 \frac{g}{mole}}{1 \frac{eq}{mole}} = 142 \frac{g}{eq}$$

while in the reaction

$$SO_4^{2-} + 2H^+ \rightarrow (HO)_2SO_2 \quad (\textit{sulfuric acid})$$

the equivalent weight of Na_2SO_4 is

$$\frac{142 \frac{g}{mole}}{2 \frac{eq}{mole}} = 71 \frac{g}{eq}$$

(b) **Equivalent Weights of Oxidizing and Reducing Agents.** In redox reactions, **the equivalent weight of the oxidizing agent** is the weight that **accepts 1 mole of electrons;** correspondingly, **the equivalent weight of a reducing agent** is the weight that **loses 1 mole of electrons.** For example, in the reaction between potassium dichromate, $K_2Cr_2O_7$, and sulfur dioxide, SO_2,

$$Cr_2O_7^{2-} + 3SO_2 + 5H^+ \rightarrow 2Cr^{3+} + 3HOSO_3^- + H_2O$$

the half-reactions are

reduction: $\qquad Cr_2O_7^{2-} + 14H^+ + 6e^- \rightarrow 2Cr^{3+} + 7H_2O$
oxidation: $\qquad\qquad SO_2 + 2H_2O - 2e^- \rightarrow HOSO_3^- + 3H^+$

One mole of $Cr_2O_7^{2-}$ ions accepts 6 moles of electrons, while 1 mole of SO_2 transfers 2 moles of electrons; hence, there are 6 equivalents in 1 mole of $Cr_2O_7^{2-}$ or in 1 mole of $K_2Cr_2O_7$, 6 equivalents in 2 moles of Cr^{3+}, and 2 equivalents in 1 mole of SO_2.

Their equivalent weights are then

$$K_2Cr_2O_7 \qquad \frac{294 \frac{g}{mole}}{6 \frac{eq}{mole}} = 49.0 \frac{g}{eq}$$

$$Cr_2O_7^{2-} \qquad \frac{216 \frac{g}{mole}}{6 \frac{eq}{mole}} = 36.0 \frac{g}{eq}$$

$$SO_2 \qquad \frac{64.1 \frac{g}{mole}}{2 \frac{eq}{mole}} = 32.1 \frac{g}{eq}$$

$$Cr^{3+} \qquad \frac{52.0 \frac{g}{mole}}{3 \frac{eq}{mole}} = 17.3 \frac{g}{eq}$$

(c) **The Equivalent Weights in Ion Combinations.** In **reactions in which ions combine** to form an insoluble solid or a soluble but practically nondissociating substance, the **number of equivalents in one mole** is equal to the **total charge of either ion** forming the precipitate or the weakly dissociated substance. For example, in the reaction

$$Ca^{2+} + SO_4^{2-} \rightarrow CaSO_4\downarrow$$

the number of equivalents in 1 mole of $CaSO_4$ is 2, the total charge of either ion forming the precipitate; there are also 2 equivalents in each mole of Ca^{2+} and SO_4^{2-}. In the reaction

$$2La^{3+} + 3C_2O_4^{2-} \rightarrow La_2(C_2O_4)_3\downarrow$$

there are 6 equivalents ($2 \times 3^+$ or $3 \times 2^-$) in 1 mole of lanthanum oxalate, $La_2(C_2O_4)_3$; there are also 3 equivalents in 1 mole of La^{3+} and 2 equivalents in 1 mole of $C_2O_4^{2-}$. In the precipitation reaction

$$2Cu^+ + 2Br^- \rightarrow Cu_2Br_2\downarrow$$

there are 2 equivalents in 1 mole of Cu_2Br_2.
In the reaction

$$Hg^{2+} + 2Cl^- \rightarrow HgCl_2 \quad (a\ nonelectrolyte)$$

there are 2 equivalents in 1 mole of $HgCl_2$.
In the reaction

$$Hg_2^{2+} + 2Cl^- \rightarrow Hg_2Cl_2\downarrow$$

there are 2 equivalents in 1 mole of Hg_2^{2+}, 2 equivalents in 1 mole of Hg_2Cl_2, and 1 equivalent in 1 mole of Cl^-.

The system of equivalence is merely a convenient but arbitrary scheme for rebalancing equations such that *1 equivalent of one substance reacts exactly with 1 equivalent of another substance to produce 1 equivalent of each product.* For example, the reaction written as

$$3Ca(OH)_2(c) + 2(HO)_3PO \rightarrow Ca_3(PO_4)_2\downarrow + 6HOH \quad (4)$$
$$\text{\textit{3 moles}} \quad + \quad \text{\textit{2 moles}} \qquad \text{\textit{1 mole}} \quad + \text{\textit{6 moles}}$$

involves 6 equivalents of each reactant and product; dividing Equation (4) by 6 also yields a balanced equation:

$$\tfrac{1}{2}Ca(OH)_2(c) + \tfrac{1}{3}(HO)_3PO \rightarrow \tfrac{1}{6}Ca_3(PO_4)_2 + \quad HOH \quad (5)$$
$$\text{\textit{1 equivalent}} \ + \text{\textit{1 equivalent}} \qquad \text{\textit{1 equivalent}} \ + \text{\textit{1 equivalent}}$$

Since the coefficients of a balanced equation merely indicate the *relative number* of moles of reactants and products, Equation (5) is as acceptable as Equation (4).

EXAMPLE 5 **(a) Give directions for the preparation of 0.5000 liter of a 0.1000N solution of sodium carbonate, Na_2CO_3, which reacts with an acid, as shown,**

$$CO_3^{2-} + 2H^+ \rightarrow CO_2 + H_2O$$

ANSWER **The solution will contain 0.1000 eq/liter; since 0.5000 liter is required, the number of equivalents needed is**

$$0.1000\ \frac{eq}{liter} \times 0.5000\ liter = 0.05000\ eq$$

For the given reaction there are 2 equivalents in 1 mole of Na_2CO_3; the equivalent weight of Na_2CO_3 is therefore

$$\frac{105.99 \frac{g}{mole}}{2 \frac{eq}{mole}} = 53.00 \frac{g}{eq}$$

Hence, the required weight is

$$0.05000 \; eq \times 53.00 \frac{g}{eq} = 2.650 \; g$$

or in one step:

$$0.1000 \frac{eq}{liter} \times 0.5000 \; liter \times 53.00 \frac{g}{eq} = 2.650 \; g$$

To prepare the solution, 2.650 g Na_2CO_3 is weighed into a 500.0-ml calibrated volumetric flask which is then about half-filled with water and shaken to dissolve the salt. Water is now added to the mark etched on the flask neck and the flask is again shaken.

(b) Label the flask in molarity units.

ANSWER Since there are 2 equivalents in 1 mole Na_2CO_3, the label should read $0.05000M$,

$$0.1000 \frac{eq}{liter} \times \frac{mole}{2 \; eq} = 0.05000 \frac{mole}{liter}$$

Relabel the flask if the Na_2CO_3 solution is to react with an acid as shown,

$$CO_3^{2-} + H^+ \rightarrow HOCO_2^-$$

ANSWER For this reaction, there is 1 equivalent in 1 mole of Na_2CO_3; whence the label should read $0.05000N$,

$$0.05000 \frac{mole}{liter} \times \frac{1 \; eq}{mole} = 0.05000 \frac{eq}{liter}$$

Example 5 illustrates the wisdom of labeling solutions in molarity, rather than normality, units.

EXAMPLE 6 1.14 g of pure fused barium chloride, $BaCl_2$, is dissolved in a 100.0-ml volumetric flask. Calculate the normality of the solution to be used in the volumetric determination of SO_4^{2-} by precipitation as $BaSO_4$.

ANSWER First calculate the quantity of $BaCl_2$ dissolved per liter of solution,

$$\frac{1.14 \; g}{100.0 \; ml} 1000 \frac{ml}{liter} = 11.4 \frac{g}{liter}$$

Since there are 2 equivalents in 1 mole of $BaCl_2$, its equivalent weight is

$$\frac{208 \frac{g}{mole}}{2 \frac{eq}{mole}} = 104 \frac{g}{eq}$$

Whence, the normality of the solution is

$$\frac{11.4 \frac{g}{liter}}{104 \frac{g}{eq}} = 0.110 \frac{eq}{liter} = 0.110 N$$

or in one step:

$$\frac{1.14 \, g}{100.0 \, ml} 1000 \frac{ml}{liter} \frac{1}{104 \frac{g}{eq}} = 0.110 \frac{eq}{liter} = 0.110 N$$

EXAMPLE 7   How many mg of silver nitrate are in 31.75 ml of $0.1242N$ solution of $AgNO_3$ used in a Cl^- titration?

ANSWER   The number of meq of $AgNO_3$ is given by

$$0.1242 \frac{meq}{ml} 31.75 \, ml = 3.943 \, meq$$

Since the equivalent weight of $AgNO_3$ is

$$\frac{169.9 \frac{g}{mole}}{1 \frac{eq}{mole}} = 169.9 \frac{g}{eq} = 169.9 \frac{mg}{meq}$$

the weight of it in the given volume is

$$3.943 \, meq \, 169.9 \frac{mg}{meq} = 670.0 \, mg$$

or in one step:

$$0.1242 \frac{meq}{ml} 31.75 \, ml \, 169.9 \frac{mg}{meq} = 670.0 \, mg$$

The following examples involve redox reactions.

EXAMPLE 8   How many grams of sodium oxalate, $Na_2C_2O_4$, are required to prepare 0.5000 liter of $0.1500N$ solution to be used as a reducing agent in the half-reaction $C_2O_4^{2-} - 2e^- \rightarrow 2CO_2$?

ANSWER   Since 1 mole of $C_2O_4^{2-}$ transfers 2 moles of electrons, there are 2 equivalents in 1 mole of $Na_2C_2O_4$; its equivalent weight is therefore

$$\frac{134.0 \ \frac{g}{mole}}{2 \ \frac{eq}{mole}} = 67.00 \ \frac{g}{eq}$$

Whence, the required number of grams is given by

$$0.5000 \ \text{liter} \times 0.1500 \ \frac{eq}{liter} \times 67.00 \ \frac{g}{eq} = 5.025 \ g$$

EXAMPLE 9   0.5692 g arsenic trioxide, As_2O_3, is dissolved and converted to arsenious acid, $(HO)AsO$,* in a 100.0-ml volumetric flask. Calculate the normality of the solution to be used as a reducing agent in the half-reaction

$$(HO)AsO + 2H_2O - 2e^- \rightarrow (HO)_3AsO + 2H^+$$

ANSWER   From the given half-reaction, there are 2 equivalents in 1 mole of arsenious acid. However, 1 mole of As_2O_3 produces 2 moles of $(HO)AsO$; hence there are 4 equivalents in 1 mole of As_2O_3 and its equivalent weight is

$$\frac{197.84 \ \frac{g}{mole}}{4 \ \frac{eq}{mole}} = 49.46 \ \frac{g}{eq}$$

The normality of the solution is then given by

$$\frac{0.5692 \ g}{100.0 \ ml} 1000 \ \frac{ml}{liter} \ \frac{1}{49.46 \ \frac{g}{eq}} = 0.1151 \ \frac{eq}{liter} = 0.1151N$$

EXAMPLE 10   How many grams of potassium permanganate, $KMnO_4$, are in 40.65 ml of $0.1572N$ solution used in a titration as an oxidizing agent in an acid solution? The half-reaction is

$$MnO_4^- + 8H^+ + 5e^- \rightarrow Mn^{2+} + 4H_2O$$

ANSWER   From the given half-reaction, the equivalent weight of $KMnO_4$ is

$$\frac{158.04 \ \frac{g}{mole}}{5 \ \frac{eq}{mole}} = 31.61 \ \frac{g}{eq}$$

Whence, the weight of it in the given volume is

$$\frac{40.65 \ ml}{1000 \ \frac{ml}{liter}} 0.1572 \ \frac{eq}{liter} 31.61 \ \frac{g}{eq} = 0.2020 \ g$$

* Arsenious acid is most likely a hydrated oxide $As_2O_3(H_2O)_x$; its formula is not definitely established.

EXAMPLE 11 What volume in ml should be taken from a stock solution of $0.30M$ $Ca(MnO_4)_2$ to prepare 250 ml of $0.12N$ solution for use in a reaction in which MnO_4^- is reduced to Mn^{2+}?

ANSWER The number of milliequivalents required is

$$250 \text{ ml } 0.12 \frac{\text{meq}}{\text{ml}} = 30 \text{ meq}$$

There are 5 milliequivalents in 1 millimole of MnO_4^- or 10 milliequivalents in 1 millimole of $Ca(MnO_4)_2$. Hence, the required number of millimoles of $Ca(MnO_4)_2$ is

$$\frac{30 \text{ meq}}{10 \dfrac{\text{meq}}{\text{mmole}}} = 3.0 \text{ mmole}$$

The stock solution contains 0.30 mmole/ml; the required volume is therefore

$$\frac{3.0 \text{ mmole}}{0.30 \dfrac{\text{mmole}}{\text{ml}}} = 10 \text{ ml}$$

EXAMPLE 12 In an acidic solution, 25.00 ml of $0.1050N$ MnO_4^- are used to oxidize Fe^{2+} to Fe^{3+}, ultimately recovered as Fe_2O_3. How many mg of Fe_2O_3 are recovered?

ANSWER The number of milliequivalents of MnO_4^- is

$$25.00 \text{ ml } 0.1050 \frac{\text{meq}}{\text{ml}} = 2.625 \text{ meq}$$

This reacts with an equal number of milliequivalents of Fe^{2+} to produce an equal number of milliequivalents of Fe^{3+} or Fe_2O_3. Hence

$$2.625 \text{ meq } MnO_4^- = 2.625 \text{ meq } Fe^{2+} = 2.625 \text{ meq } Fe^{3+} = 2.625 \text{ meq } Fe_2O_3$$

From the half-reaction, $Fe^{2+} - 1e^- \rightarrow Fe^{3+}$, there is 1 equivalent in 1 mole of Fe^{3+}; but 2 moles of Fe^{3+} produce 1 mole of Fe_2O_3. Therefore, there are 2 equivalents in 1 mole of Fe_2O_3 and its equivalent weight is

$$\frac{159.70 \dfrac{\text{g}}{\text{mole}}}{2 \dfrac{\text{eq}}{\text{mole}}} = 79.85 \frac{\text{g}}{\text{eq}} = 79.85 \frac{\text{mg}}{\text{meq}}$$

The weight of Fe_2O_3 is then given by

$$2.625 \text{ meq } 79.85 \frac{\text{mg}}{\text{meq}} = 209.6 \text{ mg}$$

or in one step:

$$25.00 \text{ ml } 0.1050 \frac{\text{meq}}{\text{ml}} \, 79.85 \frac{\text{mg}}{\text{meq}} = 209.6 \text{ mg}$$

The following examples involve titrations.

EXAMPLE 13   35.72 ml of KMnO₄ reacts completely with 25.00 ml of 0.1500N Na₂C₂O₄ in an acid solution. Calculate the normality of the permanganate solution.

ANSWER   Since any reactant reacts with the same number of equivalents of a second reactant, the number of milliequivalents in 35.72 ml KMnO₄ equals the number of milliequivalents in 25.00 ml Na₂C₂O₄; or

$$25.00 \text{ ml } 0.1500 \frac{\text{meq}}{\text{ml}} = 3.750 \text{ meq Na}_2\text{C}_2\text{O}_4 = 3.750 \text{ meq KMnO}_4$$

The normality of the KMnO₄ solution is therefore

$$\frac{3.750 \text{ meq}}{35.72 \text{ ml}} = 0.1050 \frac{\text{meq}}{\text{ml}}$$

EXAMPLE 14   How many ml of 0.1140N basic solution are required to react completely with 28.65 ml of 0.1060N acid solution?

ANSWER   The number of milliequivalents of acid is

$$28.65 \text{ ml } 0.1060 \frac{\text{meq}}{\text{ml}} = 3.037 \text{ meq}$$

Hence, 3.037 milliequivalents of base are required. Since the basic solution contains 0.1140 meq/ml, the required volume is given by

$$\frac{3.037 \text{ meq}}{0.1140 \frac{\text{meq}}{\text{ml}}} = 26.64 \text{ ml}$$

21.3   TITRATION CURVES

An important question in connection with Examples 13 and 14 has not yet been answered. Namely, in the titration of one solution with another solution, how does the chemist know when to stop the addition? In the type of titration involved in Example 13, this question has a comparatively simple answer. One drop, about 0.05 ml, of the 0.11N permanganate solution added to as much as 500 ml water suffices to impart a distinct pink color to the resultant solution. Hence, with the addition of the permanganate solution to the colorless oxalate solution, the solution remains colorless as long as oxalate ions are in excess. When just sufficient permanganate is added so that exactly equivalent (stoichiometric) quantities have reacted, the solution is still colorless. The addition of one drop of the permanganate solution *in excess* then imparts a pink color to the solution. The stage at which equivalent quantities of the standard solution and the unknown have been mixed is called the **equivalence point of the titration.** The **end point,** signaled by a sudden change in a physical or chemical property of the solution, indicates the end of the titration and the buret reading is taken.

EXAMPLE 15 **In a titration with permanganate solution the end point was signaled at 35.72 ml. The end point is in excess of the equivalence point by 0.05 ml. Calculate the titration error in percentage.**

ANSWER **The equivalence point corresponds to**

$$35.72 \text{ ml} - 0.05 \text{ ml} = 35.67 \text{ ml}$$

The percent error is therefore

$$\frac{+0.05 \text{ ml}}{35.67 \text{ ml}} \ 100 = +0.14\%$$

This is usually not a serious error.

Frequently the titration reactants do not produce a color change. It is then necessary to add an indicator to the solution being titrated to indicate the end point. A starch solution, for example, is used as the indicator in titrations with iodine solution; an excess of one drop of iodine solution imparts an unmistakable blue color to the resultant solution.

In titrations of acids and bases, advantage is taken of the observation that the *pH of the solution* being titrated *changes rapidly* as the equivalence point is approached. When an acid and a base have been mixed in equivalent quantities, they are said to have **neutralized** each other. This word is misleading, however, for the resulting solution may be neutral, acidic, or basic. Also, indicators (page 501) possess a characteristic pH range over which they exhibit a visible color change. How, then, do we decide which indicator to use? Since the object of any titration is to mix equivalent quantities of reactants, *the choice of an indicator is determined by the pH of the solution at the equivalence point.*

Let us say that an acid solution is in a beaker or a flask; the basic solution is then in the buret. Assume that the base is an ionic hydroxide, for example, NaOH. As the base is added to the acid, the pH of the solution in the beaker increases. The dependence of pH on the quantity of base added is shown in Fig. 21.2. If the acid is strong (Fig. 21.2a), the initial effect of adding the base is merely to decrease the concentration of the acid; if the acid is weak (Fig. 21.2b), the initial effect is to form a buffer solution containing the acid and its conjugate base (page 497). In either case, the pH rises slowly at first. *The curve becomes almost vertical when equivalent quantities of acid and base are present.* Hence, to provide the signal for the chemist to stop adding solution and to take the volume reading, the indicator must be so chosen that its color change is somewhere within the pH range spanned by the steeply rising portion of the curve. Fig. 21.2a shows that either phenolphthalein or methyl red is suitable for the HCl–NaOH titration while Fig. 21.2b shows that phenolphthalein, and not methyl red, is suitable for the acetic acid–NaOH titration. Simi-

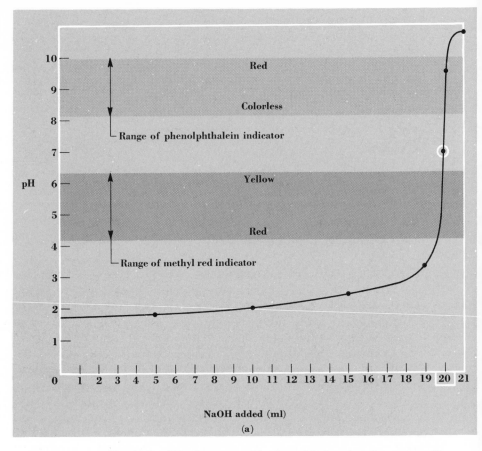

Fig. 21.2. *Titration curve; pH values plotted against the corresponding volume added from a buret. (a) 20.00 ml of 0.1000M HCl diluted to 100.0 ml and titrated with 0.1000M NaOH; (b) 20.00 ml of 0.1000M HOAc (acetic*

larly, in a titration involving a strong acid and a weak base, the indicator would have to change color on the acid side.

At the equivalence point, *the solution contains the product* of neutralization of the acid and base, but, by the definition of the equivalence point, it contains *no excess of either the acid or the base used in the titration.*

EXAMPLE 16 **25.00 ml 0.1000M acetic acid, HOAc, is diluted to 100.0 ml at 25.0°C. Select an indicator suitable for the titration of the acetic acid by 0.1000M NaOH. Sodium acetate is a strong electrolyte and may be assumed to be completely dissociated. Assume activity coefficients of HOAc and the ions are 1.00.**

ANSWER **The object here is to calculate the pH of the solution at the equivalence point. An indicator that changes color at about this calculated pH value is then selected.**

The original quantity of HOAc present is

$$25.00 \text{ ml} \times 0.1000 \frac{\text{mmole}}{\text{ml}} = 2.500 \text{ mmole}$$

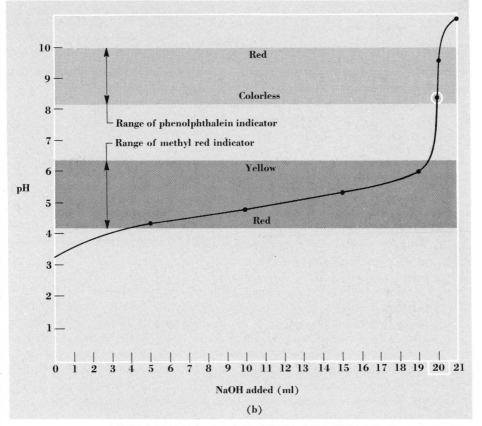

(b)

acid) diluted to 100.0 ml and titrated with 0.1000M NaOH. Temperature is 25°C. Also shown is the pH range of the indicator, the range of pH values through which visual changes in color occur. The equivalence point is circled.

HOAc and OH⁻ produce water and acetate ion,

$$HOAc + OH^- \rightarrow H_2O + OAc^-$$

2.500 mmoles of OH⁻ are therefore required to reach the equivalence point corresponding to a volume of 25.00 ml NaOH,

$$\frac{2.500 \; \text{mmole OH}^-}{0.1000 \; \dfrac{\text{mmole OH}^-}{\text{ml}}} = 25.00 \; \text{ml}$$

The volume at the equivalence point is then the original acetic acid solution, 100.0 ml, plus the added 25.00 ml NaOH, or 125.0 ml. Also, at the equivalence point, we mixed exactly equivalent amounts of HOAc and NaOH (2.500 mmoles), producing 2.500 mmoles of OAc⁻. Thus, the solution at the equivalence point is identical to a 125.0 ml solution obtained on adding water to 2.500 mmoles NaOAc. The reaction of OAc⁻ with H₂O,

$$OAc^- + H_2O \rightarrow HOAc + OH^- \qquad K_b = \frac{K_w}{K_a} = 5.77 \times 10^{-10}$$

then determines the pH of the solution (page 490),

$$[OAc^-] = \frac{2.500 \text{ mmoles}}{125.0 \text{ ml}} = 2.00 \times 10^{-2} \frac{\text{mmole}}{\text{ml}}$$

$$[HOAc] = [OH^-]$$

Since the quantity of OAc^- that reacts with water is negligible compared to the quantity present,

$$\frac{[HOAc][OH^-]}{[OAc^-]} = \frac{[OH^-]^2}{2.00 \times 10^{-2}} = 5.77 \times 10^{-10}$$

from which

$$[OH^-] = 3.40 \times 10^{-6}$$

and

$$pOH = -\log 3.40 \times 10^{-6} = 5.47$$
$$pH = 14.00 - 5.47 = 8.53$$

The indicator should change color at about pH 9; Table 19.2 (page 502) shows that phenolphthalein is suitable.

When the acid is polyprotic, different indicators may be selected to change color at each of the several equivalence points. Figure 21.3 refers to phosphoric acid, $(HO)_3PO$. At the first equivalence point (pH about 4), one mole of NaOH has been added per mole of $(HO)_3PO$, and the solution contains $Na^+ + (HO)_2PO_2^-$. At the second equivalence point (pH about 9), twice as much NaOH has been added (two moles per mole of $(HO)_3PO$), and the solution contains $2Na^+ + (HO)PO_3^{2-}$. One would expect a third equivalence point, corresponding to $3Na^+ + PO_4^{3-}$, but $(HO)PO_3^{2-}$ is so weak an acid that the reaction

$$(HO)PO_3^{2-} + OH^- \rightarrow PO_4^{3-} + H_2O$$

reaches an equilibrium in which much of the OH^- added after the second equivalence point merely remains as such, instead of reacting with the

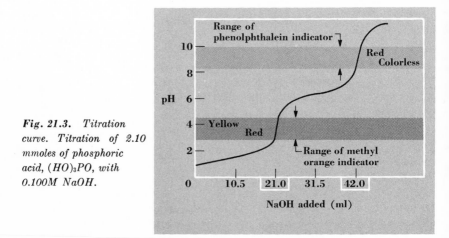

Fig. 21.3. *Titration curve. Titration of 2.10 mmoles of phosphoric acid, (HO)₃PO, with 0.100M NaOH.*

$(HO)PO_3^{2-}$. $(HO)_3PO$ thus acts in aqueous solutions as if it were only diprotic.

If an attempt is made to titrate a very weak acid, for example boric acid, for which no large change in pH occurs in the vicinity of the equivalence point, such a large volume of the base is required to change the color of an indicator that an end point would be practically impossible to detect with the eye. In these cases, the solution in the region of the equivalence point is well buffered with OH^- ions.

21.4 CALCULATION OF TITRATION CURVES

(a) **Strong Acid and Strong Base.** When a solution of a strong acid, such as HCl, is titrated with a solution of a strong base such as NaOH, the reaction

$$H^+ + OH^- \rightarrow H_2O$$

occurs but a certain quantity of H^+ is left in the solution. However, the addition of the sodium hydroxide dilutes the acid solution and this dilution affects the activity (concentration) of the remaining H^+. At the equivalence point, $a_{H^+} = a_{OH^-}$ or $[H^+] = [OH^-]$, and the solution contains Na^+ and Cl^- ions, neither of which possesses acidic or basic properties. Beyond the equivalence point, the added NaOH stays in solution as excess OH^-.

EXAMPLE 17   **20.00 ml of 0.1000N HCl is diluted to 100.0 ml at 25.0°C. What is (a) the pH of the solution and what is the pH after (b) 5.00 ml, (c) 20.00 ml, (d) 20.05 ml, (e) 21.00 ml, of 0.1000N NaOH are added? HCl and NaOH are completely dissociated. $K_w(H_2O \rightleftharpoons H^+ + OH^-)$ at 25.0°C is 1.007×10^{-14}; assume the activity coefficients of H^+ and OH^- ions remain constant at (i) 1.00 and (ii) 0.90 during the titration.**

ANSWER   (a) *0.00 ml NaOH added.* **The original quantity of HCl present is**

$$20.00 \; \text{ml} \; 0.1000 \; \frac{\text{meq}}{\text{ml}} = 2.000 \; \text{meq}$$

$$2.000 \; \text{meq} \; \frac{1 \; \text{mmole}}{1 \; \text{meq}} = 2.000 \; \text{mmole}$$

Since the volume of the solution is 100.0 ml,

$$[H^+] = \frac{2.000 \; \text{mmole}}{100.0 \; \text{ml}} = 2.000 \times 10^{-2} \frac{\text{mmole}}{\text{ml}}$$

Defining pH in terms of the activity of H^+,

(i)	(ii)
$pH = -\log a_{H^+}$	$pH = -\log a_{H^+}$
$\quad = -\log ([H^+]\gamma_{H^+})$	$\quad = -\log ([H^+]\gamma_{H^+})$
$\quad = -\log [H^+]$	$\quad = -\log (2.00 \times 10^{-2} \times 0.90)$
$\quad = -\log 2.00 \times 10^{-2}$	$\quad = 1.75$
$\quad = 1.70$	

(b) *5.00 ml NaOH added.* **The number of mmoles of NaOH added is**

$$5.00 \text{ ml} \times 0.1000 \, \frac{\text{meq}}{\text{ml}} = 0.500 \text{ meq} = 0.500 \text{ mmole}$$

Thus, 0.500 mmole of NaCl forms and 1.500 mmoles of HCl remains,

$$2.000 \text{ mmole HCl} - 0.500 \text{ mmole HCl} = 1.500 \text{ mmole HCl}$$

Since the NaCl does not possess acidic or basic properties, the [H⁺] is not affected by the presence of this salt. Hence

$$[\text{H}^+] = \frac{1.500 \text{ mmole}}{(100.0 + 5.0)\text{ml}} = 1.43 \times 10^{-2} \, \frac{\text{mmole}}{\text{ml}}$$

and

(i)	(ii)
pH $= -\log 1.43 \times 10^{-2}$	pH $= -\log (1.43 \times 10^{-2} \times 0.90)$
$= 1.85$	$= 1.89$

(c) The addition of 20.00 ml of 0.1000N NaOH corresponds exactly to the equivalence point; only NaCl and water are therefore present in the solution. Therefore

$$[\text{H}^+] = [\text{OH}^-] \qquad\qquad a_{\text{H}^+} = a_{\text{OH}^-}$$

Since

$$[\text{H}^+][\text{OH}^-] = 1.007 \times 10^{-14} \qquad a_{\text{H}^+} \cdot a_{\text{OH}^-} = 1.007 \times 10^{-14}$$

then

$$[\text{H}^+]^2 = 1.007 \times 10^{-14} \qquad\qquad a_{\text{H}^+}^2 = 1.007 \times 10^{-14}$$
$$[\text{H}^+] = 1.00 \times 10^{-7} \qquad\qquad a_{\text{H}^+} = 1.00 \times 10^{-7}$$
$$\text{pH} = 7.00^* \qquad\qquad\qquad \text{pH} = 7.00$$

(d) The addition of 20.050 ml corresponds to the addition of an excess of 0.050 ml (one drop) or 0.0050 mmole of NaOH. The effect is the same as addition of 0.0050 mmole NaOH to 120.1 ml H₂O. Hence

$$[\text{OH}^-] = \frac{0.0050 \text{ mmole}}{(100.0 + 20.1)\text{ml}}$$
$$= 4.17 \times 10^{-5} \, \frac{\text{mmole}}{\text{ml}}$$

whence

(i)	(ii)
pOH $= -\log 4.17 \times 10^{-5}$	pOH $= -\log a_{\text{OH}^-}$
$= 4.38$	$= -\log (4.17 \times 10^{-5} \times 0.90)$
	$= 4.43$
pH $= 14.00 - 4.38$	pH $= 14.00 - 4.43$
$= 9.62$	$= 9.57$

(e) The addition of 21.00 ml corresponds to the addition of an excess 1.00 ml or 0.1000 mmole NaOH. Hence

$$[\text{OH}^-] = \frac{0.1000 \text{ mmole}}{(100.0 + 21.0)\text{ml}}$$
$$= 8.26 \times 10^{-4} \, \frac{\text{mmole}}{\text{ml}}$$

* The presence of CO_2 absorbed from the air may lower the pH to about 6.

whence

(i)	(ii)
$pOH = -\log 8.26 \times 10^{-4}$	$pOH = -\log(8.26 \times 10^{-4} \times 0.90)$
$= 3.08$	$= 3.13$
$pH = 10.92$	$pH = 10.87$

These calculated pH values (ii), with other similarly calculated values, are plotted in Fig. 21.2a.

(b) Weak Acid and Strong Base. When a solution of a weak acid, such as acetic acid (HOAc), is titrated with a solution of a strong base, such as NaOH, the reaction

$$HOAc + Na^+ + OH^- \rightarrow OAc^- + H_2O$$

occurs and the acid solution is diluted. However, at the equivalence point, we now have a solution of NaOAc; unlike Cl^-, OAc^- reacts with water. Beyond the equivalence point, the OH^- and the HOAc resulting from the hydrolysis of OAc^- are so small that the added NaOH determines the pH of the solution.

EXAMPLE 18   **20.00 ml of 0.1000M acetic acid, HOAc, is diluted to 100.0 ml at 25.0°C. What is (a) the pH of the solution and what is the pH after (b) 5.00 ml, (c) 19.00 ml, (d) 20.00 ml, (e) 20.050 ml, of 0.1000M NaOH are added? K_a(HOAc $\rightleftharpoons H^+ + OAc^-$) at 25.0°C is 1.750×10^{-5} and $K_w = 1.01 \times 10^{-14}$; assume the activity coefficients of HOAc and the ions are 1.0 in the pure acetic acid solution, but that during the titration the activity coefficients of HOAc and the ions are, respectively, (i) 1.00 and 1.0; (ii) 1.00 and 0.90. Sodium acetate is a strong electrolyte and may be assumed to be completely dissociated. Further, we may _assume_ that the quantity of HOAc that dissociates is negligible compared to the quantity of HOAc present and to the quantity of sodium acetate that forms during the titration.**

ANSWER   (a) _0.00 ml NaOH added._ **The original quantity of HOAc present is**

$$20.00 \text{ ml} \times 0.1000 \frac{\text{mmole}}{\text{ml}} = 2.000 \text{ mmoles}$$

Since the volume of the solution is 100.0 ml, then

$$[HOAc] = \frac{2.000 \text{ mmole}}{100.0 \text{ ml}} = 2.000 \times 10^{-2} \frac{\text{mmole}}{\text{ml}}$$

and

(i)	(ii)
$[HOAc] = 2.00 \times 10^{-2}$	$a_{HOAc} = [HOAc]\gamma_{HOAc}$
	$= 2.00 \times 10^{-2} \times 1.00$

In acetic acid solutions

The concentration of H^+ is given by	The activity of H^+ is given by
$[H^+] = 1.75 \times 10^{-5} \dfrac{[HOAc]}{[OAc^-]}$	$a_{H^+} = 1.75 \times 10^{-5} \dfrac{a_{HOAc}}{a_{OAc^-}}$

In the pure acetic acid solution

$$[H^+] = [OAc^-] \qquad\qquad a_{H^+} = a_{OAc^-}$$

Then

$$[H^+]^2 = 1.75 \times 10^{-5} \times 2.00 \times 10^{-2} \qquad a_{H^+}^2 = 1.75 \times 10^{-5} a_{HOAc}$$
$$= 1.75 \times 10^{-5} \times 2.00 \times 10^{-2}$$
$$[H^+] = 5.92 \times 10^{-4} \qquad\qquad a_{H^+} = 5.92 \times 10^{-4}$$
$$pH = -\log [H^+] = 3.23 \qquad\qquad pH = -\log a_{H^+} = 3.23$$

(b) *5.00 ml NaOH added.* **The number of mmoles of NaOH added is**

$$5.00 \text{ ml} \times 0.1000 \frac{\text{mmole}}{\text{ml}} = 0.500 \text{ mmole}$$

Thus 0.500 mmole of NaOAc forms and 1.500 mmoles of HOAc remains,

$$2.000 \text{ mmole HOAc} - 0.500 \text{ mmole HOAc} = 1.500 \text{ mmole HOAc}$$

Hence

$$[HOAc] = \frac{1.50 \text{ mmole}}{(100.0 + 5.0)\text{ml}}$$

and

$$[OAc^-] = \frac{0.500 \text{ mmole}}{(100.0 + 5.0)\text{ml}}$$

Whence

(i)

$$[H^+] = 1.75 \times 10^{-5} \frac{\left(\dfrac{1.50}{105.0}\right)}{\left(\dfrac{0.500}{105.0}\right)}$$

$$= 1.75 \times 10^{-5} \frac{1.50}{0.500}$$

$$= 5.25 \times 10^{-5}$$

$$pH = 4.28$$

(ii)

$$a_{H^+} = 1.75 \times 10^{-5} \frac{\left(\dfrac{1.50}{105.0}\right)(1.0)}{\left(\dfrac{0.500}{105.0}\right)(0.90)}$$

$$= 1.75 \times 10^{-5} \frac{1.50}{0.500 \times 0.90}$$

$$= 5.83 \times 10^{-5}$$

$$pH = 4.24$$

(c) *19.00 ml NaOH added.* **The number of mmoles of NaOH added is 1.900 mmoles. Thus, 1.900 mmoles of NaOAc forms and 0.100 mmoles of HOAc remains. Hence**

(i)

$$[H^+] = 1.75 \times 10^{-5} \frac{0.100}{1.90}$$

$$= 9.21 \times 10^{-7}$$

(ii)

$$a_{H^+} = 1.75 \times 10^{-5} \frac{0.100 \times 1.0}{1.90 \times 0.90}$$

$$= 1.02 \times 10^{-6}$$

and

$$pH = 6.04 \qquad\qquad pH = 5.99$$

(d) The addition of 20.00 ml of 0.1000M NaOH corresponds exactly to the equivalence point; the solution contains sodium acetate and water. There-

fore, the reaction of the acetate ion with water

$$\text{OAc}^- + \text{H}_2\text{O} \rightleftharpoons \text{HOAc} + \text{OH}^- \qquad K_b = \frac{K_w}{K_a} = 5.77 \times 10^{-10}$$

determines the pH of the solution (page 490).

The number of mmoles of OAc^- present is 2.000 mmole. Hence

$$[\text{OAc}^-] = \frac{2.000 \text{ mmole}}{(100.0 + 20.0)\text{ml}} = 1.67 \times 10^{-2} \frac{\text{mmole}}{\text{ml}}$$

and

$$[\text{HOAc}] = [\text{OH}^-]$$

Since the quantity of OAc^- that reacts with water is negligible compared to the quantity present

(i)

$$\frac{[\text{HOAc}][\text{OH}^-]}{[\text{OAc}^-]} = 5.77 \times 10^{-10}$$

$$\frac{[\text{OH}^-]^2}{[\text{OAc}^-]} = 5.77 \times 10^{-10}$$

$$\frac{[\text{OH}^-]^2}{1.67 \times 10^{-2}} = 5.77 \times 10^{-10}$$

(ii)

$$\frac{a_{\text{HOAc}}a_{\text{OH}^-}}{a_{\text{OAc}^-}} = 5.77 \times 10^{-10}$$

$$\frac{[\text{HOAc}]1.0[\text{OH}^-]0.90}{[\text{OAc}^-]0.90} = 5.77 \times 10^{-10}$$

$$\frac{[\text{OH}^-]^2}{1.67 \times 10^{-2}} = 5.77 \times 10^{-10}$$

from which

$$[\text{OH}^-] = 3.10 \times 10^{-6}$$
$$\text{pOH} = -\log 3.10 \times 10^{-6}$$
$$= 5.51$$
$$\text{pH} = 14.00 - 5.51 = 8.49$$

$$[\text{OH}^-] = 3.10 \times 10^{-6}$$
$$\text{pOH} = -\log(3.10 \times 10^{-6}$$
$$\times 0.90) = 5.55$$
$$\text{pH} = 14.00 - 5.55 = 8.45$$

(e) The addition of 20.050 ml corresponds to the addition of an excess of 0.050 ml (one drop) or 0.0050 mmole of NaOH. Hence

$$[\text{OH}^-] = \frac{0.0050 \text{ mmole}}{(100.0 + 20.1)\text{ml}} = 4.17 \times 10^{-5} \frac{\text{mmole}}{\text{ml}}$$

Since this concentration of OH^- is larger than that resulting from the hydrolysis of OAc^- by at least a factor of 10, we may assume that it determines the pH of the solution:

$$\text{pOH} = -\log 4.17 \times 10^{-5}$$
$$= 4.38$$
$$\text{pH} = 9.62$$

$$\text{pOH} = -\log(4.17 \times 10^{-5} \times 0.90)$$
$$= 4.43$$
$$\text{pH} = 9.57$$

These calculated pH values (ii), with other similarly calculated values, are plotted in Fig. 21.2b.

21.5 COMBINED VOLUMETRIC AND GRAVIMETRIC ANALYSIS

Certain samples may be analyzed by a combination of volumetric and gravimetric techniques as illustrated in the following example.

EXAMPLE 19 A sample, containing Cl⁻ and I⁻ ions and inert material, requires 32.50 ml 0.1161N AgNO₃ for titration. The same quantity of the sample treated with excess AgNO₃ yields 0.7060 g of AgCl and AgI precipitate. Calculate the number of milligrams of each silver halide in the precipitate. The equivalent weights of the silver halides are, respectively, 143.3 and 234.8 mg/meq.

ANSWER From the titration data, the total number of milliequivalents of Cl⁻ and I⁻ is

$$32.50 \ \text{ml} \ 0.1161 \ \frac{\text{meq}}{\text{ml}} = 3.773 \ \text{meq}(\text{Cl}^- + \text{I}^-)$$

But the weight of the precipitate must also be equivalent to 3.773 meq. Hence, if we let x = milligrams of AgCl, then $706.0 - x$ is the weight of AgI and

$$\frac{x \ \text{mg AgCl}}{143.3 \ \frac{\text{mg AgCl}}{\text{meq}}} + \frac{(706.0 - x) \ \text{mg AgI}}{234.8 \ \frac{\text{mg AgI}}{\text{meq}}} = 3.773 \ \text{meq}$$

$$x = 282 \ \text{mg AgCl}$$

Whence, 706 mg − 282 mg AgCl = 424 mg AgI.

21.6 PRECISION AND ACCURACY

The only kind of physical quantity that can be measured with perfect accuracy is a tally of discrete objects, for example, dollars and cents or the number of objects in a museum case. In measuring a quantity capable of continuous variation, for example mass or length, there is always some uncertainty because the answer cannot be expressed by any finite number of digits. Besides errors resulting from mistakes made by the experimenter in the construction and use of measuring devices, other errors over which the experimenter has no control are inherent in measurements. Therefore, at least two, preferably three or more, determinations of any quantity should be made. The "true" value—more correctly the "accepted" value—of a quantity is chosen by some competent group, such as a committee of experts, as the most probable value from available data, examined critically for errors.

The **precision** of a measurement is a statement about the mutual agreement of repeated determinations; it is a measure of the reproducibility of an experiment. The arithmetical average of the values is usually taken as the "best" value. The simplest measure of precision is the **average deviation,** calculated by first determining the average of the series of measurements; then the deviation of each individual measurement from the average is calculated, and finally the deviations, each treated as a positive quantity, are averaged.

EXAMPLE 20 **In a series of determinations, the following values for the electronic charge were obtained:** 4.80×10^{-10}, 4.79×10^{-10}, 4.81×10^{-10}, 4.76×10^{-10} **esu. Calculate the average deviation.**

	Average of individual measurements		Individual deviations from the average
	4.80×10^{-10}		0.01×10^{-10}
	4.79×10^{-10}		0.00×10^{-10}
	4.81×10^{-10}		0.02×10^{-10}
	4.76×10^{-10}		0.03×10^{-10}

$$4 \,\big|\, 19.16 \times 10^{-10} \qquad\qquad 4 \,\big|\, 0.06 \times 10^{-10}$$

Average: 4.79×10^{-10} esu   *Average deviation:* 0.02×10^{-10} esu

These results would be reported as $(4.79 \pm 0.02) \times 10^{-10}$ esu.

Very frequently precision is expressed as the **relative average deviation**, r.a.d., defined as the average deviation divided by the average, so that the r.a.d. for the series of measurements in Example 20 is

$$\text{r.a.d.} = \frac{0.02 \times 10^{-10} \text{ esu}}{4.79 \times 10^{-10} \text{ esu}} = 0.0042 \; (dimensionless)$$

Multiplication by 100 yields the r.a.d. on a percentage basis,

$$\text{r.a.d.} = \frac{0.02 \times 10^{-10}}{4.79 \times 10^{-10}} \, 100 = 0.42\%$$

If, for reasons of numerical convenience, the r.a.d. is to be expressed as "parts per thousand parts," or "parts per million parts" (p.p.m.), the fractional value may be increased by the appropriate multiplier. Thus

$$
\begin{aligned}
0.0042 \; (fractional) &= 0.0042 \times 10^2\%, \text{ or } 0.42\% \\
&= 0.0042 \times 10^3 \; parts \; per \; thousand \; parts, \; or \; 4.2 \\
&\quad\; parts \; per \; thousand \; (p.p.t.) \\
&= 0.0042 \times 10^6 \; parts \; per \; million, \; or \; 4200 \; p.p.m.
\end{aligned}
$$

The precision of an experiment varies with the method and apparatus used. With the apparatus commonly available for quantitative analytical work, a precision of 1 part per 1000 or better is attainable by an experienced chemist for the gravimetric determination of the chloride in a water-soluble sample; with the average inexperienced student, a precision of about 10 parts per 1000 parts is more frequently obtained. With more complex analyses, the precision may decrease sharply. In planning an experiment, the experimenter must make the choice of the method and the precision of the measuring equipment in terms of the desired precision.

Precise measurements, however, are not necessarily accurate. The **accuracy** expresses the agreement of the measurement with the accepted value of the quantity. Accuracy is expressed in terms of the error,* the experimentally determined value minus the accepted value. The **relative error** is the error divided by the accepted value. If the accepted value is unknown, the accuracy cannot be ascertained.

* Also called the absolute error.

EXAMPLE 21   The accepted value for the electronic charge is 4.80298×10^{-10} esu. Calculate the error and relative error for the determination of the electronic charge in Example 20.

ANSWER

$$4.79 \times 10^{-10} \text{ the determined value}$$
$$\underline{-4.80 \times 10^{-10} \text{ the accepted value}}$$
$$-0.01 \times 10^{-10} \text{ the error}$$

From this the relative error is

$$\frac{-0.01 \times 10^{-10}}{4.80 \times 10^{-10}} \, 100 = -0.2\%.$$

Problems

1. **Gravimetric.** A sample containing Mg^{2+} and weighing 0.5020 g yields 0.2720 g magnesium pyrophosphate, $Mg_2P_2O_7$. Calculate the percentage of (*i*) Mg^{2+}, (*ii*) MgO, in the sample.

Answer. (*i*) 11.83%.

2. **Cl^- determination.** A 0.2750 g sample contains 26% Cl^-; how many ml of $0.10N$ $AgNO_3$ should be used for stoichiometric precipitation of AgCl?

3. **Gravimetric.** The pH of a solution of $Mg(OH)_2$ at 25°C is adjusted to 11.60. How many grams of Mg^{2+} remain in 400 ml of the solution? $a_{Mg^{2+}} \cdot a_{OH^-}^2 = 1.1 \times 10^{-11}$. (*i*) Assume $\gamma_{Mg^{2+}} = \gamma_{OH^-} = 1.00$; (*ii*) assume $\gamma_{Mg^{2+}} = 0.40$. What information is needed to determine whether this loss represents a serious error?

Answer. (*i*) 6.6×10^{-6} g.

4. **Equivalent weights.** Determine the number of equivalents in 1 mole of $Mg(MnO_4)_2$ and its equivalent weight for each of the following reactions or half-reactions:

(a) $MnO_4^- + Cs^+ \rightarrow CsMnO_4\downarrow$
(b) $3MnO_4^- + [Cr(NH_3)_6]^{3+} \rightarrow [Cr(NH_3)_6](MnO_4)_3$
(c) $MnO_4^- + 8H^+ + 5e^- \rightarrow Mn^{2+} + 4H_2O$
(d) $MnO_4^- + 1e^- \rightarrow MnO_4^{2-}$
(e) $MnO_4^- + 4H^+ + 3e^- \rightarrow MnO_2 + 2H_2O$

Answer. (a) 2 eq/mole, 131 g/eq. (e) 6 eq/mole, 43.7 g/eq.

5. **Volumetric analysis.** Describe the preparation of (a) 250.0 ml of a $0.1100N$ $Cr_2O_7^{2-}$ aqueous solution using $K_2Cr_2O_7$; (b) 100.0 ml of a $0.1000N$ Fe^{2+} aqueous solution using *Mohr's salt*, $Fe(NH_4)_2(SO_4)_2(H_2O)_6$; the reaction is

$$Cr_2O_7^{2-} + 6Fe^{2+} + 14H^+ \rightarrow 6Fe^{3+} + 2Cr^{3+} + 7H_2O$$

Answer. (a) 1.349 g.

6. **Titration.** 26.72 ml of sulfuric acid, $HOSO_2OH$, reacts completely with 0.2549 g Na_2CO_3 by conversion to $CO_2 + H_2O$. (a) What is the normality of the acid? (b) If 30.50 ml of the acid is required to titrate 26.65 ml of ammonia solution, calculate the normality of the NH_3 solution.

Answer. (a) $0.1800N$.

7. Volumetric. A 2.340 g limestone sample yields 35.4 mg of Al_2O_3 and Fe_2O_3. When these oxides are treated to reduce quantitatively the Fe^{3+} to Fe^{2+}, the Fe^{2+} required 2.99 ml of $0.1001N$ permanganate for complete reaction in an acid solution ($MnO_4^- \rightleftharpoons Mn^{2+}$). Calculate the weight percent of (a) Fe_2O_3 and (b) of Al_2O_3 in the limestone sample.

Answer. (a) 10.2% Fe_2O_3.

8. End point. (a) In titrating HCl, 0.05 ml (one drop) of $0.10N$ NaOH is added in excess. If the volume of the solution is 100 ml, what is its pH at the end point at 25°C? The pH at the equivalence point is 7.0. (b) Exactly equivalent amounts of NaOH and boric acid, $B(OH)_3$, are mixed; the pH of the solution at the equivalence point is 12.0. If an excess of 0.05 ml of $0.10N$ NaOH is added and the volume of the solution is 100 ml, what is the pH of the resultant solution? Will a change occur in the color of an indicator upon the addition of one drop in excess of the equivalence point in the titration of boric acid with a strong base? Can boric acid be determined by titration with a strong base?

Answer. (a) 9.7; (b) 12.0.

9. Indicator. Calculate at 25°C the pH at the equivalence point for the titration of (a) benzoic acid, C_6H_5COOH, with NaOH; (b) NH_3 with HCl. For each case assume that the concentration of the reaction product at the equivalence point is 0.100 mole per liter, and the activity coefficients of molecules and ions are (i) 1.0, (ii) 0.80 for ions and 1.0 for molecules. For the dissociation of benzoic acid, $K = 6.30 \times 10^{-5}$ and, for the ammonium ion, $K = 5.74 \times 10^{-10}$ at 25°C. For each case, select from Table 19.2 (page 502) an indicator suitable for the titration.

Answer. (a)(i) 8.60; (b)(i) 5.12.

10. Titration curve. At room temperature, 20.00 ml of $0.1000M$ NH_3 is diluted to 100.0 ml and titrated with $0.1000M$ HCl. Calculate the pH after the addition of (a) 0.00 ml, (b) 5.00 ml, (c) 10.00 ml, (d) 15.00 ml (e) 19.00 ml, (f) 20.00 ml, (g) 20.100 ml, (h) 21.00 ml, of the acid. The equilibrium constant for $NH_3 + H_2O \rightleftharpoons NH_4^+ + OH^-$ (or $NH_3(H_2O) \rightleftharpoons NH_4^+ + OH^-$) is 1.76×10^{-5}, and 5.74×10^{-10} for $NH_4^+ \rightleftharpoons H^+ + NH_3$ at 25°C. Assume (i) activity coefficients are 1.0, (ii) activity coefficients are 1.0 for molecules and 0.80 for ions. Plot the titration curve; would you expect a sharp end point? Select from Table 19.2 (page 502) a suitable indicator.

Answer. (i)(a) 10.77; (b) 9.72; (c) 9.24; (d) 8.76; (e) 7.96; (f) 5.51; (g) 3.08; (h) 2.08.

11. Precision and accuracy. Student A determined the molecular weight of an unknown substance in a time-of-flight mass spectrograph (page 96), while student B used the Dumas method (page 94). The results of replicate experiments are

Student A	Student B
77.214	78.2
77.212	78.9
77.215	78.5
77.212	

For each series, calculate (a) the average ("best") value, (b) the average deviation, and (c) the relative average deviation. If the unknown is benzene, calculate (d) the error, and (e) the relative error. Which results are (f) more precise, and (g) more accurate?

Answer. A. (a) 77.213; (b) 0.001; (c) 13 p.p.m.; (d) -0.901; (e) -1.2%.

12. Gravimetric. A sample (0.4730 g) of a silver-copper alloy was dissolved and Ag^+ was converted to AgCl (0.5660 g). Calculate the percentage of silver and of copper in the alloy.

13. Gravimetric. Assuming stoichiometric quantities are used in a Cl^- determination, calculate the loss from solubility in milligrams Cl^- in 300 ml of solution at 25°C; $K_{sp} = 1.8 \times 10^{-10}$. Assume that the activity coefficients of Ag^+ and Cl^- are equal to 1.

14. Gravimetric. The precipitation of barium sulfate is used for the gravimetric determination of Ba^{2+}, SO_4^{2-}, or sulfur in other oxidation states by oxidation to SO_4^{2-}. The solubility of $BaSO_4$ is greater in acid solution than in water. Given at 25°C,

$$[Ba^{2+}][SO_4^{2-}] = 1.1 \times 10^{-10}$$
$$\frac{[H^+][SO_4^{2-}]}{[HOSO_3^-]} = 1.03 \times 10^{-2}$$

assuming activity coefficients of the ions are practically equal to 1. A sample containing 0.14 g Ba^{2+} is precipitated in 250 ml of solution in which the equilibrium concentration of $HOSO_3^-$ is 5.0×10^{-5} moles per liter at 25°C. What should be the maximum equilibrium concentration of H^+ if the loss from solubility is not to exceed 1/1000 of the Ba^{2+} content of the sample?

Answer. $1.9 \times 10^{-2}M$.

15. Cl^- determination. With respect to the Cl^- determination: (a) silver chloride is easily reduced by organic matter. What error, positive or negative, is introduced by the use of filter paper? (b) The sensitivity of the silver halides to light is the basis of photography. The change from white silver chloride to a gray-purple solid is the result of photochemical decomposition,

$$AgCl(c) \rightarrow Ag(c) + \tfrac{1}{2}Cl_2(g)$$

Unless work is done in direct sunlight, the weight change is not significant. What error (+ or −) is introduced if decomposition occurs with excess Ag^+ present? Recall the reaction at ordinary temperatures and in hot water,

$$Cl_2 + H_2O \rightarrow H^+ + Cl^- + HOCl$$
$$3Cl_2 + 3H_2O(hot) \rightarrow 5Cl^- + ClO_3^- + 6H^+$$

(c) What error (+ or −) may result from failure to acidify the solution? (d) When Ag^+ and Cl^- are added in stoichiometric quantities, AgCl is precipitated without the formation of colloidal solution. If Ag^+ is in excess, a positive sol, $(AgCl)Ag^+$, forms; if Cl^- is in excess, a negative sol, $(AgCl)Cl^-$, forms. Explain the use of very dilute nitric acid as the wash water.

16. Gravimetric. A mixture consisting of 1.0000 g of insoluble solids and 0.4310 g of NaCl and KCl is dissolved in water, the insoluble solids are quantitatively removed by filtration, and the chlorides yield 0.8890 g AgCl. Calculate (*i*) the weight of NaCl, (*ii*) the percentage of NaCl and of KCl, in the mixture.

Answer. (*i*) 0.114 g.

17. Gravimetric. The analysis of a sample of a silicate weighing 0.4210 g yields a mixture of KCl and NaCl weighing 0.0699 g. From the KCl, 0.1499 g K_2PtCl_6 is precipitated with $(NH_4)_2PtCl_6$ in a water-alcohol solution. Calculate

(i) the weight of KCl obtained from the silicate, (ii) the percent of Na_2O in the silicate.

Answer. (i) 0.04599 g.

18. Gravimetric. Given at 25°C for

$$2Ag^+ + CrO_4^{2-} \rightleftharpoons Ag_2CrO_4\downarrow$$

that

$$a_{Ag^+}^2 \cdot a_{CrO_4^{2-}} = 1.2 \times 10^{-12}$$

and (i) $\gamma_{Ag^+} = \gamma_{CrO_4^{2-}} = 1$; ($ii$) $\gamma_{Ag^+} = 0.80$, $\gamma_{CrO_4^{2-}} = 0.41$. Calculate the solubility loss, in mg of CrO_4^{2-} per liter of solution, at 25°C in the gravimetric determination of CrO_4^{2-} when (a) the stoichiometric quantity of $AgNO_3$ is used, (b) an excess of 0.010 mmole of $AgNO_3$ per ml is used.

Answer. (i) (a) 7.8 mg/liter.
(ii) (a) 12 mg/liter.

19. Gravimetric. 100 ml 0.020M $CuSO_4$ is electrolyzed with Pt electrodes. What should be the emf of the cell

standard H_2 electrode $\|$ Cu^{2+} (0.020M $CuSO_4$) $|$ Cu

at the end of the electrolysis to insure that the loss from incomplete deposition does not exceed 1/1000 of the copper in the initial solution? The standard potential of the half-cell Cu $|$ Cu^{2+} is -0.35 volt. Assume at end of electrolysis $\gamma_{Cu^{2+}}$ (i) = 1.00; (ii) = 0.50.

Answer. (i) $+0.21$ volt.

20. Gravimetric; atomic weights. Many of the accepted atomic weights of the elements are based upon the gravimetric determination of a silver halide brought to a high degree of precision by Theodore Richards and his students. 8.3683 g of AgBr is obtained from 4.8071 g of Ag. Accepting 107.870 as the atomic weight of silver, calculate an atomic weight for bromine.

21. Equivalent weights. 0.420 g of an acid, for which the number of replaceable hydrogens is unknown, is dissolved in 100 ml water; 50.0 ml of 0.125N NaOH are added to the solution. The resultant solution is titrated with 21.4 ml of 0.110N HCl. What is the equivalent weight of the original acid? Could you answer this question if NaOH were not added in excess?

Answer. 124 g/eq.

22. Meq, mg, and mmoles. With respect to the half-reaction

$$I_2 + 2e^- \rightarrow 2I^-$$

(a) how many milliequivalents are there in (i) 10 g iodine, (ii) 10 g KI,
(iii) 10 mg I_2, (iv) 10 mg KI, (v) 25 ml 0.10M I_2 solution, (vi) 25 ml 0.10M MgI_2,
(vii) 25 ml 0.10M NaI, ($viii$) 25 ml 0.10N MgI_2, (ix) 0.10 mole I_2,
(x) 0.10 mmole AlI_3? (b) How many milligrams of I_2 are there in (i) 1.2 meq I_2,
(ii) 1.2 meq AlI_3, (iii) 1.3 mmoles I_2, (iv) 1.3 mmoles MgI_2, (v) 50 ml 0.10N I_2,
(vi) 50 ml 0.10M I_2, (vii) 50 ml 0.10N KI, ($viii$) 50 ml 0.10M KI?

Answer. (a) (i) 79 meq, (ii) 60 meq; (b) (i) 153 mg, (ii) 153 mg.

23. Meq, grams and mmoles. With respect to the half-reaction for the oxidation of oxalic acid,

$$HOC_2O_2OH - 2e^- \rightarrow 2CO_2 + 2H^+$$

(a) how many milliequivalents are there in (i) 10 g HOC_2O_2OH, (ii) 10 g $C_2O_4^{2-}$,
(iii) 10 g CO_2 (iv) 11 mg CO_2, (v) 25 ml 0.10N HOC_2O_2OH solution,
(vi) 25 ml 0.10N $C_2O_4^{2-}$, (vii) 25 ml 0.0010N CO_2, ($viii$) 25 ml 0.10M HOC_2O_2OH,

(ix) 25 ml 0.0010M CO$_2$, (x) 0.10 mole HOC$_2$O$_2$OH, (xi) 0.10 mole CO$_2$?

(b) How many grams of CO$_2$ are in, or obtainable from, (i) 1.2 mmoles CO$_2$, (ii) 1.2 meq CO$_2$, (iii) 1.2 meq HOC$_2$O$_2$OH, (iv) 1.2 meq C$_2$O$_4^{2-}$, (v) 50 ml 0.10N C$_2$O$_4^{2-}$, (vi) 50 ml 0.10N HOC$_2$O$_2$OH, (vii) 50 ml 0.0010M CO$_2$?

Answer. (a) (i) 2.2 $\times$ 10^2 meq, (ii) 2.3 $\times$ 10^2 meq; (b) (i) 5.3 $\times$ 10^{-2} g, (ii) 5.3 $\times$ 10^{-2} g.

24. Titration. (a) How many milligrams of sulfuric acid, HOSO$_2$OH, were in a solution which required 27.62 ml of 0.1224N base for titration? If the volume of HOSO$_2$OH solution was 24.86 ml, what was its normality? The reaction involves HOSO$_2$OH $\rightarrow$ SO$_4^{2-}$ + 2H$^+$.

(b) Answer the same questions as in (a) for a nonaqueous solution in which the reaction involved is HOSO$_2$OH $\rightarrow$ HSO$_4^-$ + H$^+$.

Answer. (a) 165.8 mg, 0.1360N.

25. Titration. 20.00 ml 0.1000N HCl is diluted to 100.0 ml at 25.0°C. What is the pH of the solution after 10.00 ml of 0.1000N NaOH are added? Assume activity coefficients of H$^+$ and OH$^-$ ions are (i) 1.00, (ii) 0.90.

Answer. (i) 2.04.

26. Titration. 20.00 ml of 0.1000M acetic acid (HOAc) is diluted to 100.0 ml at 25.0°C. What is the pH of the solution after 10.00 ml of 0.1000M KOH are added? Assume the activity coefficients of HOAc and the ions, respectively, are (i) 1.00 and 1.00, (ii) 1.00 and 0.90.

Answer. (i) 4.76.

27. Volumetric. You are told to add acetic acid from a stock solution (0.100M) to 1.00 liter of water at 25°C until the pH of the resultant solution is 3.88. How much of the stock solution would you add? The dissociation constant for acetic acid is 1.75 $\times$ 10^{-5} at 25°C; assume activity coefficients of molecules and ions are 1.0.

Answer. 10.2 ml.

28. Titration. (a) The rate of the reaction between permanganate and oxalate solutions at ordinary temperatures in the absence of a catalyst is very slow.* Is this reaction suitable for use in quantitative analysis at ordinary temperatures in the absence of a catalyst? Explain your answer. (b) Use Fig. 21.2a (page 566) to justify the use of either methyl red or phenolphthalein to determine the end point in the titration of HCl with NaOH; would the precision of the titration be identical for about 0.10 and 0.0010 normal solutions?

29. Volumetric. What volumes of 0.1000M acetic acid and 0.1000M NaOH stock solutions should be mixed to prepare 1.000 liter of solution of pH 6.00 at room temperature? The dissociation constant of the acid is 1.75 $\times$ 10^{-5}. Assume activity coefficients of molecules and ions are 1.0.

30. Volumetric. *Vinegar* is an aqueous solution of acetic acid, CH$_3$COOH, with small quantities of nonacidic components. 25.00 ml NaOH is titrated with 21.45 ml 0.114N HCl. A 5.00 ml portion of vinegar is diluted with water and titrated with 40.50 ml of the NaOH solution. Calculate (a) the weight of acetic acid per 100 ml vinegar, (b) the weight percent of acetic acid, if the density of the vinegar is 1.001 g per ml.

31. Analysis. A 3.2460 g sample containing Cl$^-$, Br$^-$, and NO$_3^-$ is titrated with 20.10 ml of 0.1211N AgNO$_3$; the same quantity of the sample yields a 0.3969 g precipitate of silver halides. Calculate (a) the weight of AgCl and AgBr in the precipitate, (b) the weight percent of each halide in the sample.

Answer. (a) 194 mg AgCl, 203 mg AgBr.

* This reaction is discussed in Chapter 23.

32. Analysis. Krypton and fluorine, subjected to an electrical discharge, at about 90°K and 30 torr, react to form a white solid which sublimes readily at temperatures well below 273°K. A definite quantity of the solid added to water hydrolyzes with the formation of HF and Kr; 0.153 g of Kr is recovered, and the titration of the fluoride in solution with thorium nitrate (alizarin sulfonate used as the indicator) shows the presence of 3.64×10^{-3} mmole F^-. What is the empirical formula of the krypton fluoride?

Answer. KrF_2.

33. Analysis. Analysis shows a sample contains Na^+, Fe^{2+}, Cl^-, ClO_3^-, and NO_3^- ions and inert material. 2.5641 g of the sample is dissolved in a 100.0-ml volumetric flask. A 10.00 ml portion of the solution is diluted to about 150 ml, treated with excess $AgNO_3$, and 0.02620 g $AgCl$ is obtained. A 25.00 ml portion is treated with a reducing agent converting the ClO_3^- quantitatively to the Cl^-. The solution, titrated with $0.1011N$ $AgNO_3$, required 24.32 ml. Calculate the weight percent of (a) Cl^-, (b) ClO_3^-, in the sample.

34. Volumetric analysis. When hydrochloric acid is distilled under a pressure of 760 torr, a distillate containing 20.23% HCl by weight is eventually obtained. If 50.50 g of such a solution is weighed and diluted to 2.000 liters, what is the normality of the solution?

35. Titration. 10.60 g of sodium thiosulfate, $Na_2S_2O_3$, is dissolved in 500 ml of solution. 25.00 ml of this solution reacts completely with 26.62 ml of I_2 solution. In turn, 28.73 ml of the I_2 solution is required to titrate a solution containing 0.3675 g of sample A. Sample A contains As_2O_3. Calculate the percent of As_2O_3 in sample A. The reactions may be represented as

$$2S_2O_3^{2-} + I_2 \rightarrow S_4O_6^{2-} + 2I^-$$
$$(HO)AsO + 2H_2O + I_2 \rightarrow (HO)_3AsO + 2H^+ + 2I^-$$

Answer. 48.68%.

36. Titration. A 0.6254 g sample containing Ca^{2+} is quantitatively converted to CaC_2O_4, which is then rapidly titrated in a hot acid solution with 30.25 ml of $0.1510N$ $KMnO_4$. The reaction is representable as

$$MnO_4^- + C_2O_4^{2-} + 8H^+ \rightarrow Mn^{2+} + 2CO_2 + 4H_2O$$

How many milliequivalents, and how many milligrams of (a) CaC_2O_4, (b) CaO, are in the sample? (c) What is the weight percent of CaO in the sample?

37. Volumetric. A 0.24 g mineral sample contains FeO, Fe_2O_3, and inert material. When quantitatively separated from the sample, the weight of these oxides is 120 mg; when the separated oxides are converted to Fe^{2+}, 16.0 ml of $0.100N$ acidified permanganate is required to oxidize the Fe^{2+} to Fe^{3+}. Calculate (a) the weight of FeO and of Fe_2O_3, and (b) the weight percent of Fe, in the sample.

Answer. (a) 73 mg FeO, 47 mg Fe_2O_3.

38. Concentration. 100 ml of $0.20M$ ceric sulfate $Ce(SO_4)_2$ is added to 50 ml of $0.20N$ arsenious acid, $(HO)AsO$, with water to make 500 ml of solution. The reaction

$$2Ce^{4+} + (HO)AsO + 2H_2O \rightleftharpoons 2Ce^{3+} + (HO)_3AsO + 2H^+$$

goes practically to completion. Calculate the normality and molarity of the final solution with respect to Ce^{4+}.

Answer. $0.020N$.

39. Separation. 1.4 mmoles of Ca^{2+}, 0.50 mmole Mg^{2+}, and 2.4 mmoles $C_2O_4^{2-}$ are added to a well-buffered solution, pH = 5.00, in which the equilibrium concentration of hydrogen oxalate ion, $HOC_2O_3^-$, is 4.0×10^{-3} mmole/ml; the final volume of the solution is 100 ml at room temperature. Calculate the $C_2O_4^{2-}$ concentration that would be present in the solution if no precipitation occurred. *Assuming* the precipitation of CaC_2O_4 and MgC_2O_4 occurs at comparable rates, will a separation of the two cations be effected under these conditions? Assume the activity coefficients of the ions are 1.0. The equilibrium constants at 25°C are

$$HOC_2O_3^- \rightleftharpoons H^+ + C_2O_4^{2-} \qquad K_2 = 5.0 \times 10^{-5}$$
$$a_{Ba^{2+}} \cdot a_{C_2O_4^{2-}} = 1.5 \times 10^{-8}$$
$$a_{Mg^{2+}} \cdot a_{C_2O_4^{2-}} = 8.6 \times 10^{-5}$$

Answer. $2.0 \times 10^{-2} M$.

40. Indicator. In the volumetric determination of Cl^- at room temperature, a sample is titrated with $0.1010N$ silver nitrate. (a) Calculate the concentration of Cl^- and Ag^+ ions in solution at the equivalence point. (b) Potassium chromate, 0.60 mmole, is used as the indicator; silver chloride is white but silver chromate is a red solid. If the volume of the solution at the equivalence point is 200 ml, show by calculation that Ag_2CrO_4 will not precipitate. (c) If an excess of one drop (0.05 ml) of the silver nitrate solution is now added, will the solution change color? (d) At what point would you read your buret: at the equivalence point or when the solution changes color? Explain your answer. Required data: $a_{Ag^+} \cdot a_{Cl^-} = 1.8 \times 10^{-10}$, $a_{Ag^+}^2 \cdot a_{CrO_4^{2-}} = 1.2 \times 10^{-12}$; (*i*) assume $\gamma_{Ag^+} = \gamma_{Cl^-} = \gamma_{CrO_4^{2-}} = 1.0$; (*ii*) assume $\gamma_{Ag^+} = \gamma_{Cl^-} = 0.80$, and $\gamma_{CrO_4^{2-}} = 0.41$.

Answer. (a)(*i*) $1.3 \times 10^{-5} M$.

41. Titration. Figure 21.4 is a typical titration curve for the titration of Na_2CO_3 with a strong acid. (a) What is the equivalent weight of Na_2CO_3 titrated to the (*i*) phenolphthalein end point $(CO_3^{2-} + H^+ \rightarrow HOCO_2^-)$, (*ii*) methyl orange end point $(CO_3^{2-} + 2H^+ \rightarrow (HO)_2CO_2)$? (b) What is the equivalent weight of NaOH titrated to the (*i*) phenolphthalein end point, (*ii*) methyl orange end point? (c) A sample containing only Na_2CO_3 required 21.22 ml of $0.1022N$ HCl when titrated with phenolphthalein indicator. What volume of the same acid would be required to titrate the same original sample if methyl orange were used as the indi-

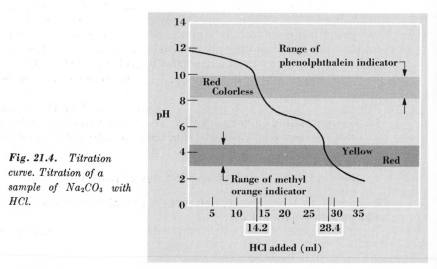

Fig. 21.4. *Titration curve. Titration of a sample of Na_2CO_3 with HCl.*

cator? (d) A sample containing only NaOH required 12.84 ml of 0.1022N HCl when titrated with phenolphthalein indicator. What volume of the same acid would be required to titrate the same original sample if methyl orange were used as the indicator? (e) A sample containing NaOH, Na_2CO_3, and inert material is dissolved and titrated with 20.46 ml of 0.1022N HCl, using phenolphthalein as the indicator. The same sample titrated with the same acid, using methyl orange indicator, required 22.66 ml of acid. (i) How many millimoles of NaOH and of Na_2CO_3 are present in the sample? (ii) If the sample weight is 0.3651 g, what is the weight percent of NaOH and of Na_2CO_3? (iii) If this weight of the sample is dissolved in 200.0 ml, what is the molarity of Na_2CO_3 and what is the normality of the Na_2CO_3 with respect to the phenolphthalein and methyl orange end points?

Answer. (a)(i) 106.0 g/eq; (ii) 53.0 g/eq. (b)(i, ii) 40.0 g/eq. (c) 42.44 ml. (d) 12.84 ml. (e)(i) 1.866 mmoles NaOH, 0.225 mmole Na_2CO_3.

42. Titration error. (a) What should be the minimum volume to add from a buret if the error due to the addition of one drop in excess is not to exceed 0.10% and the volume of a drop is (i) 0.10 ml; (ii) 0.05 ml; (iii) 0.01 ml? (b) Would you expect the pH at the equivalence point to be a sensitive function of temperature? What is the basis of your answer? (c) The accuracy desired in a particular determination is 3%. A chemical reaction that might be used as the basis of the determination proceeds at a very rapid rate and establishes equilibrium when 90% of the reactants have been converted to products. Is this reaction suitable for the determination? Explain your answer.

Answer. (a)(i) 100 ml.

43. Titration error. Calculate the error in ml NaOH if, in titrating HCl with 0.10N NaOH, the end point corresponds to a volume of 100 ml and pH = 3.50. Assume (i) $\gamma_{H^+} = 1.00$; (ii) $\gamma_{H^+} = 0.90$. Is the error positive or negative?

Answer. (i) -0.31 ml.

44. Indicator. Use Fig. 21.2b, (page 567) to estimate what fraction of the acetic acid remains unneutralized if methyl red is used as the indicator in the titration of the acetic acid with NaOH.

45. Precision and accuracy. The 1961 report of the International Commission on Atomic Weights discusses the following seven determinations of the atomic weight of silver reported by several investigators:

107.8721	107.8704	107.8698
107.8740		107.8697
107.8722		107.8714

"There appears to be no justification for discriminating among these results . . . ." Calculate (a) the relative average deviation, and (b) the error of the average, of these results.

Answer. (a) 11 p.p.m.

46. Error. What should be the minimum weight of a sample if the weighing error, on a balance with a sensitivity of 0.4 mg, is not to exceed (i) 2 parts per 1000, (ii) 2%?

Answer. (i) 0.2 g.

22

Modern
approaches to
analytical
chemistry:
Chromatography
and
spectrometry

22.1 **GENERAL**

The preceding two chapters have dealt with methods of chemical analysis of the components of aqueous solutions, or of substances that can readily be dissolved in water or converted into water-soluble matter. These methods, moreover, involve quantities of components that can be manipulated by hand—usually in the range of milligrams or grams. The analytical procedures described are time-consuming and nonautomatic; the analyst works continuously at a given determination for a number of hours. These methods are still taught to students because they provide a purposeful and challenging manner of learning about the chemistry of inorganic substances in aqueous solution, about ionic equilibria, and about the techniques of some fundamental laboratory operations. Furthermore, these methods are still used in many instances; they are not entirely obsolete. However, they cannot cope with problems like the analysis of a nanogram of a metallic powder, analysis of the components of fresh strawberry flavor, analysis of the exhaust gases from a jet engine, analysis of material sampled on the moon by an unmanned vehicle.

Recent developments in analytical methods have yielded great improvements in the separation of components of mixtures, in the measurement of properties of substances, in the estimation of quantity or concentration of material in a sample, and in the speed and ease of gathering and recording analytical information. The most effective techniques of separation belong to a group called **chromatographic methods;** these will be discussed in a later section. The most informative kinds of analytical description (both qualitative and quantitative) are those that tell how a substance responds when energy of some particular kind is transferred to or from the substance. Such descriptions are called **spectrometric methods of analysis;** some of them will also be discussed in later sections. Refinements of electronic circuitry, especially in methods of extreme, yet reliable, amplification of electronic signals, have had a profound effect in making chromatographic and spectrometric methods versatile, sensitive, and precise. Finally, the automation of data recording has increased the speed of analysis beyond all expectations, and has frequently embarrassed the analyst by giving him more information than he has time to interpret.

22.2   CRITERIA OF PURITY AND METHODS OF PURIFICATION

Any analytical method, old or modern, manual or automatic, deals with the *components* of a substance—the individual entities among which the analysis is supposed to discriminate. One may think that the limit of information obtainable by a chemical analysis is reached when the substance under examination is separated into its *pure* components, and when these components are identified or characterized and their relative quantities determined. A *pure substance* has been defined as one with a precisely fixed composition that is associated with its properties (page 3); we usually think of it as being entirely composed of like molecules. But the situation is really not so simple. When a given constituent has been separated from a mixture, and no analytical procedure succeeds in separating that constituent into additional components, we must *assume* that the substance is pure. As far as laboratory operations are concerned, we have no choice in the matter. There is no way of showing that the assumption is false except by developing a more powerful analytical method by which the "pure" substance is further separated into new components.

In laboratory practice, then, the criterion of purity of a substance is simply the inability of the experimenter to isolate or otherwise detect foreign material. It is implied, of course, that the component(s) which are to be preserved must undergo no chemical changes, unless such changes are reversed later in the purification procedure. Unwanted components may be chemically destroyed, if it is convenient to do so. This operational concept of purity requires that we consider some of the approaches to methods of purification. Only physical methods will be mentioned.

Purification implies separation. Separation implies differential motion; that is, each component to be purified must be moved to a different location. Such separation occurs as a consequence of the differences in properties among the components to be separated. Finally, the presence of the

TABLE 22.1 *Requirements for the Purification of Materials*

A. *Motive processes (processes that involve motion)*

   (a) **Gravitational or centrifugal settling**

   (b) **Motion in response to hydraulic or other mechanical force**

   (c) **Convection (motion in a moving stream of gas or liquid which acts as a carrier)**

   (d) **Acceleration in a magnetic field**

   (e) **Acceleration in an electric field**

   (f) **Diffusion or effusion (see Chapter 2)**

   (g) **Motion associated with changes in states of aggregation (examples precipitation of a solid; rise of bubbles of a vapor)**

B. *Properties in which components may differ*

   (a) **Mass**

   (b) **Density**

   (c) **Electrical properties**

   (d) **Magnetic properties**

   (e) **Cohesive or adhesive properties; temperatures at which changes of state occur**

   (f) **Solubility characteristics**

   (g) **Particle size**

C. *Sensing or detection methods*

   (a) **Direct sensations: vision, touch, taste, smell**

   (b) **Determination of physical properties of the type used by chemists since the last century for characterization of substances: melting point, boiling point, refractive indices, etc.**

   (c) **Electrical methods: detection of charge, ability to form ions on being heated or otherwise excited, acceleration in an electric field, electrical conductivity**

   (d) **Magnetic methods: deflection in magnetic fields**

   (e) **Methods that use electromagnetic radiation: light microscopy, photography, x ray diffraction, infrared or ultraviolet photometry, other spectrometric methods**

   (f) **Thermal methods: measurement of conduction of heat through a substance**

TABLE 22.2 *Examples of Purification Methods*

Method	Motive process	Differential action	Sensing or detection
In filtration,	material is moved by gravity or pressure through a sieve, paper, sand bed, or other medium.	The smaller particles move through the medium more easily than the larger ones, and	the separated components can be seen and their amounts can be determined by weighing.
In distillation,	a liquid is converted to a vapor by boiling. The vapor is lighter than the liquid and rises from it.	Components which vaporize more easily leave the liquid earlier, and	are sensed by noting the temperatures at which they are produced, or by their indices of refraction (ability to bend light).
In column chromatography,	material is carried by a liquid stream through a column of powder or porous granules of large surface area.	The components which adhere to the surface least emerge from the column earliest.	The progress of separation of colored materials can be followed visually. Colorless components may be sensed by their behavior in absorption of infrared or ultraviolet light.
In electrophoresis,	charged particles in liquid medium migrate in an electric field to a positive or negative electrode.	The components are separated according to their electric charge and	can be rendered visible by appropriate dyeing or staining methods.
In gas-liquid partition chromatography,	a mixture of vapors is carried in a stream of helium through several hundred feet of capillary tubing coated inside with a nonvolatile liquid.	The components least soluble in the stationary liquid emerge earliest.	They are detected by their ability to produce ions when they are burned in a hydrogen flame or when they are excited by energy obtained from radioactive emission. As little as about a picogram can be sensed.

purified component(s) must be sensed or detected in some way, so that we are informed of the fact that separation has occurred.

Purification thus involves (1) a motive process, (2) a differentiating action, and (3) a sensing method. An idea of the degree of variety possible in purification procedures may be gleaned from the listings in Table 22.1. Examples of methods frequently used by chemists are in Table 22.2.

Any purification process is, in effect, an analysis, because in separating the components of a mixture we gain information about them. Chromatography (described in the ensuing sections) is used for both purification and analysis; the choice between the two depends on the intent of the investigator.

22.3 CHROMATOGRAPHIC METHODS

In 1906 the Russian botanist Mikhail Tswett described how colored plant pigments, such as chlorophylls and carotenoids,* could be separated into components of different hues by passing a solution of the pigment through a column of finely divided adsorptive material, such as precipitated chalk (calcium carbonate). Even before Tswett, the American geologist David T. Day recognized that the sharply differentiated colors of oil-bearing rock, black, green, red, and white, represented a fractional separation of a single crude oil mixture that had percolated slowly through the strata of shale, clay, or limestone. The Painted Desert of Arizona is a striking result of such action.

The essentials of the Tswett method can be reproduced in the laboratory with simple equipment, as shown in Fig. 22.1. In his pioneer experiments Tswett used an extract of green leaves in a low-boiling hydrocarbon solvent, petroleum ether. This solution, on trickling through his chalk column, produced sharply differentiated colored bands, comprising various yellows and greens. This colored separation was called a **chromatogram.** Tswett's original technique did not entail waiting for the components to emerge from the bottom of the tube; he simply allowed the chromatogram to develop, and then pushed the adsorbent material out of the tube and separated the bands by slicing the column at the color boundaries with a knife. It is usually more convenient, however, to pass solvent through the column and catch the components as they emerge sequentially at the bottom; this method is called **elution.**

In modern analytical parlance, the meaning of the term *chromatogram* has broadened far beyond its initial connotation of a visible separation of colored components. **"Chromatography"** now refers to any separation process in which the motion of the components is effected by a moving stream of gas or liquid (called a **carrier fluid.**) The carrier fluid and the material to be separated move together through a tube. To effect the separation some medium (like Tswett's chalk, or Day's clay) must be present that detains different components to different degrees, and hence

* Carotenoids are yellow-red pigments that impart characteristic color to carrots, butter, and other natural organic products.

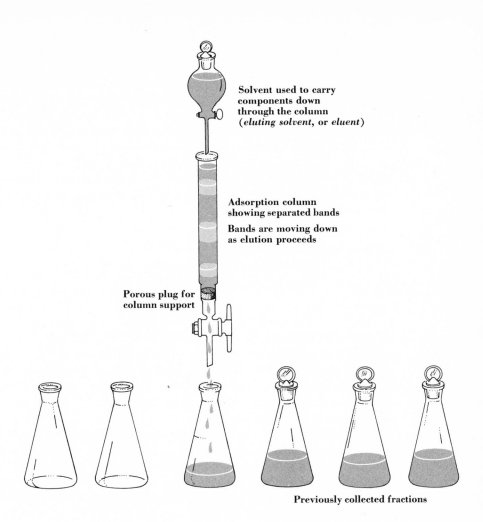

Solvent used to carry
components down
through the column
(*eluting solvent*, or *eluent*)

Adsorption column
showing separated bands

Bands are moving down
as elution proceeds

Porous plug for
column support

Previously collected fractions

Fig. 22.1. *Column chromatography.*

makes them spread apart and emerge from the tube at different times.
Finally, we must be able to detect the separated components.

The development of a great variety of highly selective detention media,
and of several very sensitive methods of detection, have made chromatographic methods the most widely used and effective methods of analytic
separation of materials. On a larger scale, such separations are also used
preparatively—that is, to obtain quantities of pure substances for further
use. An idea of the activity in this area may be gleaned from the facts that
Tswett wrote some 50 technical papers and a book entitled "Chlorophylls
in the Plant and Animal Kingdom"; a review of paper chromatography
(see Table 22.3) for the period 1944–1956 alone, listed 10,290 references;
today there are technical journals devoted exclusively to individual
branches of the general method.

TABLE 22.3 *Systems and Materials in Chromatographic Separations*

Mobile phase (carrier fluid)	Motive force
	(A) **Gravity**
(I) **Liquid**	(B) **Gas pressure**
(II) **Gas**	(C) **Capillarity**
	(D) **Electrical potential**

Immobile medium in which detention or differential migration occurs

(1) **A column of adsorbent**

(2) **A liquid that is held stationary on paper**

(3) **A liquid that is held stationary on an inert powder**

(4) **A liquid that is held stationary by wetting the inside wall of a capillary tube**

(5) **A gel**

(6) **An ionic solid in which either cations or anions are mobile**

All chromatographic methods involve the differential motion of components in a carrier fluid. A rational classification of chromatographic methods may be based on (a) whether the carrier fluid is a liquid or a gas, (b) what causes the fluid to move, and (c) what type of medium in the tube selectively detains the moving components. Such a classification appears in Table 22.3. The reader will note that this table affords 48 possible combinations; not all of them, of course, constitute practical techniques. Some of the more important methods are cited and briefly described in the ensuing sections.

22.4 SOLID-LIQUID ADSORPTION CHROMATOGRAPHY

The original Tswett method, which used petroleum ether as the carrier liquid or eluent, and chalk (an adsorbent) as the detention medium, may be described in terms of the classification of Table 22.3 as I-A-1 or, if the liquid is pushed down by gas pressure to speed up the process, I-B-1. The most important experimental problems in this type of chromatography are the selection of a combination of adsorbent and eluent (eluting agent) for best separation.

22.5 LIQUID-LIQUID PARTITION CHROMATOGRAPHY

A solute is known to distribute itself between two immiscible liquids in a proportion depending on the relative solubilities of the solute in the two liquids (see Distribution Law, also called Law of Partition, page 350). This phenomenon is used in the process of solvent **extraction** (page 350).

Different solutes will distribute themselves in different proportions between the same pair of solvents. In 1941, A. J. P. Martin and R. L. M. Synge started to investigate partition procedures in connection with a problem of determination of the amino acid composition of wool. They devised the method whereby one solvent is mobile and the other is stationary. By this means, the distribution or partition of solutes between immiscible solvents is made to serve as a chromatographic method. The mobile solvent (for example, chloroform or acetone) becomes the carrier fluid. The stationary solvent (for example, a heavy mineral oil soaked onto finely crushed firebrick) is the detention medium. Components of a solute mixture that are more soluble in the mobile liquid spend more time moving through the tube; components more soluble in the stationary phase spend less time in motion. Therefore, the components more soluble in the mobile liquid emerge earlier, and separation is thereby effected. Liquid-liquid partition methods were first used with columnar equipment (I-A-3). An ingenious application of this method is **paper chromatography** (I-C-2). In the separation of amino acids, for example, a small quantity of the mixture to be analyzed is dropped onto a cellulosic paper that holds a stationary liquid phase (usually water). The edge of the paper is then dipped into the mobile liquid, which moves through the paper by capillary action and carries the amino acids through the paper at different rates, thus effecting separation. It is an oversimplification to assume that the support for the stationary liquid phase is truly inert. The powder or paper support in partition chromatography is also, to some degree, an adsorbent. Cellulose, particularly, is chemically reactive (see Chapter 29) and often also contains ionic impurities (see ion-exchange chromatography, below). In practice it is often convenient to carry out a two-dimensional elution. One solvent is used to effect the best separation attainable in one direction; the paper is then rotated 90° and a second

Fig. 22.2. A composite two-dimensional paper chromatogram of amino acids. Solvents: (A) tertiary butyl alcohol + formic acid; (B) tertiary amyl alcohol + 2,4-lutidine. Amino acids: (1) cystine; (2) lysine; (3) arginine; (4) histidine; (5) aspartic acid; (6) glutamic acid; (7) serine; (8) glycine; (9) threonine; (10) alanine; (11) valine; (12) isoleucine; (13) leucine; (14) phenylalanine; (15) methionine; (16) tyrosine; (17) tryptophan.

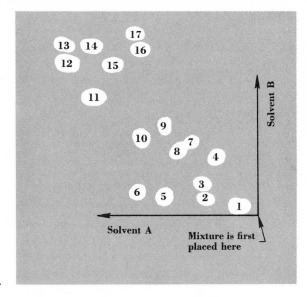

solvent, chosen so that it does not duplicate the differentiating action of the first, continues the development in the new direction. The separated amino acid spots, colorless in themselves, are rendered visible by reaction with appropriate reagents with which amino acids form colored compounds. Figure 22.2 illustrates a two-dimensional separation of 17 components.

22.6 GAS CHROMATOGRAPHY

Gas-liquid partition chromatography (II-B-3 or 4) and **gas adsorption chromatography** (II-B-1) are applications of the methods described above to the separation of gases. The methods are very widely used and are called, collectively, **gas chromatography.** The handling ease, effectiveness and versatility of separation, sensitivity of detection, and automation of data recording have progressed to such a degree in gas chromatography that it is often analytically profitable to vaporize even relatively nonvolatile liquids and solids to exploit these advantages. Equipment is commercially available that accepts a gas or liquid sample, vaporizes it if necessary, carries it through a coiled column up to several hundred feet in

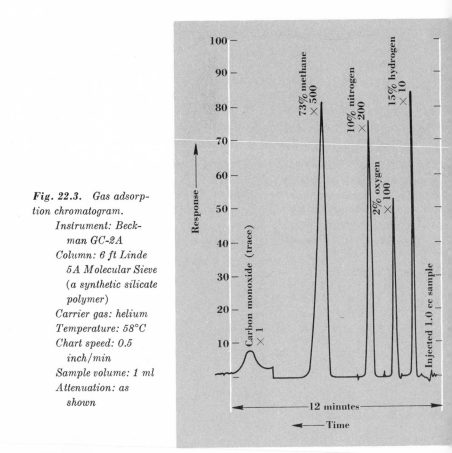

Fig. 22.3. Gas adsorp-
tion chromatogram.
Instrument: Beck-
man GC-2A
Column: 6 ft Linde
5A Molecular Sieve
(a synthetic silicate
polymer)
Carrier gas: helium
Temperature: 58°C
Chart speed: 0.5
inch/min
Sample volume: 1 ml
Attenuation: as
shown

length, senses the emerging components by an ionization method, plots the curve of quantity eluted vs. time, and prints the integrated values (areas under each peak) on a tape. Figure 22.3 is the gas adsorption chromatogram of a mixture having the following initial composition: methane, nitrogen, oxygen, hydrogen, and carbon monoxide. In this analysis, the thermal conductivity response of the effluent gas stream is plotted against time* of emergence from the column. If all the peaks were plotted along the same vertical scale, the largest one (methane) would be about 4000 times as high as the smallest (carbon monoxide), and it would be impossible to depict both satisfactorily on the same page. Therefore a scale reduction factor, called an **attenuation,** is applied to the larger responses. Each peak is attenuated by the factor necessary to keep it on the scale. The actual response in each case is therefore the indicated response times the attenuation (500, 200, 100, or 10). The chromatogram of the mixture of known composition may be used as a standard for the quantitative estimation of unknown mixtures, with the assumption that the response is directly proportional to the number of molecules present.

EXAMPLE 1 **In the analysis of a gas mixture under the conditions of Fig. 22.3, the indicated response for nitrogen is 40 units, with 50-fold attenuation. Calculate the percent nitrogen in the mixture.**

ANSWER **The analysis shown in Fig. 22.3 is used as the standard for determining the composition of the unknown. It is assumed that, if the operating conditions are the same, the quantity of component is proportional to the response. Then**

$$\text{total response} = \text{response indicated on graph} \times \text{attenuation factor}$$

$$\frac{\% \text{ N}_2 \text{ (unknown)}}{\% \text{ N}_2 \text{ (known)}} = \frac{\text{total response (unknown)}}{\text{total response (known)}}$$

$$\% \text{ N}_2 \text{ (unknown)} = 10\% \times \frac{40 \times 50}{77 \times 200}$$

$$= 1.3\%$$

22.7 ION-EXCHANGE CHROMATOGRAPHY

An **ion-exchange material** is a solid consisting of a molecular network structure containing electrically charged sites of one particular charge sign, and mobile ions of the other charge sign. In a **cation exchanger** the immobile molecular network is anionic; the mobile ions are cations. In an **anion exchanger** the charge signs are reversed. Figure 22.4 is a schematic representation of a cation exchanger. Ion exchange can be used, as the name implies, to substitute one ion for another in a solution. For example, if water containing Ca^{2+} ions flows through a column of cationic exchanger containing Na^+ ions, displacement occurs, and Na^+ ions appear in the eluent. This particular process thus converts **hard water** to

* "Time" progresses from right to left simply because the recorder paper unrolls automatically under the pen from left to right.

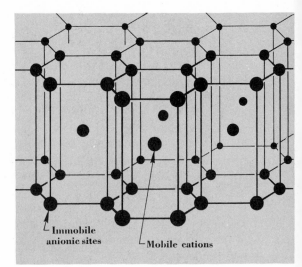

Fig. 22.4. *Cationic exchanger (schematic). Some of the atoms are charged.*

Immobile anionic sites — Mobile cations

soft water (see page 458). The action is an equilibrium that may be represented as

$$[Na_x^+ \; resin^{x-}] + \frac{x}{2} Ca^{2+} \rightleftharpoons [Ca_{x/2}^{2+} \; resin^{x-}] + xNa^+$$

A cationic resin treated with acidified water becomes populated with $H^+(aq)$ ions; an anionic resin in basic solution takes up $OH^-(aq)$ ions. When water containing mineral impurities is treated with two such resins in series, the saline cations and anions are removed and are replaced by H^+ and OH^-, respectively. This combination of substitutions amounts to the replacement of salts by water, and thus constitutes a **demineralizing** action, comparable to distillation. Thus, the removal of $CaCl_2$ from water may be represented as

$$[H_x^+ \; resin^{x-}] + [(OH^-)_x \; resin^{x+}] + \frac{x}{2} Ca^{2+} + xCl^- \rightarrow$$
$$[Ca_{x/2}^{2+} \; resin^{x-}] + [Cl_x^- \; resin^{x+}] + xH_2O$$

To extend ion-exchange actions to a chromatographic method of separation, a solution of a mixture of ions is passed through the column; different ions are detained by the solid to different degrees, and separation is achieved. The classification of this method, according to Table 22.3, is I-A-6. Ion-exchange materials comprise natural silicates (**zeolites**: for example **chabazite,** $CaAl_2Si_6O_{16}(H_2O)_8$ and **sodalite,** $Na_8Al_6Si_6O_{24}Cl_2$) and a large variety of synthetic resins. By using the cation-exchange resin Dowex 50,* it is possible to achieve a sharp separation of a mixture of 2 millimoles each of Li^+, Na^+, and K^+, with about 300 ml of $0.70M$ HCl as the carrier fluid. Ion-exchange chromatography has been used extensively

* Trade name of the Dow Chemical Co.

for the separation of lanthanide and actinide (rare earth and heavy rare earth) elements.

22.8 ELECTROCHROMATOGRAPHY

This process, also called **electrophoresis** or **ionography,** is the separation of charged particles by their differential migration in an electric field. Since flow is induced electrically, there is no tendency for the neutral solvent molecules to migrate, and therefore mechanical immobilization of the solvent is not essential. To minimize convective effects, however, the liquid medium is often stabilized by starch, agar gel, paper, or other non-migratory material. Extensive applications have been made in separations of proteins and other high-molecular-weight materials of biochemical interest. The classification of this method, according to Table 22.3, is I-D-2, I-D-3, or I-D-5.

22.9 SPECTROMETRIC METHODS

A **spectrum** (Latin, *image*) is, broadly, a separated group of components arranged in some orderly progression. The word "spectrum" is used in two senses: separation of materials and separation of energies. The separation of energies (as in a rainbow) is the earlier and more usual connotation of "spectrum." An energy spectrum can be obtained by measuring the energy emitted by a substance (**emission spectrum**) or the energy absorbed by a substance (**absorption spectrum**).

The emission spectrum is obtained when electrons that have been excited to higher energy levels return to lower energy levels; the energy difference is emitted as radiation. Examples of emission spectra appear in Fig. 8.10 (page 160). Emission spectrometry is used in the analysis of metals; the material that is excited may be the metal itself or one of its salts. Flames and electric arcs or sparks are used to produce excitation. The Bunsen burner flame is hot enough (about 1700°C) to vaporize the alkali and alkaline earth metals; oxygen-hydrocarbon flames are used for some, but not all, of the other metals. High-voltage arcs (about 1000 volts) or sparks (up to 50,000 volts) provide even higher energy sources, and can be used for excitation of all the metals.

Molecular material that would decompose under conditions of excessive thermal excitation cannot be examined by emission spectroscopy. Instead, it is convenient to measure the absorption of radiation by the substance; this method is called **absorption spectrometry.**

Radiant energy absorbed by a substance must affect the substance in some way, and an understanding of such effects is analytically useful. Refer to Fig. 8.6 (page 156), starting at the high frequency region of the spectrum. **Gamma rays** are energetic enough to produce nuclear transformations. **X rays** penetrate the inner electronic shells of the atom and can be used to probe the details of crystal structure (Chapter 3). **Ultra-**

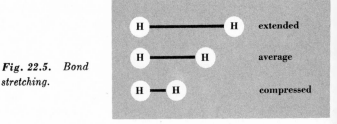

Fig. 22.5. *Bond stretching.*

violet and **visible radiations** affect primarily the valence electrons and are particularly useful in examining molecular structures characterized by π bonding. Aromatic (benzenoid) substances have been extensively examined by ultraviolet spectrometry. Molecular structures whose valence electrons are sufficiently labile to be excited by visible light are colored; **visible spectrophotometry** is thus useful in the examination of dyes. **Infrared radiation** is not energetic enough to cause electronic excitation, but can induce molecular vibration. Fortunately for the analyst, modes of vibration are characteristic of particular bonds as well as of particular molecules; **infrared spectrometry** is therefore a tool of very wide utility. Some applications will be described in the following section. Radiations less energetic than infrared can induce molecular rotations or other changes of molecular orientation. The techniques of **microwave** and **radiofrequency spectroscopy** exploit these effects.

The total energy that a molecule possesses may be considered to be the sum of the energy in the nuclei of its atoms, in its electrons, and in its motions (see Appendix I, page 776)—translational, rotational and vibrational:

$$E_{\text{total}} = E_{\text{nuclear}} + E_{\text{electronic}} + E_{\text{translational}} + E_{\text{rotational}} + E_{\text{vibrational}}$$

Thus, a molecule of water in a sample of water at ordinary conditions may be considered to possess energy because (1) its hydrogen nuclei could undergo fusion (see page 741), (2) some of its electrons could drop to lower energy levels, (3) it is moving, (4) it is rotating, and (5) it is vibrating.

Molecular vibrations can occur in any of a number of different modes. A diatomic molecule, like H_2 or HCl, can vibrate only by compression and extension, like a coiled spring (Fig. 22.5). The distance between atoms is thus constantly changing; the nominal "bond distance" is actually an average value. Molecules containing more than two atoms are characterized by valence angles (page 273); these angles, like the distances between atoms, are continuously changing under conditions of molecular vibration. Therefore "bond angle," like bond distance, is really an average, not a constant, value. The modes of molecular vibration that involve changes of bond angles are shown in Figs. 22.6 through 22.9. Scissoring (Fig. 22.6) and rocking (Fig. 22.7) involve deformation within the plane that the atoms occupy when they are in their average positions. Wagging (Fig. 22.8) and twisting (Fig. 22.9) involve out-of-plane deformations.

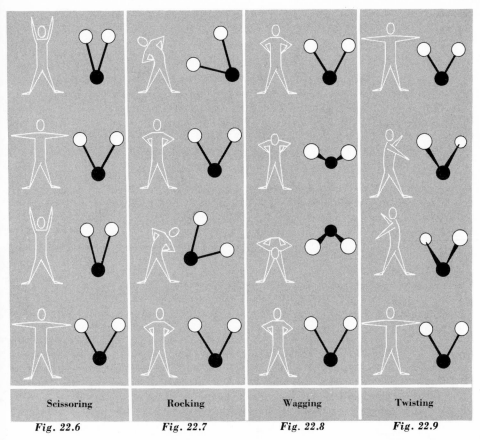

| Scissoring | Rocking | Wagging | Twisting |

Fig. 22.6   **Fig. 22.7**   **Fig. 22.8**   **Fig. 22.9**

Fig. 22.6.   *In-plane deformation (scissoring). The angle changes; the carbon atom moves in and out.*

Fig. 22.7.   *In-plane deformation (rocking). The angle is constant.*

Fig. 22.8.   *Out-of-plane deformation (wagging). Both hydrogen atoms move simultaneously up and down out of the plane.*

Fig. 22.9.   *Out-of-plane deformation (twisting). One H atom moves up and the other moves down out of the plane.*

22.10   AN EXAMPLE OF ABSORPTION SPECTROMETRY: THE INFRARED SPECTRUM

An infrared spectrophotometer consists of a source of radiation that is continuous over the range of approximately 2.5–15 microns, a prism or grating to disperse the radiation into its component wavelengths, means for selection of a particular wavelength interval for detection, a receptacle for interposing a sample of the material being analyzed in the path of the radiation, and a detection system. The spectrum itself is obtained as a plot of the infrared radiation absorbed vs. wavelength (or frequency). A particular infrared frequency that is absorbed corresponds to the energy of some specific molecular vibration. The occurrence of these absorptions has been correlated with known structures of many compounds, and many assignments of such absorptions to specific modes of vibration of

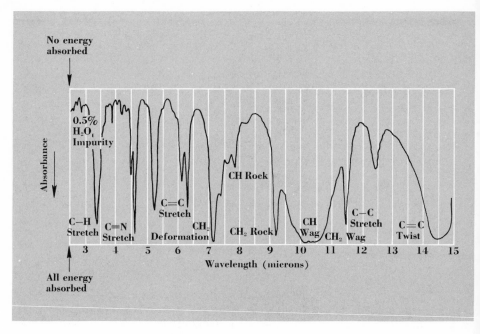

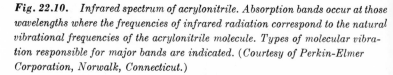

Fig. 22.10. *Infrared spectrum of acrylonitrile. Absorption bands occur at those wavelengths where the frequencies of infrared radiation correspond to the natural vibrational frequencies of the acrylonitrile molecule. Types of molecular vibration responsible for major bands are indicated. (Courtesy of Perkin-Elmer Corporation, Norwalk, Connecticut.)*

particular bonds can be made with confidence. The over-all infrared spectrum of a pure substance is a uniquely characteristic property and, like a fingerprint, can be used as an identification. The presence of absorptions that cannot be attributed to the substance under examination thus indicates the presence of impurities. Figure 22.10 shows the spectrum of acrylonitrile

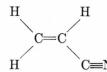

with some structural assignments.

Problems

1. Definitions. Define or explain the terms: spectrometry; absorption spectrometry; emission spectrometry; chromatography; gas chromatography; gas-liquid partition chromatography; electrophoresis; anionic exchange resin; ion-exchange demineralization.

2. Purity of matter. In 1850 a sample of water, after treatment by distillation and other methods, resisted further attempts at purification and was called "pure." Techniques available in 1950 made it possible to separate the "pure" sample into several components, including protium deuterium oxide and dideuterium oxide. Has the purity of the unchanged sample deteriorated because of advance in technique? Was the sample pure in 1850? Is it possible for future advances in methods to show that components separated out today are "impure"?

3. Purification. Black gunpowder consists of sulfur, charcoal, and potassium nitrate. Sulfur dissolves in the volatile solvent carbon bisulfide; potassium nitrate dissolves in water; charcoal is insoluble in both. Outline a procedure for separation and isolation of the components, and suggest methods to identify them.

4. Purification. For each of the following purification methods, point out the motive process, the differential action, and the sensing means:

(a) Scrap iron is recovered from junk with the aid of a magnet.

(b) Moving ionized material is deflected in a magnetic field; the lighter particles deflect to the greater extent. The separation is recorded on a photographic plate.

(c) A perfume chemist places a drop of an essential oil on a strip of blotting paper, which he leaves open to evaporation. He sniffs the paper each hour, until a constant, characteristic odor is noted.

5. Chromatography. It is found that the adsorption of anionic dyes by alumina, Al_2O_3, is enhanced if the alumina is pretreated with hydrochloric acid. Under such conditions, there is a negligible apparent heat of adsorption and the eluent gives a white precipitate with silver nitrate. Interpret these findings. How would you classify this separation, using the notation of Table 22.3 (page 590).

6. Chromatography. Assuming that the response times the attenuation is proportional to the quantity, calculate the concentration in parts per million of CO in the mixture shown in Fig. 22.3 (page 593).

Answer. 1×10^2 p.p.m.

7. Chromatography. Figure 22.11 shows, on the right, the chromatogram of a coke-oven gas mixture of composition 60% H_2, 4.0% N_2, 5.0% CO, and

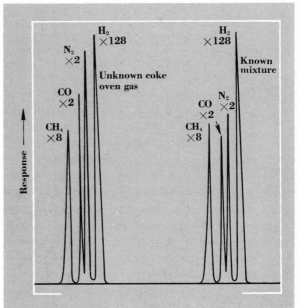

Fig. 22.11. Chromatogram of a mixture of coke-oven gases. Chromatogram of known mixture appears on the right, for a 1 ml sample at 25°C in a 4 m silica gel column, carried by argon at 100 ml/min. Chromatogram of the unknown mixture appears on the left.

30% CH_4. Approximate the composition of the mixture whose chromatogram appears on the left. If the total percentages do not add up to 100, how do you account for the difference?

8. Chromatography. The adsorbent material used in the chromatogram of Fig. 22.3 is a synthetic zeolite, containing less than 2% water. It is observed that, if the adsorbent is wetted until it contains 10% water, the analysis is completed in half the time and the CO emerges before the CH_4. Account for this speedup and reversal.

9. Chromatography. Refer to Fig. 22.2. (a) Draw the one-dimensional chromatogram that would have been formed with solvent A alone, assuming other factors were unchanged. Of the 17 components shown in Fig. 22.2, how many would have been substantially separated (less than 20% overlap of spots)? (b) Answer the same question for solvent B.

Answer. (a) about 11

10. Chromatography. An analytical technique called **thin layer chromatography** (TLC) separates substances on thin layers of adsorbents or ion exchangers, using the experimental methods of paper chromatography. Suggest a specific laboratory procedure for separating a mixture of hydrocarbons, using alumina adsorbent and a pentane-ether eluent, by TLC. Identify the various parts of the procedure in terms of the outline of Table 22.3.

11. Ion exchange. A sample of water of pH 7.00 exhibits hardness because of its content of Mg^{2+}, Ca^{2+}, Al^{3+}, and other ions whose soaps are insoluble. To assay the average equivalent concentration of such ions, some of the water is passed through a column of the hydrogen form of a sulfonic acid cation exchanger. A 10.00 ml portion of the eluent requires 14.05 ml of 0.01050M NaOH for titration to re-establish neutrality. Calculate (a) the molar concentration of H^+ in the eluent; (b) the average equivalent concentration of metal ions in the original solution. Explain the relationship between (a) and (b) in terms of the action of the ion exchanger.

Answer. (a) 0.01475M; (b) 0.01475N.

12. Ion exchange. 50.00 ml of a neutral solution of a mixture of rare earth salts is passed through a column of the hydrogen form of a cation exchanger. A 10.00 ml portion of the eluent requires 12.35 ml of 0.1040M NaOH for titration to re-establish neutrality. The exchanger is then burned completely in air, leaving a residue of rare earth sesquioxide (M_2O_3) containing 0.3555 g of metal. Calculate the mean atomic weight of the rare earth mixture. List the assumptions made with regard to the course of the analytical procedure in accepting this calculated value.

13. Infrared spectrometry. The following stretching frequencies due to unsaturated (double or triple bond) linkages are observed (R = hydrocarbon portion of the molecule):

		Frequency (cm^{-1})
Alkyne	R—C≡C—H	2100–2140
Alkyne	R—C≡C—R	2190–2260
Nitrile	R—C≡N	2240–2260
Azo compound	R—N=N—R	2120–2160
Acid chloride	R—C=O 丨 Cl	1770–1815

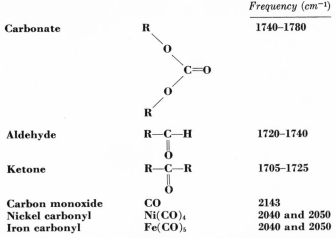

		Frequency (cm^{-1})
Carbonate		1740–1780
Aldehyde	R—C—H ‖ O	1720–1740
Ketone	R—C—R ‖ O	1705–1725
Carbon monoxide	CO	2143
Nickel carbonyl	Ni(CO)$_4$	2040 and 2050
Iron carbonyl	Fe(CO)$_5$	2040 and 2050

(a) Are the infrared absorption frequencies associated with given chemical linkages absolutely independent of their intramolecular environment? Are they independent to a degree that permits reasonable assignments of structure to unknown substances? Defend your answers. (b) Carbon monoxide has been depicted as a resonance hybrid of the structures

$$:C{=}\overset{..}{O}: \leftrightarrow :C{\equiv}O:$$

How do the infrared data bear on the question of the assignment of structure to carbon monoxide? (c) Are metal carbonyl structures more like carbon monoxide or like organic carbonyl structures? What conclusions would you draw concerning the similarity or difference between the carbon-oxygen bond in carbonyls and the organic carbon-carbon triple bond?

23

Chemical
kinetics

23.1 **INTRODUCTION**

A thermochemical equation expresses the stoichiometric relations between reactants and products and the accompanying heat change but tells us nothing about the rate of the reaction. The rate of a reaction is the change in concentration of a reactant per unit time or the number of moles of a reactant converted to products per unit time. Thus, we may write

$$C(c) + O_2(g) \rightarrow CO_2(g) \qquad \Delta H = -94.1 \text{ kcal}$$

but exposing lumps of coal* or diamond to air produces no measurable reaction. At ordinary temperatures, the rate of this reaction is immeasurably slow. Explosions, on the other hand, appear to be immeasurably fast. Many reactions proceed at rates neither extremely slow nor extremely rapid.

Such a reaction may be demonstrated by the reduction of permanganate ion, MnO_4^-, by oxalic acid, HOC_2O_2OH,

$$\underset{colored}{2MnO_4^-} + 5HOC_2O_2OH + 6H^+ \rightarrow \underset{colorless}{2Mn^{2+}} + 10CO_2 + 8H_2O$$

Add 5.0 ml of 0.030M potassium permanganate solution, $KMnO_4$, acidified with sulfuric acid, to 500 ml of water at room temperature; the resulting solution possesses the pink color characteristic of permanganate solutions. To this solution, add 5.0 ml of 0.10M HOC_2O_2OH. The time required to decolorize the solution is approximately 30 minutes. Also illustrative are the data, plotted in Fig. 23.1, for the decomposition of dinitrogen

---

* Coal is composed largely of amorphous carbon and carbon compounds.

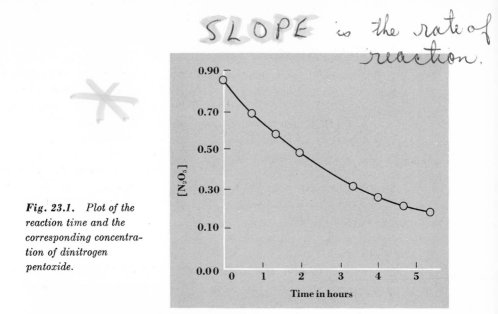

SLOPE is the rate of reaction.

Fig. 23.1. *Plot of the reaction time and the corresponding concentration of dinitrogen pentoxide.*

pentoxide dissolved in carbon tetrachloride,

$$2N_2O_5(sol)* \rightarrow 4NO_2(sol) + O_2(g)$$

During the course of the reaction, the concentration of the reactant decreases systematically.

An over-all reaction such as

$$2NO(g) + Br_2(g) \rightarrow 2NOBr(g) \tag{1}$$

tells us nothing about the **mechanism of the reaction,** the actual series of individual steps by which the reactants change to products. Does molecular bromine really combine simultaneously with 2 molecules of NO,

$$NO + NO + Br_2 \rightarrow 2NOBr$$

or, is the process the combination of one NO molecule with one Br_2 molecule in one step

$$NO + Br_2 \rightarrow NOBr_2 \tag{2}$$

followed by a second step?

$$NOBr_2 + NO \rightarrow 2NOBr \tag{3}$$

Some chemical reactions occur in a single step but, more frequently, the reaction occurs in a sequence of steps (page 618). The addition of the successive Steps (2) and (3) yields the over-all Reaction (1). The study of the rate and the mechanism of chemical reactions is known as **chemical kinetics.**

The combustion of coal is a typical **heterogeneous reaction,** a reaction occurring only at the interface (boundary) between two phases. The reaction between $NO(g)$ and $Br_2(g)$ is a typical **homogeneous reaction,** a reaction occurring in only one phase.

* Reminder: (*sol*) means *in solution*.

23.2 CONDITIONS AFFECTING REACTION RATES

Reactions occur at a definite characteristic rate when certain variables are fixed. These variables are (1) nature of the reactants, (2) concentration of the reactants, (3) particle size of the solid or liquid in a heterogeneous reaction, (4) temperature, and (5) presence of a catalyst.*

(1) Nature of Reactants. Copper or silver reacts very slowly with oxygen even in a flame, while magnesium under the same conditions burns very rapidly; white phosphorus ignites spontaneously in air, whereas red phosphorus does not. When a solution containing silver ions, Ag^+, is added to a solution containing chloride ions, Cl^-, insoluble silver chloride forms very rapidly,

$$Ag^+ + Cl^- \rightarrow AgCl\downarrow$$

On the other hand, the addition of magnesium ions, Mg^{2+}, to oxalate ions, $C_2O_4^{2-}$, produces insoluble magnesium oxalate very slowly,

$$Mg^{2+} + C_2O_4^{2-} \rightarrow MgC_2O_4\downarrow$$

The first reaction may be completed in microseconds while the second reaction may require 24 hours.

(2) Concentration of Reactants. In 1864, Cato Guldberg and Peter Waage recognized that at constant temperature the rate of a homogeneous reaction is usually proportional to some power of the concentrations of the reactants. The concentration is expressed in moles of reactant per liter of the homogeneous phase. This generalization, the **law of mass action,** simply states that for the general reaction

$$aA + bB \rightarrow cC + dD$$

the rate of formation of C or D, or the rate of disappearance of A or B, is proportional to powers of the concentrations of A and B,

$$rate \propto [A]^x[B]^y$$

in which $\propto$ denotes a proportionality, and from which

$$rate = k[A]^x[B]^y$$

The numerical value of the exponents x and y must be determined experimentally. *They cannot be deduced* from the over-all reaction or from any principle or hypothesis, and they *need not necessarily be the same as a and b.* The proportionality constant k is known as the **specific rate constant** of the reaction. The unit of k depends upon the units used for the concentration terms and the unit of time. The rate equation may also be expressed in terms of the symbols

$$-\frac{d[A]}{dt}, \quad -\frac{d[B]}{dt}, \quad +\frac{d[C]}{dt}, \quad \text{and} \quad +\frac{d[D]}{dt}$$

* Influence of solvent is not considered in this book.

in which $-d[A]/dt$ and $-d[B]/dt$ denote, respectively, *the decrease* in the concentration of A and B per unit time; $d[C]/dt$ and $d[D]/dt$ denote *the increase* in the concentration of C and D per unit time. The *plus sign* is always associated with a product of the reaction because its concentration increases, and the *minus sign* is always associated with a reactant because its concentration decreases. However, in the use of these symbols, the relative numbers of moles of reactants and products must also be stated. For example, in the reaction

$$H_2(g) + I_2(g) \rightarrow 2HI(g)$$

from the stoichiometry, we note that for *one* mole of H_2, *one* mole of I_2 reacts but *two* moles of HI are formed. This means H_2 and I_2 disappear at the same rate but HI appears at twice this rate,

$$-2\frac{d[H_2]}{dt} = -2\frac{d[I_2]}{dt} = +\frac{d[HI]}{dt}$$

or

$$-\frac{d[H_2]}{dt} = -\frac{d[I_2]}{dt} = +\tfrac{1}{2}\frac{d[HI]}{dt}$$

The rate equation may then be expressed as

$$rate = -\frac{d[H_2]}{dt} = -\frac{d[I_2]}{dt} = +\tfrac{1}{2}\frac{d[HI]}{dt} = k[H_2]^x[I_2]^y$$

In the reaction

$$2H_2(g) + O_2(g) \rightarrow 2H_2O(g)$$

H_2O appears at the same rate that H_2 disappears but this rate is twice the rate of disappearance of O_2,

$$-\frac{d[H_2]}{dt} = -2\frac{d[O_2]}{dt} = +\frac{d[H_2O]}{dt}$$

Thus, for the general reaction $aA + bB \rightarrow cC + dD$

$$rate = -\frac{d[A]}{dt} = -\frac{a}{b}\frac{d[B]}{dt} = +\frac{a}{c}\frac{d[C]}{dt} = +\frac{a}{d}\frac{d[D]}{dt} = k[A]^x[B]^y$$

EXAMPLE 1 **Dinitrogen pentoxide decomposes as shown,**

$$2N_2O_5 \rightarrow 4NO_2 + O_2$$

The rate can be expressed in three ways:

$$-\frac{d[N_2O_5]}{dt} = k[N_2O_5]$$

$$+\frac{d[NO_2]}{dt} = k'[N_2O_5]$$

$$+\frac{d[O_2]}{dt} = k''[N_2O_5]$$

How are the k' and k'' related to k?

From the stoichiometry, 2 moles of NO_2 form for every 1 mole of N_2O_5 that reacts, hence

$$k' = 2k$$

but 1 mole of O_2 forms for every 2 moles of N_2O_5 that react, hence

$$k'' = \tfrac{1}{2}k$$

The sum of the powers of the concentration terms in the rate equation is known as **the order of the reaction.** For example, the reaction

$$2NO + O_2 \rightarrow 2NO_2$$

follows the rate equation

$$-\frac{d[NO]}{dt} = k[NO]^2[O_2]$$

The reaction is therefore a third order reaction, since the sum of the exponents for the two concentration terms is 3. The reaction is said to be second order with respect to NO and first order with respect to O_2.

An example of the lack of correlation between the exponents in the rate equation and the coefficients in the chemical equation is the reaction in solution between ethyl alcohol and decaborane forming triethyl borate and hydrogen,

$$30C_2H_5OH + B_{10}H_{14} \rightarrow 10B(OC_2H_5)_3 + 22H_2(g)$$

for which the experimentally determined rate equation is

$$-\frac{d[C_2H_5OH]}{dt} = -30\frac{d[B_{10}H_{14}]}{dt} = k[C_2H_5OH][B_{10}H_{14}]$$

The exponent for each of the two concentration terms is one; this reaction is therefore said to be a second order reaction, first order with respect to C_2H_5OH and first order with respect to $B_{10}H_{14}$.

EXAMPLE 2 **For the decomposition of dinitrogen pentoxide, N_2O_5, dissolved in carbon tetrachloride,**

$$2N_2O_5 \rightarrow 4NO_2 + O_2$$

the following data at 30°C are given:

Reactant concentration $[N_2O_5]$	Rate of decomposition $-\dfrac{d[N_2O_5]}{dt}$
$0.170\ \dfrac{\text{mole}}{\text{liter}}$	$0.050\ \dfrac{\text{mole}}{\text{liter hr}}$
0.340	0.10
0.680	0.20

(a) **Write the rate equation for the reaction. What is the order of the reaction?**
(b) **Calculate the rate constant for the reaction at 30°C.**
(c) **Calculate the decomposition rate at 30°C at the instant when $[N_2O_5] = 0.540$.**

ANSWER (a) It is seen that doubling the concentration of the N_2O_5 doubles the rate; therefore, the rate of this reaction is proportional to the N_2O_5 concentration, or

$$rate = -\frac{d[N_2O_5]}{dt} = k[N_2O_5]$$

Since the rate is proportional to the first power of one reactant, the reaction is first order. (Figure 23.1 also shows that the rate is proportional to the N_2O_5 concentration.)

(b) Solving for k,

$$k = \frac{rate}{[N_2O_5]} = \frac{0.050 \frac{mole}{liter\ hr}}{0.170 \frac{mole}{liter}} = \frac{0.10}{0.34} = \frac{0.20}{0.68}$$

$$= \frac{0.29}{hr}$$

and k is thus 0.29 per hour. Kinetic data with an error of 3% are generally considered excellent.

(c) From the previous calculation

$$rate = -\frac{d[N_2O_5]}{dt} = \frac{0.29}{hr}[N_2O_5]$$

so that when $[N_2O_5] = 0.540$

$$rate = \frac{0.29}{hr}0.540\frac{mole}{liter} = 0.16\frac{mole}{liter\ hr}$$

EXAMPLE 3 The reaction

$$F_2 + 2ClO_2 \rightarrow 2FClO_2$$

has been studied in the gaseous state and the data at 250°K may be summarized as

Rate of disappearance of F_2 (mole/liter sec) $-\frac{[F_2]}{dt}$	Reactant concentration (mole/liter)	
	$[F_2]$	$[ClO_2]$
1.2×10^{-3}	0.10	0.010
4.8×10^{-3}	0.10	0.040
2.4×10^{-3}	0.20	0.010

Calculate the rate constant for the reaction and the rate of formation of $FClO_2$ at the instant when $[F_2] = 0.010$ and $[ClO_2] = 0.020$ at 250°K.

ANSWER First, use the data to determine the rate equation, from which the rate constant is then calculated. Observe that when the concentration of F_2 is constant and the concentration of ClO_2 is quadrupled, the rate is also quadrupled; hence, the rate of the reaction is proportional to $[ClO_2]$. When the concentration of ClO_2 is constant and the concentration of F_2 is doubled, the rate is also doubled; hence the rate is proportional to $[F_2]$. The rate equation is therefore

$$-\frac{d[F_2]}{dt} = k[F_2][ClO_2]$$

from which

$$k = \frac{-\dfrac{d[F_2]}{dt}}{[F_2][ClO_2]} = \frac{1.2 \times 10^{-3} \dfrac{\text{mole}}{\text{liter sec}}}{0.10 \dfrac{\text{mole}}{\text{liter}} \times 0.010 \dfrac{\text{mole}}{\text{liter}}} = \frac{4.8 \times 10^{-3}}{0.10 \times 0.040} = \frac{2.4 \times 10^{-3}}{0.20 \times 0.010}$$

$$= 1.2 \frac{\text{liter}}{\text{mole sec}}$$

The rate of disappearance of F_2 is thus given by

$$-\frac{d[F_2]}{dt} = 1.2 \frac{\text{liter}}{\text{mole sec}} [F_2][ClO_2]$$

so that when $[F_2] = 0.010$ and $[ClO_2] = 0.020$, the rate of disappearance of F_2 is

$$-\frac{d[F_2]}{dt} = 1.2 \frac{\text{liter}}{\text{mole sec}} (0.010) \frac{\text{mole}}{\text{liter}} (0.020) \frac{\text{mole}}{\text{liter}}$$

$$= 2.4 \times 10^{-4} \frac{\text{mole}}{\text{liter sec}}$$

However, *two moles of $FClO_2$ form for each mole of F_2 that disappears*; hence the rate of formation of $FClO_2$ is

$$2 \times (2.4 \times 10^{-4}) \frac{\text{mole}}{\text{liter sec}} = 4.8 \times 10^{-4} \frac{\text{mole}}{\text{liter sec}}$$

(3) **Particle Size in Heterogeneous Reactions.**   Since heterogeneous reactions occur only at the surface boundary between the reacting phases, the rate of such reactions is proportional to the surface area. When a given mass is subdivided into smaller particles, the surface area is increased; hence, as the particle size is decreased, the rate of reaction increases. Lumps of coal or zinc, for example, are difficult to ignite in air but, pulverized and dispersed in air, they react explosively.*

(4) **Effect of Temperature.**   Temperature has a striking effect on the rate of chemical reactions. Reaction rates negligibly slow at ordinary temperatures may become appreciable and even explosive at elevated temperatures. As a very rough but useful rule, the rate constant is doubled for a rise in temperature of 10 Celsius degrees. Thus a temperature change of 100 degrees may alter the rate more or less by a factor of $2^{100/10}$ or 2^{10} or

* Disastrous coal mine explosions do not result ordinarily from ignition of a gas. Bituminous ("soft") coal dust suspended in air may be ignited by a match, producing a violent explosion, the rate of pressure rise reaching as much as 40 atm per sec. The pressure increase results from the rapid expansion of the gaseous products of the reaction and air, caused by the heat evolved from the combustion reaction.

10^3. Illustrative is the effect of temperature on the rate of decomposition of hydrogen iodide; the rate constant increases by a factor of 1.7 for each 10° rise in temperature.

The effect of temperature may be demonstrated by substituting hot water in the experiment involving $KMnO_4$ and HOC_2O_2OH (page 602). With hot water the time required to decolorize the solution becomes about 2 minutes.

23.3 THEORY OF REACTION RATES

(a) **Classical Collision Theory.** According to the collision theory, molecules must "collide" to react; the rate of reaction is then proportional to the number of colliding molecules,

rate ∝ number of colliding molecules per liter per sec

The collision theory accounts for the dependence of the rate on a product (and not a sum) of concentration terms. Let us assume that molecule A combines directly with a molecule of B to form AB (A + B → AB). Visualize 5 molecules each of A and B in a box. The molecule tagged A^1 will undergo 5 collisions with the 5 B molecules; molecules tagged A^2, A^3, A^4, and A^5 will also each undergo 5 collisions with the 5 B molecules. Thus, the total number of collisions between A and B is 25, which equals 5×5 and not $5 + 5$. For a fixed volume, the concentration is proportional to the number of molecules; then

number of collisions ∝ [A][B]

But the rate is proportional to the number of collisions; hence

rate ∝ [A][B]

The number of colliding molecules calculated from the kinetic theory of gases is enormous, of the order of magnitude of 10^{32} molecules per liter per sec at standard conditions; this value does not vary considerably with different gases. Hence, if "collision" were the only requirement for reaction, all gaseous reactions should proceed at practically the same explosive rate. However, for the same reactant concentration at the same temperature, 300°C, the decomposition rate of gaseous hydrogen iodide is 4.4×10^{-3} mole/liter hr, while the decomposition rate of gaseous dinitrogen pentoxide is 9.4×10^5 moles/liter hr. Clearly, collisions between molecules cannot be the only factor involved in determining the rate of a reaction.

Chemical reactions involve redistribution of atoms, but the redistribution of atoms requires a weakening of the bonds holding the atoms together in the original molecules, and the formation of new bonds in the product molecules. For example, for the reaction $2HI \rightarrow H_2 + I_2$ to occur, the bond holding the H atom to the I atom must be weakened, and bonds must form between H atoms and I atoms. We thus postulate that molecules react only if in a collision they possess an energy equal to or greater than a certain critical value. This critical value known as the **energy of activation,**[*] E_A, is characteristic for each reaction. Thus, the salient hypothesis of the classical collision theory is that if the energy of the colliding molecules is less than E_A, no reaction occurs; if the energy of the colliding molecules is equal to or greater than E_A, reaction occurs. Then

$$rate = \frac{\text{number of colliding molecules}}{\text{liter sec}} \times \begin{array}{c}\text{fraction of colliding mole-}\\ \text{cules with energy } E_A \text{ or}\\ \text{greater}\end{array}$$

For simplicity, it is further assumed that molecules utilize only their kinetic (translational) energy to acquire E_A. This kinetic energy converted to vibrational energy (page 596) upon impact causes the atoms in the molecules to vibrate violently; the large vibrational amplitudes[†] weaken the bonds (see Fig. 23.2).

The kinetic theory of gases tells us that at any given temperature not all molecules possess the same kinetic energy. Rather, because of the enormous number of collisions, the speeds of molecules will vary from practically zero to practically the speed of light. Figure 23.3 illustrates an energy distribution curve. If we let the area under the curve represent the total number of molecules, then the shaded area represents the number of molecules possessing a velocity of 20×10^4 cm per sec or higher. Notice that comparatively few molecules possess the kinetic energy corresponding to 20×10^4 cm per sec or higher. Also notice that practically all the molecules possess the kinetic energy corresponding to 2×10^4 cm per sec or higher. Thus if the energy of activation for a reaction is 3000 cal per mole, corresponding to 20×10^4 cm per sec, then only a very small fraction of all the colliding molecules will react. On the other hand, if the energy of activation requirement is only 30 cal per mole, then practically all of the colliding molecules will react.

[*] In terms of more modern theory (page 615), the energy of activation is interpreted as an energy difference. By tradition the symbol Δ is omitted.

[†] Displacement of atoms from their equilibrium positions; the center of mass of the molecule remains stationary during vibration.

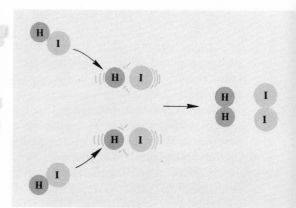

Fig. 23.2. *Chemical reaction pictured in terms of the classical collision theory. HI molecules acquire the energy necessary for reaction (E_A) upon impact; this energy converted to vibrational energy produces large vibrational amplitudes which weaken the H—I bonds.*

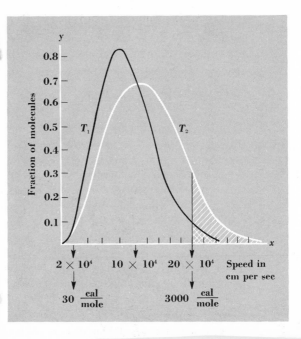

Fig. 23.3. *Kinetic energy distribution curve. The y axis gives the fraction of molecules possessing the kinetic energy indicated in cal per mole on the x axis; also included is the corresponding speed in cm per sec for a gas having a molecular weight of 6. T_2 is a temperature higher than T_1; the kinetic energy distribution is broader and the average energy higher at the higher temperature. The distribution law was first published by James Clerk Maxwell in 1860. See page 12. (An experimental verification of the Maxwellian distribution of molecular speeds is given in "Physics," by David Halliday and Robert Resnik, page 520. Wiley, New York, 1960.)*

EXAMPLE 4   **The simple form of the Maxwell velocity distribution law is, for practical purposes**

FRACTION OF MOLECULES HAVING E_m OR HIGHER $= N_E$

at T increases rate increases.

ate $=$

$$\boxed{\frac{N_E}{N} = e^{-E/RT}}$$

in which N is the total number of molecules and N_E is the number of molecules having an energy E or greater. Then

$$\frac{N_E}{N}$$

is the fraction of the molecules for which the kinetic energy is E or greater. R is the gas constant, 2.0 cal per mole per deg, and T is the temperature in absolute degrees. Calculate the fraction of the molecules of a gas at 500°K possessing kinetic energies corresponding to a minimum of (a) 3000 cal per mole, and (b) 30 cal per mole.

ANSWER   **From the distribution law**

(a)

$$\frac{E}{RT} = \frac{3000 \ \dfrac{cal}{mole}}{2.0 \ \dfrac{cal}{mole \ deg} \ 500 \ deg} = 3.0$$

$$\frac{N_{3000}}{N} = e^{-3.0}$$

Solving for the value of $e^{-3.0}$ (Appendix II, page 792),

$$e^{-3.0} = 0.05$$

Hence

$$\frac{N_{3000}}{N} = 0.05$$

(b)

$$\frac{E}{RT} = \frac{30 \ \frac{\cancel{cal}}{\cancel{mole}}}{2.0 \ \frac{\cancel{cal}}{\cancel{mole} \ \cancel{deg}} \ 500 \ \cancel{deg}} = 0.030$$

$$\frac{N_{30}}{N} = e^{-0.030} = 0.97$$

Thus, at 500°K, only 5% of the molecules possess a minimum kinetic energy of 3000 cal per mole, while 97% of them possess at least 30 cal per mole. (Note that the *fraction* of molecules possessing a given kinetic energy is *independent of the* absolute *number* of molecules involved.)

In terms of the collision theory, the rate of a reaction may then be expressed as

$$rate = \frac{\text{number of colliding molecules}}{\text{liter sec}} e^{-E_A/RT} \tag{1}$$

The *greater* is E_A, the energy the molecules must acquire before they can react, the *smaller* is the fraction of the molecules possessing this E_A, and the *slower* is the rate of the reaction.

EXAMPLE 5   Use the collision theory to estimate the rate of the reaction $2HI(g) \rightarrow H_2(g) + I_2(g)$ at 500°C. When [HI] is 1.0 mole per liter, the number of colliding molecules is 7.1×10^{34} molecules per liter per sec. The energy of activation is 4.5×10^4 cal per mole.

ANSWER   According to the collision theory, only those molecules possessing kinetic energy corresponding to 4.5×10^4 cal per mole or higher will react upon collision. Hence, first use the Maxwell distribution law to calculate what fraction of the colliding molecules possesses a minimum of 4.5×10^4 cal per mole,

$$\frac{N_{45000}}{N} = e^{-(4.5 \times 10^4)/(2 \times 773)} = e^{-29} = 2.6 \times 10^{-13}$$

Thus, only 2.6×10^{-11}% of the colliding molecules react; the rate of the reaction is therefore

$$rate = 7.1 \times 10^{34} \ \frac{\text{molecules}}{\text{liter sec}} \ 2.6 \times 10^{-13} = 18 \times 10^{21} \ \frac{\text{molecules}}{\text{liter sec}}$$

Converting to $\dfrac{\text{moles}}{\text{liter hr}}$,

$$rate = 18 \times 10^{21}\,\frac{\text{molecules}}{\text{liter } \cancel{\text{sec}}}\; \cfrac{3600\;\cancel{\text{sec}}}{6.0 \times 10^{23}\,\dfrac{\text{molecules}}{\text{mole}}}\;\text{hr}$$

$$= 11 \times 10^{1}\,\frac{\text{moles}}{\text{liter hr}}$$

This value compares very favorably with the observed rate, 126 moles/liter hr.

The velocity distribution also affords an explanation of the effect of temperature on rates of reactions. A 10 degree rise produces a negligible increase in the number of colliding molecules. On the other hand, Fig. 23.3 (page 611) illustrates that at the higher temperature T_2 the fraction of the molecules possessing a minimum of 3000 cal per mole increases appreciably. Actual calculations show that the fraction of molecules possessing a minimum of 25,000 cal per mole increases by a factor of 4 when the temperature is increased from 25° to 35°C, clearly indicating that the increase in reaction rates is due largely to an increase in the fraction of "activated molecules," the fraction possessing the required energy of activation.

There are, however, many reactions for which the collision theory yields results in extremely poor agreement with observed values; the deviations may vary from about 10^8 too large to 10^{-9} too small. Also, the energy of activation may include vibrational and rotational energies arising from the vibrational and rotational motions of molecules. Some molecules possessing the required energy apparently do not react. By analogy, the damage in flight ("reaction") resulting from the collision of two airplanes depends not only on their speeds (energy), but also on their relative positions or orientation. Thus some molecules must be oriented in a very specific manner for reaction to occur; see Fig. 23.4. This factor, the

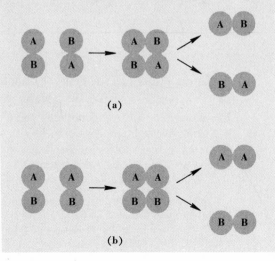

Fig. 23.4. A general representation of the possible influence of orientation of molecules on the rate of the reaction
$2AB \rightarrow A_2 + B_2$.
(*a*) *Orientation that does not lead to reaction;*
(*b*) *orientation that leads to reaction.*

(a)

(b)

orientation factor,* is known as the **entropy of activation,** $S^\ddagger$. The more specific the orientation required for the reaction to proceed, the smaller is the entropy of activation and the measured rate will be smaller than calculated on the basis of the classical collision theory, Equation (1) (page 612). Thus, more correctly, the rate is determined by three factors, the number of colliding molecules, the energy of activation, and the entropy of activation,

$$rate = \frac{\text{number of colliding molecules}}{\text{liter sec}} \, e^{-E_A/RT} e^{S^\ddagger/R}$$

$S^\ddagger$ is determined empirically in calories per mole per deg.

(b) Theory of the Activated Complex (the Transition State Theory). More modern theories, developed by Henry Eyring and others, modify the concept that reacting molecules must "collide" with a certain energy. It is believed that changes in the arrangement of the atoms in molecules commence even when the distance between molecules is greater than the separation corresponding to a classical "collision." The chemical change is visualized as a continuous series of changes in bond distances as reactant molecules approach each other. Energy changes accompany these continuous changes in configuration or arrangement of atoms. Finally, *the reacting molecules must achieve a specific configuration* before they can form the products of the reaction. This specific configuration possessing a definite energy is known as an "activated complex" or "the transition state complex." Thus, the combination of H_2 and I_2,

$$H_2(g) + I_2(g) \rightarrow 2HI(g) \qquad \Delta H = -2.6 \text{ kcal}$$

for which $E_A = 42$ kcal per mole may be visualized as shown in Schemes I and II (distances between atoms are given in angstrom units).

Scheme I

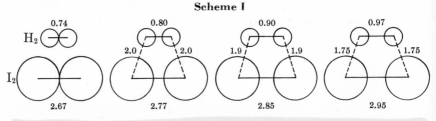

Initial reactants   **As the molecules approach** *the inter-*   *"The transition state*
molecules far apart   *atomic distances continuously change*†   *complex"*‡

The activated complex does not represent an observable substance; in principle, it cannot be isolated. Nevertheless it is assumed to possess properties common to real molecules, such as a molecular weight, interatomic distances, ability to rotate and vibrate. Further, it is endowed with theoretical properties not possessed by real molecules. Once the complex is formed,

---

* Solvent interactions also influence the magnitude of the entropy of activation.

† Interatomic distance in H_2 and I_2 increases while H and I atoms attract each other, forming finally the critical configuration called the activated complex or the transition state complex.

‡ Estimated bond distances in the complex taken from S. W. Benson, "The Foundations of Chemical Kinetics," p. 286. McGraw-Hill, New York, 1960.

it can do only one of two things: either it returns to the initial reactants, or it proceeds to form products. To simplify the application of the theory, it is commonly assumed that once the complex is formed, it will decompose to the products, as shown in Scheme II.

Scheme II

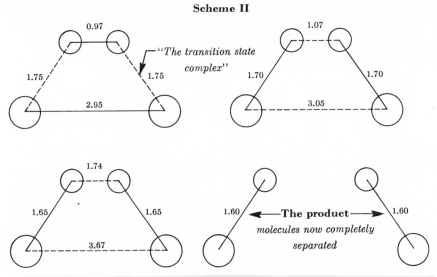

The energy changes accompanying the gradual breaking of the H—H and I—I molecules or bonds, and the gradual formation of the H—I molecules or bonds, are illustrated in Fig. 23.5. H_i is the enthalpy of the initial reactants. As the interatomic distance increases in the H—H and I—I molecules, energy is absorbed, but simultaneously H$\cdots$I starts to form and this process evolves energy. However, in forming the complex more energy is absorbed than evolved; hence, the complex possesses a larger enthalpy, H_a, than the initial reactants. The difference

$$H_a - H_i = H^{\ddagger} = 42 \text{ kcal per mole}$$

corresponds to the energy of activation.* As the complex decomposes to product, the H——H atoms and I——I atoms separate even farther, but at these distances the work required to separate them further is compara- tively small; simultaneously, the H$\cdots$I atoms now attract each other very strongly and considerable energy is evolved. Hence, the product always possesses a smaller enthalpy, H_p, than the complex. Note that for this particular reaction, the product has a smaller enthalpy than the initial reactants,

$$H_p - H_i = -2.6 \text{ kcal}$$

corresponding to ΔH for the reaction. Note also that ΔH *for the reaction depends only on the difference between H_p and H_i.*

* This statement is not strictly true; we are assuming that $H^{\ddagger}$ (the enthalpy of activation) $= E_A$ (the energy of activation). At room temperature, $H^{\ddagger}$ may be smaller by about 1.2 kcal per mole.

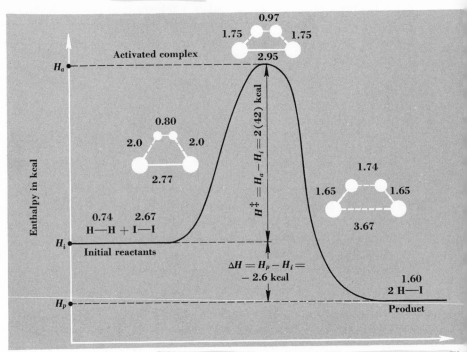

Fig. 23.5. *Reaction as the interatomic distances change (not to scale. The energy of activation is 42 kcal per mole; the diagram is given on the basis of 2 moles. 40.74 ± 0.25 kcal per mole is a more accurate value in the temperature range 633–783°C. Distances are in angstrom units.)*

From the assumption that once formed, the complex proceeds to products, it follows that the rate of a reaction is proportional to the concentration of the activated complex,

$$rate \propto [activated\ complex]$$

Cloaked in quantum mechanical terms, an equation for the rate, presently impossible of solution, is obtained; but with simplifying assumptions, when the concentration of each reactant is 1 mole per liter, **the proportionality constant becomes a universal constant** for homogeneous reactions at a given temperature,

$$rate = \frac{2.1 \times 10^{10} T}{deg\ sec}\ [activated\ complex]$$

and the concentration of the complex becomes a function of $H^{\ddagger}$ and $S^{\ddagger}$. *The smaller the $H^{\ddagger}$ and the larger the $S^{\ddagger}$ the greater is the concentration of the complex and the faster is the rate of the reaction.* As the entropy of the activated complex increases above the entropy of the initial reactants, the probability of forming the complex increases. In principle, this equation means that *all complexes, independent of their specific nature, decompose to products with the same specific rate constant.* Therefore *the rate of a reaction is controlled by the number of activated complex "molecules" per unit* *volume.* The theoretical calculation of the complex concentration, however, remains completely impracticable. Even when intelligent guesses are made by experienced scientists, as in the case of the complex for the $H_2 + I_2$ reaction, it is still a formidable and largely unsuccessful task.

This is a fair evaluation of the state of our theoretical knowledge of chemistry and physics. Applications of the principles of quantum mechanics must be guided by empirical knowledge.

And yet the concept that an activated complex possesses a hypothetical structure permits a scientist to make predictions, a basic aim of science. For example, for the reaction

$$(C_2H_5)_3N \ + \quad CH_3I \quad \rightarrow \ [(C_2H_5)_3NCH_3]^+I^-$$
triethylamine   *methyl iodide*   *triethylmethylammonium*
                                                      iodide

we guess the complex is formed by the approach of the N atom to the C atom in CH_3I, the stretching of the C—I bond, and the turning of the H atoms in the methyl iodide molecule, as shown in Scheme III.

eg.
Know.

Scheme III

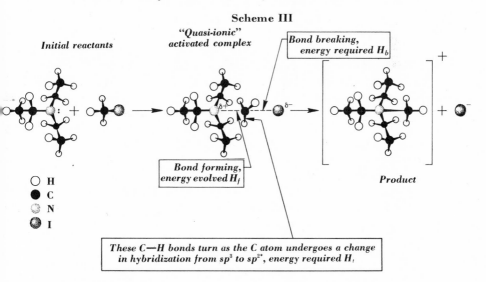

○ H
● C
◍ N
◉ I

Then $H^{\ddagger} = H_b + H_t - H_f$.

We can now predict that a change in reactants, making it more difficult for the N atom to approach the C atom, will result in an increase in the energy of activation. Thus, substitute *tert*-butyl iodide,

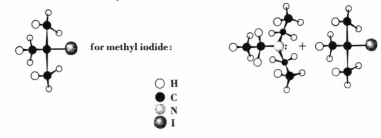

for methyl iodide:

○ H
● C
◍ N
◉ I

* The *p* orbital lies along the N---C---I axis.

It should now be more difficult for the N atom to approach the C atom from which the I atom has to be detached. Consequently, the energy of activation should increase considerably; hence, the concentration of the complex should be smaller, and therefore the rate of the reaction by this particular mechanism considerably reduced. This conclusion is in agreement with experimental results.

23.4 MECHANISM OF REACTION FROM RATE EQUATION

Unlike the reactions we have considered in the previous section, many reactions occur in several steps, each step passing through a transition state. The study of the kinetics of a reaction offers an important method of deciphering the series of processes that occur consecutively (or simultaneously) to produce the observed over-all reaction. Not to underestimate the difficulty of this intellectual endeavor, let us confess immediately that many apparently simple reactions, for example, $2H_2 + O_2 \rightarrow 2H_2O$, are devastatingly complicated, and that after a half-century of labor by many scientists the mechanisms of these reactions are not yet completely understood. Obviously, the treatment of only the simplest mechanisms will be attempted here. A study of the mechanism of the reaction $N_2 + 3H_2 \rightarrow 2NH_3$, used for the production of ammonia, reveals that the rate of this reaction is actually controlled by the rate at which nitrogen dissociates into atomic nitrogen. Thus, *any scheme* that increases the rate of the reaction $N_2 \rightarrow 2N$ *automatically* will increase the production rate of ammonia. This also brings us to a cardinal point in the study of reaction mechanisms: in the series of individual steps, *the slowest one* determines the rate of the over-all reaction and therefore determines the observed rate equation.* Hence, a reaction mechanism may be postulated from the rate equation. These ideas are further developed by the following examples.

An assembly line for the production of toasted corn puffs is set up to operate at the given rates:

Step (1) Explosion and toasting of corn kernels (125 lbs per hr)
Step (2) Cooling puffed corn (130 lbs per hr)
Step (3) Packaging (125 lbs per hr)
Step (4) Insertion of prize notice in each package (15 lbs per hr)
Step (5) Sealing package (130 lbs per hr)

In the language of the kineticists, we would say **Step 4** is the slow step, the measured production rate will be 15 pounds per hour, and any improvement in **Step 4** alone will automatically increase the production rate of toasted corn puffs.

The rate equation for the gaseous reaction

$$H_2 + I_2 \rightarrow 2HI$$

is

$$rate = -\frac{d[H_2]}{dt} = k[H_2][I_2]$$

---

* Reactions involving two or more steps of comparable rates are here disregarded.

We therefore conclude that the slowest step, also known as **the rate-determining step,** involves one molecule of H_2 and one molecule of I_2:

$$H_2 + I_2 \rightarrow \quad \begin{matrix} H \ldots I \\ | \quad | \\ H \ldots I \end{matrix} \quad \rightarrow HI + HI$$

activated complex

This mechanism, typical of the chemical reactions that occur in a single act, is consistent with the observed over-all reaction and rate equation. When the mechanism consists of a single step, it is commonly said to be a *concerted mechanism.* However, it does not follow that a simple over-all reaction, for example $H_2 + Br_2 \rightarrow 2HBr$, or $H_2 + Cl_2 \rightarrow 2HCl$, must also occur in a single step; the hydrogen-chlorine reaction occurs in a sequence of steps (considered on page 629).

Reactions that do not occur in a single act are now considered. The rate equation for the third order reaction between nitrogen oxide (nitric oxide) and hydrogen,

$$2NO + 2H_2 \rightarrow N_2 + 2H_2O$$

is

$$rate = -\frac{d[H_2]}{dt} = k[NO]^2[H_2] \tag{I}$$

We therefore conclude that the slowest step involves 2 molecules of NO and only one H_2 molecule; thus

$$NO + NO + H_2 \rightarrow activated\ complex \rightarrow intermediate\ product(s)$$

The intermediate product(s) or **intermediate(s)** is comparatively reactive and hence short-lived. However, *unlike* the activated complex, intermediates, *in principle*, exist as well-defined atoms, molecules, free radicals, or ions. But what are the intermediates? Now, we use a little imagination: since N_2 is a product of the over-all reaction we may try

$$NO + NO + H_2 \rightarrow activated\ complex \rightarrow N_2 + H_2O_2 \tag{1}$$

But we have to consume another H_2 molecule, and H_2O, not H_2O_2, is the other final product; so we postulate further that

$$H_2O_2 + H_2 \rightarrow 2H_2O \quad \left(\begin{smallmatrix}\text{comparatively}\\\text{fast*}\end{smallmatrix}\right) \tag{2}$$

Upon adding Steps (1) and (2), we obtain the observed over-all reaction

$$2NO + 2H_2 = N_2 + 2H_2O$$

and Step (1) satisfies the observed rate equation.

Another possible mechanism is

$$NO + NO + H_2 \rightarrow activated\ complex \rightarrow N_2O + H_2O \quad \left(\begin{smallmatrix}\text{comparatively}\\\text{slow}\end{smallmatrix}\right)$$
$$N_2O + H_2 \rightarrow N_2 + H_2O \quad \left(\begin{smallmatrix}\text{comparatively}\\\text{fast}\end{smallmatrix}\right)$$

* We generally concern ourselves only with the activated complex of the rate-determining step.

This mechanism also satisfies the observed over-all reaction and rate equation.

A third possible mechanism is the concept that a third order reaction may actually consist of several steps, each step involving two molecules. Thus, we may assume that an *equilibrium* between 2 molecules and an intermediate is set up in the first step,

$$NO + NO \rightleftharpoons N_2O_2 \qquad \left(\substack{\text{comparatively} \\ \text{fast}}\right) \qquad \qquad (1)$$

$$K = \frac{[N_2O_2]}{[NO]^2} \qquad \qquad (II)$$

and that the second step is rate-determining,

$$N_2O_2 + H_2 \rightarrow activated\ complex \rightarrow N_2O + H_2O \qquad \left(\substack{\text{comparatively} \\ \text{slow}}\right) \qquad (2)$$

If we let k_2 be the rate constant for Step 2, then

$$rate = -\frac{d[H_2]}{dt} = k_2[N_2O_2][H_2]$$

But, from Equation II,

$$[N_2O_2] = K[NO]^2$$

whence

$$rate = -\frac{d[H_2]}{dt} = k_2K[NO]^2[H_2]$$

Thus, according to this mechanism the experimentally observed third order rate constant k (Equation I) *is equal to the product of two constants,* k_2 and K. This mechanism then satisfies the experimental rate equation. But, to satisfy the observed net reaction, a third step is necessary,

$$N_2O + H_2 \rightarrow N_2 + H_2O \qquad \left(\substack{\text{comparatively} \\ \text{fast}}\right) \qquad \qquad (3)$$

A decision among kinetically reasonable mechanisms must then be made on some other basis, such as the detection or isolation of a postulated intermediate. Evidence against one of the proposed mechanisms may be obtained from experiments which show that the reaction

$$H_2O_2 + H_2 \rightarrow 2H_2O$$

or

$$N_2O + H_2 \rightarrow N_2 + H_2O$$

is slow. Further, studies of the dependence of the equilibrium constant (Equation II) and the third order rate constant (Equation I) upon temperature may yield evidence in favor of the third mechanism.*

Another example is the reaction between iodine chloride, ICl, and hydrogen,

$$H_2 + 2ICl \rightarrow I_2 + 2HCl$$

* The actual mechanism is not simple and not yet completely known.

studied over the temperature range 205–240°C, for which the rate equation is

$$rate = -\frac{d[H_2]}{dt} = k[ICl][H_2]$$

Again, the slow step must involve one molecule of ICl and one molecule of H_2

$$ICl + H_2 \rightarrow activated\ complex \rightarrow HI + HCl \qquad \left(\substack{comparatively\\ slow}\right)$$

and the second step may be

$$ICl + HI \rightarrow I_2 + HCl \qquad \left(\substack{comparatively\\ fast}\right)$$

A further example is the reaction between *tert*-butyl bromide

$$CH_3 \atop CH_3\!-\!C\!-\!Br \atop CH_3$$

and hydroxide ions, OH^-, in the presence of water,

$$(CH_3)_3CBr + OH^- \rightarrow (CH_3)_3COH + Br^-$$

for which the rate equation is

$$rate = \frac{d[Br^-]}{dt} = k[(CH_3)_3CBr]$$

Notice that the rate of the reaction is *independent* of the hydroxide ion concentration; this ion therefore *does not appear* in the slow step. A suggested mechanism involves the slow dissociation of the butyl bromide into ions,

$$(CH_3)_3CBr \rightarrow \{(CH_3)_3\overset{\delta+}{C}\cdots\overset{\delta-}{Br}\} \rightarrow (CH_3)_3C^+ + Br^- \qquad \left(\substack{comparatively\\ slow}\right)$$
$$activated\ complex$$

followed by the rapid reaction*

$$(CH_3)_3C^+ + OH^- \rightarrow (CH_3)_3COH \qquad \left(\substack{comparatively\\ fast}\right)$$

* The more complete mechanism is

$$(CH_3)_3CBr \longrightarrow activated\ complex \longrightarrow (CH_3)_3C^+ + Br^- \quad (slow)$$

$$(CH_3)_3C^+ + H_2O \overset{fast}{\longrightarrow} \left[(CH_3)_3CO\!\!\begin{array}{c}H\\ \diagup\\ \diagdown\\ H\end{array}\right]^+ \qquad (H_2O\ serves\ as\ a\ Lewis\ base)$$

$$\left[(CH_3)_3CO\!\!\begin{array}{c}H\\ \diagup\\ \diagdown\\ H\end{array}\right]^+ + OH^- \overset{fast}{\longrightarrow} (CH_3)_3COH + H_2O$$

The use of a carbonium ion $[(CH_3)_3C^+]$ intermediate to explain mechanisms of organic reactions was developed by Frank C. Whitmore in 1932.

On the other hand, for a simpler bromide such as ethyl bromide, C_2H_5Br,

$$C_2H_5Br + OH^- \rightarrow C_2H_5OH + Br^-$$

the rate equation

$$rate = \frac{d[Br^-]}{dt} = k[C_2H_5Br][OH^-]$$

shows that the rate depends also on the hydroxide ion concentration; the OH^- ion must now appear in the rate-determining step. The suggested mechanism

$$C_2H_5Br + OH^- \rightarrow \left\{ \begin{matrix} H & \quad CH_3 \\ & \diagdown \quad \diagup \\ HO\cdots & C\cdots Br \\ & | \\ & H \end{matrix} \right\}^- \rightarrow C_2H_5OH + Br^- \quad \left(\begin{smallmatrix}\text{comparatively}\\ \text{slow}\end{smallmatrix}\right)$$

$$\text{\textit{activated}}$$
$$\text{\textit{complex}}$$

is consistent with the rate equation.*

EXAMPLE 6 **A proposed mechanism for the oxidation of I^- by H_2O_2 in acidic solutions is**

$$H_2O_2 + I^- \rightarrow \{H_2O_2I^-\} \rightarrow OH^- + HOI \quad \left(\begin{smallmatrix}\text{comparatively}\\ \text{slow}\end{smallmatrix}\right)$$
$$\textit{activated}$$
$$\textit{complex}$$

followed by the comparatively rapid reactions

$$H^+ + OH^- \rightarrow H_2O$$
$$HOI + H^+ + I^- \rightarrow I_2 + H_2O$$

For this mechanism to be consistent with kinetic data, what must be the over-all reaction and the rate equation?

ANSWER **The mechanism of a chemical reaction is a** *hypothetical picture* **of how reactants are transformed to products; hence the addition† of the individual steps must yield the over-all reaction:**

$$H_2O_2 + 2H^+ + 2I^- \rightarrow I_2 + 2H_2O$$

The slowest step determines the rate of the over-all reaction. Since the slow step involves one molecule of H_2O_2 and one I^- ion, the rate equation should be

$$rate = -\frac{d[H_2O_2]}{dt} = k[H_2O_2][I^-]$$

* This reaction is discussed further on page 688.

† Mechanisms in which 2 or more steps are alternative rather than consecutive are sometimes written. Also, with the main reaction, other minor reactions (*side reactions*) may occur concurrently. In such cases, the equations are not expected to add up to the over-all reaction.

The *number* of species (molecules, atoms, free radicals, or ions) that come together to form an activated complex is called the **molecularity of the reaction.** The molecularity of a reaction must be an integral number. When one, two, or three molecules produce an activated complex, the reaction is said to be **unimolecular, bimolecular,** or **termolecular,** respectively. This concept is therefore theoretical, while the order of the reaction is an experimentally determined quantity (page 604). The probability that four or more species may simultaneously combine to form an activated complex is so small that reactions of molecularity higher than three are never postulated.

Thus, in general terms, let us assume for the observed chemical change

$$2B + A \rightarrow D + E$$

that the rate equation is

$$rate = k[B]^2[A]$$

The order of reaction is therefore 3, second order with respect to B and first order with respect to A. A possible mechanism for this chemical change is

Step 1 $B + B \rightarrow$ *activated complex* $\rightarrow B_2$
Step 2 $B_2 + A \rightarrow$ *activated complex* $\rightarrow AB_2$
Step 3 $AB_2 \rightarrow$ *activated complex* $\rightarrow D + E$

Steps 1 and 2 are bimolecular reactions, while Step 3 is a unimolecular reaction.*

More specifically, for the third order reaction, $2NO + O_2 \rightarrow 2NO_2$, we would refer to the steps in the following proposed mechanism,

$$2NO \rightleftarrows \text{ } activated \text{ } complex \rightleftarrows N_2O_2$$
$$N_2O_2 + O_2 \rightarrow \text{ } activated \text{ } complex \rightarrow 2NO_2$$

as two bimolecular reactions.†

23.6   CATALYSIS

Life as we know it would be impossible without the phenomenon of catalysis. Almost everyone has heard of **enzymes;** these are natural

---

  * Though the $H_2 + I_2 \rightarrow 2HI$ reaction was long considered a typical bimolecular reaction involving a 4 center complex (pages 614; 619), it has recently been shown (*Annual Review of Physical Chemistry* **11**, 57, 1960) that this reaction may also occur through another mechanism. These studies serve to emphasize that the proposed mechanism of a chemical reaction is a theoretical pathway consistent with presently known data, and that changes in proposed mechanisms will most likely result from new experimental-theoretical studies.

  † It is acceptable to write such steps simply as

$$2NO \rightleftarrows N_2O_2$$
$$N_2O_2 + O_2 \rightarrow 2NO_2$$

substances (page 771) that catalyze biochemically important reactions. Many industrial processes would be impossible without catalysts. A **catalyst** is a substance that increases the rate of a reaction and is recovered chemically unchanged at the end of the reaction. Although the catalyst is not consumed, it is universally agreed that the catalyst enters into the chemical reaction but is subsequently regenerated. Typical is the catalytic effect of nitrogen oxide on the rate of conversion of sulfur dioxide to sulfur trioxide. The reaction

$$2SO_2 + O_2 \xrightarrow{slow} 2SO_3$$

is slow. However, nitrogen oxide and oxygen react rapidly and the product of this reaction also reacts rapidly with SO_2,

$$2NO + O_2 \xrightarrow{fast} 2NO_2 \tag{1}$$

$$2NO_2 + 2SO_2 \xrightarrow{fast} 2NO + 2SO_3 \tag{2}$$

Addition of Reactions (1) and (2) yields

$$2SO_2 + O_2 \xrightarrow{fast} 2SO_3$$

It is evident that we have substituted two fast reactions for a slow one to yield the same over-all chemical reaction. In the so-called lead-chamber process for the manufacture of sulfuric acid, these oxides of nitrogen are used to catalyze the oxidation of sulfur dioxide by oxygen.

In homogeneous catalysis, the reaction occurs in one phase and the *rate is a function of the catalyst concentration*. In heterogeneous catalysis, also known as surface catalysis, the reaction occurs at the phase interface* and the rate is a function of surface area, the number of atoms or "active sites" per cm².

The catalyst increases the rate by changing the mechanism of the reaction, thereby decreasing the energy of activation.† For example, the homogeneous decomposition of acetaldehyde

$$CH_3CHO(g) \rightarrow CH_4(g) + CO(g)$$

follows the rate equation

$$-\frac{d[CH_3CHO]}{dt} = k_1[CH_3CHO]^2$$

with an energy of activation of 45 kcal per mole, suggesting the net reaction‡

$$CH_3CHO + CH_3CHO \rightarrow 2CH_4 + 2CO$$

while in the presence of iodine vapor, the rate equation becomes

$$-\frac{d[CH_3CHO]}{dt} = k_2[CH_3CHO][I_2]$$

* Solids are the most commonly used surface catalysts.
† The effect of the catalyst on $S‡$ is generally less significant.
‡ Complicated chain mechanisms (page 628) are involved in this reaction.

with an energy of activation of 33 kcal per mole, suggesting the net reactions

$$CH_3CHO + I_2 \rightarrow CH_3I + HI + CO$$
$$CH_3I + HI \rightarrow CH_4 + I_2$$

At 600°K, k_2 is about 10^7 times larger than k_1.

Catalysis may be demonstrated qualitatively by preparing an acidified solution of $KMnO_4$ and HOC_2O_2OH (given on page 602) and adding a small crystal of manganese(II) sulfate, $MnSO_4$. The reaction is catalyzed by Mn^{2+} and decolorization now occurs in about 1 minute. Note here that one of the products of the reaction, Mn^{2+}, serves as a catalyst for the over-all reaction.

A general mechanism of surface catalysis involves (a) diffusion of reactants to the surface of the catalyst, (b) a fast reaction between the molecules of the reactants and the atoms in the surface of the solid catalyst (adsorption), followed by (c) the formation of the activated complex (the rate-determining step), which then decomposes rapidly to the solid and the products. For example, at about 800°K the homogeneous decomposition of hydrogen iodide,

$$2HI(g) \rightarrow H_2(g) + I_2(g)$$

follows the rate equation

$$-\frac{d[HI]}{dt} = k_1[HI]^2$$

with an energy of activation of 45 kcal per mole, while in the presence of solid platinum, Pt, the rate equation is

$$-\frac{d[HI]}{dt} = k_2[HI][s] = k_3[HI]$$

with an energy of activation of 14 kcal per mole; [s] is number of platinum atoms ("active sites") per cm^2. The suggested mechanism is

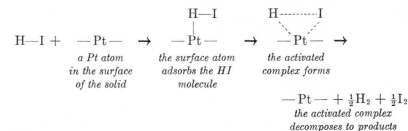

a Pt atom in the surface of the solid   *the surface atom adsorbs the HI molecule*   *the activated complex forms*

$$-Pt- + \tfrac{1}{2}H_2 + \tfrac{1}{2}I_2$$
the activated complex decomposes to products

Negative Catalysis. Substances that retard chemical reactions are known as **negative catalysts,** or **inhibitors,** or **poisons.** They generally act by interfering with the mechanism that leads to a lower energy of activation. Arsenic atoms, for example, are more strongly adsorbed on platinum than HI molecules; this destroys the catalytic effect of the platinum, since its surface is no longer available to the HI molecules.

Physiological poisons like mercuric chloride and rattlesnake venom react
with enzymes, rendering them useless for essential biochemical reactions.

The decomposition of dinitrogen pentoxide dissolved in carbon tetrachloride,

$$N_2O_5 \rightarrow 2NO_2 + \tfrac{1}{2}O_2$$

is a first order reaction:

$$rate = -\frac{d[N_2O_5]}{dt} = k[N_2O_5]$$

Rewritten as

$$-\frac{d[N_2O_5]}{[N_2O_5]} = kdt \tag{1}$$

the left side of the equation is dimensionless, and therefore the unit of k
must be reciprocal time.

Equation (1), as shown in Problem 40 (page 639) leads to

$$\ln\frac{[N_2O_5]_0}{[N_2O_5]_t} = kt$$

or

$$k = \frac{2.303}{t}\log\frac{[N_2O_5]_0}{[N_2O_5]_t} \tag{2}$$

in which $[N_2O_5]_0$ is the concentration of N_2O_5 at the start of the experiment
($t = 0$), and $[N_2O_5]_t$ is the concentration at a time t after the start of the
experiment. 2.303 is the conversion factor for changing natural log, ln, to
the base 10. Since the log term is dimensionless, Equation (2) may be
rewritten as

$$k = \frac{2.303}{t}\log\frac{q_0}{q_t} \tag{3}$$

in which q_0, the initial quantity of reactant, and q_t, the quantity at time t,
are expressible in any convenient quantity unit as moles, grams, number
of atoms, number of molecules, etc.

A measure of the rate of a reaction is the so-called **half-life,** *the time
required for one half a given quantity to react;* namely, the time t,
denoted $t_{\frac{1}{2}}$, at which $q_t = q_0/2$. Whence

$$k = \frac{2.303}{t_{\frac{1}{2}}}\log\frac{q_0}{q_0/2} = \frac{2.303}{t_{\frac{1}{2}}}\log 2 = \frac{0.693}{t_{\frac{1}{2}}}$$

$$k = \frac{0.693}{t_{\frac{1}{2}}} \tag{4}$$

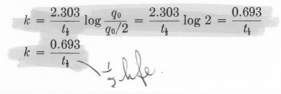

so that the half-life may be evaluated from the rate constant. The shorter the half-life, the faster the rate of a reaction. Because of this simple relationship, half-lives are frequently used to express the rates of first order reactions.

Another method of determining the half-life is to plot, as in Fig. 23.6, the quantity present at time t as a function of t; the time required for one half of any chosen quantity to react is the half-life. For example, the half-life for the decomposition of N_2O_5 in carbon tetrachloride at 30°C is 2.4 hours so that, if we start with 10 grams of N_2O_5 at $t = 0$, then, after a period of 2.4 hours, 5.0 grams remain; after a second period of 2.4 hours (total of 4.8 hours), 2.5 grams remain; after a third period of 2.4 hours (total of 7.2 hours), 1.25 grams remain, etc. For each half-life period, the

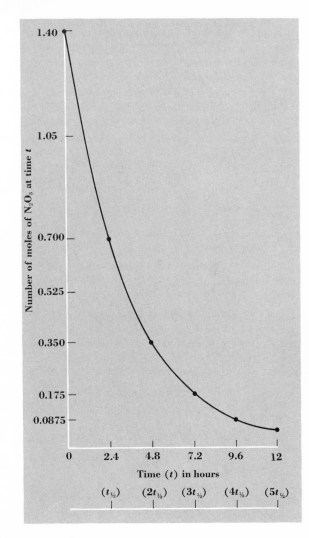

Fig. 23.6. Determination of $t_{\frac{1}{2}}$. The time required to reduce 1.40 moles of N_2O_5 to 0.70 mole is 2.4 hours; to reduce 0.70 mole to 0.35 mole the time is 2.4 hours; to reduce 0.90 mole to 0.45 mole the time is 2.4 hours, etc. Thus for each half-life period, half of the remaining quantity reacts. For convenience, the time is also given in parentheses in multiples of the half-life.

quantity present is reduced by one half, or

$$q_t = q_0(0.5)^{t/t_\frac{1}{2}} \tag{5}$$

in which $t/t_\frac{1}{2}$ gives the number of half-lives.

EXAMPLE 7 The half-life for the reaction $N_2O_5 \rightarrow 2NO_2 + \frac{1}{2}O_2$ is 2.4 hours at 30°C. (a) Starting with 10 grams, how many grams will remain after a period of 9.6 hours?

ANSWER 9.6 hours corresponds to four half-lives, 9.6 hours/2.4 hours, whence

$$q_t = 10 \text{ g } (0.5)(0.5)(0.5)(0.5) = 0.63 \text{ g}$$

or

$$q_t = 10 \text{ g } (0.5)^{9.6 \text{ hr}/2.4 \text{ hr}} = 10 \text{ g } (0.5)^4$$
$$\log q_t = \log 10 + 4 \log 0.5$$

from which

$$q_t = 0.63 \text{ g}$$

(b) Starting with 100 grams, how many grams will remain after a period of 16 hours?

ANSWER From the data, the number of half-lives is 16 hours/2.4 hours or 6.7, whence

$$q_t = 100 \text{ grams } (0.5)^{6.7} = 0.98 \text{ g}$$

(c) What period of time is required to reduce 5.0×10^{10} molecules of N_2O_5 to 10^8 molecules?

ANSWER Using Equation (5),

$$10^8 \text{ molecules} = 5.0 \times 10^{10} \text{ molecules } (0.5)^{t/2.4 \text{ hr}}$$

and solving,

$$\log \frac{10^8 \text{ molecules}}{5.0 \times 10^{10} \text{ molecules}} = \frac{t}{2.4 \text{ hr}} \log (0.5)$$

from which $t = 22$ hr.

23.8 CHAIN MECHANISM

When a chemical reaction proceeds by a mechanism in which a species consumed in one step is regenerated in a second step, the set of steps is referred to as a **chain mechanism**. Thus, in a **chain reaction** each step yields *one* species capable of producing the reaction for each *one* species consumed. For example, in the chain reaction

$$: \ddot{C}l \cdot + H_2 \rightarrow HCl + H \cdot \tag{1}$$

$$H \cdot + Cl_2 \rightarrow HCl + : \ddot{C}l \cdot \tag{2}$$

each $: \ddot{C}l \cdot$ atom used to produce an HCl molecule also forms an $H \cdot$ atom, which subsequently produces an HCl molecule and regenerates the $: \ddot{C}l \cdot$ atom; the $: \ddot{C}l \cdot$ atom produced in Step (2) reacts to form another HCl molecule and $H \cdot$ atom as in Step (1), etc.

At ordinary temperatures, hydrogen and chlorine form hydrogen chloride slowly in the dark but explosively in sunlight. The chlorine absorbs radiation* below 4785 A, producing atomic chlorine,

$$Cl_2 + h\nu \rightleftharpoons 2 : \ddot{C}l \cdot$$

Without absorption of further light energy, the atoms of chlorine initiate the chain reaction illustrated by Reactions (1) and (2).† Such chain reactions are fast but not necessarily explosive. They become explosive when the heat evolved in the over-all reaction is so large that isothermal conditions (constant temperature) cannot be maintained; as the reaction proceeds, the heat evolved increases the temperature which, in turn, increases the rate of the reaction and the liberation of heat until, finally, the rate becomes explosive.

In a **branching chain reaction,** *two* or more species capable of producing the reaction are regenerated for every *one* consumed. For example, in

$$O* + H_2 \rightarrow H_2O* \tag{3}$$
$$H_2O* + O_2 \rightarrow H_2O + 2O*‡ \tag{4}$$

for every one "excited" oxygen atom consumed in Reaction (3), two are regenerated in Reaction (4). The over-all rate then becomes infinite (see Problem 41, page 640) and, if the reaction is exothermic, an explosion results under isothermal conditions. At about 550°C, for example, the rate of the hydrogen-oxygen reaction forming water increases slowly as the concentration of either reactant is increased and then, at the same temperature, the mixture suddenly explodes, signaling the development of the branching chain reaction, illustrated by Reactions (3) and (4).

---

* Radiation is represented by $h\nu$, the amount of energy in one photon when the frequency is ν (page 158).

† The mechanism may be summarized as

$$Cl_2 + h\nu \rightleftharpoons 2Cl$$
$$Cl + H_2 \rightarrow HCl + H$$
$$H + Cl_2 \rightarrow HCl + Cl$$

but note that the over-all reaction is obtained from the sum of the last *two* steps.

‡ The asterisk is usually used to denote excited species.

1. Rate equation. For the gaseous reaction

$$2NO + 2H_2 \rightarrow N_2 + 2H_2O$$

the following data at 1100°K are given:

Rate of disappearance of NO (mole/liter sec) $-\dfrac{d[NO]}{dt}$	Reactant concentrations (mole/liter)	
	[NO]	[H₂]
2.4×10^{-5}	5.0×10^{-3}	2.0×10^{-3}
2.2×10^{-4}	15×10^{-3}	2.0×10^{-3}
4.4×10^{-4}	15×10^{-3}	4.0×10^{-3}

(a) Write the rate equation for the reaction. What is the order of the reaction
(b) Calculate the rate constant for the reaction at 1100°K.
(c) Calculate the rate, moles per liter per sec, at 1100°K at the instant when

$$[NO] = 1.1 \times 10^{-3} \quad \text{and} \quad [H_2] = 1.5 \times 10^{-3}$$

(d) Calculate the rate, moles per sec, at 1100°K at the instant when

$$[NO] = 1.1 \times 10^{-3} \quad \text{and} \quad [H_2] = 1.5 \times 10^{-3}$$

and the volume of the reacting system is 2.0 liters.
(e) At the instant when NO is reacting at the rate 1.2×10^{-5} mole per liter per sec, what is the rate at which H₂ is reacting and N₂ is forming?

Answer. (a) third; (b) $4.9 \times 10^2 \dfrac{\text{liter}^2}{\text{mole}^2 \text{ sec}}$; (c) $8.9 \times 10^{-7} \dfrac{\text{moles}}{\text{liter sec}}$; (d) $1.8 \times 10^{-6} \dfrac{\text{moles}}{\text{sec}}$; (e) $1.2 \times 10^{-5} \dfrac{\text{mole}}{\text{liter sec}}$, $6.0 \times 10^{-6} \dfrac{\text{mole}}{\text{liter sec}}$

2. Rate equation. The mechanism proposed for the decarbonylation of formic acid, HCOOH, in strongly acid solutions is

$$HCOOH + (OH)_2SO_2 \rightleftharpoons HCOOH_2^+ + HSO_4^-$$

$$HCOOH_2^+ \xrightarrow{\text{slow}} [H\!-\!C\!=\!O]^+ + H_2O$$

$$HCO^+ + H_2SO_4 \longrightarrow H_3SO_4^+ + CO$$

(*i*) Which acid, formic or sulfuric, is acting as a Bronsted acid? (*ii*) Write the over-all reaction and the rate equation for the reaction. (*iii*) In the last reaction is sulfuric acid acting as an acid or a base?

3. Rate constant. Noble gas excited atoms and ions react with other gases. Typical are the reactions

$$Xe^* + CH_4 \rightarrow XeCH_4^+ + e^- \tag{1}$$
$$Xe^+ + CH_4 + e^- \rightarrow XeCH_2 + H_2 \tag{2}$$

in which Xe* represents an excited Xe atom. The rate constant for reaction (2) is 4.5×10^{-13} cc/mole sec. Calculate the number of H₂ molecules formed per sec per liter when the concentrations of Xe⁺ and CH₄ are equal at 5.0×10^{-7} mole per cc.

4. Reaction order. The rate of electron exchange between MnO_4^{2-} and MnO_4^-,

$$MnO_4^{2-} + MnO_4^- \rightarrow MnO_4^- + MnO_4^{2-}$$

has been measured at 0°C:

$$rate = 1.5 \times 10^3 \, \frac{liter}{mole \ sec} \, [MnO_4^-][MnO_4^{2-}]$$

Is this exchange reaction first, second, or third order?

5. Mechanism. Show that the mechanism for the reaction $2NO + O_2 \rightarrow 2NO_2$ involving two bimolecular reactions, namely,

$$2NO \underset{slow}{\overset{fast}{\rightleftharpoons}} N_2O_2$$

$$N_2O_2 + O_2 \overset{slow}{\longrightarrow} 2NO_2$$

satisfies the rate equation

$$\frac{d[NO_2]}{dt} = k[NO]^2[O_2]$$

6. Mechanism. Suggest a mechanism for each of the following homogeneous reactions from the given rate equations:

(a)
$$H_2 + Cl_2 \rightarrow 2HCl$$
$$rate = -\frac{d[Cl_2]}{dt} = k[Cl_2]$$

(b)
$$2ClO_2 + 2OH^- \rightarrow ClO_3^- + ClO_2^- + H_2O$$
$$rate = -\frac{d[ClO_2]}{dt} = k[ClO_2]^2[OH^-]$$

(c) With respect to parts (a) and (b), what is the order of the reaction and what is the molecularity of each step in your proposed mechanism?

7. Temperature. If the rate of a reaction is 0.10 mole per liter per sec at 20°C, what would be its rate at (*i*) 50°C, (*ii*) 55°C, assuming the rate is doubled for each 10°C rise?

Answer. (*i*) 0.80 mole/liter sec.

8. Energy of activation. The rate constants for the decomposition of nitrogen dioxide are

Temperature	k
500°K	38 liter/mole hr
700°K	5.5×10^4

Explain the increase in the rate constants with increasing temperature.

9. Activated complex theory. (a) For the reaction

$$N_2(COO)_2^{2-} + H_3O^+ \rightarrow HN_2(COO)_2^- + H_2O$$
azodicarboxylate

the following data are given:

Solvent dielectric constant	$H^{\ddagger}$ (kcal/mole)	$S^{\ddagger}$ (cal/mole deg)
78.5	10.2	12.9
71.2	10.2	14.1

In which solvent will [activated complex] be greater and in which solvent will the rate be faster for the same concentration of reactants at the same temperature? (b) From the following data for gaseous decomposition:

Reaction	$H^{\ddagger}$ (kcal/mole)	$S^{\ddagger}$ (cal/mole deg)
$(CH_3CO)_2O \rightarrow CH_3COOH + CH_2CO$	34.5	−4
$CH_3CHCl_2 \rightarrow CH_2{=}CHCl + HCl$	49.5	−4

which reaction will be faster for the same concentration of reactants at the same temperature?

10. Catalysis. The energy of activation for the homogeneous decomposition of H_2O_2 into H_2O and O_2 is 18 kcal per mole and 6 kcal for the (catalase) enzyme-catalyzed reaction. What is the increase in rate that would be produced by this factor alone at 27°C?

Answer. 5×10^8.

11. $t_{\frac{1}{2}}$. The principal reaction in the decomposition of azomethane, at about 300°C, $CH_3NNCH_3(g) \rightarrow C_2H_6(g) + N_2(g)$, is first order. The time required for a given quantity of azomethane to decrease by one half is 0.50 hour at temperature t°C. (a) What fraction of a given quantity of azomethane remains after 1.5 hours? (b) Starting with 10 g, how many grams remain after 1.2 hours? (c) How many hours will be required to reduce 5.0 g of azomethane to 2.0 g?

Answer. (a) 0.13; (b) 1.9 g.

12. Intermediates. On each of the accompanying diagrams (a and b) identify the reactant, the product, the intermediate, the activated complex(es), and the rate-determining step. In which reaction will the intermediate have a longer life and therefore may be isolated?

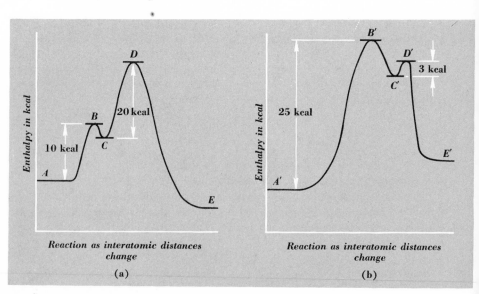

Reaction as interatomic distances change

(a)

Reaction as interatomic distances change

(b)

13. Over-all reaction. The following mechanism has been proposed for the reaction of hydrogen with oxygen.

$$H_2 \rightarrow H + H$$
$$H + O_2 \rightarrow HO + O$$
$$O + H_2 \rightarrow HO + H$$
$$HO + H_2 \rightarrow H_2O + H$$
$$H + OH \rightarrow H_2O$$
$$H + H \rightarrow H_2$$

Show how the over-all reaction may be obtained from these individual steps.

14. Rate equation. Minute tubes containing radon gas, known as "radon seeds," are used for cancer radiotherapy. Radon, Rn, changes to the element polonium, Po, kinetic data for which follow:

Rate of disappearance of Rn (mole/liter day) $-\dfrac{d[Rn]}{dt}$	Reactant concentration (mole/liter) $[Rn]$
5.43×10^{-3}	0.0300
1.62×10^{-2}	0.0900

The rate of this reaction is independent of temperature. (*i*) Write the rate equation for this reaction, and (*ii*) calculate the rate at the instant in a 10 mm³ "seed" when $[Rn] = 0.0200$.

15. Rate equation. (a) In a certain pressure range and temperature, the rate of decomposition of gaseous acetaldehyde,

$$CH_3CHO \rightarrow CH_4 + CO$$

is given by the rate equation,

$$rate = -\frac{d[CH_3CHO]}{dt} = k[CH_3CHO]^2$$

Make up some data from which this rate equation might have been obtained. (b) At a fixed temperature, the volume of a homogeneous reacting system decreases so that the concentrations of the reacting gases remain constant. Which of the following will change: the rate constant in liter/mole sec, the rate in moles/liter-sec, the rate in moles/sec? If the volume remains constant during reaction, which will change?

16. Rate equation. The over-all equation for the reaction of vanadium(IV) and chromium(VI) in acidic perchlorate solution is

$$VO^{2+} + HCrO_4^- + H^+ \rightarrow VO_2^+ + Cr^{3+} + H_2O$$

(*i*) Balance the equation. (*ii*) The rate equation at constant acidity is

$$-\frac{d[HCrO_4^-]}{dt} = \frac{k[VO^{2+}][HCrO_4^-]}{[VO_2^+]}$$

What will be the effect on the rate of disappearance of $HCrO_4^-$ if $[VO^{2+}]$, $[HCrO_4^-]$, $[VO_2^+]$ is doubled? Can you make a quantitative statement about the effect of doubling $[H^+]$?

17. Rate equation. For the decomposition of nitrosyl chloride, $2NOCl(g) \rightarrow 2NO(g) + Cl_2(g)$, the rate equation at $1020°K$ is

$$-\frac{d[NOCl]}{dt} = k[NOCl]^2 = 8.3 \times 10^5 \frac{liter}{mole\ sec}[NOCl]^2$$

The rate equation may also be expressed as

$$\frac{d[NO]}{dt} = k'[NOCl]^2$$

and

$$\frac{d[Cl_2]}{dt} = k''[NOCl]^2$$

Calculate (i) k' and (ii) k'' at $1020°K$.

Answer. (i) 8.3×10^5 liter mole^{-1} sec^{-1}

18. Types of reaction. The reaction $A(g) + B(g) \rightarrow AB(g)$ is carried out in a glass vessel. When glass beads are added at constant concentration of the gases, the rate of the reaction changes. Is the reaction homogeneous or heterogeneous?

19. Kinetics, general. Explain the statements: (a) Only the slow step can be studied by measuring the rate of reaction. (b) A chemical reaction always involves a change in the distance between atoms in molecules. (c) Chemical inertia is to be attributed to the forces resisting the deformation and the subsequent breakdown of the initial reactants.

20. Heterogeneous reaction. A zinc, Zn, sphere, $1.0\ cm^3$, density 7.1 g per cc is pulverized to a particle size (diameter) of 1.0×10^{-2} micron. Calculate (i) the number of Zn particles, and (ii) the factor by which the rate of combustion in oxygen, of constant concentration, is multiplied. Assume the particles are spherical.

Answer. (ii) 1.2×10^6

21. Energy of activation. The energy of activation for the decomposition of HI,

$$2HI(g) \rightarrow H_2(g) + I_2(g) \qquad \Delta H = +2.6\ kcal$$

is 45 kcal per mole, while the energy of activation for the decomposition of nitrogen dioxide, NO_2,

$$2NO_2(g) \rightarrow 2NO(g) + O_2(g) \qquad \Delta H = +27.0\ kcal$$

is 25 kcal per mole. At the same concentration and temperature which reaction will proceed faster? Explain your answer. (Disregard $S‡$.)

22. Mechanism. A mechanism proposed by Joseph Weiss in 1944 for the redox reaction between Sn^{2+} and Fe^{3+} is

$$SnCl_2 + 2Cl^- \rightarrow SnCl_4^{2-}$$
$$SnCl_4^{2-} + FeCl_3 \rightarrow SnCl_3 + FeCl_2 + 2Cl^-$$
$$SnCl_3 + FeCl_3 \rightarrow SnCl_4 + FeCl_2$$

What should be the observed over-all chemical reaction? What is the molecularity of the first two steps? What is the oxidation number of Sn in the intermediates $SnCl_4^{2-}$ and $SnCl_3$? What species appears to serve as a catalyst?

23. Slow step. In the following series of changes, for which the rate constants are given, which step determines, for all practical purposes, the conversion of A to D?

$$A \xrightarrow{10^4/\text{year}} B \xrightarrow{10^{-9}/\text{year}} C \xrightarrow{10/\text{year}} D \xrightarrow{0/\text{year}}$$

Is D a stable or unstable substance?

24. Collision theory. Within the error of calculation, at any given temperature and concentration, the number of colliding molecules is the same for oxygen and for nitrogen. Under comparable conditions will these gases react with another gas at the same rate? Explain your answer.

25. Collision theory. For gaseous NO_2, the number of colliding molecules is 5.2×10^{32} molecules per liter per sec when $[NO_2] = 1.0$ mole per liter at 500°K. Using also the data in Problem 21, calculate (i) the decomposition rate in molecules per liter per sec, and (ii) in moles per liter per hr. The observed value under the same conditions is 38 moles per liter per hr.

Answer. (i) 7.3×10^{21} molecules/liter sec.

26. Activated complex theory. Take a guess: if isopropyl iodide is substituted for methyl iodide (page 617), should the rate of reaction with triethylamine be closer to the rate for methyl iodide or for *tert*-butyl iodide? The configuration of isopropyl iodide is

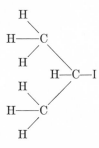

Make an attempt to justify your guess.

27. Activated complex theory. The reaction between hydrogen and bromine is very complicated, but the most likely rate-determining step is

$$H_2 + Br \rightarrow HBr + H$$

for which the activated complex may be H···H···Br. When deuterium D_2 is substituted for H_2, the rate-determining step is

$$D_2 + Br \rightarrow DBr + D$$

and the activated complex is D···D··Br. For the two hydrogen isotopes, H_2 and D_2, bond energies are about identical, the H—Br and D—Br bond energies are also about identical, the enthalpies of the two complexes are assumed to be about identical, but at a given temperature there is a significant difference in the enthalpy of H_2 and D_2 molecules, it being larger for H_2. (a) Will the energy of activation be larger for the $H_2 + Br$ or the $D_2 + Br$ reaction? (b) Will the two activated complexes decompose at the same rate or will one decompose faster? (c) Will the rate of the reaction be faster for $H_2 + Br_2$ or $D_2 + Br_2$ when the concentration of each gas is identical? (d) The reactions $H_2 + Br$ and $D_2 + Br$ are endothermic, $\Delta H = +17$ kcal for each reaction. Represent diagrammatically, on the same graph, the change in enthalpy as the reactants form the activated complex which then decomposes into products.

28. Activated complex theory. (a) Of the two bonds C—I and C—Cl, the bond energy is greater for C—Cl. When methyl chloride CH_3Cl is substituted for CH_3I, will the reaction rate with triethylamine (page 617) increase, decrease, or remain the same? Explain your answer. (b) An ethyl group is replaced in $(C_2H_5)_3N$ by an electron-releasing group (page 475) of the same size. How should the rate of reaction with methyl iodide change? Justify your guess.

29. Activated complex theory. Bond energies are H_2 104 kcal, N_2 226 kcal, HI 71 kcal; helium, He, requires 568 kcal per mole to activate it to a configuration like that of H atoms. Arrange these four in the increasing order with which they should react with oxygen in the absence of catalysts. Make an attempt to justify your guess.

30. Activated complex theory. (a) The structure of the complex assumed for the reaction

$$2NO + O_2 \rightarrow 2NO_2 \qquad \Delta H = -27.0 \text{ kcal}$$

is

$$O \cdots \overset{5.0}{\cdots} N \cdots \overset{1.22}{\cdots} O$$

$$\overset{1.32}{\cdot}$$

$$O \cdots \overset{5.0}{\cdots} N \cdots \overset{1.22}{\cdots} O$$

in which the distances are in angstrom units. Interatomic distances are

nitrogen oxide   *oxygen*   *nitrogen dioxide*

$$N \overset{1.15}{\rule{1cm}{0.4pt}} O \qquad O \overset{1.21}{\rule{1cm}{0.4pt}} O \qquad \underset{O \quad\quad O}{\overset{N}{\underset{1.24 \diagup \quad \diagdown 1.24}{}}}$$

$H^{\ddagger} = 200$ cal per mole. (a) Write the rate equation for the reaction, and (b) represent diagrammatically the change in enthalpy as the reactants form the activated complex which then decomposes into product. (c) Approximate calculations indicate that the concentration of the transition state complex for the reaction given in part (a) is 1.3×10^{-10} moles per liter when $[NO] = [O_2] = 1.0$ mole per liter at 660°K. Calculate the rate of the reaction in moles per liter per sec for these conditions. (For comparison, you may calculate the rate from the empirical equation,

$$rate = -\frac{d[NO]}{dt} = k[NO]^2[O_2]$$

At 660°K, $k = 2.5 \times 10^3$ liter^2/mole^2 sec.)

Answer. 1.8×10^3 mole/liter sec.

31. Activated complex theory. The dinitrogen pentoxide decomposition

$$2N_2O_5 \rightarrow 4NO_2 + O_2$$

is complicated, but it is agreed that one of the rate-determining steps involves

$$N_2O_5 \rightarrow NO_2 + NO_3 \tag{1}$$

The configuration of N_2O_5 is

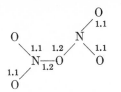

Distances are in angstrom units. Suggest a plausible configuration for the activated complex for Step (1).

32. Activated complex. If for the reaction

$$H_2O_2 + 2H^+ + 2I^- \rightarrow I_2 + 2H_2O$$

a proposed mechanism accepts

$$H_2O_2 + I^- \rightarrow OH^- + HOI$$

as the slow step, what should be the rate equation and the composition of the activated complex? If a second proposed mechanism accepts

$$H_2O_2 + H^+ + I^- \rightarrow H_2O + HOI$$

as the slow step, what should be the rate equation and the composition of the activated complex?

33. Catalysis. An acceptable mechanism for a general type of reaction known as the *Friedel-Crafts* reaction follows:

$$CH_3CH_2\ddot{C}l: + AlCl_3 \rightarrow AlCl_4^- + CH_3CH_2^+$$

ethyl chloride

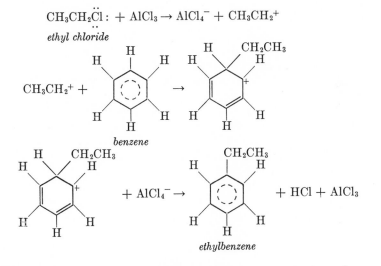

ethylbenzene

What is the observed over-all Friedel-Crafts reaction, and what substance catalyzes the formation of ethylbenzene? Are all carbon atoms similarly hybridized in the intermediate?

34. Catalysis. Upon mixing solutions of $(OH)_2SO_2$, $KMnO_4$, and HOC_2O_2OH, no appreciable decolorization occurs for a comparatively long period of time, but once decolorization occurs it proceeds rapidly. Explain.

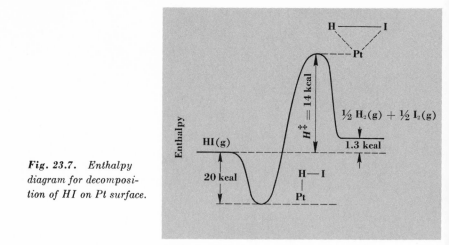

Fig. 23.7. Enthalpy
diagram for decomposi-
tion of HI on Pt surface.

35. Catalysis. From the data for acetaldehyde decomposition (page 624), calculate the k_2/k_1 ratio at 600°K due only to the change in energy of activation and compare with the measured ratio.

Answer. 2.2×10^4.

36. Catalysis. The hydrolysis of methyl trichloroacetate to trichloroacetic acid and methyl alcohol,

$$CCl_3COOCH_3 + H_2O \rightarrow CCl_3COOH + CH_3OH$$

is catalyzed by H^+. Should the time required to convert a given quantity of the acetate to products, in a given quantity of water at a given pH, be different in a buffered and an unbuffered solution? If so, in which solution should the time be shorter? Explain briefly.

37. Catalysis. Figure 23.7 represents the enthalpy diagram for the decomposition of HI on the Pt surface (page 625).

(a) Is the adsorption reaction exothermic or endothermic? Write ΔH for the adsorption reaction

$$HI + Pt \rightarrow \overset{\displaystyle H-I}{\underset{\displaystyle Pt}{|}}$$

(b) Is the reaction

$$HI(g) \rightarrow \tfrac{1}{2}H_2(g) + \tfrac{1}{2}I_2(g)$$

exothermic or endothermic? Write ΔH for this reaction.

(c) Indicate where the activated complex for the homogeneous decomposition of HI would be located on the diagram relative to (above or below) the complex

Answer. (a) $\Delta H = -20$ kcal/mole.

38. Catalysis. Ozone, O_3, an allotropic form of oxygen, is stable at room temperature, but when chlorine, Cl_2, is added a measurable reaction occurs. The suggested mechanism for the reaction is

$$Cl_2 + O_3 \rightarrow ClO + ClO_2$$
$$ClO_2 + O_3 \rightarrow ClO_3 + O_2$$
$$ClO_3 + O_3 \rightarrow ClO_2 + 2O_2$$
$$ClO_3 + ClO_3 \rightarrow Cl_2 + 3O_2$$
$$ClO \rightarrow Cl + O$$
$$ClO_2 + O \rightarrow ClO_3$$
$$Cl + \tfrac{3}{2}O_2 \rightarrow ClO_3$$

What is the over-all reaction and what is the catalyst for the reaction?

39. Negative catalysis. In a crude manner, the catalytic effect of the enzyme catalase on the decomposition of H_2O_2 into $H_2O + O_2$ may be pictured as follows:

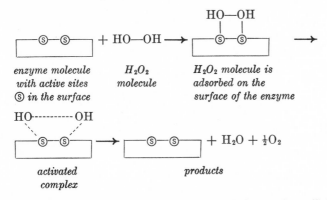

Show how a mercuric ion, Hg^{2+}, may "poison" the catalyst. (Sulfur atoms may be active sites in many proteins.)

40. $t_{\frac{1}{2}}$. Table 23.1 gives the concentration and the natural logarithm of the concentration of N_2O_5 as a function of time for the decomposition of N_2O_5 dissolved in carbon tetrachloride, and Fig. 23.8 is a plot of the data. From the equation for a straight line (Appendix II, page 793) it follows that $\ln [N_2O_5]$ at time $t = -(\text{constant})t + \ln [N_2O_5]$ at zero time, or

TABLE **23.1**[a] *Dinitrogen Pentoxide Decomposition at 30.0°C in Carbon Tetrachloride:* $N_2O_5 \rightarrow 2NO_2 + \tfrac{1}{2}O_2$

Time (hours)	$[N_2O_5]$	$\ln[N_2O_5]$
0	0.8485	-0.1648
1.333	0.5720	-0.5586
2.000	0.4715	-0.7519
4.000	0.2655	-1.3262
5.333	0.1800	-1.7148

[a] **Data taken from Henry Eyring and Farrington Daniels,** *J. Am. Chem. Soc.* **52, 1472 (1930).**

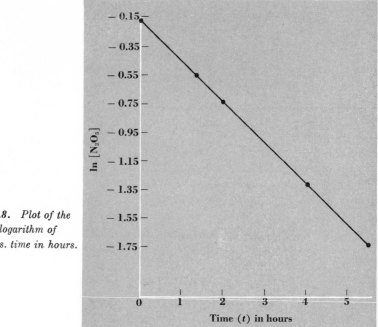

Fig. 23.8. *Plot of the natural logarithm of* $[N_2O_5]$ *vs. time in hours.*

$$\ln [N_2O_5]_t = -kt + \ln [N_2O_5]_0$$

from which

$$\ln \frac{[N_2O_5]_0}{[N_2O_5]_t} = kt$$

(a) Use the data in Table 23.1 to calculate the rate constant for the decomposition of N_2O_5. The accepted value is 0.292 per hour. (b) Use the rate constant obtained in part (a) to check the half-life obtained from the graph (page 627). (c) What is the meaning of a statement like "The half-life of the modern general chemistry book is 10 years"?

41. Chain mechanism. Assume that the rates of Reactions (1) through (4) on page 629 are identical so that 1 molecule of HCl is produced in 10^{-9} sec, while the number of H_2O molecules produced is doubled every 10^{-9} sec. Calculate (a) the number of HCl and of H_2O molecules, and (b) the number of moles of HCl and of H_2O, produced in 10^{-6} sec.

Answer. (a) 10^3, 10^{301} molecules

Molecular
geometry
and
bonding;
Symmetry

24.1 INTRODUCTION

The shape of molecules and polyatomic ions influences their physical and chemical properties. The shape and dimensions of a molecule, as fixed by bond angles and bond distances, are usually inferred from the results of (a) x ray and electron diffraction, (b) infrared, Raman, and microwave spectroscopy, and (c) dipole moment measurements. Although a detailed discussion of most of these techniques is beyond the scope of this text, in a following section we shall consider the use of dipole moments for elucidating shapes of simple molecules.

We shall be concerned principally, in this chapter, with the molecular shapes of the AB_n type molecule, where A, the central atom, is *not* a transition element, and B is a peripheral atom bonded to atom A. The shape of an AB_n molecule is determined by the relative positions of the nucleus of atom A and the nuclei of the B atoms. These relative positions are defined in terms of B—A—B bond angles. Hence, our discussion of molecular geometry will be greatly concerned with bond angles. Our discussion will not emphasize bond lengths, because distances between atoms determine mainly the size, rather than the shape, of the molecule.

Definite categories of molecular shapes are observed experimentally. Since the atoms arrange themselves so that the molecule has the lowest possible energy, it should be possible to account for these typical shapes in terms of energy considerations. Once the factors that influence the geometry of a molecule are understood, we not only can account for the experimentally determined shapes, but can also predict the shape of a molecule from its structural formula. We will first discuss the principal factors determining the typical shapes, and then consider the secondary effects causing minor but significant changes in bond angles.

24.2 PRINCIPAL FACTORS DETERMINING MOLECULAR SHAPE

(a) The σ Bonds; Tendency for Maximum Orbital Overlap.   We have seen from our discussion of the bonding of ethylene (page 276), acetylene (page 277), and benzene (page 288) that the geometry of the molecule is delineated by the σ bonds. The same is true for the AB_n type of molecule. Thus, *the σ bonds which project from the central atom define the shape of the molecule.* Since σ bonds result from overlap of atomic orbitals, it follows that the geometry of the molecule is determined essentially by the type of atomic orbitals used by the central atom, A. As long as atom B has only one σ bond, as is the case in the AB_n type molecules, the orbital it uses does *not* influence the bond angle and the molecular shape. The atomic orbitals used by atom B tends to maximize overlap with the atomic orbitals of atom A, so as to create the highest possible electron density in the region between the atoms, and in this way most effectively attract the nuclei. A σ bond has maximum overlap when the constituent atomic orbitals lie along the internuclear axis (Fig. 24.1a), rather than off the axis (Fig. 24.1b). Since σ bonds are formed from head-to-head overlap, the bond angle is defined by the atomic orbitals of the multi-σ-bonded central atom, A, rather than by the uni-σ-bonded peripheral atom, B (Fig. 24.2). We will see, however, that the relative electronegativity of atom B and the participation of atoms B and A in π bonding have secondary influences, slightly altering the B—A—B bond angles.

The tendency for maximum orbital overlap is a factor that encourages an atom, as for example the nitrogen atom in ammonia and the oxygen atom in water (page 275), to use an *s-p* type hybrid atomic orbital rather than an unhybridized *p* orbital. The following relative strengths of σ bonds formed from different atomic orbitals have been calculated from molecular orbital theory:

Type orbital	s	p	sp	sp^2	sp^3
Relative σ-bond strength	0.3	1	1.5	1.4	1.3

Fig. 24.1.   *Representation of overlap of s-p type atomic orbitals: (a) head-to-head (along axis); (b) off-axis.*

Head-to-head overlap

(a)

more effective than

Off-axis overlap

(b)

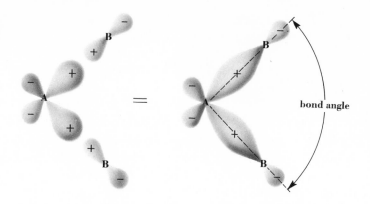

Fig. 24.2. *Representation of a typical B—A—B bond angle formed by overlap of two s-p type atomic orbitals of A, each with a p orbital of atom B. (Dotted line indicates the bond axis.)*

Fig. 24.3. *Arrangement of electron pairs to minimize repulsion: (a) two pairs—linear, (b) three pairs—plane triangle, (c) four pairs—tetrahedral, (d) five pairs—trigonal bipyramid, (e) six pairs—octahedral.*

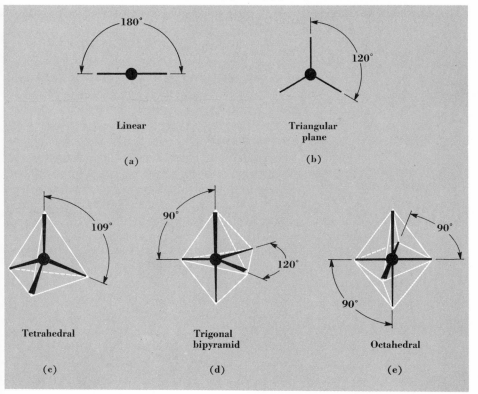

TABLE 24.1 *Shapes of Molecules and Ions of Nontransitional Elements with No Lone Pairs of Electrons on Central Atom*

General type	Example	Observed shape	Hybrid orbital number	Hybrid orbital type
AB_2	$BeCl_2$, $HgCl_2$	Linear	2	sp
AB_3	BF_3, $GaCl_3$	Triangular plane	3	sp^2
AB_4	CH_4, NH_4^+, BF_4^-, $BeCl_4^{2-}$	Tetrahedral	4	sp^3
AB_5	$SbCl_5$, PCl_5	Trigonal bipyramid	5	sp^3d
AB_6	SF_6, AlF_6^{3-}, SiF_6^{2-}	Octahedral	6	sp^3d^2

Evidently σ bonds formed from s-p type hybrid orbitals are stronger than those formed from a p orbital.

(b) **Kinds of Orbitals Used; Electron Pair Repulsion.** The central atom uses hybridized atomic orbitals for bonding in most cases. Some exceptions in which the central atom uses unhybridized p orbitals are discussed in an ensuing section. A hybrid atomic orbital is needed for each σ bond and for each lone pair of electrons. This requirement is the basis for the Hybrid Orbital Number Rule (page 280). We have previously suggested five types of hybrid atomic orbital: sp, sp^2, sp^3, sp^3d, and sp^3d^2 (pages 271; 281). Each type is associated with a definite spatial orientation (Fig. 24.3), so as to minimize repulsion between electron pairs in the outer shell of the central atom. Therefore, hybrid atomic orbitals that house electron pairs, both bonding (shared) and lone (unshared), are oriented in space so as to minimize the mutual repulsion (Fig. 24.3).

It is experimentally determined that molecules and ions of nontransitional elements with *no lone pairs of electrons* have one of the five shapes shown in Fig. 24.3, depending on the number of B atoms bonded to atom A. Table 24.1 gives the experimentally observed shapes and the associated hybrid type for some typical molecules and ions.

We have previously seen (page 275) that the tendency for repulsion between electron pairs on the same central atom is one of the reasons that atoms frequently use hybrid atomic orbitals rather than pure p orbitals to form σ bonds.

24.3 PRINCIPAL EFFECT OF A LONE PAIR

This discussion is germane to those molecules and ions in which the central atom has a lone pair, uses hybridized orbitals, and has no multiple bonds. In AB_n, replacing a B atom by a lone pair, as in $:AB_{(n-1)}$, introduces a void, thereby altering the shape. In the AB_2 type of species, this

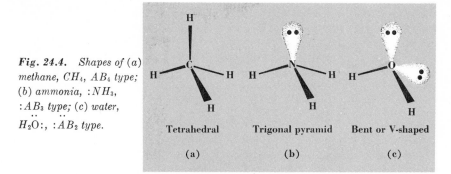

Fig. 24.4. *Shapes of (a) methane, CH_4, AB_4 type; (b) ammonia, $:NH_3$, $:AB_3$ type; (c) water, $H_2O:$, $:AB_2$ type.*

Tetrahedral   Trigonal pyramid   Bent or V-shaped

(a)   (b)   (c)

kind of change gives an :A—B molecule, such as H—Cl:. Such diatomic molecules have only one bond axis and are therefore necessarily linear. The $:AB_2$ type structure, which has no multiple bonds and in which atom A uses hybrid orbitals, is rare (Problem 17), and hence will not be discussed.

(a) Four Electron Pairs on the Central Atom. In this group, there are two types of species, $:AB_3$, as typified by ammonia, $:NH_3$, and $:AB_2$, as typified by water, $H_2O:$. In both molecules, the central atom uses sp^3 hybrid atomic orbitals. All four orbitals are equivalent, and it is therefore immaterial which orbital houses a lone pair.

It has been experimentally determined that $:NH_3$ is a **trigonal** (triangular) **pyramid;** the three H atoms form the triangular base of the pyramid with the N atom at the apex (Fig. 24.4b). The H—N—H bond angles are 107°, indicating that the orientation of the four pairs of electrons around the nitrogen atom is approximately tetrahedral. The nitrogen atom exhibits sp^3 hybridization, thereby forming stronger σ bonds with greater bond angles.

Water, $H_2O:$, is a **bent** or **V-shaped** molecule (Fig. 24.4c), with a bond angle of 105°. This value is fairly close to the tetrahedral angle, and hence oxygen is believed to use sp^3 hybrid atomic orbitals.

(b) Six Electron Pairs on the Central Atom. In this group, there are only two types, $:AB_5$, as typified by bromine pentafluoride, $:BrF_5$, and $:AB_4$, as typified by xenon tetrafluoride, $:XeF_4$. In the octahedral array for an AB_6 type of molecule, all six sp^3d^2 hybridized atomic orbitals are equivalent. We should expect that any of the six could accommodate the lone pair of electrons equally well. We find that the shape of $:BrF_5$ is a **square pyramid** (Fig. 24.5b); four of the fluorine atoms form the square base of the pyramid, and the fifth fluorine atom is at the apex.

When we consider $:XeF_4$, a new factor appears for the first time in our discussion. The two pairs of electrons can be arranged in *two* different ways about the central atom. The axes of the orbitals with the lone pairs of electrons can form either an angle of 90° (Fig. 24.5d) or an angle of 180° (Fig. 24.5c). The shape of xenon tetrafluoride is square-planar (Fig. 24.5c).

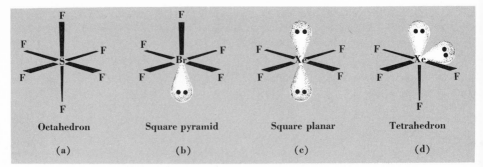

Octahedron   Square pyramid   Square planar   Tetrahedron

(a)   (b)   (c)   (d)

Fig. 24.5. Structures of typical molecules whose central atom has six pairs of electrons: (a) AB_6 type, SF_6; (b) : AB_5 type, BrF_5; (c) : AB_4 type, $\overset{..}{X}eF_4$; (d) incorrect structure for XeF_4.

The Xe atom and all four F atoms are in the same plane. The Xe atom is in the center and the fluorine atoms are at the corners of a square. Evidently the two orbitals with the lone pairs form an angle of 180° with each other, rather than an angle of 90°.

(c) **Five Electron Pairs on the Central Atom.** This group has three categories of structures: (*i*) :AB_4, as typified by tellurium tetrachloride, :$TeCl_4$; (*ii*) :AB_3, as typified by chlorine trifluoride, :ClF_3; (*iii*) :AB_2, as typified by xenon difluoride, :$\overset{..}{X}eF_2$. Of the five types of hybrid atomic orbital shown in Table 24.1, the sp^3d is unique in that not all five orbitals are equivalent (page 283). There are two sets of equivalent orbitals. The three orbitals oriented in a plane toward the corners of a triangle comprise the **equatorial** (e) group, and the two orbitals oriented perpendicular to the plane comprise the **axial** (a) group (Fig. 24.6a). The nonequivalence of the bonds is revealed by the bond distances in PCl_5; P—Cl (axial) = 2.19 A, P—Cl (equatorial) = 2.04 A. When bonding

Fig. 24.6. Shapes of typical molecules with five pairs of electrons on the central atom: (a) PCl_5, AB_5 type; (b) $\overset{..}{T}eCl_4$, :AB_4 type; (c) :ClF_3, :AB_3 type; (d) :$\overset{..}{X}eF_2$, :AB_2 type.

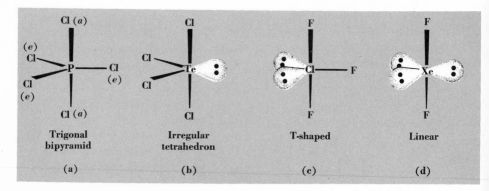

Trigonal bipyramid   Irregular tetrahedron   T-shaped   Linear

(a)   (b)   (c)   (d)

General type	Example	Shape	Orbital type	Electron pair arrangement
: AB_3	: NH_3, H_3O: $^+$, : PF_3	Trigonal pyramid	sp^3	Tetrahedral
: AB_2	$H_2\ddot{O}$:, : $\ddot{S}Cl_2$, : $\ddot{N}H_2^-$	Bent	sp^3	Tetrahedral
: AB_4	: SF_4, : $TeCl_4$	Irregular tetrahedron	sp^3d	Trigonal bipyramid
: $\ddot{A}B_3$	: $\ddot{Cl}F_3$	T-shaped	sp^3d	Trigonal bipyramid
: $\ddot{A}B_2$	: $\ddot{X}eF_2$, : $\ddot{I}Cl_2^-$	Linear	sp^3d	Trigonal bipyramid
: AB_5	: IF_5, : BrF_5	Square pyramid	sp^3d^2	Octahedral
: $\ddot{A}B_4$	: $\ddot{X}eF_4$, : $\ddot{I}Cl_4^-$	Square plane	sp^3d^2	Octahedral

pairs are replaced by lone pairs, the observed shapes of the three types of molecule indicate that the lone pairs assume equatorial positions (Fig. 24.6b–d).

We can better understand the geometry of the molecules in Fig. 24.6b–d by making a rough but useful approximation concerning the nonequivalent hybridization of the sp^3d system. The triangular planar orientation of the equatorial orbitals suggests that they are sp^2 hybridized. The two axial orbitals would then be pd hybridized. Thus, three sp^2 hybrid orbitals plus two pd hybrid orbitals equal five sp^3d hybrid orbitals. The sp^2 group is at a lower energy than the pd group. We still must answer the question of why the lone pairs are situated in the lower energy sp^2 group. A lone pair is under the influence of only one positive nucleus, and so tends to be closer to the central atom than is a bonding pair, which is under the influence of two positive nuclei. Being closer to the nucleus means being at a lower energy level. For this reason, it is suggested that the lone pairs are situated in the equatorial sp^2 orbitals, since these orbitals are at a lower energy than the axial pd orbitals. Table 24.2 summarizes the typical shapes of molecules and ions whose central atom has at least one lone pair.

24.4   MOLECULES WHOSE CENTRAL ATOMS USE UNHYBRIDIZED p ORBITALS

Although ammonia has a bond angle (107°) close to the tetrahedral value of 109.5°, the hydrides of the other members of Group V have bond angles close to 90°. The observed values are 94° for : PH_3, 92° for : AsH_3, and 91° for : SbH_3. These values are interpreted to mean that phosphorus, arsenic, and antimony use unhybridized p orbitals to form bonds to hydrogen. The lone pair in these hydrides is in an s orbital. A similar situation prevails for the hydrides of Group VI. Thus, whereas the bond angle for water is 105°, the bond angles are 92° for H_2S, 91° for H_2Se, and 90° for H_2Te. As the size of the atoms in Groups V and VI of the Periodic Table increases, the tendency to use unhybridized p orbitals for formation of a σ bond to hydrogen appears to increase. This tendency to use p orbitals seems to prevail mainly for σ bonding to hydrogen, since the bond angle in sulfur dichloride, SCl_2, is 103°, and the F—P—F angle in phosphorus trifluoride, PF_3, is 104°. A reason for this effect on the bond angle of replacing a hydrogen by a halogen atom is discussed in Section 24.6c.

24.5 SHAPES OF MULTIPLE-BONDED MOLECULES

A multiple bond consists of σ and π bonds. We have seen that the geometry of a molecule is essentially determined by the σ bonds. The π bonds are parallel to the axis of the σ bond, and hence have no primary effect on the shape. The shape of a multiple-bonded molecule or ion depends primarily on the same factors discussed in Sections 24.2 and 24.3. Table 24.3 summarizes the typical shapes of some common substances with p-p π bonds, on the basis of the number of B atoms bonded to atom A, and the number of lone pairs on atom A. Several of the substances are represented by structures showing extended π bonding (page 288). Notice that p-p π bonds occur only if the central atom is sp or sp^2 hybridized, for only then does the central atom have a p orbital available to overlap with a p orbital of atom B.

If the number of σ bonds and lone pairs (hybrid orbital number) equals 4, 5, or 6, any π bonding in the substance must be of the p-d type. In such cases, the central atom uses all its p orbitals for hybridization, and there-

TABLE 24.3 *Shapes of Molecules and Ions with p-p π Bonds*

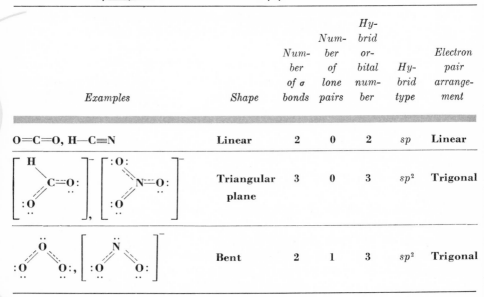

Examples	Shape	Number of σ bonds	Number of lone pairs	Hybrid orbital number	Hybrid type	Electron pair arrangement
O=C=O, H—C≡N	Linear	2	0	2	sp	Linear
(structures)	Triangular plane	3	0	3	sp^2	Trigonal
(structures)	Bent	2	1	3	sp^2	Trigonal

TABLE **24.4** *Shapes of Substances with p-d π Bonding*

Example	Shape	Number of σ bonds	Number of lone pairs	Hybrid orbital number	Hybrid type	Electron pair arrangement
(structures: P with O, Cl, Cl, Cl; $\left[\begin{array}{c} O \\ \| \\ S \\ O \quad O \quad O \end{array}\right]^{2-}$)	Tetrahedron	4	0	4	sp^3	Tetrahedral
$\left[\begin{array}{c} \ddot{C}l \\ O \quad O \quad O \end{array}\right]^{-}$	Triangular pyramid	3	1	4	sp^3	Tetrahedral
$\left[\begin{array}{c} :\ddot{C}l \\ O \quad O \end{array}\right]^{-}$	Bent	2	2	4	sp^3	Tetrahedral
$O=S$ with F F F F	Trigonal bipyramid	5	0	5	sp^3d	Trigonal bipyramid
:I with F O F O	Irregular tetrahedron	4	1	5	sp^3d	Trigonal bipyramid
I with HO O OH HO OH OH	Octahedron	6	0	6	sp^3d^2	Octahedron
Xe with F O F F F	Square pyramid	5	1	6	sp^3d^2	Octahedron

fore has only d orbitals available for $π$ bonding. Table 24.4 lists some typical shapes of molecules and ions with p-d $π$ bonds.

24.6 SECONDARY EFFECTS; MODIFICATIONS IN BOND ANGLES

(a) **Effect of Lone Pairs.** Whereas the bond angle in methane is 109.5°, the expected tetrahedral value, the introduction of a lone pair of electrons in place of a bond reduces the interbond angles in $:NH_3$ to 107°, and the replacement of two bonds by two lone pairs of electrons in

..
H_2O: causes the remaining bonds to move still closer together (105°). Evidently, *insertion of lone pairs causes contraction of the angle of the remaining bonding pairs.*

This phenomenon can be explained in terms of electron pair repulsions. Repulsion between electron pairs depends on the proximity of each pair to the central atom, as well as on the angle between them. At a fixed angle, the closer the pairs are to the central atom the closer they are to each other, and the greater is the repulsion. A lone pair is under the influence of only one positive center, and so is closer to the central atom than is a bonding pair, which is under the influence of two positive nuclei. Since a lone pair is closer to the central atom than is a bonding pair, it is believed to exert a greater repulsion. Hence, *lone pairs repel adjacent electron pairs more strongly than do bonding pairs.* Consequently, two lone pairs repel each other more than do two bonding pairs. The repulsion between a lone pair and a bonding pair is intermediate. Electron pair repulsions decrease in the order: lone pair–lone pair > lone pair–bonding pair > bonding pair–bonding pair, as shown in Fig. 24.7. Since a bonding pair experiences less repulsion from another bonding pair than from a lone pair, it can afford to be closer to the bonding pair than to the lone pair. For this reason, the presence of a lone pair contracts the angle made by the bonding pairs. One lone pair on the nitrogen atom of ammonia causes a contraction of the H—N—H bonding angles of 2°. Two lone pairs on the oxygen atom of water contracts the H—O—H bond angle by 4°.

It has been further suggested that repulsions between electron pairs in *filled* shells are greater than those between electron pairs in *partially filled* shells. For elements in the second period of the Periodic Table, the complete shell has 8 electrons, and for third-period elements, the complete shell has 18 electrons. The orbitals in a filled shell occupy all the available space. Excessive contraction of bond angles will cause appreciable interaction between adjacent orbitals, each of which has a pair of electrons, and therefore will be strongly resisted. The orbitals in partially filled shells do not occupy all the available space, and hence can approach each other more closely without causing destabilizing interaction between neighboring orbitals. Using this suggestion, we can explain the bond angle of 107° in :NH_3, compared with the bond angle of 93° in :PH_3. In :PH_3 the four electron pairs are in an incompletely filled shell, while in :NH_3 the four pairs are in a filled shell. Therefore, the bond angles in

Fig. 24.7. Schematic representation of electron pair repulsions: (a) lone pair–lone pair; (b) lone pair–bonded pair; (c) bonded pair–bonded pair.

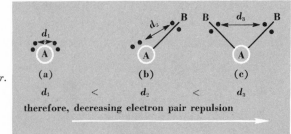

: PH_3 can be contracted more than the bond angles in : NH_3. This suggestion explains why the Group VA and VIA elements in the third and higher periods use essentially pure p orbitals when forming hydrides (page 648).

In establishing the hybrid orbital number of the methyl free radical, $H_3C\cdot$ (page 281), the statement was made that the odd electron should not be considered. Thus, $H_3C\cdot$ has a hybrid orbital number of 3, and the carbon atom is presumed to use sp^2 hybrid orbitals. This presumption is based on the experimental evidence that the structure is in fact trigonal. The three bonding pairs of electrons form an angle of 120°. The odd electron is in a p orbital, which makes an angle of 90° with the bonding pairs. Were the shape to be tetrahedral, all bond angles would be approximately 109.5°. It therefore appears that repulsion between pairs of electrons is much more important in determining the shape than repulsion between a pair of electrons and an odd electron. To have the pairs of electrons as far from each other as possible, $H_3C\cdot$ acquires the trigonal rather than the tetrahedral structure. The presence of the odd electron evidently has little or no influence on the shape. Therefore, in making predictions about the shape of simple free radicals, we can disregard the presence of the odd electron.

(b) Effect of Electronegativity of Atom B. This effect becomes apparent when we compare the following sets of bond angles:

H_2O (105°)	NH_3 (107°)	PI_3 (102°)
F_2O (103°)	NF_3 (102°)	PBr_3 (101.5°)
		PCl_3 (100°)

As the peripheral atom, B, becomes more electronegative, the bond angle evidently decreases. An F atom is more electronegative than an H atom, for example, and the F—O—F bond angle is less than the H—O—H bond angle. This observation can be explained in terms of electron pair repulsions. As the electronegativity of the peripheral atom, B, increases, the bonding electrons are displaced, thus becoming *further apart*. As a result, repulsion between the bonding electrons decreases, and the bond angle contracts.

(c) Effect of π Bonds. Although π bonds usually have no gross effect on the shape of a molecule, their presence does to some extent alter bond angles. The bond angles in formaldehyde, $H_2C{=}O$,

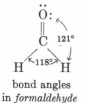

bond angles
in *formaldehyde*

substantiate this point. The carbon atom has three σ bonds, and no lone pair of electrons. It therefore uses sp^2 hybrid atomic orbitals. Hence, we expect $H_2C{=}O$ to have a triangular planar shape, with bond angles of 120°. We find that, although the molecule has the expected shape, the bond angles are somewhat distorted. The angle between the two single bonds—the H—C—H bond angle—is contracted 2°, and each angle involving the double bond—the H—C=O bond angle—is expanded 1°. Each angle involving the π bond is larger than the angles involving only the single bonds. Apparently, *the multiple bond orbitals repel neighboring orbitals more strongly than do single bond orbitals.* A multiple bond has an electron density resulting from the presence of *at least* two pairs of electrons, and hence repels the neighboring pairs of electrons more than does a single bond orbital, which always has an electron density due to the presence of *one pair* of electrons. Thus, in general, *angles involving multiple bonds tend to be larger than those involving only single bonds.*

The multiple bond may also be of the $d\text{-}p\ \pi$ type. For example, in the tetrahedral molecule, phosphorus oxytrichloride,

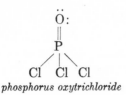

phosphorus oxytrichloride

there is a $d\text{-}p\ \pi$ bond between phosphorus and oxygen. The presence of this π bond causes the Cl—P—Cl angles to be 104° instead of 109.5°, the typical tetrahedral value.

The effect of the $d\pi\text{-}p\pi$ bonding becomes apparent when we compare the bond angles of phosphine, PH_3, phosphorus trifluoride, PF_3, and phosphorus trichloride, PCl_3:

	$:PH_3$	$:PF_3$	$:PCl_3$
bond angles	93°	104°	100°

On the basis of increasing electronegativity, we would expect the bond angles to decrease in the order $PH_3 > PCl_3 > PF_3$, since the bond angle involving the most electronegative peripheral atom should contract the most. Recall that such a contraction is observed when NH_3 and NF_3 are compared (page 651). The actual bond angles are contrary to our predictions. Our predictions are erroneous because we overlooked the presence of $d\pi\text{-}p\pi$ bonding. Phosphorus is a third-period element, and has a d orbital available for π bonding. Furthermore, fluorine can furnish at least one p orbital with a pair of electrons to complete the π bond. Each fluorine atom can participate in the $d\pi\text{-}p\pi$ bonding, and hence the F—P—F bond angles expand. In fact, the bond angles in PF_3 are closer to the tetrahedral angle expected if phosphorus were to use sp^3 hybrid atomic orbitals, than to the 90° angle expected if phosphorus were to use p orbitals.

The bond angles in PCl_3 are less than those in PF_3. The chlorine atom is larger than the fluorine atom, and hence the P—Cl bond distance is greater than the P—F bond length. As a result, the $d\pi$-$p\pi$ bonding in the phosphorus-to-chlorine bond is not so important as in the phosphorus-to-fluorine bond. There is less electron density in the P—Cl bonds, and therefore less repulsion. Consequently, the Cl—P—Cl bond angles are smaller than the F—P—F bond angles. It is of course impossible for H to engage in π bonding.

A comparison of the bond angles in sulfuryl fluoride, SO_2F_2, reveals another important feature of $d\pi$-$p\pi$ bonding:

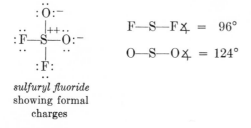

$$F—S—F \measuredangle \ = \ 96°$$

$$O—S—O \measuredangle \ = \ 124°$$

sulfuryl fluoride
showing formal
charges

Sulfuryl fluoride is a tetrahedral molecule; the sulfur atom uses sp^3 hybrid orbitals to form the four σ bonds. However, the expected tetrahedral bond angles of 109.5° are not observed. The O—S—O bond angle is expanded, and the F—S—F bond angle is contracted. The oxygen atoms participate in $d\pi$-$p\pi$ bonding more than do the fluorine atoms. Each oxygen atom has a formal charge of -1, and hence they are more apt to delocalize a pair of electrons by π bonding than are the fluorine atoms, neither of which has a formal charge.

The following generalizations are helpful for recognizing when $d\pi$-$p\pi$ bonding can occur, and for comparing qualitatively the extent of such bonding in two comparable bonds:

(1) $d\pi$-$p\pi$ bonding can occur whenever an atom with at least one lone pair of electrons is bonded to an atom that is able to utilize d orbitals.

(2) As the sizes of either atom or both atoms increase, the bond distance increases, and the $d\pi$-$p\pi$ bonding becomes less extensive. Consequently, third-period elements such as Si, P, S, and Cl can use d orbitals for such bonding more effectively than can the comparable fourth-period elements Ge, As, Se, and Br. Likewise, among the halogens, the order of ability to furnish a filled p orbital for such bonding decreases in the order F > Cl > Br > I.

(3) If the atom furnishing the p orbital has a negative formal charge, as shown in its Lewis structure (for example, the oxygen atom of sulfuryl fluoride), it participates in $d\pi$-$p\pi$ bonding to a greater extent than an atom having no negative formal charge.

Involvement in $d\pi$-$p\pi$ bonding may completely alter the shape expected from the hybrid orbital number. For example, trisilylamine, $(H_3Si)_3N:$, has a structure in which the N atom and the three Si atoms lie in a plane

with Si—N—Si bond angles of 120°,

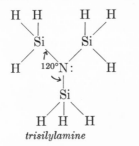

trisilylamine

This geometry is interpreted to mean that the nitrogen atom does not use the tetrahedral sp^3 hybrid orbitals predicted by the hybrid orbital number rule. Instead, the nitrogen atom uses sp^2 hybrid atomic orbitals to form the three σ bonds, and the lone pair is in a p orbital overlapping a d orbital of each Si atom; sp^2 hybridization, rather than sp^3 hybridization, permits delocalization of the electron pair of the nitrogen, and thus leads to a more stable molecule. As has been mentioned (footnote, page 290) the tendency to delocalize a pair of electrons often leads to a lower hybrid orbital number.

24.7 DEVIATED BOND ANGLES AND HYBRIDIZATION

A definite geometry is associated with each type of orbital used by the central atom for bonding (Table 24.1, page 644). However, we have seen that several factors distort the expected bond angles. How do we interpret these changes in bond angles in terms of hybridization? For example, is there a difference between the hybridized orbitals used by nitrogen in the NH_4^+ ion, where all bond angles are 109.5°, and in :NF_3, where all bond angles are 102°? If we hold to our premise that the bond angle reflects the type of hybrid orbital used, we must answer this question in the affirmative.

The lone pair of electrons in :NF_3 is closer to the nitrogen atom than are the three bonded pairs. Hence, the orbital that houses the lone pair must be at a somewhat lower energy than the orbitals possessing the bonded pairs. The lone pair orbital is said to have more s character, and the orbitals with the bonding pairs are said to have more p character, as shown in Fig. 24.8. Recall that the bond angle associated with the use of p orbitals is 90°, while the sp^3 hybrid angle is 109.5°. Hence, the angle

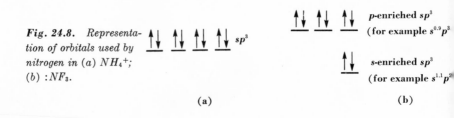

Fig. 24.8. *Representation of orbitals used by nitrogen in (a) NH_4^+; (b) :NF_3.*

(a)   (b)

made by the bonded pairs can be related to the amount of p character in the sp^3 orbitals. We should expect, as more p character is introduced into the sp^3 orbitals, the bonding pair angles to converge from 109.5° toward 90°. The more closely the lone pair is drawn to the nucleus of the central atom, the more s character there is in the lone pair orbital, and the more p character in the bonded pair orbitals. On this basis, we can account for the contraction of the bond angle when the H atoms of $:NH_3$ are replaced by F atoms, as in $:NF_3$. Fluorine is more electronegative than hydrogen, and draws electrons away from the nitrogen atom toward itself more than does hydrogen. To compensate, the N atom in $:NF_3$ draws the lone pair closer to itself. As a result, compared to the lone pair in $:NH_3$, the lone pair in $:NF_3$ is closer to the nitrogen nucleus, and is in an sp^3 hybrid orbital with more s character. The orbital in $:NF_3$ with the bonding pairs has more p character, and the bond angle is contracted.

24.8 MOLECULAR SHAPE AND DIPOLE MOMENTS

As previously mentioned, certain molecules possess a dipole moment (page 294). *The molecular dipole moment is a composite of the individual bond moments and the effect of lone pairs in* **hybrid** *atomic orbitals.* The bond and lone pair moments can be considered as vectors, the sum of which gives the molecular dipole moment. The molecular dipole moments, which are experimentally determined, are useful criteria for determining shapes of

Fig. 24.9. *Vector representation of molecular moments for (a) linear AB_2; (b) triangular plane, AB_3 and (c) tetrahedral, AB_4 molecules.*

$$B_2 \longleftarrow A \longrightarrow B_1$$

(a)

(AB$_2$ vector) + (AB$_1$ vector) = Dipole moment

$(\longleftarrow) + (\longrightarrow) = 0$

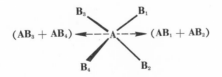

(b)   AB$_3$ vector + (AB$_1$ vector + AB$_2$ vector) = Dipole moment

$(\longleftarrow) + (\longrightarrow) = 0$

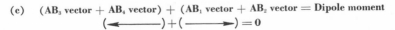

(c)   (AB$_3$ vector + AB$_4$ vector) + (AB$_1$ vector + AB$_2$ vector = Dipole moment

$(\longleftarrow) + (\longrightarrow) = 0$

molecules. For the linear, plane triangular, tetrahedral, trigonal bi-pyramidal, and octahedral shapes, the sum of the individual bond moment vectors is zero if the central atom is bonded to only one kind of atom or group. This fact is demonstrated for the linear, triangular planar, and tetrahedral structures (Fig. 24.9). For consistency it is assumed that the bonded atom is more electronegative than the central atom. The fact that compounds such as $BeCl_2$, BF_3, CCl_4, gaseous PCl_5, and SF_6 have zero dipole moments supports (but does not necessarily prove) the assigned structures. If the bonding atoms are not the same, the vector sum is no longer zero. For example, whereas carbon dioxide, $O=C=O$, has no dipole moment, carbon oxysulfide, $O=C=S$, has a finite dipole moment. Bent molecules, such as H_2O, and pyramidal molecules, such as NH_3, have dipole moments, a fact distinguishing them from linear and plane triangular molecules, respectively.

The effect of a lone pair on the molecular moment depends on the orbital in which it resides. A lone pair in an s orbital, as in H_2S, has no effect on the molecular moment, since the s orbital is symmetrically disposed around the nucleus. A lone pair in a p orbital has no effect, since the two lobes are of equal size and in opposite direction. A lone pair in an s-p type hybrid atomic orbital, as in $:NH_3$, has a definite individual moment, since the two lobes are of unequal size (page 272, Fig. 11.13). The fact that the dipole moment of $:NF_3$ is very small indicates that the moment of the lone pair almost cancels the moments of the three N—F bonds.

ONLY TO HERE.

24.9 MOLECULAR SYMMETRY

Symmetry is an important aspect of molecular shape. Intuitively, we recognize that a sphere and cube are highly symmetrical bodies. In this section are described ways of detecting the structural features, called **symmetry elements,** which make a molecule symmetrical. Discussion of these symmetry elements requires a keen understanding of the typical molecular structures previously described. Thus, the search for symmetry elements sharpens one's ability to visualize the various structures. The use of three-dimensional models is strongly recommended for developing the ability to recognize and visualize symmetry elements. Once the models have been studied, the three-dimensional projectional formulas can be more easily understood.

The symmetry of a molecule affects physical properties such as infrared and ultraviolet absorption and dipole moments. Chemical behavior is also influenced by the presence or absence of symmetry. For example, the enzymes, biochemical catalysts, are asymmetrical (nonsymmetrical) molecules that react chemically in a very specific manner. Their specificity is related to their asymmetrical structure. The properties of polymers (discussed in Chapter 29) are frequently controlled by the symmetry of their structure.

The symmetry elements that we will look for are planes, a point, and lines (axes).

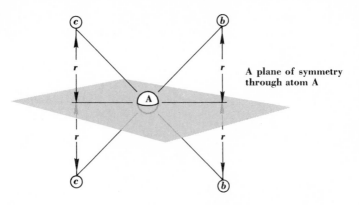

Fig. 24.10. *Example of a plane of symmetry.*

(a) **Symmetry Planes.** A symmetry plane cuts through the molecule so that a line drawn from any atom perpendicular to the plane, and extended an equal distance on the other side of the plane, terminates at the same kind of atom, as shown for a square-planar structure of the type Ab_2c_2 (Fig. 24.10). We can consider the plane as being a mirror, so that half the molecule is a mirror image of the other half. In the example cited, the plane passes through an atom, in which case it can be considered as cutting the atom into two halves that are mirror images of each other. Consequently, any planar molecule has at least one plane of symmetry, namely, the molecular plane, the plane that cuts through all its atoms. The structure in Fig. 24.10 has two planes of symmetry, the one shown and the molecular plane; evidently a structure can have more than one plane of symmetry.

A plane can pass through more than one atom along bonds, as shown in Fig. 24.11a and b.

A plane can also pass midway between atoms without incorporating any one atom, as shown in Fig. 24.12 for ethane.

In summary, a symmetry plane divides a molecule into two identical

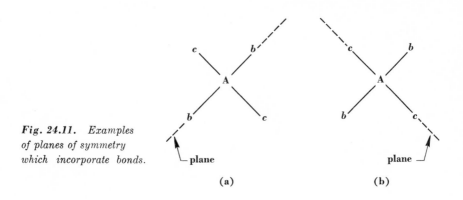

Fig. 24.11. *Examples of planes of symmetry which incorporate bonds.*

(a)   (b)

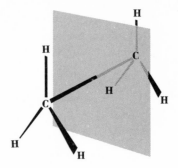

Fig. 24.12. A plane of symmetry which bisects a bond as in ethane.

halves. The plane must pass through at least one atom, or midway between atoms.

Let us examine some simple types of molecule for symmetry planes. Carbon dioxide, a typical linear molecule, has an infinite number of symmetry planes through the molecular axis, the line extending from one O atom through the C atom to the other O atom. It also has a plane through the carbon atom perpendicular to the molecular axis (Fig. 24.13).

Boron trifluoride, a typical planar triangular molecule, has, in addition to the molecular plane, three planes each passing through the B atom and a different F atom (Fig. 24.13b).

(b) Center of Symmetry. The center of symmetry is a point in the center of the molecule to which lines can be drawn from all atoms so that, when each line is extended an equal distance past the center, it comes to the same kind of atom. A simple illustration of a figure with a center of symmetry is a square with points A, A and B, B diagonally opposite each other. If the positions of an A and a B are exchanged, the center of symmetry vanishes:

<table>
<tr><td>B—A
  \| \|
A—B</td><td>B—B
  \| \|
A—A</td><td>B—A
  \| \|
C—B</td></tr>
<tr><td>has center of symmetry</td><td>no center of symmetry</td><td>no center of symmetry</td></tr>
</table>

A molecule can have only one center of symmetry, which may or may not coincide with an atom. *For a molecule to have a center of symmetry,*

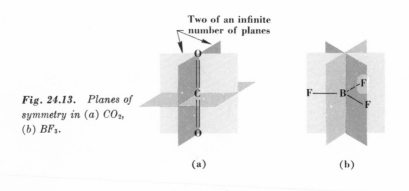

Fig. 24.13. Planes of symmetry in (a) CO₂, (b) BF₃.

Two of an infinite number of planes

(a)　　　　　(b)

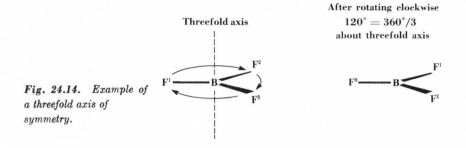

After rotating clockwise
$120° = 360°/3$
about threefold axis

Fig. 24.14. Example of a threefold axis of symmetry.

all atoms, with the exception of the one which may coincide with the center, must exist in paired sets. This restriction limits the number of molecules having centers of symmetry. In carbon dioxide, the C atom is the center of symmetry. Of the typical molecular shapes mentioned in Tables 24.1 and 24.2, only the planar square and octahedral forms, as exemplified by XeF_4 and SF_6, respectively, have centers of symmetry. In both cases, the center is at the center of the square.

(c) **Proper or Simple Axis of Symmetry.** A proper axis is a line through the molecule about which the molecule can be rotated so that the new position of the molecule is indistinguishable from its original position. The angle of rotation is equal to $360°/n$, where n is necessarily an integer, 2, 3, 4, 5, 6, ... The value of n defines the **order of the axis** expressed as n-**fold.** Therefore, for values of $n = 2$, 3, or 4, which represent rotations of 180°, 120°, or 90°, we have, respectively, a **twofold, threefold,** or **fourfold** axis. If the axis passes through one or more atoms, the positions of these atoms are unchanged during the rotation. Therefore, the molecular axis of a linear molecule is an infinite-fold axis of symmetry.

The planar BF_3 molecule serves as a good example for illustrating the presence of axes of symmetry (Fig. 24.14). The individual fluorine atoms are designated by numbers 1, 2, and 3. If the molecule is rotated 120° about an axis through the B atom perpendicular to the molecular plane, an equivalent structure is obtained. The molecule after rotation looks like the one before rotation, although the individual F atoms have changed

Fig. 24.15. Example of a twofold axis of symmetry.

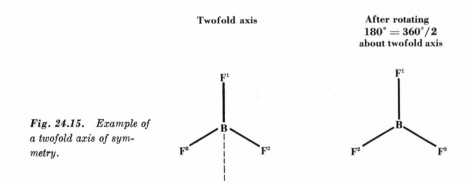

positions. Since 120° is one-third of 360°, this particular line is a threefold axis. Let us now draw a line through the B atom and one of the F atoms (Fig. 24.15). A rotation of 180° about this line gives an equivalent structure even though F-2 and F-3 have exchanged positions. This line is, therefore, a twofold axis. A similar axis can be drawn through the B atom and either of the other two F atoms; hence, BF_3 has three twofold axes in addition to one threefold axis.

Molecules possessing a plane or center of symmetry are said to be **symmetric.*** Molecules possessing *no* symmetry elements are said to be **asymmetric.**

EXAMPLE 1   **Determine the number and location of the symmetry elements in**

(a) $H_2\ddot{O}\colon$, (b) $\colon NH_3$, (c) CH_4.

ANSWER   **Write the structure showing the proper shape, and then look for planes, center, and proper axes of symmetry:**

(a)

$$\ddot{O}$$
$$\diagup \quad \diagdown$$
$$H \qquad H$$

(1) **Planes of symmetry: there are two present, the molecular plane, and the plane through the oxygen atom bisecting the angle.**

(2) **Center: not present.**

(3) **Proper axes: there is one twofold axis; it passes through the oxygen atom and bisects the bond angle.**

(b) **Consult Fig. 24.4b.**

(1) **Planes of symmetry: since there is only one nitrogen atom and an odd number of H atoms, any plane of symmetry, if present, must pass through the N atom and either one or all three of the H atoms. Only in this way can the two resulting halves be identical. Since NH_3 is not a planar molecule, no plane can include all four atoms. Consequently, we seek planes including the N atom and one H atom, and bisecting the angle involving the other two H atoms. There are *three* such planes, since any one of the three H atoms can be included in the plane.**

(2) **Center: not present.**

(3) **Proper axes: only one is present. It passes through the N atom, as it must since only one N atom is present, and is perpendicular to the plane of the three H atoms. A rotation of 120° (360°/3) brings the molecule into a position indistinguishable from the position before rotation. The axis is therefore threefold.**

(c) **To help our discussion, a ball and peg model of CH_4 is shown in Fig. 24.16.**

(1) **Planes of symmetry: any and all planes must pass through the C atom**

* A fourth symmetry element, the improper (alternating) axis, is not described here because it is difficult to locate. Fortunately, there are few molecules possessing an improper axis without possessing a plane or center of symmetry. Hence we can usually determine whether a molecule is symmetrical without looking for the improper axis.

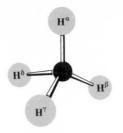

Fig. 24.16. *Ball and peg model for methane. The H atoms are designated with Greek letters.*

because only one C atom is present. The plane must pass through either all four H atoms, a pair of H atoms, or no H atoms. Since CH_4 is not a planar molecule, the plane cannot include all four H atoms. No plane of symmetry can be drawn through *only* the C atom, because of the tetrahedral arrangement of the four H atoms. Note that a plane drawn through C, H^α, and H^β also bisects the angle

The two halves of the molecule are identical, and we have a plane of symmetry. However, there are six combinations for selecting a pair of hydrogens to lie in a symmetry plane with the C atom: $H^\alpha H^\beta$; $H^\alpha H^\gamma$; $H^\alpha H^\delta$; $H^\beta H^\gamma$; $H^\beta H^\delta$; $H^\gamma H^\delta$. Therefore, methane has *six* planes of symmetry.

(2) **Center:** none present.

(3) **Proper axes:** any proper axis must pass through the C atom since it is one of a kind. In one respect, CH_4 is like $:NH_3$; three of the H atoms can be viewed as lying in a plane. The fourth H atom is projecting above the carbon atom away from the plane, just like the lone pair of electrons projecting from the N atom in $:NH_3$. If we pass an axis through the C atom and the H atom that projects above the plane comprising the other three H atoms, we have a threefold axis (as in $:NH_3$). However, we can turn the molecule so that the axis passes through the C atom and any of the four H atoms. There are, therefore, four threefold axes. Methane also has three twofold axes. To find them, we must visualize the structure differently. If we focus our attention on pairs of hydrogen atoms, we note that an axis bisecting the angle

$$\begin{matrix} H^\alpha \\ | \\ C \\ \diagup \\ H^\gamma \end{matrix}$$

emerges from the other side of the C atom and bisects the angle

$$\begin{matrix} C \\ \diagup \quad \diagdown \\ H^\delta \qquad H^\beta \end{matrix}$$

A 180° rotation about this axis leaves the molecule in an unchanged position.

This axis is therefore a twofold axis. Two other twofold axes exist: one bisects

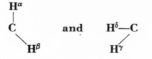

and the other bisects

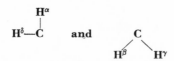

Note that each of the six possible combinations of H to C to H bond angles has been bisected by one of the three twofold axes.

24.10 STEREOISOMERISM

Isomers have been defined as compounds with the same molecular formula, but with different chemical and physical properties (page 242). Some typical examples are

$$CH_3—CH=CH—CH_3 \quad and \quad CH_2=CH—CH_2—CH_3$$
2-butene   1-butene
(b.p. 0.3°C)   (b.p. −5°C)

$$CH_3—O—CH_3 \quad and \quad CH_3—CH_2—OH$$
dimethyl ether   ethyl alcohol
(b.p. −29.7°C)   (b.p. 78.4°C)

These pairs of compounds, called **structural isomers,** differ in the sequence of bonds. There are also compounds having the same sequence of bonds and yet different properties. These compounds differ somehow in the spatial orientation (*configuration*) of the bonds, and are called **stereoisomers.** There are two broad classes of stereoisomers: **geometrical** and **optical.**

(a) **Geometrical Isomerism.** There are three compounds known with the molecular formula, $C_2H_2Cl_2$. All three have one C=C, two C—H, and two C—Cl bonds. One of the isomers has both Cl atoms attached to

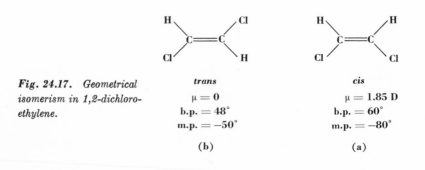

Fig. 24.17. *Geometrical isomerism in 1,2-dichloro-ethylene.*

trans	*cis*
μ = 0	μ = 1.85 D
b.p. = 48°	b.p. = 60°
m.p. = −50°	m.p. = −80°
(b)	(a)

the same carbon, $H_2C=CCl_2$, whereas in each of the other two isomers the Cl atoms are attached to different carbons, $ClCH=CHCl$. The latter two compounds have the same sequence of bonds, as shown by the condensed formula, $ClCH=CHCl$, yet are isomers. Of special significance in determining the structures is the fact that one compound, A, has a dipole moment of 1.85D, and the other compound, B, has a zero dipole moment. In compound B, the C—Cl bond moments must oppose and cancel each other, as do the C—H bond moments, and therefore the molecule has the structure shown in Fig. 24.17b. In the structure shown in Fig. 24.17a, the C—Cl bond moments substantially reinforce each other, thus accounting for the observed dipole moment. The isomer with the chlorine atoms on opposite sides of the double bond is designated *trans*, the other isomer is called *cis*. The pair constitutes an example of **geometrical isomerism.**

The butenes illustrate the structural requirements for alkenes to exhibit geometrical (*cis-trans*) isomerism. 1-Butene has *no* geometric isomers, whereas 2-butene has two.

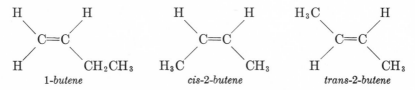

1-*butene* cis-2-*butene* trans-2-*butene*

1-Butene has two H atoms attached to the same carbon. *Whenever two like atoms or groups are attached to the same double-bonded carbon atom of an alkene, geometrical isomerism cannot occur.* In 2-butene, two different substituents, an H atom and a methyl (CH_3) group, are attached to each of the double-bonded carbons. *In order for geometrical isomerism to exist, it is necessary for each carbon of the double bond to have two different atoms or groups attached to it.*

(b) Rotation about Bonds. Geometrical isomerism is observed for substituted ethylenes, for example $ClCH=CHCl$, but can it occur in **substituted ethanes,** for example $ClCH_2CH_2Cl$ (1,2-dichloroethane)? Figure 24.18a and b shows two possible structures for the latter compound; in (a) the Cl atoms are "side-by-side", while in (b) they are opposed. However, no such isomers of this compound have been isolated, and this

Fig. 24.18. Conformations of 1,2-dichloroethane showing distance between Cl atoms; (a) eclipsed, (b) staggered.

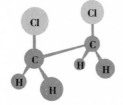 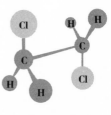

Eclipsed **Staggered**

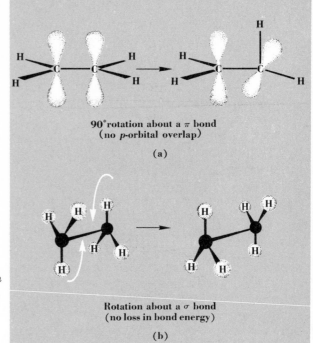

90° rotation about a π bond
(no p-orbital overlap)

(a)

Fig. 24.19. *Rotation about (a) a pi bond, (b) a sigma bond.*

Rotation about a σ bond
(no loss in bond energy)

(b)

compound, therefore, does not exhibit geometrical isomerism. The difference in behavior of $ClCH_2CH_2Cl$ and $ClCH=CHCl$ arises from the nature of the bonds joining the carbon atoms. In $ClCH=CHCl$, the carbons are joined by a σ and a π bond. Because of the π bond, the two H—C—Cl groups cannot rotate without a large expenditure of energy. Rotation can be viewed as a process whereby each carbon atom, with all its bonds, is turned around the bond axis in a direction opposite to the adjacent p orbitals destroying the π bond (Fig. 24.19a). This large barrier to rotation about the double-bond axis prevents rapid interconversion of the *cis* and *trans* isomers.

The energy requirements for interconversion of the *cis-trans* isomers is illustrated by the energy diagram in Fig. 24.20. Whenever the energy of activation at room temperature for the interconversion of stereoisomers is more than about 30 kcal/mole, the isomers will maintain their identity. Each stereoisomer can be kept in the dark in a separate bottle and, even after long periods of time, the purity of each isomer is maintained. Geometrical isomers must be kept in dark bottles because light energy may induce interconversion.

Notice that the two geometrical isomers do not possess the same ground state energy. In this case, the *trans* isomer has less energy than the *cis* isomer. We can account for the relative stabilities of geometrical isomers with the familiar postulate, "Two objects (atoms) cannot occupy the same space at the same time." Consequently, the stability of a molecule is affected by the proximity of atoms not bonded to each other. In 1,2-dichloroethene the Cl atoms are bulkier than the H atoms. In the *cis* isomer the bulky Cl atoms are on the same side of the molecule and so tend to crowd each other. In the *trans* isomer the Cl atoms are on opposite sides of the molecule and there is much less crowding. Therefore the *trans* isomer is more stable than the *cis* isomer. The more stable geometrical isomer is in general the one having the bulkier groups *trans* to each other. When a pure geometrical isomer is heated to a temperature at which rotation can occur, the resulting equilibrium mixture of *cis* and *trans* isomers is invariably richer in the more stable isomer (Problem 24).

On the other hand, σ bonds are created by head-to-head overlap of atomic orbitals (page 642), and as a result are symmetrical about the C—C bond axis. The carbon atoms can be rotated without interfering with the overlap of the atomic orbitals (Fig. 24.19b). Rotation rapidly interconverts the structures (Fig. 24.18) and consequently they are not individually isolable.

Structures, as shown in Fig. 24.18, differing as the result of rotation about one or more single bonds are called **conformations.** The structure in Fig. 24.18a is called the *eclipsed* conformation; structure (b) is the *staggered* or *anti* conformation. There is actually an infinite number of **conformations,** each with a different momentary spatial arrangement that results from rotation about the C—C bond. The *anti* and *eclipsed* forms are the extreme cases.

(c) **Optical Isomerism.** Whenever a molecule or ion lacks a plane, a center, or an improper axis of symmetry, it exhibits a type of stereoisomerism called **optical isomerism.** The most prevalent kind of mole-

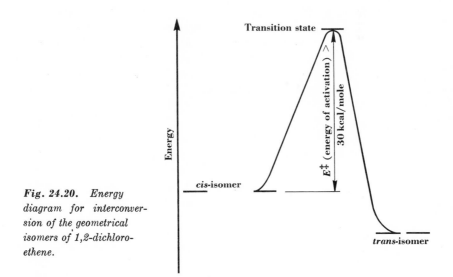

Fig. 24.20. Energy diagram for interconversion of the geometrical isomers of 1,2-dichloroethene.

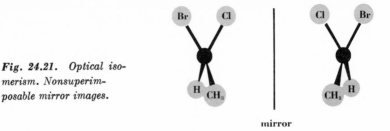

*Fig. 24.21. Optical iso-
merism. Nonsuperim-
posable mirror images.*

mirror

cule meeting these requirements is a tetrahedron in which the center atom
is bonded to *four different atoms or groups,* for example $CH_3CHBrCl$. In
such a structure, the central atom is said to be **asymmetric.** It is possible
to arrange the four different groups about an asymmetric atom to give
two structures (Fig. 24.21a and b). These structures are not superimposa-
ble; they are, however, mirror images of each other. The spatial order of
groups is called the **configuration.** Configurations are interchangeable
usually only by breaking and reforming bonds, and not by mere rotation.
For this reason, most optical isomers retain their identity and are not
readily transformed to an equilibrium mixture.

Optical isomers have the ability to rotate a beam of plane-polarized
light;* one rotates the beam to the right (**dextrorotatory**) and the other
rotates it to the left (**levorotatory**). This **optical activity** accounts for
the name given to this kind of isomerism. A mixture of equal amounts of
optical isomers, called a **racemate,** is optically inactive. Except for this
difference in optical activity, the physical properties of optical isomers
are identical. The chemical properties are also identical, unless the optical
isomers react with an optically active reagent or catalyst. For example,
enzymes, which are optically active biochemical catalysts, can promote
reactions of one optical isomer and leave the other untouched.

The explanation for the rotation of a beam of plane-polarized light by
assymmetrical molecules requires an understanding of complex physics
and mathematics. Suffice to say that the electrons in *any* molecule are
perturbed by the electrical field associated with the radiation. As a result
of this perturbation, the direction of wave polarization is altered. One
molecule has an extremely small effect, but a large number of molecules
produce a measurable net rotation of the plane-polarized light. All kinds
of molecule interact with plane-polarized light in this manner. However,
if the molecules are symmetrical, some rotate the plane to the right, and
a like number cause an equal rotation of the plane to the left. There is a
cancellation of effects, and no net rotation. The same situation prevails
for a 50–50 mixture of optical isomers. Only when there is a preponderance
of one optical isomer is there a net rotation.

* Light waves vibrate in an infinite number of planes, all of which are at right angles
to the direction in which the light travels. When ordinary light is passed through a
Nicol prism, composed of calcite (a crystalline form of $CaCO_3$), or through Polaroid,
it emerges vibrating in only one plane. Such light is **plane-polarized.**

The rotation of plane-polarized light causes no chemical or physical change. The same sample of material can be exposed innumerable times to beams of plane-polarized light and the same angle of rotation will be observed.*

Problems

1. **Electron-pair repulsion.** In terms of electron-pair repulsion, explain the following observations. (a) Proceeding from H_2S to H_2Se and H_2Te, the H—X—H bond angle contracts. (b) The Cl—C—Cl bond angle in phosgene, $Cl_2C=O$, is 111.3°, whereas the H—C—H bond angle in formaldehyde, $H_2C=O$, is 118°. (c) The O—O—H angle in H_2O_2 is 101.5° rather than 105° as in water. (d) The H—C—H bond angle in ethylene is actually 116.7° rather than the expected 120°.

2. **Orbital structures.** Show the distribution of the electrons in the outer energy level orbitals of the central atom in (a) H_2Se (H—Se—H angle, 91°); (b) CH_3OCH_3 (C—O—C angle, 110°); (c) S_8; (S—S—S angle, 105°); (d) $BeCl_4^{2-}$; (e) $(CH_3)_2Sn^{2+}$ (C—Sn—C angle, 180°); (f) planar $(CH_3)_3Sn^+$.

3. **Shapes of molecules and ions.** Draw the electronic structures and predict the shapes of the following ions and covalent molecules: (a) CdI_2; (b) CCl_4; (c) GaI_2; (d) $BeBr_4^{2-}$; (e) $SeCl_2$; (f) SeF_4; (g) BrF_3; (h) AsF_6^-; (i) BrF_4^-; (j) ICl_2^-.

4. **Orbital structures.** Show the distribution of electrons in the outer energy level of the central atom in (a) AlF_6^{3-}, (b) $SbCl_5$; (c) $O=PCl_3$; (d) $:ClO_3^-$.

5. **Shapes of multiple-bonded molecules.** Draw electronic structures and predict the shapes of the following molecules and ions: (a) nitrosyl chloride, ClNO, (b) nitryl chloride, $ClNO_2$, (c) sulfuryl chloride, Cl—SO_2—Cl, (d) IO_3^-, (e) XeO_3.

6. **Dipole moments.** Indicate which of the following molecules have an appreciable dipole moment, and represent the dipole moment by an arrow pointing from positive to negative end of the molecule. In each case, explain your answer. (a) H_2O; (b) CH_2Cl_2; (c) PF_5; (d) SF_6, (e) SO_2Cl_2.

7. **Symmetry.** Indicate the kind, number and location of each symmetry element in the following compounds: (a) $O=C=S$; (b) Cl—$\overset{\overset{..}{S}}{\underset{\underset{O}{\|}}{}}$—Cl; (c) CH_3Cl;

(d) CH_2Cl_2; (e) $Cl\overset{..}{N}H_2$.

8. **$d\pi$-$p\pi$ Bonding and shape.** (a) Explain how interplay of relative electronegativities and $d\pi$-$p\pi$ bonding can account for the following bond angles:

(i) PH_3, 93.3°; PF_3, 104°; PCl_3, 100°; PBr_3, 101°; PI_3, 102°
(ii) H_2O, 105°; OF_2, 103.2°; Cl_2O, 110.8

(b) Can $d\pi$-$p\pi$ bonding be used to account for the bond angle in NF_3? Explain. (c) Can it be used to account for the bond angle in NCl_3? Explain. (d) For what types of compound does $d\pi$-$p\pi$ bonding play a role?

* The angle of rotation does vary, however, with temperature, concentration of the solution, wavelength of the light, and length of the light path through the solution or the pure liquid.

9. Geometrical Isomers. (a) Which of the following compounds exist as geometrical isomers? Draw the isomers.

(*i*) $H_2C=C(CH_3)_2$ (*ii*) $CH_3CH=C(CH_3)_2$

(*iii*) $CH_3CH=CCH_2CH_3$ (*iv*) $CH_3CH_2C=CCH_2CH_3$
                CH_3 H_3C CH_3

(b) Underline the more stable geometrical isomer.

10. Optical Isomers. Which of the following compounds exist as optical isomers?

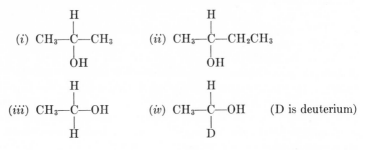

(*i*) $CH_3-\overset{\displaystyle H}{\underset{\displaystyle OH}{C}}-CH_3$ (*ii*) $CH_3-\overset{\displaystyle H}{\underset{\displaystyle OH}{C}}-CH_2CH_3$

(*iii*) $CH_3-\overset{\displaystyle H}{\underset{\displaystyle H}{C}}-OH$ (*iv*) $CH_3-\overset{\displaystyle H}{\underset{\displaystyle D}{C}}-OH$ (D is deuterium)

Additional problems

11. Dipole moment and lone pairs. After comparing experimental and calculated dipole moments, C. A. Coulson suggested that in HCl the chlorine atom is sp hybridized. (a) Give the orbital electronic structure for an sp hybridized Cl atom. (b) Which HCl molecule would have a larger dipole moment—the one in which the chlorine uses pure p, or uses sp hybrid orbitals for bonding with the H atom?

12. Shape and reactivity. (a) Compare the shape and bonding of CO_2 and SO_2. (b) Compare the shape and bonding of $HOCO_2^-$ and $HOSO_2^-$. (c) On the basis of your answers to parts (a) and (b), suggest a reason why SO_2 is a stronger acid than CO_2.

13. Multiple bond and shape. Draw two possible structures for $F_4S=O$. Predict which is the actual one. Explain.

14. Geometrical isomerism and lone pairs. Dinitrogen difluoride, N_2F_2, exists as two geometrical isomers. (a) Draw an electronic structural formula for each consistent with covalency and octet rules. (b) How could you distinguish between them?

15. Dipole moment and isomerism. The statement was made on page 656 that the zero dipole moment for CCl_4 is consistent with, but does not prove, a tetrahedral structure. Which of the following conceivable structures for CCl_4 would also have a zero dipole moment? (a) Square-planar; (b) square-pyramid (Cl atoms at the corners of a square base, C at apex); (c) irregular tetrahedron (as in $TeCl_4$).

16. Shape. In their crystalline states, PCl_5 exists as $PCl_4^+PCl_6^-$, and PBr_5 exists as $PBr_4^+Br^-$. (a) Predict the shape of all polyatomic ions above. (b) Indicate the electronic orbital structure for the P atom in each of its different types of ion. (c) Speculate as to why PCl_5 and PBr_5 do not form the same ionic species.

17. Shape and hybrid orbitals. (a) Draw the Lewis (electronic) structure for the covalent molecule $SnCl_2$. (b) Describe the types of orbital used by the Sn atom if the observed bond angle is 95°.

18. General. Distinguish clearly between (a) plane and point of symmetry; (b) optical and geometrical isomerism; (c) *cis* and *trans* isomers; (d) structural isomer and stereoisomer; (e) eclipsed and anti conformations.

19. Dipole moments. (a) Write the structural formulas for *ortho-*, *meta-*, and *para*-dichlorobenzene, and list them in the order of decreasing dipole moment. (b) Account for the fact that 1,4-dihydroxybenzene has a dipole moment.

20. $d\pi$-$p\pi$ Bonding and shape. (a) Using the hybrid orbital number rule, as applicable to oxygen, predict the Si—O—Si bond angle in *cristobalite*, a form of SiO_2 (Fig. 9.2, page 213). (b) Account for the fact that the observed bond angle is 150°. Describe the bonding between silicon and oxygen in terms of orbitals.

21. Symmetry. Indicate the kind, number, and location of each symmetry element in the following compounds: (a) ethylene; (b) *cis*-BrCH=CHBr; (c) *trans*-BrCH=CHBr; (d) benzene; (e) *staggered* conformation of ethane; (f) *eclipsed* conformation of ethane.

22. Symmetry. Indicate the kind, number, and location of each symmetry element in the following compounds: (a) PCl_5; (b) SF_6.

23. Symmetry. A cube has at its corners two A atoms, two B atoms, two C atoms, and two D atoms. Arrange the six atoms so that the cube has (a) a plane of symmetry—locate the plane; (b) a point of symmetry—locate the point; (c) a twofold axis—locate the axis.

24. Geometrical isomerism. At 227°C a *cis* isomer has 2.3 kcal per mole more free energy than its *trans* isomer. (a) Calculate the equilibrium constant (K) for the equilibrium, *trans* $\rightleftharpoons$ *cis*, at 227°C. (b) Find the percentage of *trans* isomer in the mixture.

Answer. (a) 10^{-1}; (b) 90.9%.

25. Resonance and shape. (a) Draw two contributing structures for NO_2, one with the odd electron on the nitrogen atom, and one with the odd electron on an oxygen atom. (b) Predict the shape of each contributing structure. (c) The actual bond angle is 134°. Explain.

26. Conformations. (a) Which of the following molecules possess conformations: (*i*) H_2O; (*ii*) hydrogen peroxide, HOOH; (*iii*) chloramine, H_2NCl; (*iv*) hydroxylamine, H_2NOH; (*v*) CH_3OH; (*vi*) C_6H_5Cl; (*vii*) phenol, C_6H_5OH. (b) Draw the two extreme conformations when present.

25

Transition
metal
complexes

25.1 COMPLEX FORMATION

A complex (ion or molecule) has been defined as a species composed of several parts, each of which has some independent existence in solution. It usually consists of a positive metal ion and a number of electron-rich ligands. The cation is a Lewis acid and the ligand is a Lewis base. Elements whose cations form complex ions may be classified as follows:

(a) Elements found in the B groups and Group VIII of the Periodic Table. These elements are most effective in forming complexes. Some examples are Fe, Co, Ni, Zn, Cu, Ag, Cr, and Pt. This chapter deals with the structure of the complexes of this group of elements.

(b) Representative elements whose cations lack a noble gas configuration. This group includes Pb(II), Sb(III), Sn(II), and Sn(IV).

(c) Representative elements whose cations have a noble gas configuration, but which also have a charge of $+3$ or more. This group includes Al(III) and Si(IV).

The ligands may be anions, such as CN^-, Cl^-, F^-, H^-, and OH^-, and/or molecules with lone pairs of electrons, such as $H_2\overset{..}{O}:$, $:NH_3$, $:PH_3$, and $:C\equiv O:$. Some typical examples of complex compositions are

Lewis acids	Lewis bases	Complexes
Co^{3+}	$+$ $6NH_3$	$\rightarrow Co(NH_3)_6{}^{3+}$
	neutral ligand	
Fe^{2+}	$+$ $6CN^-$	$\rightarrow Fe(CN)_6{}^{4-}$
	anionic ligand	
Pt^{4+}	$+ 2NH_3 + 4Cl^-$	$\rightarrow Pt(NH_3)_2Cl_4{}^0$
	mixed ligands	

Notice that the complex may have a positive, negative, or zero charge. *The charge is always the sum of the charges on the individual components.* In most cases, the complexes are ions, and henceforth we will refer to complex ions, rather than complexes.

25.2 COORDINATION NUMBER OR LIGANCY

The number of atoms attached to the central atom is called the **coordination number** or **ligancy.** Ligancy is one of the most puzzling problems of complex ion formation. It is undoubtedly influenced by the charge on the cation, the charge on the ligand, the radius ratio of cation to ligand, and the repulsion among ligands. However, the interplay of these factors cannot be evaluated quantitatively, and hence reliable predictions cannot be made. Fortunately, from experience, we can make a useful but not universal generalization—*a cation usually has a ligancy that is twice its charge.* Thus, some typical values are 2 for Ag^+, 4 for Cu^{2+}, 6 for Co^{3+}, 4 for Ni^{2+}, and 6 for Fe^{3+}. Some important exceptions are 6 for Fe(II), Co(II), Sn(II), and Sn(IV). The same cation can have more than one ligancy, as in $FeF_6{}^{3-}$ and $FeCl_4{}^-$. However, the ligancy is rarely more than 3 times the charge of the cation.

25.3 WERNER'S COORDINATION THEORY

Alfred Werner in 1893 proposed a rather simple theory to explain the structure of complexes. He suggested that, in addition to the common valence, certain metals possess "auxiliary" valences. Thus, Cr(III) has a valence of three in the compound $Cr_2(SO_4)_3$, and was said to have an auxiliary valence of six in the complex $(CrCl_6)^{3-}$. The common valences are satisfied only by anions, but auxiliary valences are satisfied by either anions or molecules.

The coordination complexes that Werner studied behave in solution as stable units. The ligands lose their typical chemical behavior, as exemplified by the fact that an aqueous solution of $PtCl_4 \cdot 2NH_3$ gives no precipitate of AgCl with silver nitrate, and does not neutralize sulfuric acid. Werner concluded that rather than being present in an uncombined state, Cl^- and NH_3 are intimately associated with Pt(IV) in a stable unit:

$$PtCl_4 \cdot 2NH_3 \overset{Ag^+}{\underset{(HO)_2SO_2}{\Huge[}} \begin{array}{l} \text{no AgCl, } \textit{therefore no free } Cl^- \textit{ present} \\ \\ \text{no } NH_4^+, \textit{ therefore no free } NH_3 \textit{ present} \end{array}$$

Conclusive proof of this tight association of Pt(IV), Cl^-, and NH_3 comes from the fact that an aqueous solution of this substance does not conduct an electric current, indicating the absence of free ions. Werner bracketed the complex to indicate its unit-like behavior: $[Pt(NH_3)_2Cl_4]^0$.

Another platinum(IV)-chloride-ammonia compound, $PtCl_4 \cdot 6NH_3$, on the other hand, gives four moles of AgCl per mole of complex on the addition of Ag^+, has a molar conductance indicating the presence of *five* ions, but does not neutralize sulfuric acid. Werner proposed that the formula for this compound be written $[Pt(NH_3)_6]Cl_4$, indicating the presence of the complex ion, $Pt(NH_3)_6^{4+}$ and four Cl^- ions.

Most complexes, however, are not so stable as the Co(II), Pt(IV), and Cr(III) complexes that Werner studied. For example, the $Cu(NH_3)_4^{2+}$ complex is readily decomposed by acid,

$$Cu(NH_3)_4^{2+} + 4H_3O^+ \rightarrow Cu(H_2O)_4^{2+} + 4NH_4^+$$

25.4 NOMENCLATURE

The rules presented in this section apply only to the naming of the simple coordination compounds—those with no multidentate* ligands and with only one central atom.

(1) **Naming the Ligand.** Anionic ligands are usually named by adding the letter o to the stem name, for example, Cl^- (*chloro*), CN^- (*cyano*), SO_4^{2-} (*sulfato*), NH_2^- (*amido*), NO_2^- (*nitro*), $O{-}NO^-$ (*nitrito*), and $S_2O_3^{2-}$ (*thiosulfato*). Molecular ligands are given special names, for example, H_2O (*aquo*), NH_3 (*ammine*), CO (*carbonyl*), NO (*nitrosyl*), and PH_3 (*phosphine*).

(2) **Naming Compounds with a Complex Ion.** Four rules are observed:

(a) If the compound is ionic, the cation is mentioned first, whether it is the complex ion or not.

(b) In naming the complex, the order is negative ligand, neutral ligand, and then central atom, followed by a Roman numeral in parentheses to indicate the oxidation number.

(c) If the complex is an anion, the suffix *-ate* is appended to the name of the central atom. The oxidation number then follows this suffix.

(d) The number of each kind of ligand is specified, using the Greek prefixes *di-, tri-, tetra-, penta-,* and *hexa-.*

The examples below illustrate these rules:

$[Co(NH_3)_6]Cl_3$	Hexamminecobalt(III) chloride
$K_3[Fe(CN)_6]$	Potassium hexacyanoferrate(III)
$[Cr(H_2O)_4Cl_2]Cl$	Dichlorotetraaquochromium(III) chloride
$Na_3[Ag(S_2O_3)_2]$	Sodium dithiosulfatoargentate(I)

25.5 COORDINATION NUMBER AND SHAPE

Werner suggested that the auxiliary valences were directed in space about the central atom, and that a definite spatial array is associated with each coordination number. We now know that this supposition is in accord with the wave-mechanical model for chemical bonding. The coordination num-

---

* A multidentate ligand exemplified by ethylenediamine, $H_2NCH_2CH_2NH_2$, has more than one bonding site.

bers most frequently encountered are six and four. The six-coordinate complexes are all octahedral. When the ligands are not all identical, some distortions occur because the ligands are no longer equidistant from the central atom. The four-coordinate complexes, such as $Fe(III)Cl_4^-$ and $Co(III)Br_4^-$, are usually tetrahedral, but some are square-planar. The square is the shape for $Pt(II)$ and $Au(III)$, as in $Pt(II)(NH_3)_4^{2+}$ and $Au(III)Cl_4^-$, and occurs frequently among $Ni(II)$ and $Cu(II)$ complexes. Recent findings seem to indicate that square-planar complexes are really cases of distorted octahedra, in which two loosely held molecules of water occupy the two vacant positions:

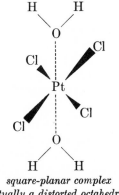

square-planar complex
(actually a distorted octahedron;
one molecule of H_2O above
and one molecule below
the plane of the paper)

A coordination number of two is observed especially for the coinage metals, Cu, Ag, and Au, in their $+1$ oxidation state. The shape of these complexes is linear, e.g., $Cu(I)Cl_2^-$, $Ag(I)(NH_3)_2^+$, and $Au(I)Cl_2^-$. Coordination numbers of five are rare and of three are very rare. The few well-defined complexes with coordination number five are trigonal bipyramids, for instance iron pentacarbonyl, $Fe(0)(CO)_5$ (0 indicates zero charge).

Bonding in transition metal complexes

Werner's coordination theory made no mention of the nature of the bonding between the central atom and ligand, yet the theory was able to account for much of the chemistry and some of the structure of complexes. However, if we wish to understand more about complexes, their color, stability, ease of formation, and magnetic properties, we must concern ourselves with the nature of the bonding. We have already seen that bonding between atoms can be viewed as two extremes: (1) electrostatic interaction between oppositely charged ions (or between an ion and a dipolar molecule); and (2) an overlap of atomic orbitals to give a covalent bond. Most often, there is a blending of the two extremes, so that many bonds have both ionic and covalent character. The same blending of bonding types prevails for the transition metal complexes. For simplicity, proponents of bonding theories usually consider only the extreme representations of bonding. Thus, the Valence Bond and Molecular Orbital* theories suppose only orbital overlap, whereas the Crystal Field theory asserts that bonding is purely electrostatic. The Crystal Field theory has been modified to take into account orbital overlap. The modified theory, called Ligand Field theory, gives slightly better predictions.

25.6 VALENCE BOND THEORY

This theory, which dates from 1935, is the contribution mainly of Linus Pauling. He introduced the concept, previously used elsewhere (page 644), that *nonequivalent atomic orbitals hybridize to give a set of equivalent hybrid atomic orbitals whose characteristic orientation determines the geometry of the complex.* Bonding may then be regarded as a result of the overlapping of a *filled* atomic orbital of the ligand with an *empty* hybrid atomic orbital of the central atom.

(a) **Six-Coordinate Complexes.** A coordination number of six requires the central atom to make available two *d*, one *s*, and three *p* orbitals for hybridization. *These hybridized atomic orbitals must be devoid of electrons since the ligand furnishes both electrons for the bond.* This frequently necessitates a *regrouping* of the *d* orbital electrons remaining in the transition metal ion. The purpose of the regrouping of the electrons is to remove electrons from the two orbitals required for hybridization. The electronic structures in the tabulation are shown for (1) a Co atom, (2) an uncomplexed (free) Co^{3+} ion, (3) a d^2sp^3 hybridized Co^{3+} ion ready to receive the six pairs of ligand electrons, and (4) a d^2sp^3 hybridized Co^{3+} ion

	1s	2s	2p	3s	3p	3d	4s	4p
(1) $_{27}Co^0$ atom	↑↓	↑↓	↑↓ ↑↓ ↑↓	↑↓	↑↓ ↑↓ ↑↓	↑↓ ↑↓ ↑ ↑ ↑	↑↓	_ _ _
(2) Co^{3+} (free)	↑↓	↑↓	↑↓ ↑↓ ↑↓	↑↓	↑↓ ↑↓ ↑↓	↑↓ ↑ ↑ ↑ ↑	_	_ _ _
(3) Co^{3+} (free) d^2sp^3 hybridized	↑↓	↑↓	↑↓ ↑↓ ↑↓	↑↓	↑↓ ↑↓ ↑↓	↑↓ ↑↓ ↑↓ _ _	_ _	_ _ _
(4) Co^{3+} (bonded) d^2sp^3 hybridized	↑↓	↑↓	↑↓ ↑↓ ↑↓	↑↓	↑↓ ↑↓ ↑↓	↑↓ ↑↓ ↑↓ 2 2	2	2 2 2

Row (3): regrouped remaining *d* electrons; six empty d^2sp^3 hybrid orbitals

Row (4): six d^2sp^3 hybrid orbitals filled with ligand electrons

---

* An understanding of the application of molecular orbital theory to the structure of complex ions requires an understanding of group theory. For this reason, the application of the theory is not discussed in this book. Interested readers are referred to a paper by H. B. Gray in *Journal of Chemical Education* **41**, 2 (1964).

TABLE 25.1   *Types of Hybrid Atomic Orbital in Transition Metal Complexes*

Ligancy	Orbital configuration	Shape	Examples	
2	sp	**Linear**	$CuCl_2^-$	$Ag(NH_3)_2^+$
4	sp^3	**Tetrahedral**	$NiCl_4^{2-}$	
4	dsp^2	**Square-planar**	$Ni(CN)_4^{2-}$	$Pt(NH_3)_4^{2+}$
6	d^2sp^3	**Octahedral**	$Co(NH_3)_6^{3+}$	$Fe(CN)_6^{3-}$

after receiving the six pairs of ligand electrons. Notice that in the "free" Co^{3+} ion, of the six $3d$ electrons, two are paired and four are unpaired, while in the d^2sp^3 hybridized Co^{3+} ion all six electrons are paired. For greatest stability, the d orbitals used for hybridization should be of the next lower principal quantum number than the s and p orbitals. These **inner** complexes are indicated by the symbol d^2sp^3, in which the d precedes the s and p. In contrast, the hexacovalent representative elements such as Al in AlF_6^{3-} (page 218), use d orbitals of the same principal quantum number as the s and p. These **outer** complexes are indicated by writing the symbol sp^3d^2.

Table 25.1 summarizes the types of hybrid orbitals most frequently used by transition elements when forming complexes.

In the above orbital representation, no attempt is made to show the relative energy levels of the hybridized and unhybridized atomic orbitals, as was done for the s-p type hybrids (page 283). However, it should be understood that the d^2sp^3 hybrid orbitals are the highest energy level orbitals used by the cation. Hence, only these orbitals are considered when predicting the shape of the complex ion. Electrons in the remaining unhybridized d orbitals are in an inner energy level, and hence do not influence the geometry of the complex ion.

The "free" Co^{3+} ion is not encountered under ordinary chemical conditions. It can be formed in the gaseous state by the ionization of cobalt vapor,

$$Co(g) \rightarrow Co^{3+}(g) + 3e^-$$

but in water, it forms an aquo complex, $Co(H_2O)_6^{3+}$. Nevertheless, the electronic structure of the so-called "free" Co^{3+} cation is shown to indicate how Hund's rule would be expected to apply, and how the rule is abandoned in order to regroup the remaining d electrons to provide two empty d orbitals for bonding.

(b) Four-Coordinate Complexes.   Nickel(II) forms both *square-planar* and *tetrahedral* four-coordinate complexes, the former being more prevalent. In tetrahedral complexes, Ni(II) uses sp^3 hybrid atomic orbitals. The typical hybridization in the square-planar complexes is dsp^2, as shown in the tabulation:

	3s	3p			3d					4s	4p		
$_{28}$Ni^0	↑↓	↑↓	↑↓	↑↓	↑↓	↑↓	↑↓	↑	↑	↑↓	__	__	__
Ni^{2+} (free)	↑↓	↑↓	↑↓	↑↓	↑↓	↑↓	↑↓	↑	↑				
Ni^{2+} (sp^3)	↑↓	↑↓	↑↓	↑↓	↑↓	↑↓	↑↓	↑	↑	2	2	2	2
											sp^3		
Ni^{2+} (dsp^2)	↑↓	↑↓	↑↓	↑↓	↑↓	↑↓	↑↓	↑↓	2	2	2	2	__
										dsp^2			

One criterion for distinguishing between these two types of complex is based on magnetic properties. The tetrahedral complex in which Ni(II) is sp^3 hybridized has two unpaired electrons, and therefore is paramagnetic. On the other hand, formation of the dsp^2 hybrid atomic orbitals for the square-planar complex of Ni(II) necessitates the pairing up of all the remaining d electrons in order to provide an empty d orbital for hybridization. Consequently, the square-planar complex is not paramagnetic.

(c) Modifications in the Valence Bond Theory. New broad theories usually stimulate further research, and Pauling's theory was no exception. New complexes were synthesized and studied, and it soon became apparent that the original theory was inadequate. For example, it was found that whereas the octahedral complex $Fe(CN)_6^{3-}$ has, as expected, one unpaired electron (see below), the octahedral complex FeF_6^{3-} has a magnetic moment corresponding to five unpaired electrons. Five unpaired electrons suggest a free Fe^{3+} ion, and Pauling actually proposed that the FeF_6^{3-} ion was formed by ionic bonding and not by orbital overlap. It was later suggested that FeF_6^{3-} was an outer sp^3d^2 complex in which Fe(III) utilizes two $4d$ rather than two $3d$ orbitals. In this way, the electronic configuration of the $3d$ orbitals is left unchanged, corresponding to a free Fe(III) ion:

	3d					4s	4p			4d			
Fe^{3+} (free)	↑	↑	↑	↑	↑	__	__	__	__	__	__	__	__
Fe^{3+} (d^2sp^3) as in Fe(CN)$_6$$^{3-}$	↑↓	↑↓	↑	2	2	2	2	2	2	__	__	__	__
				d^2sp^3 **orbitals**									
Fe^{3+} (sp^3d^2) as in FeF$_6$$^{3-}$	↑	↑	↑	↑	↑	2	2	2	2	2	2	__	__
							sp^3d^2 **orbitals**						

These modifications of the original theory came "after the fact." They cannot predict or explain the different behavior of Fe(III) toward CN$^-$ and F$^-$ ions. Nor are these modifications based on a rigorous analysis of the energy relationships involved. For example, only meager proof is offered that it is energetically feasible for Fe to use $4d$ rather than $3d$

orbitals in bonding. Also, the theory is qualitative and does not permit quantitative predictions of spectra, stabilities, and magnetic behavior. For these reasons, chemists began to explore new ideas, and both the Crystal Field and Molecular Orbital theories become popular in the 1950's.

25.7 CRYSTAL FIELD THEORY *

This theory was developed by Hans Bethe (1929) and John Van Vleck (1932), and explored by physicists. However, it was not until 1952 that Leslie Orgel popularized its use for the inorganic chemist. The theory assumes that the interaction between the transition metal ion and the ligand is purely electrostatic; it does not consider any orbital overlap. Essentially, the theory is concerned with the effect that the electron-rich ligand has on the degeneracy (page 173) of the d orbitals of the central cation. The theory is applicable only to complexes of cations with partially filled d orbitals.

(a) **Crystal Field Splitting.** Recall the shape and spatial orientation of the five d orbitals, as shown in Fig. 8.21. The d_{z^2} orbital is oriented along the z axis, the $d_{x^2-y^2}$ orbital is oriented along both the x and y axes, and the d_{xy}, d_{xz}, and d_{yz} orbitals are oriented between the x, y, and z axes. We now consider the formation of an octahedral complex, as an illustration of this theory. Analogous reasoning is used to arrive at the electronic structures of tetrahedral and square-planar complexes. The metal ion is at the origin of the x, y, and z axes, and the six ligands approach from both ends along each of these three axes† (Fig. 25.1). This approach permits the electron-rich ligands to be at the maximum distance from each other. As the electron-rich ligands approach, they exert a repulsive force on the electrons in each of the d orbitals of the metal. The d_{z^2} and the $d_{x^2-y^2}$ orbitals are oriented along an axis, and so lie directly in the path of the approaching ligands. The other three d orbitals are oriented in space between the approaching ligands. Consequently, the electrons in the d_{z^2}

---

* *Crystal Field Theory* was so named because its early proponents were interested in ionic crystals.

† For uniformity, the same axes are used to define the d orbitals as are used to describe the octahedral approach of the ligands.

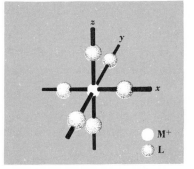

Fig. 25.1. *Approach of ligands along x, y, and z axes in an octahedral complex.*

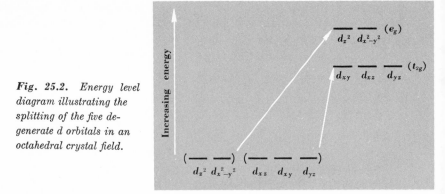

and $d_{x^2-y^2}$ orbitals suffer more repulsion than do electrons in the d_{xy}, d_{xz}, and d_{yz} orbitals.

Although all five d orbitals are raised to higher energy levels, the d_{xy}, d_{xz}, and d_{yz} orbitals are at a lower energy level than the d_{z^2} and $d_{x^2-y^2}$ orbitals. Thus when the ligand approaches, it is more favorable for an electron to be in the d_{xy}, d_{xz}, and d_{yz} orbitals than in the other two orbitals. Thus, the Crystal Field theory predicts that under the influence of the electrostatic field generated by the ligands, the five degenerate d orbitals are split into two groups of different energy (Fig. 25.2). The higher energy group is called the e_g, and the lower energy group is called the t_{2g}. The origin of these symbols will not be discussed here. The difference in energy between the two groups is called the **crystal field splitting energy,** and is designated by the symbol Δ:

$$\begin{array}{c} \overline{d_{z^2}}\ \overline{d_{x^2-y^2}} \quad (e_g) \\ \\ = \Delta \\ \\ \overline{d_{xy}}\ \overline{d_{xz}}\ \overline{d_{yz}} \quad (t_{2g}) \end{array}$$

Increasing energy

(b) Factors Influencing Δ. It was previously mentioned that the complex ions of transition metals with partially filled d orbitals are frequently colored. The Crystal Field theory suggests that color appears when, for example, in a typical octahedral complex, $Ti(H_2O)_6^{3+}$, the $3d$ electron is excited from the t_{2g} to the e_g energy level. In fact, the energy of the absorbed photon should equal the value of Δ. Studies of the absorption spectra of complex ions show that the value of Δ depends on the nature of the ligand. The splitting power for some of the more common ligands decreases in the order: $CN^- > NO_2^- > NH_3 > H_2O > OH^- > F^- > Cl^- > Br^- > I^-$. In terms of splitting power, we talk about strong and weak ligands. Thus, CN^- is a very *strong* ligand and, at the other end of the scale, I^- is a very *weak* ligand.

The greater the crystal field splitting energy, Δ, the larger is the excitation energy, ΔE. The effect of the splitting power of ligands on Δ, and the resulting effect on the wavelength of light absorbed by the complex ion is illustrated by comparing the following three colored Co(III) complex ions:

$Co(CN)_6{}^{3-}$	$Co(NH_3)_6{}^{3+}$	$Co(H_2O)_6{}^{3+}$
yellow	*yellow-orange*	*blue*
Wavelength of absorbed light is shortest	Wavelength of absorbed light is intermediate	Wavelength of absorbed light is longest
↓	↓	↓
ΔE is largest	ΔE is intermediate	ΔE is smallest
↓	↓	↓
Δ is largest	Δ is intermediate	Δ is smallest
↓	↓	↓
CN^- has strongest field splitting power	NH_3 has intermediate field splitting power	H_2O has weakest field splitting power

In applying this reasoning, one must be certain that there is no change in the geometry of the complex when the ligand is altered.

The cation also plays a role in establishing the value of Δ. To determine the nature of this role, it is imperative to compare only those cations with the same number of d electrons and the same geometry. Thus, the behavior toward the same ligand of Fe(II) and Co(III), which both have $6d$ electrons (d^6 ions), or V(II) and Cr(III), which are both d^3 ions, can be compared. It is observed that the crystal field splitting in $V(H_2O)_6{}^{2+}$ is less than in $Cr(H_2O)_6{}^{3+}$, a fact that can be interpreted in terms of the charge on the cation. The Cr^{3+} ion exerts a greater attraction for water molecules than does the V^{2+} ion, because of the greater positive charge. Hence, the water molecules approach the Cr(III) ion more closely than they approach the V(II) ion, and so exert a stronger crystal field effect on the d electrons of Cr(III).

Color is not the best criterion for comparing crystal field splitting energies, since a substance may be colored because of electronic excitations other than t_{2g} to e_g. It is thus necessary to determine the spectrum of the complex ion, making certain to select the proper absorption band for determining the value of Δ. It is also possible that the value of Δ is so small that radiation in the infrared region may cause excitation. In such cases, the complex ion would be colorless. Hence, lack of color in a complex ion of a frequently colored cation may be due to either a very large or very small value for the crystal field splitting energy.

(c) **Distribution of Electrons in the d Orbitals; Weak and Strong Crystal Field Complexes.** According to the Crystal Field theory, properties such as color, paramagnetism, stability, and geometry are greatly influenced by the manner in which the metal ion d electrons are distributed in the d orbitals. The distribution of electrons in an atom is influenced by two factors: (1) the tendency for electrons to resist pairing (Hund's rule), and (2) the tendency for electrons to occupy orbitals of lower energy before entering orbitals of higher energy. The factor that

TABLE 25.2 *Electronic Distribution in Strong and Weak Field Complexes*

No. of d electrons	Typical ion	Weak field (spin-free)	Strong field (spin-paired) t₂g	eg
d^1	Ti^{3+}	↑ _ _ _ _	↑ _ _	_ _
d^2	V^{3+}	↑ ↑ _ _ _	↑ ↑ _	_ _
d^3	Cr^{3+}, V^{2+}	↑ ↑ ↑ _ _	↑ ↑ ↑	_ _
d^4	Cr^{2+}	↑ ↑ ↑ ↑ _	↑↓ ↑ ↑	_ _
d^5	Fe^{3+}, Mn^{2+}	↑ ↑ ↑ ↑ ↑	↑↓ ↑↓ ↑	_ _
d^6	Fe^{2+}, Co^{3+}	↑↓ ↑ ↑ ↑ ↑	↑↓ ↑↓ ↑↓	_ _
d^7	Co^{2+}	↑↓ ↑↓ ↑ ↑ ↑	↑↓ ↑↓ ↑↓	↑ _
d^8	Ni^{2+}	↑↓ ↑↓ ↑↓ ↑ ↑	↑↓ ↑↓ ↑↓	↑ ↑
d^9	Cu^{2+}	↑↓ ↑↓ ↑↓ ↑↓ ↑	↑↓ ↑↓ ↑↓	↑↓ ↑

controls the electron distribution is determined by the strength of the field exerted by the ligand. A strong field causes appreciable splitting of the d orbitals, and the t_{2g} orbitals are completely paired before electrons enter the e_g orbitals. A complex with this type of electron distribution is called a **strong field (spin-paired) complex.** If the ligand exerts a weak crystal field effect there is little or no splitting, and the electrons fill all five d orbitals so as to minimize pairing of spins. The resulting aggregate is called a **weak field (spin-free) complex.** Table 25.2 shows the types of electronic arrangement for ions with differing numbers of d electrons. When there are 1, 2, 3, 8, and 9 d electrons there is no difference in the number of unpaired electrons in the weak and strong field complexes, so that magnetic behavior cannot be used to distinguish between the two kinds of complex. However, for the d^4, d^5, d^6, and d^7 electron states, there is a difference in the number of unpaired electrons and therefore in magnetic properties. We can now see how the Crystal Field theory explains the magnetic properties of $Fe(CN)_6^{3-}$ and FeF_6^{3-}; the CN^- ion engenders a strong field complex while the F^- ion gives a weak field complex.

25.8 GEOMETRICAL ISOMERISM

Geometrical isomerism is known to occur in complex ions. This discussion is restricted to square-planar complexes of the general formula MA_2B_2. The complex $Pt(NH_3)_2Cl_2$ exists as a *cis* form (Fig. 25.3a), and a *trans* form (Fig. 25.3b) having zero dipole moment.

Geometrical isomerism with respect to the central atom is *impossible* in tetrahedral complexes. The observation of geometrical isomers is therefore a way of deciding that a certain complex is square-planar rather than tetrahedral.

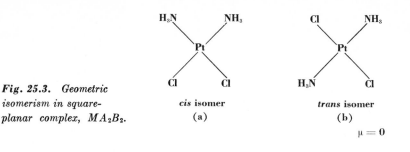

Fig. 25.3. *Geometric isomerism in square-planar complex, MA_2B_2.*

cis isomer
(a)

trans isomer
(b)

$\mu = 0$

Problems

1. Werner theory. A compound (A) has the analysis 22.0% Co, 39.8% Cl, 31.4% N, and 6.8% H. With $AgNO_3$, one mole of (A) gives three moles of AgCl. NH_4Cl is not produced when hydrochloric acid is added to (A). Write the structural formula and give the name for compound (A).

2. Nomenclature. Give a systematic name for (a) $Co(NH_3)_5ClCl_2$, (b) $Na_3Co(NO_2)_6$, (c) $K_2PtCl_4Br_2$, (d) $Ni(CO)_4$, (e) $K_2Fe(CN)_5NO$.

3. Complex formation. Indicate the number of d electrons remaining in the cation in (a) $Mn(CN)_6^{3-}$; (b) $Zn(NH_3)_4^{2+}$; (c) $Pt(NH_3)_2Br_4^0$; (d) ZnF_6^{2-}.

4. Valence bond theory. Give the shape of the ion and the electronic configuration of the central atom according to the Valence Bond theory (use *arrows* for cation electrons and *2* for ligand electrons) for (a) $Ag(NH_3)_2^+$; (b) $Ni(CN)_4^{2-}$, diamagnetic; (c) $NiBr_4^{2-}$, paramagnetic; (d) $Mn(CN)_6^{4-}$; (e) $CuCl_2Br_2^{2-}$, shows geometrical isomerism.

5. Crystal field theory. Draw the electronic configurations for the strong and weak field octahedral complexes of (a) Mn(III); (b) Ni(III).

6. Geometrical isomerism. Give the number of geometrical isomers of the square-planar complexes of (a) $Pt(NH_3)_2ClBr$; (b) $PtNH_3ClBrF^-$. Draw the structural formulas.

7. Crystal field splitting. $Mn(H_2O)_6^{3+}$ absorbs in the visible region at a shorter wavelength than does $Cr(H_2O)_6^{2+}$. Explain the significance of this finding in terms of the crystal field splitting energy and account for the difference in absorption.

8. Valence bond and crystal field theory. Give the electronic configuration of the central atom according to (a) Valence Bond theory, and (b) Crystal Field theory, for (*i*) $Co(NH_3)_6^{3+}$, diamagnetic; (*ii*) CoF_6^{3-}, paramagnetic; (*iii*) $Co(NH_3)_6^{2+}$.

Additional problems

9. Crystal field theory. Given the following standard oxidation potentials:

(1) $Co(H_2O)_6^{2+} \rightarrow Co(H_2O)_6^{3+} + e^-$ $\varepsilon° = -1.84$ volts

(2) $Co(NH_3)_6^{2+} \rightarrow Co(NH_3)_6^{3+} + e^-$ $\varepsilon° = -0.1$ volts

(3) $Co(CN)_6^{4-} \rightarrow Co(CN)_6^{3-} + e^-$ $\varepsilon° = +0.84$ volts

(a) Explain the significance of these $\mathcal{E}°$ values in terms of relative stabilities of the Co(II) and Co(III) states in these three complexes. (b) Offer an explanation in terms of the Crystal Field theory for the differences in the three $\mathcal{E}°$ values.

10. Werner theory. A compound with the *empirical* formula $Pt(II)Cl_2 \cdot 2NH_3$ (a) does not liberate NH_3 in the presence of HCl; (b) has a molar conductance corresponding to two ions; (c) gives no precipitate of AgCl with $AgNO_3$; (d) has a molecular weight of 600 g per mole. Write the formulas for two possible isomers of the compound and name them. What type of isomerism is exhibited?

11. Ligand strength. (a) Draw the MO structure for $:C{\equiv}N:^-$ and NO_2^-. (b) Do any other ligands in the series shown on page 678 have π bonds? (c) Draw a conclusion about the crystal field effect of ligands that possess π bonds. (d) About where would CO fit into the series?

12. Practical use of complexes. Explain the following phenomena in terms of complex formation, and give formula and name for the complex ion:

(a) In photography the fixing bath, $Na_2S_2O_3$, dissolves AgBr from the film.

(b) Gold is oxidized by O_2 only when NaCN is present.

(c) Platinum does not react with nitric acid, but reacts with aqua regia (3 parts HCl, 1 part $HONO_2$).

13. Crystal field theory. When two opposing (*trans*) ligands are removed from an octahedral complex, a square-planar complex results. Assume the ligands are removed from the z axis. In such a square-planar complex, for example $Ni(CN)_4^{2-}$, the d orbitals are split into four energy levels. Label the d orbitals in each level and account for the split.

14. Symmetry. Indicate the kind, number, and location of each symmetry element in (a) *cis*-$Pt(NH_3)_2Cl_2$; (b) *trans*-$Pt(NH_3)_2Cl_2$.

26

Reactions
of
covalent
bonds

▩▩▩▩▩

MOST CHEMICAL REACTIONS involve alterations in covalent bonds. The exceptions are the precipitation of insoluble ionic salts, and electron transfer between atoms and monatomic ions, for example,

$$Cu^{2+} + Zn \rightarrow Zn^{2+} + Cu$$

Even these reactions may involve a gain or loss of covalently bonded water molecules. There are myriad reactions of covalent bonds, but fortunately they can be grouped into a few broad classifications. These are decomposition, displacement or substitution, addition, elimination, and rearrangement. Addition and elimination reactions have been described (page 246).

26.1 DECOMPOSITION

Fragmentation of a covalent molecule into two or more smaller particles without the involvement of other reactants is called a **decomposition** reaction. Heat or radiation is generally used to effect the decomposition. Exposure to an energy source increases the vibration of the atoms in the molecule, and eventually causes the rupture of the weaker bonds. Bond cleavage can occur in either of two ways.

(a) *One of the atoms retains both electrons* (**heterolysis**):

$$A\!:\!\}B \rightarrow A\!: + \quad B$$

or

$$A \{ :B \rightarrow A \ + :B$$

as illustrated by

$$H_3N:B(CH_3)_3 \overset{heat}{\rightleftharpoons} H_3N: + B(CH_3)_3 \tag{a}$$

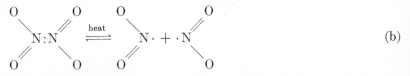

This reaction is the reverse of a Lewis acid-base reaction (page 451).

(b) *Each atom takes one electron* (**homolysis**):

$$A : B \rightarrow A\cdot + \cdot B$$

as illustrated by the decomposition of dinitrogen tetroxide,

$$\begin{array}{c}\text{O} \\ \diagdown \\ \end{array} N:N \begin{array}{c}\text{O}\\ \diagup\\ \end{array} \overset{heat}{\rightleftharpoons} \begin{array}{c}\text{O}\\ \diagdown\\ \end{array} N\cdot + \cdot N \begin{array}{c}\text{O}\\ \diagup\\ \end{array} \tag{b}$$

Reaction (b) leads to the formation of free radicals. Most free radicals are reactive species that rapidly undergo further reaction. Free radicals are frequently needed, especially in organic chemistry, to initiate reactions (page 695). Compounds with weak covalent bonds, such as the bond between less active metals and carbon, or the peroxide, —O—O— bond, are frequently used as free radical sources, as shown,

$$H_3C:Hg:CH_3 \overset{heat}{\longrightarrow} \cdot Hg\cdot + 2H_3C\cdot$$
dimethylmercury

$$H_3C:\overset{..}{\underset{:O:}{C}}—\overset{..}{\underset{..}{O}}:\overset{..}{\underset{..}{O}}—\overset{..}{\underset{:O:}{C}}:CH_3 \longrightarrow 2\left[H_3C \overset{..}{\underset{:O:}{C}} \overset{..}{O} \right] \rightarrow$$
acetyl peroxide
$$2\dot{H}_3C\cdot + 2O{=}C{=}O$$

To understand the course of these reactions (and those discussed later in the chapter), it is necessary to keep track of the assignment of electrons. To help in this "electron bookkeeping," the chemist frequently uses curved arrows to indicate the disposition of electrons, as shown above.

Decomposition can also involve more than one bond of the molecule, in which case it almost invariably is coincident with the formation of a new bond in a new molecule. For example:

(a) When phosphorus pentachloride is heated, it decomposes into the trichloride and chlorine,

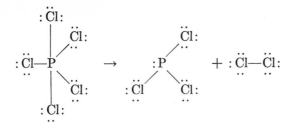

(b) When potassium chlorate is heated, it gives potassium chloride and oxygen,

$$2K^+ \left[\begin{matrix} :\ddot{O}: \\ :\ddot{O}\!-\!\overset{\displaystyle |}{\underset{\displaystyle}{Cl}}\!-\!\ddot{O}: \end{matrix} \right]^- \xrightarrow{\text{heat}} 2K^+Cl^- + 3O_2$$

potassium chlorate

as the result of a cleavage of the Cl—O bonds and formation of an O—O bond.

The hydrides of heavy atoms are usually unstable, and, on being heated, decompose into the element and hydrogen as shown for arsine, AsH_3,

$$:AsH_3 \xrightarrow{\text{heat}} \cdot\ddot{As}\cdot + 1\tfrac{1}{2}H_2$$

The decomposition of arsine, a very poisonous gas, is the essential step in the Marsh test, used to detect minute amounts of arsenic. The substance suspected of containing arsenic, for example the stomach contents of a murder victim, is heated with zinc and hydrochloric acid. This action reduces arsenic, in any of its higher oxidation states, to arsine. The arsine is burned and the arsenic is deposited on a cool, clean, white surface; the arsenic appears as a dark spot.

26.2 DISPLACEMENT OR SUBSTITUTION REACTIONS

In this frequently encountered type of reaction, one atom or group of atoms in the molecule is replaced by another atom or group of atoms,

$$X + A\!-\!Y \rightarrow X\!-\!A + Y$$

X is the **displacing** group, Y is the **leaving** group, and the displacement is said to occur on atom A. AY is frequently called the **substrate.** There are several modifications of this reaction, because of the variations in the electronic structure of X and the bonding state of A. We shall also see that there are differences in mechanism.

26.3 NUCLEOPHILIC DISPLACEMENT ON A σ-BONDED ATOM

In this type of displacement reaction, X has an unshared pair of electrons and atom A participates only in σ-bonding. X is a nucleophile (page 451), and so the reaction is called a **nucleophilic displacement.** The generalized equation is

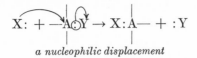

$$X: + \quad A\!-\!Y \rightarrow X:A\!- + :Y$$

a nucleophilic displacement

One of the best examples of a nucleophilic displacement is a Bronsted acid-base reaction, such as the ionization of hydrogen chloride in water,

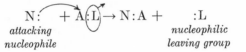

The features of this reaction are characteristic of all nucleophilic displacements. One nucleophile displaces another; the leaving group always departs from the attacked atom with the pair of electrons,

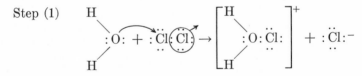

$$N: \quad + A:L \rightarrow N:A + \quad :L$$

attacking   *nucleophilic*
nucleophile   *leaving group*

Redox reactions involve a transfer of electrons. In many cases, this transfer of electrons occurs as a result of nucleophilic displacements. Consider the fairly simple auto-oxidation of chlorine in water to give hypochlorous and hydrochloric acids,

$$2H_2O + Cl_2 \rightarrow H_3O^+ + HOCl + Cl^-$$

oxidation number: 0 $+1$ -1

This reaction can be viewed as two nucleophilic displacements. In Step (1), water is the nucleophile which displaces Cl^- from a Cl atom of chlorine,

Step (1)

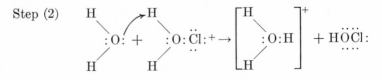

In the second step, water acting as a nucleophile attacks an H atom of H_2OCl^+, and hypochlorous acid becomes the leaving group,

Step (2) H   H   ⌈ H   ⌉+
         \   /   \ | \ |
      :O: +   :O:Cl:+ → | :O:H | + HOCl:
         /   / | / |
        H   H   ⌊ H   ⌋

The oxidation of iodide ion by chlorine can also be formulated as a two-step nucleophilic displacement:

$$:\ddot{I}:^- + :\ddot{C}l(\ddot{C}l:) \rightarrow :\ddot{I}:\ddot{C}l: + :\ddot{C}l:^-$$

$$:\ddot{I}:^- + :\ddot{I}(\ddot{C}l:) \rightarrow :\ddot{I}:\ddot{I}: + :\ddot{C}l:^-$$

$$2I^- + Cl_2 \rightarrow I_2 + 2Cl^-$$

Many redox reactions involving oxyanions and molecular oxides seem to involve a transfer of oxygen atoms as well as a transfer of electrons. A typical example is the oxidation of sulfite ion by chlorate ion,

$$SO_3^{2-} + ClO_3^- \rightarrow SO_4^{2-} + ClO_2^-$$

Although this equation is balanced, let us use the ion-electron method (page 367) to find the "half" equations:

(oxidation) $SO_3^{2-} + H_2O \rightarrow SO_4^{2-} + 2H^+ + 2e^-$
(reduction) $ClO_3^- + 2H^+ \rightarrow ClO_2^- + H_2O - 2e^-$

$$SO_3^{2-} + ClO_3^- \rightarrow SO_4^{2-} + ClO_2^-$$

It appears from the equation for the oxidation that the fourth oxygen atom needed to convert SO_3^{2-} to SO_4^{2-} comes from a water molecule. It also appears that in changing to ClO_2^-, the ClO_3^- ion loses its oxygen atom to two protons to form water. These changes occur when the reaction is carried out in a galvanic cell—that is, when the oxidation and reduction half-reactions are separated. But what happens when the reactants are mixed? To determine the fate of the various oxygen atoms, the chemist tags his materials with O^{18}, an isotope of oxygen with atomic weight of 18. When the reaction between $[SO_3{}^{16}]^{2-}$ and $[ClO_3{}^{16}]^-$ is carried out in H_2O^{18}, only an insignificant amount of O^{18} appears in the resulting sulfate ions. However, when $[ClO_3{}^{18}]^-$ is mixed with $[SO_3{}^{16}]^{2-}$ in H_2O^{16}, the resulting sulfate ion is enriched with O^{18}. These results indicate that the reaction proceeds mainly by direct transfer of an oxygen atom from chlorine to sulfur without the intervention of water:

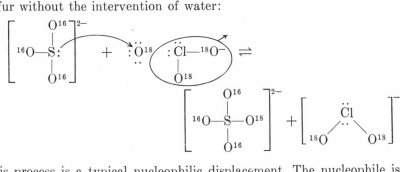

This process is a typical nucleophilic displacement. The nucleophile is SO_3^{2-}, attack occurs on an oxygen atom of the ClO_3^- ion, and the chlorite ion, ClO_2^-, is the leaving group. Thus, when the oxidant and reductant are mixed, we should not construe the partial equations as representing a mechanism for the redox reaction. As previously stated, these equations are often just atom- and electron-bookkeeping procedures.

Nucleophilic displacements on carbon are important in the synthesis of organic compounds. The thorough study of these reactions has helped to elucidate their mechanisms. The kinetics of the two most prevalent kinds of reaction have been described previously (page 621). The second order reaction, as typified by

$$H:\overset{..}{\underset{..}{O}}:^- + CH_3CH_2(Br:) \rightarrow CH_3CH_2:\overset{..}{O}H + :\overset{..}{\underset{..}{Br}}:^- \tag{1}$$

is termed the S_N2 reaction: S for substitution (displacement), N for nucleophilic, and 2 for bimolecular. It is believed that the S_N2 reaction proceeds by a concerted mechanism (page 206); *as the bond between the nucleophile and the carbon atom forms, the bond between the leaving group and the carbon atom breaks.* Since the attacking and leaving groups are both electron-rich, we should expect them to be as far away from each other as possible during the reaction. The transition state for this concerted process is shown on page 622. In the transition state, the carbon is weakly bonded to both OH and Br. The carbon atom in the transition state should not be considered as having five bonds, since it is only *partially* bonded to the Br and O atoms. As the oxygen atom bonds to carbon, it loses negative charge, and as the Br atom leaves the carbon atom, it acquires negative charge. Therefore, in the transition state, both the O and Br atoms have fractional negative charges.

The reaction between OH^- and C_2H_5Br is practically irreversible. This fact indicates an important aspect of nucleophilic displacements on carbon. *The reaction proceeds so that the stronger Brönsted base* (OH^-) *displaces the weaker Brönsted base* (Br^-). For this reason, in most S_N2 reactions on carbon that go to completion, the leaving groups are the extremely weak bases, such as I^-, Br^-, and Cl^-. These anions are referred to as "good leaving groups."

If hydrobromic acid, HBr, is added to ethyl alcohol, ethyl bromide is formed,

$$CH_3CH_2OH + HBr \rightarrow CH_3CH_2Br + HOH$$

It appears that this reaction is anomalous, in that a weak base, Br^-, has displaced a strong base, OH^-. This is not the case, however, because the Equation (1) above is irreversible; *bromide ion does not react with ethyl alcohol.* We must therefore assign a role to the H^+ which can be donated by the hydrobromic acid. Ethanol is a Bronsted base and reacts with hydrobromic acid,

$$CH_3CH_2:\overset{..}{O}H: +H(Br:) \rightleftharpoons \left[CH_3CH_2:\overset{H}{\underset{..}{O}}:H \right]^+ + :\overset{..}{\underset{..}{Br}}:^-$$

$$\text{base}_1 \qquad \text{acid}_2 \qquad \text{acid}_1 \qquad \text{base}_2$$

Now, when the Br⁻ attacks the carbon atom bonded to the oxygen, water, *a weak base*, is the leaving group,

$$\ddot{Br}:^- + \left[\begin{array}{c} H \\ | \\ H-C-\ddot{O}:H \\ / \\ CH_3 \end{array} \quad H \right]^+ \rightarrow \; :\ddot{O}:H + CH_3CH_2:\ddot{Br}:$$

Although Br⁻ is a somewhat weaker base than water, the reaction still goes mainly to form ethyl bromide. This is due to the fact that ethyl bromide is a liquid (b.p. 38.4°C) insoluble in water. As ethyl bromide forms, it "oils out" (page 305) and hence, in accord with the Le Châtelier principle, the reaction shifts to the right. Concentrated hydrobromic acid is used, and the resulting high concentration of bromide ion also favors the forward reaction. The concerted process is typical of many nucleophilic displacements. For example, the redox reactions which involve a transfer of oxygen atoms probably proceed by an S_N2-type mechanism.

The first order reaction, as typified by

$$(CH_3)_3C:\ddot{Br}: + \; :\ddot{O}:H^- \rightarrow (CH_3)_3C:\ddot{O}:H + \; :\ddot{Br}:^-$$

(page 621) is designated the S_N1 reaction: S for substitution, N for nucleophilic, and 1 for unimolecular. The S_N1 mechanism is typical of a second type of displacement reaction; *the leaving group is ejected first, and then combination with the displacing group occurs.* The addition of Ag⁺ enhances the rate of those S_N1 reactions in which halide ions are leaving groups. This observation is consistent with the proposed mechanism; the Ag⁺ ion facilitates the ionization step by forming AgBr,

$$(CH_3)_3C:Br + Ag^+ \rightarrow (CH_3)_3C^+ + Ag:Br$$
$$(CH_3)_3C^+ + 2H_2O \; \rightarrow (CH_3)_3COH + H_3O^+$$

26.5 NUCLEOPHILIC DISPLACEMENT ON ATOMS ABLE TO ACQUIRE MORE THAN AN OCTET OF ELECTRONS

Carbon tetrachloride does not react with water, sodium hydroxide, or Ag⁺; it does not undergo nucleophilic displacements by either the S_N1 or S_N2 pathway. In contrast to CCl_4, silicon tetrachloride, $SiCl_4$, reacts vigorously with water,

$$SiCl_4 + 4H_2O \rightarrow Si(OH)_4 + 4HCl$$
"silicic
acid"*

This sharp difference between the behavior of CCl_4 and $SiCl_4$ arises because silicon has d orbitals available for bonding, while carbon has none.

* Silicic acid, $Si(OH)_4$, is not a stable compound. It undergoes partial loss of water to give a gel-like form of silica hydrated by an indefinite number of water molecules, $SiO_2(H_2O)_x$.

Therefore a silicon atom can acquire more than eight "outer" electrons. Silicon tetrachloride acts as an electrophile and forms an octahedral complex (sp^3d^2) by bonding with two water molecules (ligands),

$$SiCl_4 + 2H—\overset{..}{\underset{..}{O}}—H \rightleftharpoons [SiCl_4(H_2O)_2]$$
$$\textit{intermediate}$$

The silicon atom re-establishes its octet of outer electrons by ejecting two Cl^- ions. Each of the coordinated water molecules loses a proton to the solvent,

$$[SiCl_4(H_2O)_2] + 2H_2O \rightarrow [SiCl_2(OH)_2] + 2Cl^- + 2H_3O^+$$
$$\textit{intermediate}$$

By repetition of these two steps, the final products are obtained,

$$[SiCl_2(OH)_2] + 4H_2O \rightarrow Si(OH)_4 + 2Cl^- + 2H_3O^+$$

This reaction typifies a third type of mechanism. *The displacing group bonds first to give an intermediate from which the leaving group is ejected.* This two-step combination-ejection mechanism prevails for the hydrolysis of the covalent halides of elements able to use d orbitals in bonding, some examples of which are phosphorus(III) trichloride, PCl_3, tin(IV) tetrachloride, $SnCl_4$, and arsenic(III) trichloride, $AsCl_3$.

26.6 NUCLEOPHILIC DISPLACEMENT ON π-BONDED ATOMS

When a nucleophile forms a bond with an atom that is participating in a π bond, it can be said to displace a pair of electrons to the other atom, as shown for a generalized case,

$$\overset{..}{B:} + X:\overset{..}{\underset{..}{Y}} \rightarrow B:X:\overset{..}{Y}$$

A typical example is the reaction between hydroxide ion and carbon dioxide to give the bicarbonate ion, $HOCO_2^-$,

$$H—\overset{..}{\underset{..}{O}}:^- + \overset{\overset{..}{O}:}{\underset{\overset{..}{O}:}{C}} \rightarrow \left[H—\overset{..}{\underset{..}{O}}:\overset{:\overset{..}{O}:}{\underset{:\overset{..}{O}:}{C}}\right]^- \quad or \quad \left[H—\overset{..}{O}:C\overset{\overset{..}{O}:}{\underset{\overset{..}{O}:}{\diagdown}}\right]^- \tag{2}$$

Notice that in the Lewis formula drawn for $HOCO_2^-$, it is the lone single-bonded oxygen atom that has a formal charge of -1. Actually, this oxygen atom and the double-bonded oxygen atom are indistinguishable, and the bicarbonate ion should be represented with an extended π bond.

For this reaction to be successful, there are two requirements for the $X=Y$ group which are interrelated.

(a) *The electron density of the π bond must be displaced towards atom Y, making atom X electron-deficient* and likely to react with the nucleophile. The reactivity, toward the nucleophile, of atom X is directly related to its electron deficiency.

(b) *Atom Y must be able to bear the increase in electron density resulting from the reaction.* Atom Y is usually an oxygen or nitrogen atom. Carbon dioxide meets both requirements. First, the carbon atom is much less electronegative than the oxygen atoms. The resulting polarity of the π bond is indicated by writing

$$\overset{\delta+ \quad \delta-}{O=C=O.}$$

Second, since the oxygen atom is very electronegative, it can bear the increase in electron density.

We might expect any carbonyl group, $>C=O$, to behave in a similar manner,

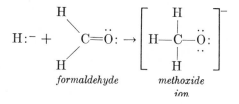

This type of reaction is observed but is reversible, and, depending on the nature of B : ⁻, the equilibrium may favor the reactants rather than the products. Thus at room temperature, *dilute* NaOH does not react noticeably with formaldehyde, $H_2C=O$. The reaction between CO_2 and OH^- (Equation 2) goes to completion because the resulting electron density in the product is dispersed over two oxygen atoms, thus making the product more stable than the reactants. However, in the unsuccessful reaction between OH^- and $H_2C=O$,

the electron density resides on only one O atom, and in this case the product is *less* stable than the reactants. This type of intermediate has a natural tendency to re-form the C=O group by ejecting the attacking base. However, if the attacking nucleophile is a very strong base, the reaction will go to completion. Thus, hydride ion, $H:^-$, reacts with formaldehyde to give the methoxide ion, the conjugate base of methanol,

formaldehyde   *methoxide ion*

In this case, the C=O bond does not re-form because H:⁻, a very powerful base, resists being ejected.

The importance of these two requirements is manifest when we consider the lack of reaction between OH⁻ and ethylene,

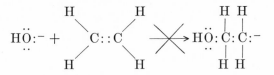

Ethylene does not meet the first requirement, since the electron density of the π bond is uniformly distributed; neither carbon atom is electron-deficient. In fact, because of the uniform electron density arising from the pair of electrons in the π bond, ethylene is itself a nucleophile (page 453), and tends to repel the approach of another nucleophile. Nor does ethylene meet the second requirement, since the increased electron density would have to be borne by carbon, an atom not nearly so electronegative as oxygen.

Let us now consider the reaction between equimolar amounts of nitrosyl chloride and OH⁻,

$$\text{HO}^- + \text{O}{=}\ddot{\text{N}}{-}\text{Cl} \rightarrow \text{O}{=}\ddot{\text{N}}{-}\text{OH} + \text{Cl}^-$$

nitrosyl   nitrous
chloride   acid

This is a typical nucleophilic displacement reaction. The nucleophile is OH⁻, the attacked atom is nitrogen, and the leaving group is Cl⁻. This reaction can be considered as occurring in two steps. The N=O group meets the two requirements for attack by a nucleophile; the N atom is less electronegative than the O atom, and oxygen can bear the resulting negative charge. Therefore, the first step is

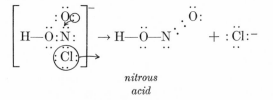

The resulting intermediate anion has a tendency to reform the N=O bond, and can do so by ejecting the weak base, Cl⁻. The second step is

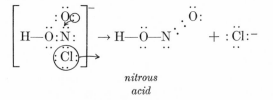

nitrous
acid

This type of combination-ejection process is expected to occur whenever a good leaving group, such as I, Br, or Cl, is attached to the X atom of an X=Y group that meets the requirements for nucleophilic attack. Compounds such as nitryl chloride, $ClNO_2$, and acetyl chloride, CH_3COCl, react vigorously, even with a weak nucleophile such as water,

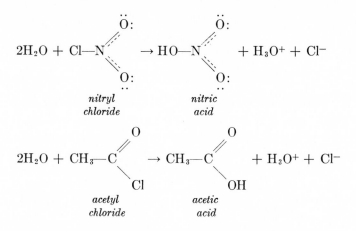

nitryl chloride → *nitric acid*

acetyl chloride → *acetic acid*

26.7 ELECTROPHILIC DISPLACEMENT ON σ-BONDED ATOMS

In an electrophilic displacement, an electrophile acts as the displacing group; the attacked atom must have an available pair of electrons, and the leaving group is an electrophile. The general equation for an *electrophilic displacement* is

$$E \quad + \quad :A:L \rightarrow E:A: + \quad L$$
electrophile   attacked   electrophile
               atom with
               available
               electrons

The solution of aluminum chloride, $AlCl_3$, in phosgene, Cl_2CO, exemplifies the reaction. Although neither substance, alone, conducts an electric current, the solution conducts. The presence of ions is explained by the following reaction:

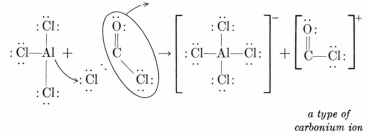

a type of carbonium ion

The electron-seeking $AlCl_3$ molecule forms a bond with the electron-rich Cl atom, and the leaving group is a carbonium ion, $[Cl—C=O]^+$.

The formation of chlorosulfonic acid from SO_3 and HCl can be pictured as an electrophilic displacement:

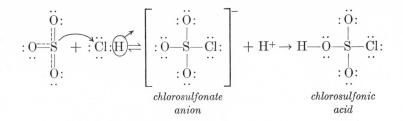

chlorosulfonate
anion

chlorosulfonic
acid

26.8 ELECTROPHILIC DISPLACEMENT ON π-BONDED ATOMS

A hydrogen atom of benzene can be replaced by a variety of atoms or groups. Three of the more common examples of such substitution reactions are bromination, chlorination, and nitration. The formula for the specific catalyst needed is shown above the arrow:

(*bromination*) $C_6H_6 + Br_2 \xrightarrow{FeBr_3} C_6H_5Br + HBr$
bromo-
benzene

(*chlorination*) $C_6H_6 + Cl_2 \xrightarrow{FeCl_3} C_6H_5Cl + HCl$
chloro-
benzene

(*nitration*) $C_6H_6 + HONO_2 \xrightarrow{(HO)_2SO_2} C_6H_5NO_2 + H_2O$
nitro-
benzene

Each of these reactions is an example of an electrophilic displacement on a π-bonded atom of the benzene ring.

The identification of the electrophiles is not self-evident from the previous equations. They are generated by the catalyst as a result of electrophilic displacements. The reaction for the formation of each electrophile, named below, is

(*bromination*)

$$:\!\overset{..}{\underset{..}{Br}}\!:\overset{..}{\underset{..}{Br}}\!:Fe \; + \; :\overset{..}{\underset{..}{Br}}\!:\overset{..}{\underset{..}{Br}}\!: \; \rightarrow \; \left[:\overset{..}{\underset{..}{Br}}\!:\overset{..}{\underset{..}{Br}}\!:Fe:\overset{..}{\underset{..}{Br}}\!: \right]^{-} \; + \; :\overset{..}{Br}^{+}$$
bromonium ion

(*chlorination*)

$$:\!\overset{..}{\underset{..}{Cl}}\!:\overset{..}{\underset{..}{Cl}}\!:Fe \; + \; :\overset{..}{\underset{..}{Cl}}\!:\overset{..}{\underset{..}{Cl}}\!: \; \rightarrow \; \left[:\overset{..}{\underset{..}{Cl}}\!:\overset{..}{\underset{..}{Cl}}\!:Fe:\overset{..}{\underset{..}{Cl}}\!: \right]^{-} \; + \; :\overset{..}{Cl}^{+}$$
chloronium ion

(*nitration*)
$$HONO_2 + 2(HO)_2SO_2 \rightarrow H_3O^+ + 2HOSO_3^- + \quad NO_2^+$$
nitronium
ion

(cf. page 451)

The extended cyclic π bond of benzene is electron-rich and therefore benzene is a nucleophile. The first step in the mechanism for the electrophilic displacement is assumed to be a combination of benzene and the electrophile, as shown for nitration,

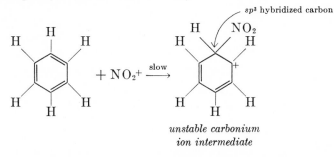

unstable carbonium
ion intermediate

The carbon to which the electrophile bonds becomes sp^3 hybridized, since it now has four σ bonds. As a result, the extended π bond is disrupted and most of the delocalization energy is lost. Therefore this step is endothermic and rate-controlling. The intermediate carbonium ion has a strong tendency to re-establish the stable cyclic π bond. This can be achieved if the NO_2^+ is ejected, thus reversing the first step, or if a proton is transferred to a base to give the substituted product, as shown,

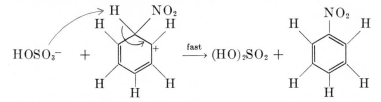

All electrophilic substitutions on benzene proceed through a similar two-step "combination-ejection" mechanism.

26.9 FREE RADICAL SUBSTITUTIONS

The displacing agent can be a free radical,

$$F\cdot + A{:}L \rightarrow F{:}A + \cdot L$$

in which case the group or atom displaced must also be a free radical. Such displacements usually occur as *intermediate* steps in reactions. This type of reaction is illustrated by the light-induced chlorination of methane,

$$CH_4 + Cl_2 \xrightarrow{\text{light}} CH_3Cl + HCl$$

In the dark, even at temperatures up to 200°C, a mixture of methane and chlorine does not react. In the presence of visible light, the reaction proceeds. We have seen (page 683) that light energy can cause bonds to rupture. Which bond breaks, the C—H bond of methane, or the Cl—Cl bond of chlorine? The answer: the bond with the lower bond energy. The Cl—Cl bond energy is $+58$ kcal/mole, and the C—H bond energy is

+101 kcal/mole. Hence, the Cl—Cl bond cleaves. In the first step, a molecule of chlorine absorbs a quantum of energy from the visible region and is cleaved into two chlorine atoms,

Step 1 $: \ddot{C}l : \ddot{C}l : \xrightarrow{\text{light}} 2 : \ddot{C}l \cdot$ $\Delta H = +58$ kcal/mole

In a second step, a chlorine atom collides with a molecule of methane and displaces a methyl free radical from a hydrogen atom,

Step 2 $: \ddot{C}l \cdot + H \cdot CH_3 \rightarrow : \ddot{C}l : H + \cdot CH_3$ $\Delta H = -4$ kcal/mole

As seen from the enthalpy of reaction, step 2 is a reasonably exothermic reaction. Notice that we have broken a C—H bond ($\Delta H = +99$ kcal/mole), and formed a new Cl—H bond ($\Delta H = -103$ kcal/mole). This change accounts for the over-all enthalpy of reaction of -4 kcal/mole. In a third step, the methyl free radical reacts with a molecule of Cl_2, producing the product, methyl chloride, and a $Cl \cdot$ atom,

Step 3 $H_3C \cdot + : \ddot{C}l : \ddot{C}l : \rightarrow \cdot \ddot{C}l : + H_3C : \ddot{C}l :$

$\Delta H = -20$ kcal/mole

The third step is also exothermic, since a Cl—Cl bond ($+58$ kcal/mole) is replaced by a C—Cl bond (-78 kcal/mole). The $Cl \cdot$ atom generated in Step 3 can react as shown in Step 2, and therefore this sequence of steps comprises a chain reaction (page 628). Chain reactions are characteristic of free radical processes. Although free radical chain reactions vary in detail, they all have certain fundamental characteristics in common. First, we find a **chain-initiating** step (Step 1), in which the absorbed energy generates the free radicals. Next, we find one or more **chain-propagating** steps (Steps 2 and 3). Since, in the example cited, the propagating steps are exothermic, once sufficient energy is supplied to create the initial free radical to start the chain, the reaction should proceed "under its own head of steam."

One might suppose that the decomposition of one molecule of Cl_2 should be sufficient to supply the $Cl \cdot$ atoms to maintain the self-propagating chain reaction. Such is rarely the case, since the chain can be terminated when two free radicals collide. The following are examples of **chain-terminating** steps:

$Cl \cdot + Cl \cdot \rightarrow Cl : Cl$
$Cl \cdot + \cdot CH_3 \rightarrow Cl : CH_3$
$H_3C \cdot + \cdot CH_3 \rightarrow H_3C : CH_3$
      ethane

Whenever two radicals combine to form a nonradical species, two chains are terminated. Fortunately, the collision of two free radicals is *rare* because the concentration of free radicals in the mixture at any given instant is extremely small. Nevertheless, such collisions occasionally occur and, consequently, a continuous source of energy is necessary for the reaction. Because of chain termination steps, most free radical reactions need a continuing supply of free radicals to reinitiate the chain processes. Chain termination is another characteristic feature of free radical reactions.

Yet another feature is the susceptibility to inhibition (page 625). If oxygen is present in the mixture of CH_4 and Cl_2, a period of time elapses (inhibition period) when no noticeable consumption of chlorine or methane occurs. Oxygen is an inhibitor; it is a free radical, and "traps" other free radicals, in this case $\cdot CH_3$,

$$H_3C\cdot \ + \ \cdot \ddot{O}\!:\!\ddot{O}\cdot \ \rightarrow H_3C\!:\!\ddot{O}\!-\!\ddot{O}\cdot$$
peroxymethyl
radical

The $H_3C\!-\!O\!-\!O\cdot$ radical is much less reactive than $CH_3\cdot$, and is incapable of participating in the chain propagating steps. Therefore, each molecule of O_2 present terminates a chain. All the oxygen must be consumed by conversion to $CH_3O\!-\!O\cdot$ before the chlorination of methane can proceed.

We can now summarize the features of a typical free radical chain process:

$$Cl_2 \xrightarrow{\text{light}} 2\ Cl\cdot \qquad\qquad \textit{chain initiation}$$

$$\left.\begin{array}{l} Cl\cdot \ + H\!:\!CH_3 \longrightarrow Cl\!:\!H \ + \ \cdot CH_3 \\ H_3C\cdot \ + Cl\!:\!Cl \ \longrightarrow H_3C\!:\!Cl + Cl\cdot \end{array}\right\} \quad \textit{chain propagation}$$

$$\left.\begin{array}{l} H_3C\cdot \ + \ \cdot Cl \ \longrightarrow H_3C\!:\!Cl \\ H_3C\cdot \ + \ \cdot CH_3 \ \longrightarrow H_3C\!:\!CH_3 \\ \quad Cl\cdot \ + \ \cdot Cl \ \longrightarrow Cl\!:\!Cl \end{array}\right\} \quad \textit{chain termination}$$

$$H_3C\cdot \ + O_2 \qquad \longrightarrow H_3C\!:\!O\!-\!O\cdot \qquad \textit{chain inhibition}$$

Inhibition is not an inherent feature of the chain since it requires the presence of an impurity.

26.10 REARRANGEMENTS

The conversion of one structural isomer into another is known as a **rearrangement reaction.** A famous rearrangement was discovered by Friedrich Wöhler in 1828, when he obtained urea by mixing silver cyanate and ammonium chloride in water. The expected product was a solution of ammonium cyanate,

$$Ag^+ + \ :\!\ddot{N}\!=\!C\!=\!\ddot{O}\!:^- + NH_4{}^+ + Cl^- \rightarrow$$
cyanate
ion

$$AgCl\!\downarrow \ + [NH_4{}^+ + \ :\!\ddot{N}\!=\!C\!=\!\ddot{O}\!:^-]^*$$
ammonium
cyanate

* The bracket in this case indicates instability.

When, however, the solution was evaporated to dryness, only urea was found; a rearrangement had occurred,

$$[NH_4^+ + N{=}C{=}O^-] \rightarrow H_2N{-}\overset{\displaystyle O}{\overset{\|}{C}}{-}NH_2$$
$$\textit{urea}$$

Prior to this experiment, it was believed that some "vital force" was essential for the synthesis of compounds by plants and animals. Urea, which is isolated from the urine of higher animals, was such a compound. Therefore, Wöhler's synthesis of urea from materials of mineral origin signaled the demise of the "Vital Force" theory. However, it took many years for the relevance of this synthesis to be recognized, and for the "Vital Force" theory to be abandoned.

Some rearrangements involve merely a movement of an H atom. For example, when PCl_3 is hydrolyzed, $P(OH)_3$ would be the expected product. However, this compound is not stable; an H atom migrates from an O atom to a P atom to give phosphorous acid

$$PCl_3 + 3H_2O \rightarrow 3HCl + [P(OH)_3]^*$$

$$[P(OH)_3] \rightarrow H{-}\underset{\diagdown OH}{\overset{\diagup OH}{P}}{-}O$$
$$\textit{phosphorous}$$
$$\textit{acid}$$

Problems

1. Decomposition. Ozone, O_3, absorbs ultraviolet radiation to give oxygen, O_2, and another fragment. (a) Write an equation using Lewis structures and symbols for the reaction. (b) Name the fragment. (c) Predict the fate of the fragment.

2. Decomposition. (a) Write a Lewis structure for dinitrogen tetrafluoride, N_2F_4. (b) When heated, N_2F_4 decomposes to NF_2, which is a fairly stable species. Write an equation for the reaction, using Lewis symbols.

3. Displacement reaction. (a) Classify the types of displacement reaction described in this chapter into three broad categories: (i) concerted, (ii) ejection followed by combination, and (iii) combination followed by ejection. (b) Account for the fact that nucleophilic displacements on a carbon atom with four σ bonds cannot proceed by a "combination-ejection" pathway. (c) Could nucleophilic displacement on boron in BCl_3 proceed by a combination-ejection pathway? Explain. (d) Give three bonding situations that permit a nucleophilic displacement to proceed by a "combination-ejection" mechanism.

4. Nucleophilic displacement. Complete the following equations, and indicate which represent redox reactions.

* The bracket in this case indicates instability.

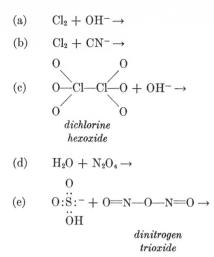

(a) $Cl_2 + OH^- \rightarrow$

(b) $Cl_2 + CN^- \rightarrow$

(c)   dichlorine hexoxide $+ OH^- \rightarrow$

(d) $H_2O + N_2O_4 \rightarrow$

(e)   dinitrogen trioxide

5. Electrophilic substitution on benzene. Write equations for all the steps for the bromination of benzene. (*Hint:* $FeBr_4^-$ is the base that removes the proton, giving $FeBr_3$ and HBr.)

6. Nucleophilic displacement on carbon. (a) Write equations for the reactions of ethyl bromide with each of the following nucleophiles: (*i*) HS^-; (*ii*) CN^-; (*iii*) H^-; (*iv*) CH_3^-; (*v*) CH_3NH_2.

7. Electrophilic substitution. Account for the facts that (a) nitrosyl chloride, Cl—N=O, and antimony pentachloride, $SbCl_5$, both of which are covalent molecules, react to form a salt; (b) a mixture of $(C_6H_5)_3C$—Cl and $AlCl_3$ conducts an electric current when dissolved in liquid SO_2, but not when dissolved in ethanol.

8. Free radical substitution. Account for the following observations: no reaction occurs when ethane and bromine are heated in the dark at 150°C; however, when a trace amount of $Pb(CH_3)_4$ is added under the same conditions, ethyl bromide and HBr are produced.

9. S_N1 vs. S_N2. Assume a substrate, RBr, may react by either the S_N1 or S_N2 mechanism. Which reaction path, S_N1 or S_N2, is favored when (a) the basicity of the attacking nucleophile is increased; (b) the polarity of the solvent is increased; (c) mercurous ion is added? Explain your answers.

Additional problems

10. Decomposition. (a) At 60–100°C the following reaction occurs:

$$H_3C-\underset{\underset{CH_3}{|}}{\overset{\overset{CN}{|}}{C}}:N=N:\underset{\underset{CH_3}{|}}{\overset{\overset{CN}{|}}{C}}-CH_3 \rightarrow 2H_3C-\underset{\underset{CH_3}{|}}{\overset{\overset{CN}{|}}{C}}\cdot \; + \; ?$$

What is the formula of the missing molecule? (b) When benzoyl peroxide

$$C_6H_5-\overset{\overset{O}{\|}}{C}-O-O-\overset{\overset{O}{\|}}{C}-C_6H_5$$

is heated, one of the products isolated is biphenyl, C_6H_5—C_6H_5. Suggest a mechanism for the formation of biphenyl. What gaseous substance is also produced?

11. Nucleophilic displacement. Suggest a mechanism by which (a) BCl_3 is converted to boric acid, $B(OH)_3$, by water; (b) F_2 reacts with OH^- in water to give F_2O; (c) hydrazine, H_2NNH_2, is obtained from NH_3 and Cl_2; (d) hypochlorous acid, $HOCl$, is obtained when NCl_3 reacts with water.

12. Free radical substitution. With the use of bond energies (page 116), account for the facts that (a) methane reacts with Cl_2 but not with I_2; (b) the reaction of $Cl\cdot$ with methane proceeds as shown on page 696 rather than as follows:

$$:\ddot{C}l\cdot + CH_4 \rightarrow CH_3Cl + H\cdot$$

13. Nucleophilic displacement (redox). Thiosulfate ion

$$\begin{array}{c} :\ddot{O}: \\ :\ddot{O}:\ddot{S}:\ddot{S}:^{2-} \\ :\ddot{O}: \end{array}$$

reduces I_2 to I^- and is oxidized to tetrathionate anion

$$\begin{array}{cc} :\ddot{O}: & :\ddot{O}: \\ :\ddot{O}:\ddot{S}:\ddot{S}:\ddot{S}:\ddot{S}:\ddot{O}:^{2-} \\ :\ddot{O}: & :\ddot{O}: \end{array}$$

Formulate this redox reaction as a two-step nucleophilic displacement reaction in which $S_2O_3{}^{2-}$ acts as the nucleophile.

14. S_N1. Account for the fact that $(CH_3)_3CBr$ reacts with OH^- in CH_3OH to give $(CH_3)_3COCH_3$ and not $(CH_3)_3COH$.

15. S_N2. (a) Account for the following observation: trimethylamine, $(CH_3)_3N$, $pK_b = 4.28$, reacts faster with $(CH_3)_2CHBr$ than does $(C_2H_5)_3N$, $pK_b = 3.25$. (b) Write equations for both reactions in part (a).

27

Metals
and
metallurgy

▬▬▬▬▬

27.1 THE PROPERTIES OF METALS

Some 80% of the elements are metallic. Metals are widely used for decorative and structural applications, and we are sufficiently familiar with their physical properties to distinguish them with confidence from nonmetallic substances after only casual observation.

The most conspicuous attribute of metals is **luster,** the bright, high-lighted appearance of a substance that reflects light well. A particularly lustrous metal is silver, a smooth surface of which throws back over 90% of the incident light; the adjective **silvery** is often used in the general sense of having high luster. Two metals, gold and copper, are colored, but none-theless lustrous from smooth surfaces. Metals dispersed in a spongy or finely divided form appear gray to black; this results from cumulated light losses occurring in many short-distance reflections from the irregular surface before the light leaves the metal. An example is **platinum black,** the precipitate obtained on the reduction of a dissolved platinum compound (such as potassium hexachloroplatinate(IV), K_2PtCl_6). Powdered aluminum and magnesium, on the other hand, retain much of their lustrous appearance. The reflectivity of ordinary glass mirrors is, of course, due largely to their metallic backing. In fact, the word **mirror** is often used to denote any smooth metal surface, especially a deposition from a chemical reaction. For example, shortly after tetraethyl lead is heated, a **lead mirror** deposits on the adjacent cool part of the tube. Many metal surfaces are overlaid with oxide or other coatings; their natural luster reappears after mechanical or chemical removal of such deposits.

Also noteworthy are the high electrical and thermal conductivities of metals. The periodic variation of these properties as a function of electronic structure is discussed in Section 27.4 and illustrated in Table 27.3. It is significant that electrical conductivity of metals is far greater than that of electrolytes (by a factor of as much as about 10^6), that it is exhibited to a high degree in both the solid and liquid states, that it is unaccompanied by detectable chemical change, and that it increases with *decrease* in temperature. In all instances of metallic conduction, it is known that the charged particles carrying the current are electrons. Electrons play a central role, too, in the conduction of heat by metals.

The densities of metals vary over a wide range, from 0.53 g/ml for lithium at 20°C to 22.5 g/ml for osmium at the same temperature. No other kinds of substance have densities as great as those of the heavy metals. The value for granite rock, for example, is only about 3 g/ml, for concrete 2 g/ml. Typical coordination numbers of atoms in metals are 8 or 12 (the maximum possible for spheres of identical size). It is this close packing that accounts in large measure for high metallic densities.

Metals can remain contiguous under severe conditions of deformation. A stick of light metal, such as sodium, may be extruded into a wire by a simple hand press; heavier metals may be fabricated into sheets, foils, or other forms by suitable tools and application of force. The ability of a solid to be flattened is called **malleability**; the ability to be drawn into a wire is called **ductility.** *What is unusual in metals is that crystalline structure is preserved under such stresses and strains.*

Alloys are mixtures of metals, with or without definite composition, sometimes containing a small proportion of a nonmetallic component. The physical properties of alloys are metallic, and alloys are therefore not superficially distinguishable from pure metals. This close resemblance persists even when the alloy is an intermetallic compound of definite composition (such as Cu_2Mg, Cr_3Os, Fe_5Zn_2), in sharp contradistinction to compounds of metals with nonmetals (such as NaCl), which lack metallic character. The physical nature of the intermetallic compounds implies the existence of a chemical bond quite different in kind from the ionic or covalent linkages discussed in previous chapters. The physical similarity of intermetallic compounds to the metallic elements implies that the same type of bond exists in both classes of substances.

27.2 THE METALLIC BOND; EARLY IDEAS OF THE "ELECTRON GAS"

It has long been recognized that the nature of the metallic bond is related in some way to the "free" state of electrons in metals. If these electrons are the media for the conduction of heat and electricity, if they are the vehicles that absorb and re-emit energy in reflection, they must therefore be the key ingredient that imparts such unique attributes to the bonds between atoms in metals and alloys. Early concepts indeed referred to a pseudo-ionic compound in which the anions are electrons (a "metallic electride"), or an array of cations dispersed in an "electronic cement" or "sea of electrons," or "electron gas."

If the "free" electrons that endow metals with their characteristic properties were literally gas-like, their energies would be distributed in the manner predicted by classical kinetic theory (Fig. 23.3, page 611). Electrons whose energies are so distributed would be able to absorb heat by being excited to higher energy levels; this capacity for heat absorption would be a property of all the "gas-like" electrons and, as a result, would endow metals with specific heats substantially greater than those of nonmetals. No such differences are found; metals do not have high specific heats. This means that the electrons in metals do not all have the capacity to be promoted to nearby vacant higher energy levels. In 1928, Arnold Sommerfeld postulated that the "electron gas" must be in a quantized arrangement in which the low-energy levels are almost fully occupied. These low-level electrons cannot absorb energy because the energy levels to which they could reasonably be expected to be promoted are all filled; there are no nearby "vacancies" for the electrons to occupy. As a result, the low-energy electrons remain at their low energy levels. This paucity of opportunities for energy-absorbing transitions accounts for the fact that the specific heats of metals are small.

27.3 THE BAND THEORY OF METALS

Ideas concerning the metallic bond were expanded by Felix Bloch in 1928 and later by Léon Brillouin and others, and have developed into what is now known as the **band theory of solids.** To understand what may constitute an electron band, and how such bands are involved in metallic bonding, it will be helpful to consider the following points.

(a) Metals typically crystallize in lattices of high coordination number. Lithium, $1s^2, 2s^1$, for example, has only 3 electrons per atom, but exists as a body-centered cubic lattice with coordination number 8. It is clear that no assignment of valence electrons to metallic bonding can account for such a high coordination number, unless it is assumed that the valence electrons are delocalized.

(b) The combination of two like atomic orbitals forms two molecular orbitals, one more stable, the other less stable, than the original atomic orbital (page 260). In general, x atomic orbitals, when they combine, yield x molecular orbitals.

(c) In metals, where many atoms may exist together so closely packed in a crystal lattice that electron delocalization occurs, the number of molecular orbitals will depend on the number of atoms in the lattice:

$$N \text{ atoms with } 1 \frac{\text{atomic orbital}}{\text{atom}} \text{ yield } N \text{ molecular orbitals}$$

$$N \text{ atoms with } x \frac{\text{atomic orbitals}}{\text{atom}} \text{ yield } Nx \text{ molecular orbitals}$$

Consider these relationships in the specific case of the lightest metal, lithium. Figure 27.1 shows that, as the number of atoms in a crystal of metallic lithium increases, the number of molecular orbitals increases and the energy difference between successive energy levels decreases. The smallest visible piece of lithium contains about 10^{19} atoms; for such a large

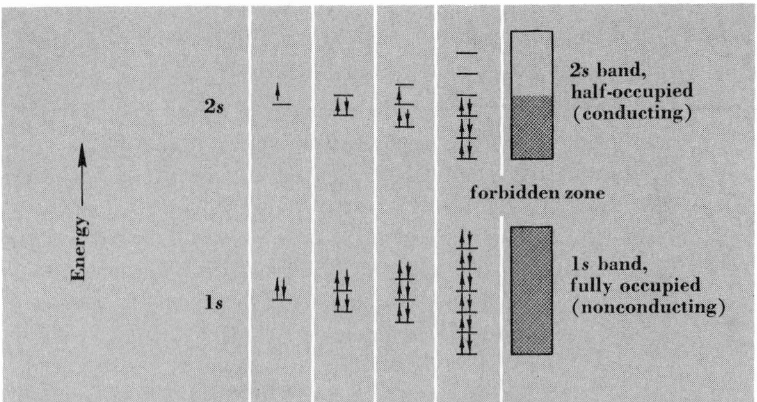

Energy →

2s   ↑   ↑↓   ↑↓   ↑↓↓ ... 2s band, half-occupied (conducting)

forbidden zone

1s   ↑↓   ↑↓   ↑↓   ↑↓ ... 1s band, fully occupied (nonconducting)

Number of atoms	1	2	3	6	N
Number of atomic orbitals if atoms were isolated	2	4	6	12	2N
Number of molecular orbitals in bonded atoms	2	4	6	12	2N
Number of electrons	3	6	9	18	3N

Fig. 27.1. *Electron bands in metallic lithium.*

number the energy difference between successive levels is so small that the levels are continuous; the group of closely associated energy levels, taken together, is called an **electron band.** In lithium, one of these bands, originating from the 1s atomic orbital, is fully occupied; the other, originating from the 2s atomic orbital, is only half-occupied. As we shall see, *metals are characterized by incompletely filled electron bands.* The energy gap between the two bands is so large that it effectively deters promotion of electrons from the lower to the higher band. Such energy gaps have come to be called **"forbidden zones."**

Let us next consider the distribution of energy bands involving both s and p orbitals. The maximum number of electrons per band will be

Energy level →

2p   maximum 6 electrons per subshell $\times$ N atoms per crystal $=$ maximum 6N electrons per band

2s   maximum 2 electrons per subshell $\times$ N atoms per crystal $=$ maximum 2N electrons per band

1s   maximum 2 electrons per subshell $\times$ N atoms per crystal $=$ maximum 2N electrons per band

Thus, for sodium (Na, $1s^2,2s^2,2p^6,3s^1$) the electron bands are $1s^{2N},2s^{2N}$, $2p^{6N},3s^N$. The $3s$ band, having a maximum capacity of $2N$ electrons, is only half-filled; this is the conduction band of sodium.

For magnesium (Mg, $1s^2,2s^2,2p^6,3s^2$), the electron bands are $1s^{2N},2s^{2N}$, $2p^{6N},3s^{2N}$. This completely filled band distribution appears to predict that magnesium should not be metallic. This apparent contradiction of fact is explained as follows. The relative energies of successive bands depend on internuclear distances. In metals, which are typified by close packing and relatively small internuclear distances, the adjacent bands may overlap. In the case of magnesium, the $3s$ and $3p$ bands overlap, that is, there is no "forbidden" energy zone between them, and promotion of electrons from the $3s$ to the empty $3p$ band occurs readily.

27.4 METALLIC PROPERTIES IN TERMS OF THE BAND THEORY

Let us now consider in more detail how an incompletely filled electron band engenders metallic character. In a completely filled band, each orbital is filled with two electrons of paired spins. When an external electric field is applied, the displacement of electrons in the field is equal in all directions, and no net current flows. In an incompletely filled band, however, the effect of the applied potential is to promote the electrons flowing in the direction of the field to higher unoccupied energy levels within the band; these electrons account for a net flow of current and the substance is a metallic conductor. A rise in temperature promotes vibration of the atoms in the crystal lattice; such vibrations interfere with the movement of electrons. Electrical conductivity of metals therefore *decreases* as the temperature increases.

The labile electrons of the conduction bands can also absorb thermal energy; the ready transport of such energy by these electrons accounts for the high thermal conductivity of metals.

The absorption and re-emission of photons of radiant energy by the labile electrons accounts for the high reflectivity of metals.

The destruction of the metallic lattice by mechanical stresses is rendered difficult by the fact that bonds can be readily broken and reformed by the promotion of electrons in the conduction bands to higher unoccupied levels by mechanical energy and by subsequent return of the electrons to their original levels. In the process, lattice structure may be altered, but yet remains contiguous, since the bonding electrons are not localized with respect to any particular atoms. This picture is in accord with the previously described ductility and malleability of metals.

It is possible to draw an analogy between delocalization of bonding electrons in a metallic crystal and in a small molecule, such as benzene, that exhibits extended π overlap. The aptness of the analogy is evidenced by the fact that an indefinitely extended benzene-like structure (graphite) conducts electricity and is thus partly metallic in nature (Fig. 10.1, page 251).

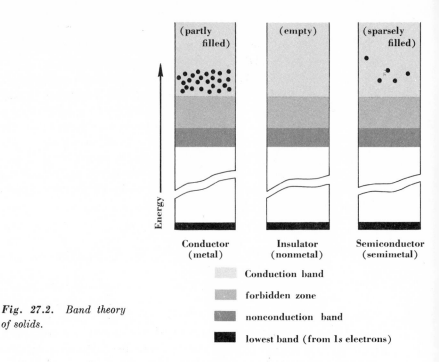

Fig. 27.2. Band theory
of solids.

(partly filled)	(empty)	(sparsely filled)
Conductor (metal)	Insulator (nonmetal)	Semiconductor (semimetal)

Conduction band

forbidden zone

nonconduction band

lowest band (from 1s electrons)

27.5 INSULATORS AND SEMICONDUCTORS

In **insulators,** the "conduction band" is empty. The forbidden zone below the conduction band represents a large energy barrier, and promotion of electrons to the conduction band normally does not occur. The electrical conductivity of a good insulator may be as small as about 10^{-24} times that of silver. For conduction to occur, the energy that must be supplied is so large that it may be accompanied by chemical or mechanical disruption; this is the phenomenon of **dielectric breakdown.**

In **semiconductors** (also called **semimetals** or **metalloids**), the conduction band is populated by electrons that are occasionally promoted to it by excitation from lower bands. The forbidden zone is narrower than in the case of insulators, and therefore constitutes less of a barrier to such promotion. Such substances show meager electrical conductivity. A rise in temperature favors excitations to the conduction band; electrical conductivity of semiconductors therefore *increases* as the temperature increases. Figure 27.2 illustrates, schematically, the arrangement of bands and forbidden zones in conductors (metals), insulators (nonmetals), and semiconductors.

27.6 METALLIC VALENCE

The considerations discussed above imply that metals are endowed with their unique properties, in the main, by a relatively small fraction of their total complement of extranuclear electrons. Let us take up the problem of how many electrons of each metal atom are actually involved in metallic bonding. This number may be called the **metallic valence.** Consider, for example, the element potassium, which has an ionic valence of 1 (in KCl) and a metallic coordination number (in the body-centered cube (page 41) in which it crystallizes) of 8. What number should be assigned to potassium as its metallic valence? If we examine the metallic atomic radii (Table 27.1) of potassium and its succeeding elements in the Fourth Period, we find a steady diminution progressing as far as chromium. Conversely, the melting points and hardness of these elements increase more or less regularly from K to Cr. These progressions are arrested in the span between chromium and nickel, and then reversed as one continues past nickel to the right in the Fourth Period. Since compactness (small radius), hardness, and high melting point are all associated with metallicity, it is appropriate to relate these changes in metallic character in some way to the stepwise increase of atomic number. The relationship in the interval between K and Cr is simple enough if we assign all the $3d$ and $4s$ electrons to metallic valence. These valences will then be K = 1, Ca = 2, Sc = 3, Ti = 4, V = 5, and Cr = 6. We should then have to explore two questions. (1) How do we explain the fact that the coordination numbers that the metals exhibit are larger than the metallic valences, and (2) how do we account for the changes in the progression of some metallic properties after Cr?

The potassium atom, with but one valence electron, is linked to 8 nearest neighbors in its crystal lattice, and this arrangement is continuous throughout the body of the crystal. Every valence electron therefore is associated with all the potassium atoms that are linked to each other, not

TABLE 27.1 *Properties of Metals of the Fourth Period*

Metal	Metallic atomic radius (A)		Melting point (°C)		Hardness (Mohs' scale: talc = 1, diamond = 10)	
K, $4s^1$	2.35	↓	63	↓	0.5	↓
Ca, $4s^2$	1.97		850		1.5	
Sc, $3d^1$, $4s^2$	1.62	*steadily decreasing*	1423	*increasing*	—	*increasing*
Ti, $3d^2$, $4s^2$	1.47		1677		—	
V, $3d^3$, $4s^2$	1.34		1917		—	
Cr, $3d^5$, $4s^1$	1.27		1900		9.0	
Mn, $3d^5$, $4s^2$	1.26		1244		5.0	
Fe, $3d^6$, $4s^2$	1.26	*approximately constant*	1539	*irregularly decreasing*	4–5	*decreasing*
Co, $3d^7$, $4s^2$	1.25		1495		—	
Ni, $3d^8$, $4s^2$	1.24		1455		—	
Cu, $3d^{10}$, $4s^1$	1.28	*increasing*	1083		2.5–3	
Zn, $3d^{10}$, $4s^2$	1.38		420		2.5	

with any one particular potassium atom. The valence electrons are then said to be *delocalized*. In this indefinitely extensive wave overlap, the electrons are distributed in a series of distinct molecular orbitals, each orbital accommodating two electrons, as discussed in the preceding sections on band theory. This delocalization produces a lowering of energy and consequent stabilization of the metallic crystal. The metallic valence of 6 assigned to Cr corresponds to the total number of electrons outside the argon core and to the highest oxidation state exhibited by Cr (as in chromates, CrO_4^{2-}, and dichromate, $Cr_2O_7^{2-}$). As the atomic number continues to increase in this series, the orbitals available for them necessarily become filled with nonbonding pairs of electrons. The maximum number of orbitals that can be singly occupied by valence electrons then progressively diminishes. This diminution is associated with the progressive loss of some attributes of metallic character.

Relationships between electronic structure and metallic character should not be pursued too closely, however. Metallic character is not a single property, but a composite; some elements are more "metallic" in some ways, less so in others. Sodium, for example, is a powerful chemical reducing agent, and is lustrous and ductile. Silver is a much poorer reducing agent than sodium, but is a better conductor of heat and electricity. Metals like chromium, manganese, and iron are not so lustrous or such good conductors of heat or electricity as sodium or silver, but are harder, denser, and stronger. No one electronic configuration, therefore, corresponds to the most pronounced over-all metallic character.

27.7 **PERIODICITY OF HEATS OF FUSION AND VAPORIZATION OF METALS AND NONMETALS**

Some insight into the nature and periodic variations of the bonding forces, metallic and nonmetallic, among like atoms can be gained by examination of the heats of fusion and vaporization of the elements. The heat of fusion (page 50) may be considered to be the energy (kcal/g-atom) required to disrupt the bonding in the crystal structure and change it to the bonding in the liquid structure. The heat of vaporization (same units) is the energy required to disrupt completely the bonding in the liquid structure. The periodic variations in these values are shown in Table 27.2 in the following manner: each rectangle has the same shape (height:width = 4:1); its area is proportional to the magnitude of the property represented. The outer rectangle denotes heat of vaporization; the inner rectangle denotes heat of fusion. An approximation of the *relative* values may be obtained by measuring the height of the rectangle in mm and substituting this quantity in one of the simple formulas shown in the key that appears in the table. The following observations and discussions refer to Table 27.2:

(a) *For all elements,* $\Delta H_{vap} \gg \Delta H_{fus}$. This means that there is a much greater difference in energy between liquid and vapor states of the elements than between liquid and solid states.

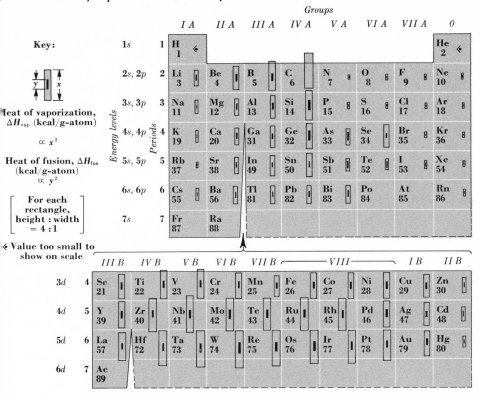

Key:

Heat of vaporization, ΔH_{vap} (kcal/g-atom) $\propto x^2$

Heat of fusion, ΔH_{fus} (kcal/g-atom) $\propto y^2$

For each rectangle, height : width = 4 : 1

◄ Value too small to show on scale

(b) *In Periods 2 and 3, both ΔH_{vap} and ΔH_{fus} increase to a high maximum in Group IV A, then drop very sharply.* The increased values from Li → Be and from Na → Mg → Al represent an increase in the strength of metallic bonding. In these sequences, the atoms are becoming smaller and denser and richer in bonding electrons. The very sharp increases Be → B → C and Al → Si are caused by a change to a network covalent bond structure, which must be destroyed partially in fusion and completely in vaporization. The low values for the Group VA and VIA elements are accounted for by the existence of molecular arrangements in the solid state (for example, N_2, S_8, P_4) that are preserved in the liquid and gaseous states. In these cases, fusion and vaporization disrupt only the intermolecular forces, and do not break the strong covalent bonds. Molecular arrangements are possible for these elements because they require fewer than 4 covalent bonds for octet completion; such electronic requirements can be met by single or multiple bonding or by cyclic structures.

(c) *Both ΔH_{fus} and ΔH_{vap} are higher for transition metals than for representative metals. Maxima are reached in Group VB or VIB.* The increasing number of *unpaired d* electrons strengthens the metallic bond and makes it more difficult to disrupt the aggregated structure of the metal by fusion or vaporization. Maximum unpairing, however, which is reached in Group VIIB (d^5 structures) imparts added stability to the atom (Chapter 8), and *electrons are less available for bonding* than would otherwise be expected. The stabilizing effect of the half-filled d sub-level, moreover, decreases with *increasing* period number. The over-all results are the maxima shown in Table 27.2 (V, Nb, W), and the abnormally low ΔH values for the lightest d^5 transition metal (Mn).

(d) $\Delta H_{vap}/\Delta H_{fus}$ *is generally greater for metals than for nonmetals.* When metallic solids melt, they preserve much of their metallic character; when they vaporize, metallic character is lost. Hence the energy involved in fusion does not greatly change the type of bonding and is therefore relatively small.

(e) ΔH_{vap} *and* ΔH_{fus} *of Group IB elements are much greater than for Group IIB elements.* Transition metals are typified by the participation of d orbitals in metallic bonding. Consequently, the metallic bond is stronger in transition than in representative elements. The ΔH_{vap} and ΔH_{fus} of Cu, Ag, and Au are large enough to suggest that, despite the assignment of a filled d^{10} sublevel to these elements, their d orbitals do participate in metallic bonding. The coinage metals can therefore be considered to be transitional; by contrast, the IIB metals, in this regard, are representative.

27.8 **PERIODICITY OF ELECTRICAL AND THERMAL CONDUCTIVITIES OF METALS AND NONMETALS**

The electrical and thermal conductivities* of the elements range very widely in value. Both properties are related in some way to the mobility of electrons in the aggregated forms of the elements, and an examination of the periodic variations in these properties may therefore yield additional understanding of bonding among like atoms. Periodic variations are shown in Table 27.3; the dark rectangles denote thermal conductivity; the light rectangles denote electrical conductivity. The following observations refer to Table 27.3:

(a) *There is a high degree of correlation between electrical and thermal conductivities.* Both properties depend on the degree to which electrons are delocalized.

(b) *Electrical and thermal conductivities of metals are much higher than those of nonmetals.* Metals are substances in which bonding electrons are delocalized, and are available for transmission of charge or energy. High

---

* Electrical conductivity (specific conductance, page 379) is the reciprocal of the electrical resistivity (specific resistance), which is the electrical resistance per cm of length of a conductor of 1 cm² cross-sectional area. The units of resistivity are ohm cm. Thermal conductivity is the amount of heat that will pass per second through 1 cm of length of a substance of 1 cm² cross-sectional area, when the temperature gradient is 1 degree per cm; the units are cal/cm deg sec.

TABLE 27.3 *Electrical and Thermal Conductivities of the Elements*

Key:

Thermal conductivity (25°C) (cal/cm deg sec) $\propto x^2$

Electrical conductivity ohm^{-1} cm^{-1} (0–20°C) $\propto y^2$

[for each rectangle, height : width = 4 : 1]

< Value too small to show on scale

g Data inappropriate because element is gaseous at these temperatures

Energy levels / Periods

	I A	II A	III A	IV A	V A	VI A	VII A	0
1s — 1	H g 1							He g 2
2s, 2p — 2	Li 3	Be 4	B < 5	C 6	N g 7	O g 8	F g 9	Ne g 10
3s, 3p — 3	Na 11	Mg 12	Al 13	Si 14	P 15	S 16	Cl g 17	Ar g 18
4s, 4p — 4	K 19	Ca 20	Ga 31	Ge 32	As 33	Se 34	Br < 35	Kr g 36
5s, 5p — 5	Rb 37	Sr 38	In 49	Sn 50	Sb 51	Te 52	I < 53	Xe g 54
6s, 6p — 6	Cs 55	Ba 56	Tl 81	Pb 82	Bi 83	Po 84	At 85	Rn 86
7s — 7	Fr 87	Ra 88						

	III B	IV B	V B	VI B	VII B	— VIII —			I B	II B
3d — 4	Sc 21	Ti 22	V 23	Cr 24	Mn 25	Fe 26	Co 27	Ni 28	Cu 29	Zn 30
4d — 5	Y 39	Zr 40	Nb 41	Mo 42	Tc 43	Ru 44	Rh 45	Pd 46	Ag 47	Cd 48
5d — 6	La 57	Hf 72	Ta 73	W 74	Re 75	Os 76	Ir 77	Pt 78	Au 79	Hg 80
6d — 7	Ac 89									

electrical and thermal conductivities are therefore an integral part of metallic character.

(c) *The "coinage" metals Cu, Ag, and Au have very high electrical and thermal conductivities. Lesser maxima are noted in Group VIB and in the middle of Group VIII.* Conductivity is related to the availability of electrons for transfer of charge or energy through the matter. Transition metals that have unpaired *s* electrons are very highly conducting. The occurrence of such single *s* electrons is favored by a filled *d* level (as in Cu, Ag, and Au) and, to a lesser extent, by a half-filled *d* level (as in Cr, Mo, and perhaps W). Note also that these electronic effects of unpaired *s* electrons in transition metals differ from those in the representative alkali metals, which are characterized by especially low ionization potentials and high chemical reactivity. Reactivity, but not conductivity, is related to the formation of electronic structures like those of the noble gases. Such configurations are achieved by Na$^+$, but not by Cu$^+$. Obviously, the electronic requirements for conductivity and for reactivity are quite different.

Elemental substances with different properties can be formed by variation of bond types among the same atoms. This phenomenon is called **allotropy.** When allotropic forms differ from each other in chemical bonding, they are said to be **primary modifications.** An allotropic difference in the mode of molecular aggregation, or in crystal habit, is called a **secondary modification;** such differences, which do not represent different molecular species, will not be considered here.

Primary allotropic modifications exist in C, O, P, S, As, Se, Sn, Sb, and Te. Carbon occurs as diamond (Fig. 9.3, page 225) and as graphite (Fig. 10.1, page 251). Both forms are very unreactive; diamond is extremely hard, while graphite is soft in consequence of the ease of layer slippage. At ordinary temperatures and pressures, graphite is the lower energy (more stable) form by about 0.5 kcal/g-atom. Graphite conducts heat and electricity fairly well, and has an appearance that suggests metallic luster.

The element oxygen exists as two gaseous forms: oxygen, O_2, and the much less stable ozone, O_3. Oxygen is light blue in the liquid state, is paramagnetic, and has two unpaired electrons per molecule. Ozone is dark blue in the liquid state, and spontaneously decomposes to oxygen. The bond angle in ozone is 127°.

Phosphorus occurs as tetrahedral P_4 molecules (phosphorus vapor, and the "white" solid form), and as two forms consisting of large molecular networks: black phosphorus and red (or violet) phosphorus. The black form is a layer lattice that shows some metallic properties (luster, conductivity of heat and electricity); the red form lacks these attributes.

Sulfur exists as ringed molecules (S_8, in liquid sulfur below about 160°C and in the rhombic and monoclinic crystal forms), as long chains ("plastic sulfur" and the liquid form $S\mu$), and as short chains of various lengths (S_6, S_4, and S_2 in the gaseous state).

Arsenic, selenium, tin, antimony, and tellurium all exist in more or less distinctly differentiated metallic and nonmetallic modifications (Table 27.4).

What generalizations can be made about the place of allotropy in the periodic classification of the elements? Oxygen is unique in exhibiting allotropy of covalently bound forms of low molecular weight. Sulfur, like oxygen, shows allotropy of covalent modifications; unlike oxygen, it can exist as an extended molecular network. Oxygen and sulfur are the most electronegative of the elements that exist in primary allotropic modifications; in consequence, neither element shows a tendency to exist in a metallic form. It is interesting to note that nitrogen, with its readiness to form multiple bonds, exists only as the stable species N_2 under ordinary conditions. In all the other cases cited, the allotropic elements occur both as distinctly nonmetallic and as more or less metallic forms. The drive toward delocalization of electrons by assumption of metallic character is evidenced even by carbon.

TABLE **27.4** *Allotropes of As, Se, Sn, Sb, Te*

| | *Allotropes* | |
Element	*Metallic or metalloidal*	*Nonmetallic*
As	Gray, metallic luster (density 5.73 g/cm³)	"Yellow arsenic," waxy (density 3.7 g/cm³)
Se	Gray, semiconductor of electricity	Red, amorphous or "vitreous" selenium
Sn	"White tin," metallic luster, conducts heat and electricity well, is soft and ductile	"Gray tin," diamond structure
Sb	Metallic luster, good conductor of heat and electricity; hard, brittle	"Yellow antimony"; also exists as a vitreous modification known as "explosive antimony"
Te	Metallic luster, poor semiconductor of electricity	Amorphous form

In summary, it may be generalized that (a) the occurrence of primary allotropy is limited to the elements in Periods 2, 3, 4, and 5 of Groups IVA, VA, and VIA of the Periodic System, (b) the allotropy of the more electronegative elements is predominantly one of differences in covalent structure, while the allotropy of the less electronegative elements is one of difference between metallic and nonmetallic forms, and (c) the less electronegative the element, the greater is the stability of the metallic allotrope. This "allotrope region" of the Periodic System corresponds roughly to the line that separates metallic from nonmetallic elements.

Notable exceptions to these generalizations are silicon and germanium, which do not exhibit primary allotropy at all. Both elements occur only in the diamond (sp^3 covalent) lattice. These elements, being beyond the second Period, do not tend to form multiple bonds and so do not exist as layer lattices with extended π bonding, the structure of graphite being unique among the Group IVA elements in this respect. Silicon and germanium are less electronegative than carbon, however, and the promotion of their electrons to higher energy levels, even from the covalent lattice, can be readily accomplished by thermal or radiative excitation. As a result, silicon and germanium show electrical conductivity which increases with increasing temperature (the reverse of the behavior shown by true metals); they are semiconductors. These elements thus show both metallic and nonmetallic properties in a single mode of aggregation; this behavior is **semimetallic** or **metalloid** (Fig. 27.2, page 706).

27.10 SOURCES OF METALS: THERMODYNAMIC CONSIDERATIONS

The earth's crust, it is believed, was formed by the cooling of fluid matter. Under such circumstances, separation of different substances occurs first when immiscible liquids stratify and, second, when fractional crystallization (the separation of materials of different solubilities by differential crystallization from a liquid phase) occurs on cooling of the liquid. During the long geological time since the formation of the earth's crust, the various solid depositions were subjected to additional differentiating actions by atmospheric weathering, by the action of water after the earth had cooled below 100°C, and by biological processes after life began. Of all these weathering effects, the most important is the action of water. The materials now remaining in the solid state must therefore be resistant to oxidation, reduction, and biological attack, and (usually) highly insoluble. Such materials, when they are used as sources for the commercial extraction of metals, are called **ores.** Relatively pure natural solids, whether they find commercial use or not, are called **minerals.** Soluble compounds are dispersed in the oceans or concentrated in landlocked bodies of water, like Great Salt Lake and the Dead, the Caspian, and the Aral Seas, or remain as evaporation residues, such as the Bonneville salt flats or the Chilean saltpeter deposits. The requirements for chemical stability are, specifically, resistance to oxidation by acid or reduction by water. The important half-reactions and their standard oxidation potentials are given below. H^+ is written in place of H_3O^+, for brevity.

$$H_2 \rightleftharpoons 2H^+ \text{ (acid)} + 2e^- \qquad \qquad \varepsilon° = 0 \text{ volts} \qquad \qquad (1)$$

and

$$2H_2O \rightleftharpoons O_2 + 4H^+ \text{ (acid)} + 4e^- \qquad \varepsilon° = -1.23 \text{ volts}$$
$$\text{(cf. Table 27.5)} \quad (2)$$

The requirement for resistance to oxidation, based on standard oxidation potentials, can be deduced from

$$\text{ore} \rightleftharpoons \text{oxidized ore} + \text{electrons}$$

Let the half-cell potential of this reaction be designated $\varepsilon°_{ore}$. Subtracting Equation (1), we have

$$\text{ore} + \text{acid} \rightleftharpoons \text{oxidized ore} + \text{hydrogen} \qquad \varepsilon° = \varepsilon°_{ore} - 0 \qquad (3)$$

Then, the condition for Reaction (3) *not* to occur (that is, for the ore to resist oxidation) is that $\varepsilon°$ must be negative, or $\varepsilon° < 0$. Then

$$\varepsilon°_{ore} < 0 \qquad \qquad (4)$$

These deductions depend on the assumptions that activities (or, roughly, molarities) are equal to 1, and that equilibrium-shifting effects are negligible even over long periods of time. To compare these predictions

TABLE 27.5   *Some Standard Oxidation Potentials Related to the Occurrence of Ores*

Half-reaction	$\mathcal{E}°$ *(volts)*
$Sn^{2+} \rightleftharpoons Sn^{4+} + 2e^-$	-0.15
$Cu^+ \rightleftharpoons Cu^{2+} + e^-$	-0.17
$Fe^{2+} \rightleftharpoons Fe^{3+} + e^-$	-0.77
$2H_2O + Mn^{2+} \rightleftharpoons MnO_2(c) + 4H^+ + 2e^-$	-1.23
$4H_2O + Mn^{2+} \rightleftharpoons MnO_4^- + 8H^+ + 5e^-$	-1.50
$PbSO_4 + 2H_2O \rightleftharpoons PbO_2(c) + SO_4^{2-} + 4H^+ + 2e^-$	-1.69
$Co^{2+} \rightleftharpoons Co^{3+} + e^-$	-1.84

with geophysical realities, let us note first which metals are found in elemental states in their ores. Equation (4) predicts that these metals will comprise all those whose oxidation potential is less than that of hydrogen (zero) (Table 16.1). Such metals include bismuth, copper, mercury, silver, gold, and the platinum group.* Native (elemental) bismuth is, in fact, found in Peru and Bolivia. Native copper is found in one important deposit in Michigan (so-called Lake Copper, now substantially exhausted); otherwise it is usually mined as the sulfide. The important source of mercury is also the sulfide (**cinnabar**, HgS), but the free metal is sometimes found finely dispersed in its ore. Silver is found as the free metal, the sulfide, or the chloride. In general, the metals lower than silver in oxidation potential (for instance, gold) are mined in the native state. Lead, on the other hand, which is slightly higher than hydrogen in the series ($\mathcal{E}° = 0.13$) is mined only from sulfides, PbS (**galena**), or oxygenated minerals, $PbCO_3$ (**cerussite**) and $PbSO_4$ (**anglesite**).

The requirement for resistance to reduction can be calculated from

$$\text{reduced ore} \rightleftharpoons \text{ore} + \text{electrons} \tag{5}$$

Let the half-cell potential of this reaction be designated $\mathcal{E}°_{red. ore}$. Subtracting Equation (5) from Equation (2), we have

$$\text{ore} + \text{water} \rightleftharpoons \text{reduced ore} + \text{oxygen} + \text{acid}$$
$$\mathcal{E}° = -1.23 \text{ volts} - \mathcal{E}°_{red. ore}$$

The condition for the reaction *not* to occur (that is, for the ore to resist reduction) is

$$-1.23 - \mathcal{E}°_{red. ore} < 0$$

or

$$\mathcal{E}°_{red. ore} > -1.23 \tag{6}$$

For ores containing metals in chemical combination, a prediction of the expected oxidation states of the metals is made from Equation (6), which

* The lower the oxidation potential of a metal, the more **noble** it is said to be. Metals like gold and platinum are called **noble metals.**

implies that a compound will survive reduction by water only if the $\mathcal{E}^{\circ}_{\text{red. ore}}$ (Equation 6) is greater (that is, less negative) than -1.23 volts. From the standard oxidation potentials shown in Table 27.5, one would predict that Cu(II), Sn(IV), and Fe(III) would be stable, that manganese would occur in the Mn^{2+} state and as MnO_2 but never in a more highly oxidized condition, and that PbO_2 would not occur in nature. These considerations therefore set an upper limit on the oxidation states of metals that could have survived on earth in the presence of liquid water. The predictions are well borne out, as evidenced by the following facts. Copper occurs as CuS (**chalcocite, covellite**). The only important mineral of tin is SnO_2 (**cassiterite**). Iron is mined as Fe_2O_3 (**hematite**). Manganese is found as MnO_2 (**pyrolusite**) and as $MnCO_3$ (**rhodochrosite**), never in an oxidation state greater than 4. The most highly oxidized form of lead in ores is $+2$.

27.11 THE WINNING OF METALS FROM ORES: GENERAL CONSIDERATIONS

Metals occur in ores in an impure and, generally, oxidized condition. The winning (the word reflects our esteem for metallurgical success) of metals therefore involves purification processes and usually reduction. Physical or chemical treatment of materials may also be needed to prepare them for effective further processing.

The first rough purification steps are called, simply, **concentration.** The last purification, which almost always takes place after reduction, is called **refining.** Between these initial and final efforts may be interposed any of a large variety of metallurgical processes, many of which are adaptations of methods developed in antiquity. Some of these processes will be briefly described in the ensuing sections, in the order in which they are most likely to be used in commercial practice.

27.12 PRELIMINARY PHYSICAL TREATMENT

Crushing and grinding operations are used to subdivide large pieces of ore to a workable particle size. Excessively fine particles also pose handling problems, and must therefore be agglomerated. A common method of agglomeration, used especially in the treatment of iron ore fines,* is **sintering,** which involves incipient melting of solid material. The edges of a solid melt before the flat surfaces, because the more highly curved edges have fewer molecules around them to help constrain them in the solid lattice. Material that is partially melted, therefore, tends to fuse together at the sharp points of contract; the aggregate thus formed is called a **sinter.** In some processes, blast furnace flue dust, which is rich in carbon, is mixed with the ore fines to serve as a fuel. During the sintering, some sulfur is lost as SO_2; thus the physical agglomeration is accompanied by some chemical action.

* "Fines" means, in industrial parlance, fine particles.

The simplest method of concentration is the removal of lumps of impurities by sorting or sieving operations. The portion of the ore that does not contain metal is considered to be impurity. It is collectively called **gangue** and includes sand and clays. When the mineral differs greatly in density from the gangue, gravity or inertial methods (which depend on differences in masses of particles) may be used. A primitive process is the **panning** of gold, in which the lighter gravel is washed down a sluice, leaving the heavier gold behind. Spiral whirling of an air-borne suspension of ore in a conical chamber called a **cyclone separator** is an effective inertial process. Magnetic separation is useful in separating ore rich in Fe_3O_4 (**magnetite**—the lodestone of antiquity) from gangue. By using magnets of different strength it is possible to separate the ore into several different concentrations. It is sometimes possible to effect an **electrostatic separation.** By this method one material (usually the gangue) retains an electric charge better than another, and can be attracted to a charged surface from which it falls or is scraped off. **Distillation** methods are sometimes used, notably in the refining of mercury.

By far the most important method of physical concentration is **flotation.** In this process, ground or crushed ore is suspended in water by air bubbling, and a differentiation is made among various types of particle on the basis of the extent to which they are wetted by water. Particles that adhere tenaciously to water do not leave the aqueous phase. Thus, an oxide (SiO_2, for example) will be more strongly hydrogen-bonded to water than a sulfide, because the oxide is more highly polar. Particles that lack affinity for water, on the other hand, are held at the boundaries between the water and the bubbles by surface tension. These nonwetted components rise to the surface as a froth and can be skimmed off and recovered, and thus separated from the wetted particles which do not float. Older techniques employed agents like pine oil or mineral oil, which coat the ore in preference to the gangue; the ore was thus rendered nonwettable by water and was separated in the froth. Modern methods accomplish much more than merely the separation of ore materials from gangue; preferential wetting of particular ores is effected by agents of high specificity, called **collectors.** The typical collector is a molecule, one end of which has an ionic or polar group that attaches itself to the ore to be separated, and the other end of which is hydrocarbon in nature to shield against the wetting action of water. An example is the use of potassium ethylxanthate

$$CH_3-CH_2-O-\overset{\overset{\displaystyle S}{\|}}{C}-S^-\ \ K^+$$

in the froth flotation of **chalcopyrite,** $CuFeS_2$. The ionic bonds of the xanthate molecules attach themselves to the $CuFeS_2$ particles, render them nonwettable, and thus permit them to be carried off in the froth. The availability of a large variety of collectors affords a wide choice of separation procedures. The method is economical in expenditure of energy and hence can be used with low-grade ores. Thus, chalcopyrite has been commercially recovered by froth flotation from ores in which it constitutes less than 1% of the total material.

27.14 CHEMICAL LEACHING

Chemical leaching is a method of extraction with the use of a liquid that renders the desired component soluble by some chemical action. For such a process to be commercially valuable in metallurgy, the leached product must be sufficiently stable for a fairly high proportion of the metal to be in the desired state at equilibrium. Because the cyano complex ions are very stable, and because NaCN and KCN are relatively cheap raw materials, cyanide leaching has been used for the recovery of valuable metals from low-grade ores. Some typical instability constants and standard electrode potentials are

$$Ag \rightleftharpoons Ag^+ + e^-$$
$$\mathcal{E}° = -0.80 \text{ volt}$$
$$Ag + 2CN^- \rightleftharpoons Ag(CN)_2^- + e^-$$
$$\mathcal{E}° = 0.35 \text{ volt}$$

the cyanide complexing promotes the oxidation of Ag

$$Ag(CN)_2^- \rightleftharpoons Ag^+ + 2CN^-$$
$$K = 1 \times 10^{-20}$$
$$Au \rightleftharpoons Au^{3+} + 3e^-$$
$$\mathcal{E}° = -1.42 \text{ volts}$$
$$Au + 2CN^- \rightleftharpoons Au(CN)_2^- + e^-$$
$$\mathcal{E}° = 0.60 \text{ volt}$$

the cyanide complexing promotes the oxidation of Au

$$Au(CN)_2^- \rightleftharpoons Au^+ + 2CN^-$$
$$K \approx 5 \times 10^{-39}$$

The cyanide leaching of native silver or gold is, as shown above, an oxidation process; the cheapest oxidant, air, is used. The half-reaction that involves oxygen is

$$4OH^- \rightleftharpoons O_2 + 2H_2O + 4e^- \qquad \mathcal{E}° = -0.40 \text{ volt}$$

The over-all reaction for silver is therefore

$$4Ag + 8CN^- + O_2 + 2H_2O \rightleftharpoons 4Ag(CN)_2^- + 4OH^-$$
$$\mathcal{E}° = +0.35 - (-0.40) = +0.75 \text{ volt}$$

An analogous equation can be written for Au. The metals are recovered from their cyanide salts by electrolytic reduction. Although similar chemical considerations would make it seem feasible to apply cyanide leaching to other metals, such as copper, the less noble metals can be treated more economically by air oxidation (roasting).

27.15 ROASTING: THERMODYNAMIC CONSIDERATIONS

Ores used in ancient metallurgy were, for the most part, surface deposits of oxides, carbonates, or native metal. The oxides and carbonates were reduced to metal by heating with wood charcoal, the gaseous products, CO and CO_2, escaping readily to the atmosphere. As mining developed in the pursuit of ores at greater depths, sulfides were increasingly encountered. It was found advantageous to convert these sulfides to oxides prior to reduction. **Roasting** is the process whereby such conversion is accomplished by heating in air. With more noble metals, careful control of the roasting process may effect reduction to the metallic state. If the temperature is fairly low (about 500°C) and the concentration of SO_2 in the gaseous environment is high, sulfates may be produced. This is an undesirable effect, because sulfates are stable and high temperatures are needed to decompose them.

Representative equations are

$$HgS + O_2 \rightarrow Hg + SO_2 \tag{7}$$
$$2ZnS + 3O_2 \rightarrow 2ZnO + 2SO_2$$
$$4FeS_2 + 11O_2 \rightarrow 2Fe_2O_3 + 8SO_2$$

(*undesirable*) $\quad 2ZnO + 2SO_2 + O_2 \rightarrow 2ZnSO_4$

(*undesirable*) $\quad 2Fe_2O_3 + 4SO_2 + O_2 \rightarrow 4FeSO_4$

Why is roasting necessary? The direct reduction of sulfides with charcoal is usually less satisfactory than the corresponding treatment of oxides for reasons that can be understood by considering the standard free energies of formation* (ΔF_f) of the substances involved. If we designate the metallic sulfide as MS, and the oxide as MO, then

$$2MS + C \rightarrow 2M + CS_2$$
(*direct reduction of sulfide, no roasting*)

This reaction can be considered as the difference between

$$C + 2S \rightarrow CS_2 \qquad \Delta F = \Delta F_{fCS_2}$$

and

$$2M + 2S \rightarrow 2MS \qquad \Delta F = 2\Delta F_{fMS}$$

Then the standard free energy of direct reduction of the sulfide must be, by difference,

$$\Delta F_{\substack{\text{reduction} \\ \text{of sulfide}}} = \Delta F_{fCS_2} - 2\Delta F_{fMS}$$

The equation for reduction of oxide is

$$2MO + C \rightarrow 2M + CO_2$$
(*reduction of oxide, obtained by roasting of sulfide*)

By steps exactly analogous to those used above, we obtain

$$\Delta F_{\substack{\text{reduction} \\ \text{of oxide}}} = \Delta F_{fCO_2} - 2\Delta F_{fMO}$$

Now, the *advantage* obtained by roasting is the greater tendency for the oxide to undergo reduction as compared with the sulfide. This may be

* ΔF_f is the free energy change involved in the formation of one mole of a substance, starting from its elements in their most stable states at 25°C.

expressed as

$$\begin{array}{l}
\textit{free energy} \\
\textit{advantage of} \\
\textit{roasting}
\end{array} = \Delta F_{\text{reduction} \atop \text{of oxide}} - \Delta F_{\text{reduction} \atop \text{of sulfide}}$$

$$= (\Delta F_{fCO_2} - 2\Delta F_{fMO}) - (\Delta F_{fCS_2} - 2\Delta F_{fMS})$$

But $\Delta F_{fCO_2} = -94.3$ kcal/mole, and $\Delta F_{fCS_2} = 15.6$ kcal/mole; substituting these values above, we have

$$\begin{array}{l}
\textit{free energy} \\
\textit{advantage} \\
\textit{of roasting}
\end{array} = -109.9 \frac{\text{kcal}}{\text{mole}} + 2(\Delta F_{fMS} - \Delta F_{fMO})$$

Remember that the driving force of a reaction is greater when the ΔF value is algebraically *less*. Now we may consider the question: Is it advantageous to roast copper sulfide ores? ΔF_f for Cu_2S is -20.6 kcal/mole; for Cu_2O, ΔF_f is -35.0 kcal/mole:

$$\Delta F_{\text{advantage} \atop \text{of roasting}} = -109.9 + 2(-20.6 + 35.0)$$

$$= -81.1 \text{ kcal/2 moles} = -40.5 \text{ kcal/mole}$$

Obviously the greater stability of the copper(I) oxide as compared to the sulfide (a difference of 14.4 kcal/mole) is much less than the greater stability of CO_2 as compared with CS_2 (109.9 kcal/mole), and roasting is therefore advantageous. For the corresponding (cupric) copper(II) compounds, $(\Delta F_{fCuS} - \Delta F_{fCuO})$ is only $+1.9$ kcal/mole; roasting is even more advantageous here. Such differences are typical and, as a result, the production of metal with carbon as a reducing agent is thermodynamically favored by using oxides rather than sulfides as starting material.

27.16 REDUCTION

Reducing agents available for treatment of ores can be classified into three major categories: (1) the atoms in the mineral that have low oxidation numbers and may therefore serve as reductants, (2) added chemical reductants, and (3) the cathode of an electrolytic cell.

When a metal is produced by direct decomposition, the anionic portion of the mineral may be considered to be the reducing agent. Thus, Equation (7) may be considered to be the production of mercury by decomposition of the sulfide, followed by oxidation of the sulfur.

Among chemical reductants, the cheapest and most widely used is carbon, usually in the form of coke (the carbonaceous residue from the destructive distillation of coal). Carbon, being a solid, does not make intimate contact with ore particles. Instead, its partial oxidation product, gaseous CO, is the effective reducing agent in most instances. The source of oxygen for conversion of carbon to CO is air, air enriched with oxygen, or sometimes even pure oxygen. Carbon dioxide that is formed by complete oxidation of carbon is reduced to carbon monoxide in the presence of excess carbon:

$$C(amorph) + O_2(g) \rightleftharpoons CO_2(g) \qquad \Delta H = -94 \text{ kcal}$$
$$C(amorph) + CO_2(g) \rightleftharpoons 2CO(g) \qquad \Delta H = +41 \text{ kcal}$$

Other reducing agents may be selected from hydrogen up to sodium (Table 16.1, page 417); the choice depends on the reducing potential needed, and on the cost that can be justified.

The Metallurgy of Iron. The metal produced in greatest quantity by reduction of an ore is iron. The ore used is usually an oxide mixed with gangue. For facility in handling, it is advantageous if the products obtained from metallurgical reduction are in a liquid condition. The siliceous gangue, however, does not liquefy at the temperature at which coke reduces iron oxide, but instead forms a soft vitreous mass that would make handling very difficult. A liquefying agent (**flux**) is therefore used to react with the gangue to convert it to a **slag,** a product obtained as an upper liquid layer in a metallurgical process. The slag serves the additional function of shielding the metal on which it floats from air oxidation. The flux is lime, formed by the decomposition of limestone (calcium carbonate). The carbon dioxide produced by this decomposition reacts with carbon to produce carbon monoxide. The changes are depicted by the following idealized equations:

$$CaCO_3(c) \rightarrow \underset{\text{lime}}{CaO(c)} + CO_2(g)$$
$$\underset{\substack{\text{lime} \\ \text{(flux)}}}{CaO(c)} + \underset{\substack{\text{silica} \\ \text{(gangue)}}}{SiO_2(c)} \rightarrow \underset{\substack{\text{calcium silicate} \\ \text{(fusible slag)}}}{CaSiO_3(l)}$$

The major sequence of reduction reactions is shown in the schematic diagram of the blast furnace (Fig. 27.3).

Other Chemical Reduction Processes. Carbon dissolves in metals to some degree, often with the formation of carbides; the removal of small residues of carbon from the metal is therefore difficult. When a pure product is needed, or when a more powerful reductant must be used, a metal with high reducing potential like aluminum may serve. In the Goldschmidt or aluminothermic process, chromium may be prepared directly from its oxide,

$$Cr_2O_3(c) + 2Al(l) \rightarrow 2Cr(l) + Al_2O_3(c)$$

The reaction is vigorously exothermic and quite rapid. Tantalum, niobium, and tungsten can also be produced by aluminothermic methods.

Hydrogen gas can reduce anything that carbon can, and may be thought to have the important advantage of leaving no impurity. It may leave some of itself, however, in the form of a hydride. It is costly, forms explosive mixtures with air, and is not widely used.

The alkali metals are not generally used as reducing agents because, when such reduction potential is needed, electrochemical methods are more satisfactory and cheaper.

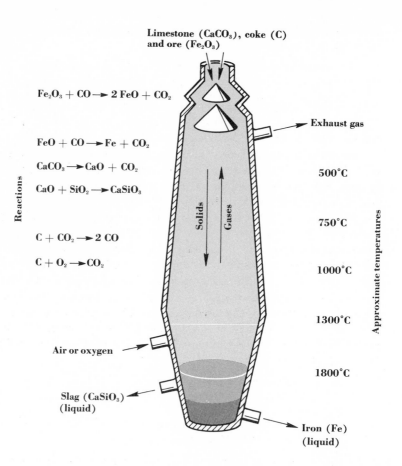

Limestone ($CaCO_3$), coke (C)
and ore (Fe_2O_3)

$Fe_2O_3 + CO \longrightarrow 2\ FeO + CO_2$

$FeO + CO \longrightarrow Fe + CO_2$

$CaCO_3 \longrightarrow CaO + CO_2$

$CaO + SiO_2 \longrightarrow CaSiO_3$

$C + CO_2 \longrightarrow 2\ CO$

$C + O_2 \longrightarrow CO_2$

Reactions

Solids Gases

Exhaust gas

500°C

750°C

1000°C

1300°C

1800°C

Approximate temperatures

Air or oxygen

Slag ($CaSiO_3$)
(liquid)

Iron (Fe)
(liquid)

Fig. 27.3. *The blast furnace for making iron (schematic).*

27.17 ELECTROMETALLURGY

The standard oxidation potentials of the alkali metals and the alkaline earth metals are so high that chemical reductants are not available for the isolation of the pure metals. Instead, the pure metals are prepared by the electrolysis of their fused salts.

A noteworthy example of commercial electrolytic reduction of an ore is the metallurgy of aluminum. The important source of the metal is **bauxite,** $Al_2O_3(H_2O)_2$. Ferric oxide and silica are the usual contaminants. Since ferric oxide will be reduced under any conditions used for the preparation of aluminum, the bauxite must be purified first if the aluminum is to be free of iron. The separation is effected by extracting the amphoteric alumina (Al_2O_3) with hot aqueous NaOH, and decanting the hot solution from the nonamphoteric ferric oxide and from the siliceous residue. The purified alumina, to be used in the electrolysis, is recovered by reversal of the equilibrium on cooling,

$$Al_2O_3 + 2OH^- + 7H_2O \rightleftharpoons 2[Al(OH)_4(H_2O)_2]^-$$

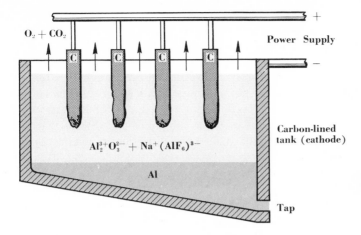

Fig. 27.4. *Apparatus for electrolytic production of aluminum by the Hall process, using carbon anodes (schematic).*

The problem of reduction of Al_2O_3 stems from the high oxidation potential of aluminum. Chemical reduction would require the use of a very powerful reducing agent like metallic sodium, which was in fact used in the early preparations of small quantities of aluminum. Attempts to use carbon were failures—aluminum carbide was the major product. Aqueous solutions are inappropriate media, because it is easier to reduce water ($\varepsilon° = +0.83$ volt) than aluminum ion ($\varepsilon° = +1.67$ volts) and therefore only hydrogen is produced at the cathode during such electrolyses. A suitable electrolyte would be one not undergoing electrolysis itself but serving as a solvent for the ionic dissociation of Al_2O_3.

The electrolyte now used is sodium fluoaluminate (**cryolite**), Na_3AlF_6. Charles M. Hall, in 1886, found that Al_2O_3 would dissolve in liquid cryolite (m.p. 1000°C) and that the solution conducted the electric current. The cryolite itself undergoes no appreciable electrolysis, because AlF_6^{3-} is resistant to oxidation and Na^+ is resistant to reduction at the voltages used. In modern industrial practice, the aluminum accumulates as a cathodic melt which is tapped off. Carbon is used as the anodic material; it undergoes oxidative attrition with evolution of CO_2. The molten aluminum itself is the cathode. The reactions are

$$(cathode) \qquad Al^{3+} + 3e^- \rightarrow Al$$
$$(anode) \qquad O^{2-} + C - 2e^- \rightarrow CO_2$$

A schematic diagram of the cell appears in Fig. 27.4.

27.18 **REFINING: ELECTROLYTIC METHOD**

Refining refers generally to any final method of bringing a metal to its highest degree of purity. Electrolytic methods are very effective and are used in a variety of processes. A discussion of the electrolytic refining of copper will illustrate the application.

The contaminants to be removed from impure copper may be classified, electrolytically, as (1) metals that are stronger reducing agents than copper, (2) metals that are weaker reducing agents than copper, and (3) nonmetallic substances. Let us typify materials in these categories as Zn, Ag, and SiO_2, respectively. The refining cell uses the impure copper as the anode, pure copper as the cathode, and aqueous $CuSO_4$ as electrolyte. The anodic oxidation potential ($Cu \rightarrow Cu^{2+}$) is equal in magnitude and opposite in sign to the cathodic reduction potential ($Cu^{2+} \rightarrow Cu$), disregarding the small effect of impurities in the copper; the sum of the two is zero and therefore no voltage should be needed to initiate current flow, except for the slight amount required to overcome the resistance of the electrolyte. The operation of the cell will increase the $[Cu^{2+}]$ near the anode and decrease it near the cathode. This effect is that of a concentration cell whose voltage opposes that of the applied potential, and this opposition, too, must be overcome to operate the cell. In practice, the sum of these resistances is small and the cell operates at voltages that produce only the following reactions.

Anodic actions:

$$Cu \rightarrow Cu^{2+} + 2e^-$$
$$Zn \rightarrow Zn^{2+} + 2e^-$$
$$Ag \rightarrow \text{no reaction (because applied voltage is less than oxidation potential for Ag)}$$
$$SiO_2 \rightarrow \text{no reaction}$$

Cathodic actions:

$$Cu^{2+} + 2e^- \rightarrow Cu$$
$$Zn^{2+} \rightarrow \text{no reaction (because applied voltage is less than deposition (reduction) potential for Zn)}$$

The net effect is that the nonmetals and the weakly reducing ("noble") metals precipitate as a residue called the **anode sludge,** which can profitably be reworked for recovery of the noble metals. The strongly reducing metals remain as ions in solution from which they can be removed from time to time. The only cathodic deposition is copper; this selectivity produces copper of purity exceeding 99.95%.

27.19 **REFINING: NONELECTROLYTIC METHODS**

The Mond Process. An interesting method of refining metals is the formation of a volatile carbonyl compound, separation from nonvolatile residual impurity, and recovery of the metal by decomposition of its carbonyl. In the **Mond process** for nickel (named for the former Mond plant near Swansea, South Wales), the crude metal is produced by roasting the sulfide, NiS, and reducing the resultant oxide at 350–400°C with "water gas," a mixture of carbon monoxide and hydrogen. Water gas is produced by the action of steam on hot carbon. The equations are

$$C(amorph) + H_2O(g) \rightarrow CO(g) + H_2(g)$$
$$NiO(c) + H_2(g) \rightarrow Ni(c) + H_2O(g)$$
$$NiO(c) + CO(g) \rightarrow Ni(c) + CO_2(g)$$

The crude nickel is then treated at 60°C with carbon monoxide, and the volatile carbonyl is formed,

$$Ni(c) + 4CO(g) \rightleftharpoons Ni(CO)_4(g)$$

Because about 97% of the reduction of the nickel oxide is brought about by hydrogen, the gaseous effluent from the reduction is substantially carbon monoxide and steam. After removal of the water by condensation, this gas is suitable for use in carbonyl formation. After purification, the carbonyl is decomposed on nickel pellets at 180°C, the released carbon monoxide being recirculated for reuse. The nonvolatile residue contains copper, cobalt, sulfur, and some precious metals.

The Parkes Process. An interesting extractive method of refining is the **Parkes process,** used to remove silver and gold from lead. The lead is melted and thoroughly agitated with about 2% of molten zinc, with which it is practically immiscible. Both silver and gold are much more soluble in zinc than in lead, and therefore will preferentially dissolve in the zinc (Distribution law, page 350). Zinc is lighter and freezes at a higher temperature than lead; the mixture can then be cooled and the solid zinc-silver-gold solution skimmed off the top of the molten lead. The zinc can be removed from the precious metals by distillation.

The Refining of Iron. The refining of iron is essentially a selective oxidation of its impurities, especially carbon, and to a lesser extent silicon, phosphorus, and sulfur. In the "open-hearth" process, the impure iron from the blast furnace (**pig iron**) is mixed with a melt consisting of iron scrap, iron ore, and lime. The ore is the oxidant. The oxidized products that do not pass off as a gas are separated from the iron as a slag. Some of the reactions are

$$Fe_2O_3 + 3C \rightarrow 3CO + 2Fe$$
$$2Fe_2O_3 + 3Si \rightarrow 3SiO_2 + 4Fe$$
$$5Fe_2O_3 + 6P \rightarrow 3P_2O_5 + 10Fe$$
$$Fe_2O_3 + 3Mn \rightarrow 3MnO + 2Fe$$
$$S + CaO + C \rightarrow CaS + CO$$

The oxidizing agent used may also be air (**Bessemer process**) or, as increasingly used in recent years, oxygen (**oxygen top-blowing process**).

The iron is then treated with various addition agents to modify its properties; the resulting product is called **steel.** Steelmaking is not, strictly speaking, refining, because it is not a purification process. The changes in composition, however, are strictly controlled and are monitored analytically during the manufacturing process. Addition agents include **ferromanganese** (an alloy containing Fe, Mn, and C), **ferrosilicon** (an alloy of Fe and Si), and other materials as required. Carbon contents of steels range from about 0.05% to about 1.50%. Nonferrous metallic components of steel include Mn, Ni, Cr, Mo, V, W, Co, and Cu.

Problems

1. Metallic properties. Iron pyrite, FeS_2, is called "fool's gold." What are the probable reasons for this confusion? What steps would you, as an amateur prospector, take to ensure that your find was metallic?

2. Metallic properties. Wax can be squeezed into a sheet; organic matter can occur as filaments like hair or fibers; fused salt conducts electricity well; cinnabar (HgS) is dense (8 g/cm³). None of these substances is metallic. Explain in each case why the property described does not demonstrate that the substance is a metal.

3. The metallic bond. Only metallic (never ionic or covalent) substances form crystals that exhibit the maximum coordination number of 12 among like-sized atoms. Account for this fact.

4. The metallic bond. Iron in FeF_2 is isoelectronic with chromium in Cr_3Os, yet the former substance is nonmetallic, the latter metallic. What is the number of electrons in the two isoelectronic species? Explain why a metallic valence cannot be assigned to Fe^{2+}. Criticize the assignment of 24 electrons to Cr.

5. Heats of fusion and vaporization. From Table 27.2, calculate the relative heats of fusion and vaporization of Si and Cu. Calculate the ratio of $\Delta H_{vap}/\Delta H_{fus}$ for each of these elements. Offer an interpretation for the difference between these ratios.

> **Answer.** Accurate values:
> ΔH_{fus} (Si) 11.1 cal/g-atom, (Cu) 3.11 cal/g-atom;
> ΔH_{vap} (Si) 105 cal/g-atom, (Cu) 72.8 cal/g-atom;
> $\Delta H_{vap}/\Delta H_{fus}$ (Si) 9.46, (Cu) 23.4.

6. Allotropy. Reproduce that portion of the Periodic Table in which primary allotropy is exhibited. Indicate, for each of the elements shown, whether covalent (C), metallic (M), or both modifications are known. Defend or criticize the statement, "The allotrope region of the Periodic Table is roughly the boundary between metals and nonmetals."

7. Occurrence of ores. Consider a planet that contains seas of liquid ammonia and whose atmosphere contains ammonia and nitrogen. Amide ion, NH_2^-, is a stronger base than hydroxide ion, OH^-, and oxygen is a more powerful oxidant than nitrogen. Would you expect to find more or fewer metals in their native state on this planet than on Earth? Would you expect the maximum oxidation states of metals in ores that occur on that planet to be greater or less than they are on Earth? Explain.

8. Concentration. You are asked to make recommendations for methods of ore concentration that are low in cost and specific in selection. What general methods would you consider? What advantages and disadvantages of each would you point out? What information about the ore would you want and how would such information affect your recommendations?

9. Roasting. (a) Write the chemical equations for the formation of CS_2, CO_2, Cu_2S, and Cu_2O from their elements. (b) Write the chemical equations for the reduction of Cu_2S, CuS, Cu_2O, and CuO by carbon. (c) From the data given on page 720, calculate ΔF for the reduction of Cu_2S and of Cu_2O by carbon. Explain how the difference between these two values constitutes a justification for the roasting process. (d) Calculate the corresponding difference between the ΔF values for the reduction of CuS and of CuO.

$\qquad$ **Answer.** (c) $+28.4$, -12.1 kcal/mole; (d) -53.0 kcal/mole.

10. Electrometallurgy. (a) Draw a diagram of a cell which could be used for winning sodium from NaCl. Label anode, cathode, and electrolyte. Write the equations for the half-reactions. (b) In one industrial process, magnesium oxide is electrolyzed in a fused bath of MgF_2, NaF, and BaF_2. This electrolyte is denser than liquid magnesium. Draw a diagram of a cell that could be used for such electrolysis. Label anode, cathode, and electrolyte. Write the equations for the half-reactions.

Additional problems

11. Metallic properties. Useful objects may be produced by a precision casting process called **powder metallurgy.** Metallic powders are first compressed to reduce void space and to increase the density, and then heated to a temperature slightly below the melting point to increase the density still further and greatly to strengthen the product. Account for these phenomena. Do you think that nonmetallic powders could be used as well? If not, what steps in the process would be unsatisfactory?

12. The metallic bond. (a) When matter is heated to temperatures around 50,000°C, it enters the **plasma** state, in which electrons are extensively dissociated from atoms. What comparisons or contrasts can you draw between plasmas and metals? (b) Some substances (for example $CaCO_3$) become metallic under extremely high pressures ($\sim 10^5$–10^6 atm), as shown by the work of Willard Libby and others. What new properties do you think might appear under such conditions to warrant describing the substance as metallic? Offer a qualitative explanation for such transformations in terms of theories of the nature of ionic and metallic bonds.

13. The metallic bond. Is it conceivable that a substance could be found whose electrical conductivity is substantially independent of temperature in some temperature range? If so, describe the qualitative energy requirements for the energy bands of such a substance.

14. Melting and boiling points. Would you expect periodic variations in melting and boiling points of the elements to correlate well with variations in ΔH_{fus} and ΔH_{vap}? Why or why not? Substantiate your answer with data from a chemical handbook.

15. Heats of vaporization. ΔH_{vap} decreases with increase of atomic number within each of the Groups IA to IVA of the representative elements; this trend is most marked in Group IVA. The trend disappears abruptly in Groups VA to VIIA. Account for these facts.

16. Properties of Mn. Both ΔH_{vap} and electrical conductivity values in the fourth period of the transition elements go through a minimum at Mn. Are these two circumstances related? Account for them in terms of electronic structure.

17. Groups IB and IIB. From the viewpoint of ΔH_{fus} and ΔH_{vap} values, classify the IB and IIB elements as to transitional or representative types. Explain.

18. Allotropy. Allotropy is not observed among the halogens. Offer an explanation for this fact.

19. Occurrence of ores. You are offered the following investments: (a) purchase of stock in a brass mine; (b) purchase of stock in a mineral deposit of cobalt(III) chloride, $CoCl_3$; and (c) of potassium permanganate, $KMnO_4$. Explain your technical recommendations with regard to the likelihood that such opportunities exist. Brass is an alloy of copper and zinc.

20. Cyanide leaching. Draw a diagram of an electrochemical cell in which a current is produced from the cyanide leaching of silver (page 718). Label anode, cathode, and all reactive chemical constituents of the cell. Suggest a method of recovering silver from the cyanide complex.

21. Reduction of ores. Silicon undergoes oxidation to the dioxide,

$$Si + O_2 \rightarrow SiO_2 \qquad \Delta H = -201 \text{ kcal/mole}$$

If elemental silicon were cheaply available, would it be useful for the industrial reduction of ores? If so, outline a practical process. If not, point out the difficulties.

22. Electrometallurgy. Zinc is produced at Trail, British Columbia, by electrolysis of a concentrated aqueous solution of the sulfate at high current density. It is found that the solution must be quite pure if the zinc is to be of satisfactory quality. Anodes are a silver-lead alloy; cathodes are aluminum. What types of impurity in the electrolyte would be most likely to contaminate the reduced zinc? Write the equations for the reactions that occur at each electrode. Account for the fact that hydrogen gas is not the major cathodic product.

23. Refining. Although zinc can be refined electrolytically, it is sometimes refined by distillation. What factors would you wish to evaluate if you were asked to make a choice between electrolysis and distillation for refining a metal? In what way would each factor influence your choice? Explain how such evaluations might dictate the choice of electrolysis for zinc.

28

*Nuclear
chemistry*

▬▬▬▬▬

IN THIS CHAPTER we examine more closely the nature of the bond (force) holding nucleons together in nuclei, and the properties of the nuclei such as radioactivity, artificial transmutations, fission, and fusion.

28.1 RADIOACTIVITY

With the discovery of x rays by Röntgen (page 151), several investigators considered the possibility of a relationship between the phosphorescence produced by the x rays in an electron beam tube and the light emitted by natural and artificial minerals upon exposure to sunlight. Probing for such a relationship, Henri Becquerel in 1896 accidentally discovered that uranium compounds emit a radiation similar in nature to x rays. *Elements such as uranium, which spontaneously emit energy without the absorption of energy, are called naturally* **radioactive.** Artificially radioactive isotopes may be produced by adding energy to stable nuclei (page 737).

Laboratory studies using electric or magnetic fields showed that the emission is composed of three distinct types. In Fig. 28.1, an electric field applied to a narrow parallel beam of the emission, obtained from a naturally radioactive source, splits the beam into three beams, labeled **alpha** (α), **beta** (β), and **gamma** (γ). The α beam, deflected to the negative plate, is therefore composed of positively charged particles; the β beam, deflected to the positive plate, must therefore be composed of negatively charged particles. The γ beam, undeflected, must be electrically neutral.

Further experimentation has demonstrated that the alpha particle carries two unit positive charges, and possesses a mass equal to that of a helium, $_2^4\text{He}$, nucleus. Alpha particles are thus helium nuclei, $_2^4\text{He}^{2+}$, ejected at high velocities from certain radioactive substances. The electric charge

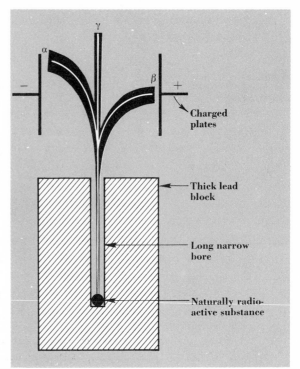

Fig. 28.1. *The behavior of α, β, and γ emissions in an electric field; apparatus is enclosed in a vacuum.*

and the mass of a β particle are equal to those of an electron. Beta particles are thus electrons ejected at very high velocities from certain radioactive isotopes (radioisotopes). The properties of γ rays are similar to those of x rays, except that their wavelengths are shorter. Gamma rays are therefore electromagnetic radiations or photons several million times higher in frequency than visible light; refer to Fig. 8.6 (page 156).

Intensive researches also demonstrated that certain radioisotopes produce other radioisotopes. Lord Rutherford, for example, found that radium continuously and spontaneously emits not only β particles but also radon, a radioactive gas.

To account for these observations, Lord Rutherford and Frederick Soddy in 1902 proposed the theory that radioactivity is the result of a spontaneous change of the atoms of one element into the atoms of another element. These "subatomic chemical changes," called nuclear reactions (transmutations, transformations, or disintegrations), involve a change in atomic number and, frequently, a change in the mass number of the radioisotope. Thus, the transmutation of radium may be represented by the equation

$$_{88}\text{Ra}^{226} \rightarrow {}_2\text{He}^4 + {}_{86}\text{Rn}^{222} \tag{1}$$

or

$$^{226}_{88}\text{Ra} \rightarrow {}^4_2\text{He} + {}^{222}_{86}\text{Rn}$$

in which the subscript is the atomic number, and the superscript is the mass number—the number of nucleons (page 155) in the nucleus.

In ordinary chemical changes, involving ions, atoms, and molecules, atoms are rearranged; they are not created or destroyed. In nuclear reactions, nucleons are rearranged; they are not destroyed or created, although a nucleon can change into a different nucleon (page 734). Hence, mass numbers are conserved: *the sum of the mass numbers of reacting nuclei and particles must equal the sum of the mass numbers of the nuclei and particles produced.* The conservation of charge requires *the sum of the atomic numbers of reacting nuclei and particles to equal the sum of the atomic numbers of the products.* The nuclear transformation represented by Equation (1) conforms to these principles. Thus, in the reaction of an α particle with $^{27}_{13}\text{Al}$, in which a neutron is produced,

$$^{27}_{13}\text{Al} + {}^{4}_{2}\text{He} \rightarrow ({}^{31}_{15}\text{P}) \rightarrow {}_{0}\text{n}^{1} + ?$$

the product nucleus must be $^{30}_{15}\text{P}$. In the reaction

$$^{235}_{92}\text{U} \rightarrow {}_{-1}\beta^{0} + ?$$

the product must be $^{235}_{93}\text{Np}$.

The intermediate nucleus formed, $({}^{31}_{15}\text{P})$, is known as a **"compound nucleus"** (a term coined to describe a nuclear system whose lifetime is longer than the time required for a nucleon to cross a nucleus).

Although neutrons, *outside the nucleus*, disintegrate into protons and electrons, they are *not* composed of protons and electrons. Experiments by Robert Hofstadter on electron scattering by protons and by neutrons— analogous to the experiments by Lord Rutherford on the scattering of α particles by nuclei—suggest that a proton consists of a neutral core, $\approx 10^{-14}$ cm, surrounded by two positively charged clouds, and that a neutron possesses a similar structure except that the inner cloud is negative. In one, the two clouds add up to one unit positive charge; in the other, the two clouds cancel each other electrically.

28.2 NUCLEAR ENERGY

The heat of nuclear reactions, ΔE, calculated from the difference between the masses of products and reactants in accordance with the Einstein law of the equivalence of mass and energy (page 118), is in agreement with the measured values within the experimental errors involved in the determination of atomic masses and of the energy of the reaction. Thus, for the transmutation of radium the masses* of the atoms involved are

$$^{226}_{88}\text{Ra} = 226.032 \qquad {}^{4}_{2}\text{He} = 4.0026$$
$$^{222}_{86}\text{Rn} = 222.024$$
$$\overline{\phantom{^{222}_{86}\text{Rn} = }226.027}$$

so that Δm, the difference in mass between the products and the initial

* Based on the mass scale $^{12}\text{C} = 12$ (exactly).

reactants, is

$$\Delta m = 226.027 - 226.032 = -0.005 \frac{g}{mole}$$

and

$$\Delta E = \Delta mc^2 = -5 \times 10^{-3} \frac{g}{mole} \left(3 \times 10^{10} \frac{cm}{sec}\right)^2$$

$$= -45 \times 10^{17} \frac{ergs}{mole}$$

or in kcal/mole

$$\Delta E = \frac{-45 \times 10^{17} \frac{ergs}{mole}}{4.18 \times 10^{10} \frac{ergs}{kcal}} = -11 \times 10^7 \frac{kcal}{mole}$$

The measured value is $\Delta E = -11 \times 10^7$ kcal per mole. A convenient energy unit is the electron volt, ev. An electron volt is equal to 1.60×10^{-12} erg or 3.83×10^{-23} kcal and one electron volt per atom is equal to 23.1 kcal per mole (page 744). Then

$$\Delta E = -11 \times 10^7 \frac{kcal}{mole} \frac{mole}{23.1} \frac{ev}{kcal} \frac{ev}{atom} = -4.8 \times 10^6 \frac{ev}{atom}$$

There are 10^6 electron volts in a Mev, a million electron volts, whence

$$\Delta E = \frac{-4.8 \times 10^6 \, ev}{10^6 \frac{ev \, atom}{Mev}} = -4.8 \frac{Mev}{atom}$$

Upon passage through matter, the energy of the emissions from radioactive nuclei is consumed by the ionization or excitation of atoms, molecules, or ions and by the disruption of chemical bonds.

Alpha particles usually cannot penetrate paper more than a few sheets in thickness. The walls of the ordinary glass beaker generally suffice to stop β particles. X and γ rays, however, are highly penetrating and require thick layers of lead or concrete to minimize penetration. To reduce the intensity of a γ ray of 10^{-12} cm wavelength by one half, about 1.8 cm of lead or almost 10 cm of concrete are required. Distance from the source is also important in minimizing exposure, since the intensity varies inversely with the square of the distance.

28.3   **THE STABILITY OF NUCLEI**

The energy required to separate a molecule in the gaseous state into its component atoms in the gaseous state corresponds to the energy evolved when these atoms combine to form the molecule in the gaseous state at a definite temperature. Similarly, the **binding** (bond) **energy of a nucleus** is the energy evolved when the nucleons combine to form the nucleus or the energy required to separate the nucleus into its component nucleons;

nuclear binding energies, however, are temperature independent. Thus, the formation of deuterium from protium and neutrons, $_0n^1 + {}_1^1H \rightarrow {}_1^2H$, liberates 5.15×10^7 kcal per mole, calculated from the masses of particles:

$$_0n^1 = 1.00866 \qquad {}_1^2H = 2.01410$$
$$\frac{{}_1^1H = 1.00783}{2.01649}$$

$$\Delta m = 2.01410 - 2.01649 = -0.00239 \frac{g}{mole}$$

$$\Delta E = \Delta mc^2 = -2.39 \times 10^{-3} \frac{g}{mole} \times \frac{9.00 \times 10^{20} \frac{cm^2}{sec^2}}{4.18 \times 10^{10} \frac{ergs}{kcal}}$$

$$= -5.15 \times 10^7 \frac{kcal}{mole}$$

Note that the use of the *atomic* weights of isotopes for the *nuclear* mass in the calculation of the heat of nuclear reactions is acceptable in these cases, since the number of electrons associated with reactants and products is identical and therefore the masses of the electrons cancel in the subtraction. This is not true, however, for the emission of a positron, $_{+1}\beta^0$, a particle identical with an electron except that the sign of its charge is positive.*

The heat of the chemical reaction $H + H \rightarrow H_2$ at 25°C is 104 kcal per mole. Evidently, the heats of nuclear reactions are about a million times larger. The nature of the force holding nucleons together must therefore be fundamentally different from the electrostatic force involved in atomic (chemical) bonding. As in chemical bonding, gravitational and magnetic forces† are not significant interaction forces. Further, the deuteron, composed of one type of charged particle (the proton) and a neutral particle, cannot be held together by electric forces. An even more striking illustration of the conclusion that nuclear forces cannot be electrical is the great stability of the nucleus of $_2^3He$ in which the coulombic interaction of the two protons is repulsive. In 1935, Hideki Yukawa, a theoretical physicist, suggested that *a particular particle oscillating between nucleons* with practically the velocity of light *is the force* that holds the nucleons together. He further predicted that this particle should have a mass about 275 ± 25 times the electron mass and may be electrically neutral, positive, or negative. We designate these particles, called "pi-mesons" or "pions," as π^0, π^+, π^-, the proton as p, and the neutron as n. The processes taking place in the deuteron that stabilize it are assumed to be

* See Problem 20 (page 748).

† This statement tacitly assumes that the gravitational and magnetic effects are identical for interactions between all bodies independent of size and velocity. See Problem 22 (page 748) and page 735.

and the reverse

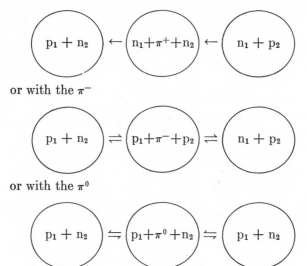

or with the π^-

or with the π^0

The proton in the nucleus then is a neutron part of the time while the neutron is a proton part of the time; the proton and the neutron are thus regarded as two different states of a single particle. The new fundamental idea in this theory is *the concept of a particle* (π^-, π^+, or π^0) *serving as an interaction force.* To be within the range of each other's forces, nucleon separations must be of the order of magnitude of a **fermi** (10^{-13} cm). This accounts for the observation that nuclear forces possess a very short range, $2\text{–}3 \times 10^{-13}$ cm, while the forces between atoms, molecules, terrestrial objects, and astronomical bodies obey an inverse square law and can be detected at large distances. Analogous to chemical bonding, the closer the nucleons, the stronger the nuclear bond. On the other hand, a small distortion or separation of nucleons leads to instability and the repulsive forces of the positive charges cause the nucleus to split into smaller fragments.

The emission of a π^- by a neutron and its almost instantaneous absorption by a proton corresponds to an exchange of the positions of the two nucleons. We emphasize, however, that a deuteron is formed by the interaction of only two particles, a proton and a neutron; addition of a third particle is not required. Rather, the proton and the neutron form a stable system by virtue of the exchange processes involving the pions "created" by the nucleons. Yukawa also predicted that these pions could be "materialized" by imparting to nuclei energies equal to about 250 electron masses (128 Mev). Experiments with high-energy particle accelerators have qualitatively confirmed the essential features of the mesonic field theory. Also, it is consistent with the more recent descriptions of the structure of the proton and the neutron (page 731) and with the observation that a β particle (+ or −) is not ejected directly from a nucleus. Rather, the process involves the ejection of a pion which then decays with the ultimate formation of a β particle:

$$\text{nuclear neutron} \rightarrow \text{nuclear proton} + \text{ejected } \pi^-$$
$$\text{ejected } \pi^- \rightarrow \mu^- \text{ (meson)} + {}_0\nu^0 \text{ (neutrino)}$$
$$\mu^- \rightarrow {}_{-1}\beta^0 + 2\,{}_0\nu^0$$

The existence of the neutrino, massless and chargeless, was predicted by Enrico Fermi and Wolfgang Pauli in 1934 to maintain conservation principles in nuclear processes.

It is interesting that the theoretical calculations carried out by Ernest Sternglass in 1961 indicate that the π^0 may be composed of a hydrogen type "atom" with the proton replaced by a positron and with each particle rotating at nearly the speed of light at distances of about 10^{-14} cm. The rotation of positron-electron pairs would give rise to strong electromagnetic forces whose interactions correspond to typical nuclear forces. He therefore suggested that positron-electron pairs in "relativistic states" (rotating at nearly the speed of light) form the basic structural elements of the mesons and nucleons and, hence, of all matter.

28.4 NUCLEAR REACTIONS

(a) **Radioactivity.** Natural nonradioactive (stable) nuclei, plotted as indicated in Fig. 28.2, fall within a narrow region of stability. Thus, in the light elements the ratio of N/Z is nearly 1, but in the heavier elements the ratio of neutrons to protons increases to about 1.5. Apparently, more neutrons are needed in the heavier nuclei to balance the electrostatic repulsion between the protons. All nuclei with atomic numbers greater than 83 are radioactive; of these, only ${}^{235}_{92}U$, ${}^{238}_{92}U$, and ${}^{232}_{90}Th$ occur on the earth in relatively large amounts. Quantitative investigations reveal that about 60% of the stable nuclei contain an even number of neutrons and an even number of protons, and that there are only four stable nuclei containing an odd number of neutrons and an odd number of protons (${}^2_1H$, ${}^6_3Li$, ${}^{10}_5B$, ${}^{14}_7N$); ${}^1_1H$ and ${}^3_2He$ are the only nuclei that contain fewer neutrons than protons. It is of interest to note that about 86% of the nuclei in the earth's crust (excluding the waters and the atmosphere) have even mass numbers.

Nuclei outside of the stability band spontaneously transform (decay) to nuclei closer to or within the stability band. Nuclei to the right of the stability band have a relative excess of protons and will transform by ${}_{+1}\beta$, ${}^1_1H$, or ${}^4_2He$ emission or electron capture; illustrations are

$$\begin{aligned}
{}^{78}_{35}Br &\rightarrow {}^{78}_{34}Se + {}_{+1}\beta^0 \\
{}^{43}_{21}Sc &\rightarrow {}^{42}_{20}Ca + {}^1_1H \\
{}^{11}_{6}C &\rightarrow {}^7_4Be + {}^4_2He \\
{}^7_4Be + e^- &\rightarrow {}^7_3Li \quad (\textit{electron capture})
\end{aligned}$$

Nuclei to the left of the stability band have a relative excess of neutrons

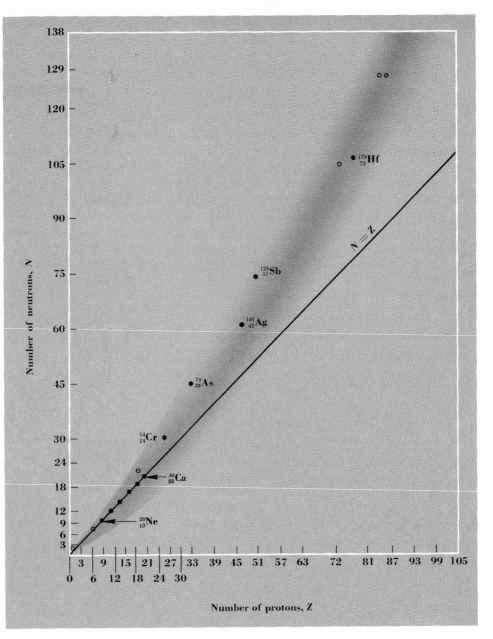

Fig 28.2. *The stability region; several naturally stable nuclei are given to serve as reference points. A few naturally occurring radioactive nuclei are indicated by open circles.*

and will decay by $_{-1}\beta^0$ or $_0n^1$ emission; illustrations are

$$_{36}^{87}\text{Kr} \rightarrow \,_{37}^{87}\text{Rb} + \,_{-1}\beta^0$$
$$_{36}^{87}\text{Kr} \rightarrow \,_{36}^{86}\text{Kr} + \,_0n^1$$

$_{92}^{235}\text{U}$, $_{92}^{238}\text{U}$, and $_{90}^{232}\text{Th}$, the parents, respectively, of three natural radioactive series, lie to the right of the extrapolated stability region and decay mostly by α particle emission. Typical of the natural radioactive series is the ^{238}U series, for which the successive transformations are shown in Fig. 28.3. Several natural radioactive nuclei, for example $^{3}_{1}$H, $^{14}_{6}$C, $^{40}_{19}$K, $^{115}_{49}$In, that are not members of these families also exist.

(b) **Artificial Transmutations.** Everyone is more or less familiar with the dreams, shattered by Daltonian chemistry, of the early chemists, who attempted to transform a cheap metal into gold. With the postulation of the nuclear theory of the atom, artificial transmutation came to appear feasible. The first induced transmutation was demonstrated in 1919 by Lord Rutherford, who exposed nitrogen to α particles from a natural source and detected the production of protons. This reaction may be represented as

$$^{14}_{7}\text{N} + {}^{4}_{2}\text{He} \rightarrow ({}^{18}_{9}\text{F}) \rightarrow {}^{17}_{8}\text{O} + {}^{1}_{1}\text{H}$$

A nitrogen nucleus captures an α particle forming a short-lived compound nucleus ($^{18}_{9}$F), which lies below the stability region and decomposes with the emission of a proton. With the removal of the α particle source, the reaction stops.

While treating light elements such as boron or aluminum with α particles from natural sources, Irene Curie and Frederic Joliot detected in 1934 the emission of positrons and neutrons. More important, they observed that the unexpected emission of positrons does not stop, although the emission of neutrons does stop, upon removal of the α particle source. The reactions may be represented as

$$^{10}_{5}\text{B} + {}^{4}_{2}\text{He} \rightarrow ({}^{14}_{7}\text{N}) \rightarrow {}^{13}_{7}\text{N}^* + {}_{0}\text{n}^1$$

followed by

$$^{13}_{7}\text{N}^* \rightarrow {}^{13}_{6}\text{C} + {}_{+1}\beta^0$$

in which $^{13}_{7}$N* is the first radioisotope artificially produced. An asterisk is sometimes used to indicate a radionucleus.

An α particle, proton, or deuteron, before it can be captured by a nucleus, must possess sufficient kinetic energy to overcome the repulsive force that develops as the positive particle approaches the positive nucleus. Particle accelerators, such as cyclotrons, were invented to increase the kinetic energy of charged particles to levels required for capture by nuclei with high atomic numbers. With the accelerators available in 1934, it was not possible to disintegrate or induce radioactivity in the elements beyond potassium. Since the neutron is electrically neutral, Enrico Fermi reasoned that a repulsive force to oppose its entry into a nucleus would probably not be set up and, therefore, that it should be possible to transform all known elements with natural sources of neutrons. The test of this hypothesis by Fermi and other investigators proved fruitful. Practically all known elements have been transformed, and in addition a number of transuranium elements were synthesized:

$$^{238}_{92}\text{U} + {}_{0}\text{n}^1 \rightarrow {}^{239}_{92}\text{U}^* \rightarrow {}^{239}_{93}\text{Np}^* + {}_{-1}\beta^0$$
$$^{239}_{93}\text{Np}^* \rightarrow {}^{239}_{94}\text{Pu}^* + {}_{-1}\beta^0$$

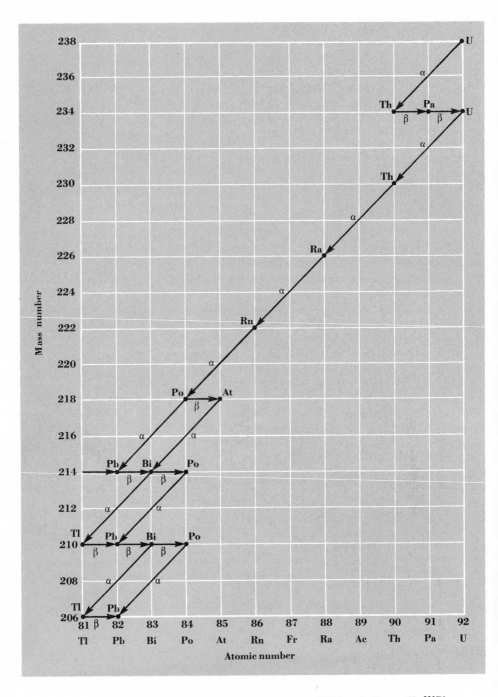

Fig. 28.3. *Uranium-238 radioactive series.* $^{238}_{92}U$ *is the "parent";* $^{206}_{82}Pb$, *nonradioactive, is the "end product." The radionuclei are either* α *or* $_{-1}\beta$ *unstable; occasionally, a fraction of the nuclei of an element, for example,* ^{218}Po, *emits* α *particles while the remainder emits* $_{-1}\beta$ *particles.*

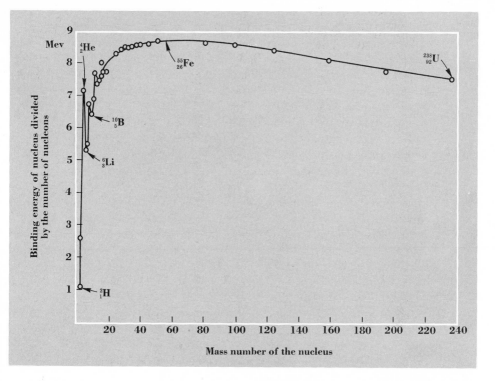

Fig. 28.4. *The average energy evolved per nucleon for natural nuclei.*

(c) Fission. It is instructive to plot, as in Fig. 28.4, the average energy released per nucleon, in the formation of a nucleus from nucleons, against the mass number. The greater the energy released per nucleon, the greater the stability of the nucleus. It is evident that the very light and the very heavy nuclei are least stable compared to the nuclei in the vicinity of $^{55}_{26}$Fe. It would be natural to expect that spontaneous changes that may occur among nuclei should include the fusion of very light nuclei into heavier nuclei, and the splitting (fission) of a very heavy nucleus into two nuclei. It is equally evident that these reactions are rich energy sources, compared with chemical changes.

Although spontaneous fission has been detected in $_{90}$Th and heavier elements, the rate is too slow for any practical purpose because of the high energy of activation (roughly 1.4×10^8 kcal per mole) required to produce the deformation of the nucleus (a slight separation of nucleons) necessary for fission. The energy of activation is usually supplied by exposure to neutrons which form deformed unstable compound nuclei; for example

$$^{235}_{92}U + {}_0n^1 \rightarrow \left({}^{236}_{92}U\right) \rightarrow {}^{137}_{53}I + {}^{97}_{39}Y + 2{}_0n^1$$

When Fermi announced in 1934 the synthesis of transuranium elements by neutron bombardment of uranium, many investigators doubted this interpretation of the chemical analytical results. In particular, Ida Noddack intimated that the uranium nuclei were being split into smaller nuclei. Considerable interest was engendered and practically every laboratory engaged in the study of nuclear reactions undertook an analytical investigation of the possible products.

Among the products of the neutron irradiation of uranium, a radioelement was found that behaved chemically like radium. Since its radioactivity differed from that of natural radium it was assumed to be an isotope of radium. However, because of the chemical similarity of barium and radium, these results do not eliminate the possibility that *the element behaving like radium could be barium.* The chemical reactions of the compounds of barium and radium are so alike that a separation may be effected only by making use of the slight differences in solubility of the corresponding chlorides or bromides. If an unknown bromide is a radium bromide, it crystallizes along with natural radium bromide; if it is a barium bromide, it stays with the natural barium bromide. Otto Hahn and Fritz Strassman in 1939 mixed the supposed isotope of radium as the bromide with natural barium bromide and natural radium bromide and, by a series of fractional crystallizations, found that the supposed isotope of radium was actually barium. The new radioelement could not be separated from barium for the simple, but unexpected, reason that it was an isotope of barium. They then concluded that the uranium nucleus had divided into two fragments and it was immediately realized that a tremendous amount of energy would accompany this division, a conclusion verified by the large readings produced by this energy in an ionization chamber.* Similar readings obtained by previous investigators had been dismissed as "electronic noises." Nuclear fission was thus discovered by chemists.

From the principle of conservation of charge, the other nucleus formed with $_{56}$Ba must be $_{36}$Kr; a typical fission reaction is

$$^{235}_{92}\text{U} + _0\text{n}^1 \rightarrow (^{236}_{92}\text{U}) \rightarrow ^{142}_{56}\text{Ba} + ^{91}_{36}\text{Kr} + 3_0\text{n}^1 \qquad \Delta E = -2 \times 10^2 \text{ Mev}$$
$$(4.6 \times 10^9 \text{ kcal per mole})$$

Since more than one neutron is produced for each one consumed and since a ^{236}U nucleus undergoes fission in about 10^{-9} sec, it becomes possible to develop a branching chain reaction (page 629, and Problem 41, page 640) leading to an "atomic explosion," the release of unprecedented quantities of energy in extremely small periods of time. However, through the use of "chain breakers," materials such as cadmium that act as neutron scavengers, the number of neutrons available for the fission of $^{235}_{92}$U may be decreased to about one for three produced. The rate of the fission reaction is then decreased, and the heat of the reaction may be utilized as a practi-

---

* A gold-leaf electroscope serves to illustrate the principle of an ionization chamber. The gold leaves diverge when a potential difference is applied between the gold leaves (similarly charged) and the case of the electroscope; the larger the charge, the greater the leaf deflection. On exposure to radiation, ions are formed in the electroscope. The ions and electrons will collect on the oppositely charged elements of the electroscope, thus decreasing the charge on the leaves, thereby decreasing the leaf deflection. The rate of collapse of the leaves may be calibrated in terms of the charge collected.

cal energy source. Also, the remaining neutrons may be used to produce desirable isotopes or to study the biological effects of neutrons.

The first controlled and sustained fission reaction was operated successfully in 1942 at the University of Chicago with comparatively impure ^{235}U and "chain breakers." The first fission branching chain reaction was successfully carried out in a test explosion with pure ^{239}Pu in 1945 near Alamogordo, New Mexico.

Fission fragments are very rich in neutrons and therefore decay by emitting $_{-1}\beta$ particles or neutrons and γ radiation, ultimately forming stable elements.

(d) **Fusion.** A tank of hydrogen does not explode with the formation of deuterium because the rate of the reaction is infinitesimally small. The rate is proportional to the number of collisions between the nuclei, but the number of collisions is essentially zero because of repulsive electrostatic forces. To increase the number of collisions, the temperature of the reactants must be increased to 10^6–10^7 °C. At these temperatures, light elements are completely stripped of orbital electrons forming a completely ionized **plasma,** a gaseous system containing an equivalent number of positive ions and electrons. For the hydrogen isotopes, the probability of reaction per collision appears to be highest for

$$^3_1H + {}^3_1H \rightarrow {}^4_2He + 2{}_0n^1$$

and least for

$$^1_1H + {}^1_1H \rightarrow {}^2_1H + {}_{+1}\beta^0$$

(e) **Stellar Energy.** The mean temperature of the sun, 4×10^6 °K, suffices for fusion between protons, ^2H, and ^3He:

$$^1_1H + {}^1_1H \rightarrow {}^2_1H + {}_{+1}\beta^0$$
$$^2_1H + {}^1_1H \rightarrow {}^3_2He$$
$$^3_2He + {}^3_2He \rightarrow {}^4_2He + 2{}^1_1H$$

Once the sun has synthesized ^3He and ^4He, further nuclear reactions involving ^3He and ^4He nuclei may lead to the production of ^{12}C, which then starts a carbon-nitrogen-oxygen cycle in which 4 protons are fused into a ^4He nucleus:

$$^{12}_{6}C + {}^1_1H \rightarrow {}^{13}_{7}N \rightarrow {}^{13}_{6}C + {}_{+1}\beta^0$$
$$^{13}_{6}C + {}^1_1H \rightarrow {}^{14}_{7}N$$
$$^{14}_{7}N + {}^1_1H \rightarrow {}^{15}_{8}O \rightarrow {}^{15}_{7}N + {}_{+1}\beta^0$$
$$^{15}_{7}N + {}^1_1H \rightarrow {}^{12}_{6}C + {}^4_2He$$

The over-all reaction is

$$4{}^1_1H \rightarrow {}^4_2He + 2{}_{+1}\beta^0 \qquad \Delta E = -4 \times 10^{-5} \text{ ergs per } \alpha \text{ particle}$$
$$= -6 \times 10^8 \text{ kcal per mole}$$

The proton-proton chain reaction and the C—N—O cycle for the burning of hydrogen to helium were first proposed in 1938–1939 by Hans Bethe and Carl von Weizsäcker.

TABLE 28.1   *Half-Lives of Some Radioisotopes*

Isotope	Decay reactions	$t_{\frac{1}{2}}$
$^{3}_{1}H$	$^{3}_{1}H \rightarrow\ ^{3}_{2}He +\ _{-1}\beta$	12.5 years
$^{15}_{8}O$	$^{15}_{8}O \rightarrow\ ^{15}_{7}N +\ _{+1}\beta$	2.0 min
$^{32}_{15}P$	$^{32}_{15}P \rightarrow\ ^{32}_{16}S +\ _{-1}\beta$	14.3 days
$^{59}_{26}Fe$	$^{59}_{26}Fe \rightarrow\ ^{59}_{27}Co +\ _{-1}\beta$	45.1 days
$^{60}_{27}Co$	$^{60}_{27}Co \rightarrow\ ^{60}_{28}Ni +\ _{-1}\beta$	5.2 years
$^{90}_{38}Sr$	$^{90}_{38}Sr \rightarrow\ ^{90}_{39}Y +\ _{-1}\beta$	27.7 years
$^{131}_{53}I$	$^{131}_{53}I \rightarrow\ ^{131}_{54}Xe +\ _{-1}\beta$	8.1 days
$^{209}_{83}Bi$	$^{209}_{83}Bi \rightarrow\ ^{205}_{81}Tl +\ \alpha$	10^{17} years

28.5   RATE OF RADIOACTIVE DECAY PROCESSES

Radioactive decay processes are also first order reactions. That is, the number of disintegrations per unit of time is directly proportional to the number of atoms present. The rate of decay is usually expressed in terms of half-lives (page 626). The half-lives of some radioactive isotopes are given in Table 28.1. The relation between q_t, the quantity at time t, and q_0, the initial quantity, is (page 628)

$$q_t = q_0(0.5)^{t/t_{\frac{1}{2}}} \tag{2}$$

EXAMPLE 1   **Radon "seeds," radon collected from a radium bromide supply and sealed in capillary tubing, are used for cancer therapy. The half-life for radon,**

$$^{222}_{86}Rn \rightarrow\ ^{218}_{84}Po +\ ^{4}_{2}He$$

is 3.825 days. (a) Starting with 0.0200 mg, how many milligrams will remain after 11.475 days?

ANSWER   **Substituting the given data into Equation (2),**

$$q_t = 0.0200\ \text{mg}\ (0.5)^{11.475\ \text{days}/3.825\ \text{days}} = 0.00250\ \text{mg}$$

The quantity left is therefore 2.50×10^{-3} mg.
(b) A radon seed initially emitted 7.0×10^4 alpha particles per sec; later, it emitted 2.1×10^4 alpha particles. What is the age of the seed?

ANSWER   **Using Equation (2),**

$$2.1 \times 10^4\ \text{particles} = 7.0 \times 10^4\ \text{particles}\ (0.5)^{t/3.8\ \text{days}}$$

from which $t = 6.6$ days. The age of the seed is therefore 6.6 days.

28.6   RADIOCHEMISTRY

(a) **Tracer Elements.**   With very few exceptions, the disintegration rate of a given radioisotope is, unlike chemical changes, independent of the chemical state and physical conditions. Hence, radioisotopes may be "traced" through chemical and physical changes, yielding valuable information about the mechanism of such changes. The fraction of ingested cholesterol, for example, that terminates in the blood stream may be determined by feeding cholesterol, enriched with $^{14}_6C^*$ of known activity, and then measuring the $^{14}_6C^*$ activity of cholesterol per unit volume of blood.

(b) Radiochemical Dating. Radiochemical dating continues to make important contributions to paleoanthropology and geology. The full significance of the discoveries of hominid* fossils at Olduvai Gorge, Tanganyika, in 1960, for example, could not be realized until the ages of the beds at the Gorge were accurately determined.

EXAMPLE 2   **The activity of $^{14}_6C^*$ found in living plants and animals and in the air is approximately constant at 14 disintegrations per min per gram (d/min-g) of carbon, the activity lost through disintegration being replenished by the production of $^{14}_6C^*$ through the interaction of cosmic radiation with $^{14}_7N$ in the atmosphere. It is assumed that this value is also true for ancient times. Then, so long as a plant or an animal is alive, the activity of $^{14}_6C^*$ per gram of carbon remains constant, but upon death the $^{14}_6C^*$ continues to decay without replenishment and the activity decreases. From the known half-life, 5.73 $\times$ 10^3 years, for $^{14}_6C^* \rightarrow {_{-1}\beta^0} + {^{14}_7N}$, the age of archeological samples may then be determined. The activity of the hair of an Egyptian woman is 7.50 disintegrations per min per gram carbon. What is the historical age of the hair?**

ANSWER   **From the statement of the problem,**

$$q_0 = 14 \frac{d}{\min g}$$

$$q_t = 7.50 \frac{d}{\min g}$$

whence, using Equation (2)

$$7.50 \frac{d}{\min g} = 14 \frac{d}{\min g} (0.5)^{t/573 \times 10 \text{ yr}}$$

from which $t = 5.10 \times 10^3$ years; the age of the hair is therefore 5.10×10^3 years. Willard Libby is largely responsible for these significant contributions to archeology.†

* Pertains to very remote ancestors of Man.

† Although the agreement between the ages obtained from historical evidence and radiocarbon dating is generally satisfactory, discrepancies have been found between ring dating and the radiocarbon dating of wood samples. In one case, ring dating yielded an age of 931 years for a tree sample while radiocarbon dating showed 1271 years. Disagreements could be accounted for by variations in the annual formation of tree rings, by incorrectness of the assumption that $^{14}C^*$ formation is constant in time and space, or by alteration of the original composition. The radiocarbon age of fresh water shells is subject to large error due to the alteration of the original shell composition, mainly by the incorporation or removal of carbonaceous material.

(c) Chemonuclear Synthesis. High-energy ionizing radiation, about 1–50 megarads (see below), is used as an energy source to initiate chemical reactions. Ethyl bromide and nitrogen trifluoride, for example, are manufactured by **chemonuclear synthesis,** reactions in which the reactants are exposed to ionizing radiation. Solid methane at 77°K is polymerized rapidly and efficiently to heavy hydrocarbons by cobalt-60 gamma rays. The product is a viscous oil consisting mainly of saturated hydrocarbons containing an average of about 20 carbon atoms per molecule.

Nitrogen in some combined form is essential to all living organisms. The proteins (page 771), important components of all living cells, are nitrogen compounds but the cells cannot assimilate the nitrogen of the air. However, the roots of some plants, notably the leguminous variety, carry *nitrogen-fixing bacteria* capable of converting atmospheric nitrogen into nitrogen compounds that are then assimilated by the plant for protein synthesis. Lightning also fixes atmospheric nitrogen into compounds. However, artificial fertilizers, made through the fixation of nitrogen, must supplement natural sources. Under investigation is the fixation of nitrogen with oxygen to nitrogen oxide,

$$N_2 + O_2 \rightarrow 2NO \qquad \Delta H = +42 \text{ kcal}$$

by the passage of air through a nuclear reactor serving as a source of ionizing radiation.

28.7   **UNITS FOR REFERENCE**

The **curie, c,** the standard used in measuring the activity of all radioactive substances, has been fixed at 3.7×10^{10} disintegrations per second (dps). A microcurie is 10^{-6} curie. All human beings are continuously exposed to radiation (exclusive of "fallout") originating within as well as outside the body; this natural source averages about 2–3 dps.

The **roentgen, r,** the standard used in measuring the intensity of x or γ radiations, is defined as the quantity of x or γ radiation that produces 1.61×10^{12} ion pairs in one gram of air, equivalent to the absorption of 84 ergs per gram of air. The **rad** is the dosage of any nuclear emanation equivalent to the absorption of 100 ergs per gram of any material.

An **electron volt** corresponds to the kinetic energy acquired by one electron (1.60×10^{-19} coulomb) when it is accelerated in an electric field produced by a potential difference of one volt:

$$1.60 \times 10^{-19} \frac{\text{coulomb}}{\text{electron}} \frac{\text{joule}}{\text{volt coulomb}} \, 10^7 \frac{\text{ergs}}{\text{joule}}$$

$$= 1.60 \times 10^{-12} \frac{\text{erg}}{\text{electron volt}}$$

$$1.60 \times 10^{-12} \frac{\text{erg}}{\text{electron volt} \, 4.18 \times 10^{10} \frac{\text{ergs}}{\text{kcal}}}$$

$$= 3.83 \times 10^{-23} \frac{\text{kcal}}{\text{electron volt}}$$

There is therefore 1.60×10^{-12} erg or 3.83×10^{-23} kcal in one electron volt. Recalling that one faraday is a mole of electrons,

$$1.60 \times 10^{-12} \; \frac{\text{erg}}{\text{electron volt}} \; 6.02 \times 10^{23} \; \frac{\text{electrons}}{\text{faraday}}$$

$$= 9.63 \times 10^{11} \; \frac{\text{ergs}}{\text{faraday volt}}$$

$$3.83 \times 10^{-23} \; \frac{\text{kcal}}{\text{electron volt}} \; 6.02 \times 10^{23} \; \frac{\text{electrons}}{\text{faraday}}$$

$$= 23.1 \; \frac{\text{kcal}}{\text{faraday volt}}$$

Thus, the kinetic energy acquired by *one mole of electrons* when they are accelerated in an electric field produced by a potential difference of one volt is 9.63×10^{11} ergs or 23.1 kcal.

Then 1 electron volt per atom is equal to 23.1 kcal/mole:

$$1 \frac{\text{electron volt}}{\text{atom}} \times 23.1 \; \frac{\text{kcal}}{\text{faraday volt}} \times 6.02 \times 10^{23} \; \frac{\text{atoms}}{\text{mole}}$$

$$\times \frac{\text{faraday}}{6.02 \times 10^{23} \; \text{electrons}} = 23.1 \; \frac{\text{kcal}}{\text{mole}}$$

In short, divide kcal/mole by 23.1 to convert to electron volt/atom; multiply electron volt/atom by 23.1 to convert to kcal/mole.

The **Mev,** a million electron volts, is the kinetic energy acquired by an electron when it is accelerated through a potential difference of 10^6 volts in an electric field.

Problems

1. α, β, γ. How is the number of protons in a nucleus changed when (*i*) a gamma ray, (*ii*) a beta particle, (*iii*) an alpha particle, is emitted from the nucleus?

2. Conservation of nucleons and charge. (a) Balance the following nuclear reactions which involve the formation of a compound nucleus [indicate symbol, mass number, and atomic number for ( ) and ?]:

$$^{93}\text{Nb} + {}^{12}_{6}\text{C} \rightarrow (\quad) \rightarrow ? + 2\,_0\text{n}^1$$
$$^{51}\text{V} + {}^{16}\text{O} \rightarrow (\quad) \rightarrow {}^{65}_{31}\text{Ga} + ?$$
$$^{12}\text{C} + {}^{12}\text{C} \rightarrow (\quad) \rightarrow {}^{22}_{11}\text{Na} + ? + ?$$

Not all nuclear processes involve the formation of a compound nucleus; when, for example, very high-energy particles are used, the energy is not shared among all the nucleons in the target nucleus. (b) Balance the following nuclear reactions which do not involve compound nuclei:

$$^{239}_{94}\text{Pu} + {}^4\text{He} \rightarrow ? + \,_0\text{n}^1$$
$$^{246}_{96}\text{Cm} + ? \rightarrow {}^{254}_{102}\text{No} + \text{neutrons}$$
$$^{252}_{98}\text{Cf} + {}^{11}_{5}\text{B} \rightarrow ? + 4\,_0\text{n}^1$$
$$^{252}_{98}\text{Cf} + {}^{13}\text{C} \rightarrow ? + 4\,_0\text{n}^1$$

(c) Balance the following nuclear reactions:

$$^{14}C + ? \rightarrow {}^{14}C + 2_0n^1 + {}^1H \rightarrow ? + {}^1H$$
$$? + 15_0n^1 \rightarrow {}^{254}_{94}Pu \rightarrow ? + 6_{-1}\beta°$$

$$^{238}_{92}U + ? \rightarrow {}^{247}_{99}E + 5_0n^1$$
$$^{75}As + {}^4He \rightarrow {}^{38}Cl + ? + 6\,{}^1H + 11_0n^1$$

3. ΔE. Calculate ΔE for the reaction

$$^7_3Li + {}^1_1H \rightarrow 2{}^4_2He$$

Atomic masses: $^7Li = 7.016$, $^1H = 1.008$, $^4He = 4.003$. The measured value is 39×10^7 kcal per mole or 17 Mev.

4. Beta decay. (a) How would you account for the production of electrons that do not exist in nuclei? (b) Write the individual processes for the nuclear reaction generally represented as

$$^{65}_{28}Ni \rightarrow {}^{65}_{29}Cu + {}_{-1}\beta^0$$

(c) Is the Yukawa theory consistent with β-decay processes? (Yes or no.) (d) Positrons do not exist as particles in nuclei. Explain $_{+1}\beta$ emission (by analogy to $_{-1}\beta$ emission).

5. Abundance. Atoms with a given Z belong to the same element. Nuclei with a given Z and A are said to belong to the same **nuclide.** For each pair pick the more abundant nuclide: (a) $^{52}_{24}Cr$, $^{59}_{27}Co$; (b) $^{19}_9F$, $^{18}_9F$; (c) $^{180}_{72}Hf$, $^{179}_{72}Hf$.

6. Radioactive series. The over-all equation for the decomposition of $^{232}_{90}Th$, the parent of the thorium natural radioactive series, is

$$^{232}_{90}Th \rightarrow 6\alpha + 3_{-1}\beta° + x$$

What are the mass number and atomic number of the end product?

7. $t_{\frac{1}{2}}$. Plot the following data for ^{144}Pr:

Time (min)	Counts per min
0	200×10^2
10	135×10^2
20	93×10^2
30	65×10^2

Use the graph to determine the half-life of ^{144}Pr. The accepted value is 18 min.

8. $t_{\frac{1}{2}}$. By beta emission, 1.000 microgram of ^{107}Cd decays to 0.125 microgram in 20.1 hours. What is the half-life of ^{107}Cd?

9. Dating. Two wood samples of well-established age (4900 ± 200 years, by historical evidence) from Egyptian tombs possess activity of 7.8 disintegrations per min per gram of carbon. Calculate the age of these wood samples from radiochemical evidence. Does this finding have any bearing on the assumption that the rate of production of $^{14}_6C^*$ in ancient times was the same as it is today?

Answer. 48×10^2 years.

10. Tracer chemistry. An animal is fed ethyl alcohol, $^*C_2H_5OH$, activity a counts per min. Subsequently, acetic acid, $^*CH_3COOH$, activity b counts per min per 10 g liver, is isolated from the liver; total weight of liver is c g. Exhaled $^*CO_2$, recovered as Ca^*CO_3, has an activity of d counts per min per liter of air; total air volume is e liters. $^*C$ activity of blood stream is zero. (a) How would you check the precision of this experiment? (b) What conclusions regarding the chemistry of ethyl alcohol would you draw from these results?

11. Radioactivity. *Scientific American,* April 1903: "Professor Curie has announced to the French Academy of Sciences that radium possesses the extraordinary property of continuously emitting heat without combustion, without chemical change of any kind, and without change in its molecular structure. Radium, he states, maintains its own temperature at a point 1.5°C above the surrounding atmosphere. Despite this constant activity, the salt apparently remains just as potent as it was at the beginning." Would you, at the present time, accept this as a correct statement? Justify your position.

12. Radioactivity. The range, R, of a particle is the distance it traverses in air before being stopped. The relation between the velocity, v, with which an α particle is ejected from a nucleus and its range in centimeters is

$$v^3 = 1.0 \times 10^{27} \frac{\text{cm}^2}{\text{sec}^3} R$$

The range of the α particles ejected by $^{214}_{84}$Po is 7 cm (15°C, 1 atm). Calculate the velocity of these α particles.

13. α, β. What is the simplest explanation you can offer to account for the observation that α particles traverse air in straight lines while β particles are easily deflected and hence describe a zigzag path?

14. α, β, γ. The emission of α and β particles from nuclei is frequently accompanied by the emission of γ ray photons, the source of the photons being the product nuclei. For example:

$$^{210}_{82}\text{Pb} \rightarrow {}^{210}_{83}\text{Bi} + {}_{-1}\beta^0 \qquad {}^{226}_{88}\text{Ra} \rightarrow {}^{222}_{86}\text{Rn} + \alpha$$
$$^{210}_{83}\text{Bi} \rightarrow {}^{210}_{83}\text{Bi} + \gamma \qquad {}^{222}_{86}\text{Rn} \rightarrow {}^{222}_{86}\text{Rn} + \gamma$$

(a) Are these particles and photons nucleons (constituents of nuclei)? (b) Calculate Δm, the difference in mass between the final and initial nuclei in g per mole for the emission of a γ ray of energy 2.6 Mev,

$$^2_1\text{H(excited)} \rightarrow {}^2_1\text{H} + \gamma$$

Answer. -2.8×10^{-3} g/mole.

15. α. Calculate the e/m ratio for an α particle. The measured value is 14.5×10^{13} esu/g.

16. Conservation of nucleons and charge. (a) Dependence of the half-life on the chemical state and physical conditions is found in radioactive processes in which orbital electrons enter directly. For example, $^7_4$Be decays by "K capture," the capture of one of its K orbital electrons (page 173); the rate is 0.14% faster for BeF_2 compared to BeO. Balance the following:

$$^7_4\text{Be (BeF}_2) + e^- \rightarrow ?$$
$$^7_4\text{Be (BeO)} + e^- \rightarrow ?$$

(b) "Element x is intensely radioactive and decays by spontaneous fission. Its chemical properties are similar to those of thulium." What is the atomic number of x? (c) Using balanced equations, give one illustration of the following statement: It is believed that transplutonium elements form from lead and bismuth by very rapid neutron absorption in thermonuclear explosions. The transplutonium elements then decay to uranium and thorium. (d) The muonium atom, a new atom consisting of a positive mu meson and an electron, is similar to what atom? Would you expect the chemistry of these two atoms to be similar? What is the basis of your answer?

17. Conservation rules. (a) Account for the orbital electrons in the nuclear reaction

$$^{226}_{88}Ra \rightarrow \alpha + {}^{222}_{86}Rn$$

(b) Do the following reactions, observed outside of nuclei, violate the law of conservation of nucleons?

$$\text{proton} \rightarrow \text{neutron} + {}_{+1}\beta^0 \qquad t_{\frac{1}{2}} > 10^{21} \text{ years}$$
$$\text{neutron} \rightarrow \text{proton} + {}_{-1}\beta^0 \qquad t_{\frac{1}{2}} = 13 \text{ min}$$

(c) Is the following process, in which charge, mass, energy, and momentum are conserved, possible?

$$\text{neutron} \rightarrow \text{meson}^+ + \text{meson}^- + \text{energy}$$

18. Conservation. The mass of a nucleus is less than the sum of the masses of the individual nucleons (protons and neutrons). Is this a violation of the conservation principles? Explain your answer.

19. Protection. Alpha particles may be stopped by paper or by the outer skin layers. Does it follow that an α emitter, internally located, presents no hazard to an animal?

20. Mass-energy. (a) Show that the energy of a ${}_{-1}\beta^0$ decay nuclear reaction, for example,

$$^{87}_{37}Rb \rightarrow {}^{87}_{38}Sr + {}_{-1}\beta^0$$

expressed in g per mole, is equal to the difference between the atomic masses of ${}^{87}Sr$ and ${}^{87}Rb$. (b) Show that the energy of a ${}_{+1}\beta^0$ decay nuclear reaction, for example,

$$^{34}_{17}Cl \rightarrow {}^{34}_{16}S + {}_{+1}\beta^0$$

expressed in g per mole, is equal to the difference between the atomic masses of ${}^{34}S$ and ${}^{34}Cl$ plus two electron masses.

21. Mass-energy. When a positron is slowed down in matter, annihilation of matter occurs with the production of two γ ray photons,

$$_{+1}\beta + {}_{-1}\beta \rightleftharpoons 2\gamma$$

The electron mass is 9.11×10^{-28} g per electron. Calculate the energy in Mev and the frequency of each photon. (Assume the energy is evenly divided between the two photons.) The measured frequency of this radiation is 1.24×10^{20} sec^{-1}. The reverse process, also observed experimentally, is known as **pair production** or the materialization of energy.

22. Nuclear forces. Nucleons cannot be held together by electric forces because the neutron carries no charge. (a) If the nature of the attractive force between the neutron and the proton in the deuteron were gravitational, the work required to separate them to very large distances would be given by

$$\frac{Gm_1m_2}{r}$$

where m_1 and m_2 are the masses of the two particles, 1.67×10^{-24} g per proton or neutron, r is the distance between the two particles, 3×10^{-13} cm (3 fermis), and G is the gravitational constant, 6.67×10^{-8} cm³/g sec², assumed to have the same value for all pairs of bodies. Predict the binding energy of the deuteron in ergs per nucleus due to gravitational attraction. The experimental binding energy is 3.6×10^{-6} erg per nucleus. The predicted value is too small or too large by what factor? (Assuming that the traditional concept of G as a universal constant is not valid for the forces operating within subatomic particles, calculate the value for a gravitational constant that would account for the experimentally observed binding energy. Lloyd Motz in 1962 theoretically calculated 1.13×10^{31} cm³/g sec² as the gravitational constant for systems with masses of the order of protons and neutrons.) (b) The work required to bring two protons from very large distances to r is e^2/r where $e = 4.8 \times 10^{-10}$ esu per proton. Calculate the work in ergs required to bring two protons within a distance of 3×10^{-13} cm (3 fermis). Required unit: esu² = dyne cm². (c) The binding energy of deuteron nuclei is 2.23 Mev. Express this quantity in kcal per mole.

Answer. (a) 6.2×10^{-43} erg/nucleus;
(b) 8×10^{-7} erg.

23. Yukawa theory. (a) Nuclear stability refers to the work necessary to separate the nucleus into its constituent nucleons. In terms of the Yukawa theory, what is the possible number of "nuclear bonds" in $^{1}_{1}\text{H}$, $^{3}_{2}\text{He}$, and $^{4}_{2}\text{He}$? Which nucleus should be most stable? Least stable? (b) Estimate the minimum energy (i) in ergs per particle and (ii) in kcal per mole that must be imparted to an α particle for it to materialize a pi meson, 3×10^2 electron masses, upon striking a nucleus. (c) The binding energies of the helium isotopes are $^{3}_{2}\text{He}$, 8 Mev; $^{4}_{2}\text{He}$, 28 Mev. By analogy to chemical bonding, what statement can you make about the relative internucleon distances in these nuclei?

Answer. (a) 1, 3, 6; (b) (i) 2.5×10^{-4} erg/particle.

24. Meson field theory. Would you accept the statement, "In fact, it is doubtful whether any 'ultimate' unit of matter exists at all"? Justify your position.

25. Stability. Pick the nuclear reaction most likely to occur:

(a) $\quad ^{135}_{56}\text{Ba} \rightarrow {}_{-1}\beta^0 + {}^{135}_{57}\text{La}$

(b) $\quad ^{120}_{56}\text{Ba} \rightarrow {}_0\text{n}^1 + {}^{119}_{56}\text{Ba}$

or

(c) $\quad ^{120}_{56}\text{Ba} \rightarrow {}_{+1}\beta^0 + {}^{120}_{55}\text{Cs}$

26. Artificial disintegration. (a) If α particles and nuclei behaved in the same way as macroparticles, should α particles be captured by nuclei? (b) Neutrons are very effective in producing nuclear transmutations. According to some cosmological theories, neutrons became available soon after the beginning of the universe. Account for the fact that disintegrations by neutrons were discovered only within the past few decades.

27. Fission. (a) Natural uranium contains about 0.7% ^{235}U atoms which split under the influence of naturally occurring neutrons. Account for the fact that uranium ores are safe to handle. (b) $^{239}_{94}\text{Pu}$ is a fissionable isotope and may be synthesized from $^{238}_{92}\text{U}$ by the reaction sequence

$$^{238}_{92}\text{U} + {}_0\text{n}^1 \rightarrow {}^{239}_{92}\text{U} \rightarrow {}^{239}_{93}\text{Np} + {}_{-1}\beta^0$$
$$^{239}_{93}\text{Np} \rightarrow {}^{239}_{94}\text{Pu} + {}_{-1}\beta^0$$

Account for the fact that certain reactors produce more fissionable atoms than are used.

28. Fission. Let us assume that the neutrons produced by ^{235}U fission travel an average distance of 5 cm before being captured by ^{235}U. The density of ^{235}U is 19 g per ml. Will a sphere of pure ^{235}U with a mass of (i) 10 g, (ii) 5 kg, explode on exposure to a stray neutron? Explain your answers.

29. Fission. Is the fission reaction

$$^{63}Cu + {}^1_1H \rightarrow {}^{24}_{11}Na + ? + {}_0n^1$$

endothermic or exothermic? Atomic masses: $^1H = 1.008$, $n^1 = 1.009$, $^{24}Na = 23.991$, $^{39}K = 38.964$, $^{63}Cu = 62.929$.

30. Fusion. The "ignition temperature," the temperature above which more energy is liberated than is lost by radiation, is 4.5×10^7 °K for the deuterium-tritium (T) reaction

$$^2_1D + {}^3_1T \rightarrow {}^4_2He + {}_0n^1 \qquad \Delta E = -17.6 \text{ Mev}$$

Calculate the energy in kcal required to convert at constant volume 10^{-3} mole of hydrogen (D_2, T_2) gas at room temperature to a plasma at the ignition temperature:

$$H_2 \text{ (25°C)} \xrightarrow[\text{volume}]{\text{constant}} 2 \text{ nuclei} + 2 \text{ electrons } (4.5 \times 10^7 \text{ °K})$$

The average specific heat of D_2 and T_2 may be assumed to be identical, 7 cal per mole per deg; the heats of dissociation may be assumed to be 10^2 kcal per mole, and the ionization energy to be 14 ev.

31. Stellar energy. (a) The thermonuclear chain reactions (page 741) evolve 4×10^{-5} erg per α particle. The sun radiates 8×10^{21} kcal per sec from its surface. Calculate the mass of hydrogen in tons (2×10^3 lb per ton) and the number of H atoms destroyed per sec. (b) The rate of helium production from hydrogen is related to

$$-\frac{d[H]}{dt} = k[H]^2$$

in which k is very small. How would you account for the production rate of energy given in part (a)?

Answer. (a) 4×10^6 tons/sec; 2×10^{35} atoms/sec.

32. Atomic energy. Matter is converted to energy through chemical or nuclear changes. Calculate the heat in kcal available at constant volume per mole of lithium for the following reactions at absolute zero:

(i) $^6_3Li + {}^1_1H \rightarrow Li^6H^1$

in which Δm is estimated to be -3×10^{-9} g per mole;

(ii) $^6_3Li + {}^1_1H \rightarrow {}^3_2He + {}^4_2He$

for which the atomic masses are $^1H = 1.0078$, $^3He = 3.0160$, $^4He = 4.0026$, $^6Li = 6.0151$.

Answer. (ii) 9.3×10^7 kcal/mole.

33. Rate. (a) The half-life is 8.1 days for ^{131}I. What is its rate constant? (b) If a sample of ^{131}I has an activity of 10×10^5 disintegrations per minute, what is the number of atoms, the number of moles, and the number of picograms (page 778) of ^{131}I in the sample?

Answer. (a) 8.6×10^{-2} day^{-1}; (b) 1.7×10^{10} atoms.

34. $t_\frac{1}{2}$. The over-all equation for the decomposition of ^{238}U$(t_\frac{1}{2} = 4.50 \times 10^9$ years) is

$$^{238}_{92}\text{U} \rightarrow \,^{206}_{82}\text{Pb} + 8\alpha + 6_{-1}\beta^0$$

The average amount of ^{238}U in the earth's crust is 4 g per metric ton. What is the maximum number of atoms and volume of helium produced at 27°C and 1 atm per metric ton in 2.25×10^9 years?

35. $t_\frac{1}{2}$. The most stable isotope of berkelium or californium has a half-life of 7×10^3 years. Accepting 4×10^9 years as the age of the earth and assuming berkelium was part of the primordial stock of elements, calculate the fraction of the original amount remaining. Is this quantity detectable?

Answer. 1 part in $10^{2 \times 10^5}$.

36. Dating. (a) Will the production of ^{14}C* in the atmosphere by other than natural means affect radiocarbon dating (i) of existing relics; (ii) of matter now living that may become future relics? If so, will the error in the age be positive or negative? (b) The over-all equation for the decomposition of ^{238}U ($t_\frac{1}{2} = 4.50 \times 10^9$ years) is

$$^{239}_{92}\text{U} \rightarrow \,^{206}_{82}\text{Pb} + 8\alpha + 6_{-1}\beta^0$$

A uranium mineral mined from a stratum corresponding to the Pre-Cambrian era contains 2.4 g ^{206}Pb to 22.8 g ^{238}U. (i) Assuming no lead was leached from or added to the mineral, calculate the weight of ^{238}U that decomposed. (ii) Assuming further that no uranium was leached or added to the mineral, calculate the age of the mineral. (iii) See Fig. 28.3 (page 738). Does the leakage of radon from uranium minerals introduce a positive or a negative error in the age of the mineral? (iv) The half-life of $^{222}_{86}$Rn is 3.83 days, while that of $^{219}_{86}$Rn, formed in the ^{235}U natural radioactive series, with ^{207}Pb as the end product, is 3.92 seconds. Which should yield more accurate age values, ^{206}Pb:^{238}U or ^{207}Pb:^{235}U weight ratios? Justify your answer.

Answer. (b) (i) 2.8 g; (ii) 7.5×10^8 years.

37. Sr-90. The studies of J. Laurence Kulp on strontium-90 in man show that the average concentration of strontium-90 in human bones in 1959 was 1.1 micro-microcuries per gram of calcium in people, age 5–19 years, in New York City, while the corresponding figure for Recife, Brazil, is 0.32. Calculate the number of ^{90}Sr atoms disintegrating per hour per gram calcium of persons in New York City and Recife.

38. Tracer chemistry. (a) Describe an experiment that would use (i) $^{18}_{6}$O, (ii) $^3_1$H*, to demonstrate that H$_2$O liquid $\rightleftarrows$ H$_2$O vapor is a dynamic equilibrium. (b) Outline how you would use ^{59}Fe* to demonstrate the efficiency of an iron compound for the production of hemoglobin. (c) CrO$_4$$^{2-}$ does not become radioactive in the presence of *Cr^{3+} in solution. If *Cr^{3+} is added to a chromic acid plating bath, the Cr deposit is not radioactive. Using *CrO$_4$$^{2-}$, the deposit is radioactive. What can you say about the mechanism of the deposition of Cr from a chromic acid bath? (d) Evidence proves a radioisotope is an isotope of either Cu or Hg. What chemical experiments would you perform to determine whether the radioisotope is an isotope of Cu or Hg?

39. Luck? Write a composition on the theme "Serendipity in Nuclear Chemical Research."

Polymers

29.1 BACKGROUND AND DEFINITIONS

In Chapter 1 "molecules" were described as small, separable, electrically neutral particles of ordinary matter. The characterization of matter as an aggregation of molecules became conceptually quite useful in the study of gases during the 18th and 19th centuries, and it is natural that ideas of molecular structure were also applied to help our understanding of liquids and solids. Gases that are available for experimental study ordinarily do not consist of molecules larger than about 10 A in diameter or greater than several hundred in molecular weight. The characterization of liquids and solids usually involves the determination of melting, boiling, or sublimation temperatures of the pure substances, or the study of the colligative properties of their solutions. Materials of high molecular weight (in the thousands or higher), however, crystallize with difficulty, decompose on vaporization, and are often only sparingly soluble. Moreover, the greater the molecular weight of a substance, the less is the measurable effect on the colligative properties of its solutions. In contrast to these and other experimental problems with macromolecular materials, the chemical study of materials of low molecular weight has yielded a great wealth of information from the beginnings of modern chemistry. As a result, chemists regarded the accidental formation of large molecules during their experiments as a plain misfortune, and referred disparagingly to their resins, and gluey or waxy residues. Nonetheless, it was important to study naturally occurring materials like cellulose, rubber, and protein, and it was realized in the latter part of the 19th century that the molecules of these substances, like the sticky residues that plagued experimenters, were very large.

Macromolecular material, difficult as it may be to describe by sharp melting or boiling points, vapor pressures, or recognizable crystal habits, nonetheless can often be uniquely characterized by the reproducibility of its decomposition products. Thus, if natural rubber is heated, the hydrocarbon isoprene, C_5H_8, distills off. If starch is chewed, the sweet taste of glucose is detected. If egg albumin (a protein) is boiled in dilute sulfuric acid, the amino acids leucine, alanine, serine, glutamic acid, methionine, and some 13 others are produced:

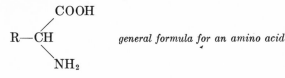

general formula for an amino acid

It is reasonable to assume that these fragments detected in the decomposition of macromolecules are indeed their units of construction. Thus, starch is called a polysaccharide (many sugar units) and, in general, materials whose molecules are made up of repetitions of individual units are called **polymers** (Greek, *many parts*). The individual unit substance of a polymer is called a **monomer.** Molecules composed of at least two different kinds of monomeric unit are called **copolymers.** When the number of units in a polymer is small and specifically known, it is often specified by use of the appropriate Greek prefix (**di**mer, **tri**mer, etc.). When the number of units is large it is not usually possible to determine it exactly, and specific numerical prefixes rapidly become inappropriate after about 4 or 5. When polymerization is so extensive that molecular weights reach the range of tens of thousands or hundreds of thousands, the substance is often called a **high polymer,** and its constituent particles are called **macromolecules.**

29.2 THE DECOMPOSITION OF NATURAL HIGH POLYMERS; MONOMERIC UNITS (MERS)

The structure of isoprene (2-methyl-1,3-butadiene) produced by the destructive distillation of natural rubber is

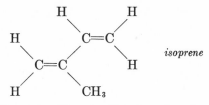

isoprene

Natural rubber itself is found to be a long chain-like structure of the type

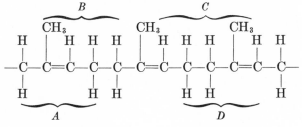

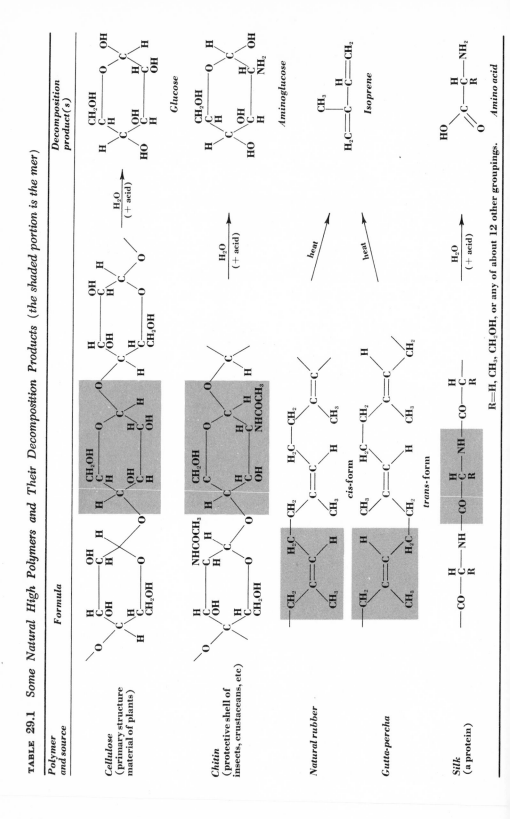

TABLE 29.1 Some Natural High Polymers and Their Decomposition Products (the shaded portion is the mer)

R=H, CH₃, CH₂OH, or any of about 12 other groupings.

(For a more appropriate rendition of bond angles, see Table 29.1.) The formula of this macromolecule can be written by repetition of any one of the portions A, B, C, or D. However, only unit A has the same atomic skeleton as isoprene, the observed decomposition product. Furthermore, the treatment of isoprene with appropriate reagents yield a rubbery solid. The repeating monomeric unit (**mer**) of natural rubber is therefore unit A, not the other geometric possibilities. In general, a mer is the repeating unit that is known by study of decomposition or synthesis to be the building block of a macromolecule.

Table 29.1 shows the formulas of some natural organic high polymers and of their decomposition products. The identification of the decomposition product, however, is far from a full description of the polymer, for the following reasons:

(a) The mode of linkage of the monomer will influence the properties of the macromolecule. Note (Table 29.1) that in natural rubber the isoprene units are linked in the *cis* form; in gutta-percha the linkage is *trans*.

(b) The sequence and extent of monomeric linkages also are important determinants of polymer structure. Cellulose and starch are both glucose polymers, but the rigid cellulose consists of linear macromolecules of about 3500 glucose units each, whereas the more pliable starch is a lower polymer (about 500 glucose units per linear chain of cornstarch) with different structural linkage of the monomeric groups and more extensive chain branching.

(c) The shape of the macromolecules and their orientation in space with respect to each other are also critical factors affecting polymer structure. Raw and cooked egg white (albumin) differ in the shape of their constituent protein molecules.

Examination of Table 29.1 shows two kinds of relationship between monomer and polymer. In rubber and gutta-percha, the repeating unit of the macromolecule is identical in atomic composition and skeletal structure with the decomposition product. If the reaction could be reversed, a simple **addition** of isoprene units to each other would form the polymer.

In cellulose, chitin, and silk, however, decomposition is accompanied by the uptake of water. A reversal of the process, if it could be effected, would require the **condensation*** of monomers with elimination of water.

Polymers of the first type are called **addition polymers** (A-polymers); those of the second type are called **condensation polymers** (C-polymers).

29.3 **THE PRODUCTION OF SYNTHETIC HIGH POLYMERS; C-POLYMERIZATION**

The controlled synthesis of high polymers by condensation methods reached a high degree of industrial success as early as the 1930's, largely

---

* Condensation is the union of two or more molecules with elimination of a smaller unit like H_2O, NH_3, etc.

as a result of the pioneer work of Wallace H. Carothers. A C-polymer must be made from monomers that contain more than one functional group so as to enable intermolecular reactions to proceed continuously. Carothers succeeded in producing C-polymers by heating the salts of diamines with dicarboxylic acids at 200–250°C, with elimination of water:

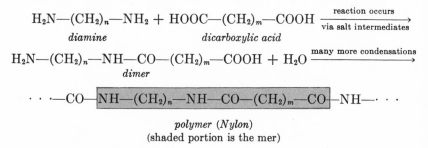

polymer (Nylon)
(shaded portion is the mer)

$+$ more H_2O

Nylon polymers are often identified by the numbers of carbon atoms in the monomeric diamine and diacid (n and $m + 2$ in the formulas above). The popular hosiery polymer is Nylon-66, the copolymer of hexamethylene diamine and adipic acid, each containing 6 carbon atoms per molecule ($n = 6$, $m = 4$). A Nylon can also be made by the simple polymerization of an amino acid, such as 6-aminohexanoic acid, which is polymerized to the material called Nylon-6:

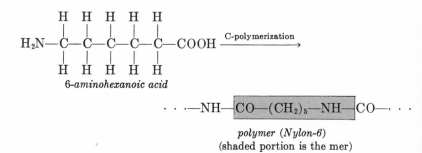

polymer (Nylon-6)
(shaded portion is the mer)

The single numeral, 6, indicates that there is but one monomer and that it has 6 carbon atoms.

29.4 A-POLYMERIZATION

In the case of addition polymerization it is necessary for the **adduct** (addition product) of two monomers to be capable of undergoing further addition, and for this process to continue to macromolecule formation. Otherwise, of course, the addition stops after a single step. Such termination occurs, for example, after the bromination of ethylene; the product is saturated and therefore lacks the capacity for undergoing further addition or chain lengthening (page 246). It is found that A-polymerizations proceed by a path involving the initial formation of some reactive species, such as free radicals or ions, and by the addition of the reactive species to another molecule with the *regeneration of the reactive feature*. In this way the addition reactions may proceed continuously. Pioneer studies in this field were carried out by Hermann Staudinger in the 1920's. An example of free radical A-polymerization (the curved arrows represent electron shifts that occur during reaction) is

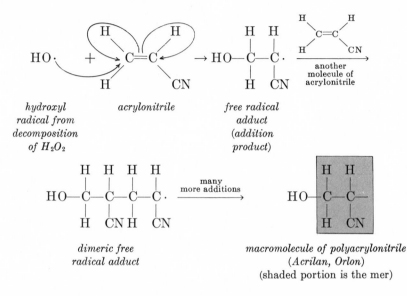

| *hydroxyl radical from decomposition of H_2O_2* | *acrylonitrile* | *free radical adduct (addition product)* |

dimeric free radical adduct

macromolecule of polyacrylonitrile (Acrilan, Orlon) (shaded portion is the mer)

An example of ionic A-polymerization is the use of sodium amide in the production of polyvinylidene nitrile:

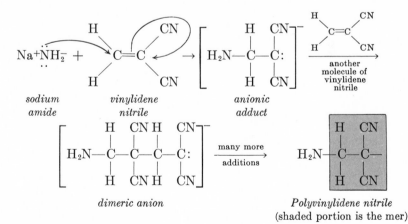

| *sodium amide* | *vinylidene nitrile* | *anionic adduct* |

dimeric anion

Polyvinylidene nitrile (shaded portion is the mer)

A-polymerization must deal with initiation and propagation reactions, as well as with terminations of the addition reactions by the union of two active species. Referring to the free-radical addition, we may represent these three types of reaction as

(a) Initiation of A-polymerization:

$$S \xrightarrow{\text{decomposition}} 2R\cdot$$

starter,
initiator,
or "catalyst"

radical

$$R\cdot + \underset{\text{monomer}}{M} \xrightarrow{\text{addition}} \underset{\substack{\text{monomer} \\ \text{radical}}}{M_1\cdot}$$

(b) Propagation:

$$M_1\cdot + M \xrightarrow{\text{propagation}} \underset{\substack{\text{dimer} \\ \text{radical}}}{M_2\cdot}$$

$$M_2\cdot + M \longrightarrow \underset{\substack{\text{trimer} \\ \text{radical}}}{M_3\cdot}$$

$$\text{etc.} \longrightarrow \underset{\substack{\text{polymer} \\ \text{radical}}}{M_x\cdot}$$

(c) Termination:

$$M_x\cdot + M_y\cdot \xrightarrow{\text{termination}} \underset{\substack{\text{nonradical} \\ \text{polymer}}}{M_{x+y}}$$

If the rate of termination of the reaction exceeds the rate of initiation, the reaction slows down and polymerization eventually ceases. If the initiation rate is the greater of the two, the over-all reaction rate will accelerate and the polymerization may progress too far or yield undesirable products. For best control of polymerization rate, initiator (catalyst) is added just fast enough to maintain a constant concentration of radicals by producing them as fast as they are destroyed.

29.5 THE MOLECULAR WEIGHTS OF MACROMOLECULES

Number-Average and Weight-Average. Not all particles (or molecules) in polymers have the same weight. Therefore we seek some average value and information regarding the distribution of the individual values.

The ordinary (unweighted) arithmetic mean is a *number-average;* each item is counted once. Thus, the number-average molecular weight ($\bar{M}_n$) of a mixture of one molecule of hydrogen (2 g/mole), one of helium (4 g/mole), and one of octane, C_8H_{18} (114 g/mole), is $\frac{1}{3}$ (2 + 4 + 114) or 40 g/mole. For any number, n, of molecules of any molecular weights, M,

$$\bar{M}_n = \frac{\Sigma M}{n}$$

	Molecular weight M	Fraction of total $\dfrac{M}{\Sigma M}$	Product $M \times \left(\dfrac{M}{\Sigma M}\right) = \dfrac{M^2}{\Sigma M}$
H_2	2	$\frac{2}{120}$	$\frac{4}{120}$
He	4	$\frac{4}{120}$	$\frac{16}{120}$
C_8H_{18}	114	$\frac{114}{120}$	$\frac{12996}{120}$
Sums	$\Sigma M = 120$	$\Sigma\left(\dfrac{M}{\Sigma M}\right) = 1$	$\dfrac{\Sigma M^2}{\Sigma M} = \dfrac{13016}{120} = 108$

(where Σ means "the sum of"). But there are instances where a number-average is deceptive and less informative than other measures. If one stands amid tropical vegetation and is hit on the head by a few falling coconuts and many pollen grains, it is somehow misleading to calculate a number-average and to say that one was bombarded by particles weighing, on the average, several milligrams. It is more important to recognize the fact that, although the coconuts were few in number, they contributed most of the total weight. The action of interest is related to the *weight* of the individual particle. Such recognition is achieved by a *weight-average*, $\bar{M}_w$, in which each item counts not as a single unit but in proportion to its weight. In the molecular weight example given above, the hydrogen molecule contributes only $\frac{2}{120}$ of the total weight, and so is counted only to the extent of this ratio. The *weight-average molecular weight* is calculated as shown in the tabulation (above).

The weight-average molecular weight is thus 108 g/mole, a value which pays respect to the major weight contribution of the octane. The general relationship is

$$\bar{M}_w = \frac{\Sigma M^2}{\Sigma M}$$

The *difference* between the two averages, $\bar{M}_w - \bar{M}_n$, is an important value because it reflects the degree of variation of molecular weights in a sample. Thus, for an equimolar mixture of O_2 (32.0 g/mole) and CO (28.0 g/mole), $\bar{M}_n = 30.0$ g/mole and $\bar{M}_w = 30.1$ g/mole. An equimolar mixture of He (4 g/mole) and butene, C_4H_8 (56 g/mole), has the same $\bar{M}_n$ (30 g/mole), but the $\bar{M}_w$ value is 53 g/mole. The greater magnitude of the $\bar{M}_w - \bar{M}_n$ difference for the helium-butene mixture reflects the fact that these molecular weights are more widely dispersed than those of the O_2–CO mixture. Since molecular weight distribution has an important influence on the properties of a polymeric material, it is useful to have both $\bar{M}_n$ and $\bar{M}_w$ values for polymers.

EXAMPLE 1 **Consider two polymers, A and B. A consists of equal numbers of molecular weights 10,000 and 40,000. B consists of equal numbers of molecular weights 20,000 and 30,000. Calculate $\bar{M}_n$ and $\bar{M}_w$ for each polymer. What is the significance of the differences?**

ANSWER **For both polymers $\bar{M}_n = 25{,}000$. For polymer A, the lighter molecules contribute $\frac{1}{5}$ and the heavier molecules $\frac{4}{5}$ of the weighted average. Then**

$$\bar{M}_w = (\tfrac{1}{5} \times 10{,}000) + (\tfrac{4}{5} \times 40{,}000) = 34{,}000$$

Similarly, for polymer B,

$$\bar{M}_w = (\tfrac{2}{5} \times 20{,}000) + (\tfrac{3}{5} \times 30{,}000) = 26{,}000$$

The difference $\bar{M}_w - \bar{M}_n$ is greater for polymer A than for polymer B, indicating the range of distribution of molecular weights to be greater for A than for B.

The variance in molecular weights is more properly measured by $(\bar{M}_w - \bar{M}_n)/\bar{M}_n$, because this ratio affords meaningful comparisons between data whose $\bar{M}_n$ values are different. The two sets given in Example 1 have the same $\bar{M}_n$, so a simple comparison of the $\bar{M}_w - \bar{M}_n$ difference is sufficient.

Colligative Properties.   The greater the molecular weight of a substance, the less is the molality of its solution of a given mass concentration. For a given quantity of solvent, the molality, m, is proportional to the number of moles, n (see page 312). But

$$n = \frac{w}{molecular\ weight}$$

Then,

$$m \propto n \propto \frac{1}{molecular\ weight}$$

The estimation of macromolecular weights of substances from the colligative properties of their solutions therefore demands great sensitivity of measurement. Cryoscopic (freezing) or ebulliometric (boiling) methods require thermometry to sense values of freezing point depression, Δt_f, or boiling point elevation, Δt_b, of about 10^{-4} C degree for a 1% solution of a polymer of molecular weight about 50,000. The most sensitive thermometry responds to temperature differences of this order of magnitude. Thermometric methods have been used with acceptable precision for the study of macromolecular weights up to about 5000. Measurement of osmotic pressure (Fig. 13.10, page 328) affords a more sensitive method of detecting changes in the properties of solutions; a value of Δt_f or Δt_b of about 10^{-3} C degree corresponds to an osmotic pressure of about 10 cm of

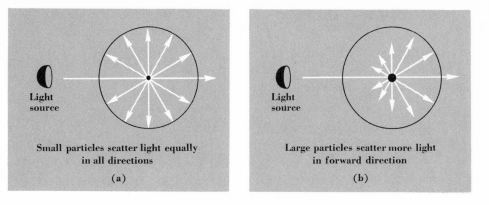

Fig. 29.1. Light scattering by particles.

a solvent of ordinary density, ~1 g/ml. It is therefore experimentally feasible to measure macromolecular weights up to about 10^6 by osmometric methods.

The molecular weights obtained from measurements of colligative properties are number-averages, because molality is, in effect, a count of the number of molecules.

Other Determinations of Molecular Weight. The molecular weights of polymers have also been determined from the rates of sedimentation in high speed centrifuges (**ultracentrifuge**), from viscosity measurements, and by optical methods such as light-scattering (Tyndall effect, page 64). Light-scattering methods can be used to calculate the weight-average molecular weight, $\bar{M}_w$, and, indirectly, to estimate the degree of compactness or elongation of the macromolecules (Fig. 29.1).

29.6 THE ORIENTATION OF MONOMERIC UNITS IN MACROMOLECULES

In a polymer made up of long, chain-like molecules, side groups may be oriented in either an orderly or disorderly pattern with respect to the chain. The name **atactic** (Greek, "without order") is used for the random arrangement, **isotactic** for a *cis* arrangement in which all the side groups lie on the same side of the chain, and **syndiotactic** for a *trans* or alternating arrangement of side groups. These are illustrated for polypropylene in Fig. 29.2. Another example of such orientations is afforded by the difference between natural rubber (*isotactic* or *cis*) and gutta-percha (*syndiotactic* or *trans*).

We have seen that molecules must provide two sites for reaction to produce a chain polymer. If more than two sites per molecule are available, then the chain may branch or a polymeric network structure may be formed. Network polymers generally extend in space in all directions and are therefore often called **three-dimensional polymers.** Chains connected to each other by occasional bridges are called **cross-linked polymers.** Short branching groups (as in the rubber or polypropylene

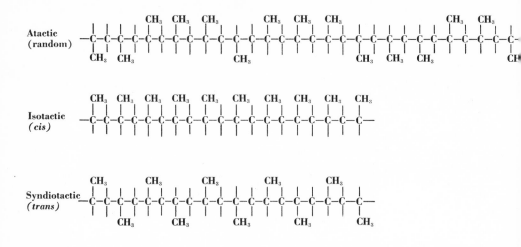

Atactic (random)

Isotactic (cis)

Syndiotactic (trans)

Fig. 29.2. *Polypropylene chain arrangements: atactic (random); isotactic (ordered and cis); syndiotactic (ordered and trans).*

chains) are not considered to be chain branches in the sense described above.

An example of a branched modification of a linear polymer is amylopectin, which is a branched starch polymer. The difference between the two is shown in Fig. 29.3. Note that the monomeric units from which the branches originate have formed linkages at three molecular sites.

A typical cross-linking bridge in protein is the diamino diacid cystine

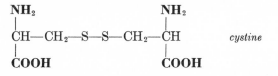

which has four sites for reaction (shown in bold face) and can serve as a ladder rung between protein chains.

A good example of difference in molecular requirements for linear and network polymers is the formation of polyesters from dihydroxy or trihydroxy alcohols. As was shown in Section 29.3 for diamines, reaction of a dialcohol with a diacid gives a linear copolymer. If a trihydroxy alcohol is used instead, a network copolymer is formed. An example is **Glyptal resin** (Fig. 29.4), produced from glycerol and phthalic acid, and used as an ingredient of paints and varnishes.

It is possible, by a suitable choice of catalysts, to control the orientation of monomeric units in A-polymerization that proceeds via ionic intermediates. An example of this control is the improvements in the synthesis of polyethylene $(—CH_2—CH_2—)_n$, one of the most widely used plastics. This material was formerly made by free-radical polymerization at high temperatures and pressures (up to 190°C and 1500 atm). These extreme conditions produced dissociation of atoms from the macromolecular chain

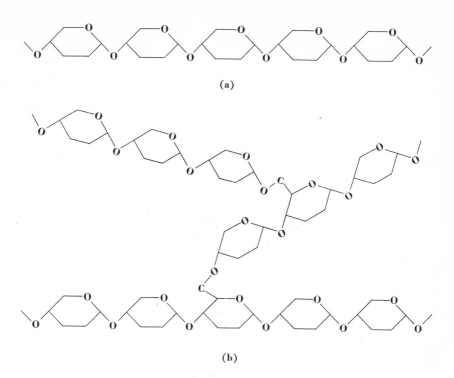

(a)

(b)

Fig. 29.3. *"Straight" (amylose) and branched-chain (amylopectin) starch molecules. (a) Straight-chain amylose starch (structural skeleton only). (b) Branched-chain amylopectin starch (structural skeleton only).*

with resulting branching from the newly created active sites. In the 1950's Karl Ziegler described the use of hydro- and organoaluminum catalysts like AlH_3, $LiAlH_4$, and AlR_3 (where R is an organic radical) that made it possible to manufacture polyethylene under very mild conditions (atmospheric pressure and 30–40°C). It is thus possible to produce unbranched macromolecules regularly arranged with respect to each other.

Even more spectacular is the series of stereospecific (spatially controlled) syntheses described by Giulio Natta during the same decade. Natta's catalysts included transition metal halides (for example, $TiCl_4$) and organometallic compounds supported on a solid carrier having a layer crystalline structure. A-polymerization occurs at the surface of this solid ionic catalyst; the macromolecule may be envisaged as "growing out" of the catalyst surface. The monomer, propylene

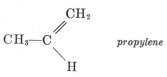

propylene

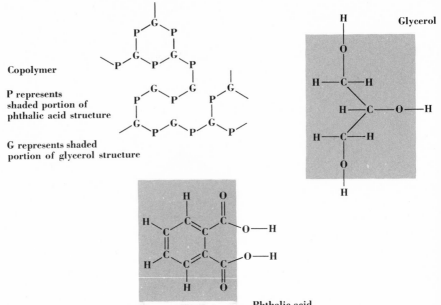

Copolymer

P represents
shaded portion of
phthalic acid structure

G represents shaded
portion of glycerol structure

Fig. 29.4. *Network copolymer of glycerol and phthalic acid.*

is not symmetrical with respect to the double bond, because there is a methyl group on only one side. There is therefore a sterically preferred mode of entrance of the propylene molecules to the points on the catalyst from which the macromolecules are emerging. When the catalyst is firmly fixed on the carrier and the temperature is low, this preference produces a regular, long, isotactic molecule. Under less rigidly controlled conditions, the chain alters its pattern from time to time and some degree of irregularity is introduced. When the catalyst carrier is amorphous, lacking entirely the ordered pattern of the layered crystal structure, disordered atactic macromolecules are formed.

Stereospecific polymerizations have solved some problems of long standing, like the synthetic duplication of natural rubber, and promise much for the future.

29.7 CRYSTALLINITY OF POLYMERS

The degree to which molecules of a substance are arranged in orderly pattern with respect to each other is, of course, a measure of crystallinity. So it is also with macromolecules. Longer molecules have more geometrical opportunities for partially crystalline arrangements, however, than shorter ones have. Consider as examples (a) a pile of neatly stacked lengths of flexible rods, and (b) a similarly stacked pile of short rods of the same material. If each pile is disturbed at the same rate by the same amount of random displacement in space, the pile of long rods will become

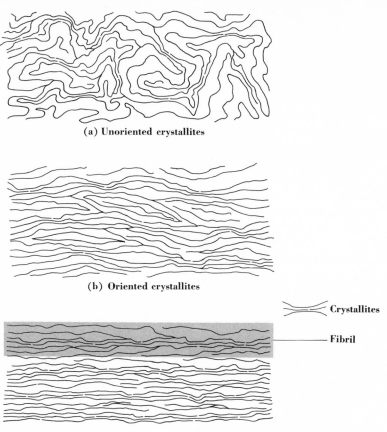

(a) Unoriented crystallites

(b) Oriented crystallites

Crystallites

Fibril

(c) Parallel crystalline areas

Fig. 29.5. *Crystallinity in chain polymers: (a) unoriented crystallites;*
(b) oriented crystallites; (c) parallel crystalline areas.

disordered (lose "crystallinity") much more slowly than the pile of short
ones. This example is given to illustrate that the distinction between
"crystalline" and "noncrystalline" is much less sharp for macromolecular
material than for substances of low molecular weights. A small region of a
macromolecular material in which portions of large molecules are linked
to each other in some regular way is called a **crystallite.** It is the orderly
orientation of crystallites with respect to each other that builds up
crystallinity in a polymer. In fibrous polymeric structures, the small
aggregates of crystallites just large enough to appear as a small thread-
like unit under a high-power microscope are called **fibrils.** In many
polymers, crystallites aggregate with each other in a manner that builds
up rounded crystalline areas called **spherulites.** Figure 29.5 shows
sketches of (a) unoriented crystallites in a polymer that is otherwise
amorphous; (b) oriented crystallites; and (c) long parallel crystalline
areas separated by amorphous areas.

Polymeric substances display wide varieties of physical and chemical properties; this is to be expected from the many possible kinds of macromolecular composition and arrangement. The broad range of fibrous, adhesive, plastic, filmy, foamy, rubbery materials so readily available to us as useful products attests to this macromolecular versatility. What generalizations can be made regarding the relationships between properties and make-up? Although the problems are complicated, considerable advances have been made in recent years.

Quite obviously, the chemical nature of the monomeric unit itself is a prime determinant of properties. Differences in thermal stability and mechanical strength of different polymers are related in part to differences in bonding and structure of the monomer. The chemical reactivity of a polymer is, in large measure, the reactivity of its molecular components. Natural rubber, for example, undergoes deterioration when ozone attacks the double bonds of the polymer chain; a saturated hydrocarbon chain, like polyethylene, resists such attack. Cellulosic polymers offer their free hydroxyl groups to a variety of reagents and thus make it possible to introduce useful modifications of properties. Reaction with nitric acid produces nitrocellulose, from which propellant (guncotton) and plastic (Celluloid) products are formed. Reaction with a derivative of acetic acid produces cellulose acetate, which can be fabricated into films, sheets, and other useful forms. Both reactions alter the free hydroxyl group of cellulose:

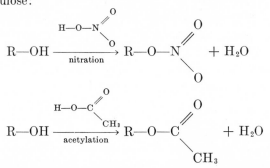

The possibilities for chemical modification and fabrication into products are very extensive.

More drastic chemical differences yield wider differences in chemical properties. Especially notable is the family of silicone polymers, in which the macromolecular chains contain —Si—O— linkages (Fig. 29.6). The great thermal stability of the O—Si bond, due in part to the p-$d\pi$ bonding of Si to O, makes it possible to use silicone products at high temperatures. The hydrocarbon side chains contribute oily or lubricating properties. There have been, of course, attempts to extend the range of "inorganic" polymers by using other varieties of linkage for the chain backbones. Potential candidates include boron-carbon, boron-oxygen, arsenic-oxygen, and beryllium-oxygen. The problems are difficult, in part because our

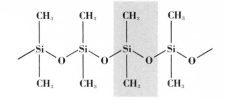

Fig. 29.6. *Methylsili-cone polymer.*

understanding of inorganic linkages, which may involve *d*-orbital π bonding and other less well-recognized interactions, lags behind our knowledge of the simpler sigma bonds and sigma-pi multiple bonds typical of simple organic molecules. Another difficulty is the annoying (to the polymer chemist) tendency of inorganic systems to cyclize in units of relatively low molecular weight. Diminution of the tendency to bond multiplicity with increasing atomic number impedes the use of the valuable A-polymerization techniques used with organic monomers like ethylene. Despite such difficulties, however, many inorganic polymers have been prepared (see Fig. 29.7), and this field of endeavor seems particularly promising.

Fig. 29.7. *Some inorganic polymers: borophane; polydichlorophosphonitrile; silazane ladder polymer; two-dimensional boron nitride polymer.*

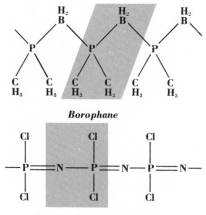

Borophane

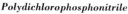

Polydichlorophosphonitrile

Silazane ladder polymer

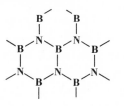

Two dimensional boron nitride polymer (The three-dimensional form, Borazon, has a diamond-like structure)

TABLE **29.2** *Properties and Molecular Make-up of Polymers*

Physical nature of polymer	Molecular requirements
Hard	High molecular weight
	High crystallinity
	Cross-linking or network structure
	Example: phenol-formaldehyde copolymer (Bakelite)
Strong	High molecular weight
(cannot easily be pulled apart)	Cross-linking or network structure
	Partly crystalline—crystallites embedded in amorphous matrix that acts like a cement
	Example: polymethylmethacrylate (Lucite, Plexiglas) reinforced with glass fiber
Fibrous	High molecular weight
	Linear macromolecules
	Long parallel arrangements of crystalline and amorphous regions
	Example: polyacrylonitrile (Acrilan, Orlon)
Leathery	High molecular weight
	Linear macromolecules with slight degree of cross-linking; fragments of the chains are free to move under stress
	Low crystallinity
	Example: vinyl chloride–vinyl acetate copolymer (Vinyl floor covering)
Rubbery	Linear macromolecules with little cross-linking; entire chains are free to move under stress
	High molecular weight
	Low crystallinity (but crystallinity increases with elongation)
	Example: polybutadiene (Buna rubber)
Soft, waxy	Low molecular weight ($<10,000$)
	Low crystallinity
	Example: polyvinyl acetate chewing gum
Thermoplastic	Linear macromolecules
(able to soften and assume new shapes by application of heat and pressure)	Little cross-linking
	Relatively low molecular weight
	Example: cellulose acetate
Thermosetting	High molecular weight
(not able to melt or flow without decomposition)	Highly cross-linked or network structure
	Example: urea-formaldehyde resin

The properties of a polymer are also determined by the form and arrangement of its macromolecules. The critical factors are the molecular weight (which is a function of the degree of polymerization), the extent of branching, cross-linking, or network structuring, the steric disposition of the monomeric units, and the degree and kind of crystallinity of the macromolecules. Certainly there is room enough for variation even without alteration of chemical functional groups. Some of these relationships are approximated in Table 29.2.

Stereoregularity (orderly arrangement in space) facilitates crystallinity and enhances those properties for which crystallinity is required. Thus, for example, stereoregularity strengthens polyethylene.

Shifts in properties also accompany the changes in molecular arrangements produced by a rise in temperature. A polymer of low crystallinity may thus progress, on heating, from a rigid glassy state, through a partly flexible leathery condition, to a rubbery condition, and finally to a flowing viscous liquid. Mechanical deformation also changes the properties of a polymer. Perhaps the most striking instance is the stretching of rubber. In the unstretched form rubber molecules undergo random motion; on stretching this motion is restricted, the entropy is reduced, and the molecules assume a linear crystalline arrangement. The consequent release of energy is familiar to anyone who has stretched a wide rubber band, touched it immediately to his lips, and felt its unexpected warmth.

29.9 BIOCHEMICALS

Macromolecular material is the stuff of life. Each time a biological cell divides, the structure of its essential parts is reconstituted. The resultant cells, in turn, retain this ability of self-replication. Therefore some sort of durable pattern must be preserved and transmitted by living things; in

Fig. 29.8. *Thymine nucleotide: phosphoric acid; deoxyribose; thymine (an organic base).*

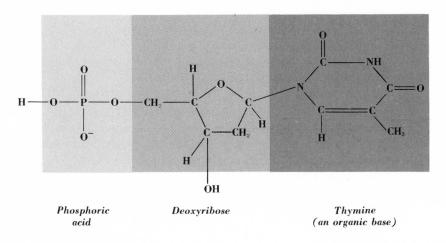

Phosphoric acid	*Deoxyribose*	*Thymine (an organic base)*

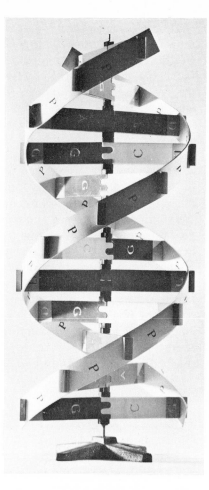

Fig. 29.9. *DNA helix (model).* KEY: *P = phosphate; D = deoxyribose; A = adenine; G = guanine; T = thymine; C = cytosine. (Photo by Fundamental Photographs, New York.)*

fact, the continuity of species depends on this durability. These patterns are called **templates** because they establish the forms needed for molecular reconstitution; it is implied, by crude analogy, that they function like dress patterns, perforated metal plates that establish positions of bolt holes, and similar mechanical devices. The biological templates are macromolecules, and the patterns are determined by the nature of the monomer, by the sequential order of different monomeric units, and by the shape of the macromolecules themselves.

In the nucleus of living cells, the fundamental determinant of replication patterns is deoxyribonucleic acid (DNA). DNA is a polymer containing 2,500–15,000 monomeric units called **mononucleotides.** Each of these units contains a phosphoric acid portion, a carbohydrate-like portion (deoxyribose), and one of four possible organic bases. An example is shown in Fig. 29.8, the shaded portions comprising the DNA monomeric unit. DNA itself is a cross-linked double-stranded helix, in which the cross-links are provided by pairs of bases joined to each other by hydrogen bonds. This model, proposed in 1953 by James D. Watson and Francis H. C. Crick, is illustrated in Fig. 29.9. The sequence of base cross-links embodies the pattern, or code, for the synthesis of proteins. Protein synthesis does not occur by direct interaction of amino acids with DNA, but rather by a complex transfer mechanism in which the DNA code (the sequence of bases) is carried by a single-stranded macromolecule, ribonucleic acid (RNA), to sites outside the cell nucleus. The amino acids, which constitute the monomeric units of the protein, are first activated by coupling with the molecule adenosine triphosphate (ATP), shown in Fig. 29.10. This activated species, with that of other amino acids, is then transferred by the RNA to a sequence that is determined by the sequence of bases in the RNA chain. In other words, the RNA is the template on which the arrangement of amino acids in protein is fixed; DNA stamps the plate.

Proteins act as catalysts for many biochemical processes—those discussed above and others. Such catalysts are called **enzymes;** the characteristics that determine their function, like those that influence macromolecular properties in general, are size, shape, and chemically reactive sites.

A great deal of effort has been expended to elucidate the structure of proteins, and much information has been accumulated. A detailed study of molecular fragmentation products has made it possible to identify the sequential order of the component amino acids. In the protein ribonuclease (the enzyme that digests RNA), for example, the positions of the 124 amino acids in the chain have been determined. This comprises 1876 atoms, totaling 13,899 in molecular weight. The spatial structure of protein molecules is, like that of DNA and RNA, helical, the helices being restrained from unwinding by hydrogen bonds and other cross-linking attachments. The mode of winding of the helix is determined by the asymmetry of naturally occurring amino acids. Refinements in the application and interpretations of x ray analysis have made it possible to establish three-dimensional shapes of protein molecules in remarkably precise detail.

Biochemical systems include, of course, a great array of nonpolymeric substances. Vitamins, lipids, sugars, and some hormones, although they

Fig. 29.10.   *Adenosine triphosphate (ATP)*

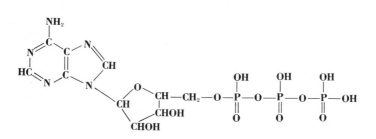

show many instances of considerable molecular complexity, are monomeric. But if the temporal key to life lies in the genetic replication of
organisms, it lies in the understanding of macromolecular behavior.

Problems

1. Monomeric units. Neoprene, a synthetic rubber introduced commercially
in 1931, is able to withstand ozone and oils more effectively than natural rubber.
It is made from "chloroprene"

$$CH_2=CCl-CH=CH_2$$

and is known to have the following structure:

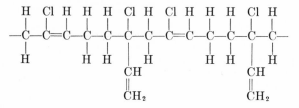

(a) Write the structures of all the geometrically possible recurring units. (b) Write
the structure of the actual monomeric unit (mer) of the rubber.

2. Polymerization. Nylon-6 has the same empirical formula as caprolactam,
the raw material used in its manufacture. (a) Write the empirical formula for
caprolactam and for Nylon-6. (b) Would you consider that Nylon-6 is a C-polymer or an A-polymer? Explain.

3. Molecular weight. Check the statement in the text that Δt_f or Δt_b is about
10^{-4} C degree for a 1% solution of a polymer of molecular weight about 50,000.
Assume the solvent is water for which $K_f = 1.86$ deg kg/mole, and $K_b = 0.52$
deg kg/mole.

4. Molecular weights. A lawn seed mixture is advertised to contain 80%
merion blue and 20% fescue by seed count and 50% of each component by weight.
(a) What is the "molecular weight" of fescue, using merion blue = 1.0 as a
standard? Calculate (b) $\bar{M}_n$, and (c) $\bar{M}_w$, for the mixture.

Answer. (a) 4.0; (b) 1.6; (c) 2.5.

5. Molecular weight distribution. The values of

$$\frac{\bar{M}_w - \bar{M}_n}{\bar{M}_n}$$

for three polymers, A, B, and C, are 0.3, 0.1, and 0.2, respectively. Which polymer
is the most homogeneous with regard to molecular weight? Which polymer is
likely to be softest in consequence of having the largest proportion of molecules
of low molecular weight? Explain your answers.

6. Orientation of monomeric units. Classify the monomer sequences in
natural rubber and gutta-percha as atactic, isotactic, or syndiotactic. Explain
your answer.

7. Orientation of monomeric units. Referring to Table 29.1 and Fig. 29.3,
do starch and cellulose differ from each other in the steric configuration of their
monomeric units, in the orientation of monomeric units with respect to each
other, or both? Explain your answer.

8. Chain cross-linking. Macromolecular chains in wool are cross-linked by cystine units. Assuming that the other monomeric units of wool are

$$R—\overset{\displaystyle H}{\underset{\displaystyle NH_2}{\overset{|}{\underset{|}{C}}}}—COOH$$

draw the structure of two sections of the chain showing the cross-linking.

9. Network structure. Draw a section of the glycerol-phthalic acid network copolymer of Fig. 29.4, showing all the atoms in each monomeric unit in place of the symbols P and G.

10. Properties of polymers. In nitration and acetylation of cellulose the free hydroxyl groups are converted to $—ONO_2$ and $—OCOCH_3$ groups, respectively. Draw the structures of the monomeric units of cellulose nitrate and cellulose acetate.

11. Properties of polymers. When polyethylene is subjected to intense ionizing radiation from a nuclear pile, it becomes much stronger, more difficult to melt, and less soluble. Account for these effects.

12. Polymers in biochemical systems. Oriented protein chains form fibrils, which in turn aggregate to produce fibers visible under the magnification of the ordinary light microscope. Proteins have been called monomeric units of fibrils, which in turn are considered to be polymers of a higher order. Discuss the aptness or ineptness of this concept.

*Definitions
and
review of
physical
concepts*

MATTER

The tendency to maintain a constant velocity is called **inertia.** Thus, unless acted on by an unbalanced force, a body at rest will remain at rest; a body in motion will remain in motion with uniform velocity.

Matter is anything that exhibits inertia: the quantity of matter is its **mass.** *Mass* is difficult to define except in terms of some specific measurements, such as the determination of the effect of an applied force on a given body. The definition of *matter* leads to a dual classification:

(a) *Matter that has mass both at rest and in motion (ordinary matter).*
   "An object at rest tends to remain at rest; an object in motion tends to remain in motion." These forms of inertia are exhibited by ordinary matter of the type that occupies space: water, air, smoke, living matter, radioactive fallout dust, electrons, etc.

(b) *Matter that does not have rest mass.* Radiation, such as visible light, involves motion and can be deflected by gravitation; the degree of deflection depends on the force of the field. In this sense radiation exhibits inertia and has mass. In the sense that it does not exhibit mass at rest, it is not ordinary matter.

The **center of mass** of an object is that point around which all of its mass can be considered to be balanced. If the object is fixed at its center of mass, but is free to rotate around this point, it will have no tendency to do so in a gravitational field, regardless of the orientation to which it is turned.

MOTION

Motion is the change of position or location in space. Motions of objects may be classified as follows:

Translational motion occurs when the center of mass of an object changes its location. *Example:* an arrow in flight.

Rotational motion occurs when some points of a moving object remain stationary. *Examples:* a spinning top (the points along its axis are stationary); a rotating molecule (the center of mass remains stationary).

Distortion is change of shape, or the motion of the points of an object relative to one another. *Example:* a sagging metal bar.

Vibration is periodic distortion and recovery of original shape (the center of mass remains stationary). *Examples:* a struck tuning fork; a vibrating molecule.

FORCE

Force is that which changes the velocity (that is, the state of rest or motion) of a body,

$$\text{force} = \text{mass} \times \text{acceleration}$$

One **dyne** is the force needed to change the velocity of a mass of 1 g by 1 cm/sec in a time of 1 sec. This is an acceleration of (1 cm/sec)/1 sec, or 1 cm/sec², and a force of 1 dyne is 1 g cm/sec².

ENERGY

The activity required to overcome inertia is called **work:**

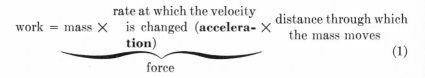

$$
\text{work} = \text{mass} \times
\underbrace{
\begin{array}{c}
\text{rate at which the velocity} \\
\text{is changed } (\textbf{accelera-} \\
\textbf{tion})
\end{array}
}_{\text{force}}
\times
\begin{array}{c}
\text{distance through which} \\
\text{the mass moves}
\end{array}
\tag{1}
$$

Energy is the capacity to do work. There is energy in a mule, a moving train, a compressed spring, a stick of dynamite, a pound of uranium or of hydrogen or of chalk. Any moving object can do work by virtue of its motion because, by collision, it can overcome the inertia of another object; this capacity is called **kinetic energy.** Energy of motion may be either translational, rotational, or vibrational. The energy that a moving body loses in a perfectly elastic collision will be transmitted to another object, and

$$
\begin{array}{c}
\text{energy (gained by object} \\
\text{that is set in motion)}
\end{array}
=
\begin{array}{c}
\text{energy (lost by object} \\
\text{that stops or slows down)}
\end{array}
$$

This is a particular instance of the Law of Conservation of Energy. The magnitude of this kinetic energy, for a body of mass m and velocity u, is derived directly from Equation (1).

Consider the energy given to a stationary body by accelerating it at a uniform rate to velocity u. Assume the energy of the stationary body is zero.

The change in velocity from 0 to u is $u - 0 = u$.

The acceleration, or change in velocity per unit time, is u/t.

The average velocity (distance/time, or d/t) from an initial value of 0 to a final value of u is $\frac{1}{2}(0 + u) = \frac{1}{2}u$. Then

$$d/t = \tfrac{1}{2}u$$

The kinetic energy is given by

$$\text{kinetic energy} = \text{mass} \times \text{acceleration} \times \text{distance}$$

$$= m \times \frac{u}{t} \times d$$

$$= m \times u \times \frac{d}{t}$$

$$= m \times u \times \tfrac{1}{2}u$$

$$= \tfrac{1}{2}mu^2$$

The energy of a body may stem from some attribute other than motion. A compressed spring, for example, may do work when it expands, a stick of dynamite when it explodes. In every case in which we attribute a quantity of energy to an object, we imagine that an event could occur in which this energy may be transmitted in some way by the object to another body. When we can no longer imagine such an event, we say the object has zero energy. Of course, the kinds of event that we imagine change with time, hence the energy that we assign to objects changes. We attribute much more energy to a pound of steam when we think of its use in an atomic fusion reactor than when we think of it in a reciprocating piston engine.

Energy is frequently named according to the kind of event we imagine: for example, we say that a substance has **chemical energy** when its energy loss would be accompanied by a change in composition, **electrical energy** by generation of an electric current, etc. The term **potential energy** is sometimes used in contradistinction to kinetic energy, but it is not really necessary to invent such a category. The energy of any object, moving or not, is "potential" in the sense that some time may elapse before an event occurs in which the energy is transmitted. Sometimes the energy-transmitting event cannot occur until some energy is absorbed first: we can think that a rock in the crater of a volcano can lose energy by rolling down to the valley, but not before it is lifted over the rim. Such a preliminary expenditure of energy that is required to bring a system to a condition in which energy is spontaneously released is called **energy of activation.**

The unit of energy is the **erg.** It is defined in terms of force and distance.

One **erg** is the work done when a force of a dyne acts over a distance of 1 cm,

$$\text{erg} = \text{dyne cm}$$
$$= \frac{\text{g cm}^2}{\text{sec}^2}$$

One **joule** is 10^7 ergs.

MASS

Standard. International Prototype Kilogram (kg): a mass of platinum-iridium at the International Bureau of Weights and Measures, Sèvres, France.

Interconversion

1 kg ≈ 2.205 pounds, avoirdupois
1 pound, avoirdupois ≈ 453.6 g

Fractions

1 gram (g)	$= 10^{-3}$ kg
1 centigram (cg)	$= 10^{-2}$ g
1 milligram (mg)	$= 10^{-3}$ g
1 microgram (μg)	$= 10^{-6}$ g
1 nanogram (ng)	$= 10^{-9}$ g
1 picogram (pg)	$= 10^{-12}$ g $= 1$ micromicrogram ($\mu\mu$g)

LENGTH

Standard. The meter (m), 1,650,763.73 wavelengths of the orange-red wavelength of krypton-86. This standard was adopted in 1960 by the General Conference on Weights and Measures, replacing the International Prototype Meter, the distance between two lines at 0°C on a platinum-iridium bar at the International Bureau of Weights and Measures, Sèvres, France.

Interconversion

1 inch = 2.54 cm (exactly)

Multiples and Fractions

1 terameter (Tm)	$= 10^{12}$ m
1 gigameter (Gm)	$= 10^{9}$ m
1 megameter (Mm)	$= 10^{6}$ m
1 kilometer (km)	$= 10^{3}$ m
1 decimeter (dm)	$= 10^{-1}$ m
1 centimeter (cm)	$= 10^{-2}$ m
1 millimeter (mm)	$= 10^{-3}$ m
1 micron (μ)	$= 10^{-6}$ m $= 10^{-4}$ cm
1 millimicron (mμ)	$= 10^{-9}$ m $= 10^{-7}$ cm
1 angstrom unit (A)	$= 10^{-8}$ cm
1 fermi	$= 10^{-13}$ cm

VOLUME

Standards

International liter = volume of 1 kg of pure water at the temperature of its maximum density (4°C).

Cubic decimeter (derived from the meter).

Interconversion

$$1 \text{ liter} = 1.000027 \text{ cubic decimeters}$$
$$= 1000.027 \text{ cubic centimeters}$$
$$\approx 1.057 \text{ U.S. liquid quarts}$$

Multiples and Fractions

1 milliliter (ml) $= 10^{-3}$ liter ≈ 1 cubic centimeter
1 microliter (μl) $= 10^{-6}$ liter $= 10^{-3}$ ml
1 nanoliter (nl) $= 10^{-9}$ liter $= 10^{-6}$ ml

DENSITY

Density is mass per unit volume; the densities of substances depend on temperature. For a granular solid (Fig. A1), the relationships are

$$\frac{\text{bulk density}}{\text{(or packing density)}} = \frac{\text{mass}}{\text{gross volume}}$$

$$\text{absolute density} = \frac{\text{mass}}{\text{gross volume} - \text{free volume}}$$

When a standard substance is used as a reference, the expression **specific gravity** is used:

$$\text{specific gravity} = \frac{\text{density of a given substance}}{\text{density of a standard substance}}$$

The temperatures of both substances must be specified; they are frequently, but not always, the same. For solids and liquids the standard substance is usually water; for gases it is usually air, or sometimes hydro-

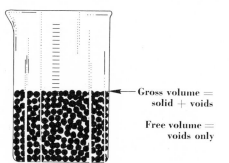

Gross volume = solid + voids

Free volume = voids only

Fig. A1. Volume of a granular solid.

gen. Thus, the specific gravity value for carbon tetrachloride, $1.594^{20°/4°}$, means that the density of this liquid at 20°C is 1.594 times as great as the density of water at 4°C. By the definition of the liter, the specific gravity$^{x°/4°}$ is numerically equal to the density in g per ml at $x°$.

PRESSURE

Pressure is force per unit area. If the pressure on any portion of matter is greater in one direction than in another, the matter will move in the direction of the lower pressure. Conversely, matter that is stationary is subject to equal pressures in all directions. Consider an infinitely thin disk submerged in a liquid, as shown in Fig. A2. The pressure from above is exerted by the combined mass of the liquid and the atmosphere above the disk. The pressure from below is exerted by the compressed liquid and by the container which is strained by the pressure of its contents. If all the liquid above the dotted line were instantaneously removed, the pressure from below would throw the disk up. Moreover, the pressure on one face of the disk will be the same as that on the other face, no matter what angle the disk assumes. Thus, the pressure of a liquid or a gas depends only on the depth (or height), and is exerted equally in all directions. At sea level, the pressure exerted by the earth's atmosphere varies around 14.7 lb per in². This value is equivalent to the pressure exerted by a column of mercury about 76 cm high, or of water about 34 feet high.

Standard. One standard atmosphere = the pressure exerted by exactly 76 cm (= exactly 760 mm) of mercury at 0°C (density 13.5951 g/cm³) and at standard gravity, 980.665 cm/sec².

It follows that

$$1 \text{ standard atm} = 13.5951 \ \frac{g}{cm^3} \times 76 \text{ cm } (exactly) \times 980.665 \ \frac{cm}{sec^2}$$

$$= 1.01325 \times 10^6 \ \frac{dynes}{cm^2}$$

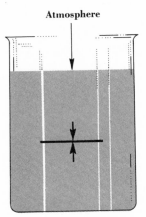

Atmosphere

Fig. A2. Pressure exerted by a liquid.

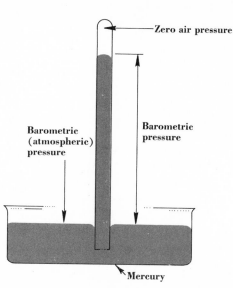

Fig. A3. Mercury barometer.

Fraction

$$1 \text{ torr}^* = \frac{\text{standard atm}}{760 \; (exactly)}$$

$$= \text{pressure exerted by 1 mm of mercury} \\ \text{at } 0°C \text{ at standard gravity}$$

A **barometer** is a device that measures atmospheric pressure. The original and simplest form was invented by Torricelli in 1643. It is made by inverting a tube longer than 76 cm filled with mercury into a dish of mercury (Fig. A3). The atmosphere will support only that height of mercury which exerts an equivalent pressure; any excess mercury will fall into the reservoir and leave a space with zero air pressure, called a torricellian vacuum, above it. Note that the height in mm, P_b, reads in torr units only if the mercury is at 0°C and standard gravity. Otherwise, appropriate corrections must be made.

Gage pressure is the value indicated by a gage that reads zero at barometric pressure:

absolute pressure = gage pressure + barometric pressure

A familiar example is the automobile tire pressure gage.

HEAT AND TEMPERATURE

One may do work on an object and yet fail to convert such work into equivalent energy of motion, electricity, magnetism, or chemical or

---

* Named after Evangelista Torricelli.

physical change. For example, one may bend an iron bar back and forth several times, or stir a liquid or a gas in a confined space, or force an electric current through a copper wire and, after all such expenditures of energy, observe that the object retains substantially its original form and position in space. In such cases, the work has had the effect of increasing the energy of random motion of all the elementary particles of the body. The same effect can be produced without doing work on the body, by letting it absorb heat from another body. Heat, like work, is a manner in which energy is transferred from one body to another. This transfer is usually recognized by changes in the **temperatures** of the bodies.* When there is a spontaneous net transfer of heat from body A to body B, then A is said to be **hotter** or at a higher temperature than B. When, despite an available path, there is no net heat transfer between two bodies, they are said to be at the same temperature. Temperature is thus the property of a body that predisposes it to lose heat: the higher the temperature, the greater the tendency for heat to flow away from the body.

Many properties of substances change with changes in temperature. Examples are density, color, ability to conduct electricity, and ability to stimulate nerve impulses. A set of values in which temperature is related to some measured property is called a **temperature scale.** A device used to obtain such measurements is a **thermometer.** Additional discussion of temperature scales appears in Chapter 2.

Standards

The triple point. The temperature at which ice, water, and water vapor coexist at equilibrium. This temperature is 273.16°K (exactly), or 0.01°C; °K refers to the Kelvin scale, °C to the Celsius (previous name, Centigrade) scale.

Absolute zero. This is 0°K (exactly), or −273.15°C.

The ice point. The temperature at which ice and water saturated with air exist together at standard atmospheric pressure. This temperature is 0°C (exactly).

The steam point. The temperature at which steam and water exist together at standard atmospheric pressure. This temperature is 100°C (exactly).

Other points frequently used are (all taken at one standard atmosphere): boiling oxygen, −182.96°C; freezing mercury, −38.87°C; boiling sulfur, +444.60°C.

1 calorie† (cal), sometimes called the thermochemical calorie, = 4.18400 × 10⁷ ergs = 4.18400 joules.

* Heat flow can also result in changing the aggregation of particles in an object (for example, solid → liquid); the heat required to produce such a change is called the **latent heat.**

† The "small calorie" or "gram-calorie" is the quantity of heat required to warm 1 g of water from 3.5°C to 4.5°C. The "normal calorie" involves the temperature change from 14.5° to 15.5°C, and the "mean calorie" is 1/100 the heat needed to warm 1 g of water from 0°C to 100°C. All of these units are nearly the same.

1 kilocalorie (kcal)
1 kilogram-calorie
1 Calorie (capital C; used in $\Big\}$ = 1000 cal
   expressing food energies)

Interconversions

$$0°C = 32° \text{ Fahrenheit (°F)}$$
$$100°C = 212° \text{ F}$$

There are thus fewer C degrees than F degrees in the temperature interval between the ice point and the steam point. The ratio is $(100 - 0)/(212 - 32)$ or 5/9. The conversion equation is

$$°C = \tfrac{5}{9} (°F - 32)$$

The **specific heat** of a substance is the heat required to warm 1 gram of the substance 1 Celsius degree (units: calories per gram per degree). The relationship is

$$\text{specific heat} = \frac{\text{heat absorbed or released (cal)}}{\text{mass (g)} \times \text{temp. rise or fall (C deg)}}$$

Specific heats vary markedly from substance to substance, and to some extent with temperature for any given substance. Some approximate values under ordinary conditions are: air (standard pressure), 0.25 cal/g deg; water, 1.00; ice, 0.5; alcohol, 0.58; copper, 0.09.

ELECTRICITY

There are several kinds of interaction among matter in the universe. Gravitation is a relatively weak attractive force seemingly exerted by all matter. Much stronger forces are exerted in **electrostatic interactions,** which may be either attractive or repulsive. Matter that exhibits such behavior is said to possess **electric charge.** To account for observed phenomena, it is postulated that two kinds of electric charge exist; they are called **positive** and **negative** (an unfortunate sign convention, since there is no implication of "greater than zero" or "less than zero"). The interaction among combinations of charged $(+, -)$ or neutral (0) points of matter are

Charge of matter		Electrostatic interaction
−	+	**Attraction**
−	−$\Big\}$	**Repulsion**
+	+	
−	0$\Big\}$	
+	0	**None**
0	0	

The magnitude of electrostatic force is given by Coulomb's law,

$$F = \frac{1}{D}\frac{q_1 q_2}{d^2}$$

where F is the force of attraction or repulsion (in dynes), q_1 and q_2 are the magnitudes (in esu) of two electric charges separated by distance d (in cm), and the **dielectric constant** D is a dimensionless number having the value of 1 (exact number) in a vacuum, and more than 1 in matter. Examples of values of D are 1.000590 for air at 1 standard atmosphere and 0°C, 24.3 for alcohol at 25°C, and 80.37 for water at 20°C.

A neutral body may have both + and − charges of equal total magnitude, but they need not be distributed homogeneously. We may arbitrarily assign a **center of positive charge** and a **center of negative charge** to each body, corresponding to the points around which the + and − charges, respectively, can be considered to be balanced. When these centers do not coincide, the body is said to have **electrical polarity,** or to be **polar,** and is called a **dipole.** The **dipole moment** is defined as the magnitude of the + or the − charge times the distance between the charge centers. Dipoles will be attracted or repelled to or from charged bodies or other dipoles, depending on the relative orientations of the bodies. But attractive forces tend to aggrandize themselves (by increasing the polarization of attracting bodies and by bringing about favorable orientations), whereas repulsive forces tend to diminish themselves. Hence attractive forces are statistically favored, and dipoles are attracted to charged bodies and to each other. Likewise, nonpolar bodies may be polarized by and attracted to charged bodies.

Standard. 1 **electrostatic unit** (esu) = charge which will exert a force of 1 dyne (1 gram cm per second per second) at a distance of 1 cm on a charge of equal magnitude in a vacuum or 1 dyne = esu^2/cm^2.

Interconversion

1 coulomb = 2.998×10^9 esu

If two points differ in electric charge, energy must be gained or lost in transferring a given charge from one point to the other. This energy is called the **potential difference** between the two points. When 10^7 ergs are gained or lost during the transfer of 1 coulomb of charge, the potential difference is said to be 1 volt. Then

10^7 ergs = 1 volt coulomb

and since

10^7 ergs = 1 joule

then

1 joule = 1 volt coulomb

A movement of charged bodies is called an **electric current.** The relationship is

$$I = Q/t$$

where I is the current (amperes), and Q is the quantity of charge (coulombs) which passes a given point in time t (seconds).

The magnitude of the current which can pass through a given section of matter depends on the potential difference (E, in volts) between the two points of reference and on the resistance imposed by the matter (R, in ohms). The expression is **Ohm's law,**

$$I = E/R$$

The reciprocal of the resistance, $1/R$, is called the **conductance,** K (units: reciprocal ohms, or mhos).

MEASUREMENT; UNCERTAINTY

Measurement is the transfer of information in terms of standard units. Information may be transferred to human beings (through sensory routes) or to machines. Any measurement culminates in a sensation; the sensing element may be the human eye or other organ, or an inanimate instrument. In any event, the sensor must be stimulated by a quantity of energy if it is to receive the measurement information. As a result, the process of measurement disturbs to some degree the matter being measured. For measurements of ordinary bodies, the magnitude of this disturbance is too small to be of consequence, but for measurements of very small bodies like individual electrons the inherent uncertainty introduced is relatively great.

Significance of Measurement Figures. Gross uncertainties in measurement are introduced through factors such as human error, malfunction of measuring devices, and experimental bias (error in one direction, as by a ruler whose "inches" are too short). Information is useful only to the extent that one can be confident of its validity. To insure such utility, each figure or digit in the numerical expression of a measurement should be significant. A **significant figure** may be defined as a number that we believe to be correct within some specified or implied limit of error. Thus, if the height of a man, expressed in significant figures, is written as 5.78 feet, it is assumed that only the **last figure** may be in error. Clearly, any uncertainty in the first or second figure would remove all significance from the last figure. (Not being certain of the number of feet, it is idle to speak of inches.) If we have reason to believe that the last figure will be in doubt by a **specified** amount, we may so indicate by expressions such as 5.78 $\pm$ 0.01 feet.

To count the significant figures in a number, read the number from left to right and count all the digits starting with the first digit that is not zero. The position of the decimal point should be ignored, because it is determined by the particular units employed. Thus, the measurements 12.2 cm and 122 mm are identical and therefore all the corresponding figures are equally significant.

The following examples will be illustrative:

Value	Number of significant figures
0.0301 lb	**3**
4.290 hours	**4**
1.030 mg	**4**
0.001030 g	**4**
5000 miles	**Ambiguous—the zeros may have measurement significance or may be merely spacers to indicate the magnitude of the first digit**
5.00×10^3 miles	**3—the zeros clearly have measurement significance; they are not needed to indicate magnitude**
6 pencils	**If this is used in the sense of a tally ("Tom has 6 pencils"), it is an exact number, and the concept of significant figures has no meaning; if it is used as a measurement ("The average student uses 6 pencils per semester"), it has 1 significant figure**
1 foot = 12 inches	**These are exact numbers which express a definition, not measurements**

We must guard against introduction of uncertainty by arithmetical procedures. The following rules will be helpful.

Rule 1. In addition or subtraction, any figure in the answer is significant only if **each number** in the problem contributes a significant figure at that decimal level. Therefore the value which terminates at the highest decimal level (that is, the level of greatest magnitude) will determine how far the significant figures should be carried in the answer:

$$
\begin{array}{r}
308.7812 \\
0.00034 \\
10.31 \\
\hline
319.09
\end{array}
$$

Rule 2. When a number is "rounded off" (nonsignificant figures discarded), the last significant figure is unchanged if the next figure is less than 5, and is increased by 1 if the next figure is 5 or more.

Rule 3. In multiplication and division, the number of significant figures in the answer is the same as that in the quantity with the fewest significant figures:

$$
\frac{3.0 \times 4297}{0.0721} = 1.8 \times 10^{-5}
$$

Rule 4. In a multistep computation, it will be convenient first to determine the number of significant figures in the answer by Rules (1), (2), and

(3) above, and to round off each number that contains excess significant figures to one more significant figure than necessary. Then round off the answer to the correct number of significant figures. This procedure will preserve significance with minimum labor.

EXAMPLE 1 **Evaluate the expression**

$$4.3 \times \frac{311.8}{273.1} \times \frac{760}{784 - 19.1}$$

ANSWER **Number of significant figures in final answer: 2. Round off according to Rules (1) and (2), to one extra significant figure:**

$$4.3 \times \frac{312}{273} \times \frac{760}{784 - 19.1}$$

Solve:

= 4.88

Round off to 2 significant figures:

= 4.9

Measurement information, to be complete, must specify the units of measurement, which are sometimes called **dimensional units.** It is valid to handle such units as algebraic terms, and one will find that such practice speeds up calculations and provides an automatic check against dimensional errors. When numbers do not imply measurement units, they are said to be dimensionless; common examples are percentages and other ratios. In handling units algebraically, learn how to manipulate identities so that the correct answer will emerge expressed in the desired units. Thus, the identity

1 foot = 12 inches

means that the fraction

$$\frac{12 \text{ inches}}{1 \text{ foot}}$$

or its reciprocal

$$\frac{1 \text{ foot}}{12 \text{ inches}}$$

has the value of unity, and can be multiplied by the numerator or denominator of any term, and be raised to any power, at will.

Dimensional units, like other algebraic terms, may have positive or negative exponents. Thus, the unit of area, square feet, is expressed as ft^2. A unit of speed may be written $miles/hr$ or $miles\ hr^{-1}$. A unit of frequency, the number of times some event occurs *per second*, is sec^{-1}.

EXAMPLE 2 **How many seconds are there in a calendar year?**

ANSWER

$$1 \text{ year} = 365 \text{ days} \times 24 \frac{\text{hrs}}{\text{day}} \times 60 \frac{\text{min}}{\text{hr}} \times 60 \frac{\text{sec}}{\text{min}}$$

$$= 31,536,000 \text{ sec}$$

This is a tally, not a measurement, and the answer is therefore an exact number.

EXAMPLE 3 **A fan blows 95.0 cubic feet of air per minute uniformly through a duct whose cross-sectional area is 72 square inches. What is the linear speed of the air in miles per hour?**

ANSWER

$$\text{Air speed} = \frac{95.0 \frac{\text{ft}^3}{\text{min}}}{72 \text{ in}^2} \times \frac{\left(12 \frac{\text{in}}{\text{ft}}\right)^2}{5280 \frac{\text{ft}}{\text{mile}}} \times 60 \frac{\text{min}}{\text{hr}}$$

$$= 2.2 \frac{\text{miles}}{\text{hr}}$$

Review of
some
mathematical
operations

EXPONENTS

In the expression x^n, x is called the **base,** and n the **exponent.** When n is an integer, the expression has the value of x multiplied by itself n times. Thus

$$2^4 = 2 \times 2 \times 2 \times 2 = 16$$

In the expression $x^{1/n}$, $1/n$ is the exponent, and n is the **root,**

$$x^{1/n} = \sqrt[n]{x}$$

Thus

$$4^{\frac{1}{2}} = \sqrt{4} = 2$$
$$16^{\frac{1}{4}} = \sqrt[4]{16} = 2.$$

In the expression $x^{m/n}$, m/n is the exponent,

$$x^{m/n} = \sqrt[n]{x^m}$$

Thus

$$4^{\frac{3}{2}} = \sqrt{4^3} = 8$$

The expression x^{-n} is the reciprocal of x^n

$$x^{-n} = \frac{1}{x^n}$$

Thus

$$4^{-1} = \tfrac{1}{4}$$

$$2^{-\frac{3}{2}} = \frac{1}{2^{\frac{3}{2}}} = \frac{1}{\sqrt{2^3}} = \frac{1}{\sqrt{8}} = \frac{1}{2\sqrt{2}} = \frac{\sqrt{2}}{4}$$

Any number to the 0th power is 1:

$$(\tfrac{1}{2})^0 = 1^0 = 8^0 = 1000^0 = (10^{23})^0 = x^0 = 1$$

When exponential expressions having the same base are multiplied, the exponents are added; when such expressions are divided, the exponents are subtracted:

$$x^m \times x^n = x^{m+n}$$

Thus

$$10^2 \times 10^3 = 10^5 \quad \text{and} \quad 10^6 \times 10^{-4} = 10^2$$

And

$$\frac{x^m}{x^n} = x^{m-n}$$

Thus

$$\frac{10^5}{10^2} = 10^3 \quad \text{and} \quad \frac{10^5}{10^{11}} = 10^{-6}$$

Exponents of exponents are multiplied:

$$(x^m)^n = x^{mn}$$

Thus

$$(10^8)^3 = 10^{24} \quad \text{and} \quad (10^{-1})^2 = 10^{-2}$$

For calculations involving multiple exponential terms and dimensional units, the following procedure is recommended:

Procedure	Example
(1) **Write the expression**	$$\dfrac{52.02\ \text{g} \times \left(10^8\ \dfrac{\text{A}}{\text{cm}}\right)^3 \times 2\ \dfrac{\text{atoms}}{\text{unit cell}}}{7.20\ \dfrac{\text{g}}{\text{cm}^3} \times \dfrac{(2.88\ \text{A})^3}{\text{unit cell}}}$$
(2) **Simplify any compound fractions; multiply exponents of exponents; evaluate dimensional units**	$$\dfrac{52.02\ \cancel{\text{g}} \times 10^{24}\ \dfrac{\cancel{\text{A}^3}}{\cancel{\text{cm}^3}} \times 2\ \dfrac{\text{atoms}}{\cancel{\text{unit cell}}}}{7.20\ \dfrac{\cancel{\text{g}}}{\cancel{\text{cm}^3}} \times \dfrac{2.88^3\ \cancel{\text{A}^3}}{\cancel{\text{unit cell}}}}$$ (final answer is in atoms)
(3) **Rewrite numbers only; check that none is omitted**	$$\dfrac{52.02 \times 10^{24} \times 2}{7.20 \times 2.88^3}$$

(4) **Decide on significant figures; avoid unnecessary computations**

3 significant figures

("2" is an exact number and does not limit significance)

(5) **Perform computation; gather exponential terms**

0.604×10^{24}

(6) **Write answer in final form with units** 6.04×10^{23} atoms

LOGARITHMS

A logarithm is an exponent:

$$a^x = N \qquad (a \text{ is the } \textbf{base}; x \text{ is the } \textbf{exponent})$$
$$\log_a N = x \qquad (a \text{ is the } \textbf{base}; x \text{ is the } \textbf{logarithm})$$

The base of logarithms used as an aid to ordinary computations is 10. Then

$$10^4 = 10{,}000$$

and

$$\log_{10} 10{,}000 = \log_{10} 10^4 = 4$$

When the base is not specified, 10 is understood,

$$\log 0.001 = \log 10^{-3} = -3$$

Because logs are exponents, logs of products are added and logs of quotients are subtracted:

$$\log (a \times b) = \log a + \log b$$
$$\log \left(\frac{a}{b}\right) = \log a - \log b$$

Logs that cannot be expressed as integral exponents are found in tables or on slide rules. Log tables present logarithms of numbers between 1 and 10; a decimal point is assumed to precede the log values given in the tables. Then

$$\log 1.21 = 0.0828$$

A number that is not between 1 and 10 may be written in proper exponential form, and the log obtained as follows:

$$\log 7040 = \log (7.040 \times 10^3)$$
$$= \log 7.040 + \log 10^3$$
$$= 0.8476 + 3 = 3.8476$$

$$\log 0.000625 = \log (6.25 \times 10^{-4})$$
$$= \log 6.25 + \log 10^{-4}$$
$$= 0.7959 + (-4) = -(3.2041)$$

The procedure can be reversed. The number, N, whose logarithm has a given value, x, is the **antilogarithm** of that value:

$$\left.\begin{array}{c} \log N = x \\ \text{antilog } x = N \end{array}\right\} (x \text{ is the } \textbf{log}; N \text{ is the } \textbf{antilog})$$

Rule for Significant Figures in Antilogarithms. The number of significant figures in the antilogarithm is equal to the number of decimal places (digits after the decimal point) in the logarithm. Some examples follow:

(*i*) $\log 100 = \log 10^2 = 2$
$\quad\quad$ antilog $2 = 10^2 = 100$

(*ii*) antilog $6.3909 = $ antilog $(6 + 0.3909)$
$\quad\quad\quad\quad\quad\quad\quad = $ antilog $6 \times$ antilog 0.3909
$\quad\quad\quad\quad\quad\quad\quad = 10^6 \times 2.460$ (from log table)
$\quad\quad\quad\quad\quad\quad\quad = 2.460 \times 10^6$

Note that only four significant figures are permitted.

(*iii*) $\quad\quad\quad\quad\quad -0.0079 = 0.9921 - 1$
$\quad\quad$ antilog $-0.0079 = $ antilog $(0.9921 - 1)$
$\quad\quad\quad\quad\quad\quad\quad\quad = $ antilog $0.9921 \times$ antilog (-1)
$\quad\quad\quad\quad\quad\quad\quad\quad = 9.820 \times 10^{-1}$
$\quad\quad\quad\quad\quad\quad\quad\quad = 0.9820$

(*iv*) $\quad\quad\quad\quad\quad -9.42 = 0.58 - 10$
$\quad\quad$ antilog $(-9.42) = $ antilog $0.58 \times$ antilog (-10)
$\quad\quad\quad\quad\quad\quad\quad\quad = 3.8 \times 10^{-10}$

Note that only two significant figures are permitted.

Logarithms to the base e are **natural logarithms** and are given the symbol ln. Thus

$\quad\quad$ ln $e^x = x$
$\quad\quad$ ln $e^{0.2} = 0.2$

The relation between the logarithms of the two bases, e and 10, is

$\quad\quad$ ln $x = 2.303 \log x$

To solve for the value of exponential functions of e, for example $e^{-3.0}$, the following procedure is recommended:

(**a**) Take the natural logarithm of $e^{-3.0}$, ln $e^{-3.0} = -3.0$
(**b**) Convert to the base 10 by dividing by 2.303,

$$\frac{-3.0}{2.3} = -1.3$$

(c) Take the antilog

$$-1.3 = 0.7 - 2$$
$$\text{antilog}\,(-1.3) = \text{antilog}\,0.7 \times \text{antilog}\,(-2)$$
$$= 5 \times 10^{-2}$$

Therefore

$$e^{-3.0} = 5 \times 10^{-2}$$

The notation, $\exp(x)$, is often used to represent e^x.

Values of exponential functions and natural logarithms are given in tables in the *Handbook of Chemistry and Physics* and other reference books. However, these tables are usually less adequate than the tables of common logarithms.

QUADRATIC EQUATIONS

A quadratic equation is one in which the highest exponent to which a variable is raised is 2. Any quadratic equation may be written as

$$ax^2 + bx + c = 0$$

The equation has two solutions, given by

$$x = \frac{-b \pm \sqrt{b^2 - 4ac}}{2a}$$

When a quadratic equation is applied to a problem dealing with physical reality, an impossible solution (such as a negative mass, or a quantity that violates a conservation law) may be dropped (an example appears on page 486):

$$x^2 \qquad +0.2x \qquad -0.1 = 0 \qquad (x \text{ is the variable})$$

$$a = 1 \qquad b = 0.2 \qquad c = 0.1$$
(understood)

Then, applying the previous equation, the solutions are

$$x = +0.23 \text{ or } -0.43$$

The negative answer is rejected because the variable in question (concentration) cannot be negative. Then

$$x = 0.23$$

GRAPHS AND PROPORTIONALITY

A straight line is represented algebraically by the equation

$$y = mx + b$$

where x and y are variables; b is the value of y when $x = 0$ ("the y intercept"); m is the slope of the line, or the change in y per unit change in x. The plot is as shown in Fig. A4.

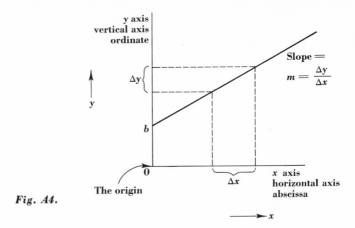

Slope $=$

$m = \dfrac{\Delta y}{\Delta x}$

Δy

y

b

0

The origin

Δx

x axis
horizontal axis
abscissa

x

Fig. A4.

A nonlinear equation may be represented by a straight line if the variables are suitably expressed (Boyle's Law, page 19):

$$V = k\left(\frac{1}{P}\right)$$

If the variables are considered to be V and P, the plot is not linear. But a plot of V vs. $(1/P)$ corresponds to the equation for a straight line, will be linear, and will pass through the origin:

$$y = mx + b$$
$$V = k\left(\frac{1}{P}\right) \quad \text{zero}$$

A **direct proportionality** is a linear relationship that passes through the origin, such as $x = ky$. Any change in one of the variables produces a proportionate (of equal portion, or equal percentage) change in the other. The symbol $\propto$ means "is proportional to." Then, $x \propto y$ is the same as $x = ky$.

In an inverse proportionality (see Boyle's law above and on page 19),

$$x \propto \frac{1}{y}$$

or

$$x = \frac{k}{y}$$

When any one variable changes by a given factor, the other variable changes by the reciprocal of that factor. Thus when x is doubled, y is halved; when x is quadrupled, y is quartered.

Of course, other proportionalities are possible. According to Graham's law (page 24) the rate (u) of diffusion of a gas is inversely proportional to the square root of its density (d),

$$u \propto \frac{1}{\sqrt{d}}$$

or

$$u = \frac{k}{\sqrt{d}} = kd^{-\frac{1}{2}}$$

It is important to recognize that for a direct proportionality, the curve must pass through the origin (both variables must be zero at the same time). A physical scale that has a *natural* beginning at zero, that is, the real value of the measurement is zero when the number 0 is assigned to it, is called an **absolute scale.** Therefore, measurements may have to be converted to absolute scales before proportionalities can be established. Examples are the conversion of the Celsius (Centigrade) scale to the Kelvin scale (page 18), and gage pressure to absolute pressure (page 781).

Bohr theory of the hydrogen atom

AS IN PRACTICALLY all modern quantum mechanical applications, Bohr assumed that the forces involved between subatomic particles are expressible in classical terms. The total energy of the electron, E, is therefore the sum of the kinetic energy and the potential energy,

$$E = \tfrac{1}{2}mv^2 - \frac{Ze^2}{r} \tag{1}$$

in which m is the mass of the electron, v is its speed, e is the charge on the electron, Ze is charge on the nucleus, r is the distance of the electron from the nucleus, and

$$-\frac{Ze^2}{r}$$

the potential energy, is minus the work required to remove the electron from the distance r to infinity.

The potential energy term is also expressible in terms of m and v. From the assumption that the electron moves in a circular orbit around the nucleus, the coulombic force of attraction balances the centrifugal force of the electron,

$$\frac{Ze^2}{r^2} = \frac{mv^2}{r}$$

or

$$\frac{Ze^2}{r} = mv^2 \qquad (2)$$

whence

$$E = \tfrac{1}{2}mv^2 - mv^2 = -\tfrac{1}{2}mv^2 \qquad (3)$$

The next problem is to restrict the values of v. Since J. W. Nicholson had concluded that the angular momentum of the electron is a multiple of $h/2\pi$, Bohr postulated that the quantization condition for the hydrogen atom is

$$angular\ momentum = mvr = \frac{nh}{2\pi} \qquad (4)$$

in which n, the principal quantum number, may take integral values of 1 to infinity. Multiplying both sides of Equation (4) by $\frac{v}{r}$ yields

$$\frac{mv^2r}{r} = \frac{nh}{2\pi}\frac{v}{r} \qquad (5)$$

But from Equations (2) and (5),

$$mv^2 = \frac{nhv}{2\pi r} = \frac{Ze^2}{r} \qquad (6)$$

The speeds of the electron are therefore restricted to the values (solving Equation (6) for v)

$$v = \frac{Ze^2 2\pi}{nh} \qquad (7)$$

Substituting Equation (7) in Equation (3) yields

$$E = -\frac{Z^2 e^4 2\pi^2 m}{n^2 h^2} \qquad (8)$$

The hydrogen atom may therefore exist only in discrete stationary states, each of which possesses a definite energy dependent upon the value of n in Equation (8). For $n = 1$, the energy of the hydrogen atom is

$$E_1 = -\frac{1^2 \times (4.8029 \times 10^{-10})^4 \dfrac{esu^4}{particle^4} 2 \times (3.1415)^2 \times 9.108 \times 10^{-28} \dfrac{g}{particle}}{1^2 \times (6.6252 \times 10^{-27})^2 \dfrac{erg^2\ sec^2}{particle^2}}$$

$$= -21.79 \times 10^{-12}\frac{erg}{atom}$$

If the correction is made for the circular motion of the proton around the mass center of the atom, the energy of the hydrogen atom becomes

$$E = -\frac{Z^2 e^4 2\pi^2 \mu}{n^2 h^2}$$

in which μ is the "reduced mass," the product of the electron mass and the proton mass divided by the sum of the electron and proton masses.

For simplicity, it is assumed that m does not vary with velocity.

In terms of wave mechanics, the motion of the electron in the hydrogen atom is represented by a mathematical function of the coordinates of the electron (wave function). The quantization conditions for the angular momenta and the energies of the stationary states follow directly, without *ad hoc* assumptions, from the mathematical solution of the Schroedinger wave equation.

Fundamental constants*

c	**Speed of light** *in vacuo*	2.997925×10^{10} cm/sec
e	**Charge on the electron**	4.80298×10^{-10} esu
		1.60210×10^{-19} coulomb
$\mathfrak{F}$	**Faraday's constant**	9.64870×10^{4} coulomb/equivalent
h	**Planck's constant**	6.6256×10^{-27} erg sec/particle
k	**Boltzmann's constant**	1.38054×10^{-16} erg/°K molecule
$\mathfrak{N}$	**Avogadro's number**	6.02252×10^{23} molecules/mole
R	**Ideal gas constant**	8.2056×10^{-2} liter atm/°K mole
		8.3143 joules/°K mole
T_0	**Ice point**	$273.15°K = 0°C$
V_0	**Molar gas volume**	22.4136 liters/mole

*Values recommended by the Committee on Fundamental Constants of the National Academy of Sciences–National Research Council, 1963 (United States).

Vapor pressure of water

Temperature (°C)	Pressure (torr)	Temperature (°C)	Pressure (torr)
0	4.6	24	22.4
5	6.5	25	23.8
10	9.2	26	25.2
11	9.8	27	26.7
12	10.5	28	28.3
13	11.2	29	30.0
14	12.0	30	31.8
15	12.8	35	42.2
16	13.6	40	55.3
17	14.5	60	149.4
18	15.5	80	355.1
19	16.5	100	760.0
20	17.5	110	1075
21	18.7		
22	19.8		
23	21.1		

Index

Ebulliometric methods, 760
Ebullition, 58
Eclipsed conformation, 665
Efficiency, current, 394 *prb*
Effusion, 24 *fig*
Einstein, A., 118, 158
Einstein law, 118, 731
Electric neutrality condition, 482
Electrical conductance and conductiv-
    ity, *see* Conductance and Conduc-
    tivity
Electrical work, 400–401
Electricity, 783–785
Electrochromatography, 595
Electrode, 360
    sign of, 408–409
Electrode concentration cell, 408
Electrode processes, 372–374
    selection of, 427–428
Electrolysis, 148, 360
    of fused salts, 374–375
    sign convention in, 408–409
Electrolytes, colligative properties of,
    360, 361 *tbl*
    conductance of, 359 *tbl*, 360
    with covalent bonds, 365
    strong, 383–384, 386
    weak, 386–387
Electrolytic dissociation, 363
Electromagnetic theory of light, 155,
    162
Electromagnetic waves, 155
    spectrum of, 156 *fig*, 160 *fig*
Electrometallurgy, 722–723
Electromotive force, 401
    and chemical equilibrium, 418–420
    dependence on concentration, 409–412
    for half-cells, 414–418, 417 *tbl*
    reversible, 402, 421
    standard, 410
Electron(s), 149, 376
    in atoms, distribution of, 173
    delocalized, 171
    e/m, 149–150, 198 *prb*
    excitation of, 531–532
    oscillating, 169
    quantization of the energy of, 161
    revolution and spin, 186–189
    s, p, d, f, etc., 172, 176
    valence, 206
Electron affinity, 194
Electron beams, 150
Electron capture, 735
Electron microscope, 167
Electron pair repulsion, 644
Electron volt, 732, 744
Electronegativity, 215, 216 *tbl*
    and bond angles, 651
Electrophile, 451
Electronic conduction, 361
Electrophilic displacement, 693–695
Electrophoresis, 595

Electrostatic effects on solubility of
    salts, 528–531
Electrostatic separation, 717
Elements, inner transition, 138, 141 *tbl*,
    142
    representative, 178 *fig*
    spectra of, 159
Elimination reaction, 248
Elution, 588
e/m, 149–150, 198 *prb*
Emission spectrum, *see* Spectrum
Empirical formulas, 83, 98
Emulsion, 4
End point, 564
Endothermic process, 50, 111
Energetics of ionic bonding, 207–208
Energy, 776–778
    of activation, 610, 624, 739, 777
    free, *see* Free energy
    materialization of, 748 *prb*
    and matter, interconvertibility of, 118
    surface, 48
    zero-point, 18
Energy levels, 162–163
Enthalpy, 113, 122; *see also* Heat
    and acidity, 456
    of activation, 615 *ftn*
Entropy, 51–53, 403
    and acidity, 456–457
    of activation, 614, 616
Enzymes, 623, 626, 656, 771
Equation, *see also* Chemical equation
    net ionic, 366–367
    partial, 368
    quadratic, 793
    of state, 14
Equilibrium(-a), 53
    and catalysis, 343
    chemical, 334–358
    combination of, 339–340
    in dissolving of gas, 303
    and e.m.f., 418–420
    and free energy, 404
    in gases, 336–341
    heterogeneous, 343–346
    homogeneous, 334–343, 346–349
    in solutions, 346–350
    and vapor pressure, 321–322
    and work, 336
Equilibrium calculations, 351–354, 479–
    526
Equilibrium constant, calculation of,
    351–352
    change with form of equation, 338–
    339
    for concentrations, 340–341
    dependence on temperature, 342
    from half-cell potentials, 418–420
    for pressures, 337
    from standard e.m.f., 418–420
    in weak electrolytes, 389
Equivalence point, 564
Equivalent conductance, 380–383,

Germanium, 131 *tbl*, 144, 233–234
Glasses, 47–48
Glucose, 753, 754 *tbl*
Glycerides, 256, 308
Glycerol, 228, 256, 305
Glyptal resin, 762
Gold, atomic radius, 311
    miscibility with silver, 311
    occurrence, 715
    reaction with O_2 and CN^-, 424
Goldschmidt process, 721
Goudsmit, S., 186
Graham's law, 15, 24–25
Gram-atom, 78
Graphite, 251, 291
Gravimetric analysis, 551, 573
Gravimetric factors, 105
Ground state, 162, 176, 186
Groups, in periodic table, 142–145
    in qualitative analysis, 536–545
Guldberg, C., 347, 604
Gutta-percha, 754 *tbl*, 755, 761

H_2^+, 266
H_2^-, 267
Haber process, 477
Hahn, O., 740
Half-cell, reference or standard, 414
Half-cell potentials, 414–418, 417 *tbl*
    for complex ions, 511 *tbl*
Half-life, 626
Halides of nonmetals, 477
Hall, C. M., 723
Halogens, 145
Hard water, 458, 600 *prb*
Heat, 781–783; *see also* Enthalpy
    of combustion, 112, 240
    of dissociation, 456
    of formation, 208
    of fusion, 50, 51 *tbl*, 708–710
    of hydrogenation, 249
    latent, 782
    of solution, 306, 528
    of vaporization, 51 *tbl*, 708–710
    and work, 113, 120–123
Heat content, 113 *ftn; see* Enthalpy
Heavy rare earth elements, *see* Actinides
Heavy water, 449
Heitler, W., 260
Hematite, 716
Henry, J., 319 *ftn*
Henry, W., 319 *ftn*
Henry's law, 319–321, 390
Herapath, J., 10
Hess's law, 114
Heterogeneity, 4
Heterogeneous equilibrium, 343–346
Heterogeneous reaction, 603, 608
Heterolysis, 683–684
High polymer, 753
Hofstadter, R., 731
Homogeneity, 4

Homogeneous equilibrium, 334–343, 346–349
Homogeneous reaction, 603
Homologous series, 239, 246
Homolysis, 684
Hückel, E., 260, 392
Humidity, 54–56
Hund, F., 260
Hund rule, 189
Hybrid orbital number rule, 280–281
Hybrid orbitals, 272–274, 282–283, 674
Hybridization, 270–276
    of *d* orbitals, 281–283
Hydration energy, 528
Hydration of ions, 364
Hydrazine, 446
Hydrazoic acid, 292 *prb*, 468 *prb*
Hydride ion, 463
Hydrides, 215 *ftn*, 462–465
Hydrobromic acid, 477
Hydrocarbons, 76, 237–258, 308, 744
    aliphatic, 239–249
    aromatic, 250–252
    derivatives of, 252–256
Hydrochloric acid, 332 *prb*
Hydrofluoric acid, 475
Hydrogen, absorption by Pd, 311
    in addition reactions, 247, 249, 255
    deviations from ideality, 29, 30 *fig*
    MO structure, 267–268
    oxides of, 73
    reactions of, 334–336, 344–345, 356 *prb*, 357 *prb*
    solubility in H_2O, 304 *tbl*
Hydrogen atom, Bohr theory of, 162, 166, 168, 796
    wave theory of, 171, 180–183
Hydrogen bonding, 296–298
    and solubility of salts, 531
Hydrogen bromide, 356 *prb*, 357 *prb*, 635 *prb*
Hydrogen chloride, 247, 355 *prb*, 629
Hydrogen cyanide, 212, 364
Hydrogen difluoride ion, 298
Hydrogen electrode, 407–408, 414
Hydrogen fluoride, 297–298, 444, 547
Hydrogen halides, acidity of, 464
Hydrogen iodide, 334–336, 610, 612, 614
Hydrogen ion, 365
Hydrogen peroxide, 371, 622
Hydrogen sulfide, 356 *prb*, 445, 496–497
Hydrolysis, of esters, 255
    of hydrides, 463
    of ions, 446–449
    of nonmetallic halides, 477
Hydronium ion, 365
Hydroxylamine, 475
Hypochlorite ion, 371
Hypochlorous acid, 438, 467, 686
Hypophosphorous acid, 228, 438, 445

preparation of, 109 *prb*
solubility in H_2O, 304 *tbl*
structure of, 217, 269
in tracer chemistry, 687
Oxyhalides, 477
Ozone, 638 *prb*, 712

p electron, 172, 176
p orbitals, unhybridized, 647–648
Palladium, 311
Palmitic acid, 256
Panning, 717
Paper chromatography, *see* Chromatography
Paraffin wax, 240
Paraffins, 240
Paramagnetism, 186
  and complexes, 676
Parent, 736
Parkes process, 725
Partial equation, 368
Partial pressure, 20
Particle accelerators, 737
Particle size, in kinetics, 608
Partition, law of, 350–351
Pascal, B., 2
Passivity, 432
Pauli, W., 735
Pauli principle, 173
Pauling, L., 190, 260, 674
pd pi bonding, 468, 653
Pentanes, 243–244, 300
Peptization, 534
Percent yield, 107
Perchlorate ion, 365, 395 *prb*
Perchloric acid, 438, 467, 470
Periodic law, 130–137
Periodic table, 133–138, 143
  from electron configuration, 177,
    178 *tbl*
Periodicity, and acidity and basicity,
    464–466
  and atomic structure, 189
  and bonding, 231–234
  in oxides, 465–467
  of valence, 138–142, 231–234
Permanganate ion, 370, 423–424, 547
Peroxides, 139 *tbl*, 144
Perpetual motion, 343, 434
Petit, A., 80
Petroleum, 239–240
Petroleum ether, 240
pH, 480, 516
  effect on solubility, 508–509
Phase, 4
Phase diagram, 61, 62 *fig*, 63 *fig*
Phosgene, 212
Phosphate ion, 547
Phosphine, 473
Phosphoric acid, 438, 476
Phosphorous acid, 438, 445, 698
Phosphorus, 144, 712
  oxyacids of, 438

Phosphorus oxytrichloride, 652
Phosphorus pentachloride, 477
  decomposition of, 685
  VB structure, 282
Photoelectrons, 158
Photon, 158, 161, 163–165, 167
Phthalic acid, 764 *fig*
Physical change, 3
Physical properties, 4
Pi bond, 265–266, 468–469
Pi mesons, 733
Pig iron, 725
p*K*, 442
Planck, M., 158
Planck's constant, 158, 159
Plane-polarized light, 666 *ftn*
Plasma, 235, 727 *prb*, 741
Plating, as protection, 431–432
Platinum, as catalyst, 337
  complexes of, 671–672
  platinized, 407
Platinum black, 701
Platinum(VI) hexafluoride, 219
Plexiglas, 768 *tbl*
pOH, 480, 516
Pohl, W., 337
Poisons, 625
Polar bonds, 214–215
Polarity and solubility, 308–309
Polarization, 299
  and color, 533, 534 *tbl*
  and solubility, 529–531
Polarization, concentration, 427
Polonium, 145
Polyacrylonitrile, 757, 768 *tbl*
Polybutadiene, 768 *tbl*
Polymers, 752–772
  addition and condensation, 755–758
  decomposition of, 753–755
  properties of, 766–769, 768 *tbl*
Polymethylmethacrylate, 768 *tbl*
Polyprotic acids and bases, 445–446,
    492–495
Polyvinyl acetate, 768 *tbl*
Polyvinylidene nitrile, 757
Positive rays, 151
Positron, 733, 735
Positronium atom, 200
Potassium chlorate, 109 *prb*, 685
Potassium chloride, 518 *tbl*
Potassium ion, 311, 545
Potassium methide, 238
Potassium permanganate, 562 *prb*, 602,
    625
Potassium sulfate, 311
Potential, electric, 400–401
  half-cell, 414–418, 417 *tbl*
  oxidation, 414–418, 417 *tbl*, 424
Potential energy, 777
Potentiometer, 402
Powder metallurgy, 727 *prb*
Precipitation, prediction of, 506–507
Precision, 574

Pressure, 12, 780
  critical, 56–58
  gage, 781
  solubility and, 304, 307
  standard, 20
Preuner, G., 344
Priestley, J., 2
Principal quantum level, 173
Principal quantum number, 162
Promotion energy, 193
Proof number, 312
Propanol, 2-methyl, 306–307
Proper axis of symmetry, 659–660
Properties, 4
Protium, 151
Protolysis, 440
  in nonaqueous media, 449–451
Proton, 151
  structure of, 731
Prussian blue, 533
Psi function, 169; *see also* Wave function
Psi square, 180–183
Psychrometer, 56
Purification, methods of, 585, 586 *tbl*,
  587 *tbl*
Purity, criteria of, 585
Pyrophosphoric acid, 438
Pyrosulfuric acid, 438, 476

Quadratic equations, 793
Qualitative analysis, of anions, 545–548
  of cations, 534–536
Quantitative analysis, 551–583
Quantization of electricity, 148
Quantized energy levels, 162
Quantum, 158
Quantum chemistry, 168
Quantum mechanics, 168–189, 616
Quantum number(s), 162, 166, 172,
  176, 186, 188
  principal, 162
Quantum theory, 158
Quotient, reaction, 336, 409

Racemate, 666
Rad, 744
Radiation, 595–596
Radicals, free, 217–218
Radioactive emissions, 729
  penetration by, 732
Radioactive series, 736
Radioactivity, 729, 735
Radiochemistry, 742
  dating by, 743
Radiofrequency spectrometry, 596
Radioisotopes, 730, 742
Radium, 544, 730, 731, 740
Radius ratio, 209–211, 209 *tbl*
  and solubility of salts, 529
Radon, 633 *prb*, 730
Raoult, F. M., 316, 360
Raoult's law, 316
  deviations from, 317–318

Rare earth elements, 138, 141–142,
  177, 178 *fig; see also* Actinides
Rate constant, 604–606
Rate-determining step, 619
Rate of dissolving, 305
Rate equation, 604–606
Reaction(s), chemonuclear, 744
  heterogeneous, 603, 608
  homogeneous, 603
  mechanism of, 453–455, 603, 618–625,
    628, 695
  nuclear, 731, 733, 735–742
  order of, 606, 623
  predicting direction of, 422–424
  rate of, conditions affecting, 604
  reversible, 334
Reaction quotient, 336, 409
Reaction rates, 602–639
  and energy of activation, 610
  and enthalpy of activation, 615, 616
  and entropy of activation, 614, 616
  and temperature, 608, 613
Rearrangements, 697–698
Redox, *see* Oxidation-reduction
Reduced mass, 798
Reducing agent, 226
  equivalent weight of, 558
Reduction, 207
Reduction potentials, 425
Refining of metals, 716, 723
Relative average deviation, 575
Relative error, 575
Relative humidity, 55–56
Representative elements, 136, 138–139,
  178 *fig*
  compounds of, 139 *tbl*
Resonance, 286–288, 291
  and basicity, 471–473
Reversible e.m.f., 402
Reversible reaction, 334
Rhodochrosite, 716
Ribonucleic acid, 771
RNA, 771
Roasting of ores, 718–720
Roentgen (unit), 744
Roman numbers, 100, 672
Röntgen, W., 151, 729
Rotational motion, *see* Motion
Rubber, 753, 754 *tbl*, 761, 766, 768 *tbl*
Rutherford, E., 730, 731, 737
Rutherford-Bohr theory of atom, 154,
  199 *prb*, 200 *prb*
Rydberg, J. R., 161 *ftn*
Rydberg constant, 161

s character and basicity, 473–474
s electron, 172, 176
Sacrificial anode, 431
Salt bridge, 406
Salt effect, 520
Salts, fused, electrolysis of, 374–375
  slightly soluble, 503–509
  weak, 387